Tuley High School
1313 N. Claremont
Chicago, Ill. 60622

Carmen Lopez

Harcourt Brace Jovanovich
Comprehensive Program for Science

Classroom Textbooks with Correlated Laboratory
Manuals, Workbooks, Teacher's Manuals, and Tests

Sequential Program for
Elementary School and Junior High School

Concepts in Science K-9
7-9: Life: Its Forms and Changes
Matter: Its Forms and Changes
Energy: Its Forms and Changes

Selective Program for
Junior High School and High School

The Earth: Its Living Things
The Earth: Its Changing Form
Exploring the Sciences
Science 700 *(a visual resource)*

Biological Science: An Inquiry into Life
BSCS Inquiry Slides
Exploring Biology
Biology 500 *(a visual resource)*
Your Health and Safety

The Physical World
Concepts in Physics
Concepts in Chemistry
Arthur W. Greenstone, Sidney P. Harris, Frank X. Sutman,
Leland G. Hollingworth

Professional Sourcebooks for the Teacher

Teaching Elementary Science: A Sourcebook for Elementary Science
Teaching High School Science: A Book of Methods
Teaching High School Science: A Sourcebook for the Biological Sciences
Teaching High School Science: A Sourcebook for the Physical Sciences

Related Materials

CLASSROOM LABORATORIES,* Independent Investigations, Science Unit
Reading for Individual Interests, and Visual Aids

*Trademark HBJ

Harcourt Brace Jovanovich, Inc.

New York   Chicago   San Francisco   Atlanta   Dallas

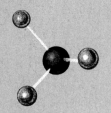

CONCEPTS IN CHEMISTRY

Second Edition

Arthur W. Greenstone

Sidney P. Harris

Frank X. Sutman

Leland G. Hollingworth

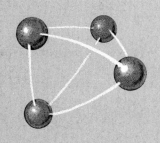

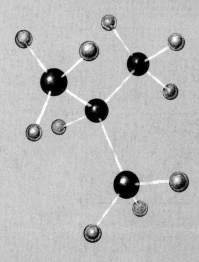

COVER AND TITLE-PAGE ILLUSTRATIONS: *Cover:* Chemical reactions occurring on a thin sheet of copper. *Title page:* Molecular structure of ice, ammonia, isobutane, and phosphorus. CREDITS: *Cover:* Harbrace by Erik Arnesen. *Title page:* Harbrace by David R. Hannum.

About the Authors:

ARTHUR W. GREENSTONE

Chairman, Physical Science Department
Bayside High School, New York, N.Y.

SIDNEY P. HARRIS

Chairman, Physical Science Department
John Bowne High School, Flushing, N.Y.

FRANK X. SUTMAN

Professor of Science, College of Education
Temple University, Philadelphia, Pa.

LELAND G. HOLLINGWORTH

Formerly Director of Science,
Brookline Public Schools
Brookline, Massachusetts

Quotation opposite page 1: Bridgman, P.W., *The Logic of Modern Physics;* reprinted with the permission of The Macmillan Company.

Copyright © 1970, 1966 by Harcourt Brace Jovanovich, Inc.

PRINTED IN THE UNITED STATES OF AMERICA
ISBN 0-15-362380-2

Preface

Science and technology go hand in hand, each gaining impetus from the other. Particularly is this true of chemistry, where the concepts that are the ground of chemistry nourish invention and are illumined by it.

Students of the enormously creative science of chemistry need insight into theory *and* technology. In order to emphasize and attend to these two faces of the science, we have, in this book, given each a different face—even as we attend to their common ground, their unity. We have, therefore, put the grounding in concepts first in the book, on pages 1–366. Then, in a different format, we have extended this grounding into the work of the chemist as artificer of new materials.

After all, chemistry streams from adventures of the mind, fashioning theory and technique in harmony.

THE AUTHORS

V

Table of Contents

UNIT 1 The Behavior of Atoms 1

Chapter 1 On "True" Appearances and Hidden Likenesses **2**

Hidden Likenesses in Matter 3
The Early Chemists and Their Elements 5
Dalton's Atomic Theory 11
Elements, Compounds, and Mixtures 15

Chapter 2 Changing Concepts of the Atom **23**

Dalton to Rutherford 23
Light and Atomic Structure 27
The Quest for Atomic Structure 30
The Bohr Atom 34

Chapter 3 A Modern Concept of the Atom **38**

Outside the Nucleus 38
A New Atomic Model Is Needed 42
The Wave-Mechanical Model of the Atom 43
Atomic Diagrams and the Wave-Mechanical Model 46

Chapter 4 Combinations of Atoms **54**

Chemically Active and Inactive Elements 54
Decomposition of Compounds 59
Composition of Compounds 62

Chapter 5 Relationships Among Atoms **71**

The Periodic Law 71
The Periodic Table 76
Relationships Among Elements 84

Chapter 6 How Atoms Combine **92**

Ionic Bonding 92
Covalent Bonding 98
Blending of Covalent and Ionic Bonds 102
Special Types of Bonds 109

Chapter 7   SKILLS—Formulas, Equations, and
Weights   **115**
Writing Chemical Formulas   115
Writing Equations   120
Interpreting Formulas in Terms of
Weights   122

Chapter 8   The Kinetic Molecular Theory   **125**
The Nature of Gases   125
The Kinetic Molecular Theory   129
The Nature of Liquids   134
The Nature of Solids   138

Chapter 9   SKILLS—The Gas Laws   **146**
Boyle's Law   146
Kelvin or Absolute Temperature Scale   147
Charles' Law   148
Gay-Lussac's Law   149
Combined Gas Law   149
Molecular Weights of Gases   150

Chapter 10   The Theory of Chemical Action   **153**
Conserving Mass and Energy   153
Energy Changes   157
Indicating Energy Changes   160
Process of Chemical Reaction   163

Chapter 11   SKILLS—Mathematics of Chemistry   **170**
Compounds: Composition and Formulas   170
The Mole Principle   172
Other Methods of Determining Weights and
Volumes   174

UNIT 2   The Behavior of Substances in Solution   179

Chapter 12   The Nature of Solutions   **180**
Solutions and Solubility   180
Expressing Concentration   186
Changes in Solvent Properties   191

Chapter 13	Particles in Solution	**201**
	Electrical Properties of Aqueous Solutions	201
	Ionization and Dissociation	205
	Behavior of Ions in Solution	209
Chapter 14	Reactions Between Ions in Solution	**217**
	Acids	217
	Bases	221
	H^+ and OH^- Ions	224
	Salts	233
Chapter 15	Acids, Bases, and Salts	**241**
	Preparation of Acids	241
	Preparation of Bases	245
	Preparation of Salts	249
	Titration	253
Chapter 16	SKILLS—Types of Reactions	**259**
	Composition Reactions	259
	Decomposition Reactions	259
	Single Replacement Reactions	259
	Double Replacement Reactions	261
Chapter 17	Controlling Chemical Reactions	**263**
	Reactions and Reaction Rates	263
	Reversible and Irreversible Reactions	268
	Controlling Equilibrium	271
Chapter 18	Oxidation and Reduction	**284**
	Oxidation–Reduction	284
	Oxidation Numbers	289
	Activity of Metals	295
	Electrochemical Cells	299
Chapter 19	SKILLS—Balancing Oxidation–Reduction Reactions	**307**
	The Nature of Electron Exchange	307
	More Complex Redox Equations	309
Chapter 20	Colloids	**311**
	The Nature of Colloids	311
	Preparing and Maintaining Colloidal Systems	316
	Charged Colloidal Particles	319

UNIT 3   The Behavior of Nuclear Particles   325

Chapter 21   The Atomic Nucleus   **326**
Discovery of Radioactivity   326
Radioactive Isotopes   331
Detecting Radiation   335
Equations for Nuclear Reactions   341

Chapter 22   Energy from Nuclear Reactions   **347**
Energy from Nuclear Fission   347
Energy from Nuclear Reactors   352
Particle Accelerators   357
Nuclear Fusion   361

UNIT 4   The Families of Elements   367

Chapter 23   The Halogen Family   **368**
Chlorine   369
Hydrochloric Acid   376
Fluorine   378
Bromine   381
Iodine   384

Chapter 24   Sulfur and the Oxygen Family   **390**
Oxygen   391
Sulfur   396
Hydrogen Sulfide and Metallic Sulfides   400
Sulfur Dioxide   402
Sulfuric Acid   405
Selenium, Tellurium, and Polonium   412

Chapter 25   The Nitrogen Family and the
Inert Gases   **417**
The Inert Gases   417
Nitrogen and the Group VA Elements   419
Ammonia and Its Compounds   428
Phosphorus, Arsenic, Antimony, and
Bismuth   433

Chapter 26   SKILLS—Testing for Negative Ions   **441**
The Hydroxide Ion   441
The Halogen Ions   443
The Ions of Sulfur   445
Ions of the Group VA Elements   446
Carbonates   447

Chapter 27   The Alkali Metals and Hydrogen   **449**
The Metals of Group IA   449
Compounds of the Alkali Metals   454
Hydrogen   459

Chapter 28   The Alkaline Earth Metals   **464**
The Alkaline Earths   464
The Compounds of Calcium   467
Hard Water   472
Compounds of Other Alkaline Earth
Metals   476

Chapter 29   The Transition Elements   **481**
Transition Heavy Metals   481
Copper   487
Silver and Gold   492

Chapter 30   The Iron Triad   **501**
Iron and Steel   502
Iron—The Element   511
Iron Compounds   516
Cobalt and Nickel   519

Chapter 31   The Aluminum Family   **524**
Aluminum and Its Metallurgy   526
Aluminum Compounds   531
Boron, Gallium, Indium, and Thallium   533

Chapter 32   SKILLS—Testing for Positive Ions   **539**
Qualitative Analysis of Metallic Ions   539
Analytical Groups IV, V, and
Specific Tests   543
Analyzing an Unknown   546

Chapter 33   The Carbon Family   **549**
                 Carbon   550
                 Chemical Behavior of Carbon   555
                 Carbon Dioxide   558
                 Carbon Monoxide   563
                 Silicon, Germanium, Tin, and Lead   565

UNIT 5   The Chemistry of Carbon Compounds   573

Chapter 34   The Hydrocarbons   **574**
                 Development of Modern Organic Theory   574
                 The Alkanes—Saturated Hydrocarbons   576
                 Unsaturated Open-Chain Hydrocarbons   582
                 Ring Hydrocarbons   587

Chapter 35   Hydrocarbon Derivatives   **592**
                 Substitution and Addition Products   592
                 Alcohols   596
                 Alcohol Derivatives   599
                 Esters   604

Chapter 36   Fuels—Source of Energy   **613**
                 Variations Among Fuels   613
                 Gaseous Fuels   617
                 Petroleum and Its Products   620

Chapter 37   Rubber, Plastics, and Fibers   **632**
                 Rubber   632
                 Plastics   638
                 Fibers   645

Chapter 38   Chemistry of the Cell   **655**
                 Carbohydrates   656
                 Proteins   663

Appendix   **673**

Index   **683**

"No one ever directly experienced an atom, and its existence is entirely inferential. The atom was invented to explain constant combining weights in chemistry. For a long time there was no other experimental evidence of its existence, and it remained a pure invention, without physical reality, useful in discussing a certain group of phenomena. It is one of the most fascinating things in physics to trace the accumulation of independent new physical information all pointing to the atom, until now we are as convinced of its physical reality as of our hands and feet."

PERCY W. BRIDGMAN
Nobel Laureate

The Behavior of Atoms

The British Air Force somehow managed to smuggle Niels Bohr, the great Danish scientist, out of Sweden. This was in 1943. Bohr (at the left), who had been in Sweden only a short time since his escape from Denmark, soon came to the United States, where he played an important role in the development of atomic energy.

At the same time, Max Planck, then eighty-five years old, had remained in his native Germany. But the war was not to leave him untouched; one of his sons was executed by the Nazi regime.

Although Bohr is known also for his work in applied science, it is for their contributions in theoretical or pure science that both he and Planck are best known—and "pure" science knows no national boundaries. In pursuing their individual concerns, each man discarded long-established ideas in science and made radically new and revolutionary assumptions. Planck's bold new assumption in explaining the transfer of energy from an incandescent solid served as a foundation on which Bohr developed his remarkable new theory of atomic structures—essentially, our present concept of the atom.

In speaking of Planck's work, Bohr said: "It is to this [Planck's] emancipation from inherited traditions of thought that we owe the wonderful progress which has been made in our knowledge of natural phenomena during the past generation." For their work both men received the Nobel prize in physics, Planck in 1918 and Bohr in 1922.

1

On "True" Appearances and Hidden Likenesses

You walk the earth today with knowledge for which scientists and philosophers of the past would have given their personal fortunes.

Perhaps the world often doesn't make sense. It seems chaotic; things are apparently without order—they seem to happen without cause. But the world of science often makes enormous sense. To the chemist, at least, the world has a certain kind of beauty and order. Take a list of things you might have seen today:

> —a plane in flight
> —an automobile en route
> —you and your friends eating lunch
> —a robin catching a worm
> —a candle burning

They seem to be very different, don't they? There seems to be no relationship among all these events. Yet the robin and the candle and the automobile and you and your friends are all producing the same substance: carbon dioxide (Fig. 1-1). Clearly the chemist sees, in all these wonderfully different objects and events, a likeness. But there is more than that. Much more.

The chemist knows—with a degree of certainty—that the plane, the automobile, the robin, the candle, and you have a deeper unity—a more profound likeness. Leucippus, a Greek, and his pupil, Democritus, had almost 2,000 years ago proposed that *all* things were made up of atoms—and this they did without benefit of a laboratory. This indicates grand hypothesizing, but not really basing thought on evidence. We must not be tempted to conclude that 2,000 years ago the Greeks were able to discern what scientists have established by way of their enormous labors in the laboratory.

Today, as a result of much searching and probing of objects and events in the laboratory, we know that outer appearances are deceiving. Only recently have scientists been able to demonstrate, by way of essential evidence, the hidden likenesses in all matter. Chairs, rocks, handkerchiefs, chromosomes, elephants, ink—things that appear so different—are basically alike in that they all consist of atoms. Continue, then, as

1-1 A hidden likeness between the inanimate candle and the animate robin is that both oxidize carbon compounds to produce carbon dioxide.

you consider the work of the ancients, the chemistry you have already begun to study. But consider as well that although scientists reason and even employ guesswork—educated guesswork to be sure—they must in the end repair to the ground of science: *evidence.* Moreover, before any single scientist's evidence is acceptable, it must be confirmed.

So scientists proceed, seeing further and further because *each stands on the shoulders of others.*

HIDDEN LIKENESSES IN MATTER

The ancients knew that appearances were deceiving. Although the world contained an infinite number of things that looked different from one another, these might well have been only different combinations of certain elementary substances. For instance, nothing appears more different from fire than water. And a piece of the solid matter from the earth's surface—say, a log of wood—appears entirely different from either. But the ancients knew that by burning a log of wood you could obtain from it fire, air, and water. From such experiments they concluded that four things—earth, air, fire, and water—were the "elements" from which all other substances derived.

This idea that there were four, and only four, elements was taught by Empedocles, an early Greek scholar, and later by Aristotle (Fig. 1-2). Largely because of the influence of Aristotle's thinking, this ancient concept of the four elements—earth, fire, water, and air—survived as a fundamental precept of science from the fourth and fifth centuries B.C. until well into the Middle Ages.

A completely different idea was proposed at about the same time by Leucippus and his pupil Democritus. They developed the notion that all the matter in the universe is made up of tiny invisible particles. These particles, Leucippus and Democritus taught, are so small and indestructible that they cannot be divided into anything smaller. Hence, they called the particles **atomos** after the Greek word for indivisible.

This idea of atoms antedated our modern concept of the atom by more than 2,000 years, but, as implied, it was slow to find acceptance. Indeed, the Arabs, in speculating on the nature of matter as late as the eighth century A.D., had only replaced the four elementary substances of the early Greeks by three "principles" which they described as "sulfur, mercury, and salt." They did not, however, mean the same thing by these terms as we do today. The idea that sulfur and mercury were **elements,** substances made up of atoms that are alike, was yet to come. The Arabs held their ideas even though they knew how to refine certain metals and to prepare the elements arsenic and antimony, as well as gold.

The Alchemists

In the ancient world there was no science of chemistry. Men like Aristotle and Democritus were philosophers, concerned with the whole scope of human knowledge. Although their speculations sometimes

	Dry	Wet
Cold	Earth	Water
Hot	Fire	Air

1-2 Early Greeks identified four elements and two pairs of contrasting traits responsible for them. If a material would burn, fire was one of its elements. Water droplets would be seen to condense on surfaces above the fire, delivered there by the escaping air. The ashes that remained were earth.

1-3 A sixteenth-century laboratory for working gold and silver, from Lazarus Ercker's "Treatise," Frankfurt, 1580.

1-4 Title page of the first edition of Boyle's *The Sceptical Chymist*, published in London in 1661.

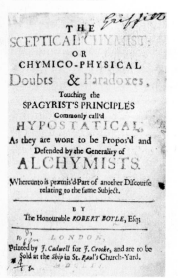

touched on the field we call chemistry, the ancients lacked the techniques for observation and measurement on which modern scientific knowledge is based. Strange as it may seem, the true antecedents of the laboratories of modern chemistry were the workshops of the alchemists (Fig. 1-3). The alchemists were chiefly concerned with trying to convert or transmute lead and other base metals into gold!

Alchemy originated in the Greek colony of Alexandria, in Egypt, during the early centuries of the Christian era. Of course, it was far from being a science in our modern sense of the word. But the alchemists' notion of transmutation was based on the old Greek idea that substances could be changed into one another. From this notion of transmutation the alchemists did uncover, so to speak, a good deal of solid chemical knowledge. By A.D. 290 they had become so successful at preparing mixtures of metals, today called *alloys,* which looked like gold that the Emperor Diocletian ordered the destruction of all their books. After the Arabs conquered Alexandria they carried the knowledge of alchemy into Spain, where it became the seed of modern European chemistry. In fact, our word chemistry comes from alchemy, a word of Arab descent meaning "pouring" or "mingling." As late as the seventeenth century many of the leading European scientists still held the alchemists' belief that it was possible to transmute base metals into gold.

Advancing the Atomic Theory

With the new birth of scientific inquiry after the Middle Ages, scientists learned to observe more accurately and to measure more carefully. They also frequently made the results of their experiments available to one another, so that gradually a reliable common fund of scientific knowledge was built up. By the 1660's the stage was set for science to take a large step forward—a step that eventually led to the formulation of an atomic theory.

No longer was the search for gold, but rather for knowledge. No longer were the required materials metals, but rather any available substances. For example, it was natural enough that scientists of this time should be experimenting with air. Air was plentiful and available everywhere. One of these men who was particularly interested in studying the physical properties of air was Robert Boyle, a young Irish nobleman passionately interested in science. Boyle is usually remembered for his experiments with gases, especially for the discovery of the relationship between the volume and pressure of gases, known as Boyle's Law (Chapter 8). But at the same time he was performing numerous experiments related to the nature of burning and the nature of elementary substances.

Boyle disproved the idea that *any substance could be resolved into fundamental elements or principles by fire.* He demonstrated that gold, when heated, does not yield earth, air, fire, or water, nor does it change into mercury, sulfur, or salt; it remains gold. In 1661 he published *The Sceptical Chymist* (Fig. 1-4) in which he defined elements as "simple bodies which, not being made of any other bodies or of one another, are the ingredients of which all those perfectly mixed bodies are immediately composed, and into which they are ultimately resolved." A few years later he stated that all matter is made up of solid particles, the atoms of modern chemistry's beginning—and its next two and one-half centuries.

QUESTIONS AND PROBLEMS

1. Which of the early ideas about elements was supported by the work of Robert Boyle? which disproved?
2. How did the work of the alchemists lay the groundwork for chemistry?
3. Contrast two different descriptions of matter proposed by Greek scholars more than 2,000 years ago.
4. What are two hidden likenesses in all matter? Compare and contrast gold and a candle on the basis of these likenesses.

THE EARLY CHEMISTS AND THEIR ELEMENTS

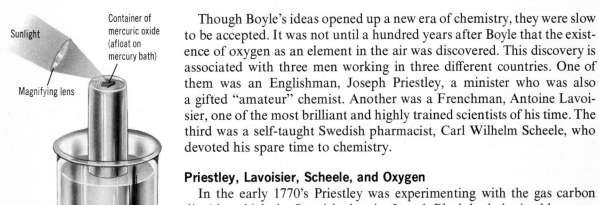

Sunlight

Magnifying lens

Container of mercuric oxide (afloat on mercury bath)

Mercury deposits on inside of glass container

Volume of gas generated

1-5 Priestley's gas discovery.

Though Boyle's ideas opened up a new era of chemistry, they were slow to be accepted. It was not until a hundred years after Boyle that the existence of oxygen as an element in the air was discovered. This discovery is associated with three men working in three different countries. One of them was an Englishman, Joseph Priestley, a minister who was also a gifted "amateur" chemist. Another was a Frenchman, Antoine Lavoisier, one of the most brilliant and highly trained scientists of his time. The third was a self-taught Swedish pharmacist, Carl Wilhelm Scheele, who devoted his spare time to chemistry.

Priestley, Lavoisier, Scheele, and Oxygen

In the early 1770's Priestley was experimenting with the gas carbon dioxide, which the Scottish chemist Joseph Black had obtained by pouring acid on chalk. By dissolving this gas in water, Priestley discovered carbonated water, the same "fizz" water that is used today in ice cream sodas. Intrigued with the results of this first experiment, Priestley became more interested in the properties of gases. In 1774 he was using a magnifying glass to focus the sun's rays on some mercuric oxide, a red powder. He observed that the powder turned black and a silvery film deposited on the inside of the container; he also collected a gas that was given off (Fig. 1-5). Was it the same gas as the carbon dioxide he had produced earlier? Priestley knew that carbon dioxide would not support combustion. What effect would this new sample of gas have on a burning object? To find out, he inserted a burning candle into the container of gas. The candle burned much more brightly than it had in ordinary air! He took a deep breath of the gas and found that he felt "much invigorated." Later he remarked (anticipating today's oxygen tent) that his new, invigorating gas might be "particularly salutary for the lungs in certain cases."

— Mercury in glass retort

— Confined volume of air

— Air entering neck of retort

— Mercuric oxide and mercury

— Decreased volume of air

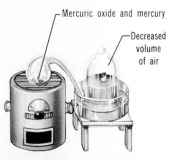

1-6 Lavoisier's apparatus for heating mercury in a confined volume of air.

That same year Priestley visited Paris, where he met and dined with Lavoisier. During the evening he told the Frenchman about his recent discovery. Lavoisier, unlike Priestley, was a well-trained scientist. After Priestley returned to London, Lavoisier repeated Priestley's experiments under the most careful conditions. Priestley had been unable to prove the exact nature of his new gas, but Lavoisier believed that it was identical with the vital part of ordinary air, the part needed for breathing and for burning. The method Lavoisier used to confirm his hypothesis was brilliant in its simplicity. He confined mercury and air together in a retort and heated it gently in an effort to produce mercuric oxide—the red powder Priestley had used (Fig. 1-6). He found that the formation of mercuric oxide continued for 12 days, then ceased. As the supply of mercury in the retort had not been exhausted, Lavoisier concluded that the gas which was necessary for the formation of the red oxide *had* been used up. In the container of air inverted over a separate mercury bath, he found that the mercury had risen one-fifth of the way into the space formerly occupied by air. From this he reasoned that one-fifth of the air is a gas that can combine with mercury. He named the gas *oxygen*. Later, Lavoisier strongly heated the red powder and liberated Priestley's "perfect air." Lavoisier had proved that Priestley's "perfect air" and the vital one-fifth of ordinary air were identical—the gas *oxygen*.

Priestley published an account of his own experiments in 1775, and the discovery of oxygen has always been associated with him and with Lavoisier. Today we know that the Swedish pharmacist and chemist Carl Wilhelm Scheele, working quite independently of the other two men, actually discovered oxygen two years earlier than Priestley. But since Scheele did not publish his discovery until two years after Priestley's book appeared, Scheele was denied acclaim for many years.

Preparing Oxygen

You might like to know more of the experiment that led Priestley to the discovery of oxygen. If so, *try the following:*

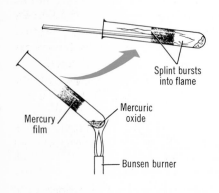

Splint bursts into flame

Mercuric oxide

Mercury film

Bunsen burner

Place 3 grams of mercuric oxide in a Pyrex* test tube. Arrange the test tube as shown at the left. Heat the test tube, gently at first, with a Bunsen burner flame, and look for a silvery film composed of small droplets of mercury on the inside of the tube. CAUTION: *Always turn the mouth of a test tube away from you when heating it.* As soon as a film of mercury forms, ignite a thin splint of wood in the Bunsen burner flame. After the wood has burned for a moment, blow out its flame, but observe that the wood continues to glow. Now thrust the glowing splint into the mouth of the test tube. What happens? This is the glowing splint test usually used to determine the presence of oxygen.

*A Pyrex test tube usually will not break on being heated.

The change that takes place as mercuric oxide is heated is usually indicated in one of three ways:

1. Mercuric oxide, when heated, yields mercury and oxygen.

2. mercuric oxide $\xrightarrow{\text{heat}}$ mercury + oxygen

3. $2\,HgO \xrightarrow{\Delta} 2\,Hg + O_2\uparrow$

All three are statements of the same event. Number 2 is a word equation. Number 3, which is a chemist's shorthand method of showing how substances react, is a chemical equation. In the equation, Hg is the symbol for mercury, O is the symbol for oxygen, Δ the symbol for heat, and $\longrightarrow$ the symbol for "yields" or "produces." The arrow next to the O_2 indicates that oxygen is given off as a gas. The meaning of the numbers used in the chemical equation is part of the subject of later chapters.

Today oxygen is prepared in the laboratory in other ways, partly because mercuric oxide is quite expensive. Frequently potassium chlorate is heated until it breaks down or decomposes to release oxygen and form potassium chloride. If you would like to, follow the procedure described below *to see for yourself how oxygen is prepared.*

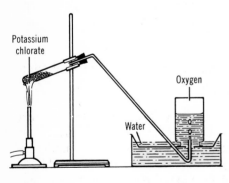

Potassium chlorate

Oxygen

Water

Arrange the equipment as shown at the left, and place a small amount of potassium chlorate in the test tube. Fill a wide-mouthed collecting bottle with water. Place a glass plate over the mouth of the bottle and invert the filled bottle into a deep dish or trough also containing water. Remove the glass plate and check the position of the delivery tube under the inverted collecting bottle.

Now heat the potassium chlorate with a Bunsen burner flame. As the potassium chlorate is heated, it changes from a solid to a liquid. When the liquid begins to bubble, oxygen escapes from the liquid, passes into the delivery tube, and escapes into the water. After a few moments in which any air trapped in the test tube escapes, insert the delivery tube under the collecting bottle and observe that the oxygen forces water out of the collecting bottle. When the collecting bottle is filled with oxygen, remove the delivery tube and slide a glass plate under the mouth of the bottle. Remove the bottle from the water and place it, mouth up, on the laboratory table. Collect a second bottle of oxygen in the same manner.

Thrust a glowing splint into the first bottle. As expected, the splint bursts into flame. But does the oxygen itself burn? Using tongs, heat a small piece of steel wool red hot in the flame of a Bunsen burner; then plunge the steel wool into the second bottle. Account for your observation that the steel wool burns brightly and gives off sparks. Again, does the oxygen burn?

This method of collecting oxygen makes use of one of its properties: it does not dissolve in water to any appreciable extent. Since the gas forces or displaces water from the collecting bottle, the technique is known as **water displacement.** The reaction that occurs can be expressed by a word equation or a chemical equation.

$$\text{potassium chlorate} \xrightarrow{\text{heat}} \text{potassium chloride} + \text{oxygen}$$

$$2\ KClO_3 \xrightarrow{\Delta} 2\ KCl + 3\ O_2\uparrow$$

Oxygen is produced very slowly by the method you used. Usually, manganese dioxide (MnO_2) is added to the potassium chlorate. The manganese dioxide causes oxygen to be released from the potassium chlorate more rapidly, yet the manganese dioxide remains unchanged. No oxygen comes from the manganese dioxide. A substance that in this way changes the *rate* at which another substance forms, but itself remains unchanged at the end of the reaction, is called a **catalyst.**

When manganese dioxide is used as a catalyst for preparing oxygen from potassium chlorate, its name is placed over the arrow in the word equation for the reaction; or, its formula (MnO_2) is placed over the arrow in the chemical equation.

$$\text{potassium chlorate} \xrightarrow[\text{heat}]{\text{manganese dioxide}} \text{potassium chloride} + \text{oxygen}$$

$$2\ KClO_3 \xrightarrow[\Delta]{MnO_2} 2\ KCl + 3\ O_2\uparrow$$

The equation is read: potassium chlorate, when heated in the presence of manganese dioxide, releases oxygen and forms potassium chloride.

Properties of Oxygen

Priestley and Scheele, in collecting samples of oxygen (Fig. 1-7) discovered four of its **properties**—the characteristics that help to distinguish one substance from another. They learned that oxygen is a gas; it is colorless; it is odorless; it is tasteless. Suppose that Scheele and Priestley, after discovering these four properties of oxygen, had then discovered a gas from another source having exactly these same properties. Would they have been correct in concluding that the two gases were one and the same? Scheele was acutely aware that other substances might have properties similar to those of oxygen. He realized that the more properties he could discover about any one gas, the better were his chances of identifying accurately that gas wherever he found it.

Scheele and Priestley continued to identify properties of oxygen. When they passed oxygen through water, they found that a small part of it did not get through. This meant that oxygen was *slightly soluble* in water. Scheele also discovered that for *supporting combustion,* oxygen was interchangeable with that part of the atmosphere which was spent when phosphorus was burned in a closed container.

Priestley had discovered that a flaming candle would burn much more brightly in oxygen than in ordinary air, and that substances such as copper, which would not burn in the atmosphere at all, would burst into

1-7 Scheele isolated "fire air" by heating sulfuric acid with potassium nitrate. Red-brown fumes were given off and absorbed by milk of lime in the bladder, which gradually became filled with colorless oxygen.

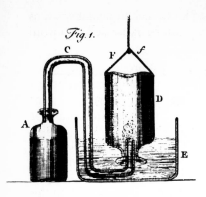

Fig. 1.

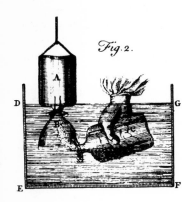

Fig. 2.

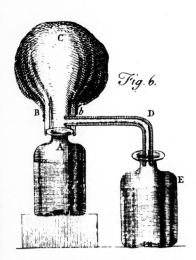

Fig. 6.

1-8 In Cavendish's first paper, "On Factitious Airs," he described collecting gases in bottles filled with water, and transferring gases by various means.

flame when heated and placed in pure oxygen. When sulfur that had been heated until it began to burn was thrust quickly into a bottle of oxygen, the sulfur burned brightly. In each instance it was observed that oxygen supports the combustion of many substances, but that oxygen itself does not burn. Is oxygen the only part of the air which supports combustion? Both Scheele and Lavoisier conducted extensive tests with "spent air" and determined that the answer to the question is always in the affirmative. You see how the list of the properties of oxygen grows. After Scheele's and Priestley's work with oxygen, many gases were subjected to series of tests in order to determine their properties. For convenience these properties have been divided into two categories: **physical** and **chemical.** For example, the physical properties of oxygen are its lack of color, odor, and taste, as well as its slight ability to dissolve in water. Its chief chemical properties, those that have to do with the way substances react with one another, are its ability to support combustion and its inability to burn.

The Search for New Elements

The discovery that oxygen could be extracted from air finally disproved the ancient notion that air itself was an element. But was oxygen an element? After repeated attempts to break it down by means of heat, light, pressure, and the then recently discovered electric cells, scientists of the late eighteenth century decided that oxygen must indeed be an element. In every test it fulfilled Boyle's definition of an element as a substance so simple that it cannot be decomposed into other substances.

Meanwhile, the search for other elements was continuing. Chemists attempted to decompose many samples of the world's matter. When they failed, they tried to make substances combine, or react, with one another. Some matter was found to be chemically **inert;** it did not react with other substances. But the great majority of the materials tested were found to be chemically **active.** That is, they would combine with other substances to form new substances. Oxygen is such a chemically active element. It combines with many other substances to form a wide variety of different kinds of matter with varying properties. Another chemically active element is hydrogen, which actually had been discovered a few years earlier than oxygen.

The Discovery of Hydrogen

In 1766 Henry Cavendish of England reported to his fellow scientists of the Royal Society that he had isolated a new gas—the gas we now call hydrogen. (About a century earlier, Boyle had collected but not identified the gas.) Cavendish reported that he obtained his new gas from the action of dilute sulfuric or hydrochloric acid on zinc, iron, or tin (Fig. 1-8). As hydrogen is highly flammable, and as he concluded incorrectly that the gas came from the metal and not from the acid, Cavendish called it "the inflammable air from metals."

While he continued to experiment with hydrogen, Cavendish came upon the answer to a question that had concerned Priestley, Lavoisier, and other scientists of the day—the composition of water. Cavendish discovered that when he exploded his flammable air (hydrogen) in a cylinder with the recently discovered oxygen, the explosion resulted in the formation of water. Lavoisier had shown that air was not an element. As a result of Cavendish's discovery, it was now clear that water, too, was not an element, but a combination of two elementary gases—hydrogen and oxygen. Lavoisier later determined the composition of water as 85 parts by weight of oxygen to 15 parts of hydrogen. This was remarkably close to our modern figure of 89 parts of oxygen to 11 parts of hydrogen.

Imagine yourself in Cavendish's laboratory in London some 200 years ago. Though his equipment (Fig. 1-8) might seem crude by modern standards, the technique and equipment he used for collecting hydrogen and other gases are essentially unchanged today. If you would like to, use a method similar to the one Cavendish used *to see for yourself how hydrogen is prepared.*

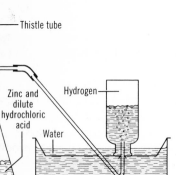

Thistle tube

Zinc and dilute hydrochloric acid

Hydrogen

Water

Place a few pieces of zinc in an Erlenmeyer flask; then arrange the apparatus for collecting a gas by water displacement as shown at the left. Make certain that the end of the thistle tube almost touches the bottom of the flask.

Now prepare dilute hydrochloric acid by half-filling a 250-milliliter (ml) beaker with water and by pouring 25 ml of concentrated hydrochloric acid into the water. Pour enough of this acid through the thistle tube to completely cover the zinc and the end of the thistle tube. Almost immediately, bubbles of hydrogen form and pass from the delivery tube into the bottle filled with water. When the bottle is filled with gas, remove the delivery tube and slide a glass plate over the mouth of the bottle. Remove the bottle from the water and place it, mouth down, on the laboratory table. Collect a second bottle of hydrogen in the same way.

From the first bottle determine the color, odor, and taste of hydrogen. Thrust a glowing splint into the second bottle, mouth down, and compare the reaction of hydrogen and oxygen. Does hydrogen support combustion?

The reaction between zinc and hydrochloric acid is represented by either of these equations:

$$\text{zinc} + \text{hydrochloric acid} \longrightarrow \text{zinc chloride} + \text{hydrogen}$$
$$\text{Zn} + 2\,\text{HCl} \longrightarrow \text{ZnCl}_2 + \text{H}_2\uparrow$$

Properties of Hydrogen

What are the properties of hydrogen? Cavendish discovered that, like oxygen, it is a colorless, odorless, tasteless gas. It is also quite insoluble

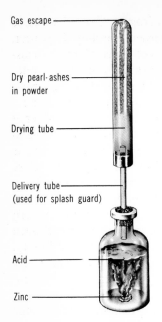

Gas escape

Dry pearl-ashes in powder

Drying tube

Delivery tube (used for splash guard)

Acid

Zinc

1-9 Cavendish weighed this apparatus—the zinc separately—before dropping the zinc into the acid. The pearl ashes in the drying tube absorbed any moisture, so that only hydrogen escaped. To determine the approximate weight of the hydrogen, Cavendish weighed the apparatus again after the reaction, adjusting his result to account for air in the bottle and tube at the start.

in water. In his studies of the weight of hydrogen, Cavendish used the special apparatus shown in Fig. 1-9. He also weighed hydrogen by more direct means, eventually concluding that it was approximately one-eleventh as heavy as ordinary air.

So far, except for weight, the physical properties of hydrogen that Cavendish discovered are much the same as those of oxygen. What of its chemical properties? Does hydrogen support combustion? When a burning splint is inserted in a bottle of hydrogen held mouth-side down, the hydrogen puts out the flame. Careful observation shows that the hydrogen itself is burning with a pale blue flame at the mouth of the bottle where the hydrogen comes in contact with the air. If the splint is slowly withdrawn from the bottle, it is reignited by the burning hydrogen. Each time these tests are made, hydrogen is seen to have two chemical properties that are exactly opposite those of oxygen. Hydrogen burns and hydrogen does not support combustion.

Sometimes a burning splint does continue to burn when thrust into a bottle of hydrogen. If the bottle has been left open so that it contains air as well as hydrogen, a whistling sound or "pop" is heard when the burning splint is inserted. Actually a mild explosion occurs as the hydrogen burns in the oxygen to form water. You will often use this characteristic "pop" as a test for hydrogen.

QUESTIONS AND PROBLEMS

1. Describe a chemical test for (a) oxygen, (b) hydrogen.
2. What physical properties do oxygen and hydrogen have in common?
3. Name two compounds that release oxygen when heated.
4. Devise an investigation to prove that no oxygen is released by the manganese dioxide (MnO_2) that is used as a catalyst in the production of oxygen from potassium chlorate ($KClO_3$).

DALTON'S ATOMIC THEORY

A quarter-century after the discovery of hydrogen and oxygen, the foundation for one of the great advances of science was laid by the Englishman John Dalton. A teacher of mathematics and natural philosophy, Dalton was also a meteorologist. Doubtless this interest led him to speculate about the gases of the atmosphere and study their physical properties—a study that provided the basis for the modern atomic theory. Dalton wondered why the heavier gases of the atmosphere, oxygen, for example, did not separate from the lighter gases, such as hydrogen. After much experimentation, he concluded that the atmospheric gases exist as small particles or "atoms" of the type proposed by Leucippus and Democritus over 2,000 years earlier. He also concluded that because the atoms of these gases are so thoroughly mixed in the atmosphere, they do not separate from each other. By extending his idea that gases are composed of very small indivisible particles to all of the elements, Dalton developed a theory of the structure of matter. This theory helped to confirm the concept of the atom that previously had been of no practical significance for chemistry.

Dalton's Early Experiments

One of Dalton's early clues to his theory came from experimentation with equal volumes of different gases. He kept equal volumes of two different gases at the same pressure; for example, a pressure of 5 pounds per square inch. Then he combined the gas from one vessel or container with the gas in the other container. He observed that the pressure in the vessel that held both gases was now equal to 10 pounds per square inch. From data collected in many experiments which were similar to this one, Dalton reasoned that the total pressure exerted by a mixture of gases is always equal to the sum of the pressures exerted by each gas acting independently. (This relationship has since become known as Dalton's Law of Partial Pressure.) Dalton further reasoned that for gases in a mixture to act independently they must consist of individual particles that intermingle with each other without combining (Fig. 1-10). Further experimentation led him to conclude that the particles of one gas differ in size and weight from the particles of another gas. These differences in sizes and weights of particles were important hypotheses for Dalton in developing the atomic theory.

As Dalton continued his experimentation during the next few years, he noted another important characteristic of these particles or "atoms," as he considered them. The atoms of one gas always combine with the atoms of another in simple ratios. In a unique experiment, he studied the volume of nitrogen that combines with a given volume of oxygen (or air). He discovered that a given volume or measure of oxygen always combines either with 36 measures of nitrogen or with 72 measures of nitrogen, "but with no intermediate quantities." From these experimental results

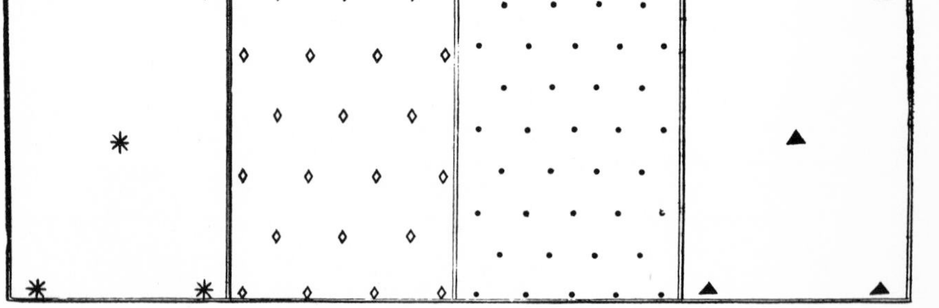

SIMPLE ATMOSPHERES.

Vol.5. Pl.8. Page. 602.

Aqueous vapour.   *Oxygenous gas*   *Azotic gas*   *Carbonic acid gas.*

1-10 One of Dalton's early manuscripts included this sketch of four gases, or "Simple Atmospheres," and a sketch of the "Compound Atmosphere" (on the opposite page). Dalton wondered why the heavier gases in the atmosphere did not settle out from the lighter ones. He concluded that the constituent gases—water vapor, oxygen, nitrogen (azotic gas), and carbon dioxide—existed in the atmosphere as small particles or atoms thoroughly mixed together.

Elements

⊙	Hydrogen
⊕	Nitrogen
●	Carbon
○	Oxygen
⊕	Sulphur
⊗	Phosphorus
⊙	Alumina
⊕	Soda
⊕	Potash
○	Copper
○	Lead

Compounds

○○	Water
○⊕	Ammonia
○●	Olefiant gas
○●	Carbonic oxide
○●○	Carbonic acid
	Sulphuric acid
	Potash alum

1-11 Symbols and formulas published in Dalton's *New System of Chemical Philosophy.*

Dalton concluded that an atom of oxygen can combine with one atom of nitrogen or two atoms of nitrogen, but never with one and one-half atoms of nitrogen. As Dalton phrased it, "Thou knowest thou canst not cut an atom."

Dalton's Explanations

By experimenting further with hydrogen and oxygen, Dalton was able to "explain" the structure of water. He hypothesized that the atoms of hydrogen are all alike since they have the same weight. For the same reason, the atoms of oxygen are all alike. In fact, he reasoned, the atoms of one element are different from the atoms of any other element because they have different weights. Using these hypotheses, Dalton proposed that water was formed by the combination of two different types of atoms, hydrogen and oxygen. In this explanation, Dalton's only mistake was to assume that a single atom of hydrogen combines with a single atom of oxygen to form a molecule of water. Today we know that water is formed by the union, or chemical combination, of two atoms of hydrogen and one of oxygen. This is the fact we represent when we write the formula for water as H_2O.

Dalton himself did not use the word *molecule.* But the **symbols** in his notebook for the year 1803 show that he understood the difference between an *atom of an element,* such as oxygen, and a *molecule of a compound,* such as water. A **compound,** as you probably know, *is a substance made up of two or more elements chemically combined.* A column of a page from Dalton's notebook is reproduced in Fig. 1-11. Each symbol in the upper half of the column represents the atom of an element; each symbol in the lower half of the column depicts the formula for a compound. Dalton's symbol for each compound includes the symbols of its elements and shows the number of atoms he assumed to be present in what we may call a molecule of each compound. Chemists before Dalton had developed many lists of symbols, but he was the first to let each symbol represent one atom of an element and to show, through his writings, a real understanding of the nature of compounds.

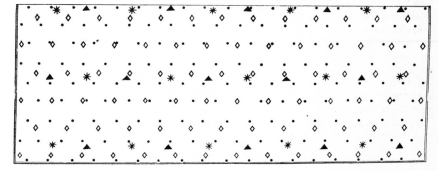

COMPOUND ATMOSPHERE.

The Theory Itself

In expanding the earlier idea of atoms, Dalton developed one of the great conceptual schemes of modern science. In the atomic theory formulated between 1803 and 1805, Dalton assumed that:

1. All matter is made up of tiny, indestructible particles called atoms.
2. An atom is the smallest particle of an element.
3. Each element is composed of atoms that are all alike.
4. The elements differ from one another because the atoms of one element are different from the atoms of any other element.
5. Atoms of different elements combine to form "atoms" (today, molecules) of compounds.
6. Only whole atoms or groups of atoms, *not* fractions of atoms, react with one another.
7. When atoms of two or more elements combine to form more than one compound, they may combine in different proportions, but always in ratios of small whole numbers.*

Today, from twentieth-century evidence, we know that certain of these assumptions are erroneous. Shortly you will learn more about the internal structure of atoms and the ways in which different atoms of the same element may differ. Nevertheless Dalton's theory is the indispensable cornerstone for much of modern chemistry.

"Proving" the Atomic Theory

Scientists have assumed for some time that all matter in the universe is made up of ninety-two natural elements. Now all matter includes not only the planets and galaxies which can be detected by use of man's most powerful telescopes, but everything in the universe—even those things lying outside the range of these telescopes. Partly for this reason, Dalton's statement about the atomic nature of "all matter" is one that can never be proved. Indeed, scientists have not as yet been able to give a photographically exact description of an atom. The internal structure of atoms cannot be detected even with the finest microscopes of today (Fig. 1-12). The illustrations of atoms you may have seen in books and magazines still are only theoretical representations of atoms. To be sure, they take into account thousands of carefully checked facts. But these illustrations are only working models; they give a picture of what we *assume* the atom to be like.

How different our knowledge of the world would be if the presently accepted assumptions about atoms had never been made, in the absence of absolute proof. We would not have the understandings from which have come such amazing developments as atomic power and rockets, and we would be unable to offer a consistent explanation for some of the simplest chemical phenomena around us. The atomic bomb that exploded over Hiroshima was not a theory but the direct result of the ideas about the nature of matter that we call the atomic theory.

1-12 This microscopy system, combining a television image with an electron microscope, increases visible magnification to 2,000,000 times.

*This statement, in modified form, is now known as the Law of Multiple Proportions.

1. On the basis of his symbols (Fig. 1-11), what would Dalton have written as the formula for each of the following: ammonia, carbonic oxide, and carbonic acid?
2. How did the "atom" of Dalton differ from the "atoms" of Leucippus and Democritus?
3. Differentiate between an element and a compound.
4. Suppose that you undertake an investigation to check one of the assumptions in Dalton's atomic theory. You find that when a fuel burns, the carbon it contains usually combines with oxygen to produce carbon dioxide; but in a limited supply of air, carbon monoxide is produced. Carbon dioxide contains 12 parts by weight of carbon for each 32 parts by weight of oxygen; carbon monoxide contains only half as much oxygen. What is the ratio by weight of carbon to oxygen in each of the compounds?

ELEMENTS, COMPOUNDS, AND MIXTURES

Dalton and his contemporaries knew of many compounds, but they had prepared and identified few elements. The list of elements continued to grow after Dalton's time until, with the discovery of astatine in 1940, it reached ninety-two. These are the natural elements, substances that cannot be broken down into simpler form by ordinary chemical processes. The lightest of them is hydrogen; the heaviest, uranium. Since 1940, nuclear scientists have produced or synthesized twelve new elements. These twelve added to the ninety-two natural ones give a present list of one hundred and four elements—a long list to write, even in symbols.

Names and Symbols

The ancient Greeks used symbols to represent the elements as they understood them. A tenth-century manuscript contains the symbols listed in the first column of Fig. 1-13. The alchemists also used picture symbols to represent the elements (Fig. 1-13, column 2). The symbols devised by Dalton were a great advance over these earlier ones. However, like those of the alchemists, they were symbols only and had little relationship to the names of the elements. Hence, symbols were used infrequently in textbooks in the early part of the nineteenth century. In 1813 the Swedish chemist Jakob Berzelius proposed a simple system to replace Dalton's circles. Based on the earlier work of Thomas Thomson, who used the symbol A for alumina and S for silica in mineral formulas, Berzelius suggested that the *symbol for an element should be the first letter, or letters, of its name.* This is the basis for the system in use today.

It is easy enough to see the origin of the symbols for most of the elements. Using the first letter of the name of the element as the symbol,

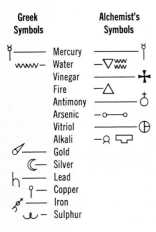

1-13 Early chemical symbols.

chemists write I for iodine, or P for phosphorus. However, where several elements begin with the same letter, for instance C, a capital and a small letter are needed to differentiate among them:

C   carbon
Ca   calcium
Cd   cadmium
Cl   chlorine
Co   cobalt
Cm   curium
Cu   copper

Some symbols, particularly of the earliest known elements, are derived from their Latin names. The symbol for copper, Cu, comes from the Latin name for copper, *cuprum.* Likewise the symbol for iron, Fe, derives from the Latin word for iron, *ferrum;* and the symbol for gold, Au, comes from the Latin name for gold, *aurum.* Some of the names of elements come from Greek words. Helium (He), for instance, comes from the Greek word for sun, *helios.* Helium was given this name because it was first discovered in the atmosphere of the sun. Some names such as hydrogen, which means "water-former" in Greek, describe a property of the element. The names of the man-made elements often honor a place or an individual. The man-made element americium (Am) is named for America, einsteinium (Es) for Albert Einstein, and curium (Cm) for Marie and Pierre Curie.

Berzelius' system of symbols has continued essentially unchanged since he devised it. Today, however, *a symbol stands not only for an element but also for one atom of that element.*

Molecules of Elements

Although the symbol for the element hydrogen is H and that for the element oxygen is O, in the equations for the preparation of hydrogen and oxygen (pages 8, 10), we represented hydrogen as H_2 and oxygen as O_2. Let's consider the reason for this.

Since Priestley's day, experimental evidence has shown that atoms of oxygen usually travel in pairs. That is, two oxygen atoms are joined together to make a *molecule* of oxygen. *A molecule is the smallest part of an element that exists under ordinary conditions and has all the properties of that element.* Only a molecule of oxygen, for instance, has all the properties of oxygen. Likewise atoms of hydrogen usually go in pairs; and a molecule of hydrogen consisting of two like atoms joined together is the smallest particle of hydrogen that has all the properties of that element. Molecules such as these, composed of two like atoms, are called **diatomic** molecules (Fig. 1-14).

In representing molecules of elements that contain two or more atoms per molecule, such as hydrogen, the symbol for the element is followed, at the lower right-hand corner, by a number called a subscript. In H_2 the

Diatomic molecules

H_2

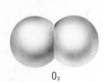

O_2

Monatomic molecules

He

Ne

1-14 Molecules of hydrogen, oxygen, and most other gaseous elements are diatomic. Molecules of helium, neon, argon, krypton, xenon, and radon are monatomic.

2 is the subscript. It indicates the number of atoms that are joined together in each molecule of the element. But we have no longer written a *symbol,* for a symbol stands for *one atom* of an element. Rather we have written a **formula,** which stands for a *molecule* of an element or a compound. While O is the symbol for the element oxygen, O_2 is the formula for a diatomic molecule of oxygen and O_3 is the formula for a molecule of ozone. Ozone is a form of oxygen in which three atoms of the gas are joined together to form each molecule.

The atoms of all but a few elements are joined together in some way. Each molecule of silicon or of a diamond (crystallized carbon) may contain anywhere from a few to many hundred atoms. By contrast, molecules of the inert gases, such as helium and neon, contain only one atom. As these gas molecules contain only a single atom, they are called **monatomic** molecules (Fig. 1-14). Since an atom and a molecule of the inert gases are the same thing, the same symbol is used for both. Thus the symbol He represents both an atom and a molecule of helium, while the symbol Ne represents monatomic neon. (Recently, xenon has been made to react under the special conditions described in Chapter 4.)

Unfortunately, the writing of symbols and formulas has not kept pace with our increased knowledge of the atomic structure of elements. As you soon will learn, if the symbol for an element is not followed by a subscript, the symbol may actually stand for one of several different kinds of molecular structures.

Chemical Compounds

Take a quick look at the names and symbols of the one hundred and three elements listed in the table on page 30. Some of these names are familiar; many are not. Now look around in the chemistry laboratory. Most of the substances you see are not elements but combinations of elements—or compounds. Mercuric oxide and potassium chlorate are compounds. The same is true of most of the substances in your daily life; they are compounds, *pure substances consisting of atoms of more than one element joined together.* Salt is a compound of the elements sodium and chlorine; sugar is a compound of carbon, hydrogen, and oxygen; and water, as you know, is a compound of hydrogen and oxygen.

The diagrams in Fig. 1-15 show how atoms of hydrogen and oxygen become rearranged to form water molecules. Observe how the like atoms in each molecule of hydrogen and oxygen break apart and rearrange themselves to form the compound.

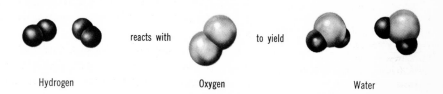

1-15 Two molecules of hydrogen react with one molecule of oxygen to form two molecules of water.

Hydrogen   reacts with   Oxygen   to yield   Water

Table 1-1 COMPOSITION OF DRY AIR

Element or compound	Percent by volume*
Nitrogen (N_2)	78.09
Oxygen (O_2)	20.95
Argon (Ar)	0.93
Carbon dioxide (CO_2)	0.03
Neon (Ne)	0.0018
Hydrogen (H_2)	0.00005

*Traces of other elements and compounds are present.

Formulas of Compounds

Although Dalton used a symbol for water, strictly speaking *we* cannot, because symbols represent elements and water is a compound. Instead we combine the symbols of the elements present in the compound into a **formula.** In the formula for water, H_2O, the subscript 2 following the symbol H indicates that each molecule of water contains two atoms of hydrogen. But there is no subscript after the symbol O. When a symbol in a compound is not followed by a subscript, the subscript is understood to be 1. Hence only one atom of oxygen combines with two atoms of hydrogen to form water.

Mixtures

Try to write a formula for soil. Look in as many books as you like; you will not be able to find such a formula. This is because soil is composed of different compounds (and elements) mixed together in varying proportions; both the ingredients and the proportions vary from place to place. Soil is certainly not an element, for it can be separated into simple substances. Nor is it a compound; no matter where a compound is found it always contains exactly the same elements combined in exactly the same proportions. Soil is a **mixture.**

Suppose you bubble oxygen into a glass of boiled water that has been cooled. If you allow the water to stand, bubbles of oxygen gas collect on the inside surface of the glass. Now when the water is heated gradually, still more bubbles escape. This is evidence that some oxygen does dissolve in cold water. The oxygen and water do not really combine chemically; they only mix together.

Air is a mixture of gases. Some of these gases, like oxygen and nitrogen, are elements; others, such as carbon dioxide, are compounds. Though Table 1-1 lists the amounts of dry gases usually found in the air, these amounts vary. A greater amount of carbon dioxide (as well as water vapor) is usually found in a room filled with people than in the open air outside. *In any mixture, unlike substances mingle with one another, but do not combine.* Mixtures are formed when unlike elements, unlike compounds, or elements and compounds mingle together.

Changes in Matter

Both mixtures and compounds can be formed from two or more elements. Is it possible for the same two elements to exist as either a mixture or a compound? You may want to *find the answer for yourself.*

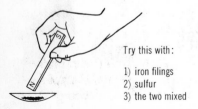

Try this with:

1) iron filings
2) sulfur
3) the two mixed

Arrange three watch glasses similar to the one at the left. Place small volumes of iron filings and powdered yellow sulfur into the first and second watch glasses, respectively. Into the third, place equal volumes of iron and sulfur that have been well mixed. Now hold a magnet over each watch glass. Do you find that the magnet attracts the iron filings in the first watch glass, has no effect upon

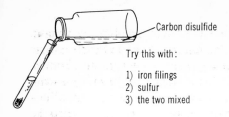
Carbon disulfide

Try this with:

1) iron filings
2) sulfur
3) the two mixed

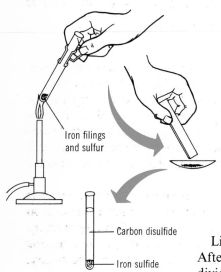
Iron filings
and sulfur

Carbon disulfide

Iron sulfide

the sulfur in the second glass, and separates the iron from the sulfur in the third glass? Mixing the two elements has obviously not changed the magnetic property of the iron.

Next, place equal amounts of carbon disulfide into three test tubes. Add small but equal amounts of iron, sulfur, and an iron-sulfur mixture to the three test tubes and shake the contents well. Observe that the iron in the first tube is unaffected, but that the sulfur in the second test tube dissolves in the carbon disulfide. Does the sulfur in the mixture of the third tube also dissolve, leaving behind the iron filings? Mixing the elements has not changed the ability of sulfur to dissolve in carbon disulfide.

Now thoroughly mix 7 grams of iron and 4 grams of sulfur and fill a large Pyrex test tube one-third full with the mixture. Heat the test tube in a Bunsen burner flame until the contents begin to glow with a cherry-red color, and then allow it to cool. If the substance does not drop easily out of the test tube, wrap the tube in several layers of paper toweling and hit it with a hammer to break the tube. Carefully remove the contents. Now try to separate the iron and the sulfur from the new substance you have made. Try the magnet. Does it separate the iron from the sulfur? Place a small amount of the substance in a test tube and add carbon disulfide. Does any dissolving occur?

Little "extra" iron or sulfur can be separated from the new substance. After being heated together, the iron and sulfur no longer retain their individual properties. By heating the mixture thoroughly, you have changed the iron and sulfur into a compound, iron sulfide. Yes, the same two elements can exist as either a mixture or a compound, but the properties of the compound are quite unlike those of the elements it contains. You can express the formation of the compound iron sulfide by the following equations:

$$\text{iron} + \text{sulfur} \longrightarrow \text{iron sulfide}$$
$$\text{Fe} + \text{S} \longrightarrow \text{FeS}$$

Physical and Chemical Changes

When you mixed the iron and sulfur together, the changes that occurred did not destroy the identity of either element. But when the mixture was heated, the properties of both elements were changed. In the first part of the investigation, the changes that occurred were physical changes. Physical changes alter the size, shape, or physical state of a substance. Breaking wood into smaller pieces, melting butter, or evaporating perfume from a bottle are all examples of physical change.

But the changes that occurred when you made iron sulfide went beyond physical changes. Heating the mixture resulted in a chemical change. A chemical change produces one or more new substances. During such a change atoms become rearranged, either by joining together or by separating. When wood burns, when heated mercuric oxide releases oxygen, or when hydrochloric acid reacts with zinc to form hydrogen, chemical changes take place.

But no matter how substances are changed chemically, they retain their hidden likenesses. Mercury and oxygen can be combined to form mercuric oxide, but the mercury and oxygen are not destroyed; the mercuric oxide can be decomposed into mercury and oxygen. Try as they may, scientists find no matter composed of anything other than combinations of the ninety-two natural and eleven man-made elements. The individual atoms of which these elements are composed follow a definite pattern. The next chapter indicates that though scientists have found it necessary to modify certain of Dalton's ideas about atoms, one basic pattern of atomic structure prevails.

QUESTIONS AND PROBLEMS

1. Write the symbol or formula for each of the following: iron, sulfur, iron sulfide, nitrogen, helium, zinc chloride. In each case indicate whether it is a symbol or a formula.
2. Write the formula for (a) carbon dioxide, which contains one carbon atom and two oxygen atoms, (b) chlorine gas, which is diatomic.
3. Differentiate among an element, a compound, and a mixture.
4. List three chemical and three physical changes (other than those mentioned in the last section of this chapter).

VALUE OF THE CONCEPT

THE CONCEPT

The idea that matter consists of atoms was proposed more than 2,000 years ago by Leucippus and Democritus. But it was not until the late 1600's that the idea of atoms as the indestructible particles of all matter began to be accepted. The isolation of the element oxygen by Scheele and Priestley, and oxygen's relation to burning, discovered by Lavoisier, provided data to support an atomic theory.

Oxygen, whether prepared from potassium chlorate or other compounds of oxygen, is a colorless, odorless, tasteless, slightly soluble gas that supports the burning of many substances. The first four characteristics are physical properties, while the last is a chemical property. Even before the discovery of oxygen, the element hydrogen had been isolated and studied by Henry Cavendish. Hydrogen is a colorless, odorless, insoluble gas that is lighter than air or oxygen. Though hydrogen does not support combustion, it burns in the presence of oxygen to form water. Elements, such as oxygen and hydrogen, that react with other elements are chemically active. A few elements do not usually react in any way; they are chemically inert.

Some 25 years after the discovery of hydrogen and oxygen, John Dalton formulated his atomic theory. Various assumptions of this theory have been revised in the light of recent experimental data. Yet our modern atomic theory, resulting from the work of many other scientists, began its development with Dalton's work.

Today we classify any matter as either an element, a compound, or a mixture. There are ninety-two natural and, at present, twelve man-made elements, pure substances that cannot be chemically changed to a simpler form. Each element, as well as one atom of the element, is represented by a symbol. Frequently elements exist in a form in which two or more atoms are joined together to form a molecule. In the formula for a molecule of an element, the subscript usually indicates the number of atoms joined together.

A chemical compound is a pure substance consisting of atoms of more than one element joined together. In the chemical formulas used to represent compounds, the subscript following each symbol represents either the actual or relative number of each type of atom present in each particle of the compound.

Mixtures consist of unlike substances mingling with one another without actually combining. In a mixture the components, whether elements, compounds, or both, are not present in a definite proportion.

USING THE CONCEPT

Using the Basic Concept

1. (a) How is the symbol for each element determined? (b) What is the significance of these symbols?
2. (a) How does an active substance differ from an inert substance? (b) Are hydrogen and oxygen active or inert? (c) Support your answer with evidence.
3. Describe the contributions to chemistry of Cavendish, Priestley, Lavoisier, and Scheele.
4. What contribution did Robert Boyle make to our modern understanding of the nature of matter?
5. (a) What is the purpose of adding manganese dioxide when preparing oxygen by heating potassium chlorate? (b) Why is "prepare" a better word than "make" for describing this process?
6. (a) How is hydrogen prepared from an acid in the laboratory? (b) List five properties of hydrogen. (c) Compare and contrast these properties with the properties of oxygen.
7. (a) What is meant by *water displacement?* (b) On what property of a gas does this process depend?
8. (a) Describe the differences among elements, compounds, and mixtures. (b) Give an example of each difference.
9. (a) How do chemical formulas differ from chemical symbols? (b) What does the subscript in the formula $ZnCl_2$ indicate?
10. (a) How does a chemical change differ from a physical change? (b) Give two examples of each type of change.
11. Write the chemical symbols for the following elements: oxygen, hydrogen, zinc, chlorine, carbon, calcium, copper, gold, helium, curium.
12. Write the name of the element represented by each of the following symbols: Cd, Co, Au, Am, Ne, Hg, K, Mn.
13. Write the chemical formula for each of the following: molecular hydrogen, molecular oxygen, ozone, water, manganese dioxide, potassium chlorate, monatomic helium.
14. Write the name of the substance represented by each of the following formulas: HgO, HCl, Cl_2, CuO, CO_2.
15. Write a word equation representing each of the following chemical changes: (a) adding water to sodium peroxide to form sodium hydroxide and release oxygen, (b) decomposing water (by electricity) into hydrogen and oxygen, (c) forming mercuric oxide from mercury and oxygen, (d) producing hydrogen from hydrochloric acid and iron.
16. Write a chemical equation for (b) and for (c) in Question 15.
17. Which of the following substances cannot be used as a source of oxygen: Na_2O_2, HCl, FeS, O_3, H_2O, CuS? Give a reason for your answer.

Relating Terms Within the Concept

Select the letter of the term in Column B that is most closely related to each term in Column A. Do not use a term more than once.

COLUMN A	COLUMN B
1. element	a. collection of oxygen
2. compound	b. colorless gas
3. mixture	c. CuS
4. atom	d. 104 elements
5. molecule	e. Fe
6. formula	f. Hg, O_2, FeS
7. symbol	g. melting of ice
8. equation	h. mercury
9. water displacement	i. potassium chlorate
10. chemical property	j. smallest part of an element having all properties of the element
11. physical change	k. smallest basic unit of an element
	l. sugar and sulfur
	m. supports combustion
	n. $2\,HgO \longrightarrow 2\,Hg + O_2$

Solving Problems Within the Concept

1. In repeating Dalton's investigation related to combining volumes of oxygen and nitrogen, chemists find that one volume of oxygen combines with one volume of nitrogen. If it should be discovered that oxygen and nitrogen combine in still another way, with what larger volume of nitrogen could one volume of oxygen also combine?

2. You have equal volumes of two different gases, one at a pressure of 3 pounds per square inch and the other at a pressure of 5 pounds per square inch. If the gas from the first container is combined with the gas in the second, what is the pressure of the gases in the second container?

Applying the Concept

1. How could you prove that water is not an element, but a compound?
2. How could you prove that air is a mixture, not an element?
3. Why has it always been important for scientists to keep accurate records of their data, and to publish the results of their work?
4. In the light of today's knowledge of matter, restate the first assumption of John Dalton's atomic theory.
5. Explain the cherry-red glow that remains after a test tube of heated Fe and S is removed from the heat source.

Reading Further

Medieval and Early Modern Science, 2 vols., by A. C. Crombie, New York, Anchor Books, 1959. Two paperbacks that present much information about the contributions of early men of science.

The Growth of Physical Science, by Sir James Jeans, New York, Premier, 1958. A brief history of the physical sciences, beginning with the contributions in early Egypt.

The Alchemists, by Michel Caron and Serge Hutin, New York, Grove Press, 1961. Stresses the positive contributions of the alchemists to chemistry.

2

Changing Concepts of the Atom

With his atomic theory Dalton laid the foundation for modern chemistry. But the theory left many important questions, such as how elements combine, unanswered. Numerous experiments performed during the next hundred and twenty-five years resulted in modification of Dalton's concept of the atom. It was finally abandoned when it became clear that an atom was mostly "empty" space around a dense, positively charged nucleus. But these changes do not detract from Dalton's contribution; it was his very insistence that matter is made of indestructible atoms that caused men to experiment further to determine the real nature of atoms.

DALTON TO RUTHERFORD

Almost immediately following the formulation of Dalton's Theory, various investigators, while studying the nature of electricity, concluded that the attraction between atoms was electrical and that each atom of a compound must have a definite electrical charge. Yet the experiments leading to the concept that atoms are composed of minute subatomic particles in rapid and constant motion in relatively vast spaces were not to be undertaken until the last quarter of the nineteenth century.

The Electron

To perform certain experiments concerning the nature of the atom, investigators used various Crookes tubes. These glass tubes were evacuated and sealed with an electrode in each end. The negative electrode is called the **cathode,** the positive electrode, the **anode.** When a high voltage source is connected across one of these tubes, rays seem to come from the cathode (Fig. 2-1). Hence, these rays are called **cathode rays.**

Numerous experiments with Crookes tubes revealed that cathode rays travel in straight lines from the cathode to the anode. Other experiments in which a horseshoe magnet was placed around a Crookes tube indicated from the direction of the bending of the rays, that cathode rays carry a negative charge. By using Crookes tubes containing two horizontal, parallel plates, oppositely charged, scientists found that cathode rays are repelled by the negative plate and attracted by the positive plate. This confirmed that cathode rays have a negative charge.

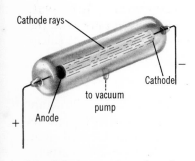

2-1 Cathode rays stream from the cathode to the anode in a Crookes tube.

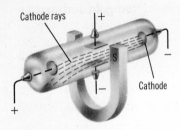

Cathode rays

+

S

Cathode

+

2-2 Sir J. J. Thomson used a modified Crookes tube in which electrons were deflected by both electric and magnetic fields to determine the charge-mass ratio of the electron.

By using both a magnet and oppositely-charged parallel plates in a modified Crookes tube (Fig. 2-2), J. J. Thomson of England calculated the speed of the negative particles, now called **electrons,** at one-fifth the speed of light. Unfortunately, two other properties of the electron, its charge (e) and its mass (m) remained unknown. Although Thomson was unable to determine individual values for the charge and for the mass, he was able to report the charge-mass ratio (e/m) of the electron. He found that *no matter what metal the cathode was composed of, the speed and charge-mass ratio of the electrons remained the same.* Thus he established that all electrons are identical particles.

The Thomson Atom

With the knowledge that all atoms contained electrons, Thomson proposed a model of the atom showing all of its then known constituents in 1898. A few years later he elaborated upon his idea by suggesting that the atom consisted of "a sphere of uniform positive electrification" in which the electrons were embedded (Fig. 2-3). Moreover, he proposed that the electrons were arranged in concentric shells, and that the electron arrangement differed for each atom.

Millikan's Oil Drops

The actual charge on the electron was determined experimentally by Robert A. Millikan, an American physicist, between 1909 and 1911. In designing the apparatus for his now famous oil-drop experiment, Millikan reasoned that neutral oil drops sprayed between two oppositely charged plates would settle down to the bottom plate because of gravity (Fig. 2-4). If, however, he could give the oil drops a negative charge, they would be attracted upward to the positive plate. To remain suspended, a negatively charged drop must have an electrical attraction upward to the positive plate exactly equaled by its weight acting downward.

Millikan reasoned that the oil drops could become charged negatively by picking up one or more electrons but that the smallest possible charge would result if an oil drop picked up a single electron. Millikan thus interpreted his results to mean that a single electron has a negative charge of 1.60×10^{-19} coulomb—the smallest unit of charge he measured.

Once the charge on the electron was determined, its mass was calculated as 9.11×10^{-28} gram. Even today this minute mass has to be calculated because no balance can determine the mass of a single electron.

The Rutherford Atom

The next great stride in expanding our concept of atomic structure came from the laboratories of Sir Ernest Rutherford in 1911. He and his collaborators were studying the positively charged particles, called alpha particles, given off by radioactive elements. They directed alpha particles from polonium in narrow beams at very thin films of metals, such as gold foil. What happened to the particles striking the gold foil? The experi-

2-3 Thomson accounted for the discovery of electrons by modifying Dalton's one-piece model of the atom. Each "atom" above shows electrons embedded in a positively charged sphere.

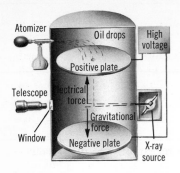

2-4 In Millikan's oil-drop apparatus electrons, which are knocked from the atoms in the air by means of X rays, are picked up by the oil drops. By observing the movement of the charged drops between the oppositely charged plates, Millikan determined the charge on the electron.

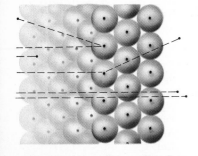

2-5 When Rutherford found that a few particles were deflected 90 degrees or more, he stated: "It was about as credible as if you had fired a 15-inch shell at a piece of tissue paper and it came back and hit you."

menters made observations from directly behind the gold foil and at many angles on either side (Fig. 2-5). They found that most alpha particles passed through the foil without a change in direction, but that some of the alpha particles were deflected slightly. Incredibly, a few of the particles were deflected through an angle of 90 degrees or more.

From these experiments Rutherford concluded that the atoms of the gold foil consist mainly of "empty" space in which electrons are orbiting. He reasoned that each atom contains a very small, dense nucleus carrying all of the positive charge, and that the few large deflections of alpha particles resulted when a positively charged alpha particle was deflected by the small positively charged nucleus of an atom of gold. Assuming that an alpha particle could approach the nucleus of a gold atom head-on before the alpha particle is deflected, Rutherford calculated that the nucleus has a radius of less than 3×10^{-12} centimeter.

As a result of these experiments, the Thomson model of the atom, which consisted of electrons moving in a sphere of positive charges, was replaced by the *nuclear atom* of Rutherford. In his model of the atom, Rutherford pictured the positive charge concentrated in a small dense region known as the *nucleus* around which orbited rapidly moving electrons equal in number to the positive charge of the nucleus.

Atomic Weights

In Dalton's time and later, scientists—even as they developed their changing concepts of the atom—attempted to determine the actual weights of different atoms. Unfortunately, individual atoms are much too small to be weighed, and even today some indirect method has to be used. Dalton developed the idea of using relative weights of atoms, although he did not know how many atoms of each element combined with each other. Dalton called the number that represents the *relative* weight of the atoms of each different element compared with hydrogen (relative weight 1) the **atomic weight** of the element. Although it is more correct to speak of *atomic mass,* we shall follow Dalton's lead and use the term *atomic weight.*

Dalton's atomic weights have, as you would expect, been revised several times. In fact, as recently as 1961 a particular type of carbon atom was assigned an atomic weight of 12.0000, and this carbon-12 atom was adopted as the standard for atomic weights used today. (The significance of the number 12 will become clear shortly.)

Chemists express atomic weight in *atomic mass units.* One atomic mass unit (abbreviated amu) is defined as one-twelfth the weight of an atom of carbon-12. The atomic weight of any given element is now defined as the relative weight of that element, in atomic mass units, compared to the weight of an atom of carbon-12. The presently accepted atomic weight of the elements are listed, in increasing order (with minor exceptions), in Table 2-1 (page 26). Note that these precise atomic weights are not whole numbers. The reason why proved to be a real challenge for scientists.

Table 2-1 ATOMIC WEIGHTS

Name of element	Symbol	Atomic number	Atomic weight*	Name of element	Symbol	Atomic number	Atomic weight
Hydrogen	H	1	1.00797	Iodine	I	53	126.9044
Helium	He	2	4.0026	Xenon	Xe	54	131.30
Lithium	Li	3	6.939	Cesium	Cs	55	132.905
Beryllium	Be	4	9.0122	Barium	Ba	56	137.34
Boron	B	5	10.811	Lanthanum	La	57	138.91
Carbon	C	6	12.01115	Cerium	Ce	58	140.12
Nitrogen	N	7	14.0067	Praseodymium	Pr	59	140.907
Oxygen	O	8	15.9994	Neodymium	Nd	60	144.24
Fluorine	F	9	18.9984	Promethium	Pm	61	[147]†
Neon	Ne	10	20.183	Samarium	Sm	62	150.35
Sodium	Na	11	22.9898	Europium	Eu	63	151.96
Magnesium	Mg	12	24.312	Gadolinium	Gd	64	157.25
Aluminum	Al	13	26.9815	Terbium	Tb	65	158.924
Silicon	Si	14	28.086	Dysprosium	Dy	66	162.50
Phosphorus	P	15	30.9738	Holmium	Ho	67	164.930
Sulfur	S	16	32.064	Erbium	Er	68	167.26
Chlorine	Cl	17	35.453	Thulium	Tm	69	168.934
Argon	Ar	18	39.948	Ytterbium	Yb	70	173.04
Potassium	K	19	39.102	Lutetium	Lu	71	174.97
Calcium	Ca	20	40.08	Hafnium	Hf	72	178.49
Scandium	Sc	21	44.956	Tantalum	Ta	73	180.948
Titanium	Ti	22	47.90	Tungsten	W	74	183.85
Vanadium	V	23	50.942	Rhenium	Re	75	186.2
Chromium	Cr	24	51.996	Osmium	Os	76	190.2
Manganese	Mn	25	54.9380	Iridium	Ir	77	192.2
Iron	Fe	26	55.847	Platinum	Pt	78	195.09
Cobalt	Co	27	58.9332	Gold	Au	79	196.967
Nickel	Ni	28	58.71	Mercury	Hg	80	200.59
Copper	Cu	29	63.54	Thallium	Tl	81	204.37
Zinc	Zn	30	65.37	Lead	Pb	82	207.19
Gallium	Ga	31	69.72	Bismuth	Bi	83	208.980
Germanium	Ge	32	72.59	Polonium	Po	84	[210]
Arsenic	As	33	74.9216	Astatine	At	85	[210]
Selenium	Se	34	78.96	Radon	Rn	86	[222]
Bromine	Br	35	79.909	Francium	Fr	87	[223]
Krypton	Kr	36	83.80	Radium	Ra	88	[226]
Rubidium	Rb	37	85.47	Actinium	Ac	89	[227]
Strontium	Sr	38	87.62	Thorium	Th	90	232.038
Yttrium	Y	39	88.905	Protactinium	Pa	91	[231]
Zirconium	Zr	40	91.22	Uranium	U	92	238.03
Niobium	Nb	41	92.906	Neptunium	Np	93	[237]
Molybdenum	Mo	42	95.94	Plutonium	Pu	94	[242]
Technetium	Tc	43	[99]	Americium	Am	95	[243]
Ruthenium	Ru	44	101.07	Curium	Cm	96	[247]
Rhodium	Rh	45	102.905	Berkelium	Bk	97	[247]
Palladium	Pd	46	106.4	Californium	Cf	98	[249]
Silver	Ag	47	107.870	Einsteinium	Es	99	[254]
Cadmium	Cd	48	112.40	Fermium	Fm	100	[253]
Indium	In	49	114.82	Mendelevium	Md	101	[256]
Tin	Sn	50	118.69	Nobelium	No	102	[253]
Antimony	Sb	51	121.75	Lawrencium	Lw	103	[257]
Tellurium	Te	52	127.60	(Name undetermined)		104	[257]

* Based on carbon-12; adopted 1961.
† Brackets denote replacement of atomic weight by the mass number of the isotope with the longest half life.

1. Indicate evidence for the following descriptions of atoms: (a) Atoms consist of negatively and positively charged particles. (b) The core of the atom is small, massive, and positively charged. (c) The space between the nucleus and electron shells is relatively vast.
2. Define the terms *electron* and *cathode ray*.
3. (a) Define the term *atomic weight*. (b) Why is atomic weight expressed in amu's? (c) What is the basis for the present system?
4. Compare and contrast (a) the Dalton and the Thomson atoms, (b) the Thomson and the Rutherford atoms.

LIGHT AND ATOMIC STRUCTURE

The path toward understanding the nature of the atom is not direct. We have seen that during the nineteenth and twentieth centuries, many investigators working in many areas in chemistry and physics contributed to our understanding of the atom. But for the moment, let us go back to one of the great seventeenth-century scientists and his study of light.

The Continuous Spectrum

Rainbows are visible in bright sunlight after a rainstorm—and with good reason. The water droplets in the air disperse the sunlight into an array of colors from red to violet. This complete array of colors forms a **continuous spectrum.** No doubt you know that a triangular glass prism disperses the light from an incandescent light bulb into the same type of continuous spectrum.

Three centuries ago, Isaac Newton passed a narrow beam of sunlight through such a prism and viewed the same spectrum on a white screen.

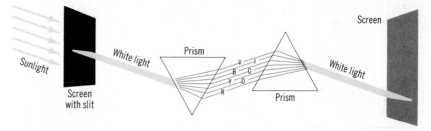

·6 When sunlight is passed through a prism, a continuous spectrum is produced. A second prism, if inverted, recombines the spectrum into white light.

Next Newton tried an experiment using two prisms—but with the second prism inverted (Fig. 2-6). Are you surprised that he was able to obtain white light by this procedure? The first prism, with its apex downward, produced a continuous spectrum. The second prism, however, with its base downward, recombined all of the visible colors into white light. Newton concluded that sunlight was white light, and that white light was actually composed of the colors of the spectrum.

Bright-line Spectrum

A different type of spectrum is more significant to the chemist. If you use a spectroscope, *you can observe this type of spectrum for yourself.*

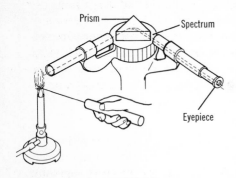

Prism — Spectrum — Eyepiece

First, clean one end of a platinum (or nichrome) wire by dipping it in a concentrated solution of hydrochloric acid. Then heat it in the hottest part of the Bunsen flame. Now dip the wire into a sodium chloride solution and place it in the same part of the Bunsen flame. Observe the spectrum through the eyepiece of the spectroscope. Do you observe two closely spaced yellow lines as shown in the color plate facing p. 84? *Be sure to clean the wire after each test.* Now place the wire in a lithium chloride solution, heat the wire in the Bunsen flame, and observe the spectrum obtained. Repeat the spectral analysis for solutions of strontium nitrate, barium nitrate, and potassium nitrate. The colors and spectral lines are different for each of these five solutions. Now describe the spectra obtained by testing separately solutions of sodium sulfate and sodium bromide. Do you observe the same double yellow lines in the spectra obtained from each of the three sodium compounds?

As sodium is the only element common to these solutions, the double yellow line must be characteristic of sodium. The visible spectrum obtained from each of the other elements is different. Such spectra in which definite lines may be seen are called **bright-line spectra.** You could have obtained bright-line spectra for gases by spectral analysis. A similar type of tube is the familiar gas-filled tubing used in various colored "neon" signs.

Of the bright-line spectra you observed, the simplest is that of sodium and the most complex that of barium. Yet it is difficult to describe these spectra further except by comparison with photographs, such as those facing page 84. There seems to be no order or system to the bright-line spectra, but *each element has a spectrum unlike that of any other element.*

Light as Wave Motion

An understanding of the nature of light can help to simplify the description of spectra. In the nineteenth century, scientists found that such common phenomena as the colors in soap bubbles and oil films could be explained only if light were considered to be transmitted by a *wave motion.* Think of a wave moving gently in a calm lake—or of a diagram of such a wave as represented by wave *A* in Figure 2-7. In any wave, the distance between any two successive identical points, such as *aa'*, is called the **wavelength.** Now consider both wave *A* and wave *B*. The distances *aa'* and *bb'* each represent one wavelength. The wavelength of wave *A* is much longer than the wavelength of wave *B*. But if we assume that both waves travel at the same velocity, then more waves with the shorter wavelengths would pass a given point each second than waves with longer wavelengths. Since the number of waves that pass a given point each sec-

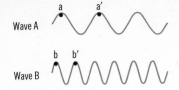

Wave A

Wave B

2-7 The wavelength, aa', of wave A is longer than the wavelength, bb', of wave B. But if both waves are traveling at the same velocity, the frequency of wave A is less than the frequency of wave B. For waves traveling at the same velocity, as the wavelength decreases, the frequency increases.

ond is called *frequency,* then the frequency of wave *B* is much greater than the frequency of wave *A*.

Observe again the two waves in Fig. 2-7, but this time think of them as "light waves." Since the velocity in air of all colors of light is the same, for the various colors of light *as the wavelength decreases, the frequency increases* and vice versa.

The wavelength of light is measured in units called Ångstroms (Å; 1 Å = 10^{-8} cm). In the visible spectrum violet light has the shortest wavelength, approximately 4,000 Å, and red the longest, approximately 7,000 Å. But since *wavelength is inversely proportioned to frequency,* violet light has a higher frequency than red light. We can express this relationship by an equation in which velocity (*c*) is equal to frequency (*v,* or nu) times wavelength (λ, or lambda):

$$c = v\lambda$$

Quantum Theory of Light

To explain new experimental results, Max Planck, in 1900, suggested that light is emitted as particles, later called **photons,** carrying definite quantities, or **quanta,** of energy. Furthermore, the energy is *not* identical for all photons. According to Planck, photons of violet light contain more energy than those of green light, which in turn have more energy than those of red light. It was, of course, already well-established that violet, green, and red light differed in frequency and wavelength. Exactly how is the energy of a photon of light (radiation) related to the frequency of light?

Planck's new **quantum theory** of light as photons of definite energy traveling with a wave motion—a startlingly new concept confirmed experimentally by later investigators—led to an exact relationship between energy (*E*), frequency (*v*), and a constant (*h*), later named Planck's constant in his honor:

$$E = hv$$

According to this equation, the *energy of the photon is directly proportional to the frequency of the light (radiation).* And since frequency is inversely proportional to wavelength (*c = v*λ), *the energy of the photon is* directly proportional to the frequency of the light and *inversely proportional to its wavelength.*

Planck's formula can, therefore, be used to determine the energy of a photon. For example, it can be determined that the energy of an orange-red photon, with a wavelength of 6,200 Å is 2.00 ev (a unit of energy called an electron volt). If the radiation consists of ultraviolet photons having a wavelength of 3,100 Å, each photon has 4.00 ev of energy.

Light has been shown to have a particle nature and to be transmitted by a wave motion. But the origin of light, or more particularly how the spectral lines result when the various elements are observed through a spectroscope, was yet to be explained. Once again, the work of the physicist and the chemist was to overlap extensively.

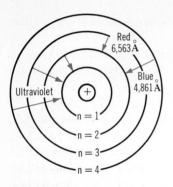

2-8 According to Bohr, various spectral lines of the hydrogen atom resulted when electrons fell from specific higher to lower energy levels. Electrons may occupy only the energy levels shown and designated n, or levels with higher values of n.

1. Indicate whether each of the following emits a continuous or bright-line spectrum: heated potassium gas, a glowing incandescent light bulb, sunlight, heated neon gas.
2. Define the terms *quanta* (singular, *quantum*), *photon, frequency, wavelength, quantum theory of light.*
3. Arrange in proper order photons of yellow, ultraviolet, blue, and infrared light (radiation) with respect to increasing (a) frequency, (b) wavelength, (c) energy.
4. What equations would you use to determine each of the following: (a) the wavelength of a light wave whose frequency is known, (b) the energy of a light wave whose wavelength is known, (c) the energy of a light wave whose frequency is known?

THE QUEST FOR ATOMIC STRUCTURE

In 1913, Neils Bohr proposed a model of the hydrogen atom that explained all of the known experimental facts. He retained the small, dense, positively charged nucleus suggested by Rutherford and also made use of Planck's quantum theory of light to develop and support his new theory of atomic structure.

In developing his model of the atom, Bohr had to answer two very perplexing questions scientists were asking. First, in Rutherford's model of the atom, why didn't the moving electrons radiate away energy and spiral back into the nucleus? And, second, what was the origin of the spectra of the various elements?

The Hydrogen Atom

To answer both of these questions, Bohr took a bold step. He proposed that electrons revolve about the nucleus in certain, fixed orbits, or *stationary states,* and that an electron does *not* radiate energy while it is in a fixed orbit. Further, Bohr proposed that there were several orbits around the nucleus, and that each orbit represented a definite but different amount of energy. The association of definite quantities of energy with each orbit has led to the use of the term **energy level** as interchangeable with orbit. According to Bohr, specific amounts of energy are released when an electron makes a transition, or "falls," from a higher energy level to a lower energy level (Fig. 2-8). Moreover, the energy that is radiated is of a specific frequency, and this frequency can be determined by Planck's quantum theory equation.

If E_2 is the energy of the atom when the electron is in the higher energy level and E_1 its energy when it is in a lower energy level, then the transition of an electron from the higher energy state to the lower energy state will give off a photon with energy equal to E_2 minus E_1 ($E_2 - E_1$). Sub-

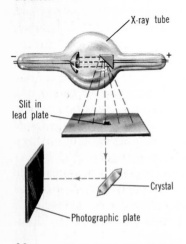

2-9 Apparatus for preparing X-ray diffraction photographs. High speed electrons produce X rays as they strike the triangular-shaped anode within the X-ray tube. The wavelengths of the resulting X rays, which fall on the photographic plate, depend upon the element used as the anode.

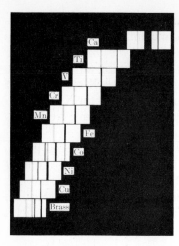

2-10 In a study of the characteristic X rays of various elements, Moseley used a photographic method in which the position of the lines on the plate were directly related to the wavelengths of the X rays. This now historic photograph shows how the X-ray spectra change in a regular manner with increasing atomic number.

stituting this value for E in Planck's equation, we have

$$E_2 - E_1 = h\nu$$

By using this equation, we can readily find that each transition gives a spectral line of definite frequency (or wave length).

Bohr found that in the hydrogen atom the return of the electron from the third energy level, $n = 3$, to the second—a decrease in energy—produced photons having an energy of 1.9 ev. Using the formula above, he determined precisely the frequency, and hence the wavelength, of the spectral line produced. Further, Bohr found that the electrons falling back to the second energy level ($n = 2$) accounted for the complete visible spectrum of hydrogen (facing page 84). The electrons dropping back to the lowest energy level, or *ground state* ($n = 1$), produced the known spectral lines in the ultraviolet region.

According to Bohr, the single electron in a hydrogen atom in the ground state followed a circular (or spherical) path around the nucleus at a radius of 0.53 Å. And the radius calculated by Bohr was identical with that determined by independent experimenters. But what makes the electron jump to the next higher orbit, that is, to be in an *excited state*? Bohr determined that the electron had to receive a photon of ultraviolet light with an energy of 10.2 ev. He also reasoned that in jumping outward to any of the orbits more distant from the nuclei, the electron in the ground state required photons of increasing but definite quantities of energy. Moreover, the energy emitted when an electron returned from a more distant orbit to an orbit closer to the nucleus was precisely the same as the energy needed to raise the electron to the higher energy level.

Using his ideas that electrons are in orbits at discrete, or exact, distances from the nucleus, Bohr accounted for every spectral line of hydrogen. Because even a very small quantity of hydrogen contains an enormous number of atoms, energized, or *excited,* hydrogen has many atoms going through every possible transition in which the electron falls from a higher energy level to a lower energy level. This makes a complete spectrum possible.

Atomic Number

In late 1913, Henry G. J. Moseley, a young English physicist, studied the rays emitted by X-ray tubes in which the anodes were made of various elements (Fig. 2-9). The wavelengths of the X rays emitted were measured by using a crystal of known spacing as the fundamental distance measuring device. When he arranged the X-ray spectra in the order of increasing atomic weights, Moseley found that, with three exceptions, the wavelengths fell into regular order (Fig. 2-10). From these results he concluded that "there is in the atom a fundamental quantity which increases by regular steps as we pass from one element to the next. This quantity can only be the charge on the atomic nucleus." Moseley called this positive nuclear charge the **atomic number** of the element.

Table 2-2   MOSELEY'S ARRANGEMENT OF ELEMENTS

Element	Atomic number	Atomic weight	Principal wavelength (Å)
Iron	26	55.85	1.94
Cobalt	27	58.93	1.80
Nickel	28	58.71	1.68

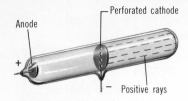

2-11 In this modified Crookes tube, "positive rays" emerged on the side away from the anode. When the tube was filled with hydrogen, Rutherford was able to identify one of the types of particles as the "long sought positive electron."

Table 2-2 illustrates Moseley's arrangement of the elements iron, cobalt, and nickel according to increasing atomic number. Observe that *the order of decreasing principal wavelengths agrees with the order of increasing atomic number* rather than with the order of increasing atomic weights.

But this was not all. The close similarity among the X-ray spectra of various elements (see Fig. 2-10) indicated to Moseley that the X rays originated in the part of the atom nearest the nucleus, the innermost electrons common to all atoms.

The outcome of Moseley's work was that it gave experimental justification for the extension of Bohr's model of the hydrogen atom to atoms of every element. In the year 1913, it seemed that the concept of the atom as electrons revolving in discrete orbits about a nucleus had been clarified. However, experimental evidence concerning the subatomic particles within the nucleus was yet to come.

The Proton

By 1914 Rutherford had described a particle much more massive than an electron, with a positive charge equal and opposite to that of the electron (Fig. 2-11). By 1920 the long sought, subatomic particle that gives the nucleus its positive charge had been isolated and named the **proton.**

Moseley, as you know, described the atomic number of an element as equal to the charge on its nucleus. This positive charge, which increases by one unit from each element to the next, is equal to the number of protons. The charge on a proton is the same as the charge on an electron but is opposite in sign. For simplicity, we can describe each as having one unit of charge. The mass of a proton has been determined experimentally as 1.672×10^{-24} gram. This is an inconveniently small number. Thus chemists usually convert it to atomic mass units (amu). The mass of a proton is 1.007 amu, or approximately 1 amu.

Using similar methods, chemists have determined that the mass of an electron is 0.000549 amu, only 1/1,836 the mass of a proton. Its approximate mass is considered 0 amu, and it is usually disregarded in determining the atomic weight of an element.

The Neutron

The most common atom of carbon has a mass approximately twelve times the mass of a hydrogen nucleus. The atomic number of carbon is 6, indicating that there are six protons having a mass of approximately 6 amu. What nuclear particles are responsible for the extra 6 amu in carbon atoms? Rutherford predicted that the nucleus contains a neutral particle that he called a **neutron.** An extensive search for evidence of the existence of the neutron was unsuccessful until 1932, when James Chadwick demonstrated that a penetrating radiation was caused by high-speed neutrons. From further experimentation, the neutron was found to have a mass almost exactly equal to the mass of a proton, 1.009 amu. The nucleus of an atom indeed contains neutrons and protons. Table 2-3 summarizes the properties of these subatomic particles.

Table 2-3 **PROPERTIES OF SUBATOMIC PARTICLES**

Particle	Symbol	Charge	Approximate atomic mass units
Proton	p	+1	1.0
Neutron	n	0	1.0
Electron	e^-	−1	0.0

2-12 Thomson interpreted the parabolic streaks in this photograph to mean that although most neon particles had a mass of 20 amu, some had a mass of 22 amu—all neon particles are not identical.

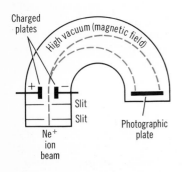

2-13 The diagram above shows the cross section of a mass spectrometer based on Aston's original instrument. Although all neon ions have the same charge, +1, they do not have the same mass. Ions of different masses follow different paths, with the lighter particles following a smaller curved path.

Isotopes

Examine the Table of Atomic Weights (page 26). Do you find any that are whole numbers? The explanation for the existence of fractional atomic weights was first given by Sir J. J. Thomson in 1912. Neon was known to have an atomic weight of approximately 20.2. When a narrow beam of positive rays of neon fell on a photographic plate, Thomson found a series of parabolic streaks (Fig. 2-12). In addition to the expected neon line for atoms with a mass of 20 amu, he found a fainter line indicating a few neon particles with a mass of 22 amu. According to Thomson, there could "be little doubt that what has been called neon is not a single gas, but a mixture of two gases, one of which has an atomic weight of about 20 and the other about 22."

F. W. Aston, who was then working in Thomson's laboratory, attempted to separate the two forms of neon. To do so, he devised an apparatus capable of sorting out positively charged particles, or positive *ions*, according to their masses. Such a device is called a **mass spectrometer** (Fig. 2-13). Aston introduced a small amount of neon gas into his mass spectrometer. Each neon atom was bombarded with very high-speed electrons, causing the neon atom to lose an electron. The resulting particles were positively charged neon particles, or neon *ions*, written Ne^+. Under the influence of a magnetic field, each Ne^+ ion followed a curved path consistent with its mass and fell on a photographic plate.

Aston showed that the relative amounts of the two forms of neon were in the ratio of 10:1. From this he accounted for the fractional atomic weight of neon by calculating the *weighted* average atomic weight of neon:

$$\frac{(10 \text{ neon atoms} \times 20.00 \text{ amu}) + (1 \text{ neon atom} \times 22.00 \text{ amu})}{11 \text{ neon atoms}} = 20.18 \text{ amu}$$

For convenience, the letters amu are usually *not* written when expressing atomic weights—the atomic weight of neon is 20.18.

In connection with his studies of the radioactive decay of uranium, F. Soddy, a British physicist, recognized in 1910 that there were at least two different kinds of atoms of uranium. He soon gave the name **isotopes** to atoms of the same element having different weights—and all elements have two or more isotopes. The weighted average of all naturally occurring isotopes of an element gives the atomic weight of the element.

But why do isotopes of the same element have different atomic weights? An atom of neon-20 has 10 protons and 10 neutrons in its nucleus, while an atom of neon-22 contains 10 protons and 12 neutrons. The whole number following the name of the element is called the **mass number.** This *mass number is equal to the sum of the number of protons and neutrons in the nucleus of that atom.* Hydrogen, for example, has three isotopes with mass numbers 1, 2, and 3. All hydrogen atoms have 1 proton. But while hydrogen-1 has no neutrons, hydrogen-2, or **deuterium,** has 1 neutron, and hydrogen-3, or **tritium,** has 2 neutrons. Note in Fig. 2-14 that the mass number of each isotope equals the sum of the protons and neutrons.

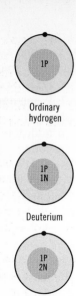

Ordinary
hydrogen

Deuterium

Tritium

2-14 Isotopes of hydrogen.

Atomic Notation

Chlorine-35 and chlorine-37 are two common isotopes of chlorine. The chemist often writes these isotopes as $^{35}_{17}Cl$ and $^{37}_{17}Cl$. The subscript gives the atomic number, which is the number of protons *or* electrons. The superscript gives the mass number, the number of protons *and* neutrons. Thus $^{35}_{17}Cl$ contains 17 protons and 18 neutrons in its nucleus, as well as 17 electrons outside the nucleus. $^{37}_{17}Cl$, the heavier of the two naturally occurring isotopes, differs only in having an *additional* two neutrons in its nucleus. (In discussing radioactive elements, as in Unit 3, scientists often delete the atomic number. Thus $^{35}_{17}Cl$ becomes ^{35}Cl.)

QUESTIONS AND PROBLEMS

1. Answer each of the following questions: (a) Why must the assigned nuclear charge of an atom be a positive whole number? (b) Why are the atomic weights of most elements not whole numbers?
2. (a) Differentiate between the atomic number and the atomic weight of an element. (b) What is the mass number of an isotope?
3. What is the weight in grams of an atom of each of the following: $^{24}_{12}Mg$, $^{14}_{7}N$, ^{2}H, ^{40}Ar? Why can the weight of the electrons be disregarded in these calculations?
4. (a) How did Bohr account for every spectral line of hydrogen? (b) Why is the term *energy level* used interchangeably with *orbit?*
5. A chemist determines that an element, Q, consists of 60 percent ^{100}Q and 40 percent ^{105}Q. Determine the atomic weight of Q.

THE BOHR ATOM

Helium

The year 1913 marked a great turning point in atomic theory. Bohr developed a detailed picture of the hydrogen atom, and Moseley determined the charge on the nuclei of atoms. But what of other atoms? How are the electrons of other atoms distributed about the nucleus? How, for example, are the 2 electrons of helium or the 10 electrons of neon distributed in electron shells, or energy levels?

Electron Structure and the Inert Gases

From his X-ray experiments Moseley had concluded that there is *a maximum of two electrons in the first energy level, or innermost electron shell, of atoms of any element with an atomic number 2 or greater.* Moreover, the helium atom, which contains only two electrons, has these two electrons in a *completed* first shell ($n = 1$).

Beginning in 1894, Sir William Ramsay and his coworkers discovered helium and the whole group of inert gaseous elements to which it belongs. All these gases resembled helium in their inactivity. Perhaps, like helium, each of these elements contains a maximum number of electrons in their outermost electron shell. This is indeed the case. The number turns out to be 8 electrons for each of these elements except helium (Fig. 2-15).

Neon

2-15 The maximum number of electrons in the outer shell of an inert gas is eight except helium, in which the maximum number is two.

Table 2-4 WEIGHTS OF ELEMENTS AND ISOTOPES

Elements and isotopes	Atomic weight
Hydrogen	1.00797
Hydrogen-1	1.0078252
Hydrogen-2	2.0141022
Hydrogen-3	3.017005
Oxygen	15.9994
Oxygen-16	15.9949149
Oxygen-17	16.999133
Oxygen-18	17.9991598
Sulfur	32.064
Sulfur-32	31.9822
Sulfur-33	32.9819
Sulfur-34	33.9786
Sulfur-36	35.9784
Chlorine	35.453
Chlorine-35	34.97990
Chlorine-37	36.97754

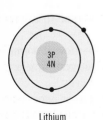

Lithium

2-16 In an atom of lithium, two electrons complete the first, or K, shell; the third electron enters the second, or L, shell.

Thus neon, which contains 10 electrons as indicated by its atomic number 10, has 2 electrons in the first shell and 8 electrons in the second shell ($n = 2$). In fact, W. Kossel of Germany pointed out in 1916 that the *octet* of electrons, or 8 electrons, in the outermost shell of the inert gases was responsible for great stability. Yet the question remains: What is the electronic structure of elements with atomic numbers between 2 and 10?

Bohr's Atomic Model

An atom of lithium (Li), atomic number 3, has 3 protons in its nucleus, giving it a charge of +3. As any positive charge on the nucleus is always balanced by an equal negative charge, the atom must contain 3 electrons. Two of the electrons complete the first, or K, shell, and a single electron is found in the second, or L, shell (Fig. 2-16). How did Bohr relate these structures to the structure of lithium?

He treated the +3 nucleus and the two electrons in the first shell as an inner part of the atom having a total charge of +1. He thought of the one electron in the second shell as revolving around this +1 inner structure, much as in a hydrogen atom, where the one electron is also attracted to the nucleus with a charge of +1. The outermost electron, on receiving a photon of energy, would jump to a higher shell, or energy level. A spectral line would be produced as the excited electron fell back to a lower energy level. Bohr's calculations, using this model, gave close agreement with the known spectrum of lithium.

According to Bohr's atomic model, beryllium (Be), atomic number 4, has 2 electrons in the first shell and 2 electrons in the second shell. Each succeeding element has one more electron in the second shell, until a maximum of 8 is reached for neon, atomic number 10.

Atoms of all succeeding elements contain two completed shells of electrons: the first shell has a maximum of 2 electrons and the second a maximum of 8 electrons. With sodium, atomic number 11, a third, or M, shell begins. In sodium, the third shell contains one electron. Each of the succeeding elements contains one more electron in its third shell, until this shell is complete with 8 electrons in argon (Ar), atomic number 18.

Bohr's structure of atoms with electrons in definite shells, or energy levels, could explain molecule formation, the spectra of elements, and much more. The understanding of the atom had advanced to a high point 125 years after Dalton's Atomic Theory. But unexpected details about atomic structure were yet to come. Their discovery is the province of the next chapter.

QUESTIONS AND PROBLEMS

1. Draw electron shell diagrams of atoms of the following isotopes: ^3_2He, $^{10}_5\text{B}$, $^{14}_6\text{C}$, $^{26}_{12}\text{Mg}$, $^{32}_{16}\text{S}$, $^{39}_{18}\text{Ar}$.
2. (a) Predict the number of electrons in each electron shell of an atom of potassium, $^{39}_{19}\text{K}$. (b) What is the basis of your prediction?
3. What is the significance of an octet of electrons?

VALUE OF THE CONCEPT

THE CONCEPT

By 1880 experimental evidence began to indicate that Dalton's solid, indestructible atoms were made up of smaller subatomic particles. In 1911 Rutherford's work yielded convincing evidence that the mass and positive charge of each atom were concentrated in the core, or nucleus, which is surrounded by relatively vast space containing the negatively charged electrons.

In 1900, Max Planck formulated the quantum theory, according to which light consists of quanta or photons of definite energy traveling with a wave motion ($E = h\nu$). Using this theory and experimental evidence of bright-line spectra, Niels Bohr in 1913 proposed that the electron of a hydrogen atom revolves around the nucleus in one of several circular orbits, each at a definite distance from the nucleus. Bohr further asserted that electrons do not radiate energy while in an orbit, or energy level, but do so when changing from an outer orbit to an orbit nearer the nucleus. A definite amount of energy is associated with each orbit, or energy level, and the energy increases with increasing distance from the nucleus.

By 1923 experimentation indicated that atoms are made up of protons and neutrons in a dense, massive nucleus, surrounded by electrons moving in discrete three-dimensional shells at relatively great distances. There is a maximum of two electrons in the first, or K, shell; a maximum of 8 electrons in the second, or L, shell; and a maximum of 8 electrons in the third shell (M) of atoms of elements with atomic numbers through 20.

Atoms differ in their atomic weights or masses. Atomic weights are never whole numbers, partly because of the existence of isotopes—atoms of the same element having different weights. The existence of isotopes is explained by the different numbers of neutrons within the nuclei of atoms of the same element. The number of protons and neutrons in the nucleus of an isotope determines its mass number. The number of protons in any atom of an element determines the atomic number of the element. The mass number minus the atomic number equals the number of neutrons in each atom of the isotope.

USING THE CONCEPT

Using the Basic Concept

1. How did Thomson's original atomic model differ from Dalton's model?
2. In terms of subatomic particles, explain why atoms are neutral particles.
3. Describe how evidence from Rutherford's gold foil experiment changed scientists' concept of the atom.
4. What is meant by atomic number?
5. In relation to atomic structure, indicate the significance of these terms: *electron shells, quanta, energy levels, octet.*
6. Why is the term *energy level* frequently used in discussion of the electron structure of atoms?
7. (a) Define *atomic weight* as Dalton used the term and as we use the term today. (b) What is an atomic mass unit, or amu?
8. (a) What are isotopes? (b) What is the mass number of an isotope? (c) Is the atomic weight or atomic number the same for isotopes of a given element? Why?
9. (a) Differentiate between an electron in the excited state and the ground state in a hydrogen atom. (b) How is the location of an electron related to its energy?
10. (a) What happens to the electrons of sodium when sodium chloride is placed in a Bunsen burner flame? (b) What determines the spectrum produced?
11. (a) What is the quantum theory of light? (b) What is its significance to the study of atomic structures?
12. If you know the frequency of a photon of green light, how can you determine its (a) wavelength, (b) energy?
13. How does the energy of various colors of light vary with their (a) frequency, (b) wavelength?
14. Draw an electron shell diagram of each of the following isotopes: ^2_1H, $^{18}_8O$.

15. List the number of electrons, protons, and neutrons present in each atom of the following pairs of isotopes: $^{12}_{6}C$, $^{14}_{6}C$; $^{16}_{8}O$, $^{17}_{8}O$; $^{1}_{1}H$, $^{3}_{1}H$; $^{13}_{7}N$; $^{14}_{7}N$; $^{3}_{2}He$, $^{4}_{2}He$.

16. If you know the wavelength of a photon of ultraviolet light, how can you determine its energy?

Relating Terms Within the Concept

From the terms below, select the term that best completes each of the following statements. Do not use a term more than once. *atom, atomic nucleus, atomic number, atomic weight, cathode rays, electrons, energy level, isotopes, mass number, neutrons, protons, quanta*

1. Atoms of the same element containing equal numbers of protons but different numbers of neutrons are _____.
2. In any element the number of protons plus the number of neutrons equals the _____.
3. The shells surrounding the nucleus of an atom contain _____.
4. The number of electrons in an atom equals the number of _____.
5. The positively charged, relatively dense part of an atom is the _____.
6. The beams of electrons in certain types of Crookes tubes form _____.
7. The number of protons in an atom determines its _____.
8. The relative weight (or mass) of an element compared to the weight of carbon-12 is the element's _____.
9. Neutral particles that are approximately equal in mass to protons are _____.
10. The discrete amounts of energy that electrons gain or lose as they move from one orbit to another are expressed in _____.

Solving Problems Within the Concept

1. Analysis shows that a 28-gram sample of carbon monoxide contains 12 grams of carbon and 16 grams of oxygen. Assuming that each molecule of carbon monoxide contains one atom each of carbon and oxygen, and accepting 12 amu or simply 12 as the atomic weight of carbon, what is the atomic weight of oxygen? Show how you obtain the answer.

2. Boron consists of two isotopes having masses of 10.0 and 11.0. As the atomic weight of boron is 10.81, what is the percentage of each isotope?

3. If each hydrogen atom weighs approximately 1.67×10^{-24} gram, and if each carbon atom is about twelve times as heavy as a hydrogen atom, how much does each carbon atom weigh?

Applying the Concept

1. An electron of a hydrogen atom falls from the third to the first energy level. List *in proper sequence* the equations you would use to determine the wavelength of the photon emitted if you know the energy of the atom in the excited state and the ground state.

2. Fifty percent by weight of a sulfur dioxide sample is sulfur and 50 percent is oxygen. Each sulfur dioxide molecule contains one atom of sulfur and two atoms of oxygen. From this data show that the atomic weight of sulfur is 32.

3. When atoms of certain elements are bombarded with high-energy particles their nuclei become altered. Sometimes a nucleus gives off 2 protons and 2 neutrons (an alpha particle). (a) What effect does this change have upon the atomic number of the element involved? (b) Is a different element formed? How do you know?

Reading Further

Physics, 2d. ed., by the Physical Science Study Committee, Boston, Heath, 1965. Chapter VII, "Mass and the Elements," as well as Chapter VIII, "Atoms and Molecules," are excellent reading for background material related to the structure of atoms.

3

A Modern Concept of the Atom

Consider any small, light object—say, a nickel coin. You know how easy it is to flip a nickel. This isn't surprising because a nickel weighs only about 5.5 grams. But suppose you packed the same-sized nickel with matter from which the electrons had been removed. You would then have a nickel composed entirely of nuclear material—and it would be so heavy that you couldn't lift it! The weight of this imaginary nuclear nickel would be about 1×10^{14} grams, or nearly 100,000,000 tons!

OUTSIDE THE NUCLEUS

Even today the only subatomic particle known to exist outside the extremely heavy nucleus is the extremely light electron. Yet it is these very electrons that are responsible for the myriad of chemical compounds and reactions. Hence, when certain experimental evidence could not be explained on the basis of Bohr's atomic model, chemists and physicists continued to pursue their study of the atom—particularly of the electron. What are some of the experimental details that helped these scientists reach a better understanding of atomic structure?

Ionization Energy

You know that a certain amount of energy can raise the electron in a hydrogen atom from the ground state to the second energy level. *This energy is quantized, or packaged, in that it occurs only in definite amounts.* The energy may be an ultraviolet photon (quantum) having an energy of 10.2 ev. If the energy is heat or that of a bombarding electron, the quantum of energy must still be 10.2 ev. When the *excited* electron, or electron raised above its ground state, returns from the second to the first energy level, a photon of ultraviolet light with 10.2 ev of energy is emitted.

What happens if the energy of the bombarding electron is increased above 10.2 ev? If the energy of the bombarding electrons is 13.6 ev or higher, the electron of hydrogen is removed *completely* from the atom (Fig. 3-1). The atom is no longer neutral; it is a positively charged particle, or *positive ion*, with a charge of $+1$, H^+ (or H^{+1}).

$$H + 13.6 \text{ ev} \longrightarrow H^+ + e^-$$

Today scientists know that any quantum of energy of 13.6 ev or higher,

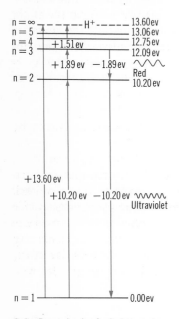

3-1 Energy levels of a hydrogen atom. A quantum of energy of 10.2 ev raises the electron from the first to the second energy level, and a photon of ultraviolet light is emitted as the electron falls back. Any quantum of energy of 13.6 ev or higher removes the electron completely from the atom, leaving a hydrogen ion.

can cause an electron to break away from the atom altogether, that is, to bring about the **ionization** of a hydrogen atom. In fact, for each element there is a different quantum of energy that will remove an electron from an atom. This quantity of energy is called the **ionization energy** of the atom. When expressed in electron volts, it is commonly called the **ionization potential.** The electron removed always comes from the highest energy level, and *the first ionization potential for an atom of any element is the minimum energy that will remove an electron from its highest energy level.*

Consider again your investigation of the spectrum of sodium. The excited outermost electron loses 2.1 ev of energy in emitting a photon (quantum) of yellow light and falling back to the ground state in the third energy level. Hence 2.1 ev of energy would also raise the electron from the third energy level to a higher level. If, however, 5.1 ev of energy are added to the atom, the electron is removed completely from the atom, or the atom becomes a sodium ion, Na^+:

$$Na + 5.1 \text{ ev} \longrightarrow Na^+ + e^-$$

Here, as in hydrogen and all other elements, the minimum energy to remove an electron, the ionization energy, is much greater than the energy required to raise an electron to a higher energy level within the atom.

The ionization process does not necessarily stop with the removal of one electron. If we use bombarding electrons of progressively higher energy, it is possible to remove a second electron from the atom, that is, to form a positive ion with a charge of $+2$.

$$Na^+ + 47.3 \text{ ev} \longrightarrow Na^{+2} + e^-$$

But this second ionization potential (47.3 ev) is approximately 9 times the first ionization potential. Why?

In a neutral atom, the positively charged protons in the nucleus exert an attractive force on an equal number of electrons. Energy must be used to overcome the attraction of the nucleus for the electron being removed. But after the first electron is removed, *the same nuclear charge is now attracting a smaller number of electrons.* The remaining electrons are pulled closer to the nucleus, and the nuclear attraction on the remaining electrons is greater than in the neutral atom. It is not surprising, therefore, that more energy is required to remove a second, third, or fourth electron.

Ionization Potential and Atomic Structure

Now let us consider why the second ionization potential of a sodium atom is so much greater than for a magnesium atom. From the electron-shell diagram of these atoms in Figure 3-2, observe that each atom has the same number of electron shells. After one electron is removed from a magnesium atom, one electron will still remain in the third shell. However, after one electron has been removed from a sodium atom, the second electron must come from the *second* shell, which is much closer to

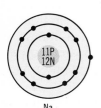

Na

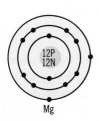

Mg

3-2 Although both atoms have the same numbers of electron shells, the outer shell of magnesium contains two electrons while the outer shell of sodium contains only one.

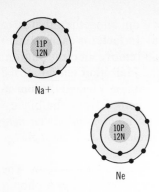

Na+

Ne

3-3 The electron configuration of the sodium ion and the inert neon atom are identical. How do these particles differ?

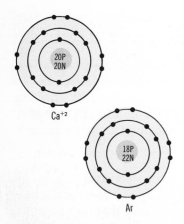

Ca+2

Ar

3-4 The calcium ion has the same electron configuration as the argon atom. The inert gas configuration of filled outer electron shells has great stability.

the nucleus. The force exerted by the nucleus is much greater on electrons in the second shell, since they are much closer to the positive nucleus.

Notice in Table 3-1 that for each element the *ionization potential on the right side of the double line is much greater than the preceding ionization potential on the left side of the same double line.* This marked increase in ionization potential is much greater than the increase between any other two consecutive ionization potentials for that element. Observe that the second ionization potential for sodium, Na, atomic number 11, which is much higher than the first, is at the right of the double line. And the third ionization potential of magnesium, Mg, atomic number 12, which is much higher than either the first or second, is also at the right of the double line. Thus, for each element the values at the right of the double line are for electrons in *an energy level closer to the nucleus.* In other words, in any atom more energy is required to remove each successive electron in the outer shell, but *a sudden marked increase in energy is required to remove an electron from an inner shell.*

Ionization Potential and the Inert Gases

Another interesting observation we can make from Table 3-1 is that the highest ionization potentials are those of the three inert gases: helium, He; neon, Ne; and argon, Ar, atomic numbers 2, 10, and 18, respectively. This could have been expected from the low chemical reactivity of this group of elements. Also notice that the elements lithium, Li; sodium, Na; and potassium, K, which immediately follow the respective inert gases, have the lowest first ionization potentials. When these elements react, their atoms lose one electron, and each atom acquires a single positive charge. These charged particles, or ions, are represented as Na+, Li+, and K+, respectively (Fig. 3-3). Whenever atoms of beryllium, Be; magnesium, Mg; and calcium, Ca, react, they each lose two electrons to reach the respective inert gas configuration (Fig. 3-4). The ions formed by these elements are Be+2, Mg+2, and Ca+2, respectively. Apparently, special stability is attached to the inert gas electron configuration of filled outer shells.

Thus far our examination of the successive ionization potentials gives strong support to the Bohr model of the atom. Perhaps there is further information hidden in the Table of Ionization Potentials.

Some Apparent Inconsistencies

Examine once again the first ionization potentials of the elements in Table 3-1 (and the graph of these values on page 75). Observe that there is a gradual increase in ionization potential from lithium to neon, and from sodium to argon. Although there is a trend toward a gradual increase with atomic numbers, there are several unexpected values: boron, B, atomic number 5, has a lower ionization potential than beryllium, Be, atomic number 4. And oxygen, atomic number 8, has a lower ionization potential than nitrogen, atomic number 7.

Table 3-1   IONIZATION POTENTIALS

Element	Symbol	Atomic number	Ionization potential*							
			1st	*2nd*	*3rd*	*4th*	*5th*	*6th*	*7th*	*8th*
Hydrogen	H	1	13.6							
Helium	He	2	24.6	54.4						
Lithium	Li	3	5.4||	75.6	122					
Beryllium	Be	4	9.3	18.2||	154	218				
Boron	B	5	8.3	25.2	37.9||	259	339			
Carbon	C	6	11.3	24.4	47.9	64.5||	391			
Nitrogen	N	7	14.5	29.6	47.4	77.5	98.0||	508	665	
Oxygen	O	8	13.6	35.2	54.9	77.4	114	138||	736	876
Fluorine	F	9	17.4	35.0	62.7	87.2	114	156	202||	950
Neon	Ne	10	21.6	41.1	64.0	97.2				
Sodium	Na	11	5.1||	47.3	71.7	98.9				
Magnesium	Mg	12	7.6	15.0||	80.1	109				
Aluminum	Al	13	6.0	18.8	28.4||	120				
Silicon	Si	14	8.2	16.3	33.5	45.1||	166			
Phosphorus	P	15	11.0	19.7	30.2	51.4	65 ||			
Sulfur	S	16	10.4	23.4	35.0	47.3	72.2	87.2||		
Chlorine	Cl	17	13.0	23.8	39.9	53.5	67.8	96.8	114||	
Argon	Ar	18	15.8	27.6	40.9	59.8				
Potassium	K	19	4.3||	31.8						
Calcium	Ca	20	6.1	11.8||	51.0					
Scandium	Sc	21	6.6	12.9	24.8||	73.9				
Titanium	Ti	22	6.8	13.6	27.5	43.1||	100			
Vanadium	V	23	6.7	14.1	26.5	48.5	64.0||	131		
Chromium	Cr	24	6.8	16.7	32.2	51.0	72.8	90.0||	168	
Manganese	Mn	25	7.4	15.6	34.0	53.1	75.9	101	118||	206

* In electron volts per atom

These unexpected ionization potentials not only raised question about the Bohr model, but also had to be resolved before any new atomic model could be accepted. Did any other experimental evidence also point to the need for a revised concept of the atom?

QUESTIONS AND PROBLEMS

1. (a) Which group of elements has the highest ionization potentials? (b) How many electrons are there in the outer shell in each of these elements? (c) How many electrons are there in the outer shell of the three elements with the lowest ionization potentials?
2. Why is the third ionization potential of beryllium (Be) almost nine times as great as its second ionization potential?
3. Why is the first ionization potential of calcium greater than that of potassium, while the second ionization of potassium is greater than that of calcium?

4. How many electrons must be removed from an atom of each of the following elements before there is a great increase in the energy required to remove the next electron: boron (B), carbon (C), nitrogen (N), oxygen (O), and fluorine (F)?
5. Write equations including the ionization potentials to produce (a) Al^+ from Al, (b) Al^{+2} from Al^+, (c) Al^{+3} from Al^{+2}.

A NEW ATOMIC MODEL IS NEEDED

The double yellow line in the spectrum of sodium is but one example of many such double lines. For example, every spectral line of hydrogen has been found, under great magnification, to consist of closely spaced lines, or **doublets.** Could it be that the small difference in wavelength in all doublets means that the energy levels in atoms are much closer to each other than Bohr had postulated?

Other spectra indicated that there may be many more energy levels, or shells, than in Bohr's model of the atom. Moreover, even the jumping electron, the cause of the bright-line spectra, was found to have a strange, unforeseen character.

Wave Nature of the Electron

In 1924 the French physicist Louis de Broglie suggested as a result of his theoretical work that every moving particle, just like light, has a wave nature associated with it. And only three years later, C. J. Davisson of the United States and G. P. Thomson of England independently interpreted the results of their experiments on the scattering of electrons by a metal surface to mean that electrons have a wave nature (Fig. 3-5).

In similar experiments scientists have found that the electron may reach a velocity almost half the velocity of light. Wavelengths of 0.05Å have been measured for such electrons. The electron does indeed have a dual nature—particle and wave. Under these conditions, how can we possibly determine the precise position of an electron in an atom?

The Uncertainty Principle

In answer to this question, Werner Heisenberg of Germany announced his *uncertainty principle* in 1927. According to this principle, it is impossible to determine simultaneously the position and velocity of any minute body such as an electron or a photon. Although Heisenberg developed the principle on a theoretical basis, let us think of it on an experimental basis. We see a moving airplane because photons of light from the sun strike the plane and are reflected to our eyes. Since the photons have such a small mass, we would hardly expect them to alter the motion of the plane in any way.

On the other hand, photons of very short wavelengths (high energy) would be required to illuminate an electron. Such photons colliding with an electron would so completely change the motion of the electron

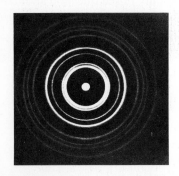

3-5 This photograph resulted when G. P. Thomson passed a stream of electrons through very thin gold foil and allowed the resulting beam to fall on a photographic plate. The concentric circles indicate the wave nature of the electron.

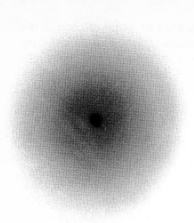

3-6 Illustrating the invisible requires imagination. Some scientists visualize an electron cloud as the pattern made by a bee flying about a flower. As the bee spends most of its time near the pollen, the bee's path, when plotted, is darker near the center. However the path has no distinct edges.

that any attempt to determine the position of the electron a second time would be impossible. Hence the net result of the uncertainty principle is that it is impossible to determine precisely the position of an electron within the atom at any given moment.

The existence of so many spectral lines, the irregularities of ionization potentials, the wave nature of the electron, and the impossibility of describing the precise path of an electron all pointed to the need for a revised model of the atom.

QUESTIONS AND PROBLEMS

1. Describe briefly three conditions that pointed to the need for a revision of the Bohr model of the electron structure of the atom.
2. How is the work of de Broglie, Davisson, and G. P. Thomson related to our understanding of the nature of the electron?
3. Why can't a calcium atom (diameter 3.94 Å) be seen with visible light?
4. The yellow light emitted by sodium has wavelengths of 5896 Å and 5890 Å. What name is given to such closely spaced wavelengths?
5. What is the significance of the uncertainty principle to atomic structure?

THE WAVE-MECHANICAL MODEL OF THE ATOM

Imagine the first rose of the year. A bee flies about it with an erratic motion. Most of the time the bee is near the pollen—above it, beside it, beneath it—but on occasion it may be at any distance, in any direction from the flower. If the position of the bee were plotted at one-second intervals, you would obtain a pattern similar to that in Fig. 3-6.

According to our present concept of the atom, if the electron in a hydrogen atom in the ground state were plotted at much shorter intervals, you would get the same type of spherical pattern—often called an electron cloud, or *charge cloud,* diagram. The electron is actually believed to travel toward and away from the nucleus in every possible direction to give the effect of a spherical atom or an electron cloud with decreasing density at greater distances from the nucleus and with no distinct edge. How did scientists develop this concept of the atom?

Schroedinger and Wave Mechanics

By 1925 many chemists and physicists had turned their attention to developing a concept of the atom that would incorporate Bohr's idea of fixed energy levels, Heisenberg's uncertainty principle, and de Broglie's wave nature of the electron. In 1926, Erwin Schroedinger of Austria proposed his idea of **wave mechanics,** or **quantum mechanics.** According to his *wave-mechanical model* of the atom, the electron is a three-dimensional wave surrounding the nucleus of the atom.

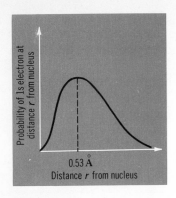

3-7 In keeping with Heisenberg's uncertainty principle, no definite path can be traced for an electron. Hence the graph indicates the probability of finding a 1s electron at distance r from the nucleus. What is the maximum probability of r?

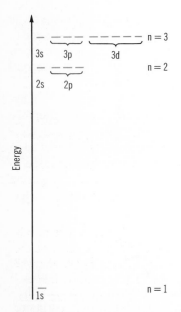

3-8 In this diagram of hydrogen orbitals, observe that the number of orbitals increases with the value of the energy level, designated n.

According to wave mechanics, electrons, as Bohr had postulated, were in fixed energy states and could move about the nucleus without radiating away their energy. However, we can not assign an exact position to the electron; rather, we can say that an electron has a *maximum probability* of being at a certain distance from the nucleus. Interestingly enough, calculations from the wave equation indicate that 0.53 Å is the most probable distance from the nucleus of an electron in a hydrogen atom in the ground state—and this is the same distance that Bohr had predicted. But while Bohr thought that the electron of hydrogen was *always* at that distance, the wave-mechanics model indicates that the electron is *most likely* at that distance.

In more precise terms, there is a greater probability that the electron is at a distance of 0.53 Å from the nucleus than at any other distance, as shown in Fig. 3-7. However, the electron can be closer to or farther from the nucleus. In keeping with Heisenberg's uncertainty principle, no definite path can be plotted for the electron.

Orbitals of the Hydrogen Atom

In keeping with the wave-mechanics model of the atom, the spherical probability in Fig. 3-6 also represents a 1s **orbital.** An orbital is a three-dimensional space about the nucleus in which an electron of a given energy is likely to be found. Experimental evidence, especially spectral evidence, indicates that energy levels are composed of one or more sublevels (or subshells), each having a slightly different energy. These sublevels, in turn, are composed of one or more orbitals. The number of sublevels in an energy level is equal to the number of the energy level. The first energy level contains only one sublevel, labeled s; the second energy level contains two sublevels, s and p; the third energy level has three sublevels, s, p, and d; while the fourth energy level has four sublevels, s, p, d, and f.

Recall what happens when a hydrogen atom in the ground state is excited by a photon with an energy of 10.2 ev. The electron jumps to the second energy level and enters any of the *four orbitals in that energy level* (Fig. 3-8). These orbitals, which are described as 2s, $2p_x$, $2p_y$, and $2p_z$, are illustrated in Fig. 3-9. The coefficient before each letter indicates the energy level of the orbital. The p orbitals are given the subscripts x, y, and z to indicate their axes and direction in space. These orbitals are located at right angles to each other. Observe that the 2s orbital is spherical and shows two dark areas. The darker the area, the greater is the chance of finding that elusive electron in the area. Compare this electron-cloud diagram with that of the 1s orbital, with only a single dark area.

What happens when an electron in any orbital of the second energy level receives an additional photon having an energy of 1.9 ev? The electron jumps to any one of *nine different orbitals in the third energy level.* These orbitals include one s, three p, and five d orbitals, two of which are shown in Fig. 3-10. While the p orbitals are all dumbbell shaped, the d orbitals have more unusual shapes. Again, the s orbital is spherical, and it shows three distinct areas of high probability for the location of an electron. Notice that in all s orbitals, the electron has a high probability of being at the nucleus or very close to it.

Perhaps you have observed that *each energy level contains* n² *different orbitals,* with *n* being a whole number corresponding to the energy level. Thus in the first energy level, in which $n = 1$, there is 1 orbital (1^2); while in the second energy level, $n = 2$, there are 4 orbitals (2^2), and in the third energy level, $n = 3$, there are 9 orbitals. Satisfy yourself that there are 16 orbitals in the fourth energy level. This energy level contains one s, three p, five d, and seven f orbitals.

Thus far we have accounted for every feature of the hydrogen spectrum except the doublet composition of each spectral line. To resolve this problem, we must consider the atom in terms of wave mechanics, or quantum mechanics, as it developed from 1925 to 1927. According to this modern theory no two electrons can have identical motion. Although there is no way of distinguishing one electron from another, we can describe an electron in terms of *four quantum numbers.*

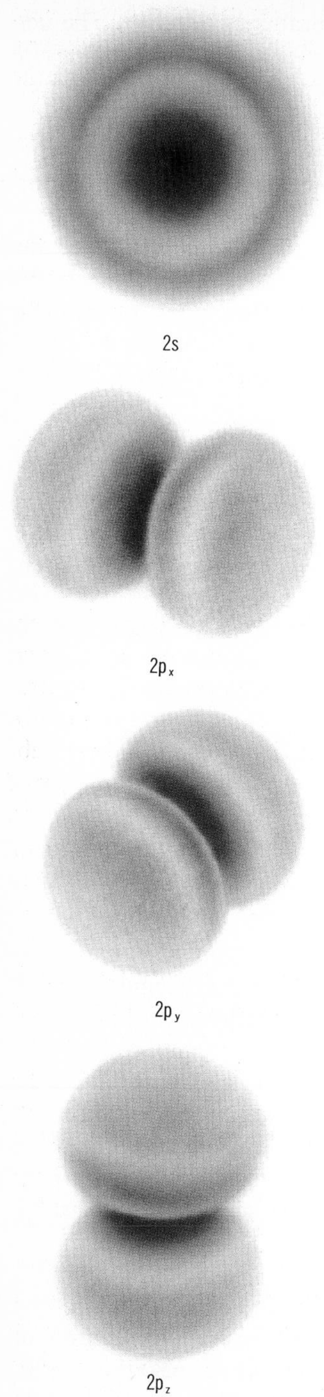

Quantum Numbers

The *first,* or *principal, quantum number, n,* indicates the energy level of the electron. The energy levels, starting with the lowest, are the first, or K level; the second, or L level; the third, or M level; and so on. In principle there is an infinite number of energy levels, but only the first seven or eight usually needs be considered. According to Bohr, remember, the electron must be in one of these principal energy levels and cannot have energy values that are between the values of the energy levels.

The *second quantum number* indicates the *shape,* or type, of the orbital. This number tells us whether the electron involved is in an s, p, d, or f orbital.

The *third quantum number* describes the orientation, or direction in space, occupied by the orbital. For example, this number distinguishes a p_x from a p_y orbital.

The *fourth quantum number* describes a characteristic of the electron we have not considered before—the so-called *spin of the electron.*

The Spin Numbers

At the same time an electron is moving rapidly around the nucleus, it is spinning like a top. If we observe the top from above, we can describe the rotation as being either clockwise or counterclockwise or, as the chemist would say, as being either positive or negative. Thus some electrons in hydrogen atoms have a positive spin number, and presumably an equal number have a negative spin number (Fig. 3-11). Since any spinning charged particle has a magnetic field around it, the magnetic effect of the spin of the electron interacts with the magnetic effect of the same electron as it revolves about the nucleus. If the spin number is positive, the elec-

2s

2p$_x$

2p$_y$

2p$_z$

3-9 Electron cloud representations of the 2s and the three 2 p orbitals.

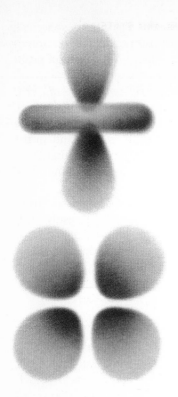

3-10 Electron cloud representations of two of the unusual-shaped 3d orbitals.

tron has higher energy than when the spin number is negative. The net effect of these slight energy differences is that single electrons, such as in hydrogen atoms, give doublet spectral lines rather than the single line observed when their spectra were first examined.

In 1925, the same year that electron spin was postulated, Wolfgang Pauli pointed out that no two electrons in an atom can have all four quantum numbers identical. According to this Pauli *exclusion principle, no more than two electrons can occupy the same orbital in an atom, and the two electrons must have opposite spins.* Moreover, if there are two electrons in the same orbital, their magnetic effects cancel each other. In the next section we will extend these ideas of quantum numbers and the Pauli exclusion principle to atoms of elements more complex than hydrogen.

QUESTIONS AND PROBLEMS

1. According to wave mechanics, (a) what is an electron, (b) what is the significance of the distance 0.53 Å from the nucleus of the hydrogen atom?
2. (a) How many different orbitals are there in the first, second, third, fourth, and fifth energy levels of the hydrogen atom? (b) Name and describe the shape of the orbitals in the sublevels of the second energy level.
3. What does an electron cloud diagram of hydrogen represent?
4. What properties of orbitals or electrons does each of the four quantum numbers describe?

ATOMIC DIAGRAMS AND THE WAVE-MECHANICAL MODEL

Because a hydrogen atom has only a single electron, scientists have been able to solve the complex wave equation for that element and to determine exactly its electron system. Because of mathematical difficulty, the wave equation has not been solved exactly for atoms of other elements. Rather, the electron system of atoms of other elements have been determined only by mathematical approximation. Experimental results have confirmed the approximations so closely, however, that the wave mechanics model—with its four quantum numbers indicating electrons in orbitals of principal energy levels about the nucleus—is established.

Orbital Diagrams

Let us consider the orbital structure, or electron configuration, of the elements *in their ground states.* The electron configuration of an atom of hydrogen is represented pictorially as $\boxed{\uparrow}$ and by orbital notation as $1s^1$. The coefficient 1 refers to the first quantum number, the principal energy level. The exponent 1 indicates that there is only one electron in the orbital. Some hydrogen atoms have an electron with a positive spin while otherwise identical atoms have an electron with a negative spin $\boxed{\downarrow}$.

↑ + spin   ↓ − spin

3-11 The two electrons in any orbital spin in opposite directions. Electrons that spin in a clockwise motion, when considered from above, are assigned a positive spin number; those that spin counterclockwise, a negative spin number.

Table 3-2 ELECTRON CONFIGURATIONS OF ATOMS IN THE GROUND STATE

Name	Symbol	Atomic number	1s	2s	2p	3s	3p	3d	4s	Orbital notation
Hydrogen	H	1	↑							$1s^1$
Helium	He	2	↑↓							$1s^2$
Lithium	Li	3	↑↓	↑						$1s^2 2s^1$
Beryllium	Be	4	↑↓	↑↓						$1s^2 2s^2$
Boron	B	5	↑↓	↑↓	↑					$1s^2 2s^2 2p^1$
Carbon	C	6	↑↓	↑↓	↑ ↑					$1s^2 2s^2 2p^2$
Nitrogen	N	7	↑↓	↑↓	↑ ↑ ↑					$1s^2 2s^2 2p^3$
Oxygen	O	8	↑↓	↑↓	↑↓ ↑ ↑					$1s^2 2s^2 2p^4$
Fluorine	F	9	↑↓	↑↓	↑↓ ↑↓ ↑					$1s^2 2s^2 2p^5$
Neon	Ne	10	↑↓	↑↓	↑↓ ↑↓ ↑↓					$1s^2 2s^2 2p^6$
Sodium	Na	11	↑↓	↑↓	↑↓ ↑↓ ↑↓	↑				$1s^2 2s^2 2p^6 3s^1$
Magnesium	Mg	12	↑↓	↑↓	↑↓ ↑↓ ↑↓	↑↓				$1s^2 2s^2 2p^6 3s^2$
Aluminum	Al	13	↑↓	↑↓	↑↓ ↑↓ ↑↓	↑↓	↑			$1s^2 2s^2 2p^6 3s^2 3p^1$
Silicon	Si	14	↑↓	↑↓	↑↓ ↑↓ ↑↓	↑↓	↑ ↑			$1s^2 2s^2 2p^6 3s^2 3p^2$
Phosphorus	P	15	↑↓	↑↓	↑↓ ↑↓ ↑↓	↑↓	↑ ↑ ↑			$1s^2 2s^2 2p^6 3s^2 3p^3$
Sulfur	S	16	↑↓	↑↓	↑↓ ↑↓ ↑↓	↑↓	↑↓ ↑ ↑			$1s^2 2s^2 2p^6 3s^2 3p^4$
Chlorine	Cl	17	↑↓	↑↓	↑↓ ↑↓ ↑↓	↑↓	↑↓ ↑↓ ↑			$1s^2 2s^2 2p^6 3s^2 3p^5$
Argon	Ar	18	↑↓	↑↓	↑↓ ↑↓ ↑↓	↑↓	↑↓ ↑↓ ↑↓			$1s^2 2s^2 2p^6 3s^2 3p^6$
Potassium	K	19	↑↓	↑↓	↑↓ ↑↓ ↑↓	↑↓	↑↓ ↑↓ ↑↓		↑	$1s^2 2s^2 2p^6 3s^2 3p^6 4s^1$
Calcium	Ca	20	↑↓	↑↓	↑↓ ↑↓ ↑↓	↑↓	↑↓ ↑↓ ↑↓		↑↓	$1s^2 2s^2 2p^6 3s^2 3p^6 4s^2$
Scandium	Sc	21	↑↓	↑↓	↑↓ ↑↓ ↑↓	↑↓	↑↓ ↑↓ ↑↓	↑	↑↓	$1s^2 2s^2 2p^6 3s^2 3p^6 3d^1 4s^2$

Helium, He, atomic number 2, is represented pictorially as ↑↓. This paired electron condition indicates that the orbital is *filled* and that there is no net magnetic effect because of the opposite spin of the electrons. Helium has an orbital notation $1s^2$. According to helium's orbital notation, $1s^2$, two electrons, or an electron pair, occupy the same orbital in the first principal energy level.

Lithium, atomic number 3, must use a higher-energy orbital for its third electron, since the first energy level can contain only two electrons. Hence, its orbital representation is ↑↓ ↑, and its orbital notation is $1s^2\ 2s^1$. For beryllium, atomic number 4, the electron configuration is

$\boxed{\uparrow\downarrow}\;\boxed{\uparrow\downarrow}$, and its orbital notation is $1s^2\,2s^2$. The next element, boron, atomic number 5, must have its fifth electron in one of the three 2p orbitals. Although the 2p orbitals are higher in energy than the 2s orbitals, they are still part of principal energy level two. The orbital representation and notation for boron, B, are shown in Table 3-2, which gives the orbital representation and notation for the first twenty-one elements. Observe that two of the three 2p orbitals of boron are empty.

Now study the electron configuration for carbon, C, atomic number 6. Why is the sixth electron shown in the $2p_y$ orbital rather than in the $2p_x$ orbital? It has been determined experimentally that the electron configuration $1s^2\,2s^2\,2p_x{}^2$, which you *might* have anticipated for carbon, is 1.3 ev above the ground state. But scientists have found that the *lowest energy state is the most stable,* and, in general, *when p, d, or f orbitals are being "filled," successive electrons enter an unfilled orbital having the same energy, and the electron spins remain parallel.* Thus, if $1s^2\,2s^2\,2p_x{}^2$ were the configuration, the electrons would not occupy the lowest energy levels, and the carbon atom would not be in its most stable state.

Now follow the atomic orbital configurations of the elements until all three p orbitals are complete in neon, Ne, atomic number 10. Observe that in the second principal energy level one electron enters each of the p orbitals *before a second electron enters any* p *orbital.*

Electron Configurations and Higher Energy Levels

The next eight succeeding elements, from sodium, Na, atomic number 11, through argon, Ar, atomic number 18, show a regular buildup in the s and p orbitals of the third principal energy level. Notice once again that one electron enters each of the p orbitals before a second electron enters any of the p orbitals.

Principal energy level three, as you know, has nine different orbitals one 3s, three 3p, and five 3d orbitals; and the energy of the orbitals increases in the same order: s, p, d. Argon, Ar, with eighteen electrons has the electron configuration $1s^2\,2s^2\,2p^6\,3s^2\,3p^6$. Predict the electron configuration for the ground state of potassium, K, with nineteen electrons. Before doing so, you should know two important facts. First, although the third energy level consists of nine *p* orbitals that can contain a maximum of 18 electrons, *the outermost shell of any atom can contain no more than 8 electrons.* Second, potassium resembles lithium and sodium in chemical activity, and each of these two elements contains a single s electron in its highest energy level. Actually, it has been determined that in its highest energy level, potassium contains a single electron in the 4s orbital rather than in the 3*d* orbital as you might have expected. Its orbital configuration is $1s^2\,2s^2\,2p^6\,3s^2\,3p^6\,4s^1$. If this trend continues, calcium, Ca, atomic number 20, should have a completed 4s orbital, and it does.

Study carefully Figure 3-12 of the orbital energies of the first thirty elements. The values graphed there have been determined experimentally from spectroscopic evidence. According to this graph, *the 4s orbital is lower in energy than the 3d orbital for all elements having atomic numbers*

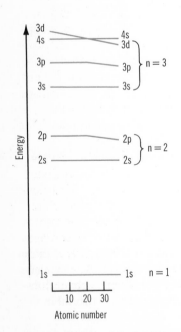

3-12 Orbital energies of the first thirty elements. For all elements with atomic numbers less than 21, the 4s orbital is lower in energy than the 3d orbital.

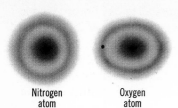

Nitrogen atom   Oxygen atom

3-13 Because an oxygen and a nitrogen atom differ in shape, an electron at the position indicated by the dot in the oxygen atom is further from the nucleus than a similar electron in the nitrogen atom. Hence an electron in the second energy level is lost more readily by an oxygen atom than by a nitrogen atom.

less than 21. In an atom of scandium in the ground state, an electron enters the 3d orbital for the first time. Hence, the orbital configuration for scandium is $1s^2\, 2s^2\, 2p^6\, 3s^2\, 3p^6\, 3d^1\, 4s^2$. Now consider how orbital configurations are used to answer another question raised by the Bohr atom.

Electron Configurations and Ionization Potentials

The reasons for some irregularities in ionization potentials (shown in Table 3-1) can now be explained. Why does oxygen, atomic number 8, have a lower first-ionization potential than nitrogen, atomic number 7? An empirical rule chemists use to explain this apparent inconsistency is that filled or half-filled p, d, or f orbitals are very stable. According to Table 3-2, when an oxygen atom loses one electron from the $2p_x$ orbital, it assumes the stable configuration of a nitrogen atom—which has only filled or half-filled orbitals. A more basic understanding comes from wave mechanics. Calculations indicate that the nitrogen atom is spherical, while the oxygen atom has the shape of a somewhat flattened sphere, or ellipsoid. Compared with an electron in a nitrogen atom, an electron in an oxygen is more readily lost when it is farthest from the nucleus (Fig. 3-13). Now locate another element with an unexpected ionization potential situation that you can explain in the same way. Did you select sulfur?

Why does boron, atomic number 5, have a lower first-ionization potential than beryllium, atomic number 4? From Table 3-2 you can determine that the first electron lost by a boron atom is the 2p electron. Such an electron is further away from the nucleus, on the average, than the pair of 2s electrons in the same atom. The 1s and 2s electrons, which spend appreciable time near the nucleus of the atom, effectively shield the positively charged nucleus from the 2p electron. Hence the 2p electron can be fairly easily removed from the boron atom. In the beryllium atom, all four electrons spend appreciable time near the nucleus. Also, all four electrons are paired, and extra energy is needed to separate paired electrons.

Electron Cloud Diagrams

In terms of wave mechanics, how does a total atom appear when we consider all its electrons and their probable locations? Look at Figure 3-14, which represents an atom of sodium, atomic number 11. This electron cloud diagram, which gives a total probability picture of all eleven electrons, shows three darkened spherical regions, or shells. The two 1s electrons form the innermost shell, or energy level. The next shell contains eight electrons—two 2s electrons and six 2p electrons. The darker area of the outermost shell is due largely to the single 3s electron. Thus, in electron cloud diagrams each darkened area consists of all the electrons having the same principal energy level, or same quantum number.

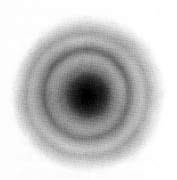

3-14 According to wave mechanics, the three darkened areas in this electron cloud diagram of a sodium atom represent the regions of greatest probabilities of finding the first, second, and third energy level electrons.

Electron Dot Diagrams

Electron cloud diagrams of atoms are difficult to draw properly and do not reveal sufficiently the changes going on in atoms during chemical reactions. In chemical changes only the electrons in the outermost shell,

3-15 Changes in the concept of the atom are developments of experimental chemistry that you should be able to reconstruct efficiently. Beginning with evidence for Dalton's model, cite the experimental evidence responsible for each model.

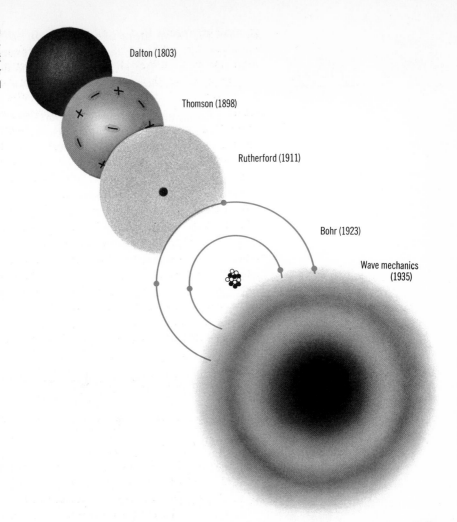

Dalton (1803)

Thomson (1898)

Rutherford (1911)

Bohr (1923)

Wave mechanics (1935)

or energy level, of the atom are involved. The electrons in the inner shells of atoms and their nuclei remain unchanged. To illustrate chemical changes, therefore, electron-dot diagrams *showing only the electrons in the outer shell* are widely used. In electron dot diagrams, the symbol for the element is surrounded by a number of dots, each representing an electron in the highest energy level. In such a diagram the letter symbol represents the *kernel* of the atom. This kernel represents both the nucleus and the electrons in all the energy levels, or shells, of the atom except the outer shell.

In the electron-dot diagrams below, the dots are arranged to show the orbital representations of elements with atomic numbers 1 through 10.

H· He: Li· Be: B: ·C· ·N: ·O: :F: :Ne:

The pair of electrons at the right of symbol He (helium) represents two 1s electrons, while those at the right of symbol Be (beryllium) represent two 2s electrons. Similarly, the two electrons at the right of the symbol B (boron) represent two 2s electrons, while the single dot beneath the B stands for the single 2p electrons. In this way chemists represent the three electrons in highest energy level of a boron atom.

Now consider the electron dot diagram for nitrogen. The pair of dots at the right of the symbol N represents the two 2s electrons. The three single dots on the other three sides of the symbol N represent the electrons in the three different 2p orbitals. In the electron dot diagram for oxygen, the pair of dots beneath the symbol O represent the filled $2p_x$ orbital, while in the diagrams for fluorine (F) and neon (Ne), the additional paired dots represent the electron pairs in the $2p_y$ and $2p_z$ orbitals, respectively.

Today, our concept of the atom is a far cry from the atom of Dalton—or even the atoms of Rutherford and Bohr. The total history of the atom as it has been revealed by advances in science over the past 150 years is summarized in Figure 3-15. These diagrams represent the structure of individual atoms. But atoms combine; in fact, atoms are seldom found singly. Atoms of the same kind combine to form elements, and unlike atoms combine to form compounds. Why are some elements usually found uncombined, while others are always found in compounds? Why are some elements more active than others? Is a given compound always the same? The next chapter discusses the answers to these and related questions.

QUESTIONS AND PROBLEMS

1. Which element has each of the following electron notations:
   (a) $1s^2\, 2s^1$, (b) $1s^2\, 2s^2\, 2p^1$, (c) $1s^2\, 2s^2\, 2p^6$, (d) $1s^2\, 2s^2\, 2p^6\, 3s^2$, (e) $1s^2\, 2s^2\, 2p^6\, 3s^2\, 3p^6\, 3d^2\, 4s^2$.
2. (a) Draw the electron dot diagram for each atom in question 1. (b) Draw the electron orbital representation for each atom.
3. (a) Write the symbols of two elements that have an electron dot structure of $:\overset{.}{X}:$ (b) Write the symbols of three elements that have an electron dot structure of $Y\cdot$.
4. Which *orbitals* are represented by the electron dot diagrams for the following atoms in the ground state: (a) $\underset{.}{Al}:$, (b) $Mg:$, (c) $\cdot Si:$, (d) $:\overset{.}{Ne}:$, (e) $\cdot\overset{.}{\underset{.}{P}}:$?
5. On the basis of electron configuration, explain why sulfur has a lower ionization potential than phosphorus.

VALUE OF THE CONCEPT

THE CONCEPT

Experimental evidences such as the observations of the details of each line in a bright-line spectrum and the existence of irregularities in ionization potential trends led chemists to seek a more satisfactory model of the atom. The wave nature of the high-speed electron and the uncertainty principle changed their ideas about the existence of definite orbits for electrons.

According to the wave-mechanical model of the atom, most of the space around the small, positively charged nucleus is occupied by rapidly moving electrons. These electrons move about the nucleus in fixed energy levels, but no definite path can be plotted. The precise position of an electron cannot be determined; rather, there is a maximum probability of its being at a given distance from the nucleus at any given moment.

Electrons are found in definite orbitals within sublevels making up the principal energy levels. Each orbital can contain a maximum of two electrons—each having opposite spin. The electrons in atoms 1 to 18 occupy orbitals in the definite order: 1s, 2s, 2p, 3s, 3p. There are three p orbitals, p_x, p_y, and p_z, each at right angles to each other. In each successive principal energy level, there is a maximum of 1, 2^2, 3^2, and 4^2 orbitals in the order of s, p, d, and f. There can be twice as many electrons as orbitals, but in no case can an outermost shell contain more than eight electrons. The orbitals, sublevels, and principal energy levels need not be filled to capacity; the outer energy levels of atoms of most elements are unfilled.

Each electron can be described in terms of four quantum numbers. These indicate, in turn, the energy level, the orbital, the direction of the orbital, and the direction of electron spin.

The knowledge of the orbital configuration of the electrons in an atom enables the drawing of electron cloud and electron dot diagrams. The latter are useful in representing chemical changes, which usually involve only the electron in the highest principal energy level.

USING THE CONCEPT

Using the Basic Concept

1. (a) Describe what is meant by an electron cloud. (b) How does an atom represented by an electron cloud diagram differ from that represented by an electron shell diagram?

2. (a) What is the ionization potential of an element? (b) What are the first ionization potentials of H, He, Li, and Al? (c) Distinguish between the first and second ionization potentials of an atom.

3. (a) Compare the first ionization potential of a sodium atom with the energy needed to excite the outermost electron so that it emits a photon of yellow light when it drops back to the ground state in the third energy level. (b) Why are the values so different?

4. The first ionization potential of beryllium is greater than that of lithium, but the second ionization potential of lithium is greater than that of beryllium. Why?

5. How did the work of each of the following scientists affect our concept of the atom: (a) de Broglie, (b) Davisson, (c) Heisenberg, (d) Schroedinger?

6. (a) What is a *doublet*? (b) What is the significance of doublets in the changing picture of atomic structure?

7. Describe an atom according to the wave-mechanical model. (Include the idea of quantum numbers in your description.)

8. (a) Using the table of electron configurations, indicate the total number of electrons in the first energy level of H and He atoms in the ground state. (b) Determine the total number of electrons in each electron shell for elements through atomic number 22.

9. (a) What is the maximum number of electrons each energy level, sublevel, and orbital can contain? (b) Differentiate between a filled and an unfilled orbital.

10. What does each of the following symbols represent: 2s, 3d, 4p, $2s^1$, $4f^2$?

11. (a) Give a general rule that describes the relative energies of orbitals within a particular atom. (b) Why are there exceptions to this rule?

12. (a) What is the maximum number of electrons the outer electron shell can contain? (b) Identify three elements whose atoms in the ground state contain this number of electrons in their outer shell.

13. What is the atomic number and the symbol for each element whose atoms have the following electron configurations: (a) $1s^1$, (b) $1s^2\ 2s^2\ 2p_x^1\ 2p_y^1$ (c) $1s^2\ 2s^2\ 2p^6\ 3s^2\ 3p^6$, (d) $1s^2\ 2s^2\ 2p^6\ 3s^2\ 3p^2$, (e) $1s^2\ 2s^2\ 2p_x^1\ 2p_y^1\ 2p_z^1$, (f) $1s^2\ 2s^2\ 2p_x^1$?

14. Draw the electron-dot structures for each atom in Question 13.
15. Draw an orbital representation for each atom in Question 13.

Relating Terms Within the Concept

Each of the following exercises consists of five terms. From the last four, select the term or terms most closely related to the *italicized* term.

1. *Doublet:* three-dimensional space, subshell, first quantum number, close spectral lines
2. *Electron dot diagram:* isotope, kernel, outer electron shell, uncertainty principle
3. *Orbital:* maximum of 2 electrons, maximum of 8 electrons, minimum of 1 electron, minimum of 0 electrons
4. *Electron-cloud diagram:* particle nature of electron, wave nature of electron, X rays, maximum probability
5. *Ionization potential:* bright-line spectrum, continuous spectrum, excited state, electron removal
6. *Excited atom:* $1s^2$, $1s^2 2s^1$, $1s^2 2s^2 2p^6 3p^1$, $1s^2 2s^2 2p^6 3s^1$
7. *Third energy level:* 1s 2p 3s, 2s 2p 3s, 3s 3p 3d, 3p 3d 4s

Solving Problems Within the Concept

1. The yellow doublet in the sodium bright-line spectrum is separated by 6×10^{-8} cm. Convert this separation to angstrom (Å) units.
2. Wavelengths of visible light vary between 3800 Å and 7600 Å. Compare the frequencies corresponding to these wavelengths. Compare the energy of photons having these wavelengths.
3. In the fourth, or N, shell, the orbitals are described as s, p, d, and f in order of increasing energy. How many of each kind of orbital can exist?
4. An excited sodium atom has the electron configuration $1s^2 2s^2 2p^6 3p^1$. The atom emits a photon having an energy of 2.1 ev

in returning to the ground state. Write an equation including the energy term and electron notations to show how the excited atom reaches the ground state.

Applying the Concept

1. You can easily predict the electron distribution of atoms of elements with atomic numbers 1 through 22. However, the electron distribution of a vanadium atom (atomic number 23) is 2, 8, 11, 2, *not* 2, 8, 13 as might be anticipated. Explain why, in terms of the energy level diagram in Fig. 3-12.
2. (a) From the table of ionization potentials (page 41), compare the energy needed to remove the 2s electron from a lithium atom and the energy needed to remove the first 1s electron from a helium atom. (b) Which electron is harder to remove? Account for the difference.
3. (a) Write a symbol that might appropriately represent the particle remaining after 4.3 ev are applied to a potassium atom. (b) Does the suggested symbol represent an atom? Explain.
4. Prepare an orbital diagram to represent the electron distribution of an atom of bromine, atomic number 35. Write the orbital notation for the atom.
5. Derive a formula for finding the maximum number of electrons in each principal energy level. (Hint: Use n to represent each energy level.)

Reading Further

General Chemistry, by M. A. Paul, E. J. King, and L. H. Farinholt, New York, Harcourt, Brace & World, 1967. A clear and concise presentation of the development of atomic structure from the Bohr model to the wave mechanics model.

Introduction to Atomic and Nuclear Physics, by Henry Semat, New York, Holt, Rinehart and Winston, 4th ed., 1962. An excellent book about the structure of the atom.

4

Combinations of Atoms

Look around you any morning at the breakfast table; most of the substances you see are compounds. The salt you use for seasoning looks simple and harmless enough. Little wonder the early chemists were so unaware that salt could be separated into two elements that are far from harmless. One of these elements is sodium, a silvery-white metal that is dangerous to touch. The other is chlorine, a greenish-yellow gas that has a choking odor and is highly poisonous. Or consider water; how incredible it must have seemed that gaseous hydrogen and oxygen combined to form a liquid.

Oxygen normally exists as a gas mixed with other gases in the atmosphere. Could it be that the oxygen in the air is the same element as that which combines with hydrogen in water—or with iron in certain iron ores? In its uncombined state the element sulfur is found as a yellow solid, mixed with other solids in the earth's crust. Or it can exist in various combinations; for instance, with iron in a compound which looks so much like gold that it is called fool's gold. Are there any elements that are always found uncombined?

CHEMICALLY ACTIVE AND INACTIVE ELEMENTS

Only six of the first ninety-two elements are always found free, or uncombined, or so it was thought until 1962. These so-called chemically "inert" elements are all gases: helium, neon, argon, krypton, xenon, and radon. Their discovery dates back to 1894, when Sir William Ramsay was extracting nitrogen gas from the air. He noticed that the nitrogen he obtained had a greater density than the same gas he obtained from nitrogen compounds in the laboratory. Ramsay was intrigued by this mystery and, in collaboration with his friend Lord Rayleigh, he continued his search. After a few months of work, the two men made a surprising announcement. The earth's atmosphere contained an elementary gas which was entirely new to science. Since this gas would not combine with any other element, they named it *argon* after the Greek word meaning "lazy." Ramsay suspected that there might be a whole family of such **inert gases.** His hunch proved correct, as you know from Chapter 2. Ramsay's research led to the eventual discovery of helium, neon, krypton, xenon, and

Table 4-1   RARE GASES IN THE AIR

Rare gas	Percent by volume
Helium	0.00052
Neon	0.0018
Argon	0.93
Krypton	0.0001
Xenon	0.000008
Radon	Trace

4-1 Crystals of xenon tetrafluoride are evidence that the "inert" gases are not actually inert. Previously such a compound had been thought to be impossible.

radon. Because these six gases are all found in comparatively small quantities (Table 4-1) on earth, they are also called the **rare gases.**

Are the Inert Gases Really Inert?

The story of the discovery of these gases is an exciting chapter in modern science. But the discovery of their "activity" is even more exciting. Though a number of rare gas compounds had been reported earlier, it was only as recently as 1962 that their existence was confirmed. Neil Bartlett, working at the University of British Columbia, produced a yellow powdery compound of xenon, platinum, and fluorine. Shortly thereafter a team of scientists at the Argonne National Laboratory found that xenon, when heated with fluorine for an hour at 400° C and then cooled to −78° C, combines with fluorine to form a colorless, crystalline substance (Fig. 4-1). Upon analysis, this substance was identified as the compound xenon tetrafluoride, XeF_4.

As fluorine is the most active nonmetallic element known, its choice in these experiments was obvious—and it worked! In fact, the existence of several other compounds containing xenon and fluorine has been confirmed. Radon, the densest "inert" gas, has also been combined with fluorine to produce radon fluoride. The discovery that several rare gases combine with fluorine leads chemists to speculate that the "inert" gases are probably not so inert as they were once thought to be.

All the elements, we now suspect, combine with other elements to form compounds. However, as the elements other than the rare gases combine much more readily, they are called *chemically active* elements. Why should the inert gases be relatively inactive while all the other elements are active? Why should some elements, such as oxygen and sulfur, be found both uncombined and in compounds while others, such as sodium and fluorine, are never found free? The answer takes us back to our understanding of atomic structure, particularly to electron structure.

Electron Arrangements of Atoms

Because of differing electron arrangements within atoms, elements are chemically different from one another. Study the distribution of electrons within the main shells for the atoms of elements with atomic numbers 1 through 20 in Table 4-2 on the following page. When the first twenty elements are listed consecutively according to atomic number, the number of electrons in one atom of each succeeding element also increases by one.

As you know, the atom with the simplest structure is the hydrogen atom; it contains 1 electron in its K shell (Fig. 4-2). After hydrogen, the next simplest atom is helium. Here, as in hydrogen, the outer shell is still the K shell; but in helium the outer shell contains 2 electrons. As 2 is the maximum number of electrons that the K shell of an atom can have, the outer shell of the helium atom cannot obtain additional electrons; this shell, or the 1s orbital, is filled or complete.

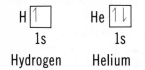

4-2 The maximum number of electrons in the K shell, which is composed of a single 1s orbital, is two.

Table 4-2 **DISTRIBUTION OF ELECTRONS AMONG ELECTRON SHELLS AND SUBSHELLS**

Atomic number	Name	Symbol	K or 1 (s)	L or 2 (s)	L or 2 (p)	Atomic number	Name	Symbol	K or 1 (s)	L or 2 (s)	L or 2 (p)	M or 3 (s)	M or 3 (p)	M or 3 (d)	N or 4 (s)
1	Hydrogen	H	1			11	Sodium	Na	2	2	6	1			
2	Helium	He	2			12	Magnesium	Mg	2	2	6	2			
3	Lithium	Li	2	1		13	Aluminum	Al	2	2	6	2	1		
4	Beryllium	Be	2	2		14	Silicon	Si	2	2	6	2	2		
5	Boron	B	2	2	1	15	Phosphorus	P	2	2	6	2	3		
6	Carbon	C	2	2	2	16	Sulfur	S	2	2	6	2	4		
7	Nitrogen	N	2	2	3	17	Chlorine	Cl	2	2	6	2	5		
8	Oxygen	O	2	2	4	18	Argon	Ar	2	2	6	2	6		
9	Fluorine	F	2	2	5	19	Potassium	K	2	2	6	2	6		1
10	Neon	Ne	2	2	6	20	Calcium	Ca	2	2	6	2	6		2

Beginning with atoms of lithium (Fig. 4-3), the L shell increases consecutively by one until it reaches a maximum of 8 in neon. Beginning with sodium, the M shell begins to fill. Once again, the number of electrons in the M shell increases successively by one until it reaches a maximum of 8 in argon. Then the N shell begins to fill. Recall that the *maximum* number of electrons in the outer shell (except the K shell) of any atom is 8.

Here you note again that the atoms with complete outer shells are helium, neon, and argon—atoms of the inert gases. Atoms whose outer shells are complete are relatively inert. Atoms of all the other elements listed are chemically active because their outer shells are incomplete.

Relative Activity of Elements

Though most elements are active to some extent, some are more active than others. If, for example, you place a small piece of sodium in a dish of cool water, the sodium reacts with the water, and hydrogen is produced. The reaction is so vigorous that the chemicals may spatter. CAUTION: *Do not try this for yourself.* To determine what happens if you substitute an element such as magnesium for the sodium, *try the following:*

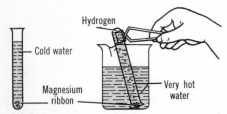

Hydrogen
Cold water
Magnesium ribbon
Very hot water

Clean a small piece of magnesium ribbon with fine sandpaper and place the magnesium in a test tube of cold water. Are any bubbles of gas produced? If not, place the magnesium ribbon in a test tube of very hot water and invert the test tube into a beaker of very hot water, as shown at the left. Use the burning splint test to determine if the gas produced is hydrogen.

Though the sodium liberates hydrogen from cold water, the magnesium ribbon does not. It is necessary to heat the water before magnesium reacts with it to liberate hydrogen. Sodium is more active than magnesium.

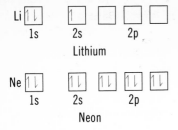

Li [↑↓] [↑] [ ] [ ] [ ]
　　1s　　2s　　　　2p
Lithium

Ne [↑↓] [↑↓] [↑↓] [↑↓] [↑↓]
　　1s　　2s　　　　2p
Neon

4-3 The number of electrons in the L shell, including the 2s and 2p orbitals, increases from one in an atom of lithium to a maximum of eight in an atom of neon.

A·

·B:

:C:

D:

·E:

4-4 From the number of electrons in their dot diagrams, determine which of the elements indicated above are metals and which are nonmetals.

The more active sodium atom has only 1 electron in its outer shell while the less active magnesium atom has 2 electrons in its outer shell. Or consider chlorine with only one more electron than sulfur. Chlorine with its 7 outer-shell electrons is so active that it is rarely found uncombined in nature; sulfur, with 6 outer electrons, is frequently found free. Much experimental data indicates that elements vary in their degree of activity, and that the activity of an element is related to the number of electrons in the outer shell of its atoms. In general, *the fewer the electrons an atom must lose or gain to complete its outer shell, the more active the element.*

Toward a Stable Structure

What would happen if you could bring an atom of sodium close to an atom of chlorine? Both atoms are active, since the outer shells of both are incomplete. The outer shell of the chlorine atom contains 7 electrons; the outer shell of sodium contains 1. The atoms of these two active elements combine to form a compound, sodium chloride (NaCl), if enough energy is supplied.

As a result of the changes in structure that take place during the formation of compounds, the active elements acquire a complete outer electron shell and thus a more stable structure. You will study this transfer of electrons between elements in detail in Chapter 6.

Activity of Metals and Nonmetals

The active elements, such as sodium and chlorine, can be separated into two classes: **metals** and **nonmetals.** Metals have certain physical properties in common. Though they are often dense and hard they are *malleable* (can be hammered into sheets without cracking) and *ductile* (can be drawn into wire). Too, they are good conductors of heat and electricity. Metals usually have a high luster, and, with the exception of gold and copper, tend to be silvery-gray in color. Iron, silver, and sodium are other examples of metals. Nonmetallic elements, on the other hand, are usually gaseous, like oxygen, or soft solids, like phosphorus. They are frequently colorless and are poor thermal and electrical conductors.

Chemists do not have to rely on such physical properties to distinguish between metals and nonmetals. They can distinguish between these two classes of elements on the basis of the number of electrons in their outer shells. *Atoms of metals usually contain 1, 2, or 3 electrons in their outer shells.* This is less than half the number of electrons required to make the outer shell complete. By contrast, atoms of *nonmetals usually have outer shells with 5 to 7 electrons,* or more than half the number needed to make a complete outer shell (Fig. 4-4).

Refer again to Table 4-2. Notice that an atom of the metal sodium has 1 electron in its outer shell, while calcium has 2 electrons and aluminum 3 electrons. By contrast, an atom of the nonmetal fluorine has 7 electrons in its outer shell, while sulfur has 6 electrons, and nitrogen 5 electrons. When the outer shell of an atom is half-full—has 4 electrons—the element seems to have neither distinctly metallic nor nonmetallic properties.

4-5 An unusual high-voltage X-ray diffraction photograph of an aluminum crystal. The diffraction "spots" appear as streaks because of the thickness (2 cm) of the crystal.

Carbon, the best-known of these elements, forms thousands of compounds with both metals and nonmetals.

Effect of Atomic Size in Metals and Nonmetals

You have seen that the fewer the number of electrons to be gained or lost from the outer shell of an atom, the greater the activity of a nonmetal or metal respectively. There is also another factor which affects atomic activity. This is the size of the atom, or the **atomic radius.**

Because they are so extremely small, we cannot measure the diameter of atoms directly. Some indirect method, such as X-ray diffraction, must be used. If a crystal of a pure substance, for example, a crystal of aluminum, is bombarded with X rays, the rays are reflected in a specific pattern (Fig. 4-5). By studying the X-ray patterns of various substances, scientists can determine the distance between atoms, and thus acquire an indication of the size of the atoms that make up the substance. Usually the size of an atom is given in terms of its radius. The atomic radius is defined, in precise terms, as *one-half the average distance between the nuclei of adjacent atoms in the solid (or liquid) state.*

In considering the effect of atomic size on the activity of atoms, we find that there is a sharp difference between metals and nonmetals. *In metals, the larger the atomic radius, the more chemically active the atom.* Gold (Au) is a fairly inactive metal that is often found free in nature; potassium (K), is so active that it is never found free. So it is not surprising to find that an atom of potassium has a larger atomic radius than an atom of gold (Table 4-3). This positive relationship between atomic size and activity in metals might have been anticipated. The larger the atomic radius, the farther the outer-shell electrons are from the nucleus and the lower the ionization potential. Hence the electrons are removed more easily.

With nonmetals, the rule is exactly the reverse. *In nonmetals, the smaller the atomic radius, the more chemically active the element.* Each atom of fluorine (F), chemically the most active element known, has a very small atomic radius. Each atom of iodine (I), a much less active nonmetal than fluorine, has a much greater atomic radius. Can you account for this relationship between atomic size and activity among nonmetals? The smaller the atomic size, the closer the outer-shell electrons are to the nucleus, and the higher the ionization potential. Under these conditions an electron is not lost easily, but electrons are added with relative ease.

Electron Affinity

You have seen that *positive ions* are formed when atoms lose electrons. For example, a sodium atom, Na, loses 1 electron to become a sodium ion, Na^+. Similarly, atoms of elements with 5, 6, or 7 electrons in their outer shells gain electrons to form *negative ions.* Chlorine, for example, has 7 electrons in its outer shell. If 1 electron is added to a chlorine atom, Cl, a chloride ion, Cl^-, is formed. Notice that the name of this negative ion ends in *ide:* we speak of a chlor*ine* atom but a chlor*ide* ion.

Table 4-3 **ATOMIC RADII**

Element	Symbol	Atomic radius*
Potassium	K	2.31
Gold	Au	1.44
Fluorine	F	0.72
Iodine	I	1.33

* In angstroms.

58 BEHAVIOR OF ATOMS

Table 4-4
ELECTRON AFFINITIES

Element	Symbol	Electron affinity*
Fluorine	F	3.6
Chlorine	Cl	3.8
Bromine	Br	3.5
Iodine	I	3.2
Oxygen	O	1.5
Phosphorus	P	0.7

* In electron volts.

The energy involved when an electron is added to an atom is called the *electron affinity*. For example, when one electron is *added* to a chlorine atom to form a chloride ion, 3.8 ev are released:

$$Cl + e^- \longrightarrow Cl^- + 3.8 \text{ ev}$$

Since 13 ev of energy are required to *remove* an electron from a chlorine atom, it is not surprising that the addition of an electron to the same atom results in the release of energy. Chlorine and the members of its family have the highest electron affinities of all elements (Table 4-4).

QUESTIONS AND PROBLEMS

1. Draw an orbital and an electron dot diagram of an atom of each of these elements: oxygen, magnesium, silicon, chlorine, and potassium.
2. On the basis of the number of electrons in their outer shells, indicate the more active element of each of these pairs of elements: (a) oxygen and fluorine (b) sulfur and phosphorus (c) potassium and calcium (d) lithium and beryllium (e) chlorine and argon.
3. On the basis of the number of electrons in their outer shells, indicate whether each element is a metal or a nonmetal: potassium, chlorine, lithium, phosphorus, beryllium, sulfur, magnesium, and bromine.
4. On the basis of atomic radius and ionization potential, differentiate between atoms of metallic and nonmetallic elements.

DECOMPOSITION OF COMPOUNDS

Clearly, the atoms of all elements except those of the "inert" gases are chemically active, yet the great majority of the elements have been identified within the past 250 years. Why did it take men so long to identify all the natural elements in the earth's crust? A mere eight of these natural elements account, by weight, for 98.6 percent of the earth's crust, while oxygen and nitrogen account for 99.1 percent of its atmosphere. By contrast, consider the element xenon, which exists in the earth's atmosphere to the extent of only one part in 125,000!

Another reason for the comparatively late identification of certain elements is that *some of them exist as gases difficult to detect*. Men of early civilizations used silver, copper, gold, and iron, elements which normally exist as solids. Even mercury has been mined in the form of one of its solid compounds for centuries. With elements such as oxygen it was a different matter. Oxygen normally exists as a gas, and scientists knew very little about the nature of gases until the seventeenth century.

A final reason for the late discovery of some elements is *they exist only in compounds that are difficult to decompose*. Marble and limestone, used in the building trades for centuries, contain calcium, the fifth most abundant element in the earth's crust; yet calcium was not isolated until 1808.

—Ion of
chlorine

—Ion of
sodium

4-6a A crystal of sodium chloride is composed of numerous ions of chlorine and sodium arranged in an orderly pattern. By comparison with the sodium ions, the chloride ions are relatively large.

4-6b The camera confirms that crystals of sodium chloride have a definite shape and structure.

When exposed to the air, highly active calcium reacts readily to form an oxygen compound that is difficult to decompose.

The Nature of Compounds

Before determining how compounds are decomposed, let us look briefly at their composition. An element results when all the atoms of a substance are the same, but when unlike atoms combine, they form compounds. Some compounds, such as carbon dioxide, are composed of molecules that contain only a few atoms. In contrast, a molecule of hemoglobin is made up of 9,512 atoms. Strangely enough, molecules of compounds, whether they contain few or many atoms, consist of relatively few elements, usually from two to six or seven.

Some compounds, however, are not composed of molecules. Instead they are made up of *ions*. In the formation of sodium chloride (page 93), an electron from each sodium atom moves to the outer shell of a chlorine atom. Each atom is no longer neutral but becomes a *charged particle or ion*. You will learn more about ions in Chapter 6. Ions, rather than uniting to form molecules, usually arrange themselves (in the solid state) in orderly patterns to form crystals (Figs. 4-6a and 4-6b). Even a minute crystal of sodium chloride contains an incredibly large number of ions.

What, then, do we mean when we write the formula for sodium chloride as NaCl? We simply mean that for each sodium ion present in the compound there is also one chloride ion. Similarly, magnesium bromide, $MgBr_2$, contains one magnesium ion for every two bromide ions in the compound. In short, these formulas do not represent the actual number of different ions present in the compound; they indicate the *simplest ratio* of ions present. A formula of this kind is called an **empirical formula.** CaO and $KClO_3$ are other examples of empirical formulas of compounds.

The Stability of Compounds

The method used in decomposing a compound depends, in part, upon the stability of the compound. Nitrogen triiodide (NI_3) is so unstable that a breeze can cause it to decompose into nitrogen and iodine. Mercuric oxide, which is more stable, can be decomposed by heating. Atoms of chemically active elements combine to form the more stable compounds, such as sodium chloride. Atoms of less chemically active elements combine to form less stable compounds, such as mercuric oxide. The relative amount of energy needed to decompose a compound is an indication of its stability. Consequently, when attempts are made to decompose these compounds, more energy is required to decompose the more stable than the less stable, or unstable, compound. Now let us consider some of the methods used in decomposing compounds.

Decomposition by Electrolysis

Electricity passing through water causes it to decompose into the elements hydrogen and oxygen. *Why not investigate this for yourself* by using a simple electrolysis procedure?

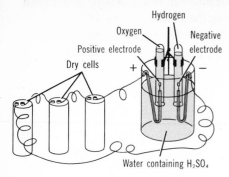

Hydrogen

Oxygen

Negative electrode

Positive electrode

Dry cells

Water containing H_2SO_4

Set up the apparatus as shown at the left, being sure to use two similar test tubes. Fill the battery jar with water and add a few drops of concentrated sulfuric acid. Completely fill the test tubes with water, insert them, and clamp them in place. Insert the platinum (or carbon) electrodes under the test tubes, and connect the wires from the electrodes to a low-voltage, direct current source (several dry cells in series or a rectifier-transformer). Let the electrolysis continue until one test tube is almost completely filled with gas; then disconnect the wires from the battery. Quickly but carefully remove this test tube and place your thumb over its mouth. Try the burning splint test to prove that the tube contains hydrogen. How can you prove that the other test tube contains oxygen?

Chemists may also use electrolysis to decompose compounds that usually exist as solids if they can be either liquefied by heat or dissolved. Magnesium is extracted from magnesium chloride by this process. First the solid compound is heated until it becomes molten. Electricity is then passed through the hot liquid to cause it to decompose, isolating the magnesium.

Decomposition by Heat

Ice melts when heated, but not all compounds are easily changed into liquids by heating. In some cases heating causes the compound to decompose. Recall that both oxygen and mercury were produced by the heating of red mercuric oxide. Suppose you want to decompose sugar into its elements; *you could proceed as follows:*

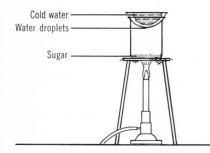

Cold water

Water droplets

Sugar

Cover the bottom of a beaker with $\frac{1}{4}$ inch of sugar, and place an evaporating dish filled with cold water into the top of the beaker, as in the diagram at the left. Heat the beaker steadily. At first the sugar caramelizes and the evaporating dish is unaffected. Continue heating the sugar until it starts to char. Do droplets of water gradually collect on the bottom of the evaporating dish? Continue heating the sugar; eventually nothing is left in the beaker but a black substance. What is it? How could you prove that the droplets on the bottom of the evaporating dish are water?

The substance in the dish is the element carbon; you probably recognized it. The water collected on the evaporating dish could be collected and decomposed by electrolysis into its two elements, hydrogen and oxygen. Sugar is composed of three elements, hydrogen, oxygen, and carbon.

Decomposition by Reactions with Other Substances

Elements can also be extracted from certain compounds by causing the compounds to react with different substances. This is how iron, used in making steel, is extracted from certain iron ores. Carbon, in the form of coke, is mixed with the iron ore and the mixture is heated. In a series of reactions (summarized in the equation below), the carbon of the coal combines with the oxygen in the ore to form carbon dioxide. In this way the element iron remains.

$$\text{iron ore} + \text{carbon} \longrightarrow \text{iron} + \text{carbon dioxide}$$
$$2\,Fe_2O_3 + 3\,C \longrightarrow 4\,Fe + 3\,CO_2\uparrow$$

In your more detailed study of the elements, you will find that other procedures can be used to decompose certain specific compounds. Nevertheless, the most common procedures are those just discussed.

QUESTIONS AND PROBLEMS

1. The last of the ninety-two natural elements was identified in 1945. Give three (or more) reasons for the late discovery of some elements.
2. The empirical formula for sodium oxide is Na_2O; the molecular formula for sulfur dioxide is SO_2. How do they differ in composition?
3. (a) List three methods by which compounds are decomposed into elements. (b) Give an example *not described in this section* of a compound decomposed by each method. (Use the index if necessary.)

COMPOSITION OF COMPOUNDS

True, the early chemists knew the elements present in many compounds—but how much of each element? Or as the chemist would say, what is the composition of the compound? One method of expressing the ratio of each element in a compound is in terms of the *weight* of each element present. How much hydrogen and oxygen by weight are present, for instance, in 1 gram of water? A second method of expressing the ratio of gaseous elements that combine to form a compound is in terms of *volume*.

The early chemists developed and learned to use chemical balances and other instruments to determine the composition of compounds. The first instruments were crude and not highly accurate, yet the numerical data obtained with these instruments made it possible for these early chemists to learn the compositions both by volume and by weight of a number of compounds.

Combining Volumes

Electrolysis has been used for many years to determine the ratio by volume in which hydrogen and oxygen combine to form water. During electrolysis the space above the water in the left-hand tube of the Hoffman apparatus shown in Fig. 4-7 fills with hydrogen gas, while the opposite tube becomes filled with oxygen. The exact volumes of the two

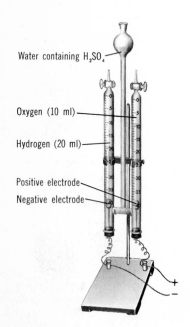

Water containing H_2SO_4

Oxygen (10 ml)

Hydrogen (20 ml)

Positive electrode

Negative electrode

4-7 The electrolysis of water.

gases can be measured by using the scale marked on the side of the tubes. This scale gives the volume in milliliters, a unit of volume in the metric system (see Appendix A). The abbreviation for this unit of volume is ml. It is clear from the results of the procedure shown in Fig. 4-7 that 20 ml of hydrogen and 10 ml of oxygen are produced. In other words, twice as much hydrogen as oxygen is produced. This proportion is always the same in any decomposition of water. If the electrolysis had formed 70 ml of hdrogen, you would have had 35 ml of oxygen. In breaking down water, the ratio by volume of hydrogen to oxygen is always 2 to 1 (Table 4-5).

Table 4-5   RATIO OF HYDROGEN TO OXYGEN *BY VOLUME* IN WATER

Element	Actual volume		Ratio by volume
	Trial 1	Trial 2	
Hydrogen	20 ml	70 ml	2
Oxygen	10 ml	35 ml	1

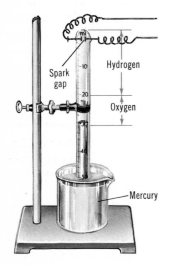

4-8 Electric discharge across the spark gap provides a test of the combining ratio of hydrogen to oxygen in water. How far will the mercury rise in the tube?

Chemists have used electrolysis to determine the ratio by volume of the gaseous elements in a great many compounds besides water. They have discovered that the volumes of the gases produced in this way are always in a ratio of small *whole* numbers. For instance, the electrolysis of concentrated hydrochloric acid shows that the ratio of its two elementary gases, hydrogen and chlorine, is always 1 to 1. What is the ratio of nitrogen to hydrogen in ammonia (NH_3)?

The ratio of two volumes of hydrogen to one volume of oxygen in water can be verified if we try to combine these gases to form water. If 20 ml of hydrogen and 10 ml of oxygen are placed in a eudiometer tube (Fig. 4-8) and ignited, the two gases combine completely to form water. No gas is left over. If 20 ml of hydrogen and 20 ml of oxygen are used, 10 ml of oxygen remain uncombined. The combining ratio of hydrogen to oxygen in water is always 2 to 1. When hydrogen and chlorine combine to form the compound hydrogen chloride (HCl), 60 ml of hydrogen combine with 60 ml of chlorine. Similarly, 30 ml of hydrogen combine with 30 ml of chlorine. In hydrogen chloride, these two gases always combine in a ratio by volume of 1 to 1 (Table 4-6).

Table 4-6   RATIO OF HYDROGEN TO CHLORINE *BY VOLUME* IN FORMATION OF HYDROCHLORIC ACID

Element	Actual volume		Ratio by volume
	Trial 1	Trial 2	
Hydrogen	60 ml	30 ml	1
Chlorine	60 ml	30 ml	1

Table 4-7 **RATIO OF COMBINING GASES** *BY VOLUME*

Compound	Formula	Volume of first gas	Volume of second gas	Ratio of gases by volume
Water	H_2O	2 hydrogen	1 oxygen	2:1
Hydrogen chloride	HCl	1 hydrogen	1 chlorine	1:1
Ammonia	NH_3	1 nitrogen	3 hydrogen	1:3
Nitrogen dioxide	NO_2	1 nitrogen	2 oxygen	1:2

The ratios by volume in which various gaseous elements combine to form compounds are listed in Table 4-7. Notice that these ratios are all ratios of small whole numbers. The relationship between the volumes of combining gases is expressed by **Gay-Lussac's Law of Combining Volumes of Gases.** This law states that *whenever gases combine to form new substances, the volumes of the combining gases and the product, if gaseous, are in ratios of small whole numbers.*

Definite Proportions

You have been measuring the ratio of the different elements in a compound in terms of volume. Next, we shall measure such ratios in terms of *weight*. What do we find in the electrolysis of water? By decomposing 9 grams of water, we obtain 1 gram of hydrogen and 8 grams of oxygen: the ratio by weight of hydrogen to oxygen in water is 1 to 8. Suppose we electrolyze 18 grams of water; this gives us 2 grams of hydrogen and 16 grams of oxygen. The ratio by weight of the gases is still 1 to 8. No matter how many times chemists decompose water, the ratio by weight of hydrogen to oxygen is always the same (Table 4-8).

Table 4-8 **RATIO OF HYDROGEN TO OXYGEN** *BY WEIGHT* **IN WATER**

Element	Actual weight		Ratio by weight
	Trial 1	Trial 2	
Hydrogen	1 gram	2 grams	1
Oxygen	8 grams	16 grams	8

Chemists have discovered that no matter what method is used to decompose a given compound into its elements, the ratio by weight of the elements formed during the decomposition is always the same. For example, the ratio by weight of copper to sulfur in the compound cupric sulfide (CuS) is approximately 2 to 1. This means that 96 grams of the compound cupric sulfide contain about 64 grams of the element copper and 32 grams of the element sulfur. Forty-eight grams of cupric sulfide contain about 32 grams of copper and 16 grams of sulfur (Table 4-9).

Dalton, you recall, was the first scientist to suggest that in any given compound the elements are always found in a definite proportion by

Table 4-9 **RATIO OF COPPER TO SULFUR** *BY WEIGHT* **IN CUPRIC SULFIDE**

| | Actual weight | | Ratio by |
Element	Trial 1	Trial 2	weight
Copper	64 grams	32 grams	2
Sulfur	32 grams	16 grams	1

weight. But it was Louis Proust, a French chemist, who first formulated this idea as a law. He called it the **Law of Definite Proportions** (or Definite Composition). In terms of this law, *a compound may be defined as a chemical combination of elements in definite proportions by weight.*

Does this constant weight relationship hold true whenever elements are combined to form compounds? As evidence that it does, consider the burning of the element magnesium (Mg) in oxygen, which produces a dazzling light and forms magnesium oxide (MgO). If 24 grams of magnesium are burned completely, they combine with 16 grams of oxygen to form 40 grams of magnesium oxide. When 12 grams of magnesium burn completely, they combine with 8 grams of oxygen to form 20 grams of magnesium oxide. No matter what quantities are used, the ratio by weight of magnesium to oxygen that combines to form MgO is 24 to 16—or approximately 1.5 to 1 (Table 4-10). Yes, the Law of Definite Proportions is confirmed by the formation of compounds from elements.

Table 4-10 **RATIO OF MAGNESIUM TO OXYGEN** *BY WEIGHT* **IN FORMATION OF MAGNESIUM OXIDE**

| | Actual weight | | Ratio by |
Element	Trial 1	Trial 2	weight
Magnesium	24 grams	12 grams	1.5
Oxygen	16 grams	8 grams	1

Isotopes: An Exception?

In formulating this law, Proust assumed that since all atoms of an element were alike in chemical properties, they were alike in all respects. Today we know this is not so. Isotopes of the same element have different weights. In the common form of water, most of the hydrogen atoms have an atomic weight of 1, and the oxygen atoms an atomic weight of 16. Since each molecule of ordinary water contains two atoms of hydrogen and one of oxygen, the ratio by weight of hydrogen to oxygen in a molecule of water is 1 to 8 (2 parts hydrogen to 16 parts oxygen). But suppose we decompose water in which hydrogen is in the form of deuterium, the isotope with mass number 2 (H^2). When two deuterium atoms combine with an atom of oxygen to form a molecule of water, the ratio

Table 4-11   **RATIO OF HYDROGEN TO OXYGEN IN HEAVY WATER**

Element	Actual weight	Ratio by weight
Hydrogen-2	4 grams	1
Oxygen	16 grams	4

by weight of the hydrogen to the oxygen is no longer 1 to 8 but 1 to 4 (4 parts hydrogen to 16 parts oxygen; Table 4-11). Water formed in this way is called **heavy water;** it is a very important substance in nuclear research.

In view of the discovery of isotopes, the ratio by weight of elements in the same compound may differ. Consequently, a different definition of a compound is in order. Today, *a compound may be defined as a substance composed of a definite number of atoms of two or more elements chemically combined together in a particular ratio.* Here again is an example of how scientific understandings change in the light of new evidence.

Multiple Proportions

Even before isotopes were discovered, scientists had begun to question the Law of Definite Proportions. Their experiments had shown that in certain cases the same elements can combine to form different compounds. Consider the two compounds, water and hydrogen peroxide. Both are formed from the same elements, hydrogen and oxygen. But the ratio by weight of the two elements is different in each case. In ordinary water the proportion by weight of hydrogen to oxygen is 1 to 8. In hydrogen peroxide the proportion, again by weight, is 1 to 16. To find the formula for hydrogen peroxide, compare the weights of oxygen in the two compounds. In these compounds the amount of oxygen is in the ratio of 1 to 2. Since the formula for water is H_2O, the formula for hydrogen peroxide must be H_2O_2 (Table 4-12).

Chemists, through repeated investigation, have found that copper reacts with sulfur dissolved in carbon disulfide to form a compound in which copper and sulfur combine in a ratio of 2 to 1 by weight. For example, 6.4 grams of copper combine with 3.2 grams of sulfur to form 9.4 grams of *cupric sulfide.* You can perform an investigation *to demonstrate for yourself* that copper and sulfur combine in a different ratio by weight to form a different compound.

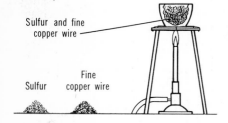

Sulfur and fine copper wire

Sulfur   Fine copper wire

Under a hood, heat an excess of sulfur and 12.8 grams of fine copper wire in a crucible until the combination of the elements is complete (shown at the left). Heat the crucible until any excess sulfur burns completely; then let the crucible cool. Now weigh the compound produced. Does it weigh about 16.0 grams? This time, 12.8 grams of copper combine with 3.2 grams of sulfur. The ratio of 12.8 grams of copper to 3.2 grams of sulfur is 4 to 1, not 2 to 1.

Table 4-12   **RATIO OF OXYGEN** *BY WEIGHT* **IN WATER AND HYDROGEN PEROXIDE**

Compound	Formula	Fixed weight of hydrogen	Weight of oxygen	Ratio of weight of oxygen
Water	H_2O	1 gram	8 grams	1
Hydrogen peroxide	H_2O_2	1 gram	16 grams	2

Table 4-13 **RATIO OF COPPER** *BY WEIGHT* **IN CUPRIC AND CUPROUS SULFIDE**

Compound	Formula	Fixed weight of sulfur	Weight of copper	Ratio by weight of copper
Cupric sulfide	CuS	3.2 grams	6.4 grams	1
Cuprous sulfide	Cu_2S	3.2 grams	12.8 grams	2

Evidently two compounds containing copper and sulfur exist. In cup*ric* sulfide, 1 part by weight of sulfur combines with 2 parts by weight of copper. In the second compound, the same 1 part by weight of sulfur combines with 4 parts by weight of copper. The ratio of weight of copper combined with the same weight of sulfur in the two compounds is 1 to 2. As the correct formula for cupric sulfide is CuS, and as in the second compound the ratio by weight of copper to sulfur is twice that in CuS, the formula for the second compound must be Cu_2S. The compound whose formula is Cu_2S is called *cuprous sulfide* (Table 4-13).

The compounds of nitrogen and oxygen listed in Table 4-14 are another example of compounds in which the same elements are found combined in different proportions by weight. Note, however, that in any one compound of nitrogen and oxygen the elements are always found in a definite proportion by weight. And you are familiar with carbon monoxide (CO) and carbon dioxide (CO_2). From the formulas you can determine that 1 part of carbon combines with either 1 or 2 parts of oxygen by weight.

That certain elements often combine to form more than one compound is expressed by the **Law of Multiple Proportions.** This law states that *when the same elements combine to form more than one compound, if the weight of one element is fixed, the weight of the other element always varies in a ratio of small whole numbers.*

Atoms combine to form elements and compounds. But does the combination have any pattern—or is it helter-skelter? Does a given atom have a relationship to another atom so that we can predict how they both combine? Are the properties of atoms predictable? Chemists constantly try to find a pattern in the behavior of the matter they observe. In the next chapter, we too search for one of these basic patterns.

Table 4-14 **COMPOUNDS OF NITROGEN AND OXYGEN**

Compound	Formula	Fixed weight of nitrogen	Weight of oxygen	Ratio of weight of oxygen
Nitrous oxide	N_2O	28	16	1
Nitric oxide	NO	28	32	2
Nitrogen trioxide	N_2O_3	28	48	3
Nitrogen dioxide	NO_2	28	64	4
Nitrogen pentoxide	N_2O_5	28	80	5

1. A molecule of carbon dioxide (CO_2) contains one carbon atom with mass number 12 and two oxygen atoms with mass number 16. What is the approximate ratio by weight of carbon to oxygen in this compound? If the CO_2 molecule contained a carbon-14 atom, what would be the ratio by weight of carbon to oxygen?
2. The analysis of two compounds, A and B, containing mercury and oxygen shows that they have the following composition:

Elements	Compound A	Compound B
Hg	100 grams	200 grams
O	8 grams	8 grams

If the atomic weight of mercury is 12.5 times as much as that of oxygen, and if the formula for compound A is HgO, what is the formula for compound B?

VALUE OF THE CONCEPT

THE CONCEPT

Most elements are found in the form of their compounds. Only six elements, the inert or rare gases, are always found uncombined in nature. Many of the ninety-two natural elements were not identified until relatively recently because, among many reasons, (1) many elements exist in very small quantities, (2) some exist as gases difficult to detect, and (3) some elements exist only in compounds that are difficult to decompose.

The difficulty in decomposing some compounds is due, in part, to the chemical activity of most elements. Even the "inert" gases are not totally inactive chemically. The chemical activity of an element is determined by the arrangement and number of electrons in its atoms, and by the size of its atoms. On the basis of chemical activity, many elements are classed as metallic or nonmetallic. Atoms of metallic elements are relatively large and contain 1, 2, or 3 electrons in their outer shells. Atoms of nonmetallic elements are relatively small and contain from 5 to 7 electrons in their outer shells. Each atom of the inert elements contains a complete outer shell of 8 electrons, except helium, whose outer shell is complete with 2 electrons. Atoms of chemically active metals lose few electrons to achieve a complete outer electron shell, while atoms of chemically active nonmetals gain few electrons to achieve a similar stable structure.

Compounds are composed of unlike atoms joined to form molecules or ions. Ions (charged particles) arrange themselves in orderly patterns to form crystals. Ionic and molecular compounds are decomposed into their elements by electrolysis, by heating, or by heating with other substances. Atoms of chemically active elements combine to form the most stable compounds; they are decomposed with difficulty. Atoms of chemically less active elements combine to form unstable compounds that decompose readily.

Among the laws describing the characteristics of compounds in Gay-Lussac's Law of Combining Volumes. This law states that *whenever gases combine to form new substances, they combine in ratios of small whole numbers by volume.* In terms of the Law of Definite Proportions, a compound is defined as a chemical combination of elements in a definite proportion by weight. With the discovery of isotopes, a compound is better defined as a substance composed of a definite ratio of atoms of two or more elements bound together. The Law of Multiple Proportions indicates that whenever the same elements combine to form more than one compound, if the weight of one element is fixed, the weight of the other element always varies in a ratio of small whole numbers.

USING THE CONCEPT

Using the Basic Concept

1. Give three reasons why only a few elements were known until about 250 years ago.
2. Explain each of the following statements: (a) Some elements are found free in nature, others never are. (b) Two elements may combine to form more than one compound. (c) An element that is part of a mixture is "free."
3. Oxygen is sometimes found as part of a mixture, and sometimes as part of a compound. Give two examples of each type of substance.
4. (a) Define the term *chemically inert*. (b) In terms of electron structure, why are certain elements chemically inert?
5. (a) Draw an orbital diagram for a krypton atom. (b) Is this atom relatively stable or unstable? Why?
6. Contrast three chemical properties of metals and nonmetals.
7. (a) Compare the physical properties of active metals and active nonmetals. (b) Give two examples of each.
8. How do atoms of metallic and nonmetallic elements differ in atomic radius and number of outer-shell electrons?
9. (a) What is meant by *an empirical formula?* (b) Give two examples of empirical formulas, and indicate what each formula represents.
10. (a) List three methods by which compounds may be broken down or decomposed. (b) Give one example of a compound decomposed by each of these methods.
11. (a) What is Gay-Lussac's Law of Combining Volumes? (b) How could you prove that whenever water is formed, one volume of oxygen reacts with twice its volume of hydrogen?
12. State and give an example of: (a) the Law of Definite Proportions and (b) the Law of Multiple Proportions.
13. How has the discovery of isotopes changed chemists' understanding of the nature of compounds? (Refer to specific compounds in answering this question.)

Relating Terms Within the Concept

Select the letter of the term in Column B that is most closely related to each term in Column A. Do not use a term more than once.

COLUMN A	COLUMN B
1. free element	a. atoms contain few electrons in outer shell and relatively large atomic radius
2. inert element	
3. chemically active metal	
4. atom with complete outer shell	b. CO
5. atom of a nonmetal	c. describes the composition of compounds
6. high thermal and electrical conductivity	d. electron affinity
	e. found uncombined in nature
7. empirical formula	f. incomplete outer shell usually with 5 or more electrons
8. definite proportions	
9. multiple proportions	g. K shell with 2 electrons
	h. N_2O and NO_2
	i. normal energy state of atoms
	j. normally not an active element
	k. silver and copper
	l. simplest ratio of each type of particle present

Solving Problems Within the Concept

1. (a) What is the simplest ratio of different ions present in each of the following compounds: AlF_3, KCl, $BaCl_2$, $NaBr$? (b) What are the actual numbers of different atoms present in a molecule of each of the following compounds: CO, CS_2, NH_3?

2. (a) How many milliliters of H_2 will combine with 100 ml of O_2 to form H_2O? (b) How many milliliters of H_2 will combine with 100 ml of Cl_2 to form HCl?

3. (a) How many grams of H_2 are also formed when 8 grams of O_2 are produced during the decomposition of water? (b) How many grams of O_2 are formed when 24 grams of H_2 are produced?

4. How many grams each of copper and sulfur do 48 grams of CuS contain?

5. Which contains more hydrogen by weight: 1 kilogram of water or 1 kilogram of hydrogen chloride? (Explain how you determined your answer.)

6. How many grams of deuterium are contained in 5 grams of deuterium oxide (heavy water)? 10 grams of deuterium oxide?

7. Compare the number of grams of oxygen contained in 5 grams of heavy water and 4.5 grams of ordinary water.

8. The analysis of two compounds, both containing hydrogen and oxygen, produced the following results:

Compound (assumed formula)	Weight of hydrogen	Weight of oxygen
H_2O	2 grams	16 grams
X	2 grams	32 grams

If H_2O is the formula assumed for the first compound, show from this data that the formula for the second compound (labeled X) must be H_2O_2.

Applying the Concept

1. If you wish to obtain pure copper, which compound would you decompose, cupric sulfide or cuprous sulfide? In determining your answer, assume that the cost per gram of both compounds is the same.

2. Fifty milliliters of H_2 and 50 ml of O_2 are available. What additional volume of H_2 or O_2 must be added to assure that no pure element remains after the H_2 and O_2 are allowed to react to form H_2O?

3. (a) Indicate whether each of the following compounds decomposes easily or with difficulty: $NaCl$, XeF_4, NaF, H_2O. (b) Give a reason for each answer you give.

4. Below is a table showing the radii of three types of atoms, X, Y, and Z, as well as the number of electrons in each of their shells. Which one of these would most likely be found free in nature? Give two reasons for your choice.

Type of atom	Shells→	1	2		3			4	Radii in Å
	Subshells→	s	s	p	s	p	d	s	
X		2	2	6	1				1.86
Y		2	2	6	2	6		2	1.97
Z		2	2	6					1.12

Reading Further

Harvard Case Histories in Experimental Science, 2 vols., edited by J. B. Conant and L. K. Nash, Cambridge, Mass., Harvard University Press, 1957. Many interesting accounts of discoveries and developments in chemistry and other sciences, such as Case 4, "The Atomic-Molecular Theory."

Fundamentals of Physical Science, 5th ed., by K. Krauskopf, and A. Beiser, New York, McGraw-Hill, 1966. One of the best presentations of the Law of Definite Composition and Law of Combining Volumes.

5

Relationships Among Atoms

Tomorrow morning the sun will rise. There isn't the slightest doubt that this will happen. Experience has shown that the sun rises and sets with the regularity of clockwork. Because we are so certain of the laws which "govern" the solar system, various predictions can be made with absolute confidence. We can say exactly when the moon will wax and wane; we can foretell the ebb and flow of the tides, and the changes in the seasons.

Just as the solar system operates according to unchangeable laws, so the properties of atoms recur in patterns which never vary. From these patterns, chemists can usually predict exactly what changes will occur under any given set of conditions. When something occurs over and over again like this, with regularity, we say that it occurs "periodically." In this chapter we are going to examine some of the periodic properties of atoms on which the chemist bases his predictions.

THE PERIODIC LAW

Even before Dalton had outlined his Atomic Theory of matter, chemists had used ratios of elements by weight to determine the formulas for many compounds. Comparison by weight was one of the methods used to find the formulas for the oxides of many elements. An oxide of an element is a compound of that element and oxygen. For instance CO_2, carbon dioxide, is an oxide of carbon, and Na_2O, sodium oxide, is an oxide of sodium. Table 5-1 lists the formulas for the most common oxides of elements with atomic numbers 1 through 20. Notice that some of these formulas follow the same pattern—for example, the formulas for hydrogen oxide (water), lithium oxide, sodium oxide, and potassium oxide. The formula for water is H_2O; that for lithium oxide is Li_2O; that for sodium oxide is Na_2O; and that for potassium oxide is K_2O. In each of these compounds a single atom of oxygen is combined with two atoms of another element.

Or notice the way in which the formulas for beryllium oxide (BeO), magnesium oxide (MgO), and calcium oxide (CaO) are alike. Here a single atom of beryllium, magnesium, or calcium is combined with a single atom of oxygen. Again there is a similarity between the most common oxide of nitrogen (N_2O_5) and the most common oxide of phospho-

Table 5-1 **FORMULAS OF THE MOST COMMON OXIDES OF ELEMENTS WITH ATOMIC NUMBERS 1 THROUGH 20**

Element	Symbol	Atomic number	Name of oxide	Formula of oxide	Element	Symbol	Atomic number	Name of oxide	Formula of oxide
Hydrogen	H	1	Water	H_2O	Sodium	Na	11	Sodium oxide	Na_2O
Helium	He	2	None	None	Magnesium	Mg	12	Magnesium oxide	MgO
Lithium	Li	3	Lithium oxide	Li_2O	Aluminum	Al	13	Aluminum oxide	Al_2O_3
Beryllium	Be	4	Beryllium oxide	BeO	Silicon	Si	14	Silicon dioxide	SiO_2
Boron	B	5	Boron oxide	B_2O_3	Phosphorus	P	15	Phosphorus pentoxide	P_4O_{10} $[P_2O_5]$
Carbon	C	6	Carbon dioxide	CO_2	Sulfur	S	16	Sulfur dioxide	SO_2
Nitrogen	N	7	Nitrogen pentoxide	N_2O_5	Chlorine	Cl	17	Chlorine oxide	OCl_2
Oxygen	O	8	Diatomic oxygen	O_2	Argon	Ar	18	None	None
Fluorine	F	9	Fluorine oxide	OF_2	Potassium	K	19	Potassium oxide	K_2O
Neon	Ne	10	None	None	Calcium	Ca	20	Calcium oxide	CaO

rus (P_4O_{10}). In both cases the proportion is five atoms of oxygen to two atoms of the other element. And note the similarity between boron oxide (B_2O_3) and aluminum oxide (Al_2O_3).

Oxides which have similar formulas are listed in the same vertical column in Table 5-2. Since none of the inert gases combine with oxygen (or usually with other elements) they are listed in a separate column at the right. Notice that the elements whose oxides are listed increase consecutively in atomic number as you read from left to right across the table. Also notice that similar formulas tend to recur. Clearly, then, in the extent to which they combine with oxygen, elements follow a definite periodic pattern.

Table 5-2 **PERIODIC ARRANGEMENT OF COMMON OXIDES**

General Formula*							
X_2O	XO	X_2O_3	XO_2	X_2O_5	O_2	OX_2	X
H_2O							He
Li_2O	BeO	B_2O_3	CO_2	N_2O_5	O_2	OF_2	Ne
Na_2O	MgO	Al_2O_3	SiO_2	P_2O_5 $[P_4O_{10}]$	SO_2	OCl_2	A
K_2O	CaO						

* X represents an element other than oxygen.

Table 5-3 **VALENCE ELECTRONS FOR FIRST TWENTY ELEMENTS IN ORDER OF INCREASING ATOMIC NUMBER**

Name	Symbol	Atomic number	Number of valence electrons	Name	Symbol	Atomic number	Number of valence electrons
Hydrogen	H	1	1	Sodium	Na	11	1
Helium	He	2	2	Magnesium	Mg	12	2
Lithium	Li	3	1	Aluminum	Al	13	3
Beryllium	Be	4	2	Silicon	Si	14	4
Boron	B	5	3	Phosphorus	P	15	5
Carbon	C	6	4	Sulfur	S	16	6
Nitrogen	N	7	5	Chlorine	Cl	17	7
Oxygen	O	8	6	Argon	Ar	18	8
Fluorine	F	9	7	Potassium	K	19	1
Neon	Ne	10	8	Calcium	Ca	20	2

Valence Electrons

Another interesting relationship among different elements appears as you examine Table 5-3. For the atoms of the first twenty elements listed in order of increasing atomic number, observe the number of outer-shell electrons—called **valence electrons.** You see that atoms of hydrogen, lithium, sodium, and potassium each contain 1 valence electron. Atoms of helium, beryllium, magnesium, sodium, and calcium each contain 2 valence electrons; boron and aluminum atoms contain 3, and so on. When you read *down* any column in Table 5-4, it becomes apparent that you can place different atoms in groups according to the number of electrons found in their outer shells.

If you read horizontally from left to right in Table 5-4, you see that the elements are listed consecutively in the order of their atomic numbers. In this horizontal listing, the number of valence electrons does not increase consecutively; it increases and decreases repeatedly. But you find again the pattern of recurrence. The same number of electrons in the outer shell occurs periodically.

Table 5-4   **GROUPS OF ELEMENTS AND VALENCE ELECTRONS**

Number of Valence Electrons							
1	2	3	4	5	6	7	8
H	He						
Li	Be	B	C	N	O	F	Ne
Na	Mg	Al	Si	P	S	Cl	A
K	Ca						

Density

A third important property of any atom is its density. Density, as you know, refers to the mass of a unit volume of a substance. Since a volume

Table 5-5 **SOME PROPERTIES OF THE FIRST TWENTY ELEMENTS**

Name	Symbol	Atomic number	Density*	Atomic radius†	Ionization potential‡
Hydrogen	H	1	0.00009	0.53	13.6
Helium	He	2	0.00018	0.93	24.6
Lithium	Li	3	0.53	1.52	5.4
Beryllium	Be	4	1.8	1.12	9.3
Boron	B	5	2.5	0.80	8.3
Carbon	C	6	3.5	0.77	11.3
Nitrogen	N	7	0.00125	0.74	14.5
Oxygen	O	8	0.00143	0.74	13.6
Fluorine	F	9	0.0017	0.72	17.4
Neon	Ne	10	0.0009	1.12	21.6
Sodium	Na	11	0.97	1.86	5.1
Magnesium	Mg	12	1.74	1.60	7.6
Aluminum	Al	13	2.7	1.43	6.0
Silicon	Si	14	2.4	1.17	8.1
Phosphorus	P	15	2.2	1.10	11.0
Sulfur	S	16	2.1	1.06	10.4
Chlorine	Cl	17	0.0032	0.97	13.0
Argon	Ar	18	0.0018	1.54	15.8
Potassium	K	19	0.86	2.31	4.3
Calcium	Ca	20	1.55	1.97	6.1

* g/ml   †angstroms   ‡electron volts

of 1 milliliter of water has a mass of 1 gram, the density of water is 1 gram per milliliter. This value is abbreviated as 1 g/ml.

You know that protons and neutrons that make up the tightly packed nucleus of an atom account for most of its mass. Thus you might expect that as the elements increase in atomic number—indicating an additional proton in the nucleus—there would be a corresponding increase in density. But a glance at column 4 of Table 5-5 shows that this is not so. The gaseous elements have low densities. There is, however, a periodic pattern for the densities of the elements. It is a pattern of increase followed by decrease, increase then decrease, as the atomic numbers become larger. While no two elements have exactly the same densities, many have densities which are very similar. Lithium, sodium, and potassium, for example, all have densities between 0.5 g/ml and 1 g/ml. The densities of helium, neon, and argon are all a small fraction of 1 g/ml.

Atomic Size

Though all atoms are extremely small in size, recall that there is a difference in size among them. As you study the atomic radii of the first twenty elements listed in column 5 of Table 5-5, a pattern emerges. Except for hydrogen and the inert gases, the atomic size decreases then increases, decreases then increases. Once again a property of elements—atomic size—recurs periodically. Though no two elements have the identical atomic radius, there is a recurring pattern.

Just as there is a similarity of densities and electron structure among certain elements, there is a similarity of atomic radii among them. The relatively large atomic radii of atoms of lithium, sodium, and potassium are in contrast with the very small values for atoms of fluorine and chlorine. As a further indication that a relationship exists among helium, neon, and argon, observe in Table 5-5 that each inert gas interrupts the regularity of decrease and increase observed for the other elements.

Ionization Potential

You remember that the ionization potential of an element is the amount of energy required to remove a single electron from an atom of that element. The ionization potentials of the first twenty elements are listed in column 6 of Table 5-5. What is the pattern here?

Ionization potentials can also be shown in the form of a graph (Fig. 5-1) where the potentials for different elements are plotted against their atomic numbers. Following the line of this graph, you see that the ionization potentials increase then decrease, over and over again. Thus ionization potentials—like the ability of elements to combine with oxygen, the number of valence electrons in different elements, and atomic size— follow a pattern of periodic recurrence. This does not mean that any two ionization potentials are exactly the same; they are not. But *similar* ionization potentials recur.

Only a small percentage of the elements are listed in the previous tables and graph of ionization potentials. But the same pattern holds true for all the one hundred and four known elements. Chemists have found that when the elements are listed consecutively in order of increasing atomic number, their chemical and physical properties recur periodically.

This periodic recurrence of properties enables us to classify elements into groups. Thus an examination of the graph of ionization potentials shows that helium (He), neon (Ne), and argon (Ar) can be placed in a single group. The ionization potential of each of these inert gases is quite high and about the same. By contrast, the ionization potentials of

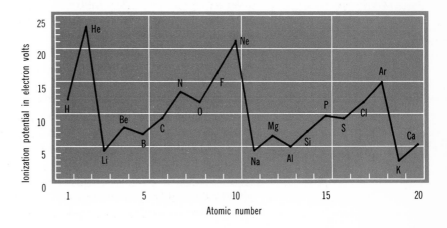

5-1 The ionization potentials of the first 20 elements in the gaseous state show a periodic recurrence. The values are for the first ionization potential, or the energy required to remove one electron from the atom.

lithium (Li), sodium (Na), and potassium (K) are low. Consequently, they fall together in another group. So it goes with all the various properties of the different elements. Each of these properties recurs in a definite pattern and we group the elements accordingly.

Since the chemical and physical properties of the elements repeat themselves in a way that is systematic and not arbitrary, they are said to recur *periodically*. The properties of the elements follow a definite pattern that is related to their atomic numbers. The statement which describes this periodic recurrence of the properties of the elements is called the **Periodic Law.** It can be stated as follows: *When the elements are arranged in order of increasing atomic numbers, their properties vary periodically.*

QUESTIONS AND PROBLEMS

1. What is the electron structure of atoms of the group of elements with the largest atomic radii? the highest ionization potentials?
2. From Table 5-5 determine the atomic numbers of the elements with the approximate ionization potentials of 4 electron volts, 9 electron volts, 22 electron volts.
3. On the basis of information in the various tables, what two elements should be placed in the same group as beryllium? Explain why you selected the elements you did.

THE PERIODIC TABLE

By 1864 John Newlands in England and J. Lothar Meyer in Germany had recognized that the chemical and physical properties of the elements repeat themselves. They related this repetition of properties to increasing *atomic weights*. Because the atomic weights of the heavier elements were incorrectly determined at the time, they found many exceptions to their rule. The properties of the heavier elements, especially, did not seem to be directly dependent upon atomic weights.

By 1869 some of these faulty atomic weights had been corrected. In that year Dmitri Mendeleev, a Russian chemist, organized much of the data about the sixty-three elements then known into a table according to increasing atomic weights. It is a modification of this table which today we call the **periodic table,** or periodic chart, of the elements (Fig. 5-2). When listed in this way, elements with similar properties fell together into separate vertical columns. These Mendeleev called **families** of elements. Mendeleev realized there were certain discrepancies when the elements were listed according to their increasing atomic weights. Tellurium (Te) and iodine (I) [as well as potassium (K) and argon (Ar) upon its discovery] did not fall into the appropriate columns on the basis of their properties. The same was true for cobalt (Co) and nickel (Ni) which, along with iron (Fe), fell into a special column. Even with these discrepancies, Mendeleev proposed a periodic law to describe his table. This first

Fig. 5-2 REVISED FORM OF MENDELEEV'S PERIODIC CHART

Period	0	I-A	I-B	II-A	II-B	III-A	III-B	IV-A	IV-B	V-A	V-B	VI-A	VI-B	VII-A	VII-B	VIII	VIII	VIII
1		H 1.008																
2	He 4.0	Li 6.9		Be 9.0		B 10.8		C 12.0		N 14.0		O 16.*		F 19.*				
3	Ne 20.2	Na 23.*		Mg 24.3		Al 27.*		Si 28.1		P 31.*		S 32.1		Cl 35.5				
4	Ar 39.9	K 39.1		Ca 40.1			Sc 45.*	Ti 47.9		V 50.9		Cr 52.*		Mn 54.9		Fe 55.8	Co 58.9	Ni 58.7
4			Cu 63.5		Zn 65.4		Ga 69.7		Ge 72.6		As 74.9		Se 79.*		Br 79.9			
5	Kr 83.8	Rb 85.5		Sr 87.6			Y 88.9	Zr 91.2		Nb 92.9		Mo 95.9		Tc [99]		Ru 101.1	Rh 102.9	Pd 106.4
5			Ag 107.9		Cd 112.4		In 114.8		Sn 118.7		Sb 121.8		Te 127.6		I 126.9			
6	Xe 131.3	Cs 132.9		Ba 137.3			La* 138.9	Hf 178.5		Ta 180.9		W 183.9		Re 186.2		Os 190.2	Ir 192.2	Pt 195.1
6			Au 197.*		Hg 200.6		Tl 204.4		Pb 207.2		Bi 209.*		Po [210]		At [210]			
7	Rn [222]	Fr [223]		Ra [226]			Ac** [227]	— [257]										

*Lanthanides	Ce 140.1	Pr 140.9	Nd 144.2	Pm [147]	Sm 150.4	Eu 152.*	Gd 157.3	Tb 158.9	Dy 162.5	Ho 164.9	Er 167.3	Tm 168.9	Yb 173.0	Lu 175.*
**Actinides	Th 232.0	Pa [231]	U 238.0	Np [237]	Pu [242]	Am [243]	Cm [247]	Bk [247]	Cf [249]	Es [254]	Fm [253]	Md [256]	No [253]	Lw [257]

* Indicates decimal value of .95 or more, rounded off to next whole number.

formulation of the periodic law stated that when the elements are arranged in order of increasing *atomic weight* their properties vary periodically.

As you remember from Chapter 2, by 1915 H. G. J. Moseley had discovered that a definite pattern exists among the X-ray spectra of the elements. He used this pattern as a basis for listing the elements in a definite order, then numbered the elements consecutively to represent this order. Moseley called these consecutive numbers atomic numbers. Later, the atomic number of each element was found to represent the number of protons in the nucleus of each atom of the element.

Moseley also showed that when the elements were placed in the order of their increasing *atomic numbers,* rather than increasing atomic weights, argon and potassium, cobalt and nickel, and tellurium and iodine all fell into their correct families of elements. In this way the discrepancies which had puzzled Mendeleev were eliminated. In the revised periodic table in widespread use today, the elements are listed in the more useful order of increasing atomic numbers.

Even with the discrepancies in Mendeleev's listing, his understanding of the relationships among the properties of the elements was remarkable. He was even able to leave spaces in his orginal table for many elements that had not yet been discovered in his time. Further, he made amazingly accurate predictions about the properties of these still unknown elements. In the next section we shall see why Mendeleev's original periodic table, and the longer, revised form in widespread use today, constitute one of the chemist's most valuable tools.

Atomic Numbers versus Atomic Weights

The usefulness of the periodic table can best be understood if we study it in some detail. We shall be concerned chiefly with the **long form** or **extended form** of the table. As you shall see in the following discussion, this form has several advantages over the short form, which is the form Mendeleev developed.

The long form of the periodic table follows page 84. As you read from left to right across this table, notice that the elements are listed consecutively in order of their atomic numbers through to lanthanum (La, atomic number 57). On this table the atomic number of each element is placed directly above the symbol for the element. There is a break in the order after lanthanum. But the consecutive order of atomic numbers begins again with the element hafnium (Hf, atomic number 72) and continues through to actinium (Ac, atomic number 89).

Two rows of elements at the bottom of the page are separated from the main body of the table. The elements from cerium (Ce, atomic number 58) through lutecium (Lu, atomic number 71) are listed consecutively in a horizontal column. Directly beneath this group of fourteen elements are listed the elements from atomic number 90 (Th, thorium) through to lawrencium (Lw, atomic number 103). The recently discovered element 104 is in the main body of the table. The reason why the two horizontal rows are isolated will be clear shortly.

Now examine closely the atomic weights of the elements in the periodic table. The atomic weight is given directly below the symbol for the element. Locate these three pairs of elements: argon (Ar) and potassium (K), atomic numbers 18 and 19; cobalt (Co) and nickel (Ni), atomic numbers 27 and 28; and tellurium (Te) and iodine (I), atomic numbers 52 and 53. Notice that their atomic weights are not in increasing order. The element in each pair which has the greater atomic weight comes first rather than second as we would expect. This is the discrepancy we have already mentioned. To explain it we must assume that the element in each pair which has the lower atomic number must have a greater number of heavy isotopes. This would give the element with the lower atomic number a greater atomic weight.

There are several other pairs of elements which are not listed in order of their increasing atomic weights but are listed according to increasing atomic number. Can you find them? (Look in the second row of elements beneath the main body of the table.) The fact that discrepancies in chemical and physical properties appear when we list the elements by atomic weight, but not when we list them by atomic number, suggests an important relationship: properties such as density, ionization potential, atomic size, and the number of valence electrons are more closely related to the atomic number of an element than they are to its atomic weight.

Groups of Elements

As the properties of elements recur, it is possible to place elements with related properties in single groups. Following Mendeleev's description, these groups are referred to as families of elements. The elements lithium (Li), sodium (Na), potassium (K), rubidium (Rb), cesium (Cs), and francium (Fr) are grouped together in the first vertical column at the left side of the periodic table. The atoms of all these elements contain 1 valence electron, their ionization potentials and atomic size are related, and their densities are similar. This group, labeled IA, is sometimes called the *alkali metal family*. The name alkali comes from the Arabic *al-kali* meaning "the ashes." The Arabs used this term for these metals because they found that the ashes of plants were composed chiefly of sodium and potassium carbonates.

Examine the periodic table to determine that it is divided into eighteen vertical columns. Except for the three columns labeled with Roman numeral VIII, and the single column to the far right labeled O (zero), each column is labeled with a Roman numeral followed by the letters A or B. Each of these vertical columns constitutes a numbered **group,** or a certain family of elements. To the right of group IA, the alkali metal family, is group IIA, the *alkaline earth family*. This group gets its name from the fact that compounds of these elements are somewhat related in their properties to the alkali metals, but were originally obtained from earth rather than from ashes. The name of group VIIA, the *halogen family,* comes from the Greek words meaning "salt from the sea." The first halogen that was discovered in the history of chemistry, chlorine (Cl), was taken from salt obtained from sea water.

Some groups take their name from the first element in the group. Thus group IVA is referred to as the *carbon family*. In the same way group VIA is called the *oxygen family*.

All of the elements in groups labeled with a Roman numeral followed by the letter B, together with the nine elements under Roman numeral VIII, are referred to as the *transition elements*. This name was selected because these elements, which are fairly active metals, represent a long series, or transition, between the active metals and the active nonmetals. Most of the elements which man has known for thousands of years fall into this transition metal group. For instance, under IB we find copper

(Cu), silver (Ag), and gold (Au). In group VIII are iron (Fe) and nickel (Ni). Zinc (Zn) is found in group IIB.

The chemistry of the transition metals is complex, since changes in these groups involve both valence electrons and electrons from the shell next to the outer shell. Therefore, let us consider first the electron structure of the group A elements.

Groups and Electron Structure

The number of electron shells in the atoms of each element and the distribution of electrons among these shells are indicated to the left of the symbol for each element in the long form of the periodic table. Carefully examine the number of valence electrons for the atoms of elements in each of the A groups shown in the table. Observe that the number of valence electrons corresponds to the number of the group to which the element belongs. All of the elements in group IA, for example, have 1 electron in the outer shells of their atoms. All the elements in group IIA have 2 electrons in their outer shells; the elements in group VIIA contain 7 electrons in their valence shells.

Notice that hydrogen is shown separated slightly from the other elements in group IA. This is done to indicate that although the single shell of a hydrogen atom contains 1 electron, hydrogen has properties different from the other elements in group IA. In fact, hydrogen is sometimes also shown at the top of group VIIA. As with elements of the halogen family, 1 electron is required to complete its outer shell; and in some properties it reacts similarly to the halogens. As a helium atom contains 2 electrons in its K shell, it might be thought to be a member of group IIA. Conventionally, however, helium appears in group O because its K shell is complete when occupied by 2 electrons. Helium, like neon, argon, and the rest of the rare gases, is therefore essentially inert; its atoms need no electrons to complete the outer shell.

Periods and Electron Structure

In addition to being divided into vertical columns or groups, the periodic table is also divided into horizontal rows. There are seven horizontal rows in the main part of the table and two rows at the bottom of the table, slightly removed from the rest. The Arabic numbers 1 through 7 down the left side of the table are used to label the first seven horizontal rows. Each row is called a **period** and consists of elements of consecutive atomic numbers. The first row is called period one, the second period two, and so on. Notice that the first horizontal row below the main body of the table is part of period six. The row beneath it is part of period seven.

Each period consists of elements whose atoms have the same number of electron shells. *Period one* contains only two elements, hydrogen (H) and helium (He). From the number of electron shells indicated at the left of each symbol in the periodic table, observe that both hydrogen and helium in period one contain only one electron shell, its 1s orbital.

Observe that all the elements in *period two* have 2 electron shells. From the left side of Table 4-2 (pg. 56) notice that, in passing from lithium (Li) to beryllium (Be), the 2s orbital is completed. The buildup of the three 2p orbitals begins with boron (B) and is completed with six 2p electrons in neon (Ne), atomic number 10. Thus neon has filled 2s and 2p orbitals.

The elements in *period three* have 3 electron shells. From Table 4-2, note the buildup of a completed third shell. Sodium (Na) and magnesium (Mg) each has two complete shells (the neon structure) plus one and two 3s electrons, respectively. This places sodium under lithium in column IA and magnesium under beryllium (Be) in column IIA of the periodic table. The next element, aluminum (Al), atomic number 13, has one electron in a 3p orbital. Thus, aluminum is placed in the IIIA family underneath boron. The buildup of the three 3p orbitals to 6 electrons is completed with argon (Ar).

How many elements are there in *each* of the first three periods?

Period four, the first *long period,* includes eighteen elements, each containing 4 electron shells. In Chapter 3 we saw that the next two elements, potassium and calcium, atomic numbers 19 and 20, have their outer-shell electrons in the 4s orbital. Thus, potassium is a member of the IA family, and calcium is a member of the IIA family. However, from Fig. 5-3 we see that beginning with scandium (Sc) atomic number 21, the 3d energy level falls below the 4s energy level. Table 5-6 shows the electron configuration for the transition elements of numbers 21 through 30. The "Ar" noted on the table indicates that each of these elements has the argon electron structure in its inner shells. The 18 electrons of argon are distributed as follows: $1s^2\ 2s^2\ 2p^6\ 3s^2\ 3p^6$.

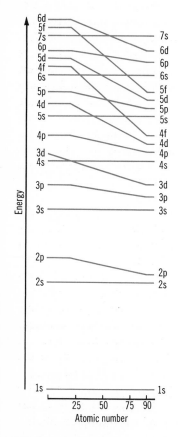

All the elements in Table 5-6 are metals and their atoms complete *an inner subshell* consisting of five 3d orbitals. There are two somewhat unexpected electron configurations in these transition elements. Can you find them? Chemists attribute the configuration in chromium and copper to the *great stability of half-filled and completely filled d orbitals.*

Gallium (Ga), atomic number 31, is a member of the IIIA family, as one electron enters the 4p orbital. The buildup of the three 4p orbitals is completed with krypton (Kr), atomic number 36. Thus, the outer shell of krypton contains a total of 8 electrons in the 4s and 4p subshells. All inert gases (except helium) have 8 electrons in their outer s and p subshells.

Period five consists of the elements containing 5 electron shells per atom. The first two elements, rubidium (Rb) and strontium (Sr), have $5s^1$ and $5s^2$ outer electron-shell configurations. Hence, rubidium and strontium are members of the IA and IIA families, respectively. At the next element, yttrium (Y), atomic number 39, the 4d energy level falls below the 5s energy level (Fig. 5-3), and a second row of transition elements begins. This part of the fifth period shows a consecutive buildup of the five 4d orbitals. Table 5-6 also gives the electron configuration of these elements. (The krypton core of electrons $1s^2\ 2s^2\ 2p^6\ 3s^2\ 3p^6\ 3d^{10}\ 4s^2\ 4p^6$ is shown as "Kr.")

5-3 Energy level crossovers.

The irregularities in electron structure of the fifth-period transition elements are even greater than those in the fourth-period transition elements. The 4d and 5s energy levels are so close in these fifth-period elements that the stability of the half-filled and completely filled 4d orbitals is especially important here. Both sets of transition elements are composed of metals and very often the d orbitals (3d and 4d) take part in the bonding with molecules or negative ions.

Beginning with indium (In), atomic number 49, the buildup of the three 5p orbitals occurs. Indium is a member of the IIIA family. The regular order of buildup of the three 5p orbitals continues until the process is completed with xenon (Xe), atomic number 54, having $5s^2$ and $5p^6$ orbitals. Thus a second *long period* of 18 elements is completed.

Period six is a much longer period containing elements from atomic number 55, cesium (Cs), to atomic number 86, radon (Rn), a total of 32 elements. All of these elements have six electron shells. The first two elements, cesium (Cs) and barium (Ba), can be described as having the structures "Xe" $6s^1$ and "Xe" $6s^2$ and are thus members of the IA and IIA families, respectively. Lanthanum (La), atomic number 57, has the electron arrangement, "Xe" $5d^1 6s^2$ because the 5d energy level falls below the 6s level at this point (Fig. 5-3). Lanthanum begins the third row of transition elements. When you inspect the periodic table, a strange situation appears. The element to the right of lanthanum is hafnium (Hf), atomic number 72. Why are the missing 14 elements set off at the bottom of the periodic table as the *lanthanide series?* You recall that there are seven 4f orbitals that can hold a maximum of 14 electrons. Indeed, beginning with cerium (Ce) and ending with ytterbium (Yb), the 4f orbitals fill to a total of 14 electrons. All of these elements are metals which form similar compounds, usually with the lanthanides having a valence number of 3. The lanthanides are so similar because their outer shells are the same; it is in the 4f subshell that these elements differ. Thus, the lanthanides are sometimes called *inner transition elements.*

When we come back to the main body of the periodic table, we find that the third row of transition elements continues with hafnium (Hf) until the 5d orbitals are filled with a total of 10 electrons in gold (Au) and mercury (Hg). Following this, the three 6p orbitals fill to a total of 6 electrons in the inert gas radon (Rn).

The *seventh period* elements contain 7 shells of electrons. A new series of inner transition elements appears and is again set off at the bottom of the periodic table as the *actinide series.* Most of these elements are man-made. The electron structure of several of these elements is uncertain, but lawrencium (Lw), atomic number 103, apparently completes the second inner transition series with 14 electrons in its 5f orbitals. The recently produced element 104 is the first of the fourth-row transition elements in which the five 6d orbitals are filled. In the years ahead, more new elements will undoubtedly be produced. Predict the maximum number of elements in the seventh or *unfinished period.*

Table 5-6 ELECTRON CONFIGURATION OF THE TRANSITION ELEMENTS

Fourth-period Elements			Orbital Representation		Orbital notation	Fifth-period Elements			Orbital representation		Orbital notation
Name	Symbol	Atomic number	3d	4s		Name	Symbol	Atomic number	4d	5s	
Scandium	Sc	21			$3d^1 4s^2$	Yttrium	Y	39			$4d^1 5s^2$
Titanium	Ti	22			$3d^2 4s^2$	Zirconium	Zr	40			$4d^2 5s^2$
Vanadium	V	23			$3d^3 4s^2$	Niobium	Nb	41			$4d^4 5s^1$
Chromium	Cr	24			$3d^5 4s^1$	Molybdenum	Mo	42			$4d^5 5s^1$
Manganese	Mn	25			$3d^5 4s^2$	Technetium	Tc	43			$4d^6 5s^1$
Iron	Fe	26	"Ar"	"Ar"	$3d^6 4s^2$	Ruthenium	Ru	44	"Kr"	"Kr"	$4d^7 5s^1$
Cobalt	Co	27			$3d^7 4s^2$	Rhodium	Rh	45			$4d^8 5s^1$
Nickel	Ni	28			$3d^8 4s^2$	Palladium	Pd	46			$4d^{10}$
Copper	Cu	29			$3d^{10} 4s^1$	Silver	Ag	47			$4d^{10} 5s^1$
Zinc	Zn	30			$3d^{10} 4s^2$	Cadmium	Cd	48			$4d^{10} 5s^2$

Summary of the Periodic Table (Long Form)

The IA and IIA families have s electrons in their outer shells. The transition elements are completing d orbitals in the next to the outer shell and generally have s electrons in their outermost shells. The IIIA, IVA, VA, VIA, and VIIA families have p electrons in their outermost subshells. The inert gases have three completed p orbitals in their highest energy subshells, except helium, which has only a completed 1s orbital. The lanthanides are completing the 4f subshell, while having 8 electrons in their fifth shell and 2 electrons in their sixth shell. The actinides are completing the 5f subshell, while having electrons in their sixth and seventh shells.

Families and Electron Structure

Since each family of elements consists of one element from each different period, the atoms of the elements in a family (a vertical column) contain an increasing number of electron shells. For example, atoms of carbon, the first element listed in group IVA, contain two shells each; atoms of silicon, the next element in this group, contain three shells; the germanium atoms four shells, and so on. However, as you can see by examining the periodic table, the atoms of the different elements in a family *do* have the same number of valence electrons—four. The orbital and electron dot diagrams in Figure 5-4 represent the outer electron shell of an atom of any element in group IVA. Each of these elements has atoms with a pair of s electrons and two unpaired p electrons in their outer shells. The four valence electrons in each element explain many of the similarities of chemical properties among the members of this family. Yet, although similar, the properties are not exactly alike, because those

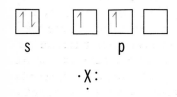

5-4 Why do these orbital and electron dot diagrams represent any element in group IVA?

elements with more shells can lose electrons more readily and thus act as metals.

B Groups and the Short Form

You have been studying the long form of the periodic table because that form is preferred by chemists. But it is well to know how the long form differs from the older and shorter form of the same table. In the long form of the table, the B families occupy the central portion of the chart beginning with period four. In examining the elements in this period, you will notice a certain similarity in their atomic structure. For instance, all the atoms in this group have one or more shells which contain more than 8 electrons. Also many of these elements, though not all, have inner electron shells that are unfilled even though they contain more than 8 electrons. Consider, for example, the M shell in atoms of chromium (Cr, atomic number 24) and iron (Fe, atomic number 26). In chromium this shell contains 13 electrons, in iron it contains 14. Since the M shell can contain 18 electrons (unless it is the outer shell of an atom) this shell is unfilled in both chromium and iron.

In the short form (Fig. 5-2) both A and B families are listed together in single vertical columns. The IA and IB families appear together in the same column at the left of the table. In this arrangement the labels A and B stand for two subgroups, or subfamilies, under each main heading. A comparison of the short and long forms reveals that there is a slightly different arrangement of the elements in the A and B categories in groups III and IV. Don't be misled by the short form to conclude that elements of the A groups are similar in their properties to elements of the B groups. They are not. Nearly all the B group elements—the transition elements or transition heavy metals—are hard, brittle substances with fairly high melting points. Also, with the exception of the elements in group VII, all the B group elements are less active than those in group A.

QUESTIONS AND PROBLEMS

1. In terms of electron structure, how are the transition elements in period five related to each other?
2. Predict the electron configuration of element 107. Explain the reason for your prediction.
3. Give the name, atomic number, atomic weight, and electron structure of the element in group IIA and period five.
4. Compare and contrast the elements in group IVA with the elements in period four with respect to electron configuration.

RELATIONSHIPS AMONG ELEMENTS

How has the periodic table helped chemists gain a better understanding of the elements and the different relationships among them? In 1869

EMISSION SPECTRA

Continuous Spectrum

Incandescent
Lamp

Every incandescent solid emits a continuous spectrum. Hot
gases, including vapors from solids, emit bright-line spectra.

Bright-line Spectra

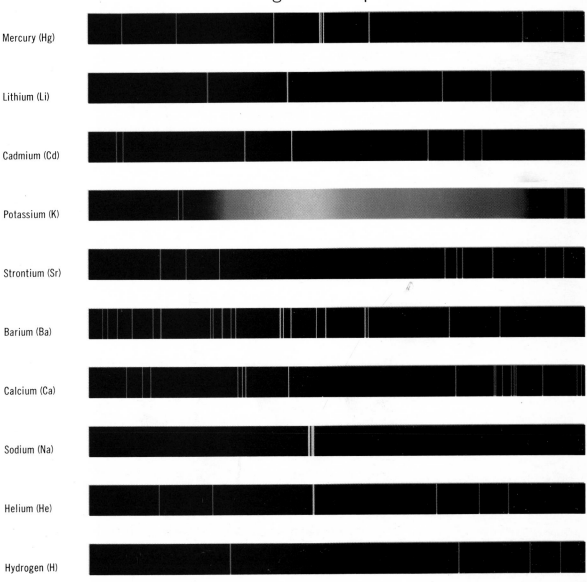

Mercury (Hg)

Lithium (Li)

Cadmium (Cd)

Potassium (K)

Strontium (Sr)

Barium (Ba)

Calcium (Ca)

Sodium (Na)

Helium (He)

Hydrogen (H)

IA

1		1 **H** 1.00797

IIA

TRANSITION ELEMENTS

	2 1	3 **Li** 6.939	2 2	4 **Be** 9.0122
2				

VIII

	2 8 1	11 **Na** 22.9898	2 8 2	12 **Mg** 24.312
3				

		IIIB		IVB		VB		VIB		VIIB					

4	2 8 8 1	19 **K** 39.102	2 8 8 2	20 **Ca** 40.08	2 8 9 2	21 **Sc** 44.956	2 8 10 2	22 **Ti** 47.90	2 8 11 2	23 **V** 50.942	2 8 13 1	24 **Cr** 51.996	2 8 13 2	25 **Mn** 54.9380	2 8 14 2	26 **Fe** 55.847	2 8 15 2	27 **Co** 58.9332
5	2 8 18 1	37 **Rb** 85.47	2 8 18 2	38 **Sr** 87.62	2 8 18 9 2	39 **Y** 88.905	2 8 18 10 2	40 **Zr** 91.22	2 8 18 12 1	41 **Nb** 92.906	2 8 18 13 1	42 **Mo** 95.94	2 8 18 14 1	43 **Tc** [99]	2 8 18 15 1	44 **Ru** 101.07	2 8 18 16 1	45 **Rh** 102.905
6	2 8 18 8 1	55 **Cs** 132.905	2 8 18 8 2	56 **Ba** 137.34	2 8 18 9 2	57 **La** 138.91	2 8 18 32 10 2	72 **Hf** 178.49	2 8 18 32 11 2	73 **Ta** 180.948	2 8 18 32 12 2	74 **W** 183.85	2 8 18 32 13 2	75 **Re** 186.2	2 8 18 32 14 2	76 **Os** 190.2	2 8 18 32 17	77 **Ir** 192.2
7	2 8 18 32 18 8 1	87 **Fr** [223]	2 8 18 32 18 8 2	88 **Ra** [226]	2 8 18 32 18 9 2	89 **Ac** [227]	2 8 18 32 18 10 2	104 — [257]										

LANTHANIDE SERIES	2 8 18 20 8 2	58 **Ce** 140.12	2 8 18 21 8 2	59 **Pr** 140.907	2 8 18 22 8 2	60 **Nd** 144.24	2 8 18 23 8 2	61 **Pm** [147]
ACTINIDE SERIES	2 8 18 32 18 10 2	90 **Th** 232.038	2 8 18 32 20 9 2	91 **Pa** [231]	2 8 18 32 21 9 2	92 **U** 238.03	2 8 18 32 22 9 2	93 **Np** [237]

Brackets denote replacement of atomic weight by the mass number of the isotope with the longest half life.

TABLE

NONMETALS

IIIA	IVA	VA	VIA	VIIA

| | | | | | 2 / 2 / He / 4.0026 |

| 2 3 / 5 / B / 10.811 | 2 4 / 6 / C / 12.01115 | 2 5 / 7 / N / 14.0067 | 2 6 / 8 / O / 15.9944 | 2 7 / 9 / F / 18.9984 | 2 8 / 10 / Ne / 20.183 |

| IB | IIB | 2 8 3 / 13 / Al / 26.9815 | 2 8 4 / 14 / Si / 28.086 | 2 8 5 / 15 / P / 30.9738 | 2 8 6 / 16 / S / 32.064 | 2 8 7 / 17 / Cl / 35.453 | 2 8 8 / 18 / Ar / 39.948 |

| 2 8 16 2 / 28 / Ni / 58.71 | 2 8 18 1 / 29 / Cu / 63.54 | 2 8 18 2 / 30 / Zn / 65.37 | 2 8 18 3 / 31 / Ga / 69.72 | 2 8 18 4 / 32 / Ge / 72.59 | 2 8 18 5 / 33 / As / 74.9216 | 2 8 18 6 / 34 / Se / 78.96 | 2 8 18 7 / 35 / Br / 79.909 | 2 8 18 8 / 36 / Kr / 83.80 |

| 2 8 18 18 / 46 / Pd / 106.4 | 2 8 18 18 1 / 47 / Ag / 107.870 | 2 8 18 18 2 / 48 / Cd / 112.40 | 2 8 18 18 3 / 49 / In / 114.82 | 2 8 18 18 4 / 50 / Sn / 118.69 | 2 8 18 18 5 / 51 / Sb / 121.75 | 2 8 18 18 6 / 52 / Te / 127.60 | 2 8 18 18 7 / 53 / I / 126.9044 | 2 8 18 18 8 / 54 / Xe / 131.30 |

| 2 8 18 32 17 1 / 78 / Pt / 195.09 | 2 8 18 32 18 1 / 79 / Au / 196.967 | 2 8 18 32 18 2 / 80 / Hg / 200.59 | 2 8 18 32 18 3 / 81 / Tl / 204.37 | 2 8 18 32 18 4 / 82 / Pb / 207.19 | 2 8 18 32 18 5 / 83 / Bi / 208.980 | 2 8 18 32 18 6 / 84 / Po / [210] | 2 8 18 32 18 7 / 85 / At / [210] | 2 8 18 32 18 8 / 86 / Rn / [222] |

| 2 8 18 24 8 2 / 62 / Sm / 150.35 | 2 8 18 25 8 2 / 63 / Eu / 151.96 | 2 8 18 25 9 2 / 64 / Gd / 157.25 | 2 8 18 27 8 2 / 65 / Tb / 158.924 | 2 8 18 28 8 2 / 66 / Dy / 162.50 | 2 8 18 29 8 2 / 67 / Ho / 164.930 | 2 8 18 30 8 2 / 68 / Er / 167.26 | 2 8 18 31 8 2 / 69 / Tm / 168.934 | 2 8 18 32 8 2 / 70 / Yb / 173.04 | 2 8 18 32 9 2 / 71 / Lu / 174.97 |

| 2 8 18 32 24 9 2 / 94 / Pu / [242] | 2 8 18 32 25 9 2 / 95 / Am / [243] | 2 8 18 32 25 9 2 / 96 / Cm / [247] | 2 8 18 32 27 8 2 / 97 / Bk / [247] | 2 8 18 32 28 8 2 / 98 / Cf / [249] | 2 8 18 32 29 9 2 / 99 / Es / [254] | 2 8 18 32 29 9 2 / 100 / Fm / [253] | 2 8 18 32 30 9 2 / 101 / Md / [256] | 2 8 18 32 31 9 2 / 102 / No / [253] | 2 8 18 32 32 9 2 / 103 / Lw / [257] |

Table 5-7 IONIZATION POTENTIALS OF THE ELEMENTS*

IA	IIA	IIIB	IVB	VB	VIB	VIIB	VIII	VIII	VIII	IB	IIB	IIIA	IVA	VA	VIA	VIIA	O
1 H 13.6																	2 He 24.6
3 Li 5.4	4 Be 9.3											5 B 8.3	6 C 11.3	7 N 14.5	8 O 13.6	9 F 17.4	10 Ne 21.6
11 Na 5.1	12 Mg 7.6											13 Al 6.0	14 Si 8.1	15 P 11.0	16 S 10.4	17 Cl 13.0	18 Ar 15.8
19 K 4.3	20 Ca 6.1	21 Sc 6.6	22 Ti 6.8	23 V 6.7	24 Cr 6.8	25 Mn 7.4	26 Fe 7.9	27 Co 7.9	28 Ni 7.6	29 Cu 7.7	30 Zn 9.4	31 Ga 6.0	32 Ge 8.1	33 As 10	34 Se 9.8	35 Br 11.8	36 Kr 14.0
37 Rb 4.2	38 Sr 5.7	39 Y 6.6	40 Zr 7.0	41 Nb 6.8	42 Mo 7.2	43 Tc –	44 Ru 7.5	45 Rh 7.7	46 Pd 8.3	47 Ag 7.6	48 Cd 9.0	49 In 5.8	50 Sn 7.3	51 Sb 8.6	52 Te 9.0	53 I 10.4	54 Xe 12.1
55 Cs 3.9	56 Ba 5.2	57 La 5.6	72 Hf 5.5	73 Ta 6	74 W 8.0	75 Re 7.9	76 Os 8.7	77 Ir 9.2	78 Pt 9.0	79 Au 9.2	80 Hg 10.4	81 Tl 6.1	82 Pb 7.4	83 Bi 8	84 Po –	85 At –	86 Rn 10.7
87 Fr –	88 Ra 5.3	89 Ac –	104 –														

58 Ce 6.9	59 Pr 5.8	60 Nd 6.3	61 Pm –	62 Sm 5.6	63 Eu 5.7	64 Gd 6.2	65 Tb 6.7	66 Dy 6.8	67 Ho –	68 Er –	69 Tm –	70 Yb 6.2	71 Lu 5.0
90 Th –	91 Pa –	92 U 4	93 Np –	94 Pu –	95 Am –	96 Cm –	97 Bk –	98 Cf –	99 Es –	100 Fm –	101 Md –	102 No –	103 Lw –

* In electron volts, for the first electron removed

Table 5-8 ATOMIC RADII*

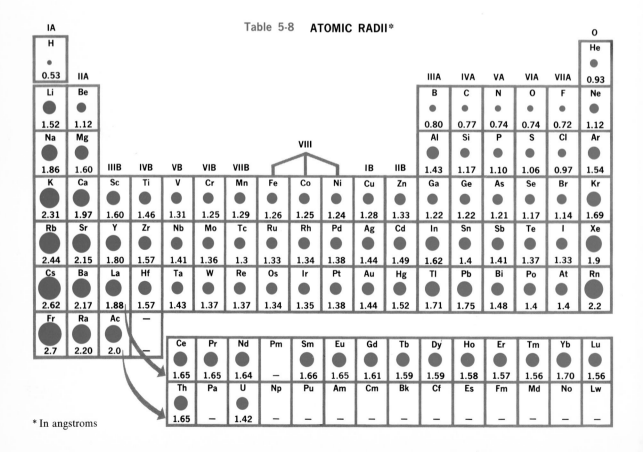

IA	IIA	IIIB	IVB	VB	VIB	VIIB	VIII	VIII	VIII	IB	IIB	IIIA	IVA	VA	VIA	VIIA	O
H 0.53																	He 0.93
Li 1.52	Be 1.12											B 0.80	C 0.77	N 0.74	O 0.74	F 0.72	Ne 1.12
Na 1.86	Mg 1.60											Al 1.43	Si 1.17	P 1.10	S 1.06	Cl 0.97	Ar 1.54
K 2.31	Ca 1.97	Sc 1.60	Ti 1.46	V 1.31	Cr 1.25	Mn 1.29	Fe 1.26	Co 1.25	Ni 1.24	Cu 1.28	Zn 1.33	Ga 1.22	Ge 1.22	As 1.21	Se 1.17	Br 1.14	Kr 1.69
Rb 2.44	Sr 2.15	Y 1.80	Zr 1.57	Nb 1.41	Mo 1.36	Tc 1.3	Ru 1.33	Rh 1.34	Pd 1.38	Ag 1.44	Cd 1.49	In 1.62	Sn 1.4	Sb 1.41	Te 1.37	I 1.33	Xe 1.9
Cs 2.62	Ba 2.17	La 1.88	Hf 1.57	Ta 1.43	W 1.37	Re 1.37	Os 1.34	Ir 1.35	Pt 1.38	Au 1.44	Hg 1.52	Tl 1.71	Pb 1.75	Bi 1.48	Po 1.4	At 1.4	Rn 2.2
Fr 2.7	Ra 2.20	Ac 2.0	–														

Ce 1.65	Pr 1.65	Nd 1.64	Pm –	Sm 1.66	Eu 1.65	Gd 1.61	Tb 1.59	Dy 1.59	Ho 1.58	Er 1.57	Tm 1.56	Yb 1.70	Lu 1.56
Th 1.65	Pa –	U 1.42	Np –	Pu –	Am –	Cm –	Bk –	Cf –	Es –	Fm –	Md –	No –	Lw –

* In angstroms

when Mendeleev developed the table, he did not have the amount of information about the elements that we have today. He didn't know about ionization potentials or atomic sizes. He didn't even know about the electron structures of atoms. Yet even with such information as he did have—atomic weights, densities, melting points, and boiling points—he was able, with the table, to predict the properties of elements as yet undiscovered. Today all of the natural elements are known and many of their properties have been determined. While chemists can use the periodic table to predict further properties, its most important use today consists in something else—in determining the relationships that exist among the properties of elements.

Ionization Potentials

Compare the ionization potentials of the elements in period two by studying Table 5-7 facing page 85. Generally, ionization potentials increase as you proceed horizontally from left to right. If you make the same comparison for the elements of period three, the same relationship exists. Whatever the period, the ionization potentials of elements increase across the table from left to right. This means that it is more and more difficult to remove each successive valence electron from each element as you move across the table. For example, it is more than three times as difficult to remove the first valence electron from a fluorine atom (ionization potential 17.4) as from a lithium atom (ionization potential 5.4).

Now study the atomic radii from Table 5-8 facing page 85. As indicated earlier, except for hydrogen and the elements in group O at the far right of the table, the atoms of the elements at the left of each period are larger than the atoms of elements at the right of the same period. Picture to yourself a valence electron in the outer shell of a large atom and the same electron in the outer shell of a small atom. In which atom is the electron attracted to the nucleus with greater force? Since the electron in the smaller atom is closer to the nucleus, you are right in thinking that the attraction here is greater than in the large atom. For this reason, it is more difficult to remove a valence electron from the smaller atom. In each period, the ionization potentials for the smaller atoms are higher than those for the larger ones.

Not only is there a pattern of increasing ionization potentials going across the table but there is also a pattern within the different families represented by the vertical columns. The atoms increase in size as we go down the table, one reason being that the number of electron shells increases. True, the nuclear charge also increases, but the effect of increasing distance of the electrons from the nucleus is greater. Hence the ionization potentials grow less as one reads down the table in any column. For example, the ionization potential of cesium (3.9) near the bottom of group IA is a little more than half that for lithium (5.4) near the top of the group. The ionization potential of iodine (10.4) near the bottom of group VIIA is likewise about half that of fluorine (17.4) at the top of the group.

Metals and Nonmetals

In the periodic table, the label LIGHT METALS appears over groups IA and IIA. The B groups are labeled TRANSITION ELEMENTS, while group VIIA and parts of groups IIIA through VIIA are labeled NONMETALS. Let's consider what these terms mean. In everyday life we are in constant contact with substances that are either metallic or nonmetallic. The steel body of an automobile, for instance, is metallic while the plastic covers inside the car are nonmetallic. The terms "metal" and "nonmetal" bring to mind certain physical properties. Metals, such as silver and iron, are dense, lustrous substances. They are also good conductors of heat and electricity. Nonmetals, like sulfur and oxygen, have low densities, do not have metallic luster, and do not readily conduct heat and electricity.

Not only do chemists associate these physical properties with metals and nonmetals, but also they use the terms metal and nonmetal with regard to certain chemical properties of elements. One of the physical properties of metals—their ability to conduct electricity—offers a clue to a chemical difference between metals and nonmetals. Scientists believe that electricity moving through a wire of copper or aluminum is actually a flow of electrons from one atom to another. Electricity flows easily through metals because of the unique arrangement of electrons in a *piece* of metal (as detailed in Chapter 6). Since it takes comparatively little energy to remove an electron from a metallic atom, the ionization potentials of metals must be relatively low. Confirm from Table 5-7 these relatively low ionization potentials of metals. As ionization potentials become higher as we proceed across the periodic table, the ionization potentials of the metals, which are shown on the left side of the table, are lower than those of the nonmetals on the right. Thus we can consider a metallic element as a substance with a relatively low ionization potential; a nonmetallic element is a substance whose ionization potential is relatively high.

Recall from the previous chapter that atoms of metals usually contain 1, 2, or 3 valence electrons while atoms of nonmetals usually have outer shells with 5 to 7 electrons. In terms of electron structure, therefore, the metals are the elements at the left and in the center of the periodic table, while nonmetals are located at the right.

From a study of ionization potentials and electron structure, as well as from other data such as atomic size and the loss or gain of electrons, the elements are separated into metals and nonmetals in the periodic table. Those elements which are to the left of the dark zigzag line in the periodic table, starting at the left of the element boron at the top of group IIIA, are the metals. All of the commonly known metals, such as iron and lead, can be found to the left of this line. The elements to the right of the line, except those in group O, are the nonmetals. The elements in group O are considered to be neither metallic nor nonmetallic. With the exception of this O group, the elements become less metallic (or more nonmetallic) as we proceed from left to right across any given period. For instance, in period three, sodium is the most metallic element; aluminum is also metallic but less so than sodium; phosphorus, which is still less metallic than aluminum, is considered a nonmetal. Silicon, which has certain properties characteristic of metals and other properties characteristic of nonmetals, is sometimes classed as a **metalloid.** Several other elements, such as boron and arsenic, on the zigzag line of the periodic table may also be classed as metalloids.

The terms *metal* and *nonmetal* can also be used to differentiate among elements within a family. Within group IA the ionization potentials of these light metals decrease as we proceed down the group. As low ionization potentials are characteristic of metals, we can predict correctly that the elements at the top of group IA are less metallic than those at the bottom, but the extent of variation is small. Look at the ionization potentials for the elements in group VIIA (Table 5-7). While all these elements are considered to be nonmetals (they are all to the right of the zigzag line), it is clear that some of them are more nonmetallic than others. The elements near the top of group VIIA (fluorine and chlorine) have higher ionization potentials than the elements below (bromine and iodine). Iodine, indeed, is so much more metallic than fluorine that in its solid state iodine actually consists of gray-black crystals. Proceeding down any family, the elements become more and more metallic, or less and less nonmetallic.

The relative proportions of metals and nonmetals in each family make it possible to generalize about the relative positions of metals and non-metals on the periodic table as a whole. The most metallic elements—those with the lowest ionization potentials—are found toward the lower left-hand corner of the table. As you move in a diagonal from the lower left side of the table to the upper right side, the elements become less metallic (or more nonmetallic). The elements in the upper right-hand corner of the table (except the inert gases) are the least metallic of all. As you would expect, they also have the highest ionization potentials.

Predicting Properties

Suppose a chemist wants to know something about the properties of tellurium (Te, atomic number 52). Is tellurium a metal? What are its density and atomic weight? What are its relative atomic size and ionization potential?

Tellurium falls in group VIA and period five of the periodic table (Fig. 5-5). By considering the position of tellurium relative to that of other elements on the table, and by knowing the properties of the elements near tellurium, chemists can give at least approximate answers to these questions.

Metallic or Nonmetallic. Iodine (I), directly to the right of tellurium, is nonmetallic. However, in its solid state iodine looks somewhat like a metal. As tellurium is left of iodine in the same period, yet just to the right

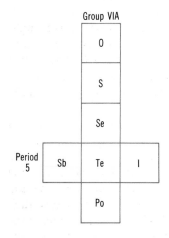

5-5 A portion of the periodic table, including parts of group VIA and period five. How are the properties of tellurium related to its group and period?

of the dark zigzag line on the periodic table, it must be slightly more metallic than iodine. Since tellurium is below sulfur in the same family, it must be more metallic than sulfur.

Density. If tellurium is more metallic than either sulfur or iodine, it should also be more dense than either of them; experience shows that metals are usually more dense than nonmetals. By experiment it has been found that the density of tellurium is 6.2 g/ml. This is about three times the density of sulfur and 1.3 times that of iodine.

Atomic Weight. From the table on the inside back cover of this book, list the atomic weights for the elements in group VIA, with the exception of tellurium. These weights increase as one proceeds down the group. Since tellurium is between selenium (Se, atomic weight 79) and polonium (Po, atomic weight 210), the atomic weight of tellurium should lie between 79 and 210. Observe that the atomic weight of sulfur is twice that of oxygen, while the atomic weight of selenium is a little more than twice that of sulfur and four times the atomic weight of oxygen. This approximate doubling of atomic weight appears to lessen somewhat as we continue down the group; polonium's atomic weight of 210 is somewhat less than four times the atomic weight of selenium. The atomic weight of tellurium, therefore, should be less than double the atomic weight of selenium (less than $79 \times 2 = 158$), and more than half that of polonium (more than $\frac{1}{2} \times 210 = 105$). The atomic weight of tellurium is actually found experimentally to be about 128. The position of tellurium in the periodic table does indeed make possible a reasonably accurate prediction about its atomic weight.

Atomic Radii and Ionization Potentials. The position of tellurium below sulfur in group VIA indicates that tellurium atoms are larger than atoms of sulfur. Since tellurium is to the left of iodine in period five, its atoms must also be larger than those of iodine and its ionization potential must be lower. Compare these predictions with the experimental data given in Tables 5-7 and 5-8. How accurate are they?

These are just a few examples of the kind of prediction that can be made about the properties of an element by observing its position in the periodic table. Using the appropriate tables, see what predictions you make for the density, atomic weight, atomic radius, and ionization potential of the element chlorine (Cl, atomic number 17). Then compare your predictions with the data for chlorine given in Table 5-9 below.

From what you have learned about the periodic table, you can see that it serves as a basic pattern for studying the elements. The next chapter explains how elements in certain groups combine with elements in other groups in a definite pattern. If you look back at the table of contents, you can see from their titles that the chapters in Unit 4 are devoted to a family-by-family study of the 104 elements. A student of chemistry without the periodic table would indeed be like an early explorer without a map.

Table 5-9 SOME PREDICTED AND DETERMINED PROPERTIES OF CHLORINE

Property	Predicted value	Determined value
Density	0.0034 g/ml	0.0032 g/ml
Atomic weight	39	35.5
Atomic radius	0.99 Å	0.97 Å
Ionization potential	14.4 ev	13.0 ev

QUESTIONS AND PROBLEMS

1. On the basis of the position of elements in the periodic table (a) which of the two elements, Na (atomic number 11) or Rb (rubidium, atomic number 37) has the lower ionization potential? Which of these two elements has the larger atomic radius? (b) Which of the two elements, K (atomic number 19) or Br (atomic number 35), has the higher ionization potential? Which of these two has the larger atomic radius?
2. (a) On the basis of the position of metals and nonmetals in the periodic table, which element is the most metallic: Cs, Fe, or Cl? (b) List the three elements F, K, and Ca in order of their decreasing metallic properties.
3. Predict the density, atomic weight, relative atomic size, and ionization potential of the element phosphorus (P, atomic number 15). On what data did you base your prediction?

VALUE OF THE CONCEPT

THE CONCEPT

By 1864 John Newlands and J. Lothar Meyer had realized that the chemical and physical properties of the elements repeat themselves when the elements are listed in order of increasing atomic weights. By 1869 Dimitri Mendeleev had organized much of the data about the elements then known into a table which we call the periodic table. In Mendeleev's Periodic Table the elements were listed in order of increasing atomic weights. From the data, Mendeleev concluded that when the elements are arranged in order of increasing *atomic weights,* their properties vary periodically. This was known as the Periodic Law. The work of H. G. J. Moseley, by 1915, resulted in the revision of the Periodic Law: when the elements are ar-ranged in order of increasing *atomic number,* their properties vary periodically.

The modern periodic table, which lists the elements consecutively in order of atomic number, divides the elements into horizontal rows called periods and into vertical columns called groups or families. Each group consists of elements that have similar or related properties, and whose atoms have the same number of valence electrons. The atoms of elements in any given period contain the same number of electron shells. The number of electron shells in the atoms of each element in a period corresponds to the number of that period.

The elements as listed in the periodic table fall into three main divisions: the metals to the left, the nonmetals to the right, and the inert elements to the far right. The metals are further divided into the active metals (group A metals) and the transition elements (group B metals).

Two related generalizations can be made about the relative properties of the elements:

1. Except for hydrogen and the elements in group O, the atoms of elements to the left of a period are larger than those to the right. There is also an increase in size going from top to bottom of a group.

2. In a given period the ionization potentials increase going from left to right; they decrease going from top to bottom of any group.

USING THE CONCEPT

Using the Basic Concept

1. (a) Precisely what does the word *periodic* mean in relation to the properties of the elements? (b) State the Periodic Law as we know it today.
2. List four properties of elements that vary periodically.
3. How did the formulas for compounds of elements help lead to a statement of the Periodic Law?
4. Describe the discrepancies in data in Mendeleev's Periodic Table. Why did these discrepancies occur?
5. Differentiate between a *group* (or family) of elements and a *period* of elements.
6. (a) Give an alternate name for each of the following groups of elements: IA, IIA, IVA, VIA, and VIIA. (b) What is the signficance of each name?
7. Describe an important difference between the short form and the long form of the periodic table.
8. (a) What is meant by the term *group B elements?* (b) Name eight commonly known group B elements.
9. What relationship exists between the number of a period and the electron structure of atoms of elements in the period?
10. Describe the change in electron configuration of the atoms of elements as you proceed from left to right in (a) period two of the periodic table, (b) period five, (c) period six.

11. (a) Describe two characteristics of the lanthanide series of elements and two characteristics of the actinide series. (b) Of what period is the lanthanide series a part? the actinide series?
12. (a) In terms of the periodic table, define a short period. (b) Give an example of such a period.
13. Describe one similarity and one difference among the different elements within a single A group (or family) of the periodic table.
14. In terms of the electron configurations of their atoms, how do the group B elements differ from the related group A elements?

Relating Terms Within the Concept

From the *italicized* terms below select the term that best completes each of the following statements. Do not use a term more than once. *actinide series, alkali metals, group, group B elements, halogen family, long period, metalloid, nonmetals, period, period four, period six, Periodic Law, rare earths, unfinished period.*

1. Elements with similar or related properties form a _____ .
2. Elements listed in order of increasing atomic number between elements with recurring properties form a _____ .
3. The transition elements are also known as the heavy metals or the _____ .
4. Uranium and lawrencium are part of the _____ .
5. Sodium and potassium are _____ .
6. All elements in group VIIA and most elements in groups VA and VIA are _____ .
7. Relationships among the properties of elements are described by the _____ .
8. The lanthanide series is commonly known as the _____ .
9. The 5f subshell is being completed in the _____ .
10. The 4f orbitals build up from 2 to 14 electrons in the _____ .

Solving Problems Within the Concept

1. The atomic numbers and atomic weights of five different elements are:

	Al	Ga	Cd	Sn	Tl
Atomic number	13	31	48	50	81
Atomic weight	27	70	112	119	204

From the position of these elements in the periodic table, predict the atomic weight of In, atomic number 49. Compare your estimated value with the actual value.

2. Study the electron configurations below for three different atoms. (a) To what period and group of the periodic table does each atom belong? (b) Give a reason for each choice you make.

(a) $1s^2\ 2s^2\ 2p^5$
(b) $1s^2\ 2s^2\ 2p^6\ 3s^2\ 3p^2$
(c) $1s^2\ 2s^2\ 2p^6\ 3s^2\ 3p^6\ 3d^{10}\ 4s^2\ 4p^6\ 5s^2$

Applying the Concept

1. The ionization potential of fluorine, a nonmetal, is 17.4 electron volts. Only two other elements, both of which are inert, have higher ionization potentials. (a) From this information, predict the number of valence electrons and the relative size of fluorine atoms. (b) How did you arrive at your answer?

2. The radius of the rubidium atom is smaller than that of cesium. From this information, predict the relative ionization potentials of these two elements.

3. Account for the fact that ionization potentials of the transition metals are higher than those of the group A metals, but generally lower than the ionization potentials of the nonmetals.

4. The ionization potentials and other properties of many members of the actinide series are unknown. Why?

Reading Further

Chemistry: Principles and Properties, by M. J. Sienko and R. A. Plane, New York, McGraw-Hill, 1966. An excellent presentation of modern chemistry, including the significance of the periodic table.

"A New Periodic Table Based on the Energy Sequence of Atomic Orbitals," by W. R. Walker and G. C. Curthoys, *Journal of Chemical Education,* 1956, vol. 33, p. 68. Describes one of a number of different approaches for classifying the elements.

6

How Atoms Combine

Had you studied chemistry in the nineteenth century, you might have drawn lines between chemical symbols of two elements in a compound to represent the bond between them. Though the formula might have been correct, the way in which the atoms were bonded together to form molecules was not understood. Chemists knew that in a given compound, the *number* of the atoms of each element in the compound never varied. Consider the compound of calcium and oxygen called calcium oxide (CaO). Here a single atom of calcium is always found combined with a single atom of oxygen. Or consider the combination of calcium and fluorine which forms the compound calcium fluoride (CaF_2). Here the proportion is invariably one atom of calcium to two of fluorine.

Without offering any explanation for the grouping of atoms in such simple, and more complex compounds, Edward Frankland of England proposed in 1852 that "no matter what the character of the uniting atoms may be, the combining power of the attracting elements, if I may be allowed the term, is always satisfied by the same number of atoms." This combining ability of the different atoms is known as **valence.** Early chemists assigned each element a number representing its valence. This number was based upon the known formulas for a few compounds. It was not until after the discovery of the electron, however, that really fruitful attempts were made to explain the nature of valence and its relation to chemical bonds between atoms.

IONIC BONDING

In 1916 the American chemist G. N. Lewis published a brief article entitled "The Atom and the Molecule," which forms the basis of the modern theory of valence. In this paper, he proposed that the outer shell of electrons in the inert gases contains 8 electrons and that the outer shell of other atoms tends to become 8 either by gaining or losing electrons or by sharing electrons in pairs with other atoms.

Lewis' ideas have been developed further, and today's chemists, with their more precise knowledge of electrons, can explain in detail how the valence or combining ability of atoms is determined by the arrangement of electrons within the atoms. To understand how the electron arrangement determines the valence of atoms, consider first the inert gases. As the atoms of these elements usually do not combine with either like or unlike atoms, they have a valence of zero.

The reason these elements are so stable is suggested by Table 5-7 facing page 85. All the inert elements have high ionization potentials. It takes a great deal of energy to remove an electron from the outer shell of any of these atoms. You know that ionization potential usually has a direct relation to the size of an atom. The greater the atomic radius (that is, the greater the distance between the nucleus and the outer shell), the lower the ionization potential of the atom. But size alone does not explain the high ionization potentials of the inert elements; for while the atoms of some of these elements are small, others are comparatively large. The great stability of the inert gases results, in part, from the fact that their atoms all have outer shells which are *complete*—they contain the maximum number of electrons which these outer shells will hold.

The elements in group O are the only ones whose atoms have complete outer shells. The outer shells of all other atoms contain less than the maximum number of electrons and hence are *incomplete*. In contrast to the inert gases, all these elements are chemically active and exhibit a valence. For example, oxygen atoms have an outer shell which contains 6 electrons, or 2 less than the shell will hold. Thus oxygen atoms exhibit a valence and will combine with like or unlike atoms.

Electron Rearrangement

Chemists have evidence which supports the idea that there is a rearrangement of outer-shell electrons between atoms to complete their outer shells. Because the number and arrangement of electrons in the outer shell determines the combining capacity or valence of an atom, these electrons, as you know, are called valence electrons. Except for the transition elements, most chemical reactions we will study involve only valence electrons. For this reason we shall be concerned at present only with the rearrangement of valence (outer-shell) electrons between atoms.

One of the ways in which this rearrangement of electrons occurs is by the formation of ions. Ions, as you know, are charged particles, and an ion results when an atom or group of atoms gains or loses electrons in order to complete the outer shell. A sodium atom with a relatively low ionization potential can lose its 1 valence electron easily. In contrast, chlorine with 7 valence electrons and a relatively high electron affinity readily accepts electrons. Hence, when an atom of sodium is brought close to an atom of chlorine, the sodium atom may lose an electron to the chlorine atom, while the chlorine atom gains this same electron. Atoms like sodium that usually lose electrons are said to *donate* them, while atoms like chlorine that gain electrons are said to *accept* them.

The changes that occur when sodium chloride (NaCl) is formed are illustrated in Fig. 6-1. Since each sodium atom contains only 1 valence electron in its M shell, it needs to lose only this 1 electron to have a com-

6-1 When a sodium atom donates one electron to a chlorine atom, the resulting sodium ion has a charge of $+1$, the chloride ion a charge of -1. This happens many times to form an ionic crystal of sodium chloride which, with equal number of Na^+ and Cl^- ions, is electrically neutral.

plete outer shell in the next shell nearer the nucleus, the L shell. With the loss of this 1 electron, the sodium atom is no longer neutral. It now has only 10 electrons, but 11 protons. Thus the original neutral sodium atom has been changed to a *positively charged* sodium ion with a charge of $+1$, Na^+.

A neutral chlorine atom containing 17 protons and 17 electrons requires the addition of 1 electron to complete its outermost, or M, shell of 7 electrons. After gaining this 1 electron from the sodium atom, the chlorine atom, too, is no longer neutral. It now has one more electron than proton. Hence the once-neutral chlorine atom is now a *negatively charged* chloride ion with a charge of -1, Cl^-.

Study the *electron* structure of a chloride ion indicated in Fig. 6-2. Note that the electron structure of the chloride ion is similar to that of an inert argon atom. Similarly, the electron structure of the sodium ion is like that of an inert atom of neon. The outer shells of all four of these particles are complete.

The Ionic Bond

The transfer of an electron from a sodium atom to a chlorine atom results in an **ionic compound,** sodium chloride. Such a transfer of electrons is one way in which chemical reactions take place. Whenever valence electrons are completely lost and gained in this manner, ionic compounds are formed. The forces that hold the ions together in these compounds are called **ionic bonds.**

Ions, held together by ionic bonds, are usually arranged in definite crystalline patterns. Sodium chloride crystals, for example, are cubic in shape. In an ionic substance the positive and negative charges are distributed throughout each crystal. In the crystal of sodium chloride diagrammed in Fig. 6-3, an equal number of positive sodium ions and negative chloride ions are held together by the attraction of oppositely charged particles. Observe that each negative chloride ion is ionically bonded to six positive sodium ions; in turn, each sodium ion is ionically bonded to six chloride ions. It should be clearly understood that ionic compounds (also referred to as *electrovalent* compounds) such as sodium chloride are *not* made up of molecules. They are composed of charged particles—ions.

In an ionic bond, there are usually relatively large attractive forces between the oppositely charged ions. As a result, a great deal of energy must be added to break the bonds between the ions in an ionic solid as it melts.

Ionic Compounds

Simple ionic compounds result when atoms of active metals lose electrons which are accepted by atoms of active nonmetals. Calcium oxide (CaO), like sodium chloride, is an example of an ionic compound. Calcium oxide forms when each calcium atom (group IIA) donates its 2 va-

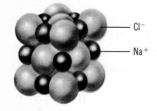

Cl⁻
Na⁺

6-3 A crystal of sodium chloride is composed of indefinite but equal numbers of sodium and chloride ions. Within the crystal, as below, each chloride ion is bonded to six sodium ions.

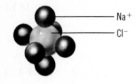

Na⁺
Cl⁻

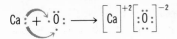

6-4 A calcium atom donates two electrons to an oxygen atom to form a calcium ion and an oxide ion. In calcium oxide, each calcium and oxide ion has a complete outer electron shell.

lence electrons to form a calcium ion with a charge of $+2$ (Ca^{+2}). At the same time each oxygen atom, with 6 valence electrons, accepts 2 electrons to form a complete outer shell. Thus each oxygen atom is changed into a negative *oxide* ion with a charge of -2 (O^{-2}). Since only one oxygen atom is needed to accept the 2 valence electrons donated by each calcium atom, calcium oxide always contains one oxide ion for each calcium ion present. Its formula is therefore CaO (Fig. 6-4). In calcium oxide each calcium ion (Ca^{+2}) and each oxide ion (O^{-2}) has a complete outer shell. The electron structure of the calcium ion is similar to that of an argon atom, while the oxide ion has an electron structure like that of the neon atom.

Now consider the formula for calcium fluoride. When calcium fluoride is formed, the calcium atom loses 2 electrons to form a calcium ion. Since each fluorine atom, which contains 7 valence electrons, can accept only 1 of the 2 electrons donated by each calcium atom, a second fluorine atom must be present to gain the additional electron (Fig. 6-5). Thus the ratio of calcium to fluoride ions in calcium fluoride must always be 1 to 2; so the formula is CaF_2.

Ionic Radii

How does the loss or gain of electrons affect the size of the ion produced? In each instance the atomic radius is different from the ionic radius. *Positively charged ions are smaller* than their corresponding atoms because the loss of the outer-shell electrons results in increased attraction of the nucleus for the fewer remaining electrons. In contrast, *negatively charged ions are larger* than their corresponding atoms because the nuclear attraction is less for an increased number of electrons.

Observe in Table 6-1 that there is a periodic relationship among ionic radii when the ions are arranged in the form of the periodic table (with the transition elements omitted). There is a gradual decrease in the size of *positive ions* going from left to right across each period. Beginning with group VA the *negative ions,* though much larger than the positive ions, also decrease gradually in size as you continue across each row. As expected, there is an increase in ionic radius as you proceed down each group.

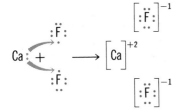

6-5 In a reaction that forms calcium fluoride, CaF_2, an atom of calcium donates two electrons, one to each of two fluorine atoms.

Formulas in Ionic Form

Chemists write the formulas for ionic compounds in the manner we have illustrated. To grasp the true significance of the formulas for ionic compounds, it is sometimes helpful to express them in their ionic form, which includes the charge for each ion in the compound. Thus in the ionic form, sodium chloride becomes Na^+Cl^-, and calcium oxide is $Ca^{+2}O^{-2}$. When the ratio of the different ions in a compound is not 1 to 1, a coefficient is used before the symbol; calcium fluoride becomes $Ca^{+2}2F^-$. Here the coefficient "one" before Ca^{+2} is understood. The coefficient 2 before the F^- indicates that the compound calcium fluo-

Table 6-1   **IONIC RADII***

IA							O
H							He
	IIA	IIIA	IVA	VA	VIA	VIIA	
Li^{+1}	Be^{+2}	B^{+3}	C^{+4}	N^{-3}	O^{-2}	F^{-1}	Ne
0.60	0.31	0.20	0.15	1.71	1.40	1.36	
Na^{+1}	Mg^{+2}	Al^{+3}	Si^{+4}	P^{-3}	S^{-2}	Cl^{-1}	Ar
0.95	0.65	0.50	0.41	2.12	1.84	1.81	
K^{+1}	Ca^{+2}	Ga^{+3}	Ge^{+4}	As^{-3}	Se^{-2}	Br^{-1}	Kr
1.33	0.99	0.62	0.53	2.22	1.98	1.95	
Rb^{+1}	Sr^{+2}	In^{+3}	Sn^{+4}	Sb^{-3}	Te^{-2}	I^{-1}	Xe
1.48	1.13	0.81	0.71	2.45	2.21	2.16	
Cs^{+1}	Ba^{+2}	Tl^{+3}	Pb^{+4}	Bi^{+5}	Po	At	Rn
1.69	1.35	0.95	0.84	0.79			

*In angstroms.

ride contains twice as many fluoride ions as calcium ions. The formulas for several ionic compounds, expressed in ionic form, are listed in Table 6-2. You will find them useful later, when you learn to write ionic equations for certain chemical reactions.

Valence Numbers and Ionic Compounds

Before the nature of chemical combination was fully understood, chemists assigned a number to each type of atom, a number representing the combining abilities or valences of the different atoms. In light of more recent knowledge of the way atoms combine, the term *valence* is now usually used to mean *the number of electrons an atom gains, loses,*

Table 6-2   **FORMULAS FOR SOME COMMON IONIC COMPOUNDS**

Name	Formula	Ionic form	Name	Formula	Ionic form
Potassium chloride	KCl	$K^{+1} Cl^{-1}$	Sodium sulfide	Na_2S	$2Na^{+1} S^{-2}$
Magnesium oxide	MgO	$Mg^{+2} O^{-2}$	Aluminum chloride	$AlCl_3$	$Al^{+3} 3Cl^{-1}$
Barium chloride	$BaCl_2$	$Ba^{+2} 2Cl^{-1}$	Manganese dioxide	MnO_2	$Mn^{+4} 2O^{-2}$

or shares when bonding with one or more atoms. Hence, the valence of hydrogen is 1, as a hydrogen atom can gain, lose, or share one electron in forming compounds.

In the original valence system, the number representing sodium was 1 and the number representing calcium was 2. Compare these numbers with charges of $+1$ and $+2$ for the sodium and calcium ions respectively. The original number representing the valence of chlorine was 1 and that of oxygen was 2. Again compare these numbers with charges of -1 and -2 for the chloride and oxide ions. In each case, though the two numbers are the same, a plus or minus sign precedes the number representing the charge on the ion. To aid in writing formulas for ionic compounds, chemists today assign to each type of atom a number that represents the relative charge of its corresponding ion. *The charge of the ion assigned to the corresponding atom is called the ionic valence number or simply the valence number of the atom.* Under this system, atoms that lose electrons have a positive valence number and atoms that gain electrons have a negative valence number. The valence number of sodium, following this system, is $+1$. The valence number of calcium is $+2$, of chlorine -1, and of oxygen -2.

Historically, "valence" has had several meanings, and there is a lack of agreement among chemists as to the best use of the term. For the present we shall continue to use the terms valence and valence numbers with the meaning developed in this section. Valence represents the combining ability or bonding capacity of an atom; valence number indicates the charge of the ion assigned to the corresponding atom. In the next chapter you will study in detail the use of valence numbers in writing formulas for compounds.

QUESTIONS AND PROBLEMS

1. Draw electron dot diagrams of each of the following ionic compounds: (a) potassium fluoride (KF), (b) lithium oxide (Li_2O), (c) magnesium sulfide (MgS), (d) calcium chloride ($CaCl_2$).
2. Differentiate between (a) a potassium *atom* and a potassium *ion,* (b) a fluorine *atom* and a fluoride *ion.*
3. What is the difference (a) between a bromide *ion* and a krypton *atom,* (b) among a potassium *ion,* a chloride *ion,* and an argon *atom?*
4. Define the terms *valence number, ion,* and *ionic bond.*
5. (a) Potassium loses one electron to bromine in the compound potassium bromide (KBr). What is the valence of each element? the valence number? (b) What is the valence number of each atom in the compound lithium oxide (Li_2O)?
6. Which member of each of the following pairs has the larger radius: (a) a potassium *atom* or a potassium *ion,* (b) a sulfide *ion* or a sulfur *atom,* (c) a magnesium *ion* or a calcium *ion?* Explain your answer.

We have seen that ions result when atoms completely gain or lose electrons in order to complete their outer shells. But not all substances are composed of ions; in fact, most chemical substances are composed of molecules. Water, at room temperature, is a liquid composed of molecules; table sugar (sucrose) is a crystalline molecular solid; while hydrogen and chlorine are molecular gases. In molecules, the atoms complete their outer shells by *sharing* electrons. To understand this process of electron sharing, let's consider several elements, beginning with hydrogen.

Molecules of Hydrogen

Each atom in a diatomic molecule of hydrogen gas has 1 electron, its valence electron. One hydrogen atom could hardly lose its valence electron to another hydrogen atom since the two atoms are exactly alike. Instead, chemists believe that one hydrogen atom *shares* its electron with the other atom. When two hydrogen atoms are near each other, the protons repel each other and the electrons repel each other. As their atoms approach so close that the electron clouds overlap (Fig. 6-6), the situa-

6-6 When two H atoms approach one another so closely that their electron clouds overlap, the electron of each H atom is simultaneously attracted by both nuclei, and a chemical bond forms.

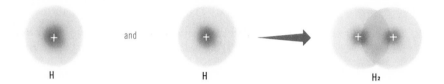

H   and   H   H₂

tion changes. The protons still repel each other and the parts of the electron cloud that do not overlap repel each other. *But in the parts of the electron clouds that overlap, the 2 electrons are simultaneously attracted by the 2 protons.* The attractive forces are now stronger than the repulsive forces, and a chemical bond forms. The bond that forms from the equal sharing of electrons between atoms is called a **covalent bond.** In ionic compounds the bonds also form because electrons are simultaneously attracted to both nuclei, *but* the electrons are so strongly attracted to one nucleus that the electrons *act as if* they were transferred completely from one nucleus to another.

Another way of representing the idea of covalent bonding is indicated in Fig. 6-7, which shows the orbital diagrams of two separate hydrogen atoms combined in an orbital overlap diagram to form a hydrogen molecule. It is clear that in the molecule each of the two atoms shares its single electron with the other to complete their outer shells. Molecules formed by atoms sharing their electrons are called **covalent molecules.**

The electrons which hold covalent molecules together are usually shared in pairs, with each atom donating 1 electron. As this pair of electrons constitutes a covalent bond, we say that the two atoms in a

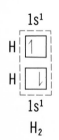

$1s^1$

H ⊓ ↑

H ⊔ ↓

$1s^1$

H_2

6-7 The reaction of Figure 6-6, represented here by an orbital overlap diagram, indicates that the covalent bond consists of two 1s electrons with opposite spins.

covalent molecule of hydrogen are held together by a single covalent bond. In a hydrogen molecule, a third atom cannot combine with the other two because each hydrogen atom can accommodate only one shared pair of electrons in its 1s orbital. In inert helium the 1s orbital is already complete with 2 electrons *and bonding does not usually occur.*

Representing a Hydrogen Molecule

An electron dot diagram can also be used to indicate how electrons are rearranged when two hydrogen atoms combine in this way. In the equation below, the electron dot diagrams to the left of the arrow stand for each of two hydrogen atoms. The dot at the side of each symbol represents the single electron of each hydrogen atom. The diagram to the right of the arrow indicates a hydrogen molecule. Here the two dots between the two H's represent the pair of shared electrons, or covalent bond, which holds together the two atoms of the molecule.

one hydrogen   one hydrogen   one hydrogen
atom   atom   molecule

H·   +   ·H $\longrightarrow$ H:H
                               ↑
                        covalent bond

Another way of showing the electron structure of a hydrogen molecule is the solid, or **space-filling model,** shown in Fig. 6-8. Here the electron clouds from each hydrogen atom overlap. This three-dimensional model *probably* comes the closest of any to depicting the molecule's shape.

Other Diatomic Elements

Chlorine gas, like hydrogen, exists at room temperature as a substance made up of diatomic molecules. The orbital overlap diagrams in Fig. 6-9 indicate what happens when two chlorine atoms combine to form a covalent molecule of chlorine. The diagrams show the two original chlorine atoms, each with its 7 valence electrons. Each atom shares 1 valence electron with the other atom. As a result, when combined into a molecule, both atoms have outer shells complete with 8 electrons.

An electron dot diagram can also show the arrangement of valence electrons when two chlorine atoms combine to form a chlorine molecule.

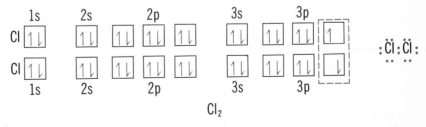

6-9 The overlap of one 3p orbital from each atom, in which the unpaired electrons have opposite spins, forms a diatomic molecule of chlorine.

Oxygen. Oxygen molecules are also diatomic. Each oxygen atom contains 6 valence electrons (Fig. 6-4). When combined into an oxygen

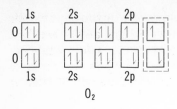

1s 2s 2p

O $\boxed{1\downarrow}$ $\boxed{1\downarrow}$ $\boxed{1\downarrow}$ $\boxed{1}$ $\boxed{1}$

O $\boxed{1\downarrow}$ $\boxed{1\downarrow}$ $\boxed{1\downarrow}$ $\boxed{\downarrow}$ $\boxed{\downarrow}$

1s 2s 2p

O_2

$$:\overset{..}{O}\cdot \; + \; \cdot\overset{..}{O}: \longrightarrow \; :\overset{..}{O}:\overset{..}{O}:$$

6-10 The overlap of 2p orbitals forms a bond with electrons of opposite spins. The one unpaired electron remaining in each atom accounts for the slight magnetic properties of the oxygen molecule.

molecule, each of the two atoms might be expected to have an outer shell that was complete with 8 electrons. Thus each of the two atoms would share not 1 but 2 electrons with the other atom. It would seem that two pairs of electrons are necessary to hold the oxygen atoms together and that two covalent bonds exist between them. For a long time chemists believed this to be the case. But in recent years they have discovered that molecular oxygen is slightly magnetic. To explain the magnetic properties of oxygen, chemists now assume that each of the atoms in an oxygen molecule shares only 1 electron with the other. This leaves the remaining valence electron in each atom *unpaired* (Fig. 6-10). It is this unpaired valence electron that accounts for the slightly magnetic property of oxygen (as well as for the magnetic properties of some of the transition elements). When the electron is unpaired its magnetic effect is not canceled out by that of another electron with an opposite spin. Here is another example of how theory is constantly changing in the light of new data. Evidently oxygen atoms, even when combined into molecules, do not have outer electron shells which are complete.

In the electron dot diagram of an oxygen molecule, observe two dots (:) between the atoms of oxygen. These represent a pair of shared electrons. The single dot below each O represents the unshared valence electron of each atom in an oxygen molecule.

Molecules of Covalent Compounds

So far we have been discussing the sharing of electrons that occurs when *like* atoms combine to form molecules of *elements*. The same process also takes place when *unlike* atoms are combined to form molecules of *compounds*. Compounds in which unlike atoms are held together by covalent bonds are called **covalent compounds.** Hydrogen chloride, water, methane, and ammonia are all examples of such compounds.

6-11 Orbital overlap and electron dot diagrams of molecules of covalent compounds.

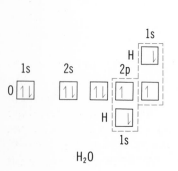

H_2O

CH_4

NH_3

Hydrogen Chloride. The electron structure of a hydrogen chloride molecule is indicated in Fig. 6-11. The two unlike atoms are held together by a pair of shared electrons which constitutes a covalent bond. This covalent bond between the hydrogen and the chlorine atom gives each atom a complete outer shell. The electron dot diagram is another way of indicating this covalent bonding.

Water. In each molecule of water, covalent bonds hold together two atoms of hydrogen and one of oxygen. The oxygen atom has 6 valence electrons while each hydrogen atom has 1. Complete outer shells can be provided for both elements only if two hydrogen atoms each share 1 electron with a single oxygen atom. Thus two covalent bonds, one uniting each atom of hydrogen with the oxygen atom, now exist.

The electron orbital diagram of a water molecule shows how electrons are shared between each hydrogen atom and the atom of oxygen.

Methane. Each methane molecule, CH_4, is composed of one carbon atom with 4 valence electrons, and four hydrogen atoms, each with a single electron. Since a carbon atom needs 4 additional electrons to complete its outer shell, it can share all 4 of its valence electrons with other atoms. In methane the carbon shares 1 valence electron with each of the four hydrogen atoms. Thus a covalent bond exists between each one of the hydrogen atoms and the single atom of carbon. As a result, the hydrogen atoms and the carbon atom all have complete outer shells.

Ammonia. In a molecule of ammonia, NH_3, a nitrogen atom, with 5 valence electrons, is combined with three hydrogen atoms. All four atoms achieve complete outer shells when the nitrogen atom shares 3 electrons, one with each of the hydrogen atoms. The hydrogen atoms, in turn, each share one electron with the nitrogen atom. Thus a covalent bond exists between the nitrogen atom and each of the three hydrogen atoms (Fig. 6-11).

Multiple Covalent Bonds

In each of the molecules diagrammed in Fig. 6-11, observe that only one pair of electrons is shared by each pair of atoms. When only a single pair of electrons holds two atoms together in a molecule, a **single covalent bond**, or **single bond,** exists between the atoms. Single covalent bonds occur in both elements and compounds. The two like atoms in a hydrogen molecule, and the hydrogen and chlorine atoms in a hydrogen chloride molecule, are held together by a single bond. A molecule of methane contains four single bonds.

In some molecules two atoms are held together by two pairs of electrons, making two covalent bonds. For instance, in a molecule of sulfur monoxide (SO) both the sulfur atom and the oxygen atom each contain 6 valence electrons. The sulfur atom and the oxygen atom must share two pairs of electrons if the outer shells of both atoms are to be complete. The two pairs of shared electrons between the sulfur atom and the oxygen atom produce two covalent bonds (Fig. 6-12). A pair of covalent

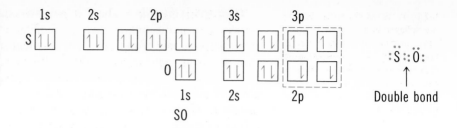

6-12 When an atom of sulfur bonds with an atom of oxygen to form sulfur monoxide, the atoms share two pairs of electrons (4 electrons) to produce a double covalent bond between them. The double bond may be shown by an orbital overlap or an electron dot diagram.

bonds between two atoms is a **double covalent bond,** or a **double bond.** In the electron dot diagram of sulfur monoxide, the four dots between the S and the O symbols represent the two pairs of shared electrons that hold the atoms together. The group of four dots indicates a double bond.

Molecules of compounds that contain three or more atoms, such as carbon dioxide (CO_2), may contain more than one double bond. In the electron dot diagram of carbon dioxide (Fig. 6-13), the four electrons between each oxygen atom and the carbon atom represent a double bond. Each molecule of carbon dioxide contains two double bonds.

In certain substances as many as three covalent bonds exist between two atoms in a molecule. Nitrogen (N_2) is an example. A nitrogen molecule consists of two like atoms held together by three pairs of shared electrons. Since each of the two nitrogen atoms contains 5 valence electrons, each must share 3 electrons with the other in order to have a complete outer shell (Fig. 6-13). These shared electrons form a **triple bond.**

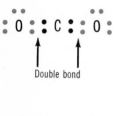

Double bond

Triple bond

6-13 In a carbon dioxide molecule, each double bond is formed by association of 2 electrons of the carbon atom with 2 electrons of an oxygen atom, as indicated by the colors of the dots. In a nitrogen molecule, the triple bond is formed by 3 electrons from each nitrogen atom.

QUESTIONS AND PROBLEMS

1. Draw an orbital overlap and an electron dot diagram of a molecule of bromine, of hydrogen fluoride, and of hydrogen sulfide.
2. How does the bonding in a molecule of hydrogen chloride (HCl) differ from the bonding in lithium chloride (LiCl)?
3. (a) Predict the number of covalent bonds between each of the atoms in molecules of F_2 and PN. (b) Draw an orbital overlap and an electron dot diagram for each of these molecules.

BLENDING OF COVALENT AND IONIC BONDS

The molecules which make up a covalent substance are composed of atoms held together by one or more covalent bonds. In such a bond the atoms *share* electrons to complete their outer shells. Since each molecule has the same number of electrons as protons, the molecule is a neutral particle. Ionic substances, on the other hand, are composed of charged particles called ions. These ions are held together by ionic bonds. In an ionic bond, instead of a sharing of electrons there is a *transfer* of one or more electrons between two different kinds of atoms or groups of atoms. Because of this transfer the number of protons and electrons in an ion is not evenly balanced and the ion has an electrical charge.

6-14 As the pair of electrons bonding two hydrogen atoms together is shared equally by the atoms, the center of negative charge is equidistant between the two nuclei. The center of positive charge is also equidistant between the nuclei. The centers of negative and positive charge therefore coincide.

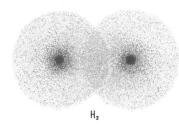

H_2

6-15 Electron cloud diagrams paired with solid models for three molecules. In each molecule the electron pairs bonding the atoms together are attracted toward the nonmetallic element with the greater electronegativity—chlorine, oxygen, and oxygen, respectively. Since the centers of partial negative and positive charge do not coincide in HCl and H_2O, these molecules are polar; CO_2 is nonpolar.

This difference established, it must be said at once that most substances are neither completely covalent nor completely ionic. There is seldom an equal sharing or a complete transfer of electrons. If the electron pair is neither shared completely by two atoms nor transferred completely to one of them, a bond of intermediate character must exist. In actual fact, diatomic molecules of elements are among the few completely covalent substances. In most other substances the difference between ionic and covalent bonding is one of degree. To indicate the extent to which their electron pairs are shared unequally, that is, *the extent to which they are partly ionic,* covalent substances are further differentiated into two types—nonpolar and polar.

Nonpolar Covalent Bonds

Since the nucleus of each atom in a hydrogen molecule has a charge of $+1$, the pair of shared electrons is attracted equally by the two nuclei. The bond formed when the electron pair is equally attracted to both atoms is called a **nonpolar bond.** Diatomic molecules containing a single nonpolar bond are called **nonpolar molecules.** When two identical atoms are held together by a nonpolar bond, the result is always a nonpolar covalent molecule. Because the pair of electrons holding the two atoms together is shared equally in such molecules, the center of negative charge (electrons) is located between the two nuclei. Therefore, the center of negative charge coincides with the center of positive charge which is also equidistant between the protons (Fig. 6-14).

Polar Covalent Bonds

In a molecule of hydrogen chloride the nucleus of the atom of chlorine has a much greater attraction for the shared electron pair than the hydro-

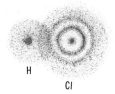

H

Cl

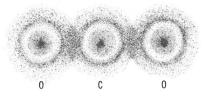

O   C   O

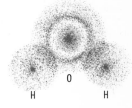

O

H   H

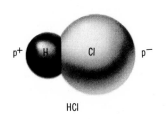

p^+ H   Cl p^-

HCl

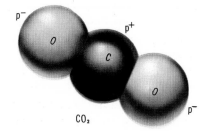

p^- O

p^+ C

O p^-

CO_2

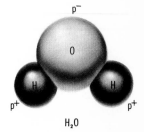

p^-

O

H   H

p^+ p^+

H_2O

gen atom. For this reason, the pair of electrons which holds the two unlike atoms together is not shared equally, but is more strongly attracted to the chlorine atom than to the hydrogen atom. The positive and negative charges, or electrical poles, therefore tend to be concentrated at different ends of the molecule (Fig. 6-15). Since the electron pair is attracted more toward the chlorine atom, that end of the molecule has a greater negative charge, while the hydrogen end is more positively charged. Thus, although the hydrogen chloride molecule *as a whole* is neutral, it contains within itself two poles or centers of charge, one positive and one negative. The bond in a molecule where the electron pair is attracted more to one atom than the other is called a **polar bond.** Since *the electrons are not transferred completely,* the unlike atoms in a polar bond acquire a *partial charge*—a partial negative charge, P^-, for chlorine, and a partial positive charge, P^+, for hydrogen (Fig. 6-15).

Molecules such as hydrogen chloride, which have two centers of charge, are called polar molecules, or **dipoles.** Polar covalent molecules or dipoles always result when two unlike atoms are held together by a polar bond, as in hydrogen chloride.

Triatomic Molecules

A triatomic molecule is composed of three atoms. To see how the bonds between these atoms affect their polarity, consider a molecule of carbon dioxide. Each of the two oxygen atoms is joined to a single carbon atom by a double bond. The oxygen atoms have a partial negative charge (P^-), while the carbon atom has a partial positive charge (P^+). This results because the electron pairs between each atom of oxygen and the atom of carbon are more strongly attracted to the oxygen atoms. Both the double covalent bonds in a molecule of carbon dioxide are polar.

Since the bonds within a carbon dioxide molecule are polar, it might be assumed that the molecule itself is polar. However, experiments show that molecules of carbon dioxide are nonpolar. The solid model of a carbon dioxide molecule in Fig. 6-15 helps explain why. Observe that the atoms in this molecule are bonded together in a straight line, called a **linear** arrangement. Because the center of negative charge coincides with that of the positive charge, the effects of the two polar bonds on opposite sides of the molecule cancel each other out; the result is a nonpolar molecule of carbon dioxide.

Water molecules also consist of three atoms held together, as you have seen, by two single covalent bonds. Each of these covalent bonds is polar since the electron pair is more strongly attracted to the oxygen atom, with its greater electron affinity, than to the hydrogen atom. Here the three atoms in each molecule, unlike those in carbon dioxide, are not arranged in a straight line. Instead, the two polar bonds are separated by an angle of 104.5°. Consequently the effects of the two polar bonds do not cancel each other out, and the water molecule is polar. Both covalent bonds occur on the same side of a water molecule. For this reason each pair of electrons tends more toward the oxygen end of the molecule; the oxygen end is more negative while the hydrogen end is more positive (Fig. 6-15). Here the center of negative charge does *not* coincide with the center of positive charge. This polarity of water molecules has many important chemical effects. It is particularly important in the dissolving of both ionic and covalent compounds in water.

The previous discussion of the polarity of molecules indicates why most molecules have two centers of charge and why there is no sharp line of distinction between covalent and ionic substances. Only those covalent substances which are entirely nonpolar, such as hydrogen and chlorine, have no centers of charge whatever. Most molecular or covalent substances are polar to a certain extent: the sharing of electrons is not equal and the substances have ionic properties to some degree. A comparison of certain properties of different substances—nonpolar covalent, polar covalent, and ionic substances—is given in Table 6-3.

Table 6-3   **PROPERTIES OF NONPOLAR COVALENT, POLAR COVALENT, AND IONIC SUBSTANCES**

Type of substance	Electron distribution	Molecular or nonmolecular	Centers of charge	Examples
Nonpolar covalent	Shared equally	Molecular	One	H_2, N_2
Polar covalent	Shared unequally	Molecular	Two	HCl, NH_3
Ionic	Transferred	Nonmolecular	—	$NaCl, CaF_2$

Predicting Bond Types

Is it possible to predict the type of chemical bond in a compound? A direct method depends upon the development of a scale in which the elements are arranged in the order of their tendency to attract shared electrons. It is called the scale of **electronegativity.** The electronegativity scale is an *arbitrary* scale based on a number of factors; among them are the ionization potentials of atoms, electron affinity, or the energy involved when an electron is added to an atom, the tendency of a dipole to turn in an electric field, and the energy required to break a bond between atoms.

The electronegativities of the elements, arranged in the form of the periodic table, are shown in Table 6-4. Notice that fluorine has the highest electronegativity (4.0). This means that fluorine has the greatest tendency to attract shared electrons and form a *negative* ion. Cesium and francium have the lowest electronegativity (0.7). Thus these two elements have the least ability to attract shared electrons and the greatest tendency to form a *positive* ion. Since the inert elements usually do not form chemical bonds, no electronegativities are assigned to them. In general, as we go from left to right across a period, and as the nuclear charge increases, the electronegativity of the elements also increases. The elements at the far left of the periodic table have low electronegativities.

Table 6-4 ELECTRONEGATIVITIES OF THE ELEMENTS

IA	IIA	IIIB	IVB	VB	VIB	VIIB	VIII	VIII	VIII	IB	IIB	IIIA	IVA	VA	VIA	VIIA	O
1 H 2.1																	2 He —
3 Li 1.0	4 Be 1.5											5 B 2.0	6 C 2.5	7 N 3.0	8 O 3.5	9 F 4.0	10 Ne —
11 Na 0.9	12 Mg 1.2											13 Al 1.5	14 Si 1.8	15 P 2.1	16 S 2.5	17 Cl 3.0	18 Ar —
19 K 0.8	20 Ca 1.0	21 Sc 1.3	22 Ti 1.5	23 V 1.6	24 Cr 1.6	25 Mn 1.5	26 Fe 1.8	27 Co 1.8	28 Ni 1.8	29 Cu 1.9	30 Zn 1.6	31 Ga 1.6	32 Ge 1.8	33 As 2.0	34 Se 2.4	35 Br 2.8	36 Kr —
37 Rb 0.8	38 Sr 1.0	39 Y 1.2	40 Zr 1.4	41 Nb 1.6	42 Mo 1.8	43 Tc 1.9	44 Ru 2.2	45 Rh 2.2	46 Pd 2.2	47 Ag 1.9	48 Cd 1.7	49 In 1.7	50 Sn 1.8	51 Sb 1.9	52 Te 2.1	53 I 2.5	54 Xe —
55 Cs 0.7	56 Ba 0.9	57 La 1.1	72 Hf 1.3	73 Ta 1.5	74 W 1.7	75 Re 1.9	76 Os 2.2	77 Ir 2.2	78 Pt 2.2	79 Au 2.4	80 Hg 1.9	81 Tl 1.8	82 Pb 1.8	83 Bi 1.9	84 Po 2.0	85 At 2.2	86 Rn —
87 Fr 0.7	88 Ra 0.9	89 Ac 1.1															

Those at the far right of the table, with the exception of the inert elements in group O, have high electronegativities. In general, electronegativity decreases as we go down a group and the atoms increase in size.

The use of these electronegatives enables us to predict which compounds have covalent bonds and which ionic. If the difference in electronegativity between the elements in a compound is greater than 1.7, the bond is usually ionic. Thus sodium (Na), with an electronegativity of only 0.9, has a low ability to attract electrons. Chlorine, with an electronegativity of 3.0, has a high attraction for electrons. Therefore, you can expect the bond of the compound sodium chloride (NaCl) to be ionic. Electronegativities support the expectation that when alkali elements and elements of group II are combined with elements of groups VI and VII, the bonds of the compounds will be ionic. In contrast, when elements have electronegativities that are more nearly equal, such as hydrogen (H, 2.1) and iodine (I, 2.5), the bonds uniting them are covalent.

The electronegativity scale enables us to predict the degree of polarity of a covalent bond. If the difference in electronegativity is zero, the bond is nonpolar covalent. If the difference is less than 1.7, the bond is polar covalent. The further apart in electronegativity the two elements, the more polar the bond holding them together. In a polar covalent bond the electrons spend more time near the more electronegative atom and thus give it a P^- charge. The other atom in the bond acquires a P^+ charge.

Shapes of Molecules

In addition to the type of bond, the shape of a molecule is important in determining its properties. On page 103 you saw that water molecules

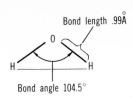

Bond length .99Å

Bond angle 104.5°

H_2O

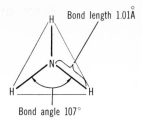

Bond length 1.01Å

Bond angle 107°

NH_3

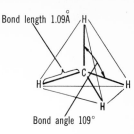

Bond length 1.09Å

Bond angle 109°

CH_4

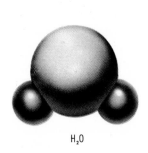

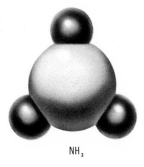

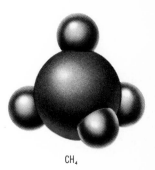

6-16 By studying bond angles and bond lengths, scientists have determined the geometric shapes of molecules. The water molecule is angular in shape, the ammonia molecule is pyramidal, and the methane molecule is tetrahedral.

are **angular** and that the nuclei of the hydrogen and oxygen atoms all lie in the same plane. Now consider further the actual shape of a water molecule—a three-dimensional molecule. In determining the geometric shape of a molecule, scientists consider the distance between the nuclei of any two atoms the **bond length** of the two atoms. In water the bond length of O—H is .99 Å (Fig. 6-16). Now if you could measure **bond angle,** the angle between any two intersecting lines representing bond lengths, you would find that bond angle H—O—H is, as mentioned previously, 104.5°.

Usually the hydrides and fluorides of oxygen and sulfur, group VIA elements requiring 2 electrons to complete their outer shell, are angular molecules. Chemists predict the shape of such molecules, for example, H_2S, from the arrangement of the orbitals involved in the bonding. In H_2O the half-filled p orbitals of the oxygen atom are at 90° to each other. This arrangement largely determines the shape of the molecule.

By means of X-ray diffraction, it has been determined that many molecules are neither angular nor linear. An ammonia (NH_3) molecule, for example, has a **pyramidal** shape (Fig. 6-16). Note that a hydrogen atom occupies each corner of the base of the pyramid, while the nitrogen atom occupies the top (apex). The N atom is known as the **central atom** of the pyramid, and the H atoms are all equidistant from this central atom. In the pyramid all the H—N—H bond angles are 107°. Hydrides and fluorides of nitrogen and phosphorus, elements in group VA, are pyramidal in shape. Both the PH_3 and the NF_3 molecules, for example, are pyramidal.

A third shape is found in many molecules, particularly the hydrides and fluorides of carbon (group IVA). Study the methane (CH_4) molecule (Fig. 6-16). The methane molecule is **tetrahedral** in shape. The carbon atom is the central atom and the hydrogen atoms occupy the four corners of the tetrahedron. The four H atoms are all equidistant from the central C atom. Each H—C—H angle is found experimentally to be approximately 109°. The shape of a carbon tetrafluoride (CF_4) molecule is also tetrahedral. Though more complex shapes occur among many molecules, we have diagrammed three important geometric shapes. Recall that the CO_2 molecule was described (page 104) as a linear molecule.

Valence Numbers and Covalent Compounds

Having learned something of the actual bonding and molecular shapes in covalent compounds, we can now consider the modified system of valence used in predicting the formulas for covalent compounds. The combining ability of atoms which form covalent compounds may be represented by the number of pairs of electrons they share. Today chemists assign **covalence numbers** or simply valence numbers to atoms that share their electrons, and in this way predict the formulas for simple molecules. The valence number of each atom, in simple molecules, is numerically equal to the number of electrons that the atom can share. This valence number also represents the total number of electron pairs or covalent bonds that exists between one atom and other atoms joined to it.

The sign of the valence number of each atom in a covalent compound is determined by observing the type of atom to which the electron pair or pairs are more strongly attracted. *The atom to which the electron pairs are more strongly attracted is assigned a negative covalence number,* while *the atom which has the weaker attraction for the electron pairs is assigned a positive covalence number.* Since in the compound hydrogen chloride the single pair of electrons between the two atoms is attracted more by each chlorine atom than by each hydrogen atom, a valence number of −1 is assigned to chlorine and a valence number of +1 is assigned to hydrogen. Because the electron pairs in a water molecule are attracted more by the oxygen atom than by the hydrogen atoms, oxygen is assigned a valence number of −2. Because each hydrogen atom shares only 1 electron, the valence number of hydrogen in H_2O, as in HCl, is +1.

QUESTIONS AND PROBLEMS

1. Answer each of the following questions: (a) Why may a polar covalent bond be considered a partly ionic bond? (b) What is the difference between a polar and a nonpolar covalent bond? (c) What is a dipole?
2. (a) What type of bond exists in a molecule of each of the following: nitrogen, bromine, silicon dioxide (SiO_2)? (b) Give a reason for your answers.

3. Use the table of electronegativities on page 106 to predict (a) whether each of the following is an ionic or covalent compound: potassium iodide (KI), magnesium oxide (MgO), hydrogen fluoride (HF), nitrogen dioxide (NO_2); (b) whether each of the following covalent substances is polar or nonpolar: nitric oxide (NO), sulfur dioxide (SO_2), fluorine (F_2).
4. (a) In a molecule of carbon dioxide which element has a positive valence (covalence) number? a negative valence number? (b) In a molecule of hydrogen bromide (HBr) the single pair of shared electrons is attracted more by each bromine atom than by each hydrogen atom. What is the valence number of each element?
5. (a) Draw a diagram to show the shape of each of the following molecules: H_2S, PH_3, and CF_4. (b) Name the geometric shape of each molecule.

SPECIAL TYPES OF BONDS

Thus far we have been dealing with relatively simple substances consisting of the atoms of only one or two elements. In these cases the atoms are joined together either solely by covalent bonds, as in carbon dioxide, or solely by ionic bonds, as in calcium fluoride. But many compounds are composed of more than two elements. In certain of these compounds some atoms are joined together by covalent bonds and yet the compounds as a whole are ionic. How can this be?

Radicals

The compound sodium hydroxide is composed of three elements: sodium, hydrogen, and oxygen. In sodium hydroxide, an atom of oxygen and an atom of hydrogen are joined together by a covalent bond (Fig. 6-17). Since the oxygen atom contains 6 valence electrons and the hydrogen atom contains 1, only the hydrogen atom has a complete outer shell as a result of this combination. The outer shell of the oxygen atom still contains only 7 valence electrons; it is 1 electron short of completion. The electron needed to complete the outer shell of the oxygen atom is donated by the atom of sodium in the compound. Since the sodium atom completely loses 1 electron in this transfer, a positive sodium ion (Na^+) is formed. At the same time, in accepting the electron from the sodium atom, the covalently bonded oxygen and hydrogen atoms are changed to a negative ion. This ion is called the **hydroxide ion** and its formula is OH^-. In the compound as a whole, these covalently bonded negative hydroxide ions are ionically bonded to the positive ions of sodium.

The hydroxide ion is one of many ions made up of more than one element. A group of atoms of unlike elements joined together to form an ion is called a radical ion or simply a **radical**. The hydroxide ion is often referred to as the hydroxide radical. Most radicals, such as hydroxide (OH^-), sulfate (SO_4^{-2}), and nitrate (NO_3^-), are negatively charged.

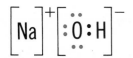

6-17 An oxygen atom has six valence electrons, while a hydrogen atom has one. The eighth dot represents an electron donated by a sodium atom. The oxygen-hydrogen bond within the OH^- radical is polar covalent.

Table 6-5
COMMON RADICALS

Name	Formula
Ammonium	NH_4^{+1}
Acetate	$C_2H_3O_2^{-1}$
Bicarbonate	HCO_3^{-1}
Carbonate	CO_3^{-2}
Chlorate	ClO_3^{-1}
Hydroxide	OH^{-1}
Nitrate	NO_3^{-1}
Phosphate	PO_4^{-3}
Sulfate	SO_4^{-2}
Sulfite	SO_3^{-2}

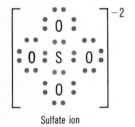

Sulfate ion

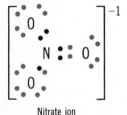

Nitrate ion

6-18 The five-atom sulfate ion contains two extra electrons. Two of the four oxygen atoms have coordinate bonds. Find the coordinate bonds in both of the ions.

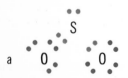

a

6-19 The sulfur dioxide molecule is a resonance hybrid, not like either **a** (above), or **b** (next page), but somehow a combination of both molecular formulas.

Fewer positively charged radicals, like the ammonium radical (NH_4^+), are known. The names and formulas of several radicals are given in Table 6-5. Notice in this table that all radicals have a definite positive or negative charge; this shows that they are true ions. Because radicals are relatively stable, that is, the bonds between the atoms in radicals are strong, they usually remain unchanged during chemical reactions.

Coordinate Bonds

In the usual covalent bond, two atoms share a pair of electrons, one electron being supplied by each atom. But in some covalent bonds one of the atoms supplies *both* electrons. Such a bond is called a **coordinate covalent bond** or simply a **coordinate bond.**

The ammonium ion (NH_4^+) contains an example of coordinate bonding. The ammonium ion results when a molecule of ammonia (NH_3) reacts with a hydrogen nucleus (H^+ or proton without surrounding electrons). In the ammonia molecule the nitrogen atom contains a single pair of unshared electrons.

$$H^+ + H:\overset{\cdot\cdot}{\underset{}{N}}:H \longrightarrow \left[H:\overset{\cdot\cdot}{\underset{H}{N}}:H \right]^+$$

hydrogen   ammonia   ammonium ion
nucleus

When a hydrogen nucleus combines with ammonia, the hydrogen nucleus readily shares the single electron pair donated by the nitrogen atom—the hydrogen nucleus is bonded to the nitrogen atom by a coordinate covalent bond. Because the particle formed has 1 more proton than electron (9 protons and 8 electrons), the resulting ammonium ion, NH_4^+, is positively charged.

Numerous other radicals also contain coordinate bonds. The sulfate radical (SO_4^{-2}), for example, contains two such bonds (Fig. 6-18). How many coordinate covalent bonds are present in the nitrate radical also shown in Fig. 6-18?

Resonance Hybrids

Try to draw an electron dot diagram for sulfur dioxide (SO_2). You probably drew one of the two diagrams in Fig. 6-19. From diagram (a) you might assume that a coordinate bond exists between the sulfur atom and the oxygen atom at the right, while a double covalent bond exists between the sulfur atom and the oxygen atom at the left. In diagram (b) the bonds are indicated in reverse.

Actually, experimental evidence shows that the bonds are identical in length and angle, and that neither diagram is correct. Each molecule of sulfur dioxide is best described as a blend or combination of both electron structures. A molecule that exhibits such a blend of electron struc-

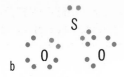

b

tures is known as a **resonance hybrid.** The term *resonance* is an unfortunate one, as it implies that the electrons jump from one bond to another. But this is not true. The SO_2 molecule has only one form; the problem is in describing and diagramming it. To indicate resonance, a diagram of the molecular structure would have to combine the two formulas. In practice this is not done, and chemists use either but not both of the electron dot diagrams.

Metallic Bonds

Metals do not behave like molecules or ions, and we cannot explain their properties in terms of either covalent or ionic bonding. Instead, metals involve a third type of bond—the **metallic bond.**

Substances such as silver, aluminum, and iron are solids at room temperature. Yet, unlike ionic or molecular solids, metals are good conductors of electricity. Molecular substances are never good conductors and ionic substances can become so only when they have been liquefied. Chemists explain the peculiar properties of metals by saying that metals consist of positively charged ions surrounded by a "sea of electrons." Although metallic atoms vary in size, they are relatively large; their valence electrons are not held tightly to their nuclei. Instead, these valence electrons can move around the heavy, positively charged metallic ions with great freedom. In a crystal of silver, for example, the positively charged silver ions (Ag^+) are held together by a continuous sea of valence electrons which constitutes the metallic bond (Fig. 6-20). The nature of metallic bonds explains why metals are such good conductors of electricity. An electric current is simply the flow of electrons through a wire. Since the electrons in metal are so free, they can be removed easily from one end of a wire while at the same time they can be added just as easily at the other end to produce an electron flow.

All elements and compounds, whether they are solids, liquids, or gases, are bonded together by ionic, covalent, or metallic bonds, or some combination of these bonds. But try as they may, chemists can find no relationship between the type of bond and the physical state of a particular substance. Once the bond has been established, it is neither altered nor broken by changing the physical state of the substance. Whether carbon dioxide is in the form of dry ice, a liquid under pressure, or gaseous bubbles in soda water, each molecule contains two polar covalent bonds. In Chapter 8 we shall see what actually does determine the physical state of a substance and why, under varying conditions, the same substance can exist as a solid, a liquid, or a gas.

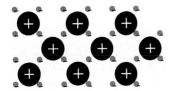

6-20 In this section of silver "wire" positively charged metallic ions are surrounded by a "sea of electrons." Silver is an excellent conductor of electricity because the electrons can be moved easily along the length of the wire.

QUESTIONS AND PROBLEMS

1. (a) Why is a radical considered a true ion? (b) How does a coordinate covalent bond differ from most covalent bonds?

2. Draw an electron dot diagram to show both the ionic and covalent bonding in potassium hydroxide (KOH), ammonium chloride (NH_4Cl), and sodium nitrate ($NaNO_3$).

3. Draw an electron dot diagram to show the coordinate covalent bond in the hydroxide ion (OH^-), the carbonate ion (CO_3^{-2}), and sodium sulfate (Na_2SO_4).

4. (a) What is meant by the statement that a molecule of sulfur trioxide (SO_3) is a resonance hybrid that may be assigned three resonance forms? (b) At the left is one electron dot diagram (SO_3); draw two other possible diagrams.

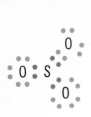

5. Differentiate among the bonding in a piece of metallic potassium, a potassium chloride crystal, and hydrogen chloride gas.

6. Why are wires used in electric circuits made of metals such as copper or aluminum?

VALUE OF THE CONCEPT

THE CONCEPT

The combining ability of different atoms, called valence, is determined by the arrangements of the outer-shell or valence electrons. Usually atoms with incomplete outer shells undergo a valence electron rearrangement to complete their outer shells. This rearrangement of electrons occurs in two ways: by a complete loss or gain of electrons to form ions, or by a sharing of electrons to form molecules. In either case the exchange usually occurs until the outer shells of all atoms involved become complete; that is until each outer shell contains 8 electrons (except 2 for hydrogen and helium).

The forces that hold ions together in compounds are called ionic bonds while those holding atoms in molecules of both elements and compounds are referred to as covalent bonds. Each covalent bond consists of a pair of shared electrons, 1 electron from each of two atoms. Atoms may share two or even three pairs of electrons, forming double and triple bonds, respectively. These molecules have various geometric shapes depending upon their bond angles and bond lengths.

The difference between ionic and covalent bonding is one of degree. To indicate the extent to which electron pairs are shared (or to which the bonds are partly ionic) covalent bonds are differentiated into nonpolar and polar bonds. The bond formed when the electron pair is equally attracted to two like atoms is a nonpolar bond, and the resulting molecule is nonpolar. In diatomic molecules consisting of two unlike atoms bonded together, the shared electrons are generally attracted more to the atom having the greater positive nuclear charge, producing a polar bond, and a polar molecule or dipole. Unlike atoms in more complex molecules may contain polar bonds, but these molecules as a whole may be either polar or nonpolar.

In an ionic compound, valence number is the charge of the ion assigned to the corresponding atom; in covalent compounds, valence number is determined by the number of electron pairs and the atom to which they are most strongly attracted. The valence number of the inert gases, with complete outer electron shells, is zero. Compared with the corresponding atomic radii, ionic radii are smaller for positive ions and larger for negative ions.

It is possible to predict the type of chemical bond in a compound by using the electronegativity scale which gives an indication of each atom's tendency to attract shared electrons. Elements whose electronegativities vary greatly combine to form ionic bonds, while elements whose electronegativities are more nearly equal combine to form covalent bonds. The farther apart in electronegativity the two elements, the more polar the covalent bond holding them together.

Many compounds exist in which some atoms are joined together by covalent bonds, and yet the compounds as a whole are ionic. In such compounds groups of atoms of different elements are joined together to form ions. These ions, referred to as radicals, are relatively stable particles, chemically difficult to decompose. In a number of radicals, atoms are held together by a special type of electron sharing called a coordinate covalent bond—in which a single atom supplies both the electrons of an electron pair. Some radicals (and compounds) are resonance hybrids—a blend of two or more possible electron structures.

Metallic atoms are held together by metallic bonds. In metals, a sea of valence electrons continuously moves about the positively charged metallic ions. The metallic bond exists between the positive nuclei and the negative electrons.

USING THE CONCEPT

Using the Basic Concept

1. (a) What is the valence number of an element? (b) In general, what determines valence number? (c) Under what conditions do atoms of elements have a zero valence number? (d) What elements have a zero valence number?

2. (a) Describe each of the following ways by which atoms combine: formation of ionic bonds, formation of covalent bonds, formation of coordinate covalent bonds, formation of metallic bonds. (b) Give an example of each method of combination.

3. (a) Which of the four types of bonds listed in Question 2 never occur in elements? (b) Which never occur in compounds?

4. (a) Draw an electron dot diagram for the ionic compound sodium bromide. (b) Why would you predict that each particle of this compound is an ion? (c) Draw electron dot diagrams for the ionic compounds: CaF_2, NaI, Na_2O, CaO.

5. (a) Draw an orbital overlap diagram for the covalent molecular compound carbon dioxide. (b) How do you know that each molecule of this compound is neutral? (c) Repeat this procedure for these molecular substances: H_2O, C_2H_6, P_4.

6. (a) Define each of the following: *polar bond, polar molecule, nonpolar bond, nonpolar molecule.* (b) Give an example of each.

7. Give the valence number of each element in each of the following compounds: (a) ionic sodium iodide (NaI), (b) ionic calcium chloride ($CaCl_2$), (c) polar covalent hydrogen fluoride (HF).

8. (a) What is a radical ion, or radical? (b) Draw an electron dot diagram for the NH_4^+ and H_3O^+ radicals, each of which contains a coordinate covalent bond.

9. (a) What does the scale of electronegativity indicate? (b) How is the electronegativity scale used to predict whether atoms of two different elements combine to form polar or nonpolar covalent bonds, or ionic bonds?

10. Write ionic expressions for: KCl, $MgCl_2$, $Ca(OH)_2$, MgS.

11. Which member of each of the following pairs has the smaller radius (a) a lithium atom or a lithium ion, (b) a chlorine atom or a chloride ion, (c) an oxide ion or a fluoride ion?

12. (a) What is a resonance hybrid? (b) Name a radical exhibiting resonance.

13. (a) Draw diagrams to show the geometric shapes of the compounds NF_3, CCl_4, OF_2. (b) Name each geometric shape.

Relating Terms Within the Concept

Each of the following statements contains two *italicized* terms. Select the *italicized* term that makes the statement correct.

1. Electrons transfer from one atom to another in compounds that form by (*covalent bonds, ionic bonds*).

2. The covalent bond between like atoms is a (*polar bond, nonpolar bond*).
3. The $+1$ charge on the sodium ion, when assigned to the sodium atom, is its (*valence number, covalence number*).
4. If two pairs of electrons are shared by two atoms, the molecule contains (*a coordinate covalent bond, a double bond*).
5. An example of a radical is (CO_3^{-2}, NH_3).
6. The scale in which elements are arranged in the order of their tendency to attract shared electrons is the (*electronegativity scale, ionization potential scale*).
7. If both electrons in the electron pair shared by two atoms come from the same atom, the bond is most accurately classified as a (*covalent bond, coordinate bond*).
8. Compared to their corresponding atoms, positively charged ions are (*larger, smaller*).
9. The geometric shape of the ammonia molecule is (*tetrahedral, pyramidal*).
10. Any molecule which appears to be a blend or combination of two electron structures is a (*resonance hybrid, dipole*).

Solving Problems Within the Concept
1. Draw an electron orbital and an electron dot diagram for an ethane (C_2H_6) molecule. From the total number of protons and electrons present, show that a molecule of ethane has no charge.
2. (a) Use the table of electronegativities to predict whether the type of bond between each of the following pairs of atoms is ionic or covalent: Cl and Cl; K and Br; Ca and S. (b) Indicate which of the following molecules contains distinctly polar bonds, slightly polar bonds, nonpolar bonds: S_8, NH_3, CH_4. Give a reason for each choice.
3. Using the table of ionic radii, draw to scale solid-model diagrams of sodium chloride and barium fluoride.
4. Draw the electron dot diagram for the ionic compound ammonium sulfide ($NH_4)_2S$. Label the radicals, the coordi-

nate bonds, and the covalent bonds. Show that each ammonium radical must have a charge of $+1$.

Applying the Concept
1. Draw the electron dot diagram for the ionic compound ammonium sulfate ($NH_4)_2SO_4$.
2. Like electrostatic charges repel each other while unlike electrostatic charges attract. (a) Using this information, formulate a possible explanation for the dissolving of ionic NaCl in polar H_2O. (b) Would you expect CH_4 molecules to dissolve in water? Why or why not?
3. When H_2 reacts with Cl_2, molecules of HCl form. (a) Describe the nature of the bonds in H_2 and Cl_2 and the nature of the bonds in HCl. (b) Predict whether the bonds between hydrogen atoms, or those between hydrogen and chlorine atoms, are the more stable. On what data did you base your prediction?
4. (a) Draw the electron dot diagrams for a fluorine molecule (F_2) and a hydrogen peroxide molecule (H_2O_2). (b) Describe two similarities between these molecules.
5. From its position in the periodic table, its electronegativity, and its ionization potential, predict the valence number and ionic radius of francium.

Reading Further
College Chemistry, 3d. ed., by Linus Pauling, San Francisco, Freeman, 1964. The author, who won the 1954 Nobel prize in chemistry for determining the nature of the chemical bond and molecular structure, includes much interesting information concerning bonding between atoms.

Chemistry: An Investigative Approach, by F. A. Cotton and L. D. Lynch, Boston, Houghton Mifflin, 1968. Includes data about the types of bonds between atoms and molecules as well as an elementary discussion of the shapes of particles produced through the various types of chemical bonding.

7

SKILLS—Formulas, Equations, and Weights

Chemists, like all scientists, have developed ways of communicating with other chemists. You are aware that they use a special language in noting chemical reactions. Like all sciences, chemistry also has its own special techniques and procedures; to work effectively in the laboratory, one must have mastered certain skills. These procedures, techniques, and skills are presented in separate chapters throughout the book. This, the first chapter concerned with skills, deals with the writing of chemical formulas and equations.

Throughout this chapter you will find a number of problems. By completing each set of problems before going on to the next section, you will develop a pattern for writing formulas and equations and find it an interesting business rather than a tedious job.

WRITING CHEMICAL FORMULAS

In the early days of chemistry, formulas were used as a shorthand method of representing compounds—but the correct formulas for even simple compounds were rarely known. John Dalton, for instance, believed that water contained an equal number of hydrogen and oxygen atoms. Using modern chemical symbols, he would have assigned water the formula of HO.

Though compounds are still often referred to by name, today's chemists find it ever more convenient and useful to assign formulas to compounds. The name calcium chloride, for example, indicates only that the compound contains two elements, calcium and chlorine. The formula, $CaCl_2$, indicates the simplest ratio of ions of each element present in the compound. In this formula the subscript 2 appears to the right of the Cl; no subscript appears after the Ca. When no subscript appears after a symbol in a formula, the subscript is understood to be 1. Therefore the formula $CaCl_2$ indicates that calcium chloride can be broken down into twice as many chloride ions as calcium ions.

Formulas are the chemist's way of expressing information that has been proved by experimentation; formulas assigned to compounds are *not* proof of their compositions. Today, however, it is not always necessary for the chemist to analyze a compound in order to write its formula. It is now possible, by knowing the combining abilities and *valence numbers* of different atoms, to predict the formulas for many of the simpler compounds.

Writing Formulas for Compounds

In writing the formula for any compound, keep in mind that *the sum of the plus and minus valence numbers of all the different atoms in the compound must be zero.*

To write the correct formula for potassium chloride, first write the symbols for the two types of atoms involved:

$$KCl$$

Now, as superscripts to the right of each symbol, write the valence number of each atom. (These valence numbers can be obtained from Table 7-1, or they can be determined by knowing how many electrons each atom donates or accepts.) Since the valence number of potassium is $+1$ and the valence number of chlorine is -1, write:

$$K^{+1}Cl^{-1}$$

The valence numbers ($+1$ and -1) add up to zero. The formula for potassium chloride therefore is KCl. Note that *the atom with the positive valence number is customarily written first.*

To write the formula for magnesium sulfide first write the symbols for the two elements:

$$MgS$$

Next place the valence numbers as superscripts to the right of each symbol. The valence number

Table 7-1 VALENCE NUMBER OF SOME COMMON ELEMENTS AND RADICALS

Element	Symbol and valence number	Element	Symbol and valence number	Radical	Symbol and valence number
Aluminum	Al^{+3}	Bromine	Br^{-1}	Ammonium	NH_4^{+1}
Barium	Ba^{+2}	Chlorine	Cl^{-1}	Acetate	$C_2H_3O_2^{-1}$
Bismuth	Bi^{+3}	Fluorine	F^{-1}	Bicarbonate	HCO_3^{-1}
Calcium	Ca^{+2}	Iodine	I^{-1}	Bisulfite	HSO_3^{-1}
Cobalt	Co^{+2}	Nitrogen†	N^{-3}	Carbonate	CO_3^{-2}
Copper	$Cu^{+1,+2}$	Oxygen	O^{-2}	Chlorate	ClO_3^{-1}
Hydrogen	H^{+1}	Phosphorus†	P^{-3}	Chromate	CrO_4^{-2}
Iron	$Fe^{+2,+3}$	Sulfur†	S^{-2}	Hydroxide	OH^{-1}
Magnesium	Mg^{+2}			Nitrate	NO_3^{-1}
Mercury*	Hg_2^{+2}, Hg^{+2}			Nitrite	NO_2^{-1}
Potassium	K^{+1}			Phosphate	PO_4^{-3}
Silver	Ag^{+1}			Sulfate	SO_4^{-2}
Sodium	Na^{+1}			Sulfite	SO_3^{-2}
Tin	$Sn^{+2,+4}$				
Zinc	Zn^{+2}				

* X-ray analysis of solid mercury salts reveals mercurous ion is Hg_2^{+2}.
† Other valence numbers possible.

of magnesium is $+2$; the valence number of sulfur is -2:

$$Mg^{+2}S^{-2}$$

Again, the valence numbers add up to zero; the formula for magnesium sulfide is MgS.

What is the formula for magnesium chloride? Write the symbols for the two types of atoms, placing the valence numbers of each atom as a superscript to the right of each symbol:

$$Mg^{+2}Cl^{-1}$$

The valence numbers do *not* add up to zero; MgCl is *not* the correct formula. Because each magnesium atom gives up 2 electrons and each chlorine atom accepts only 1, two atoms of chlorine are needed to accept the electrons from a single magnesium atom. The combination of one atom of magnesium with two atoms of chlorine is indicated by placing the subscript 2 to the right of the chlorine. The subscript 1 is understood to be at the right of the magnesium atom. The formula for magnesium chloride is $MgCl_2$.

A *simplified way of determining subscripts is to write the valence number* (ignoring its sign) *for each element as a subscript to the right of the*

opposite symbol. The valence number of magnesium is $+2$; therefore write the subscript 2 to the right of the Cl. Since the valence number of Cl is -1, place a 1 at the right of the Mg. Following this criss-cross procedure,

$$Mg_1^{+2}Cl_2^{-1} \quad \text{becomes} \quad MgCl_2$$

What is the formula for aluminum oxide? The valence number of aluminum is $+3$ while that of oxygen is -2. The symbols for the two elements with their valence numbers are written as: $Al^{+3}O^{-2}$. Using the criss-cross procedure, write the subscript 2 to the right of the symbol Al and the subscript 3 to the right of the symbol O: $Al_2^{+3}O_3^{-2}$. The formula for the compound becomes simply Al_2O_3.

Finally, consider again the formula for magnesium sulfide. By the criss-cross method, $Mg_2^{+2}S_2^{-2}$, the formula might appear to be Mg_2S_2. If the subscripts in such a formula are identical, they are omitted. An equality of valence number means that one atom can donate or share exactly the number of electrons another atom can accept or share. The formula written correctly is MgS.

Using valence numbers, write the formulas for the following compounds: sodium fluoride, sodium sulfide, potassium oxide, calcium iodide, magnesium oxide, aluminum fluoride, aluminum sulfide, boric oxide, carbon dioxide, and carbon tetrachloride.

Formulas for Compounds Containing Radicals

In some compounds atoms are found combined in the form of radicals, ions consisting of more than one type of atom. Sodium hydroxide, potassium sulfate, calcium nitrate, and ammonium chloride are examples of compounds that contain radicals. To show that these four compounds contain radicals, they are represented below in ionic form:

Name	Formula	Ionic form
Sodium hydroxide	NaOH	$Na^{+1} OH^{-1}$
Sulfate	K_2SO_4	$2K^{+1} (SO_4)^{-2}$
Calcium nitrate	$Ca(NO_3)_2$	$Ca^{+2} 2(NO_3)^{-1}$
Ammonium chloride	NH_4Cl	$NH_4^{+1} Cl^{-1}$

In the ionic form the charge of each ion is shown. The charge of the hydroxide ion (OH) is -1, of the sulfate ion (SO_4), -2, and of the nitrate ion (NO_3), -1. The ammonium radical bears a positive charge of $+1$.

The charge of a radical is usually considered to be the valence number of the radical. The formulas for compounds containing radicals can be written quickly by the same procedure as for simpler compounds. In writing the formula for a compound containing a radical, *consider the radical as a single unit with a predetermined formula. Never separate the radical into its individual elements when determining formulas.*

To write the formula for calcium sulfate, determine from Table 7-1 that the valence number of calcium is $+2$, and that the charge of the sulfate ion is -2. Written together they become:

$$Ca^{+2}SO_4^{-2}$$

Since the $+2$ charge of the calcium ion and the -2 charge of the sulfate ion add up to zero, the formula for calcium sulfate must be $CaSO_4$. When the subscripts are the same for both the element and the radical, the subscripts are omitted.

Now write the formula for aluminum sulfate. The valence number of aluminum is $+3$, while the sulfate ion has a valence number of -2. Written together they become:

$$Al^{+3}SO_4^{-2}$$

By the simplified criss-cross method of placing the number 2 as a subscript to the right of Al^{+3} and the number 3 to the right of the SO_4^{-2}, the total ionic charge adds up to zero [$(2 \times +3)$ plus $(3 \times -2) = 0$].

$$Al_2^{+3}(SO_4)_3^{-2}$$

The correct formula for aluminum sulfate must be $Al_2(SO_4)_3$. *Parentheses are placed around the SO_4 to indicate that the subscript 3 refers to the whole sulfate radical, the formula of which may not be changed.* The parentheses also prevent confusion between the subscript and any number in the radical.

Write correct formulas for each of the following compounds: potassium hydroxide, sodium bicarbonate, magnesium hydroxide, sodium nitrate, aluminum sulfite, and ammonium sulfate. (Refer to Table 7-1 for the valence numbers of elements and radicals.)

Variable Valence

You know that more than one compound containing copper and sulfur does exist (page 66). One of these compounds, Cu_2S, is cuprous sulfide; the other, CuS, is cupric sulfide. Copper is capable of losing either 1 or 2 electrons to form cuprous ions and cupric ions respectively.

$$Cu^0 - 1e^- \longrightarrow Cu^{+1}$$
$$Cu^0 - 2e^- \longrightarrow Cu^{+2}$$

For this reason, two valence numbers, $+1$ and $+2$, are assigned to copper. Certain other elements have this same property of **variable valence.** Mercury atoms, for instance, can form mercurous ions (Hg_2^{+2}) or mercuric ions (Hg^{+2}), and iron atoms can form ferrous ions (Fe^{+2}) and ferric ions (Fe^{+3}). For each element with variable valence the ion with the lower valence ends in *-ous* and the ion with the higher valence ends in *-ic*. (The reason why certain atoms have a variable valence is considered in Chapter 15.) These suffixes merely indicate a higher or lower value; they do not reveal the actual valence number. The more recent Stock system, devised by the chemist Alfred Stock, avoids this difficulty. A Roman numeral indicating the proper valence number is enclosed in parentheses following the symbol for the element. Thus, cuprous sulfide, Cu_2S, is designated copper(I) sulfide, while iron(III) chloride is synonymous with ferric chloride, $FeCl_3$.

When writing formulas that contain copper, iron, mercury, or any other element that forms more than one type of ion, be sure that the proper valence number has been assigned to each atom. These valence numbers are shown in Table 7-2.

Table 7-2 ELEMENTS WITH VARIABLE VALENCE NUMBERS

Name	Stock system	Symbol and valence number	Name	Stock system	Symbol and valence number
Cuprous	Copper I	Cu^{+1}	Ferrous	Iron II	Fe^{+2}
Cupric	Copper II	Cu^{+2}	Ferric	Iron III	Fe^{+3}
Mercurous	Mercury I	Hg_2^{+2}	Stannous	Tin II	Sn^{+2}
Mercuric	Mercury II	Hg^{+2}	Stannic	Tin IV	Sn^{+4}

PROBLEM

1. Write the formulas for cuprous oxide, cupric oxide, mercurous chloride, mercuric chloride, ferrous nitrate, and ferric nitrate.
2. Give the name of each of the following compounds: Cu_2CO_3, $SnSO_4$, $HgClO_3$, $Fe(OH)_2$.
3. Write the names of the compounds in questions 1 and 2 according to the Stock system.

Valence Numbers and the Periodic Table

Thus far you have obtained valence numbers from tables, but the periodic table may also be used in determining valence numbers for atoms of elements in the A groups. In using the periodic table, the rule to follow is that each of the elements in groups IA, IIA, and IIIA has a positive valence number that is the same as the group number. Sodium, for instance, in group IA, has a valence number of $+1$ and calcium, in group IIA, has a valence number of $+2$.

Elements in groups VA, VIA, and VIIA *may* have positive valence numbers equal to the group number, but this situation is infrequent. When these elements are electron-acceptors, their *negative* valence numbers are readily found by subtracting 8 (the number of electrons in a complete outer shell) from the group number. For example, phosphorus in sodium phosphide, Na_3P, in which it has accepted electrons, has a valence number of -3 ($5 - 8 = -3$). More often the elements in these groups share electrons; the sign of the valence number then depends on the relative electronegativity of the two elements sharing electrons (see page 106).

In group IVA, atoms of each element such as carbon have valence numbers of $+4$ or -4.

PROBLEM

Using the periodic table, determine the usual valence numbers for atoms of each of the following elements: K, Sr, Ba, B, Si, N, S, F, and O. Indicate in each case how you decided upon the correct valence number.

Valence Numbers of Radicals from Formulas

If a table of valence numbers for radicals is unavailable, their valence numbers can be determined indirectly from the formulas of a group of compounds called acids—compounds that contain hydrogen and another element or radical. (The compounds are considered in some detail in Chapter 14). Refer to Table 7-3 for the formulas of a number of acids. The hydrogen, represented by H in each formula, is assigned a

Table 7-3 SOME COMMON ACIDS

Name	Formula	Name	Formula
Acetic	$HC_2H_3O_2$	Nitrous	HNO_2
Carbonic	H_2CO_3	Phosphoric	H_3PO_4
Hydrochloric	HCl	Sulfuric	H_2SO_4
Nitric	HNO_3	Sulfurous	H_2SO_3

valence number of $+1$. Since the sum of the valence numbers in any compound must equal zero, the valence number of each radical in the formula for an acid must be negative and equal to the subscript of the H. Use this rule to determine the valence number for the sulfite radical found in sulfurous acid (hydrogen sulfite). The formula for hydrogen sulfite is H_2SO_3. The subscript of the H is 2; the charge on the sulfite radical, or its valence number, must be -2:

$$H_2^{+1}(SO_3)^{-2}$$

When a charge of -2 is assigned to the sulfite radical, the total charge represented in the formula for hydrogen sulfite is zero.

valence number of hydrogen
$$\downarrow$$
$$[(2 \times +1) + (1 \times -2) = 0]$$
$$\uparrow$$
subscript of $(SO_3)^{-2}$

Now determine the charge of the phosphate radical, PO_4, from the formula for phosphoric acid, H_3PO_4. Since the subscript to the right of the H is 3, the charge of the phosphate radical must be -3 $[(3 \times +1) + (1 \times -3) = 0]$. When a charge of -3 is assigned to the phosphate radical, the total charge represented in the formula equals zero.

PROBLEM

Determine the valence number, or charge, of the radical represented in each of the following formulas: H_2CO_3, H_2SO_4, H_3PO_3, $HClO_3$, and $HC_2H_3O_2$.

Coefficients

If a chemist wishes to indicate a single molecule of water, he simply writes H_2O. (The number 1 is usually not written before a formula: it is understood to be present.) If he wishes to indicate two molecules of water, he writes $2\,H_2O$. Numbers such as 2, 3, 4 (1 being understood) placed before formulas are called **coefficients**. *A coefficient is used to indicate the number of molecules or ionic units* represented by the formula following the coefficient.

If one molecule of H_2O contains two hydrogen atoms and one oxygen atom, then $2\,H_2O$ (two molecules of water) must contain four atoms of hydrogen and two atoms of oxygen. The total number of each type of atom represented by a formula preceded by a coefficient is determined by multiplying the subscript following each symbol by the coefficient. For example, $4\,KClO_3$ represents a total of four potassium atoms (4×1), four chlorine atoms (4×1), and twelve oxygen atoms (4×3). (Recall that subscripts of 1 are not written after the K and Cl.) To determine the number of atoms in $5\,Al_2(SO_4)_3$ first consider that the subscript 3 to the right of the sulfate radical means that three sulfur atoms (1 understood $\times$ 3) and twelve oxygen atoms (4×3) are present for each two atoms of aluminum. Therefore, a total of ten aluminum atoms (5×2), fifteen sulfur atoms (5×3), and sixty oxygen atoms (5×12) is present in $5\,Al_2(SO_4)_3$. Now to determine the total number of atoms present in $5\,Al_2(SO_4)_3$, add the number of atoms of each element. The total number of atoms is 85 $(10 + 15 + 60)$.

This same data is more conveniently written in tabular form:

Element	Number of atoms
Aluminum	$(5 \times 2) = 10$
Sulfur	$5\,(1 \times 3) = 15$
Oxygen	$5\,(4 \times 3) = \underline{60}$
	85 Total number of atoms

To determine the total number of atoms, simply add the figures in the right-hand column.

1. How many atoms of each element are represented by each of the following: $4 H_2O$, $5 H_2SO_4$, $3 KClO_3$, $3 (NH_4)_2SO_4$?

2. What is the total number of atoms represented by $2 H_3PO_4$? by $4 Fe(NO_3)_2$?

WRITING EQUATIONS

As with any skill, practice in writing chemical formulas and in determining the number of atoms represented by formulas, including any coefficients, makes these processes second nature to you. While being able to write formulas is important, the use of these formulas in chemical equations is equally important, for chemical equations are used to represent chemical changes in matter.

Meaning of Chemical Equations

Recall from Chapter 1 the equation used to indicate the chemical change or reaction that occurs when iron and sulfur are heated.

$$Fe + S \xrightarrow{\Delta} FeS$$

The symbols Fe and S to the left of the arrow represent the substances that are reacting together, the **reactants.** The arrow, as you know, is a shorthand symbol which means "yields" or "produces," and heat is indicated by the Δ (delta) above the arrow. FeS is the formula for iron sulfide (ferrous sulfide), the **product** of the reaction.

Every chemical equation is written to indicate a specific chemical reaction that is known to occur or that chemists have predicted will occur. A chemical equation must represent the reaction as accurately as possible. The first thing to ascertain when writing an equation is that the reactants and products are stated correctly. Next, the correct formulas for the reactants and the products must be written.

A fact well established by experimentation is that during a chemical change atoms of an element are never lost or gained. The equation for each chemical reaction, therefore, must include the same number of each type of atom in the products as in the reactants. The above equation shows that one atom of iron (Fe) combines with one atom of sulfur (S) to form one ionic unit of iron sulfide (FeS). Observe that the same number of iron and sulfur atoms, one each, is shown as product and as reactant.

Writing Chemical Equations

Consider again the reaction that occurs when mercuric oxide is heated. Mercury and oxygen are the products formed. You know that mercury and oxygen are represented by Hg and O_2, respectively. If you do not remember the formula for mercuric oxide, use the criss-cross procedure to determine it. Did you obtain HgO? Once correct formulas have been written they must *never* be changed. Now combine these three formulas into an equation. Because HgO is the reactant, it is written to the left of the arrow. The products Hg and O_2 are written to the right.

$$HgO \longrightarrow Hg + O_2\uparrow$$

After the equation is written it should be carefully inspected to determine if the reactant and products both contain the same number of each type of atom. The term **balanced equation** is used to describe an equation in which the reactants and products contain the same numbers of each type of atom. The above equation is *not* balanced; there are twice as many oxygen atoms represented on the right side as on the left. The equation incorrectly indicates that oxygen atoms have been created during the reaction.

Balancing an Equation

A chemical equation is "balanced" by placing the appropriate coefficient before each formula. In the above equation, the coefficient 1 is understood to appear before each formula. The HgO represents one ionic particle of mercuric oxide. The Hg represents one atom of mercury and O_2 represents one molecule of oxygen.

The formulas for reactant and products are correctly written and may not be changed; therefore the coefficient 1 understood for one or more of the formulas in the equation must be changed to balance the equation. From a rather quick inspection of this "unbalanced equation" it can be seen that the formulas on each side of the equation represent one atom of mercury but that the formula HgO on the left side represents one atom of oxygen while that on the right represents two atoms of oxygen. To balance the oxygen, place the coefficient 2 in front of the HgO.

$$2\, HgO \longrightarrow Hg + O_2\uparrow$$

Now, as the coefficient multiplies each element in the formula by 2, two atoms of oxygen and also two atoms of mercury are represented. The oxygen atoms are in balance but the mercury atoms are not balanced. There are now two mercury atoms represented on the left side of the equation and only one on the right. The coefficient 2 placed in front of the Hg on the right balances the mercury without affecting the oxygen balance. The balanced equation is:

$$2\, HgO \longrightarrow 2\, Hg \quad + \quad O_2\uparrow$$

| 2 atoms of mercury | 2 atoms of mercury | 2 atoms of oxygen |
| 2 atoms of oxygen | | |

The Inspection Method

The procedure just described is often referred to as the **inspection method.** This method can be used to balance many chemical equations. As a second example of the inspection method, balance the equation for the usual laboratory preparation of oxygen.

To write the balanced equation for the heating of potassium chlorate to yield potassium chloride and oxygen, follow the steps below:

Step 1: Write an equation including the correct formulas for reactants and products.

$$KClO_3 \longrightarrow KCl + O_2\uparrow$$

Step 2: Inspect the equation to see if the same number of atoms of each element appears in both reactants and products.

While both the formulas for reactants and products represent one atom each of potassium and chlorine, the $KClO_3$ represents three atoms

of oxygen on the left side of the equation while the O_2 represents only two atoms of oxygen. The equation is not balanced; you have not accounted for one atom of oxygen.

Step 3: To balance the equation, determine by inspection the correct coefficient to be placed before each formula.

To balance the number of oxygen atoms, *find the least common multiple of the subscripts 3 and 2;* it is 6. To indicate six atoms of oxygen on each side of the equation, place the coefficient 2 in front of the $KClO_3$ and the coefficient 3 in front of the O_2.

$$2\, KClO_3 \longrightarrow KCl + 3\, O_2\uparrow$$

Now the potassium and chlorine are no longer in balance; two atoms of each are represented on the left side of the equation and only one atom of each on the right. Place the coefficient 2 in front of the KCl, and the equation is balanced.

$$2\, KClO_3 \longrightarrow 2\, KCl \quad + \quad 3\, O_2\uparrow$$

2 atoms of potassium	2 atoms of potassium	6 atoms of oxygen
2 atoms of chlorine	2 atoms of chlorine	
6 atoms of oxygen		

PROBLEMS

1. Write balanced equations for the following reactions:
   (a) Zinc reacts with chlorine to form zinc chloride.
   (b) Phosphorus reacts with oxygen to form phosphorus pentoxide.
   (c) Iron reacts with chlorine to form ferric chloride.
   (d) Carbon reacts with oxygen to form carbon dioxide.
   (e) Sodium reacts with water to form sodium hydroxide and hydrogen.

2. Balance each of the following unbalanced equations:
   (a) $O_3 \longrightarrow O_2\uparrow$
   (b) $Fe + O_2 \longrightarrow Fe_2O_3$
   (c) $CH_4 + O_2 \longrightarrow C + H_2O$
   (d) $H_2O + C \longrightarrow H_2 + CO_2\uparrow$

INTERPRETING FORMULAS IN TERMS OF WEIGHTS

Since the time of John Dalton, atomic weights have been considered an important property of each element. The atomic weight of an element is the relative weight in atomic mass units (amu) of the element compared to the standard carbon-12 (page 29). By referring to the table of atomic weights on page 30, you find that the atomic weight of hydrogen is 1.00797 amu, the atomic weight of oxygen is 15.9994 amu, and that of sulfur is 32.064 amu. The atomic weights given in this table are used as a basis for determining the weights, in atomic mass units, of molecular and ionic compounds. These, in turn, are used in many of the calculations necessary to chemistry.

Molecular Weights

How much does a molecule of hydrogen weigh —or, as the chemist usually asks, what is the **molecular weight** (**MW**) of hydrogen? The molecular weight of a molecule is its weight expressed in atomic mass units. To find the molecular weight of a molecule it is necessary only to add together the weights of all of the atoms in the molecule, whether the atoms are alike or different. Since hydrogen molecules, for example, each consist of two atoms of hydrogen, the molecular weight of hydrogen is equal to two times its atomic weight.

2 × atomic weight of hydrogen = **MW**
2 × 1.00797 amu = 2.01594 amu

To determine the molecular weight of a water molecule, multiply the atomic weight of hydrogen, 1.00797 amu, by 2. Then add the atomic weight of oxygen, 15.9994 amu. The procedure for determining the molecular weight of water is summarized below:

Symbol for element	Number of atoms in molecule		Atomic weight		Total atomic weight
H	2	×	1.00797 amu	=	2.01594 amu
O	1	×	15.9994 amu	=	15.9994 amu
			MW of H_2O	=	18.01534 amu

Formula Weights

Since ionic substances do not form molecules, they do not have molecular weights. But the formula for each ionic substance can be used to determine its **formula weight** (**FW**). *The formula weight of an ionic substance is the sum of the atomic weights of all atoms represented by its formula.* Formula weights for ionic compounds are determined in the same way as molecular weights for molecular compounds.

The formula weight of calcium phosphate, $Ca_3(PO_4)_2$, is determined as follows:

Symbol for element	Number of atoms represented by formula		Atomic weight		Total atomic weight
Ca	3	×	40.08 amu	=	120.24 amu
P	2	×	30.9738 amu	=	61.9476 amu
O	8	×	15.9994 amu	=	127.9952 amu
			FW of $Ca_3(PO_4)_2$	=	310.1828 amu

Simplified Molecular and Formula Weights

When determining molecular and formula weights, the atomic weights of the elements in each formula are calculated usually to the nearest whole number or to one decimal place (if approximately 0.5). (The reason for this has to do with ease of calculating and with **significant figures.** See Appendix B.) Following this procedure, the atomic weight of oxygen becomes 16 amu instead of 15.9994 amu. The atomic weight of potassium becomes 39 amu rather than 39.102 amu, and the atomic weight of chlorine becomes 35.5 amu instead of 35.453 amu. You will find a table of atomic weights accurate to one decimal place located conveniently on the inside back cover of this book.

In problems dealing with molecular and formula weights, the amu following each number is usually dropped, since the amu units cancel out during the solution to the problem in which these units appear. Dropping amu's simplifies the procedure for determining and expressing molecular and formula weights. The molecular weight of carbon dioxide, CO_2, determined by this simplified procedure is:

Symbol for element	Number of atoms represented by formula	Atomic weight	Total atomic weight
C	1 ×	12 =	12
O	2 ×	16 =	32
		MW of CO_2 =	44

What is the formula weight of crystal copper sulfate, $CuSO_4 \cdot 5 H_2O$? The $\cdot 5 H_2O$ indicates that the crystal contains water, and its weight is included in determining the weight of the compound:

Symbol for Element	Number of atoms represented by formula	Atomic weight	Total atomic weight
Cu	1 ×	63.5 =	63.5
S	1 ×	32 =	32
O	9 ×	16 =	144
H	10 ×	1 =	10
		FW of $CuSO_4 \cdot 5H_2O$ =	249.5

PROBLEM

Use the simplified procedure to determine the molecular weight or the formula weight for each of the following substances: Cl_2, N_2, O_3, C_2H_6, NaCl, $CaCO_3$, $Al_2(SO_4)_3$, $Mg_3(PO_4)_2 \cdot 4H_2O$. Indicate which answers are molecular weights and which are formula weights.

Equation Weights and Actual Weights

In an equation, the coefficient before each formula represents the relative number of atomic, molecular, or formula weights of each substance that takes part in the specific reaction. To understand the use of coefficients in determining the number of these weights, consider again the decomposition of mercuric oxide. The coefficients preceding the formulas in the equation for this reaction indicate that 2 formula weights of mercuric oxide when heated yield 2 atomic weights of mercury and 1 molecular weight of oxygen.

$$2 \, HgO \longrightarrow 2 \, Hg + O_2$$
number of weights   2   2   1

By multiplying the formula, atomic, and molecular weights of mercuric oxide, mercury, and oxygen, respectively, by the appropriate coefficient, the *relative* amount of each substance by *weight* is found.

$$2 \, HgO \longrightarrow 2 \, Hg + O_2$$
$$2(201 + 16) \longrightarrow 2(201) + (2 \times 16)$$
$$434 \longrightarrow 402 + 32$$

The numbers 434, 402, and 32 represent the relative amount by weight of each substance. These numbers indicate that 434 of any weight units of HgO produce 402 of the same weight units of Hg and 32 similar weight units of O_2. These relative weights are often called **equation weights.** Any unit of weight may follow these equation weights as long as the unit of weight is the same throughout. For instance, 434 grams of HgO form 402 grams of Hg and 32 grams of O_2, or 434 pounds of HgO form 402 pounds of Hg and 32 pounds of O_2. The relative weight of each substance in a chemical equation indicates the proportion *by weight* of each substance in the reaction.

PROBLEM

What are the weights in grams, ounces, and pounds of the substances in the reaction that occurs when potassium chlorate is decomposed?

Gram Atomic, Gram Molecular, and Gram Formula Weights

Chemists often find it convenient to express the atomic weight of an element or the molecular or formula weight of a compound in grams. Atomic weights expressed in grams are called **gram atomic weights (GAW)**, while molecular weights expressed in grams are referred to as **gram molecular weights (GMW)**. The atomic weight of oxygen is 16; its gram atomic weight is 16 grams. The molecular weight of O_2 is 32; its gram molecular weight is 32 grams. Likewise, since the molecular weight of H_2O is 18, its gram molecular weight is 18 grams.

Similarly, formula weights of ionic substances expressed in gram units are known as **gram formula weights (GFW)**. Since, for example, the formula weight of $NaCl$ is 58.4, its gram formula weight is 58.4 grams. Likewise, the gram formula weight of Na_2SO_4 is 142 grams.

PROBLEMS

1. What is the gram atomic weight of each of the following elements: iron, nitrogen, and calcium?

2. Determine the gram molecular weight of each compound: CH_4, CCl_4, NH_3, $C_6H_{10}O_5$.

3. What is the gram formula weight of each of the following compounds: KCl, $NaOH$, MgO, Li_2CO_3, $Pb(NO_3)_2$, $Fe_2(CO_3)_3$?

ADDITIONAL PROBLEMS

1. Determine the formula for each of the following compounds: potassium bromide, barium hydroxide, sodium acetate, sodium sulfate, sodium phosphate, calcium phosphate, zinc chromate, magnesium sulfite, aluminum nitrate, aluminum carbonate, mercurous chloride, mercuric iodide, ferrous hydroxide, ferric hydroxide, cuprous oxide, cupric nitrate, ammonium chloride.

2. From the periodic table determine the valence number or numbers of each of the following elements: Li, Be, Al, Sn, As, Se, Br.

3. How many atoms of each element are represented by each of the following: $6\,HCl$, $7\,HNO_3$, $3\,N_2O$, $2\,KMnO_4$, $2\,HC_2H_3O_2$, $2\,(NH_4)_2CO_3$?

4. What is the total number of atoms represented by each of the following formulas: $4\,NO$, $6\,H_3PO_2$, $3\,Al_2(CrO_4)_3$, $2\,K_3Fe(CN)_6$, $5\,Ag(NH_3)_2Cl$?

5. Write a balanced equation representing each of the following reactions:
   (a) zinc + sulfuric acid $\longrightarrow$
       zinc sulfate + hydrogen
   (b) potassium + water $\longrightarrow$
       potassium hydroxide + hydrogen
   (c) carbon monoxide + water $\longrightarrow$
       carbon dioxide + hydrogen
   (d) carbon + oxygen $\longrightarrow$
       carbon monoxide

6. Balance each of the following unbalanced equations:
   (a) $O_2 \xrightarrow{\text{electricity}} O_3\uparrow$
   (b) $Na_2O_2 + H_2O \longrightarrow NaOH + O_2\uparrow$
   (c) $C_3H_8 + H_2O \longrightarrow CO_2 + H_2\uparrow$
   (d) $Fe + O_2 \longrightarrow Fe_3O_4$
   (e) $C + N_2O \longrightarrow CO_2 + N_2\uparrow$
   (f) $Cu + AgNO_3 \longrightarrow Cu(NO_3)_2 + Ag$
   (g) $NaCl + H_2SO_4 \longrightarrow Na_2SO_4 + HCl\uparrow$

7. Determine the molecular or formula weight of each of the following: F_2, I_2, C_3H_8, $NaOH$, $MgCl_2$, $CaSO_4$, $Al_2(SO_3)_3$, $CoCl_2 \cdot 6\,H_2O$.

8. What are the weights in grams, ounces, and pounds of the substances in the reaction that occurs when zinc reacts with hydrochloric acid?

9. Determine the gram atomic weight of each of the following elements: copper, fluorine, neon, potassium, silicon, radium.

10. Determine the gram formula or gram molecular weight of each of the following compounds. For each compound indicate whether you have determined the gram formula or gram molecular weight: CO, HI, Na_2CO_3, $BaSO_4$, $ZnCl_2$, $KMnO_4$, $C_6H_{12}O_6$, FeO, $CuSO_4$, $AgNO_3$, HNO_3, SO_2, $Na_2B_4O_7 \cdot 10\,H_2O$.

8

The Kinetic Molecular Theory

It was not until the seventeenth century that experiments seem to have been undertaken to prove that the earth was surrounded by a "sea of air" that exerts pressure. Probably an attempt to prove that the air exerts pressure led Evangelista Torricelli, a young pupil of Galileo, to invent the barometer in 1643. Torricelli's original barometer was basically the same instrument that we still use for measuring air pressure today (Fig. 8-1). This device, which first made it possible to measure the pressure of gases, opened a new era in the study of gases. And it was through studying the properties of gases that scientists arrived at one of their most useful explanations for the nature of all matter—the kinetic molecular theory.

THE NATURE OF GASES

Less than twenty years later, Robert Boyle of England developed a device to "pump" air into or out of a confined space. Basically this pump was much like one of the cylinders and pistons in a modern automobile engine. Using his pump, Boyle showed that when a gas like air is confined inside the cylinder, it can be compressed by applying pressure on the piston. As more force is applied, the pressure on the gas in the cylinder is increased. And with every increase in pressure, as the piston moves down the cylinder, the confined gas occupies less and less volume. Conversely, as the piston is raised and the pressure of the gas reduced, the gas occupies an ever greater volume. Boyle called this characteristic —the compression of gas under pressure and the expansion of gas when pressure is released—the "springiness" of the air.

Gases and Pressure Changes

Is there a precise relation between the volume a confined gas occupies and the pressure applied to it? You can answer this question yourself *by a simple investigation.*

Arrange a glass tube, open at one end and bent in the form of a **J,** and a meter stick. Use an eyedropper to add mercury to the long arm of the tube until the level of mercury in both arms is the

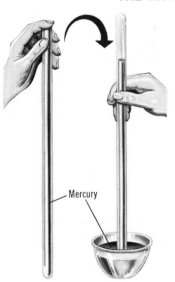

Mercury

8-1 Making a Torricelli barometer.

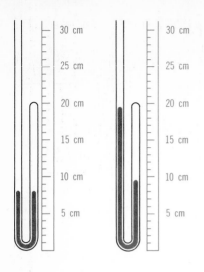

same. Observe that air is trapped at the closed end. The volume of the gas measured in cubic centimeters (cm³ or cc) is numerically equal to the height of the column of confined air measured in centimeters (cm) if the tube has a cross-sectional area of 1 square centimeter (cm²). But what is the pressure on the confined gas?

When the mercury is at the same level in both arms, the pressure on both surfaces of the mercury must be the same. The pressure on the mercury in the open arm is *normal atmospheric pressure* of 76 cm at sea level (also expressed as 760 mm, 760 **Torr** in honor of Torricelli, or 1 atmosphere). Hence, the pressure on the confined gas is also 76 cm. Continue adding mercury and observe that the volume of the trapped gas becomes less; but the level of mercury in the two arms is no longer the same. The pressure on the trapped gas is equal to the *difference* in the levels of the mercury columns *plus* the atmospheric pressure. Observe and record the volume of gas when the mercury columns are level and when the difference in the mercury columns is 10 cm, 18 cm, and 38 cm, respectively.

Perhaps when the mercury columns are level, the volume of trapped gas occupies 12 cm³. If so, when the difference in levels of the mercury columns is 10 cm, the volume of gas has decreased to 10.6 cm³—*but the actual pressure on the gas is 86 cm (10 cm + 76 cm)*. When the difference in levels in the mercury columns is 18 cm, do you find that the volume of the air column is 9.7 cm³? When the difference is 38 cm, is the volume of the air column 8 cm³? Observe that in each trial, when you multiply the number representing *total* pressure by the corresponding number representing volume, you get the same numerical answer—912. Your data so far indicates that the product of these two numbers is a constant (Table 8-1). *Now return to your investigation.*

Add mercury to the long arm until the difference in the mercury columns is 76 cm. The total pressure is now 152 cm (76 cm + 76 cm); the pressure on the gas is doubled. Observe the column of confined gas. It is reduced by half, from 12 cm³ to 6 cm³. When you double the pressure, the volume of the gas becomes half as great—and the product remains constant (152 × 6 = 912).

Table 8-1   **PRESSURE × VOLUME = CONSTANT VALUE FOR GASES**

Trial	Atmospheric pressure (cm)	Difference in mercury levels (cm)	Total pressure (cm)	Volume of trapped air (cm³)	Constant (P × V)
1	76	0	76	12.0	912
2	76	10	86	10.6	912
3	76	18	94	9.7	912
4	76	38	114	8.0	912
5	76	76	152	6.0	912

1 atmosphere   2 atmospheres   3 atmospheres

600 ml   300 ml   200 ml

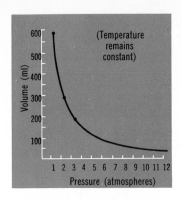

8-2 As pressure on the gas molecules in a closed cylinder increases, the volume of the gas decreases. From the graph that indicates this inverse relationship, determine the volume the gas would occupy at 4 atmospheres.

As further evidence of the inverse relationship between pressure and volume, study Fig. 8-2, which shows a cylinder of gas sealed at one end by a movable piston. Observe once again that as the pressure (measured in atmospheres) increases, the volume (measured in milliliters) decreases, but the product remains the same.

Boyle was the first scientist to describe this relationship between the pressure and volume of a confined gas in precise terms. Known as **Boyle's Law,** his discovery may be stated thus: *The volume of a confined gas varies inversely with the pressure, provided the temperature of the gas remains constant.* (Procedures for solving numerical problems involving this and other gas laws are detailed in Skills Chapter 9.)

Gases and Temperature Change

This relationship between the pressure and volume of a confined gas holds true *only* if the temperature remains constant. *You can observe* the effect of temperature changes on a confined gas quite simply.

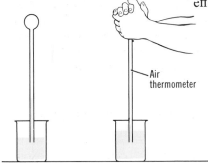

Cup your hands around the bulb of an air thermometer for about half a minute. Quickly place the open end of the stem in a beaker of colored water and observe the level of the water in the stem of the air-thermometer bulb. Cup your hands around the bulb itself and observe that the water level in the stem goes down gradually. Remove your hands from the bulb and continue to observe the water level in the stem. Does it rise, fall, or remain stationary?

The heat from your hands warms the air in the air-thermometer bulb. As the warmed air inside the bulb expands, the water level goes down; as the air cools, it contracts, and the water level slowly rises.

The changes that occur in the volume of a given mass of gas as it is heated or cooled were first measured by the French scientist Jacques Charles, in 1801. Charles concluded that any given volume of gas,

THE KINETIC MOLECULAR THEORY   127

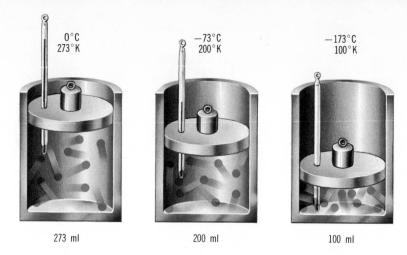

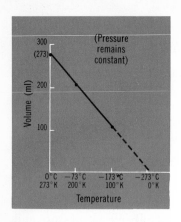

8-3 As the temperature of a confined gas decreases, the volume of the gas also decreases. From the graph that indicates this direct relationship, determine the volume the gas would occupy at 50° K.

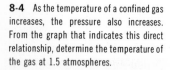

8-4 As the temperature of a confined gas increases, the pressure also increases. From the graph that indicates this direct relationship, determine the temperature of the gas at 1.5 atmospheres.

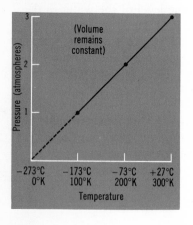

measured at 0° C*, increases in volume by 1/273 for each degree rise in temperature if the pressure remains unchanged. Conversely, when the gas is cooled and the pressure remains the same, the original volume at 0° C decreases by 1/273 for every one-degree drop on the Celsius scale.

Suppose that 273 ml of a gas are measured at 0° C. What happens theoretically when it is cooled to various temperatures is indicated in Fig. 8-3, which shows a cylinder of gas sealed at one end by a movable piston. Note that since the gas decreases 1/273 of its original volume (or 1 ml) for each temperature change of 1C°, it decreases 273/273 of the original volume (a total of 273 ml) by the time a temperature of −273° C is reached. Therefore at −273° C the volume of the gas *theoretically* becomes zero. In actual fact, a given mass of gas never attains a volume of zero as it is cooled. This is because the relationship described by Charles holds true only so long as a substance *remains a gas*. Before a temperature of −273° C is reached, any known gas turns into a liquid or a solid.

Today Charles' statement of the relationship between the temperature and volume of gases is expressed in a law that bears his name. **Charles' Law** states that *the volume of a gas varies directly with the absolute† temperature provided the pressure remains constant.*

Relating Pressure and Temperature Changes

Charles' Law holds true only as long as the pressure remains constant. When a gas is put under pressure, as when air is compressed by a tire pump, its temperature rises. If the pressure on a gas is released, as when gas escapes from a cylinder of compressed oxygen, the temperature of the gas falls. Moreover, the pressure exerted by a *confined* gas becomes greater when the temperature is raised, and becomes less when the temperature cools (Fig. 8-4). A law describing this relationship between the

*By international agreement, the centigrade scale is now called the *Celsius* scale in honor of the man who developed it. The symbol ° C refers to degrees Celsius.
†On the absolute temperature scale, 0° K equals −273° C; for details see page 147.

pressure exerted by a confined gas and its temperature was first proposed by Gay-Lussac of France. **Gay-Lussac's Law** relating pressure and temperature states that *the pressure exerted by a gas varies directly with its absolute temperature, provided the volume remains constant.*

As all gases theoretically follow the same *gas laws,* we assume that physically all gases are much alike. But scientists ask a further question: What is it in the nature of gases that makes them behave as they do?

QUESTIONS AND PROBLEMS

1. How does volume of a confined gas relate to changes in (a) pressure (at constant temperature)? (b) temperature (at constant pressure)?
2. How is Gay-Lussac's Law related to both Charles' and Boyle's Laws?
3. From the data in Figure 8-4, predict the temperature of the gas at (a) 1.5 atmospheres pressure, (b) 3.5 atmospheres pressure.

THE KINETIC MOLECULAR THEORY

8-5 Place a few small particles of mercuric oxide in a drop of water on a microscope slide and observe the slide under a microscope. Can you follow the zigzag path of a particle?

In 1827 Robert Brown, an English botanist, added pollen grains to water and observed them under the microscope. The pollen did not come to rest, but continually darted back and forth in zigzag, straight-line paths. When Brown repeated his experiment with other kinds of small particles, he observed the same type of motion. He incorrectly assumed that the particles were molecules and that he was observing molecular motion. Today we know that the particles Brown observed were not molecules but that the motion of particles was due to their bombardment by molecules (Fig. 8-5). **Brownian movement,** as this phenomenon is called, is indeed convincing evidence of molecular motion.

Based on such evidences as Brownian movement and the observations about gases made by Charles, Boyle, and others, several scientists soon developed a reasonable explanation for the behavior of gases. The scientists theorized that the behavior of gases could be accounted for by assuming that gases are composed of discrete particles, called molecules, in constant motion. The assumptions that gases are composed of molecules, and that molecules possess energy of motion, or *kinetic energy,* were soon developed into a detailed **kinetic molecular theory** of gases.

So much experimental evidence has been collected to support these assumptions that today the kinetic molecular theory is not only accepted as an explanation for the physical nature of gases but has been amplified to explain the physical nature of liquids and solids as well. It is, indeed, a kinetic molecular theory of matter. The two essential postulates of the theory are that *molecules of all matter are in continuous motion* and that *an increase in temperature increases the molecular movement and hence the kinetic energy of a substance.* Since the kinetic energy of any substance is a measure of the motion of its molecules, and since heat increases the motion of molecules, heat can change a solid into a liquid, and a liquid into a gas. For the moment, however, let us consider the early assumptions of the kinetic molecular theory as it was developed in relation to gases.

The Physical Nature of Gases

According to modern kinetic molecular theory, although gases are composed of molecules, the molecules themselves occupy an extremely small space compared to the spaces between the molecules. As the spaces between the gas molecules are relatively so vast, the attraction of the molecules for one another is almost negligible. It is also postulated that each molecule in a gas is in continuous, and very rapid, straight-line motion and that a particle changes its direction only after it collides with another gas molecule or with the walls of the container. When the molecules do collide with each other, they bounce apart with no loss in kinetic energy. Consequently, the total kinetic energy of the gas remains unchanged. However, there may be a transfer of energy from one molecule to another. Therefore, the individual molecules in a gas are traveling at different speeds and have different amounts of kinetic energy. Finally it is assumed that the average kinetic energy of the molecules is proportional to the *absolute temperature* of the gas. Doubling the absolute temperature doubles the average kinetic energy of the gas molecules.

How do these assumptions of the kinetic molecular theory explain the behavior of gases as described by the gas laws?

The Kinetic Theory and the Gas Laws

To explain the inverse relationship between the pressure and volume of a gas (Boyle's Law), visualize once again a cylinder sealed at one end by a movable piston (Fig. 8-2). The kinetic theory tells us that the gas in the cylinder consists of a definite number of molecules widely separated from one another. The molecules have little attraction for one another and are free to move about. As a result, they bump into each other and into the walls of the cylinder. Because the molecules have weight (mass), they exert a force when they hit the cylinder walls. It is this force, over the total area of the walls, which causes the internal pressure of the gas in the cylinder. The pressure of the piston at the closed end of the cylinder must be equal to the pressure of the gas inside, otherwise the gas would force the piston upward. When additional external pressure is applied to the piston, the gas particles inside the cylinder are pushed closer together so that the gas now takes up less volume. Since the same number of gas particles now hits a smaller area of the cylinder wall, the pressure against the wall is increased.

The direct relationship between the temperature and volume of a gas as expressed by Charles' Law can also be explained in terms of the kinetic theory. Consider once more a gas sealed into a cylinder by a movable piston. The molecules of the gas are moving to and fro, bump-

8-6 If the molecules in the lefthand cylinder are heated, they move faster and faster, striking the cylinder wall and the piston more frequently and vigorously. The pressure is increased, and the piston moves upward.

ing into each other and continually hitting the walls of the container. Now suppose that the gas is heated by some outside source. This increases the average kinetic energy of the molecules. They now collide with the walls of the container more vigorously and frequently than before, producing a greater pressure on the piston. The piston is thus pushed upward and this in turn increases the volume of gas in the container (Fig. 8-6).

Van der Waals Forces

The attraction of gas molecules for each other under certain circumstances accounts for the fact that Boyle's Law must be modified to describe the behavior of gases under *very high pressure*. For a similar reason, Charles' Law does not apply to gases at such *low temperatures* that they are near the point of liquefying. Unlike liquids and solids, gases always fill the container in which they are placed because their molecules can move freely. But compressing or cooling the gas beyond a certain point "pushes" the molecules of the gas so close together that the attractive forces between them become effective. These intermolecular forces resulting from *the attraction of the positive nuclei of one molecule for the electron cloud of a nearby molecule* are known as **van der Waals forces** (Fig. 8-7). They were named after the Dutch scientist Johannes Diderils van der Waals (1837–1923), who was the first to recognize their importance. Although van der Waals forces are present in all matter, they come into play in gases only when the gases are under high pressure or at temperatures near the point of liquefaction. At high pressures or at reduced temperatures, the gas molecules possess less kinetic energy to counteract the attraction of the van der Waals forces. Moreover, the greater the number of electrons in a molecule, usually the greater is the force of attraction between the molecules.

Avogadro's Law

We have seen that by 1801 Charles and Boyle had shown that equal volumes of all gases behave in the same way when their temperatures and pressures are changed. The question then arose in the minds of scientists as to why it should make no difference whether the container was filled with air, oxygen, or carbon dioxide. Seven years later Gay-Lussac demonstrated that in reactions in which the reactants and products are gases, the ratio by volume of the original reacting gases and the final gaseous product can always be expressed in small whole numbers. This is the *Law of Combining Volumes* discussed on page 64.

In 1811 an Italian scientist, Amadeo Avogadro, offered an explanation for Boyle's and Charles' Laws. He said that if equal volumes of all gases react in the same way to changes in temperature and pressure, it must be because equal volumes of different gases contain the same number of molecules under the same conditions of temperature and pressure. Furthermore, reasoning from Gay-Lussac's findings, Avogadro declared

8-7 Van der Waals forces become effective when gases are compressed or cooled so that the molecules are brought closer together. These intermolecular forces result from the attraction of the positive nuclei of one molecule for the electrons of an adjacent molecule.

that the smallest particles of gases were not necessarily atoms but were combinations of atoms "united to form a single molecule." Avogadro combined these two ideas into the principle we know today as **Avogadro's Law**: *Equal volumes of all gases, under the same conditions of temperature and pressure, contain the same number of molecules.*

Gay-Lussac had shown that one volume of hydrogen reacts with one volume of chlorine to produce two volumes of hydrogen chloride:

$$\text{hydrogen} \ + \ \text{chlorine} \longrightarrow \text{hydrogen chloride}$$

1 volume	1 volume	2 volumes

According to Avogadro's reasoning, the two volumes of hydrogen chloride must contain twice as many molecules as either the single volume of hydrogen or the single volume of chlorine. Thus if the two volumes of hydrogen chloride contained 2,000 molecules, the original volumes of hydrogen and chlorine must have contained 1,000 molecules each.

$$\text{hydrogen} \ + \ \text{chlorine} \longrightarrow \text{hydrogen chloride}$$

1,000 molecules	1,000 molecules	2,000 molecules

Now if each hydrogen particle and each chlorine particle consisted of only a single atom, 1,000 atoms of hydrogen would combine with 1,000 atoms of chlorine to produce 1,000 molecules of hydrogen chloride (HCl). But two volumes of HCl must contain 2,000 molecules to behave in the manner determined by Charles and others. Hence Avogadro reasoned that each particle of hydrogen and of chlorine must consist *not* of a single atom, but of two atoms each. In short, each was a diatomic molecule (Fig. 8-8).

8-8 Avogadro reasoned that if each particle of hydrogen and each particle of chlorine consisted of only one atom, two molecules of hydrogen chloride could not be formed when they combined.

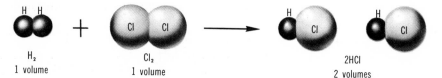

H_2	Cl_2	2HCl
1 volume	1 volume	2 volumes

If we assume that each molecule of hydrogen and of chlorine is diatomic, we can write the following equation:

$$H_2 \ + \ Cl_2 \longrightarrow 2\,HCl$$

1,000 molecules	1,000 molecules	2,000 molecules

Avogadro reasoned that the molecules of some gaseous elements were diatomic. Thus he explained how one volume of nitrogen reacts with three volumes of hydrogen to yield two volumes of ammonia:

$$N_2 \ + \ 3\,H_2 \longrightarrow 2\,NH_3$$

1 volume	3 volumes	2 volumes
1,000 molecules	3,000 molecules	2,000 molecules
2,000 atoms	6,000 atoms	8,000 atoms

Avogadro's Number

Since Avogadro's time, enough additional experimental evidence has been found to give his hypothesis the status of a law. Scientists have verified the diatomic nature of many gaseous elements (except the rare gases) and have determined the actual number of molecules that a given volume of a particular gas must contain. Today we know, for example, that 22.4 liters of any gas (measured at standard temperature and pressure*) contain 602,350,000,000,000,000,000,000 or 6.02×10^{23} molecules. This number is referred to as **Avogadro's number** in recognition of his work with gases. This number of molecules is also known as a *mole* of molecules.

A mole of diatomic oxygen molecules contains 6.02×10^{23} molecules and weighs 32 grams; a mole of monatomic helium molecules also contains 6.02×10^{23} molecules and weighs 4 grams; while a mole of HCl contains Avogadro's number of molecules and weighs 36.5 grams. *One mole or 1 gram molecular weight of any gaseous element or compound contains 6.02×10^{23} molecules and occupies 22.4 liters* (at standard conditions).

Since a volume of 22.4 liters (at standard conditions) contains a mole of gas molecules, it is sometimes called a **molar volume** of gas (Fig. 8-9). Molar volumes of nitrogen, hydrogen, and ammonia each occupy 22.4 liters. In terms of molar volumes (or moles) therefore, we may also write the previous equation as:

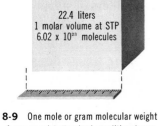

22.4 liters
1 molar volume at STP
6.02×10^{23} molecules

8-9 One mole or gram molecular weight of any gas (at standard conditions) contains 6.02×10^{23} molecules and occupies 22.4 liters, or 1 molar volume. This volume is a little less than 1 cubic foot.

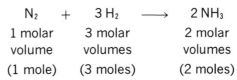

N_2	+	$3 H_2$	$\longrightarrow$	$2 NH_3$
1 molar volume		3 molar volumes		2 molar volumes
(1 mole)		(3 moles)		(2 moles)

Avogadro's Number—And a Mole

Gradually the number 6.02×10^{23} has taken on added significance. Originally the term *mole* meant the molecular weight of a compound expressed in grams. Soon it was found that 1 **GMW** of any molecular substance contained 6.02×10^{23} molecules. Today the term *mole* is used to mean *Avogadro's number of particles of any type.* Thus we speak of a mole of atoms or a mole of ions, as well as a mole of molecules.

A mole of oxygen atoms, for example, contains 6.02×10^{23} atoms, while a mole of oxygen molecules contains the same number of molecules. A gram formula weight of ionic NaCl contains 2 moles of ions: 1 mole of sodium ions and 1 mole of chloride ions. Similarly, 1 gram formula weight of ionic $Ca_3(PO_4)_2$ contains 5 moles of ions, 3 moles of calcium ions and 2 moles of phosphate ions. Indeed, a **GFW** of any ionic compound contains some whole-number multiple of 6.02×10^{23} ions.

*See page 149 for details of standard temperature and pressure, known as standard conditions.

1. (a) In terms of kinetic molecular theory and van der Waals forces, explain why the volume of a gas in a closed cylinder decreases with an increase in pressure (if the temperature remains constant). (b) What law expresses this relationship?
2. (a) In terms of kinetic molecular theory and van der Waals forces, explain why the volume of a gas in a closed cylinder decreases with a decrease in temperature (if the pressure remains constant). (b) What law expresses this relationship?
3. With reference to gaseous molecules, define straight-line motion and average kinetic energy.

4. 2 liters of hydrogen + 1 liter of oxygen $\longrightarrow$ 2 liters of steam

   Using this equation and Avogadro's Law, show that hydrogen and oxygen are composed of diatomic molecules.
5. (a) How many moles of atoms are present in 16 grams of oxygen atoms? (b) How many moles of molecules are present in 1 gram molecular weight of oxygen? (c) Why must 1 **GFW** of an ionic compound always contain 2 or more moles of ions?
6. (a) How many moles of gaseous carbon dioxide occupy 22.4 liters (at 0° C and normal atmospheric pressure)? How many molecules are present in (b) half a mole of CO_2? (c) a molar volume of CO_2?

THE NATURE OF LIQUIDS

Experience has taught you that gases and liquids bear a close relationship to each other. All liquids can be evaporated, some more easily than others. Ether and alcohol, for example, evaporate readily at room temperature; mineral oil and glycerine must be heated to bring about this change. In the vapor state, molecules of these substances resemble those in a gas. Conversely, all gases can be changed to liquids; for instance, water vapor in the air cools to form droplets of water on the outside of a cool glass. This process of changing a gas into a liquid by cooling is called **condensation**—water vapor, a gas, condenses to form water, a liquid.

Condensation

The way in which water vapor condenses can be explained by the kinetic molecular theory. When the temperature of a gas, such as water vapor, is lowered, the molecules move more slowly and the kinetic energy of the gas is reduced. The van der Waals forces between the molecules become effective, pulling the molecules closer together. And as the molecules draw near to one another, the attractive strength of the van der Waals forces becomes still more effective. Eventually, at reduced temperatures, the forces are strong enough to cause the molecules to cohere to one another and the gas is changed into a liquid.

Table 8-2 **CRITICAL TEMPERATURES OF GASES**

Gas	Formula	Critical temperature
Water vapor	H_2O	647° K
Hydrogen chloride	HCl	324° K
Hydrogen	H_2	35° K
Helium	He	5° K

But even after the change into a liquid, the molecules still retain a considerable amount of kinetic energy; therefore they are still free to slide and tumble over one another. But they are not so free that they fly apart in all directions as they did in the gaseous state. A liquid is formed when the van der Waals forces among molecules are strong enough to overcome the effects of kinetic energy. Increased pressure, by forcing the molecules of a gas closer together, also causes condensation. But every gas has a temperature, called the **critical temperature,** above which condensation due to pressure cannot occur. This critical temperature is different for each gas, and only when the gas is below this temperature is it possible to liquefy the gas solely by applying pressure (Table 8-2).

Evaporation

All liquids evaporate when left standing. The earth's water cycle depends upon the evaporation of water from the earth's surface. How does the kinetic molecular theory explain this process of evaporation? Molecules move at different speeds in a gas. The same is true of liquids. Since, however, the molecules in a liquid are much closer than those in a gas, they have a stronger mutual attraction and move more slowly. Yet some of the molecules in a liquid have much more kinetic energy than others and move faster than the rest. In a liquid there are always a few molecules which have enough energy to break bonds to adjacent molecules and to escape, or *evaporate,* from the surface of the liquid. As these more energetic molecules evaporate, the average kinetic energy of the remaining molecules is lowered. As a result, there is a drop in the liquid's temperature. Evaporation of a liquid is therefore a *cooling* process.

Suppose we cover the water in a beaker with a bell jar. The molecules evaporate from the surface of the water into the enclosed area above, and for a time, the level of the water in the beaker falls. Eventually the space above the water surface becomes saturated with vapor (no more can be absorbed) and the level of water in the beaker ceases to drop. This does not mean that evaporation has stopped. It is still going on, but water molecules are now returning to the liquid at the same rate as they are evaporating from it. When evaporation and condensation occur at the same rate, a **state of equilibrium** exists. At equilibrium the space above the liquid is saturated with vapor, and the rates of evaporation and condensation are equal.

Vapor Pressure

Place 20 ml of ethyl alcohol in one beaker and 20 ml of water in another beaker of the same size. Next, place a bell jar over each beaker, as shown at the left. (Keep the bell jars close to each other to insure that the temperatures of the liquids remain the same). Observe the level of the liquid in each beaker after several hours and again the next day. Were you surprised to find that more alcohol than water evaporated?

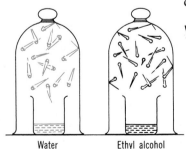

Water   Ethyl alcohol

To determine why this happens, consider that the molecules of vapor above each liquid have weight and thus exert pressure on the bell jar and on the liquid. The pressure exerted by the vapor—known as **vapor pressure**—increases as evaporation increases until at equilibrium each liquid has a specific equilibrium vapor pressure. At equilibrium, a volatile (easily vaporized) liquid such as alcohol has more particles of vapor in the enclosed area above it than a less volatile liquid such as water. Hence, a volatile liquid, in which the attractive forces between the molecules are relatively low, has a higher equilibrium vapor pressure at any given temperature than does a nonvolatile liquid. Returning to the investigation, we see that more molecules of alcohol than water escape and enter the enclosed area. Consequently, the level of liquid in the beaker of alcohol drops lower than the level of liquid in the beaker of water.

If the temperature of each liquid were increased, the space above it would contain even more particles of vapor. This indicates that the vapor pressure of a liquid increases with rising temperatures. A graph indicating the increasing vapor pressure of water and ethyl alcohol as temperatures change from 0° C to 100° C is shown in Fig. 8-10.

External Pressure and Boiling Point

If heat is applied to a container of pure water at sea level, the water boils at a temperature of 100° C. In Denver, Colorado, some 5,000 feet above sea level, the same pure water boils at a temperature of close to 94° C. Why? The **boiling point** of any liquid is that temperature at which the vapor pressure of the liquid is just equal to the atmospheric pressure. At sea level, the vapor pressure of water is equal to normal atmospheric pressure (760 mm) at 100° C—the normal boiling point of water. The atmospheric pressure at Denver is less than that at sea level since Denver is nearly a mile closer to the "top" of the atmosphere. The temperature at which the vapor pressure of water will equal the atmospheric pressure at Denver is therefore lower than it would be at sea level.

In contrast to the lower boiling point for water at Denver, consider the higher boiling point of water in a pressure cooker. In the latter, the steam that forms becomes trapped underneath the tightly sealed lid, causing the vapor pressure over the water to increase. The fact that food inside a pressure cooker cooks faster than normal indicates that the water, under increased pressure, is boiling at a temperature higher than normal. From repeated investigation, scientists have determined precisely how the boiling temperature of water changes with changes in the pressure above it. For example, when the pressure above water is lowered to 355 millimeters (mm), the water boils at 80° C. However, if the pressure above water is raised to 2,710 millimeters, the water boils at 140° C.

Hydrogen Bonding

By heating numerous other hydrogen compounds, it has been found that water, compared with these compounds, has an unusually high

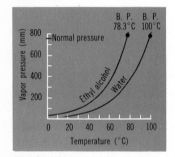

8-10 The vapor pressures of ethyl alcohol and water increase with an increase in temperature. The graph indicates that at any given temperature, ethyl alcohol has a higher equilibrium vapor pressure than water.

136 BEHAVIOR OF ATOMS

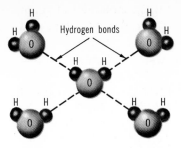

8-11 Each hydrogen atom in water is simultaneously attracted to the oxygen atoms of its own and another water molecule. These hydrogen bonds between oxygen atoms result in a giant water molecule.

boiling point. This property, and its low evaporation rate, occur because water molecules are more strongly attracted to one another than the molecules of most other liquids. Recall that water is a polar covalent molecule in which electrons are attracted more to the oxygen atom than to the hydrogen atoms. In fact, each hydrogen atom has such small attraction for the electron pair that the atom is almost like a proton without its surrounding electron. Such a proton can attract another atom. However, because of the proton's small size, it can attract only two atoms.

In water, a hydrogen atom is attracted simultaneously to the oxygen atom of the water molecule of which it is a part and to the oxygen atom of another water molecule. In effect, the hydrogen acts as a bridge between the two oxygen atoms of adjacent molecules. Such a bridge or attractive force is called a **hydrogen bond** (Fig. 8-11). As a result of this hydrogen bonding, water molecules group together or associate to form a cluster of water molecules. In the resulting giant molecule, each oxygen molecule is surrounded by four hydrogen atoms. In fact, some experimental evidence strongly indicates that a glassful of water is really one giant molecule whose formula might best be written as $(H_2O)_n$.

The force of the hydrogen bonds holding the molecules together is sufficiently strong so that a large amount of heat or kinetic energy is required to separate one molecule from the remainder of the liquid. It is this hydrogen bonding that accounts for the unexpectedly high boiling point of water. But water is not the only hydrogen compound that has an unusually high boiling point. Hydrogen fluoride has a much higher boiling point than the other halides (HCl, HBr, and HI). There is evidence that hydrogen bonds are formed between hydrogen and elements with high electronegativities, such as fluorine and nitrogen. In a molecule of hydrogen fluoride (HF), the highly electronegative fluorine atom strongly attracts the electron from the hydrogen atom. Each hydrogen atom is therefore able to bond to another fluorine atom or to form a strong hydrogen bond. These strong attractive forces result in the relatively high boiling point of hydrogen fluoride (Fig. 8-12).

Kinetic Theory and Boiling

While water or any liquid boils, the temperature remains constant. If you are skeptical, prove this for yourself by placing a thermometer in a small pan of water and observing the temperature as the water boils away. Visualize what happens to a liquid from the time it begins to be heated until it boils. As heat is absorbed by the molecules of a liquid, they gain more and more kinetic energy. Eventually the kinetic energy of these molecules is increased to such a point that the attractive forces between them are overcome. The now highly energetic molecules break away from each other, forming a gas, or vapor.

Once the liquid boils, the heat that is added causes more and more molecules to pull completely away from the liquid. The additional heat causes further vaporization, while the liquid that remains stays at a constant

8-12 Single molecules of hydrogen fluoride, HF, do not exist in the liquid phase. The high boiling point of HF results from long chains caused by the hydrogen bonding between molecules.

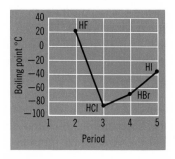

temperature. The amount of heat required to change a given amount of liquid to a gas without a change in temperature is its **heat of vaporization.** The heat of vaporization of water is 9,720 calories per mole. It is used largely to break the hydrogen bonds between water molecules.

QUESTIONS AND PROBLEMS

1. From the information in Fig. 8-10, determine: (a) the vapor pressure of water that is boiling at a temperature of 90° C, (b) the boiling point of water when the vapor pressure is 1,000 millimeters.
2. In terms of the kinetic molecular theory explain *evaporation, condensation,* and *heat of vaporization.*
3. Draw a diagram to show hydrogen bonding in hydrogen fluoride.

THE NATURE OF SOLIDS

We usually think of rock as a solid. Yet lava flows as a liquid rock. We think of the constituents of the atmosphere as gaseous. But dry ice is carbon dioxide in the solid state. According to the kinetic theory, the state, or phase, in which matter is found—whether gaseous, liquid, or solid—depends chiefly on the kinetic energy of its molecules.

The change that liquid matter undergoes to form a solid is called **freezing.** According to the kinetic molecular theory, a liquid freezes only after its particles have lost so much kinetic energy that they no longer have freedom of motion. Yet each particle of a solid, although not free to move about, is still free to vibrate about a fixed point. Because of this limited motion of their particles, solids are confined to definite shapes.

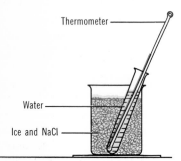

Thermometer

Water

Ice and NaCl

Freezing Point

Place a thermometer in a Pyrex test tube and add pure water until the test tube is three-fourths full. Immerse the test tube in a beaker containing ice and salt (NaCl). Observe the thermometer until ice just begins to form in the test tube, and record this temperature. Continue your observation; at first there is a mixture of ice and water, but eventually the water is frozen completely. Does the temperature remain at 0° C during this change?

In this process of removing heat from the particles of a liquid, the point at which the liquids begins to freeze is called the **freezing point.** The freezing point is the temperature at which liquid and solid exist in equilibrium with one another. At equilibrium, for each particle of liquid that freezes, a particle of solid melts and returns to the liquid state. Thus the freezing point of the liquid is also the **melting point** of the solid. The freezing point of water is 0° C at normal atmospheric pressure.

You might have varied the investigation by determining the melting point of ice. Here again the mixture of ice and water would have remained

8-13 This heating curve shows the energy changes necessary to change one mole of ice (18 grams) at −10°C to one mole of water vapor at 110°C.

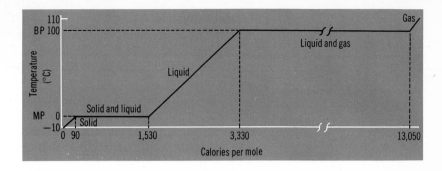

at 0° C until all the ice melted. The amount of heat required to change a given amount of solid to a liquid without a change in temperature is called **heat of fusion.** The heat of fusion of ice is 1440 calories per mole. How many calories of heat would be needed to melt 18 grams of ice?

Phase Changes in Crystalline Solids

Water forms the most common crystalline solid—ice. Yet, water does exist in three different states or phases: solid, liquid, and gas. If you heat an ice cube, the solid melts to the liquid phase. If you continue heating the liquid water, its temperature increases from 0° C to 100° C. If you continue the heating still further, the liquid boils away as it enters the gaseous phase. These changes and heat necessary to bring them about are summarized in the heating curve in Fig. 8-13.

Any pure crystalline solid displays the same behavior on being heated. The graph for each substance has two horizontal regions similar to those shown in this heating curve. The first of these indicates the melting of the solid as it forms the liquid phase. The second horizontal region indicates the boiling of the liquid as it forms the gaseous phase.

Structure of Solids

Although the particles of solids vibrate back and forth, they remain in a relatively fixed position. These relatively fixed particles may become arranged in definite patterns to form crystals. The particles in many common solids, such as ice, iron, salt (NaCl) and diamond, are always arranged as crystals. In a few solids, such as glass and some forms of sulfur, the particles do not always form definite patterns. Instead, in these substances the particles take on a random arrangement at times. Such noncrystalline substances are called **amorphous** solids.

The rigid arrangement of particles within a crystalline solid is called a **space lattice.** The space lattice of a sodium chloride crystal is shown in Fig. 8-16. The smallest portion of a space lattice that represents the recurring pattern of the entire crystal is called a **unit cell.** Observe the arrangement of sodium and chloride ions in a unit cell of sodium chloride in Fig. 8-14. In sodium chloride, as in all crystals, the unit cell structure is repeated over and over again in each crystal of the substance.

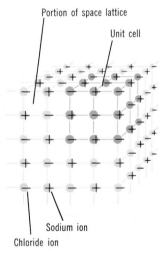

Portion of space lattice

Unit cell

Sodium ion

Chloride ion

8-14 The unit cell of sodium chloride is repeated again and again to form the space lattice of the salt crystal. The relative size and close arrangement of the sodium and chloride ions is shown in Figure 6-3.

THE KINETIC MOLECULAR THEORY   139

Cubic crystal   Tetragonal crystal

Orthorhombic crystal   Monoclinic crystal

Triclinic crystal   Hexagonal crystal

8-15 Six major types of crystals.

8-16 Packing in cubic crystals.

Simple cubic crystal

Body-centered cubic crystal

Face-centered cubic crystal

Types of Crystals

There are many types of crystals, depending on the way their particles are arranged or "packed" in the unit cell. On the basis of this particle arrangement, crystallographers classify crystals into six major types as shown in Fig. 8-15.

In turn, there are numerous variations in the way the particles can be arranged, or packed, in each of these major crystal types. Three different forms of "packing" of particles in **cubic crystals** are diagrammed in Fig. 8-16. Each dot in the unit cells shown represents a point, called a **lattice point,** at which a particle is located. Observe that in the **simple cubic crystal,** particles appear only at the corners of the unit cell while in the **body-centered cubic crystal** an additional particle appears in the center of the unit cell. In the **face-centered cubic crystal,** particles are located at points in the middle of each face as well as at the corners of the cube. This latter type of arrangement is known as close packing because each particle has the largest possible number of adjacent particles.

Three of the most frequently found crystal structures of interest to chemists are **body-centered cubic packing, face-centered cubic close packing,** and **hexagonal close packing.** In the latter, the particles are arranged at the points of a hexagonal crystal so that each particle has the largest possible number of near neighbors (Fig. 8-17). The two close-packing arrangements are usually found in metals. Crystals of magnesium and beryllium are hexagonally close-packed while those of copper, silver, and gold are face-centered cubic close-packed. The third common type of packing, body-centered cubic packing, is found in some alkali metals, such as sodium. Some metals, such as iron and calcium, exist in different packing arrangements at different temperature ranges. At present no method has been developed for predicting the crystal structure of a metal; it must be determined by experimentation.

Particles in Solids

Solids can also be classified on the basis of the type of particle that occupies the points of the space lattice. In sodium chloride the lattice points are occupied by positive and negative ions. For this reason we classify sodium chloride as an **ionic solid.** Ionic solids are hard and brittle. Since it takes a great deal of energy to overcome the attraction between the positive and negative ions, ionic solids will melt only at fairly high temperatures. (See Table 8-3.)

In **metallic solids,** such as solid sodium and copper, the points of each space lattice are occupied by positive ions which are immersed in a cloud of valence electrons. The attractive force between the positive ions and the cloud of electrons holds the metal together. As we saw on page 111, the fact that these electrons are so free to move makes metals good conductors of electricity.

In a few solids, such as diamond, the lattice points are occupied by atoms or a complex arrangement of atoms covalently bonded together.

Close-packed hexagonal crystal

8-17 This packing arrangement gives each particle in a hexagonal crystal the largest possible number of other particles as "near neighbors."

Table 8-3 **CLASSIFICATION OF SOLIDS**

Type of solid	Unit at lattice point	Properties	Examples
Ionic	Negative and positive ions	Hard, brittle, fairly high melting point	NaCl
Metallic	Positive ions in cloud of electrons	Good conductors, hard or soft	Cu, Ag
Network	Atoms in complex arrangements	Hard, very high melting point	Diamond
Molecular	Molecules	Soft, very low melting point	Ice, Dry ice

Because of this covalent bonding these **network** or macromolecular solids, as they are called, are very hard and melt only at extremely high temperatures. *Much more energy is required to break bonds between atoms in a molecule than to break bonds between molecules.*

The points in the space lattices of certain other solids are occupied by molecules. Ice is an example of such a **molecular solid.** Like all molecular solids, ice is relatively soft and has a relatively low melting point. This results because bonds between molecules are relatively weak.

The Structure of Ice

When most liquids cool and solidify, their volumes become smaller. For example, molten iron in a container contracts and pulls away from the sides of the container as the iron turns to a solid. Water, however, behaves in a special manner. It contracts until it reaches a temperature of 3.98° C; below this point it begins to expand. As the water turns to ice, there is a considerable increase in volume.

Observe the space lattice of ice diagrammed in Fig. 8-18. Any four oxygen atoms form a regular tetrahedron or pyramid structure. Also, as a result of hydrogen bonding each oxygen atom has attached to it four hydrogen atoms. Each set of six oxygen atoms with the hydrogen atoms surrounding them forms a rigid six-sided or honeycomblike opening. Because of these openings, ice takes up more volume than the corresponding water from which it forms. When ice melts the particles composing it begin to move faster, filling the openings in the honeycomb. Consequently, the water that forms occupies less space than the ice. As the ice turns to water, its rigid crystal structure collapses.

Sublimation

Moth balls, made of naphthalene or paradichlorobenzene, and dry ice appear to evaporate, or vaporize, without first turning into a liquid. As with liquids and gases, some of the particles in such a solid are more energetic than others. Those particles with higher kinetic energies break away from the others and escape from the surface of the solid to form a

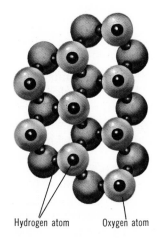

Hydrogen atom   Oxygen atom

8-18 Each set of six water molecules, associated by hydrogen bonding, form a rigid, six-sided opening at freezing temperatures. Because of these openings, ice occupies more space than the water from which it forms.

THE KINETIC MOLECULAR THEORY   141

gas. This process by which a solid changes directly into a gas is called **sublimation.**

In solids that sublime, the intermolecular or attractive forces are usually low and the tendency for molecules to escape, or vaporize, is fairly high. The odor of moth balls is evidence that vapors are given off by the naphthalene or paradichlorobenzene crystals at room temperature. Solids, therefore, as well as liquids, exhibit vapor pressure; and for solids that sublime the vapor pressures are fairly high. Similarly, dry ice and other solids that undergo sublimation have relatively low intermolecular forces and relatively high vapor pressures.

Clearly, solids can become liquids and liquids can change into gases. It is just as certain that this change of state can be reversed and gases can become liquids, and liquids can become solids. But does a change of state, say from ice to water and from water to gas, mean that mass is lost and energy is gained in any particular reaction—or vice versa? Both chemists and physicists have sought an answer to this question. In the next chapter, we too shall seek an answer.

QUESTIONS AND PROBLEMS

1. Differentiate between the terms in each of the following pairs:
   (a) *amorphous solid* and *crystalline solid*
   (b) *freezing point* and *melting point*
   (c) *space lattice* and *unit cell*
   (d) *heat of vaporization* and *heat of fusion*
2. Describe the types of particles occurring at the lattice points of each of the four types of crystalline solids. Give several examples of each type of crystal.
3. By means of diagrams, show the differences among crystals with body-centered cubic packing, face-centered cubic close packing, and hexagonal close packing.
4. After a snowstorm, why does some snow disappear by sublimation?

VALUE OF THE CONCEPT

THE CONCEPT

Three important laws describing the physical properties of gases are those of Boyle, Charles, and Gay-Lussac. Boyle's Law states that the volume of a confined gas varies inversely with the pressure, provided the temperature remains constant. Charles' Law states that the volume of a gas varies directly with the absolute temperature, provided the pressure remains constant. Gay-Lussac's Law states that the pressure exerted by a gas varies directly with its absolute temperature, provided the volume of the gas remains constant.

A most important law describing the chemical combinations of gases is Gay-Lussac's Law of Combining Volumes. This law states that gases combine in ratios of small whole numbers by volume. An outgrowth of Gay-Lussac's Law and the other gas laws is Avogadro's Law which states that equal volumes of all gases, under the same conditions of temperature and pressure, contain the same number of molecules. This law led to the understanding that molecules of gaseous elements are diatomic. More recently it has led to the understanding that 1 mole of any gas contains 6.02×10^{23} molecules and occupies a volume of 22.4 liters (at $0°$ C and normal atmospheric pressure).

Two essential postulates of the kinetic molecular theory, developed from an understanding of the gas laws, are that molecules of all matter are in continuous motion and that an increase in temperature increases the molecular movement and hence the kinetic energy of a substance. In gases the molecules themselves occupy very little of the total volume. Since gaseous particles are far apart, they have virtually no attraction for each other. When gases are cooled the molecules move less rapidly; and when gases are compressed the molecules move together. In either instance, the intermolecular, or van der Waals, forces begin to overcome the kinetic energy of the molecules. Eventually, upon continued cooling and compressing, gases become liquids by condensation. The molecules in liquids still retain a considerable amount of kinetic energy, leaving them free to slide and tumble over one another. Further cooling causes liquids to change (freeze) into solids. The molecules in solids contain relatively little kinetic energy, and each individual particle is free only to vibrate about a fixed point.

Particles within solids are often arranged in rigid geometric patterns to form crystals. The rigid arrangement of particles within a crystalline solid forms a space lattice; the smallest portion of a space lattice which represents the recurring pattern of the entire crystal is a unit cell. The points in space lattices of crystals can be occupied by ions, atoms, complex arrangements of atoms, or molecules. Crystals are classified by the shapes that result from the positions of the particles within space lattices. Three of the most frequently found crystal structures which are of interest to chemists are body-centered cubic packing, face-centered cubic close packing, and hexagonal close packing.

In terms of the kinetic theory, evaporation is the escape from liquids of molecules having high kinetic energies. When condensation and evaporation are in equilibrium in a liquid, the pressure exerted by the vapor above the liquid reaches an equilibrium vapor pressure characteristic of the liquid at a definite temperature. Liquids boil when their vapor pressures are just equal to the atmospheric pressure above them.

Some solids in which intermolecular forces are low change directly to gases, or sublime. In water, and in some other hydrogen compounds, the weak intermolecular forces manifest themselves as hydrogen bonds.

USING THE CONCEPT

Using the Basic Concept

1. Describe each of the following laws: Boyle's Law, Charles' Law, Gay-Lussac's Law relating the pressure and temperature of gases.
2. State (a) Gay-Lussac's Law of Combining Volumes, (b) Avogadro's Law.
3. (a) What are the two main postulates of the kinetic molecular theory? (b) What assumptions about the nature of gases are contained in the kinetic molecular theory?
4. Use the kinetic molecular theory to explain Boyle's Law and Charles' Law.
5. Use the kinetic molecular theory to differentiate among the solid, liquid, and gaseous states, or phases, of matter.
6. (a) What are van der Waals forces? (b) In what states of matter are they effective?
7. What relationship exists among 1 mole, 1 molar volume, and 1 gram molecular weight of gaseous CO_2? Explain.
8. Explain why 22.4 liters of hydrogen, helium, and ammonia each contain the same number of molecules but a different number of atoms.
9. Differentiate between (a) heat of vaporization and heat of fusion, (b) condensation and evaporation.

10. Why does water expand as it freezes?
11. Define the following terms: *melting point, freezing point, amorphous solid, crystal, space lattice, unit cell, lattice points, cubic crystal, hexagonal crystal.*
12. (a) What is meant by the packing of particles within a crystal? (b) How does a body-centered cubic crystal differ from a face-centered cubic crystal? (c) What is especially significant about a hexagonal close-packed crystal?
13. Describe the differences in properties between solids of ionic crystals and solids of molecular crystals.

Relating Terms Within the Concept
Select the letter of the term in Column B that is most closely related to each term in Column A. *Do not use a term more than once.*

COLUMN A	COLUMN B
1. Celsius	a. arrangement of particles within crystals
2. kinetic molecular theory	
3. van der Waals forces	b. Avogadro's number
	c. explains chemical behavior of matter
4. vapor pressure	d. explains physical behavior of matter
5. amorphous solid	
6. space lattice	e. Gay-Lussac's Law of Combining Volumes
7. sublimation	
8. hydrogen bonding	
9. 22.4 liters	f. giant molecules of water
10. evaporation	g. intermolecular attraction
11. 6.02×10^{23}	
12. face-centered	h. largest number of adjacent particles
	i. molecules of vapor above a liquid
	j. noncrystalline
	k. 1 mole of any gas
	l. reverse of condensation
	m. solid changes directly to a gas
	n. temperature scale

Solving Problems Within the Concept
1. How many volumes of nitrogen dioxide are produced when two volumes of nitric oxide (NO) combine with one volume of oxygen?
2. At normal atmospheric pressure, how many liters does each of the following occupy: (a) 1 mole of N_2, (b) 0.5 mole of NH_3?
3. How many molecules does each of the following contain: (a) 1 mole of Cl_2, (b) 0.5 mole of N_2O_5, (c) 3 moles of F_2, (d) 5 moles of HBr?
4. (a) How many moles of atoms are present in 1 gram atomic weight of fluorine? (b) How many moles of molecules are present in 2 gram molecular weights of fluorine? (c) How many moles of sodium carbonate are present in 1 gram formula weight of Na_2CO_3? (d) how many moles of ions?
5. A gas occupies 11.2 liters (at $0°$ C and normal atmospheric pressure). (a) How many molecules does it contain? (b) If the gas weighs 10 grams, what is its gram molecular weight?
6. 22.4 liters of oxygen combine with 22.4 liters of nitrogen to produce nitric oxide (NO). (a) How many liters of NO are produced? (b) How many molecules of each gas take part in the reaction? (c) how many moles?
7. How many calories are required to (a) melt 25 grams of ice at $0°$ C? (b) change 25 grams of water at $100°$ C to steam? (c) In terms of the kinetic molecular theory, account for the large difference in the two numerical values you have determined.

Applying the Concept
1. Why does boiling usually begin at the bottom of a liquid while evaporation occurs only at the surface?
2. Compare the electronegativities of oxygen and sulfur. Then in terms of hydro-

gen bonds explain why you would expect H_2S to have a lower boiling point than H_2O.

3. Are boiling and freezing physical changes or chemical changes? Explain.

4. Which would be more easily liquefied, a gas with a high critical temperature or a gas with a low critical temperature? Explain your answer.

5. One mole of hydrogen reacts with 1 mole of bromine gas to form 2 moles of hydrogen bromide. Show from this data that each bromine molecule is diatomic.

6. What assumption must be made before evaporation can be explained by the kinetic molecular theory?

7. Describe experimentally how equilibrium can be reached between evaporation and condensation.

8. Devise an investigation to demonstrate (a) how the vapor pressure of a liquid is affected by an increase in temperature, (b) how the boiling point of a liquid is affected by an increase in the pressure above the liquid.

9. What evidence do you have that the hydrogen bonds holding water molecules together are weaker than the covalent bonds between the atoms within each molecule of water?

Reading Further

Chemical Systems, by Chemical Bond Approach Project, New York, Webster McGraw-Hill, 1964. Chapters 11 and 12 give a detailed account of crystal structure, the packing of crystals, and the relationship of crystal structure to the behavior of metals.

Moments of Discovery, 2 vols., by George Schwartz and P. W. Bishop, New York, Basic Books, 1958. The three chapters on Boyle, Gay-Lussac, and Avogadro present these scientists' accounts of their developing knowledge of the properties of gases.

9

SKILLS—The Gas Laws

At the beginning of the last chapter, you were introduced to the gas laws—Boyle's Law, Charles' Law, and Gay-Lussac's Law. These laws which describe the relationships among the pressure, temperature, and volume of gases have many applications. For example, they have to be considered in designing internal combustion engines for automobiles. In this skills chapter, you will learn to solve numerical problems related to these laws. In addition, you will learn to determine the molecular weight of any gas.

BOYLE'S LAW

Boyle, you remember, found that the volume of a confined gas varies inversely with pressure, provided the temperature remains constant. Since Boyle's time, it has become customary in measuring air pressure to take the pressure at sea level as standard. This pressure is 14.7 lb/sq in—or a pressure that supports a column of mercury 760 mm high. A figure below 760 mm shows that the air pressure is below standard; a figure higher than 760 mm indicates a pressure above standard. Today gas pressure is usually expressed in millimeters of mercury, or in Torr (pg. 126), rather than in pounds per square inch. A pressure of 760 mm, or 760 Torr, is known as **standard pressure.**

In the problems that follow, it is assumed that the gas is confined in a cylinder with a movable piston that varies the pressure on the gas.

Suppose a liter of gas (1,000 ml) is measured at a pressure of 760 mm. If the pressure is doubled to 1,520 mm, the temperature of the gas

remaining constant, the volume of the gas becomes one-half of a liter (500 ml). If the pressure is tripled to 2,280 mm, the new volume is one-third of a liter. On the other hand, if the original pressure is reduced by one-half—to 380 mm—the volume becomes 2 liters, or double the original volume. This data is summarized in Table 9-1. Here the symbol P_0 represents the *original* pressure of 760 mm, while V_0 represents the *original* volume of one liter (1,000 ml). The new pressures are represented by P_1, P_2, and P_3: 1,520 mm, 2,280 mm, and 380 mm, respectively. Similarly V_1, V_2, and V_3 represent the corresponding new volumes: 500 ml, $333\frac{1}{3}$ ml, and 2,000 ml, respectively.

Observe in Table 9-1 that each of these pressures multiplied by its corresponding volume $(P \times V)$ gives the same numerical value: 760,000.

Table 9-1   BOYLE'S LAW

Pressure (P) (mm)	×	Volume (V) (ml)	=	Constant (P × V)
P_0 760	×	V_0 1,000	=	760,000
P_1 1,520	×	V_1 500	=	760,000
P_2 2,280	×	V_2 $333\frac{1}{3}$	=	760,000
P_3 380	×	V_3 2,000	=	760,000

Since the product of pressure times volume remains constant (760,000), any one pressure times its corresponding volume must be equal to any other pressure times *its* corresponding volume. This fact can be expressed in the following way:

$$P_0 \times V_0 = P_1 \times V_1 = P_2 \times V_2 = P_3 \times V_3 = P_n \times V_n$$

The subscript n in P_n and V_n in the above mathematical equation represents any new set of conditions of pressure and volume; that is, the same pressure-volume relationship applies for any figures we might choose. Since both $P_0 \times V_0$ and $P_n \times V_n$ equal the same constant—760,000 —they are equal to each other:

$$P_0 \times V_0 = P_n \times V_n$$

If any three of the four values in this equation are known, it is possible to determine the fourth.

A useful variation of the basic equation for Boyle's Law can be obtained by solving the equation to obtain a value for V_n:

$$V_n = V_o \times \frac{P_o}{P_n}$$

This equation gives a convenient way of solving for an unknown volume (V_n) when the original volume (V_o), the original pressure (P_o), and the final pressure (P_n) are known. If the new pressure is greater than the original pressure, then P_o/P_n will be less than 1, and the new volume will be smaller than the original volume. If the new pressure is less than the original pressure, then P_o/P_n will be more than 1, and the new volume will be greater than the original volume.

To understand the numerical application of Boyle's Law, consider the problem below.

A gas has an original volume of 330 ml measured at standard pressure. What volume will the gas occupy when the pressure is reduced to 660 mm, the temperature remaining constant?

The new pressure (660 mm) is less than the original (or standard) pressure (760 mm). This means that P_o/P_n is greater than 1. Hence the new volume must be greater than the original volume of 330 ml. To obtain this new volume we multiply 330 ml by 760 mm/660 mm:

$$V_o \times \frac{P_o}{P_n} = V_n$$

$$330 \text{ ml} \times \frac{760 \text{ mm}}{660 \text{ mm}} = 380 \text{ ml (answer)}$$

Consider now the reverse situation in which pressure is increased. The original volume of a gas, measured at 700 mm, is 1,200 ml. If we change the pressure to 800 mm, what volume does the gas occupy (temperature is constant)?

Since the new pressure (800 mm) is greater than the original pressure (700 mm), P_o/P_n will be less than 1. Hence, the new volume will be less than 1,200 ml. To obtain this new volume multiply 1,200 ml by 700 mm/800 mm:

$$1{,}200 \text{ ml} \times \frac{700 \text{ mm}}{800 \text{ mm}} = 1{,}050 \text{ ml (answer)}$$

PROBLEM

The original volume of a gas, measured at 800 mm pressure, is 500 ml. At constant temperature, what volume will the gas occupy if the pressure is changed to each of the following new pressures: (a) 400 mm, (b) 1,200 mm, (c) 640 Torr, (d) standard pressure?

KELVIN OR ABSOLUTE TEMPERATURE SCALE

In the previous chapter you learned that Charles determined that at $-273°$ C the volume of a gas theoretically becomes zero. Though gases liquefy above this temperature, observations seem to indicate that $-273°$ C is the lowest temperature that can exist. For this reason $-273°$ is called **absolute zero.**

Sir William Thompson (Lord Kelvin), a British scientist, used the idea of absolute zero to develop a temperature scale which we call by his name today. Each degree on the Kelvin scale (° K), which is also known as the absolute temperature scale (A), is equal to one degree Celsius. But since 0° K is equal to $-273°$ C, there are no negative temperatures on the Kelvin, or absolute, scale.

To convert ° C to ° K, simply add 273° to the number of degrees on the Celsius scale. For example, 40° C equals 313° K.

$$° K = ° C + 273°$$
$$313° K = 40° + 273°$$

To convert ° K to ° C, subtract 273° from the number on the Kelvin scale; thus, 323° K equals 50° C.

$$° C = ° K - 273°$$
$$50° C = 323° - 273°$$

PROBLEMS

1. Convert 10° C and $-40°$ C to degrees Kelvin (Absolute).

2. Convert 163° K and 305° K to degrees Celsius.

CHARLES' LAW

The Kelvin scale makes possible our previous statement of Charles' Law: the volume of a gas varies directly with the absolute temperature provided pressure remains constant. Suppose that a gas occupies a volume of 1 liter at 273° K. According to Charles, if the pressure on the gas remains constant, this same gas occupies a volume of one-half liter when the temperature is reduced by one-half to 136.5° K, and one-third liter when the temperature is reduced by two-thirds (91° K). If the absolute temperature is doubled to 540° K, the volume of the gas is also doubled—to 2 liters.

This data is summarized in Table 9-2. Here the symbol V_0 represents the *original* volume of 1,000 ml (1 liter), while the symbol T_0 represents the *original* temperature of 273° C. Similarly, V_1, V_2, and V_3 stand for new volumes; and T_1, T_2, and T_3 for the corresponding new temperatures.

Observe in this table that each volume divided by its corresponding absolute temperature (V_0/T_0) equals the same numerical value, 3.66.

Table 9-2   CHARLES' LAW

Volume (V) (ml)	÷	Temperature (T) (°K)	=	Constant $\left(\dfrac{V}{T}\right)$
V_0 1,000	÷	T_0 273	=	3.66
V_1 500	÷	T_1 136.5	=	3.66
V_2 $333\frac{1}{3}$	÷	T_2 91	=	3.66
V_3 2,000	÷	T_3 546	=	3.66

Since any one volume divided by its absolute temperature is equal to any other volume divided by *its* absolute temperature, we can write the following equation:

$$\frac{V_0}{T_0} = \frac{V_1}{T_1} = \frac{V_2}{T_2} = \frac{V_3}{T_3} = \frac{V_n}{T_n}$$

Here V_n and T_n represent any new set of conditions for volume and absolute temperature.

Compare the result of dividing the original volume (V_0) by the original absolute temperature

(T_0) with the result of dividing V_n by T_n. Since both V_0/T_0 and V_n/T_n equal the same constant, they must be equal to each other. We note this relationship in the following way:

$$\frac{V_0}{T_0} = \frac{V_n}{T_n}$$

If the numerical values for any three of the above symbols are known, the numerical value of the fourth can be found.

We can vary the form of the basic equation for Charles' Law by solving to obtain a value for V_n:

$$V_n = V_0 \times \frac{T_n}{T_0}$$

This new equation gives us a direct means of finding the unknown volume (V_n) of the gas under the new conditions of temperature (T_n) provided the original volume and temperature are known. To find the new volume we multiply the original volume (V_0) by the ratio of the new absolute temperature to the original absolute temperature (T_n/T_0). If the new absolute temperature is greater than the original one, then T_n/T_0 will be more than 1, and the new volume will be greater than the original volume. If the new absolute temperature is less than the original, T_n/T_0 will be less than 1, and the new volume will be less than the original volume.

To understand the numerical application of Charles' Law, consider these problems. In doing so, you should know that 0° C (273° K), the normal freezing point of pure water, is referred to as **standard temperature.**

A gas has an original volume of 546 ml measured at 0° C. If the pressure is unchanged, what volume will the gas occupy when it is heated to 30° C? First, change the temperatures to ° K:

T_0 is 0° C or (0 + 273) = 273° K
T_n is 30° C or (30 + 273) = 303° K

Because the new temperature (303° K) is greater than the original (273° K), T_n/T_0 will be greater than 1. The original volume (V_0 = 546 ml) is multiplied by the fraction 303° K/273° K:

$$V_0 \times \frac{T_n}{T_0} = V_n$$

$$546 \text{ ml} \times \frac{303° \text{ K}}{273° \text{ K}} = 606 \text{ ml (answer)}$$

Consider now the reverse situation in which temperature is decreased. The original volume of a gas, measured at 27° C, is 900 ml. The temperature is changed to 10° C. If the pressure remains unchanged, what volume does the gas occupy?

The new temperature (283° K) being less than the old (300° K), T_n/T_0 will be less than 1. The original volume (900 ml) is therefore multiplied by 283° K/300° K:

$$900 \text{ ml} \times \frac{283° \text{ K}}{300° \text{ K}} = 849 \text{ ml (answer)}$$

PROBLEM

The original volume of a gas measured at standard temperature is 1,000 ml. If the pressure remains unchanged, what volume will the gas occupy at each of the following temperatures: (a) −20° C, (b) 30° C, (c) 273° C, and (d) 500° K?

GAY-LUSSAC'S LAW

According to Gay-Lussac's Law relating temperature and pressure, if the original absolute temperature of a volume of gas is doubled, then the pressure exerted by the gas on the walls of its container will also be doubled. If the original absolute temperature is halved, then the pressure exerted by the gas will likewise be reduced by half. The following equation is one way of expressing the relationship just described:

$$\frac{P_0}{P_n} = \frac{T_0}{T_n}$$

P_0 represents the original pressure, P_n the new pressure, T_0 the original absolute temperature, and T_n the new absolute temperature. If P_0, T_0, and T_n are known, P_n can be determined readily by using the following form of the above equation:

$$P_n = P_0 \times \frac{T_n}{T_0}$$

PROBLEM

A cubic foot of gas at 300° K exerts a pressure of 20 pounds per square inch on the walls of a container. What pressure will the gas exert when the temperature (a) increases to 400° K, (b) decreases to 250° K, (c) changes to 27° C, (d) changes to −73° C?

COMBINED GAS LAW

To determine what happens to gases when both temperature and pressure changes occur, we could use Boyle's and Charles' Laws independently. First we could determine the new volume resulting from a change in pressure only; then we could determine the effect of a temperature change on this new volume. In practice, such problems are solved by using a single equation representing a combination of Boyle's Law and Charles' Law.

The combination of the two laws is often referred to as the **combined gas law.** To determine an equation for the combined gas law, combine the equations for Boyle's Law and Charles' Law in the following manner:

(Boyle's Law) $\qquad V_n = V_0 \times \dfrac{P_0}{P_n}$

(Charles' Law) $\qquad V_n = V_0 \times \dfrac{T_n}{T_0}$

(Combined gas law) $\qquad V_n = V_0 \times \dfrac{P_0}{P_n} \times \dfrac{T_n}{T_0}$

Now see how this equation is applied by following the solution of the problem below.

During an experiment, 600 ml of carbon dioxide gas are collected at a temperature of 18° C and a pressure of 730 mm. What volume will the gas occupy at standard temperature and pressure (known as standard conditions and abbreviated **STP**)?

First, organize the given data as follows:

$V_0 = 600$ ml
$V_n =$ unknown
$T_0 = 18°$ C
$T_n = 0°$ C (standard temperature)
$P_0 = 730$ mm
$P_n = 760$ mm (standard pressure)

By changing the given temperatures to ° K, you find that:

T_0 is 18° C or (18 + 273) = 291° K
T_n is 0° C or (0 + 273) = 273° K

There is a decrease in temperature from 291° K to 273° K which causes a decrease in volume. At the same time, an increase in pressure from 730 mm to 760 mm causes a further decrease in volume. Therefore both fractions—P_0/P_n and T_n/T_0—will be less than 1. Did you predict that the changes in both temperature and pressure would produce a decrease in the volume of the gas?

Substituting numbers for the symbols in the combined gas law equation:

$$V_n = V_0 \times \frac{P_0}{P_n} \times \frac{T_n}{T_0}$$

$$V_n = 600 \text{ ml} \times \frac{730 \text{ mm}}{760 \text{ mm}} \times \frac{273° \text{ K}}{291° \text{ K}}$$

$$V_n = 540.7 \text{ ml}$$

To check your understanding of the use of the combined gas law equation, study the sample problem at the right.

SAMPLE GAS LAW PROBLEM

Problem

200 ml of hydrogen are collected at 800 mm pressure and 0° C. What volume will the hydrogen occupy at 760 mm pressure and 27° C?

Procedure

1. Change the temperatures to the Kelvin scale.
2. Correct for the change in pressure. If the pressure decreases, P_0/P_n will be more than 1; if the pressure increases, P_0/P_n will be less than 1.
3. Correct for the change in temperature. If the temperature decreases, T_n/T_0 will be less than 1; if the temperature increases, T_n/T_0 will be more than 1.
4. Substitute the appropriate values in the combined gas law equation and solve for V_n.

Solution

$$0° \text{ C} + 273° = 273° \text{ K}$$
$$27° \text{ C} + 273° = 300° \text{ K}$$
$$V_n = 200 \text{ ml} \times \frac{800 \text{ mm}}{760 \text{ mm}} \times \frac{300° \text{ K}}{273° \text{ K}}$$
$$V_n = 231.3 \text{ ml}$$

PROBLEMS

1. A 1,200-ml volume of nitrogen is collected at 819 mm pressure and 0° C. What volume will this nitrogen occupy when its temperature rises to 20° C and the pressure increases to 879 mm?

2. During an experiment 546 ml of oxygen gas were collected at **STP** (standard temperature and pressure). What volume will the gas occupy at a temperature of −5° C and a pressure of 536 mm?

MOLECULAR WEIGHTS OF GASES

How can the molecular weight of a gas such as oxygen be determined experimentally? If you collect exactly 22.4 liters (*l*) of oxygen and weigh the gas at **STP**, it weighs 32 grams. Since 1 mole of any gas occupies 22.4 *l* (under standard conditions), the weight in grams of 22.4 *l* of a gaseous element or compound is equal to its gram molecular weight.

But it is unnecessary to collect exactly 22.4 *l* to determine the molecular weight of a gas. Suppose an investigation indicates that under standard conditions the weight of 1 liter of oxygen gas is 1.43 grams. If 1 liter of oxygen gas weighs 1.43 grams, 22.4 l (1 molar volume) of the gas will weigh 32 grams:

$$1.43 \text{ grams}/l \times 22.4 \ l = 32 \text{ grams}$$

Since gram molecular weight and molecular weight are numerically equal, drop the grams unit to obtain the molecular weight of the gas. The molecular weight of oxygen is 32.

From the results of similar investigations, the following formula for determining the molecular weight of any gas has been developed:

$$\frac{\text{weight of gas in grams}}{\text{volume of gas in liters}} \times 22.4 \ l =$$

$$\text{molecular weight of gas}$$

Now use this formula to determine the molecular weight of methane.

The weight of 100 ml of methane gas (at **STP**) has been determined experimentally to be 0.0717 grams. In substituting in the formula, remember that since 1 liter contains 1,000 ml, 100 ml is equal to 0.1 liter. Therefore:

$$\frac{0.0717 \text{ gram}}{0.1 \ l} \times 22.4 \ l = \frac{1.60608}{0.1}$$

$$= 16 \text{ grams}$$

The **GMW** of methane is 16 grams; its molecular weight therefore is 16.

How would you find the molecular weight of methane if its density were given? Density is defined as weight (mass) per unit volume, and the density of methane is 0.717 gram/l. Consequently, the calculation is essentially the same as that above:

$$0.717 \text{ gram}/l \times 22.4 \ l = 16 \text{ grams}$$

And the molecular weight of methane, as determined previously, is 16.

PROBLEMS

1. If 250 ml of sulfur trioxide (**STP**) weigh 0.893 gram, what is the molecular weight of SO_3?

2. The density of carbon dioxide gas (**STP**) is 0.196 gram/100 ml. Determine its molecular weight.

ADDITIONAL PROBLEMS

1. Convert $-30°$ C and $121°$ C to degrees Kelvin (Absolute).

2. Convert $298°$ K and $183°$ K to degrees Celsius.

3. The original volume of a gas measured at 200 mm pressure is 600 ml. If the temperature remains unchanged, what volume will the gas occupy if the pressure is changed to (a) 500 mm, (b) 100 mm, (c) standard pressure?

4. A gas has a volume of 120 ml at 80 mm pressure. What pressure is required to (a) reduce the volume to 30 ml, (b) increase the volume to 200 ml (at constant temperature)?

5. The original volume of a gas, measured at $0°$ C, is 800 ml. If the pressure remains unchanged, what volume will the gas occupy at (a) $-10°$ C, (b) $20°$ C, (c) $200°$ K?

6. The pressure on 1 liter of a confined gas is changed from standard pressure to a pressure of 380 mm. (a) What volume does the gas now occupy? (b) What would the new volume be if the pressure had been changed to 1,520 mm? (Assume no change in temperature.)

7. The temperature of 500 ml of a confined gas is changed from standard temperature to $273°$ C. (a) What volume does the gas now occupy? (b) What would the new volume be if the gas were now cooled to $100°$ C? (Assume no change in pressure.)

8. A gas has a volume of 546 ml at $0°$ C. What temperature is required to (a) reduce the volume to 364 ml, (b) increase the volume to 819 ml?

9. One liter of oxygen is collected at standard conditions. The temperature of the gas is then raised to 409.5° C. Under what pressure will the gas be at this temperature?

10. A cubic foot of gas at 400° K exerts a pressure of 25 pounds per square inch on the walls of a container. What pressure will the gas exert (**STP**) when the temperature (a) increases to 500° K, (b) decreases to 200° K?

11. During an investigation, 22.4 liters of oxygen gas are collected at a temperature of 20° C and a pressure of 750 Torr. What volume will the gas occupy at standard temperature and pressure?

12. If 200 ml of a gas at 27° C and normal pressure are warmed to 327° C, what pressure on the gas will maintain the original volume?

13. A 1,500-ml volume of gas is collected at 283 Torr pressure and 10° C. What volume will this gas occupy when its temperature is changed to 30° C and its pressure to 849 Torr?

14. During an investigation, 1,000 ml of hydrogen were collected at **STP**. What volume will the gas occupy at a temperature of −10° C and a pressure of 500 Torr?

15. If 200 ml of acetylene weigh 0.232 gram, what is the molecular weight of the gas (**STP**)?

16. The density of hydrogen sulfide is 1.539 grams per liter (**STP**). Determine its molecular weight.

17. The molecular weight of ethane is 30. How many liters will 40 grams of the gas occupy at **STP?**

10

The Theory of
Chemical Action

Though we occasionally still hear tragic news of coal mine explosions, early miners were indebted to Sir Humphry Davy for his invention of the safety lamp, which considerably reduced the hazards of their job. The gas that collects in coal mines is highly flammable, and the heat from a single match may cause an explosion. And just as the gas in a mine does not explode until heat is applied, so too, hydrogen and oxygen do not react to form water until heated. If you fill a container two-thirds full with hydrogen and one-third full with oxygen, the two gases merely mix; they do not combine as you might have expected. Only when the mixture is ignited by a flame or spark is there an explosive reaction; then the two gases unite with each other to form water. Similarly, wood, coal, and natural gas are useful fuels. But they will not burn until they are heated to their kindling temperatures in the presence of air.

Why is heat necessary to cause these chemical changes? The answer involves the kinetic molecular theory. In light of that theory, we shall take a closer look to see what actually happens when a chemical reaction takes place.

CONSERVING MASS AND ENERGY

In studying chemical reactions it is usually difficult to detect the actual processes involved. When equilibrium exists between a liquid and the vapor in the space above it, it is not easy to observe the dynamic processes of evaporation and condensation. In the same way, it is hard to see exactly the several processes that occur when two substances such as hydrogen and oxygen combine to form water. In searching for the actual processes occurring during chemical reactions, chemists find it convenient to narrow their focus of study on a *closed system.*

The term *system* refers to any material which, for the purposes of study, has been isolated as completely as possible from the things around it. Thus when you make a study of conditions in your home or your school, in a beaker of water or in the human body, you are considering each of these things as a self-enclosed system. Of course they are not truly self-enclosed. In reality, every system studied is connected with

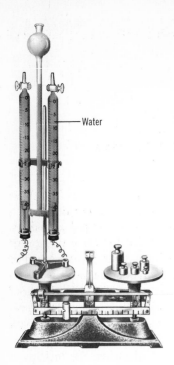

Water

innumerable things outside it. But if we try to follow up all these outside connections, we might lose our way and never arrive at any conclusions about the actual subject at hand. It is much more convenient and fruitful to focus our attention upon a given area as though it were complete in itself.

Conservation of Mass

When a small amount of sulfuric acid is added to water, and the water placed in an electrolysis apparatus, you have a system—one that enables you to arrive at some important conclusions. The total mass of the equipment and the water can be found by placing the entire set-up on a balance. When an electric current is passed through the water, electrolysis occurs: the water decomposes into two elements, hydrogen and oxygen. A chemical change has taken place; yet, as shown in Fig. 10-1, there is no change in the weight shown on the balance as a result of this electrolysis. From this procedure we can conclude that although a chemical change occurs during the electrolysis of water, there is no change in mass.

mass of original H_2O = mass of remaining H_2O + mass of H_2 and O_2

Why not *investigate this problem further?*

> Prepare 15 ml each of solutions of lead nitrate [$Pb(NO_3)_2$] and potassium iodide (KI). Place the solutions in separate beakers; by means of a balance, determine the mass of the two beakers and the solutions they contain, *as shown at the right.* Now combine the solutions. The formation of a yellow precipitate of lead iodide (PbI_2) indicates that a chemical reaction has occurred. Again, determine the mass of the beaker containing the lead iodide and the empty beaker. Does careful measurement show that any change in mass has resulted from the chemical change?

Many similar investigations have demonstrated that although great activity occurs within a chemical system, no measurable amount of mass is created or destroyed during a chemical reaction. This fact gives rise to the **Law of the Conservation of Mass** which says: *During a chemical reaction mass is neither created nor destroyed, but is changed from one form to another.*

Because mass is conserved during every chemical change, it is theoretically possible to predict the amount of product that will result from the change. Suppose, for example, that 18 grams of water are decomposed completely by electrolysis. From the Law of the Conservation of Mass we know that the total mass of the hydrogen and oxygen resulting from this decomposition will still be 18 grams. Since water consists, by weight, of ⅑ hydrogen and ⅘ oxygen, and since the same number of oxygen atoms and hydrogen atoms are found in the reactants and the product,

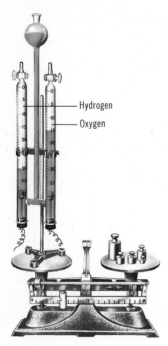

Hydrogen

Oxygen

10-1 No change in mass occurs during the electrolysis of water.

154   BEHAVIOR OF ATOMS

we can also predict that the 18 grams of product will contain 2 grams of hydrogen and 16 grams of oxygen.

hydrogen: $\frac{1}{9} \times 18$ grams $= 2$ grams
oxygen: $\frac{8}{9} \times 18$ grams $= 16$ grams

reactant	products
$2\,H_2O$	$\longrightarrow$ $2\,H_2 + O_2$
18 grams	2 grams + 16 grams

Mass and Physical Changes

Does the Law of the Conservation of Mass still hold true when there is a change of state? Consider what happens when a beaker containing 18 grams of ice are heated on a hot plate. As heat is applied, the particles of ice gain energy to break apart the crystals. Although the resulting water takes up less volume than the ice, the water still has the same mass as the original ice—18 grams. When the water is heated still further, it eventually forms steam. The volume of steam is more than 1,700 times that of the original ice. The mass of the steam, however, like the mass of the water from which it was formed, is still 18 grams. Mass is conserved even when a substance passes from one state to another.

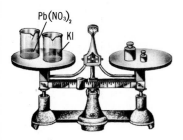

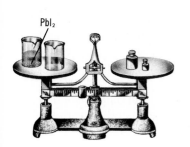

Measuring Energy

In both the electrolysis of water—a chemical change, and the melting of ice—a physical change, energy had to be supplied from outside the system to produce the desired change. In the electrolysis investigation, electricity provided the energy. In the investigation with ice, the change of state was caused by heat energy from a hot plate.

Heat and electricity are both forms of energy, and one form can be converted into the other. Electric energy is measured in *watt-hours* (or kilowatt-hours), while heat energy is measured in *calories* (or kilocalories). When electric energy is converted into heat energy, a definite number of kilowatt-hours of electricity is transformed into a definite number of kilocalories (kcal). To determine the kilocalories of heat energy absorbed or released by a system, a **calorimeter** (Fig. 10-2) is used.

A calorimeter is essentially a sealed metal chamber in which a reaction can occur. Surrounding the chamber is a container with a known quantity of water, whose temperature is measured at the start of the reaction. This container, in turn, is surrounded by an insulating container. During the reaction any heat generated in the inner chamber is transmitted to the water, which is stirred constantly to insure a uniform distribution of the heat. From the change in the temperature of the water, the amount of heat resulting from the reaction can be determined.

Conservation of Energy

If the number of watt-hours required to decompose 18 grams of water into hydrogen and oxygen is measured and then converted into kilo-

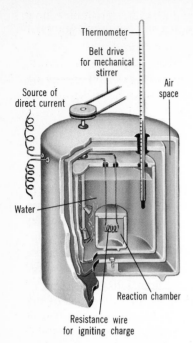

10-2 When a substance in the reaction chamber of a calorimeter is ignited, the heat produced is transmitted to the water in the adjoining chamber. The immersed thermometer indicates the resulting change in temperature.

Thermometer

Belt drive for mechanical stirrer

Source of direct current

Air space

Water

Reaction chamber

Resistance wire for igniting charge

calories, a value of 68.3 kilocalories is obtained. Since this amount of energy has been put *into* the operation, the resulting 2 grams of hydrogen and 16 grams of oxygen together contain 68.3 kilocalories *more* energy than the 18 grams of water from which they were produced. When the reaction is reversed by combining 2 grams of hydrogen and 16 grams of oxygen, the two elements combine again to re-form 18 grams of water. In this recombination, 68.3 kilocalories are *released*. The energy changes in these two operations can be represented as follows:

$$68.3 \text{ kcal (of energy)} + 18 \text{ grams } H_2O \text{ (liquid)} \longrightarrow$$
$$16 \text{ grams } O_2 \text{ (gas)} + 2 \text{ grams } H_2 \text{ (gas)}$$

$$16 \text{ grams } O_2 \text{ (gas)} + 2 \text{ grams } H_2 \text{ (gas)} \longrightarrow$$
$$18 \text{ grams } H_2O \text{ (liquid)} + 68.3 \text{ kcal (of energy)}$$

The exact amount of energy supplied to the original reaction is released when the reaction is reversed—energy is conserved. This fact is stated in the **Law of the Conservation of Energy** which says: *During a chemical reaction, energy is neither created nor destroyed, but is changed from one form to another.*

Energy and Physical Changes

Measurements with a calorimeter show that nearly 13 kilocalories (12.96 kcal) of heat energy are needed to change 18 grams of ice at 0° C to steam at 100° C. Conversely, as 18 grams of steam at 100° C are cooled to water and then to ice at 0° C, the same amount of heat energy is given off.

$$13 \text{ kcal} + 18 \text{ grams ice at } 0° \text{ C} \longrightarrow 18 \text{ grams steam at } 100° \text{ C}$$

$$18 \text{ grams steam at } 100° \text{ C} \longrightarrow 18 \text{ grams ice at } 0° \text{ C} + 13 \text{ kcal}$$

Similar experiments show that energy is never lost during a change of state or other physical change. The exact amount of energy required to complete any physical process is released when that process is reversed.

Compare the amount of energy needed to decompose 18 grams of water into hydrogen and oxygen (68.3 kcal) with the amount required to change 18 grams of ice into steam (13 kcal). The chemical change requires about five times as much energy as the physical change. Far more energy is necessary to disrupt molecules and rearrange the atoms into new patterns than to separate molecules from one another. In the former reaction it is necessary to break and re-form chemical bonds; in the latter, it is only necessary to overcome the comparatively weak forces, largely hydrogen bonds, that attract molecules to each other.

QUESTIONS AND PROBLEMS

1. (a) If in a closed system 216.6 grams of mercuric oxide (HgO) are decomposed into mercury and oxygen, how many grams of mercury and

of oxygen are formed? (b) If the mercury and oxygen recombine, how much mercuric oxide is formed? (c) Write the equation for each reaction. (d) What law is demonstrated by these reactions?

2. (a) When a mole of hydrogen burns in a mole of chlorine to produce 2 moles of hydrogen chloride (HCl), 44 kilocalories of heat energy are released. How many kilocalories are required to decompose 2 moles of HCl? (b) Write the equation for each reaction. (c) What law is demonstrated by these reactions?

3. (a) The amount of heat energy required to vaporize 1 mole of chloroform ($CHCl_3$) is 7.04 kilocalories. Predict whether more or fewer kilocalories are required to decompose 1 mole of chloroform into its component carbon, hydrogen, and chlorine atoms. (b) Give a reason for your answer.

ENERGY CHANGES

Consider a heavy book on the top shelf of a high bookcase. As it rests there it seems to have no energy. Yet if it falls to the floor, it may smash a china object in its path. Obviously, the book possesses kinetic energy, or energy of motion, while it is falling. If you lift the book back to the same shelf, you contribute to it exactly the same amount of kinetic energy as the book released when it fell. Evidently the book in its position at the top of the bookcase had energy stored in it. This energy of position is known as **potential energy.** As the book fell, potential energy was changed into kinetic energy. Similarly, the kinetic energy used to return the book to the bookcase was converted into potential energy.

Another example of energy conversion is shown in Fig. 10-3. Here two balls are connected by a rubber band. In order to pull the balls apart and stretch the band, energy must be expended. When the balls are stretched apart, the exact amount of this kinetic energy is stored in them as potential energy. When the balls are released, this stored energy is converted into kinetic energy as the balls fly together again.

Our examples of the book on the bookcase and the two balls held together by a taut rubber band refer to energy changes in physical reactions. In both examples energy is conserved. Likewise, energy in a system undergoing a chemical change is neither created nor destroyed. It too can be accounted for in terms of kinetic and potential energy.

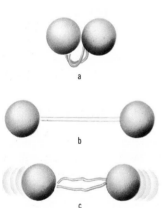

10-3 The kinetic energy expended in pulling apart the two balls in **a** is stored in them as potential energy in **b.** When the balls fly together again in **c,** potential energy is converted into kinetic energy.

Potential Energy of Particles

The kinetic molecular theory tells us that all matter—whether gaseous, liquid, or solid—is composed of particles which are in constant motion. But if this energy of motion were the only influence at work, there would be no stability in matter at all. The matter of the universe would be in a continual chaos of movement. We would not have compounds which exist in fixed proportions like sodium chloride or water, or solids whose stability and strength could be used in construction. Obviously, there must be a form of energy that counteracts the random motion of molecules, atoms, and ions associated with kinetic energy.

This stabilizing energy is supplied by the forces of attraction among molecules as well as the forces among ions and atoms. The forces holding the molecules together are dipole-dipole forces, or the forces between polar molecules, hydrogen bonds, and van der Waals forces. The *potential energy* involved in each of these is the *force of attraction multiplied by the distance between the particles.*

The bonds which unite the atoms within molecules are **covalent bond forces.** When a solid is ionic, such as sodium chloride, its ions are held together by **interionic** (or **electrostatic**) **forces.** All chemical bonds result from forces between particles, and these forces are directly proportional to the potential energy. If sufficient energy is added to a system, the bonds *between* molecules are broken. Much more energy is needed to break apart the bonds *within* molecules. Whenever bonds are formed, energy is given off from the system.

Overcoming Intermolecular Forces

In a molecular solid, the forces between molecules are the bonds that hold the particles together. As the temperature increases, the increasingly strong vibrations finally break the bonds between molecules. To help in understanding the changes that take place as kinetic energy gradually overcomes the forces that hold the molecules together, visualize a model of a CO_2 molecule like the one shown in Fig. 10-4. This model consists of a gray ball representing the carbon atom and two green balls representing the oxygen atoms. The green balls are attached to the gray one by means of springs. The springs represent the double bonds that hold the oxygen atoms to the carbon atom.

Now that the model is constructed, it is possible to move it in three different ways without breaking the spring that holds the model together (Fig. 10-4). First, the entire model can move through space from one point to another in a straight line. This represents a type of molecular motion called **translational motion.** One of the early assumptions of the kinetic molecular theory was that molecules move in this way. Next, the model can spin as it moves, causing it to turn end over end. This represents a somersaultlike motion of molecules called **rotational motion.** Finally, the springs in the model can be compressed and released, causing the balls representing atoms to vibrate back and forth as the model moves. The back-and-forth motion of the springs represents a **vibrational motion** of molecules.

Even in the most stable solid, the particles have a certain degree of motion, and hence a certain amount of kinetic energy. Where a solid, such as dry ice (CO_2), is composed of molecules, each molecule is so closely hemmed in by its neighbors that the only motion possible is vibrational motion. As the solid is heated, its molecules gain kinetic energy and have much greater freedom of action. The liquid state

a. Translational motion

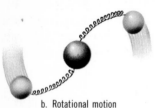

b. Rotational motion

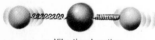

c. Vibrational motion

10-4 In gases intermolecular forces are overcome and molecules exhibit all three of these types of motion. In a liquid most molecules exhibit rotational and vibrational motion, but not translational motion. In a solid the molecules exhibit only vibrational motion.

is reached when the molecules, in addition to vibrating, possess enough kinetic energy to have rotational and even some translational motion. In the gas phase, the molecules have become so widely separated that the mutual attraction or the effect of any intermolecular forces has become negligible. In this gaseous state all the molecules have enough kinetic energy to exhibit all three types of motion: vibrational, rotational, and translational.

Overcoming Chemical Bond Forces

In ionic solids, the random motion of the particles is overcome by interionic or electrostatic forces which hold the ions together. Because these forces are relatively strong, it takes a large amount of kinetic energy to overcome them. As you remember, the ions in an ionic solid are arranged in an ionic lattice. Hence the energy used to break this structure is called **lattice energy.** Lattice energy can be supplied directly in the form of heat or electricity. Or, as you will learn in Chapter 13, it may result from dissolving the ionic solid in a liquid.

Molecular compounds consist of two or more atoms held together by covalent bonds. A reaction between such substances (for example, H_2 and Cl_2) can take place only when enough energy is added to the reactant molecules to break these bonds. Once the covalent bonds are broken, the atoms are free to move about with considerable freedom. Eventually these atoms may bond together in new arrangements (HCl). These new arrangements represent the products of chemical reactions. Most of the energy involved in any chemical reaction is related to breaking and re-forming chemical bonds.

Exothermic and Endothermic Reactions

Consider once more what happens, in terms of energy, when hydrogen and oxygen are combined to form water. Once a small amount of energy has been added to the mixture of the two gases, the initial reaction continues to completion. No additional energy has to be added during the course of this process to keep the reaction going. This means that once energy has been supplied to break the covalent bonds within the first molecules of hydrogen and oxygen, the liberated atoms of hydrogen and oxygen combine to form molecules of water *and release energy.* Enough energy is released to break down additional molecules of hydrogen and oxygen, and so on, until the reaction is complete. The extra energy that is released in this process is given off as heat.

Such a reaction—in which the reaction itself produces more than enough energy to keep it going—is called an **exothermic reaction.** Exothermic reactions are always characterized by the liberation of heat (Fig. 10-5). The burning of a piece of paper offers another example of an exothermic reaction. Once you have ignited the paper with a match, it continues to burn. The initial burning produces enough heat energy to keep the reaction going.

10-5 In exothermic reactions, as in the formation of water from hydrogen and oxygen, sufficient heat energy is released to keep the reaction going. In endothermic reactions, as in the decomposition of water, heat is absorbed; energy must be supplied continuously to sustain the reaction.

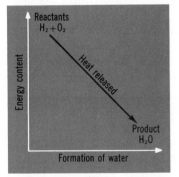

a. Exothermic reaction

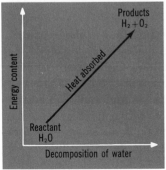

b. Endothermic reaction

Now consider what happens when water is decomposed by electrolysis into hydrogen and oxygen. The electrical energy passing through the system breaks the covalent bonds uniting the atoms of hydrogen with atoms of oxygen. The atoms are thus freed to rearrange themselves. The hydrogen atoms become bonded together in pairs to form molecules of hydrogen gas; the oxygen atoms likewise come together in pairs to form molecules of oxygen. Though the formation of these new bonds releases appreciable energy, it is not enough energy to keep the reaction going. Not only is this released energy reabsorbed, but also additional energy must be added to complete the reaction (Fig. 10-5).

The electrolysis of water is an example of an **endothermic reaction.** In an endothermic reaction the initial reaction does *not* produce enough energy to keep the process going. Energy must be supplied continuously from outside until the reaction is completed. In electrolysis, for example, the reaction is cut short if the electricity is turned off. Endothermic reactions are always characterized by the absorption of energy. The production of oxygen from mercuric oxide is another example of an endothermic reaction. The compound will decompose into oxygen and mercury only as long as heat is applied.

QUESTIONS AND PROBLEMS

1. (a) What are van der Waals forces? (b) How do they differ from chemical bond forces?
2. Define each of the following terms with respect to elements or compounds: *potential energy, kinetic energy, interionic forces, covalent bonds, lattice energy.*
3. Differentiate among translational, rotational, and vibrational types of motion.
4. (a) Differentiate between exothermic and endothermic reactions. (b) Is the dissolving of sugar in water, a process that absorbs heat, an exothermic or an endothermic reaction?

INDICATING ENERGY CHANGES

Since energy changes often provide important clues to the structures of the reactants and the final product, it is customary to include the energy changes in the equation for a reaction. The amount of heat evolved or absorbed during a reaction measures the energy changes that occur during the reaction. We saw earlier that for each mole (18 grams) of water produced from hydrogen and oxygen, 68.3 kilocalories of heat are given off. This indicates that the energy of the hydrogen and oxygen when uncombined is greater than the energy of the water (Fig. 10-6). The difference in *heat content* between product and reactants is represented by the symbol ΔH, or delta H ($\Delta H_{reaction} = H_{products} - H_{reactants}$).

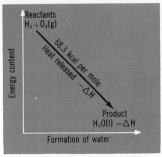

a. Exothermic reaction

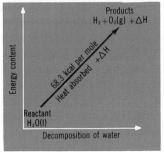

b. Endothermic reaction

10-6 Heat produced per mole of product in the formation of water is exactly equal to heat absorbed in the decomposition of the water.

Using ΔH in Equations

The symbol ΔH is placed at the end of the equation. If the equation represents an exothermic reaction, ΔH has a negative value: $\Delta H = -\text{kcal}$. The minus sign indicates that the heat content of the products is *less* than the heat content of the reactants, or that a loss in heat content has occurred. The equation for the formation of water is:

$$2 H_2 + O_2 \longrightarrow 2 H_2O \qquad \Delta H = -\text{kcal}$$

For an endothermic reaction, ΔH has a positive value: $\Delta H = +\text{kcal}$. The plus sign indicates that the heat content of the products is *greater* than the heat content of the reactants, or that a gain in heat content has occurred. The equation for the decomposition of water is:

$$2 H_2O \longrightarrow 2 H_2 + O_2 \qquad \Delta H = +\text{kcal}$$

A Value for ΔH

Numerical values for ΔH can be determined both experimentally and mathematically. These values are usually expressed in kilocalories of heat produced *per mole of a product.* When ΔH is expressed in these units it is called the **heat of reaction.** The heat of reaction can be greatly affected by changes in state. For this reason, the state of reactants and products is usually indicated in any equation that includes a value for ΔH. The state is indicated by placing the letter (*s*) for solid, (*l*) for liquid, or (*g*) for gas after each formula in the equation.

$$2 H_2(g) + O_2(g) \longrightarrow 2 H_2O(l) \qquad \Delta H = -136.6 \text{ kcal}$$
$$2 H_2(g) + O_2(g) \longrightarrow 2 H_2O(g) \qquad \Delta H = -116 \text{ kcal}$$

The first equation indicates that 136.6 kilocalories of heat are given off for each 2 moles of liquid water produced. The second indicates that 116 kilocalories of heat are given off for each 2 moles of water vapor produced.

To determine the heat given off in the production of a single mole of water, simply divide the numerical values above by 2. Thus 68.3 kilocalories of heat energy are released per mole of liquid water formed and 58 kilocalories per mole of water vapor. The heat of reaction per mole of liquid water is 10.3 kilocalories greater than the corresponding heat of reaction of 1 mole of water vapor. By subtracting the heat of reaction of water vapor from the heat of reaction of liquid water [−68.3 kcal − (−58 kcal)], we find that 10.3 kilocalories of heat energy are released as each mole of water vapor is changed to liquid water.

Compare these equations with that for the formation of water on page 156. There we were concerned with heat *lost to the surroundings;* here the equations are in terms of the difference in energy content of products and reactants. Both notations indicate the same relationship.

Equations for endothermic reactions can be written to give the same information. The equation for decomposition of sodium bicarbonate is:

$$2 NaHCO_3(s) \longrightarrow Na_2CO_3(s) + CO_2(g) + H_2O(g) \qquad \Delta H = +31 \text{ kcal}$$

This equation indicates the following: when heated, solid sodium bicarbonate produces solid sodium carbonate, carbon dioxide gas, and water vapor. During this reaction the system absorbs 31 kilocalories of heat per mole of water vapor formed.

Heat of Reaction and Stability

When carbon is burned in oxygen to form carbon dioxide, the heat of reaction is 94 kilocalories. This is also known as the *heat of formation*, when one mole of a compound is formed from its constituent elements.

$$C(s) + O_2(g) \longrightarrow CO_2(g) \qquad \Delta H = -94 \text{ kcal}$$

Compare this 94 kilocalories with the 68.3 kilocalories of heat produced when a mole of hydrogen burns in oxygen to form water vapor. Note that both reactions are exothermic and the heat of reaction is higher in the formation of CO_2. As a mole of either CO_2 or H_2O contains the same number of molecules (6.02×10^{23} molecules), more heat is given off in the formation of a molecule of carbon dioxide than in the formation of a molecule of water vapor. Since this heat is the result of chemical changes, you can predict that each molecule of CO_2 contains less energy than a molecule of H_2O. Because they contain less energy, CO_2 molecules are more stable than H_2O molecules. Consequently, it takes more energy to pull apart the atoms in a molecule of CO_2 than the atoms in a molecule of H_2O.

If nitrogen is made to react with oxygen at the very high temperature of an electric arc, nitric oxide (NO) is formed. The heat of reaction of nitric oxide is +21.5 kilocalories per mole. This positive heat of reaction indicates that nitric oxide is relatively unstable; and indeed it is. From these and numerous other reactions, it has been found that compounds with high negative heats of reaction are the most stable compounds (Fig. 10-7). Conversely, the less stable or unstable compounds have low positive or negative heats of reaction. Compounds with very high positive heats of reaction tend to be explosive.

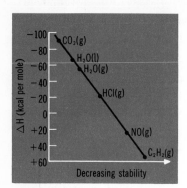

10-7 Heat of formation of six compounds. The more negative the heat of formation, the more stable the compound—or the greater the energy required to decompose the compound.

QUESTIONS AND PROBLEMS

1. Study the equation below for the formation of carbon disulfide (CS_2) from carbon and sulfur:

$$C(s) + 2 S(s) \longrightarrow CS_2(g) \qquad \Delta H = +28.7 \text{ kcal}$$

(a) Is the reaction exothermic or endothermic? Explain your answer.
(b) What is the significance of the letters (s) and (g) in the equation?
2. Differentiate between positive ΔH and negative ΔH.
3. (a) The heats of reaction for several hydrogen halides are given at the left. Indicate which halide is easiest to decompose, and which halogen compound is most stable. (b) Justify your answer.

Hydrogen halide	Heats of reaction (ΔH kcal per mole)
HF	−64
HCl	−22
HBr	−8.7
HI	+6.0

From the foregoing discussion of chemical reactions, you might conclude that reactions always occur when the molecules of the system have been supplied with a large amount of kinetic energy. Yet experiments show that this is not always so. For example, most sulfuric acid is made commercially by a process which includes the union of sulfur dioxide (SO_2) and oxygen to produce sulfur trioxide (SO_3). For many years it had been known that even high temperatures were not favorable to the reaction. Yet if sulfur dioxide and oxygen are drawn over heated platinum, sulfur trioxide is formed readily. However, if traces of arsenic are present in the sulfur, the reaction slows down considerably. Evidently the kinetic theory alone does not explain every chemical reaction.

The Collision Theory

At room temperature there are approximately 10^{28} collisions per second between gas molecules in every cubic centimeter of gas. Why then do reactions between the gases not take place immediately? The best explanation chemists have found—the collision theory—is limited to the case of particles so far apart that chance alone determines their collisions.

The collision theory (Fig. 10-8) is based on the following assumptions: (1) Particles—whether atoms, ions, or molecules—must collide before they can combine with one another. (2) Particles do not always collide as they move about, but an increase in temperature increases the chances of collision. (3) Not all collisions result in chemical changes. The collision has to be forceful enough to overcome the mutual repulsion of the particles' electron clouds; otherwise they will be repelled, unchanged. If either or both particles have enough kinetic energy to overcome the repulsion and also collide at the proper angle, the particles *may* combine.

As an example of the collision theory, consider once again the reaction between hydrogen and oxygen. You found that a small amount of heat or electrical energy must be applied if these two elements are to combine. The minimum amount of energy which will bring about such a reaction is called the **activation energy.** Note that activation energy is not the same as the energy which brings about collisions, since some collisions will occur at any given time. Rather, activation energy is that *minimal amount of energy* which insures that the collision will result in a chemical reaction. Of course, the higher the temperature, the more frequent the collisions between hydrogen and oxygen molecules will be. But the important point is that at these higher temperatures some of the molecules contain enough kinetic energy for their collisions to result in a rearrangement of chemical bonds—a chemical reaction takes place.

Activated Complex

In all reactions, even those which are exothermic, a small amount of initial energy must be supplied to get the reaction going. The chemist's

10-8 In the upper vessel the molecules are in motion but may not collide. At a higher temperature in the middle vessel, the two molecules at the left have just had "a near miss"; while at a still higher temperature in the lower vessel, the two molecules at the right have collided. In which vessel is a chemical change most likely to occur?

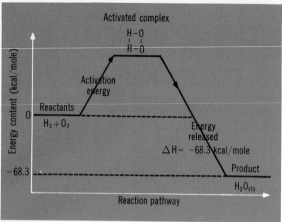

a. Exothermic reaction

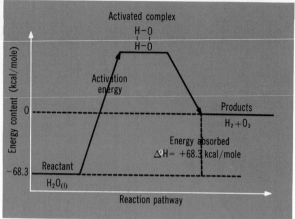

b. Endothermic reaction

10-9 In an exothermic reaction, energy is required only to activate the "complex." Once started, the reaction continues; the product has a lower energy content than the reactants. In an endothermic reaction, activation energy is required not only to start but also to sustain the reaction. The products have a higher energy content than the reactant.

explanation of this phenomenon is that in every reaction, activation energy rearranges the atoms of the reactants in such a way that they form an intermediate, or temporary, product. This temporary product is called an **activated complex.** Since some energy is absorbed in the formation of an activated complex, the complex must contain more potential energy than the original reactants.

In exothermic reactions, as in the combination of oxygen and hydrogen to form water, only the amount of energy necessary to form the activated complex has to be supplied from outside the system. When the activated complex rearranges to form the product, energy is liberated. In this way, the heat of the reaction itself supplies enough energy to form more of the activated complex, which continues the process (Fig. 10-9).

On the other hand, endothermic reactions, such as the decomposition of water by electrolysis, require more energy than the exothermic type to form an activated complex. Here, after the first activated complex has been formed, the reaction itself does not supply enough energy to form more of the complex. Hence, to maintain an endothermic reaction, energy must be continuously supplied from outside the system (Fig. 10-9).

The energy changes that occur in both exothermic and endothermic reactions are shown in the model in Fig. 10-10. Parts a and b illustrate an exothermic reaction. Two balls, attached to one another by a short string, rest in a shallow groove near the edge of a table. Each ball, like the reactants in an exothermic reaction, contains a certain amount of potential energy. Before one of the balls can fall to the floor, it must be pushed out of the groove. The small amount of energy this requires can be compared to the small amount of activation energy needed to form an activated complex in an exothermic reaction. After one of the balls has been lifted to the top of the groove and released, it falls to the ground, carrying the other ball with it. In the same way, once the initial

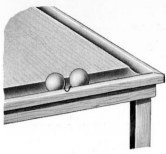

a. At outset

b. Exothermic reaction

c. Endothermic reaction

10-10 In this analogy to chemical reactions, pushing one ball out of the groove, as from **a** to **b,** requires little "activation energy"—and enough energy is released to pull the other ball out. A greater "activation energy" is needed to lift the balls from the floor to the table, as in **c**—and the second ball will not make it without additional energy input.

energy is supplied to produce an exothermic reaction, the reaction continues on its own until no more reactants remain.

An endothermic reaction, which is the previously described process in reverse, is illustrated in part c of Fig. 10-10. Now the two balls are resting on the ground, and they have no potential energy relative to the table; they represent the reactants in an endothermic reaction. A relatively large amount of energy is needed to raise one of the balls to the top of the table. In the same way, in an endothermic reaction, a large amount of activation energy is needed to produce an activated complex. After one ball is raised to the top of the table, it falls easily enough into the groove. But it does not carry the other ball into the groove with it. To accomplish that, an additional "outside" source of energy is required. In the same way, in an endothermic reaction, energy must be continuously applied until all of the desired final product is formed.

Catalysts

In the laboratory you found that when potassium chlorate ($KClO_3$) was heated in a test tube, oxygen was produced—but very slowly. By increasing the temperature, the rate at which the oxygen formed was increased. But the oxygen formed quite rapidly, and at a comparatively low temperature, if a little manganese dioxide (MnO_2) was added to potassium chlorate. Evidently, manganese dioxide in some way takes the place of heat energy in this chemical reaction. After all the oxygen has been freed from the mixture of $KClO_3$ and MnO_2, the materials that remain can be separated from one another by adding water to them and then filtering. When this is done, a dark gray solid is left in the filter paper. This solid, the MnO_2, can be used repeatedly with new supplies of $KClO_3$ to speed up the rate at which oxygen is produced. The MnO_2 does *not* break down to release oxygen.

Only by repeated experiments have chemists discovered such substances which can cause specific reactions to occur rapidly, even at temperatures which are quite low. They have also uncovered other substances which can slow down specific reactions at relatively high temperatures. In both cases the substances themselves, although they affect chemical reactions, do not seem to be changed by the reactions. Such substances that either speed up or slow down the rate of a chemical reaction yet themselves remain unchanged are called **catalysts.**

A substance that speeds up a reaction is called a positive catalyst. Manganese dioxide when it is used to prepare oxygen from potassium chlorate or the platinum used in the formation of sulfur trioxide from sulfur dioxide and oxygen are positive catalysts. A substance that slows down a reaction is called a negative catalyst. An example is the tetraethyl lead added to gasoline to prevent the gasoline from burning too rapidly. Thousands of catalysts have been discovered; they include special catalysts present inside living organisms. These catalysts, including ptyalin and pepsin, are complex molecules known as *enzymes.*

Action of Catalysts

Just how a catalyst performs its function is still not perfectly understood. The following explanation, based upon the collision theory, offers at least a partial answer. A positive catalyst, recall, eliminates the need for adding excessive amounts of heat to chemical reactions. It might appear that such a positive catalyst, like an increase in temperature, speeds up a chemical reaction by producing more collisions between particles. But this cannot be the entire answer, for without a catalyst some reactions, such as the combination of carbon monoxide with hydrogen to produce synthetic gasoline, proceed very slowly even at relatively high temperatures. Evidently in reactions like this so much activation energy is needed to start the reaction going, that although many particles collide, few of them react. The explanation may be that a catalyst in some way allows a different sort of activated complex to form. The formation of this different activated complex requires *less* activation energy, and the reaction proceeds faster with the positive catalyst than without it.

Some evidence indicates that the addition of a catalyst may increase the number of steps in a reaction before the final product is achieved. Nevertheless, the catalyzed reaction occurs more rapidly because less energy is needed to start the original reaction.

A negative catalyst, more properly called an *inhibitor,* slows down a reaction by combining with one of the reactants (as indicated on page 267).

Mechanism of Reactions

In recent years chemists have given more and more attention to the successive steps occurring in a chemical reaction while the product is being formed. This series of steps is called the **mechanism of the reaction.** The mechanisms for relatively few chemical reactions are understood completely. Experiments with the speed of reactions indicate that some mechanisms are fairly simple while others are extremely complex.

The formation of hydrogen iodide (HI) from hydrogen (H_2) and iodine (I_2) is an example of what may be learned by the study of a reaction mechanism. At first, this reaction was thought to consist of a single step; now it is known to involve two steps. In the first, for example, 1 mole of I_2 molecules requires 36 kcal of energy to dissociate into 2 moles of I atoms. Following this step, if the molecules have an activation energy of 5.3 kcal per mole and if a mole of hydrogen molecules collide at the proper angles with 2 moles of iodine atoms, the activated complex (H_2I_2) is formed.

$$I_2 + 36 \text{ kcal} \longrightarrow 2\,I$$

$$H_2 + 2\,I + 5.3 \text{ kcal} \longrightarrow \begin{array}{c} H\text{---}H \\ \vdots \quad \vdots \\ I\text{----}I \end{array} \longrightarrow HI + HI + 43.8 \text{ kcal}$$

This complex breaks down quickly to form 2 moles of hydrogen iodide (2HI). Because the activated complex has such a short life that it cannot be isolated, it is shown with dashed lines between the atoms.

10-11 Hydrogen and iodine molecules react to form an activated complex [H_2I_2] which breaks down quickly to yield two molecules of hydrogen iodide.

You might expect that the reactions which have relatively simple mechanisms would proceed fairly rapidly, while those with more complex mechanisms would proceed slowly. Though this is often true, it is not invariably so. In fact, the study of reaction mechanisms is one of the many areas of chemistry which requires more research. In the next unit we shall examine the many and varied reactions which occur when substances are in solution. We shall also take a closer look at reaction mechanisms—a frontier of chemical knowledge.

QUESTIONS AND PROBLEMS

1. (a) Why is energy required to start an exothermic reaction but not to sustain it? (b) Why is energy required both to start and sustain an endothermic reaction?
2. Define *activation energy, activated complex,* and *mechanism of a reaction.*
3. In terms of the collision theory, explain the action of a positive catalyst in a chemical reaction.

VALUE OF THE CONCEPT

THE CONCEPT

Detailed studies of closed systems indicate that both mass and energy are conserved during chemical as well as physical changes. The Law of the Conservation of Mass states that during a chemical reaction mass is neither created nor destroyed, but is changed from one form to another. The Law of the Conservation of Energy states that during a chemical reaction energy is neither created nor destroyed, but is changed from one form to another.

A calorimeter can be used to determine the amount of heat released or absorbed by a system during a chemical reaction. This energy is usually measured in kilocalories. A chemical reaction which produces more than enough energy to keep itself going is an exothermic reaction; a reaction to which energy must be added to maintain the reaction is an endothermic reaction. Exothermic reactions are characterized by the liberation of heat, while endothermic reactions absorb heat. A negative ΔH represents heat given off during

a reaction while a positive ΔH indicates that heat is absorbed. When ΔH is measured in kilocalories per mole, it is referred to as the heat of reaction.

Though all particles in motion contain kinetic energy, the forces of attraction among molecules, ions, and atoms represent potential energy; that is, van der Waals forces and chemical bonds have potential energy associated with them. Overcoming or weakening intermolecular forces results in three types of molecular motion: translational, rotational, and vibrational. Overcoming chemical bond forces results in chemical changes.

The collision theory, which attempts to explain the process by which chemical reactions occur, is based upon the following assumptions: (1) particles must collide before they can combine with one another; (2) increasing their temperature increases their chances of collision; (3) not all collisions result in chemical changes. A minimum amount of energy, known as activation energy, is required to bring about a chemical change. In a chemical reaction the atoms of the reactants are rearranged to form an intermediate product, or activated complex, which is at a higher energy state than the original reactants. Once the activated complex forms, the final products will be produced. In exothermic reactions, only the amount of energy necessary to begin the formation of the activated complex need be supplied from outside the system. In endothermic reactions, additional energy must be supplied after the activated complex begins to form, since the reaction itself does not supply enough energy to form more of the activated complex.

By enabling different activated complexes to form, catalysts may speed up or slow down the rate of a chemical reaction. The stages through which a chemical reaction goes in forming products constitutes the mechanism of the reaction.

USING THE CONCEPT

Using the Basic Concept

1. (a) State the Law of the Conservation of Mass. (b) Describe an investigation to verify this law.
2. (a) State the Law of the Conservation of Energy. (b) Describe an investigation to verify it.
3. (a) Differentiate between an exothermic and an endothermic chemical reaction. (b) Give two examples of each type of reaction.
4. (a) What happens to the 68.3 kilocalories of energy used to break apart 18 grams of water? (b) Give evidence to support your answer to this question.
5. Explain why less energy is required to change 18 grams of ice to steam than to change 18 grams of water to hydrogen and oxygen.
6. In each of the following examples indicate whether kinetic energy is changed to potential energy or vice versa: (a) a book falls from your hand, (b) a car climbs a steep hill.
7. In each of the following indicate whether the kinetic energy of the system increases or decreases: (a) van der Waals forces between molecules become effective (b) hy-

drogen bonds holding H_2O molecules together are broken.

8. (a) Describe the motion of molecules in solids, in liquids, and in gases. (b) Explain why molecules in gases collide with one another more frequently than molecules in solids.
9. Why is the physical state of each reactant and each product indicated in an equation containing the heat of reaction?
10. When solid magnesium is burned in gaseous oxygen, solid magnesium oxide forms. The heat of reaction for this chemical reaction is −143.8 kilocalories per mole of magnesium burned. Write the complete equation for this reaction showing the reactants and products, their states, and the heat produced.
11. (a) List the assumptions of the collision theory. (b) Using these assumptions, explain how a chemical reaction occurs between C_2 and O_2 molecules. Use the terms *activation energy, activated complex, collisions, kinetic energy, exothermic reaction,* and *chemical bonds* in your explanation.
12. (a) What is a catalyst? (b) What is an enzyme? (c) Give one explanation of how a catalyst works. (d) Use the terms *activation energy, kinetic energy,* and *activated complex* to explain how MnO_2 catalyzes the decomposition of $KClO_3$ to form oxygen.
13. Explain the difference between a positive and a negative catalyst. Use the terms *kinetic energy, activated complex,* and *product* in your answer.
14. (a) What is meant by the mechanism of a chemical reaction? (b) Why is it so difficult to determine the mechanisms for chemical reaction?

Relating Terms Within the Concept

Each statement on the facing page contains two *italicized* terms. Select the italicized term that makes each statement correct.

1. The intermediate product formed when activation energy rearranges the atoms of the reaction is (*an activated complex, a reaction mechanism*).
2. The energy related to interionic attraction is (*kinetic energy, potential energy*).
3. The energy needed to overcome interionic attraction is (*lattice energy, activation energy*).
4. A reaction that once started supplies enough energy to produce more of the activated complex is an (*exothermic reaction, endothermic reaction*).
5. In an equation, the heat involved in an endothermic reaction is represented by (*positive ΔH, negative ΔH*).
6. Material that is isolated from its surroundings for purposes of study forms a (*system, mechanism*).
7. The chemist uses kilocalories per mole to express (*interparticle attraction, heat of reaction*).
8. The energy of particles in motion is (*kinetic energy, potential energy*).
9. In a solid, the molecular motion is (*translational motion, vibrational motion.*)
10. According to the collision theory, a catalyst seems to change the rate of reaction by forming a different (*heat of formation, activated complex*).

Solving Problems Within the Concept
1. (a) How many grams of water (liquid) will be formed from the complete burning of 2 grams of hydrogen in oxygen? (b) How much energy will be liberated during the reaction?
2. (a) How many molecules of water will be formed during the reaction in Question 1? (b) How many moles of water will be formed?
3. Carbon monoxide gas burns completely in gaseous oxygen to form gaseous carbon dioxide. During the burning of 2 moles of carbon monoxide, 67.6 kilocalories of heat are liberated. After writing the equation for this reaction, determine the heat of the reaction (that is, the kilocalories of heat produced per mole of carbon monoxide burned.)
4. How much more energy is needed to decompose a mole of liquid H_2O than to convert a mole of ice at $0°$ C to steam at $100°$ C?

Applying the Concept
1. (a) For certain reactions ΔH is referred to as the heat of combustion. Write an equation for a reaction for which either the term heat of formation or heat of combustion appropriately describes ΔH. (b) Could the heat of combustion ever be represented by a positive ΔH?
2. How might impurities in a positive catalyst, such as arsenic in platinum, serve to "poison" or prevent the catalyst from working?
3. Explain, in terms of the collision theory, why a lighted match is usually unable to start a wood fire, while the same lighted match can instantaneously ignite coal gas inside a coal mine.
4. Would you expect the heat of reaction of a good quality fuel to have a high positive or a high negative value? Explain your answer.
5. Many reactions in which elements combine to form compounds are exothermic; some are not. Why might you have expected all such reactions to be exothermic?

Reading Further
Foundations of Modern Physical Science, by Gerald Holton and Duane Roller, Reading, Mass., Addison-Wesley, 1958. The presentation of the Law of the Conservation of Energy is excellent.

Chemistry, 3d. ed., by Michell Sienko and Robert Plane, New York, McGraw-Hill, 1966. A concise discussion of the collision theory is only one of the interesting presentations in this text.

11

SKILLS—Mathematics of Chemistry

Two gaseous compounds with similar properties are found to contain only carbon and hydrogen. On analysis, the chemist finds that both compounds have the same percentage by weight of the two elements. Do both samples represent the same compound? He could, of course, investigate in the laboratory. But the chemist has a simpler procedure, proven reliable because its results have been verified repeatedly by actual experimentation. What is the procedure? What is its fundamental basis? How is it applied?

COMPOUNDS: COMPOSITION AND FORMULAS

Formulas and equations are more than a shorthand way of representing compounds or chemical reactions. The formula $MgCl_2$, for example, identifies the elements in the compound and gives the simplest ratio of their ions in combination. But since atoms have weight, we know that 24 grams of magnesium are combined with 71 (2×35.5) grams of chlorine. From this data, it is only a short step to determine the percentage by weight of each element in the compound.

In this section, we shall consider two important relationships, each of which can be expressed in the form of a question. Given the formula of a compound, what percentage by weight of each element is present in it? Or, as the chemist would say, what is its **percentage composition?** The second relationship, actually the reverse of the first, is: How can the simplest formula and true formula of a compound be determined from its known percentage composition?

Percentage Composition from the Formula

Suppose a chemist wished to supply nitrogen in fertilizer by using potassium nitrate (KNO_3). To determine the percentage by weight of nitrogen in KNO_3, study the following procedure. First, find the formula weight (**FW**) of KNO_3.

Element	Number of atoms		Atomic weight		Weight of elements in compound
K	1	×	39	=	39
N	1	×	14	=	14
O	3	×	16	=	48
	FW of KNO_3			=	101

Then determine the fractional part of the formula weight contributed by each element, and convert the fraction to a percent. This is accomplished by dividing the weight contributed by each element by the formula weight, and multiplying each fraction obtained by 100.

Element	Fractional part		Convert to percent		Percentage composition
K	$\frac{39}{101}$	×	100	=	38.7%
N	$\frac{14}{101}$	×	100	=	13.8%
O	$\frac{48}{101}$	×	100	=	47.5%

Always check your calculations by observing whether the sum of these percentages is 100.

The same procedure applies to determining percentage composition of a molecular compound such as pentane, C_5H_{12}; only here we use molecular weights (**MW**) rather than formula weights. First determine that its molecular weight is 72 ($[5 \times 12] + [12 \times 1]$). Then determine its percentage composition.

Element	Fractional part		Convert to percent		Percentage composition
C	$\frac{60}{72}$	×	100	=	83.3%
H	$\frac{12}{72}$	×	100	=	16.7%

1. Determine the percentage composition of the molecular compounds NH_3 and $C_{12}H_{22}$.

2. Determine the percentage composition of the ionic substances $NaCl$, $CaCO_3$, and Na_3PO_4.

3. Find the percentage of water in the compound $Na_2CO_3 \cdot 10 \; H_2O$.

Determining Simplest Formula of a Compound

In the laboratory, it is sometimes necessary to determine the formula of an unknown compound. To do so, the compound is analyzed to identify its elements and to determine its percentage composition. It is then possible to determine its **simplest** or **empirical formula.**

Let us consider a compound whose analysis shows 85.7 percent carbon and 14.3 percent hydrogen by weight. How many atoms of each element do these figures represent? The first step in solving this problem is to find the simplest ratio of atoms of carbon and hydrogen present in the compound. To do this, *divide the percentage of each element present by its atomic weight.*

Element	Percentage of element Atomic weight		Simplest ratio of atoms
C	$\dfrac{85.7}{12}$	$=$	7.1
H	$\dfrac{14.3}{1}$	$=$	14.3

The simplest formula for this compound *cannot* be $C_{7.1}H_{14.3}$, since fractional parts of atoms do not exist. The ratio 7.1 to 14.3 must be changed to a ratio of whole numbers. This is accomplished by *dividing the relative number of atoms of each element by the smaller relative number in this ratio.*

Element	Relative number of atoms Smallest relative number of atoms	Smallest ratio of atoms
C	$\dfrac{7.1}{7.1}$	1
H	$\dfrac{14.3}{7.1}$	2

At the moment, it appears that the formula for this compound is CH_2. But the same percentage composition given in this problem would also hold true for the compounds C_2H_4, C_3H_6, or any C_nH_{2n}, in which the ratio of the number of atoms of carbon to hydrogen is also 1 to 2. The simplest or empirical formula is therefore *not* necessarily the **true** or **molecular formula.** How can the chemist determine which of these possibilities is the true formula?

The answer depends on the fact that CH_2, C_2H_4, and C_3H_6 *all have different molecular weights.* Once the molecular weight has been established, the true, or molecular, formula of the compound is easily determined. From Chapter 9 you know that the weight in grams of 22.4 liters of a gaseous compound at **STP** is numerically equal to the molecular weight. Assume that by applying this principle, you determine that the gas under study at **STP** has a molecular weight of 28.

If the compound's simplest formula, CH_2, were also its true formula, the compound would have a molecular weight of 14 (12 + 2). But its true molecular weight is 28. Therefore, divide the compound's true molecular weight by its hypothetical molecular weight to reveal the whole-number multiple by which each subscript in the empirical formula must be multiplied.

$$\frac{\text{true molecular weight}}{\text{hypothetical molecular weight}}$$
$$= \text{whole-number multiple}$$

$$\frac{28}{14} = 2$$

Hence, the unknown compound is ethene, with the molecular formula of C_2H_4 ($2 \times CH_2$) rather than CH_2 (**MW** = 14) or C_3H_6 (**MW** = 42).

1. Determine the simplest formula for a compound with the following percentage composition: 92.3 percent C and 7.7 percent H.

2. Determine the empirical formula for a compound that is 31.9 percent K, 28.8 percent Cl, and 39.3 percent O.

3. The molecular weight of the compound containing 82.8 percent C and 17.2 percent H by weight is 58. What is the true or molecular formula for the compound?

4. The molecular weight of the compound containing 2.0 percent H, 32.7 percent S, and 65.3 percent O by weight is 98. What is the true or molecular formula for the compound?

THE MOLE PRINCIPLE

How many grams of chlorine will react with 10 grams of hydrogen? What volume (STP) will this chlorine occupy? What is the weight of the product? What is the volume of the product? At first glance, it appears that four different problems are involved here. But all the information sought can be determined by using a single fundamental principle you have already learned—the **mole principle.** Let us see how this principle applies to the foregoing series of questions.

The equation for the reaction being considered is

$$H_2 + Cl_2 \longrightarrow 2\ HCl$$

All these materials are gaseous at standard conditions. *This equation has many interpretations;* let us look briefly at a few of them.

$$H_2 + Cl_2 \longrightarrow 2\ HCl\uparrow$$

| one molecule | + | one molecule | → | two molecules |

But chemical reactions involve far more than four or five molecules with exceedingly trifling weights. If we choose a more convenient unit for laboratory investigations—the gram—our interpretation becomes more meaningful.

$$H_2 + Cl_2 \longrightarrow 2\ HCl\uparrow$$

| 2 grams of hydrogen | + | 71 grams of chlorine | → | 73 grams of hydrogen chloride |

From the balanced equation, we know not only the weights of the individual elements and compounds but also the relative weights of the substances that combine and that are produced. Thus, in this equation, we can calculate (as on page 123) that 2 grams (2×1) of hydrogen combine with 71 grams (2×35.5) of chlorine to produce 73 grams [$2 \times (1 + 35.5)$] of hydrogen chloride. The values for hydrogen and chlorine *each represent 1 gram-molecular weight, or 1 mole, of the gas,* while the value for hydrogen chloride *represents 2 gram-molecular weights, or 2 moles.* Thus, we may also interpret the equation to read

| 1 mole of hydrogen | + | 1 mole of chlorine | → | 2 moles of hydrogen chloride |

| 1 molar volume of hydrogen | + | 1 molar volume of chlorine | → | 2 molar volumes of hydrogen chloride |

| 22.4 liters of hydrogen | + | 22.4 liters of chlorine | → | 2 × 22.4 liters of hydrogen chloride |

Finally, as 1 mole of any substance contains the Avogadro number of molecules, we can say:

| 6.02×10^{23} molecules of hydrogen | + | 6.02×10^{23} molecules of chlorine | → | $2 \times (6.02 \times 10^{23})$ molecules of hydrogen chloride |

Let us see how the mole principle, with its many interpretations, can provide the answers to the questions at the opening of this section.

The *first* step is, of course, to write the balanced equation for the reaction.

$$H_2 + Cl_2 \longrightarrow 2\ HCl\uparrow$$

As the *second* step, examine the coefficients in the equation to determine how many moles of each substance are represented. In this equation

1 mole of H_2 reacts with 1 mole of Cl_2 to produce 2 moles of HCl. Place these numbers beneath the respective substances in the equation:

$$H_2 \;+\; Cl_2 \longrightarrow 2\,HCl\uparrow$$
$$\text{1 mole} + \text{1 mole} \longrightarrow \text{2 moles}$$

The *third* step is to convert the given number of grams of hydrogen to moles. To do so, first ˌermine the number of grams per mole of hyˌgen: 2 grams/mole. Then divide the given ˌht of 10 grams by this value:

$$\frac{10 \text{ grams}}{2 \text{ grams/mole}} = 5 \text{ moles}$$

ˌ this number of moles above the H_2 and an x ˌe the Cl_2.

$$\begin{array}{ccc} 5 \text{ moles} & & x \\ H_2 & + & Cl_2 \longrightarrow 2\,HCl\uparrow \\ 1 \text{ mole} & & 1 \text{ mole} \end{array}$$

As the *fourth* step, set up the correct proportion and solve for x:

$$5 \text{ moles}:x = 1 \text{ mole}:1 \text{ mole}$$
$$x = \frac{5 \text{ moles} \times 1 \text{ mole}}{1 \text{ mole}}$$
$$x = 5 \text{ moles of } Cl_2$$

But the problem calls for the *weight* of chlorine. So, for the *fifth* step, convert the moles to actual weights. As 1 mole of Cl_2 weighs 71 grams (2×35.5), 5 moles of Cl_2 contain 355 grams:

$$5 \text{ moles} \times \frac{71 \text{ grams}}{\text{mole}} = 355 \text{ grams}$$

The reasoning in this *final* step can be modified to reveal immediately the volume occupied by 5 moles, or 355 grams of chlorine. Since 1 mole of any gaseous element or compound occupies 22.4 liters at **STP,** 5 moles of chlorine occupy 112 liters:

$$5 \text{ moles} \times \frac{22.4 \text{ liters}}{\text{mole}} = 112 \text{ liters}$$

Finally, you were asked to find the weight and volume of the HCl. To do so, repeat only the last part of step three and steps four and five from the previous part of the problem.

For step *three,* set up the correct relationship in terms of moles:

$$\begin{array}{ccc} 5 \text{ moles} & & x \\ H_2 & + & Cl_2 \longrightarrow 2\,HCl\uparrow \\ 1 \text{ mole} & & 2 \text{ moles} \end{array}$$

As step *four,* set up the correct proportion to determine the number of moles of HCl:

$$5 \text{ moles}:x = 1 \text{ mole}:2 \text{ moles}$$
$$x = \frac{5 \text{ moles} \times 2 \text{ moles}}{1 \text{ mole}}$$
$$x = 10 \text{ moles of HCl}$$

Then the weight of the HCl is determined in step *five:*

$$10 \text{ moles} \times \frac{36.5 \text{ grams}}{\text{mole}} = 365 \text{ grams of HCl}$$

The *final* step indicates the volume of HCl:

$$10 \text{ moles} \times \frac{22.4 \text{ liters}}{\text{mole}} = 224 \text{ liters of HCl}$$

Observe that in this complete series of calculations, you converted a weight in grams to moles, a number of moles to grams, and another number of moles to a volume in liters. But however one of these values is transformed into another, the relationship involved is always that of the *mole principle.*

To check your understanding of the mole method, study the sample problem on page 174.

PROBLEMS

1. Determine the volume of oxygen that combines with 93 grams of phosphorus to produce phosphorus pentoxide.

$$P_4 + 5\,O_2 \longrightarrow P_4O_{10}$$

2. Determine the weight of calcium oxide and the volume of carbon dioxide produced when 200 grams of calcium carbonate are decomposed by heating.

3. Determine the volume of hydrogen that could combine with 100 ml of nitrogen to produce ammonia, NH_3.

SAMPLE PROBLEM: MOLE METHOD

Problem

What weight of sodium is obtained by the electrolysis of 29.25 grams of molten NaCl?

Procedure

1. Write the balanced equation for the reaction.
2. Examine the coefficients of the appropriate substances to determine the number of moles of each. Place the correct number of moles beneath the respective formulas.
3. Determine the gram formula weight of the NaCl. Divide the given weight of NaCl by the number of grams per mole to convert the given weight to moles. Place the correct number of moles above the formula for NaCl. Place the letter x for an unknown number of moles of Na above its formula.
4. Set up the proportion and solve for x.
5. Convert the numerical value determined for x to weight in grams.

Solution

$$\frac{29.25 \text{ grams}}{58.5 \text{ grams/mole}} = 0.5 \text{ mole}$$

$$\begin{array}{cc} 0.5 \text{ mole} & x \\ \textbf{2 NaCl} \longrightarrow & \textbf{2 Na} + \textbf{Cl}_2\uparrow \\ 2 \text{ moles} & 2 \text{ moles} \end{array}$$

$$0.5 \text{ mole}:x = 2 \text{ moles}:2 \text{ moles}$$

$$x = \frac{0.5 \text{ mole} \times 2 \text{ moles}}{2 \text{ moles}}$$

$$x = 0.5 \text{ mole of Na}$$

$$0.5 \text{ mole} \times 23 \frac{\text{grams}}{\text{mole}} = 11.5 \text{ grams of Na}$$

OTHER METHODS OF DETERMINING WEIGHTS AND VOLUMES

Although there are other methods for solving problems in which an unknown weight or volume must be determined, *these methods are also dependent on a full and accurate interpretation of a balanced equation.* When both the reactants and products are in terms of weight, the problem is called a **weight-weight** problem, and the formulas involved *must* be interpreted *in terms of weight.* Similarily, when both the reactants and products are in terms of volume, the problem is called a **volume-volume** problem and the formulas must be interpreted *in terms of the volumes they represent.* With these ideas you can solve problems involving the weights and volumes of substances.

Weight-Weight Problems

Iron is extracted from iron(III) oxide by reducing it with carbon to produce iron and carbon dioxide. Suppose a chemist wishes to extract all the iron in 2,000 grams of pure iron oxide. What is the minimum weight of carbon needed?

The *first* step is to write a balanced equation for the reaction described:

$$2 \text{ Fe}_2\text{O}_3 + 3 \text{ C} \longrightarrow 4 \text{ Fe} + 3 \text{ CO}_2\uparrow$$

The *second* step is to determine from the formulas the formula weight or molecular weight of each reactant (Fe_2O_3 and C). Then multiply each weight by the coefficient preceding the formula to determine the relative weights, or equation weights, of each substance. Write these equation weights beneath their respective formulas. These equation weights, remember, may be followed by any unit of weight. Since in this problem the weight of Fe_2O_3 is in grams, it is most convenient to express equation weights in the same units.

$$\begin{array}{ccc} 2 \text{ Fe}_2\text{O}_3 & + & 3 \text{ C} \longrightarrow 4 \text{ Fe} + 3 \text{ CO}_2\uparrow \\ 2[2(56) + 3(16)] \text{ g} & & 3(12) \text{ g} \\ 320 \text{ g} & & 36 \text{ g} \end{array}$$

The *third* step may be reasoned as follows. If 36 grams of C are needed to react with 320 grams of Fe_2O_3, then x grams of C will be needed to react with 2,000 grams of Fe_2O_3. This is expressed by placing the given weight of ferric oxide above the Fe_2O_3 and an x above the carbon, the substance whose weight is to be determined:

$$\begin{array}{cc} 2{,}000 \text{ g} & x \\ 2 \text{ Fe}_2\text{O}_3 + 3 \text{ C} \longrightarrow 4 \text{ Fe} + 3 \text{ CO}_2\uparrow \\ 320 \text{ g} & 36 \text{ g} \end{array}$$

The *fourth* step requires setting up a proportion between the actual weights in the original problem and the equation weights, and solving for x:

$$2{,}000 \text{ g}:x = 320 \text{ g}:36 \text{ g}$$
$$320 \text{ g}:x = 2{,}000 \text{ g}:36 \text{ g}$$
$$x = \frac{2{,}000 \text{ g}:36 \text{ g}}{320 \text{ g}}$$
$$x = 225 \text{ g of C}$$

These calculations show that 225 grams of carbon is the minimum amount of carbon needed to react with 2,000 grams of Fe_2O_3.

Problems which involve determining only the weights of substances that take part in reactions are as you know, considered weight-weight problems. Check your understanding of weight-weight problems by the sample problem at the right.

PROBLEMS

1. How much zinc is needed to react with H_2SO_4 to produce 6 grams of hydrogen gas?

2. If 500 pounds of limestone ($CaCO_3$) are heated, what weight of lime (CaO) and what weight of CO_2 are produced?

3. What is the maximum amount of carbon disulfide (CS_2) produced when 1,000 grams of sulfur combine with carbon?

Volume-Volume Problems

During the electrolysis of water, hydrogen and oxygen are produced in a definite ratio by volume. Determine how many liters of oxygen are produced if 50 liters of hydrogen are produced.

This problem involving *volumes of two gases* is solved by much the same procedure as the previous ones, but the numbers involved in such a problem are usually quite simple. As each mole of any gas occupies the same molar volume (22.4 l at STP), the coefficient preceding the formula for each gas *represents the relative number of molar volumes taking part in the reaction. If only gases* are involved in a problem, only the combining volumes of the gases need be considered. Such problems, as you know, are usually called volume-volume problems.

SAMPLE WEIGHT-WEIGHT PROBLEM

Problem
What weight of water is needed to produce 60 grams of sodium hydroxide when sodium reacts with water?

Procedure
1. Write the balanced equation for the reaction.
2. Determine the formula weight of NaOH and the molecular weight of H_2O, and multiply each by the appropriate coefficient. Place these equation weights, expressed in the appropriate units, beneath the respective formulas.
3. Place the given weight of NaOH above its formula. Place the letter x, for the unknown weight of H_2O, above its formula.
4. Set up the proportion and solve for x.

Solution

$$\begin{array}{cc} & x \\ 2 \text{ Na} + & 2 \text{ H}_2\text{O} \longrightarrow \\ & 2(2 + 16) \text{ g} \qquad 60 \text{ g} \\ & 36 \text{ g} \qquad 2 \text{ NaOH} \quad + \text{ H}_2\uparrow \\ & \qquad 2(23 + 16 + 1) \text{ g} \\ & \qquad 80 \text{ g} \end{array}$$

$$x:60 \text{ g} = 36 \text{ g}:80 \text{ g}$$
$$x = \frac{60 \text{ g} \times 36 \text{ g}}{80 \text{ g}}$$
$$x = 27 \text{ g of } H_2O$$

The *first* step, as in other problems, is to write a balanced equation for the reaction.

$$2\,H_2O \xrightarrow[\text{DC}]{H_2SO_4} 2\,H_2\uparrow + O_2\uparrow$$

In the *second* step write beneath each gas the combining volume of the gas as represented by its coefficient.

$$2\,H_2O \longrightarrow \underset{\text{2 volumes}}{2\,H_2\uparrow} + \underset{\text{1 volume}}{O_2\uparrow}$$

As the *third* step write above the H_2 the number of liters of hydrogen produced and place an x above the O_2.

$$2\,H_2O \longrightarrow \overset{50\ l}{\underset{\text{2 volumes}}{2\,H_2\uparrow}} + \overset{x}{\underset{\text{1 volume}}{O_2\uparrow}}$$

The *fourth* step includes setting up the correct proportion and solving for x.

$$50\ l:x = 2\ \text{volumes}:1\ \text{volume}$$
$$x = \frac{50\ l \times 1\ \text{volume}}{2\ \text{volumes}}$$
$$x = 25\ l\ \text{of oxygen}$$

Solving the proportion shows that for each 50 liters of hydrogen produced by the electrolysis of water, 25 liters of oxygen are produced. You probably anticipated the answer since you determined by electrolysis that in H_2O the volume of hydrogen to oxygen is in the ratio of $2:1$.

Check your understanding of volume-volume problems by the sample problem at the right.

PROBLEMS

1. What volume of hydrogen chloride gas (at **STP**) will be formed if 10 liters of chlorine gas react completely with an excess of hydrogen gas?

2. How many milliliters of nitrogen dioxide (NO_2) are produced when 25 ml of nitric oxide (NO) react with excess oxygen (at **STP**)?

SAMPLE VOLUME-VOLUME PROBLEM

Problem

How many cubic feet of oxygen react with 10 cubic feet of acetylene (C_2H_2) to produce carbon dioxide and water?

Procedure

1. Write the balanced equation for the reaction.
2. Write below the formula of each gas, acetylene and oxygen, the combining volumes of the gas as represented by its coefficient.
3. Place the given volume of C_2H_2 above its formula. Place the letter x, for the unknown volume of O_2, above its formula.
4. Set up the proportion and solve for x.

Solution

$$\overset{\text{10 cubic ft}}{\underset{\text{2 volumes}}{2\,C_2H_2}} + \overset{x}{\underset{\text{5 volumes}}{5\,O_2}} \longrightarrow 4\,CO_2\uparrow + 2\,H_2O$$

$$10\ \text{cubic ft}:x = 2\ \text{volumes}:5\ \text{volumes}$$
$$x = \frac{10\ \text{cubic ft} \times 5\ \text{volumes}}{2\ \text{volumes}}$$
$$x = 25\ \text{cubic ft of}\ O_2$$

Weight-Volume Problems

Have you prepared oxygen by heating potassium chlorate. What *volume* of oxygen was produced by heating 20 grams of potassium chlorate?

In this problem we are concerned with finding the *volume* of a gas produced from a given *weight* of a substance—an example of a **weight-volume** problem. The procedure for solving this problem is similar to that already established for other problems—with one important difference. Since we are asked for the *volume* of oxygen, we must ask ourselves the *volume* represented by the oxygen from a known *weight* of solid.

Once again the *first* step is to write a balanced equation for the reaction.

$$2 \text{ KClO}_3 \longrightarrow 2 \text{ KCl} + 3 \text{ O}_2\uparrow$$

To complete step *two*, we must ask ourselves what *volume* is represented by "3 O_2." Since 1 mole of oxygen occupies 22.4 l (at **STP**), then 3 moles of oxygen must occupy $3 \times 22.4\ l$. Place this value under the oxygen and also the equation weight of $KClO_3$ under the formula:

$$\begin{array}{cc} 2 \text{ KClO}_3 & \longrightarrow \quad 2 \text{ KCl} + \quad 3 \text{ O}_2\uparrow \\ 2[39 + 35.5 + 3(16)] \text{ g} & 3(22.4)\ l \\ 245 \text{ g} & 67.2\ l \end{array}$$

For step *three* the problem now becomes: "If 67.2 l of oxygen (at **STP**) can be obtained by decomposing 245 gms of $KClO_3$, what volume should we expect on decomposing 20 grams of the solid?" To show this relationship, write the given weight of $KClO_3$ above the formula and place an x above the oxygen:

$$\begin{array}{cc} 20 \text{ g} & x \\ 2 \text{ KClO}_3 \longrightarrow & 2 \text{ KCl} + 3 \text{ O}_2\uparrow \\ 245 \text{ g} & 67.2\ l \end{array}$$

The *fourth* step provides the answer when you set up the correct proportion and solve for x:

$$20 \text{ g}:x = 245 \text{ g}:67.2\ l$$
$$x = \frac{20 \text{ g}:67.2\ l}{245 \text{ g}}$$
$$x = 5.49\ l$$

The complete decomposition of 20 grams of $KClO_3$ releases 5.49 l of oxygen (at **STP**). The proper interpretation of "3 O_2" does indeed lead to an answer in terms of liters—a unit of *volume*.

Check your understanding of weight-volume problems by the sample problem at the right.

PROBLEMS

1. How many liters of carbon monoxide (at **STP**) are produced when zinc is obtained from zinc oxide by heating 1,000 grams of zinc oxide with carbon? $\text{ZnO} + \text{C} \longrightarrow \text{Zn} + \text{CO}_2\uparrow$

2. Powdered antimony sprinkled into a jar of moist chlorine ignites spontaneously and forms antimony trichloride. How many liters of chlorine (at **STP**) are required to produce 50 grams of antimony trichloride?

$$2\text{Sb} + 3\text{Cl}_2 \longrightarrow 2\text{SbCl}_3$$

SAMPLE WEIGHT-VOLUME PROBLEM

Problem

What volume of hydrogen chloride (at **STP**) is produced when sodium chloride reacts with excess sulfuric acid to produce 20 grams of sodium sulfate in addition to hydrogen chloride?

Procedure

1. Write the balanced equation for the reaction.
2. Determine the formula weight of Na_2SO_4 and the gram molecular volume of the gas by multiplying 22.4 l by the coefficient of HCl. Place these values, expressed in the appropriate units, beneath the respective formulas.
3. Place the given weight of Na_2SO_4 above its formula. Place the letter x, for the unknown volume of HCl, above its formula.
4. Set up the proportion and solve for x.

Solution

$$2 \text{ NaCl} + \text{H}_2\text{SO}_4 \longrightarrow$$

$$\begin{array}{cc} 20 \text{ g} & x \\ \text{Na}_2\text{SO}_4 & + \quad 2 \text{ HCl}\uparrow \\ [(2 \times 23) + 32 + (4 \times 16)] \text{ g} & 2(22.4)\ l \\ 142 \text{ g} & 44.8\ l \end{array}$$

$$20 \text{ g}:x = 142 \text{ g}:44.8\ l$$
$$x = \frac{20 \text{ g} \times 44.8\ l}{142 \text{ g}}$$
$$x = 6.3\ l \text{ of HCl}$$

A Final Word

A review of the problems labeled weight-weight, weight-volume, or volume-volume problems will alert you to a significant observation— *all these problems can be solved by using the mole method.* A weight in grams or a volume in liters can be converted into moles, and moles can be converted into weight in grams or volume in liters, if we are dealing with a gas. It is for this reason that the mole method has become a powerful tool of the chemist in solving problems like those in this chapter.

ADDITIONAL PROBLEMS

1. Determine the percentage composition of each of the following compounds: HCl, $C_6H_{12}O_6$, H_2O_2, KCl, $NaNO_3$, $Al_2(SO_4)_3$, $NiSO_4 \cdot 7 H_2O$.

2. Find the percentage of water in the compound $CuSO_4 \cdot 5 H_2O$.

3. Determine the simplest (empirical) formula for the two compounds of carbon and hydrogen with the following percentage compositions:
   (a) 91.3 percent C and 8.7 percent H
   (b) 75 percent C and 25 percent H.

4. An oxide of copper contains 88.8 percent copper and 11.2 percent oxygen. What is the simplest formula of the compound?

5. The molecular weight of the compound containing 5.9 percent hydrogen and 94.1 percent oxygen is 34. Determine the true (or molecular) formula of the compound.

6. The molecular weight of the compound containing 40 percent carbon, 6.7 percent hydrogen, and 53.3 percent oxygen is 180. What is its molecular formula?

7. How many grams of mercuric oxide are needed to produce 40 grams of oxygen?

8. What is the maximum amount of copper obtained when 50 pounds of cuprous oxide react with an unlimited supply of cuprous sulfide to form metallic copper and sulfur dioxide ($2 Cu_2O + Cu_2S \longrightarrow 6 Cu + SO_2$)?

9. (a) When cuprous oxide combines with cuprous sulfide to form metallic copper (see Question 8), what volume of sulfur dioxide is released? (b) what weight of sulfur dioxide?

10. (a) What volume of chlorine gas (**STP**) is required to replace (release) the bromine from 178.5 grams of potassium bromide? (b) How much will this volume of gas weigh?

11. (a) How many grams of sodium react vigorously with water to produce sodium hydroxide and 10 grams of hydrogen? (b) How much sodium hydroxide is produced from this same weight of sodium?

12. When carbon dioxide is bubbled into limewater [$Ca(OH)_2$], calcium carbonate precipitates and water is formed. How much carbon dioxide, both by weight and by volume, is needed to cause the precipitation of 10 grams of calcium carbonate?

13. (a) Determine the weight of sodium carbonate produced when 50 pounds of sodium hydrogen carbonate ($NaHCO_3$) are heated to produce sodium carbonate, water, and carbon dioxide. (b) Determine the volume of water produced. (c) Determine the volume of CO_2 produced. (Use the mole method.)

14. (a) Determine the volume of oxygen that combines with 300 grams of lead sulfide to produce lead oxide and sulfur dioxide. (b) Determine the volume and weight of sulfur dioxide produced. (Use the mole method.)

15. When 200 grams of methane (CH_4) are burned completely in air, carbon dioxide and water are produced. (a) What volume of carbon dioxide is produced? (b) What weight of water is produced? (Use the mole method.)

The Behavior
of Substances in Solution

The nineteenth-century scientist, busy discovering new facts, found himself perplexed by many of his observations. The shaker on his dining room table contained sodium chloride, known to contain sodium and chlorine—yet the solid did not, like sodium, react violently with water nor was it, like chlorine, greenish-yellow in color. When he sprinkled some of this white solid into water that was just boiling, the boiling stopped—but it quickly resumed at a slightly higher temperature. And if electrodes connected to a source of current were introduced, the solution would conduct a current, although neither pure water nor solid table salt would do so.

Svante Arrhenius, the Swedish scientist who provided an explanation of these apparently unrelated phenomena, was only twenty-three years of age when he approached his professor (at the University of Uppsala in Sweden) with the statement that he had developed a working hypothesis to account for the facts. The rejection of his bold new ideas was most disheartening. But Arrehenius persisted in his work—work that met with repeated opposition. Finally, with the aid of other, more open-minded scientists, Arrhenius succeeded in having his original statement of the theory of electrolytic dissociation printed in the *Journal of Physical Chemistry*. Gradually opposition to his theory was overcome. Full recognition of his work came when he was awarded the Nobel prize in chemistry in 1903.

12

The Nature of Solutions

The water in the ocean is not pure water. It is a solution, containing sodium chloride and many other minerals. As a salt solution, this sea water has few practical uses. It cannot be used for drinking and is useless to the farmer in irrigating his crops. But when sea water is *desalinated*—when the salt is removed—it has all the life-giving properties of ordinary water.

The water supply of our country is limited and man is using it faster than nature can replace it. That is why the Federal Government is spending millions of dollars to develop an inexpensive, practical way of desalinating the sea water. With our population growing constantly, an adequate water supply will be a life-or-death matter for future generations.

SOLUTIONS AND SOLUBILITY

Millions of years ago the water in the ocean contained less salt than it does today. Gradually, as the rain washed the salt and other minerals of the earth's crust into the sea, the water became saltier. Since the particles of all substances are in constant motion, the minerals intermingled and became thoroughly mixed with the sea water. If we examine a sample of the mixture that resulted—the sea water today—every part of the sample tastes and looks very much the same. Sea water is truly a *homogeneous* substance.

Suppose we take a sample of sea water and add more salt to it. After gentle stirring, the salt "disappears" and the sample of water becomes homogeneous once more. The water has the same appearance it had before but it tastes "saltier." Evidently, then, sea water must be a mixture and not a compound. It can contain salt in different proportions by weight, whereas the proportions in a compound are always the same.

Homogeneous mixtures, such as sea water, which contain two or more substances are called **solutions.** The substances that are mixed together in the solution are called the *components* of the solution. One component of the solution is said to dissolve in the other component. This dissolving may result solely from physical mixing, or it may be aided by chemical

12-1 Brass is a solid solution in which the lattice points are occupied in a random arrangement by copper and zinc ions of about the same size.

12-2 Iodine dissolves readily in alcohol . . .

. . . but is almost insoluble in water.

Oil and carbon tetrachloride are miscible liquids . . .

. . . but oil and water are immiscible.

reactions. Whatever the circumstances, dissolving alters the properties of the components, and solutions involving combinations of all three states of matter—even two solids—exist.

Gaseous and Solid Solutions

Air is an example of a **gaseous solution.** It is a mixture of several gaseous substances dissolved in each other. Though oxygen, nitrogen, carbon dioxide, and water vapor make up most of the air, they represent only a few of its gaseous substances. Although the amount of each pure substance found in air is usually the same, variations are noted. For example, the amount of water vapor found in air (its humidity) varies from day to day. Because the molecules of gases have little attraction for each other, they can be mixed together in all proportions. Among the many useful gaseous solutions are the mixture of gasoline vapor and air in the carburetor of a car, as well as water gas, a mixture of carbon monoxide and hydrogen used industrially.

Some of our most familiar solids are also solutions—that is, they are homogeneous mixtures rather than compounds. Alloys such as solder and sterling silver are examples. Solder is a mixture of lead and tin dissolved in each other. Sterling silver is a solution of silver and copper. In many solids, you recall, positive ions are arranged in a definite pattern or space lattice. When elements have ions of about the same size and the same type of electron structure, such as the copper and zinc ions in brass, the ions of the metals often replace one another to form relatively rigid *solid solutions* (Fig. 12-1). A definite space lattice still exists, but there is no definite arrangement or order as to which lattice points are occupied by ions of a particular metallic element. On the other hand, since the structure of some steel alloys is not homogeneous, but consists of separate tiny crystals of the components, steel is not a solid solution.

Liquid Solutions

Liquid solutions are commonplace. Gases or solids may be dissolved in a liquid, and two liquids may be mutually soluble. Soda water, for example, consists of carbon dioxide gas dissolved in water. A salt solution represents a solid dissolved in a liquid. Two liquids, such as alcohol and water, which mix uniformly with one another in all proportions are *miscible;* while two liquids, such as kerosene and water, which hardly dissolve in each other, are *immiscible.*

Liquids may dissolve different substances to form liquid solutions. For example, if a crystal of iodine is placed in alcohol it dissolves, but the same iodine hardly dissolves in water. Carbon tetrachloride is useful in cleaning clothes because it dissolves many greases and oils; neither grease nor oil dissolves in water (Fig. 12-2). Most of the solutions used in high school chemistry are liquid solutions containing water as one of the components. For this reason we shall consider the nature of water or **aqueous** solutions in some detail.

Without aqueous solutions no form of life could exist, at least on this planet. Before any animal, including man, can use food as a source of energy, that food must first be digested, and then dissolved in the plasma (mainly water) portion of the blood. Green plants that make their own food depend upon minerals from the soil; but the plants cannot use these minerals unless they are first dissolved in water. Whenever a solid dissolves in a liquid, the solid is called the **solute** and the liquid is referred to as the **solvent.** Thus, salt dissolved in water is an example of a solute dissolved in a solvent.

Solubility

Salt dissolves in water; fat does not. A lump of sugar placed in a cup of very hot tea dissolves completely; but if a lump of sugar is dropped into a glass of iced tea, some of the sugar does not dissolve, but settles to the bottom of the glass.

When you remove the cap from a bottle of soda pop, bubbles of carbon dioxide gas begin to escape. If the bottle is allowed to remain open for some time, the gas escapes almost completely; the soda tastes flat. You have probably also found that heat affects the rate at which the carbon dioxide escapes from the open bottle of soda. If the bottle is warm, the CO_2 gas escapes faster from the water. Since gases dissolve more readily in colder liquids, increasing the temperature of a liquid causes more dissolved gas to come out of solution. The ability of substances to dissolve is referred to as **solubility.** Besides temperature, solubility is also determined by the chemical nature of both the solvent and solute particles. Moreover, for gases dissolved in liquids, pressure is an important factor in solubility—at any given temperature, solubility increases with pressure.

You have already noted the contrast between carbon tetrachloride and water as solvents for grease. The grease does not dissolve in water, but it does dissolve in carbon tetrachloride and other "cleaning fluids." Salt, on the other hand, is soluble in water but not in carbon tetrachloride. Are water and carbon tetrachloride miscible? If you try to mix the two, the denser carbon tetrachloride sinks to the bottom of the container; no mixing occurs. Since carbon tetrachloride is a nonpolar compound, its electronic charge is distributed evenly throughout each of its molecules. Water molecules, on the other hand, are polar. The oxygen end of each molecule is more negatively charged than the hydrogen end. Molecules of grease or fat, like molecules of carbon tetrachloride, are nonpolar. From these various examples you can infer several things. Ionic compounds such as sodium chloride usually dissolve in polar substances such as water. Nonpolar substances such as fat dissolve in other nonpolar substances such as ether. Polar and nonpolar molecules do not usually dissolve in each other. The more alike any two substances are in their electronic structure, the more chance there is that they will form a solution.

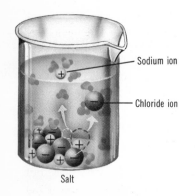

Sodium ion

Chloride ion

Salt

12-3a When sodium chloride dissolves in water, the ions become hydrated: each sodium ion (+) is surrounded by the negative ends of water molecules; each chloride ion (−) is surrounded by the positive ends of water molecules.

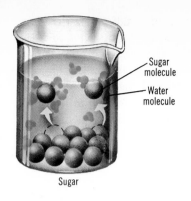

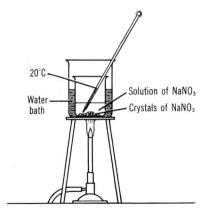

Sugar molecule
Water molecule

Sugar

12-3b When sugar dissolves in water, the molecules become hydrated: each sugar molecule is hydrogen-bonded to a cluster of water molecules.

20°C
Water bath

Solution of NaNO₃
Crystals of NaNO₃

While the solution process is not completely understood, chemists believe that they have at least some understanding of why solutions are formed by particles which are similar. When an ionic substance comes in contact with polar water molecules, the negative end of each water molecule is attracted toward a positive ion (Fig. 12-3a). In this way each positive ion becomes surrounded by water molecules. In the same way, negative ions attract to themselves the positive ends of water molecules; thus each negative ion also becomes surrounded by water molecules. Such ions surrounded by water molecules are called **hydrated ions.** (In liquids other than water, the ions of the solute are said to be *solvated.*) When ions become hydrated, **hydration energy** is given off. If this hydration energy is greater than the lattice energy, the bonds in the lattice will be broken and the hydrated ions will be free to move apart.

In all probability, when molecular substances, such as sugar or alcohol, dissolve in water, the molecules of these solutes also become hydrated. In other words, each molecule of sugar or alcohol becomes surrounded by a cluster of water molecules. The way this hydration is believed to take place is shown in Fig. 12-3b. Each hydrogen atom in water acts as a connecting link between two oxygen atoms—between the oxygen atom in a molecule of water and an oxygen atom in a molecule of sugar or alcohol. Here is another example of the special type of linkage known as hydrogen bonding.

Limit of Solubility

If you place a lump of sugar in a beaker of water at room temperature, and an equal weight of granulated sugar in another beaker, the smaller particles of the granulated sugar are found to dissolve more rapidly. You can increase the rate of dissolving of the lump sugar by heating the water. Stirring the hot water increases the rate of solution still further. It is evident, then, that the rate at which a solid dissolves in a liquid is affected by three things: by the size of the solute particles, by heat, and by stirring. *Try the following investigation* to determine more precisely the importance of heat and stirring.

Place 96 grams of powdered sodium nitrate in a beaker containing 100 grams of water and stir the solution. The sodium nitrate (NaNO₃) begins to dissolve. Keep the solution of sodium nitrate at a temperature of 20° C by using a water bath like that shown at the left. Continue to stir the solution until no further effect is noted. Does all the sodium nitrate in the beaker dissolve?

If not, gradually heat the solution while stirring it. *(Never allow a thermometer to touch the bottom of a beaker that is being heated.)* At what temperature does all of the solute dissolve? If it dissolves at 30° C, maintain this temperature and add more sodium nitrate. Stir the solution. If the additional sodium nitrate settles to the bottom of the beaker, determine how you can make it dissolve.

Table 12-1 SOLUTE DIS-SOLVED PER 100 GRAMS OF WATER

Compound	Amount at 20° C (grams)
AgCl	0.00015
AgNO$_3$	222.0
Ce$_2$(SO$_4$)$_3$	8.69
KI	144.0
LiOH	12.8
NaCl	36.0
NaNO$_3$	88.0
NH$_4$Cl	37.2
PbI$_2$	0.068

12-4 Solubility curves indicate that the solubility of most compounds increases with an increase in temperature.

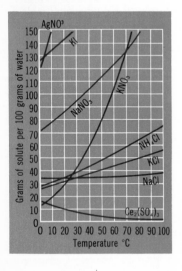

Evidently 100 grams of water at a temperature of 20° C can dissolve only a certain amount of sodium nitrate. Experimentation has proved that the greatest amount of sodium nitrate that will dissolve in 100 grams of water at 20° C is 88 grams. Hence 8 grams of the original 96 grams of sodium nitrate remain undissolved at the bottom of the beaker. Increasing the temperature of the water will, however, increase the limit of solubility. At 30° C, all 96 grams of sodium nitrate dissolve. When a solution contains as much solute as can possibly be dissolved at a given temperature, the solution is **saturated.** A solution that contains less than the amount of solute which can be dissolved at a given temperature is **unsaturated.**

The greater the amount of solid that will dissolve in a given amount of solvent to form a saturated solution, the more soluble that solute is. The weights of several solutes that will dissolve in 100 grams of water at 20° C are shown in Table 12-1. Notice that some of these solids, like sodium nitrate, are quite soluble. Others, like lead iodide (PbI$_2$), are considered slightly soluble. Substances like silver chloride (AgCl), whose saturated solutions contain very little solute, are said to be negligibly soluble or **insoluble.**

Do not think that once any solution is saturated, no further reaction takes place. If you place a relatively large crystal of sodium nitrate in a saturated solution of the compound, the weight of the crystal remains unchanged. Yet the crystal changes its shape over a period of time. Why? Ions are constantly breaking away from the solid crystal lattice and going into solution. But for each ion that dissolves, another ion leaves the solution and becomes part of the lattice structure of the crystal. While the system as a whole appears to be unchanged, two processes, the solution of ions and the precipitation of ions from the solution, are occurring continuously *at the same speed.* To demonstrate this, break off one corner of a perfectly formed crystal before placing it in a filtered saturated solution. Cover the solution to prevent evaporation, and observe that, over a long period of time, a perfect crystal re-forms. Such a crystal may appear to have a slightly smaller size because the ions have been redistributed. A solid in contact with its saturated solution is another example of a system in dynamic equilibrium. In a saturated solution the dissolved solute is in equilibrium with the undissolved solute.

Solubility Curves

A convenient way of showing how the solubility of solid substances changes with temperature appears in the graph in Fig. 12-4. This graph indicates the amounts of different solids that will dissolve in 100 grams of water at various temperatures. Observe that just below 20° C, 100 grams of water dissolve 36 grams of either NH$_4$Cl or NaCl. In other words, at about 20° C a saturated solution of either of these substances contains 36 grams of solute per 100 grams of water. How many grams of KI would a saturated solution contain at this temperature?

Each line or curve on the graph in Fig. 12-4 indicates the solubility of a solid at different temperatures. It is called a **solubility curve.** Studying individual curves and comparing one curve with another can tell us a good deal. For example, the gradual slope of the solubility curve for NaCl indicates that the solubility of NaCl is not greatly affected by increased temperature. The steeper slope of the curve labeled KNO_3 shows that even a slight change in temperature causes extreme changes in the solubility of this substance. Notice also that KNO_3 is far more soluble than NaCl at the temperatures shown. And notice that one compound on the graph actually becomes less soluble with increased temperatures. Which compound is it?

Supersaturation

If you are a camera enthusiast, you know that occasionally crystals appear in a bottle of hypo solution. To understand why this happens, *try this investigation.*

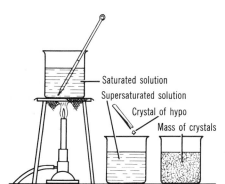

Saturated solution
Supersaturated solution
Crystal of hypo
Mass of crystals

Add 300 grams of photographer's hypo ($Na_2S_2O_3 \cdot 5\,H_2O$) to 100 grams of water and heat the mixture to 45° C. A few of the hypo crystals remain at the bottom of the beaker. The hypo solution is saturated, and in equilibrium with the remaining solid hypo crystals.

Raise the temperature to 75° C, and add sufficient hypo crystals to make sure that the solution is saturated at this higher temperature. Now raise the temperature to 80° C to make sure that all of this additional solid has dissolved. To make quite certain that the hot solution is clear it may be necessary to filter it.

Place a cover over the clear solution to prevent dust from entering it and allow the solution to cool *undisturbed* to at least 45° C. Probably no change occurs. Now jar the solution quickly. If nothing happens, add a tiny additional crystal of hypo to the solution. Does a large amount of hypo immediately crystallize out and remain in equilibrium with a saturated solution of the compound?

As long as the solution is undisturbed in any way, it remains clear. No hypo settles to the bottom of the beaker even though the cooling continues below the 45° C point. Obviously this cool, undisturbed solution contains far more than the 300 grams of hypo which originally made the solution saturated at 45° C. A solution that has a higher concentration of solute than a saturated solution normally would have at that temperature is **supersaturated.** As your investigation indicates, supersaturated solutions are very unstable.

Concentrated and Dilute Solutions

Observe the labels on the bottles of some of the solutions in your chemistry room, for example, those marked concentrated sulfuric acid

12-5 A saturated solution of the highly soluble salt potassium iodide is a concentrated solution; a saturated solution of the almost insoluble salt silver chloride is a dilute solution.

and dilute sulfuric acid. Concentrated sulfuric acid, as the name implies, contains a fairly large amount of solute dissolved in water. It contains about 95 percent by weight of hydrogen sulfate to 5 percent water. Dilute sulfuric acid, on the other hand, can be made by cautiously and gradually pouring a very small amount of concentrated sulfuric acid into water. Also observe several bottles of sodium hydroxide. These and other hydroxides—which are also known as *bases*—are prepared in both concentrated and dilute form.

The terms "concentrated" and "dilute" refer to the *relative* amounts of solute and solvent in a solution. Any solution that contains a large amount of solute in relation to the amount of solvent is said to be *concentrated*. If the amount of solute is low in relation to the amount of solvent, the solution is *dilute*.

Is a saturated solution necessarily a concentrated solution? Refer again to Table 12-1. Observe that a saturated solution of potassium iodide (KI) at 20° C contains 144 grams of solute for each 100 grams of water. This is an example of a solution which is both concentrated and saturated. On the other hand, observe that a saturated solution of silver chloride (AgCl) at 20° C contains only 0.00015 grams of solute in 100 grams of water (Fig. 12-5). This solution is dilute even though it is saturated. Further study of other compounds listed in the table will reveal that some saturated solutions are concentrated, while others are dilute.

QUESTIONS AND PROBLEMS

1. (a) List three factors that affect the solubility of any solid. (b) How does the effect of temperature on the solubility of a gas differ from its effect on most solids?
2. Define the terms *solute, solvent, miscible, immiscible, hydrated ion*.
3. (a) Chemists frequently say that "like dissolves like." Explain the meaning of this statement in terms of polar, nonpolar, and ionic compounds. (b) Contrast the way in which ionic potassium chloride (KCl) dissolves in water with the way in which covalent glucose ($C_6H_{12}O_6$) dissolves.
4. (a) Differentiate among a saturated solution, an unsaturated solution, and a supersaturated solution. (b) Some saturated solutions are concentrated, while others are dilute. Explain, using compounds from the table on page 184.

EXPRESSING CONCENTRATION

To express the concentration of a solution precisely, we often use a numerical value. One commonly used method of expressing concentration numerically is percent by weight. Perhaps you have used a 5 percent salt solution or a 10 percent sugar solution. Such percentages tell us how many parts by weight of the solute are present in 100 parts by weight of the solution.

For the chemist, however, percent by weight is not usually a very satisfactory way of expressing the concentration of solutions. He finds three other methods more useful for his purpose. These methods of expressing concentration, all of which are used in preparing **standard solutions** or solutions which can be used to determine the concentration of other solutions, are **molar** concentration, **normal** concentration, and **molal** concentration. Let's examine them in turn.

Molar Concentration

Because of the many chemical reactions occurring between solutes, it is often important for the chemist to know the number of solute particles in a given amount of solution. Therefore, he often expresses the concentration of a solution by indicating the number of moles (either gram molecular weights or gram formula weights) of the solute present in each liter of solution. This is called the **molar concentration,** or simply the **molarity,** of the solution. Thus *a 1 molar solution* (designated 1 *M*) *contains 1 mole of solute per liter of solution.* (Though occasionally the term *formal concentration* is used to apply specifically to such solutions of nonmolecular substances, we shall follow the usual procedure and use molar concentration to apply to both molecular and nonmolecular solutions.)

To make a solution of a specific molarity two things must be known: the **GMW** or **GFW** of the solute and the total volume of the solution that is required. Suppose, for instance, that a chemist wants to make 1 liter of a 1 molar solution of sucrose ($C_{12}H_{22}O_{11}$). Since the **GMW** of sucrose is 342 grams, he makes the solution by dissolving 342 grams of sucrose in enough water to make *1 liter of the solution* (Fig. 12-6). For a 2 *M* solution of sucrose, he would dissolve 2 **GMW** (2 × 342 grams) or 684 grams of sucrose in enough water to make 1 liter of solution.

Suppose that a 1 *M* solution of sodium chloride is required. Since the **GFW** of NaCl is 58.5 grams, a 1 *M* solution is made by dissolving 58.5 grams of the solute in sufficient water to make a liter of solution. Possibly only a 0.1 *M* solution is needed. In that case, one-tenth of the **GFW** of NaCl, or 5.85 grams, is added to water to make 1 liter of solution. Or perhaps the requirement is for only one-half a liter of a 1 *M* solution of the same solute. In that case half the **GFW** of NaCl, 29.25 grams, is dissolved in enough water to make half a liter, 500 ml, of the solution.

Number of Solute Particles in Molar Solutions

The number of *solute* particles in a molar solution can be found if three things are known: the molarity of the solution, its volume, and the nature of the dissolved solute. Both the molarity of a solution and the identity of the solute will be indicated on its container. The volume is either known or can be measured quite easily. Both molecular and ionic

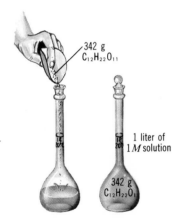

342 g
$C_{12}H_{22}O_{11}$

1 liter of
1 *M* solution

342 g
$C_{12}H_{22}O_{11}$

12-6 A 1 molar solution of sucrose is made by dissolving 1 mole, or gram molecular weight, of sucrose (342 grams) in enough water to make 1 liter of solution.

particles exist in solution. If the solute is molecular, each liter of a 1 M solution contains 1 mole (6.02×10^{23}) of the solute particles. One liter of a 2 M solution would therefore contain 2 moles (12.04×10^{23}) of the solute molecules.

It is also important for the chemist to know how many ions are present in solutions which contain either ionic solutes or substances that form ions when placed in water. (In the next chapter you will learn that not only do ionic solids dissolve in water but also some molecular substances, notably the strong acids, form ions when in water.) One **GFW** of an ionic substance will contain two, three, four, or some other whole number of moles of ions. For instance, a liter of 1 M solution of sodium chloride contains one mole of Na^+ ions and one of Cl^- ions—or a total of 2 moles of ions. Similarly, a liter of 1 M sodium hydroxide (NaOH) contains 1 mole of sodium ions and 1 mole of hydroxide ions. On the other hand, a liter of 1 M sodium sulfate (Na_2SO_4) contains 2 moles of sodium ions and 1 mole of sulfate ions—a total of 3 moles of ions. A liter of 1 M sulfuric acid (H_2SO_4) also contains 3 moles of ions, 2 moles of hydrogen ions and 1 mole of sulfate ions. From all these examples, observe that the total number of moles of ions present in each liter of a 1 M ionic solution always equals the sum of the number of ions represented by the formula for the solute or the number of ions formed when a molecular solute, such as an acid, is placed in water.

Normal Solutions of Acids

Not all 1 molar solutions contain the same number of solute particles. Yet for certain purposes (such as titration, to be considered in Chapter 15) it is helpful if the chemist can use solutions in which equal volumes *do* contain the same number of *either* positive *or* negative solute ions. To prepare solutions in which equal volumes of acids contain the same number of positive (H^+) ions, and in which equal volumes of bases contain the same number of negative (OH^-) ions, chemists use the method of expressing concentration called **normal concentration,** or **normality.**

As there are twice as many hydrogen ions in a liter of 1 M H_2SO_4 as in a liter of 1 M HCl, a half-liter of 1 molar H_2SO_4 contains the *same* number of H^+ ions as in 1 liter of 1 molar solution of HCl—1 mole in each case. The weight in grams of acid that is needed to supply 1 mole of H^+ ions is called the **gram equivalent weight (GEW)** of that acid.

Hence *a 1 normal solution* (designated 1 N) *contains one gram equivalent weight per liter of solution.* As a rule of thumb, *the* **GEW** *of an acid can be found by dividing its gram molecular weight by the subscript that follows the symbol for hydrogen* in the formula for the acid. Thus:

$$\text{GEW} \atop (\text{acid}) = \frac{\text{GMW}}{\text{subscript following H symbol in formula}}$$

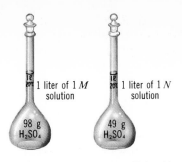

12-7 A liter of 1 molar sulfuric acid contains 1 gram molecular weight, or 98 grams, of H_2SO_4; a 1 normal solution contains 1 gram equivalent weight, or 49 grams, of H_2SO_4.

Using this formula, you can determine easily that the **GEW** of HCl is equal to its **GMW**—or 36.5 grams. The **GEW** of H_2SO_4 is equal to its **GMW** (98 grams) divided by 2—or 49 grams. Thus 1 liter of a 1 N solution of hydrochloric acid contains 36.5 grams of pure HCl while 1 liter of a 1 N sulfuric acid solution contains only 49 grams of pure H_2SO_4. Also, 1 liter of 2 N hydrochloric acid contains 73 grams (2 × 36.5 grams) of HCl while a 2 N solution of sulfuric acid contains 98 grams (2 × 49 grams) per liter. Chemists often use solutions of 0.1 N acid. One liter of 0.1 N solution of H_2SO_4 therefore contains 4.9 grams (¹⁄₁₀ × 49 grams) of pure H_2SO_4. Prove to yourself that a 1 normal solution of HCl is also 1 molar, but that a 1 normal solution of H_2SO_4 is only 0.5 M (Fig. 12-7).

Normal Solutions of Bases

Normal solutions of bases are determined in a manner similar to that used for acids. One liter of a *normal* solution of any base contains the same number of OH^- ions—1 mole in each case. The weight in grams of the amount of base needed to supply 1 mole of OH^- ions is the *gram equivalent weight* of that base. *The **GEW** of a base can be determined quickly by dividing its gram formula weight by the subscript that follows the OH^- radical in the formula for the base.* Thus the **GEW** of NaOH equals its **GFW**—40 grams. The **GEW** of $Ba(OH)_2$ is equal to its **GFW** (171 grams) divided by 2, or 85.5 grams. One liter of 1 *molar* sodium hydroxide, which contains 1 mole of OH^- ions, is also 1 *normal*. But 1 liter of 1 *molar* barium hydroxide, which contains 2 moles of OH^- ions, is therefore 2 *normal*.

A liter of a 1 N solution of sodium hydroxide contains 40 grams of NaOH, while 1 liter of 1 N barium hydroxide contains only 85.5 grams (171 grams ÷ 2) of $Ba(OH)_2$. Also, a liter of 2 N sodium hydroxide contains 80 grams (2 × 40 grams) of NaOH while a 2 N solution of calcium hydroxide contains 74 grams per liter. Similarly, 1 liter of a 0.1 N solution of NaOH contains 4 grams (¹⁄₁₀ × 40 grams) of NaOH, while 1 liter of a 0.1 N solution of $Ba(OH)_2$ contains 8.55 grams (¹⁄₁₀ × 85.5 grams) of $Ba(OH)_2$.

Molal Concentration

It is virtually impossible to find the exact number of *solvent* particles or total number of particles (solvent and solute) in a molar or normal solution. To do this the chemist would need to know the *exact* volume of the solvent which must be added to the solute to make a liter of the solution. To get around his inability to determine the exact number of particles in the solution, the chemist uses a **molal solution.** In molal solutions a specified amount of solvent is always used. A *1 molal solution* (designated 1 *m*) *contains 1 mole of solute per 1,000 grams of solvent.*

The terms *molar* and *molal* are similar, and it is important not to confuse them. **Molal concentration,** or **molality,** indicates the number of

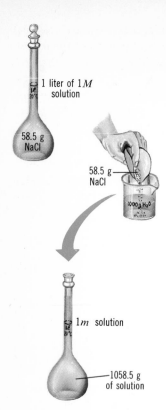

1 liter of 1M solution

58.5 g NaCl

58.5 g NaCl

1000g H₂O

1m solution

1058.5 g of solution

12-8 A 1 molar solution of sodium chloride contains 1 mole, or 58.5 grams, of NaCl in enough water to make 1 liter of solution. A 1 molal solution is made by dissolving 58.5 grams of NaCl in 1,000 grams of solvent.

moles (**GFW** or **GMW**) of solute present in *1,000 grams of solvent. Molar* concentration, remember, refers to the number of moles (**GFW** or **GMW**) of solute in *1 liter of solution.* A 1 molal (1 *m*) solution of sucrose, therefore, is a solution in which 342 grams of sucrose have been dissolved in 1,000 grams of water, while a 1 *m* NaCl solution is one in which 58.5 grams of NaCl have been dissolved in 1,000 grams of water (Fig. 12-8). In a 2 *m* NaCl solution, 117 grams of NaCl (58.5 grams × 2) have been dissolved in 1,000 grams of water—in each case the solute is dissolved in the same specified amount of solvent, 1,000 grams. If a 0.5 molal solution is needed, it can be made by dissolving half the **GFW** weight of the NaCl (29.25 grams) in 1000 grams of water. (This actually gives 1029.25 grams of solution.)

To determine the *total* number of particles in a molal solution, three things must be known: the molality of the solution, the nature of the solute particles, and the weight of the solvent. What, for example, is the total number of particles if 1 mole of sucrose dissolves in 1000 grams of water? First determine the number of *moles of particles* in the solution, and then find the actual *number of particles.* You know that 1 **GMW** of sucrose contains 1 mole of sucrose molecules. To find the number of solvent particles, recall that the **GMW** of water is 18 grams. Therefore 1,000 grams of water contain 55.6 moles of water molecules.

$$\frac{1,000 \text{ grams H}_2\text{O}}{18 \text{ grams/mole}} = 55.6 \text{ moles H}_2\text{O}$$

The total number of moles of particles in the 1 *m* solution is equal to the number of moles of particles in the solution plus the number of moles of particles in the solvent, or 56.6 moles (1 mole of $C_{12}H_{22}O_{11}$ + 55.6 moles of H_2O). To find the actual number of particles in the solution, multiply the total number of moles by 6.02×10^{23}; the solution contains 340.7×10^{23} molecules. Or take a 2 *m* solution of NaCl, made by dissolving 2 moles of NaCl in 1,000 grams of water. The solution then contains 59.6 moles of particles: 2 moles of Na^+ ions, 2 moles of Cl^- ions, and 55.6 moles of water molecules. What is the total number of particles in the solution?

QUESTIONS AND PROBLEMS

1. (a) Describe the preparation of 1 liter of each of the following solutions: 1 *M* glucose ($C_6H_{12}O_6$) solution, 1 *M* potassium nitrate (KNO_3) solution, and 2 *M* KNO_3 solution. (b) How would you make 250 ml of a 1 *M* barium hydroxide [$Ba(OH)_2$] solution? (c) How would you prepare a liter of 0.1 *M* solution of KNO_3?
2. Indicate the number of moles of each type of ion present in a 1 *M* solution of each of the following: nitric acid (HNO_3), sodium hydroxide (NaOH), barium hydroxide [$Ba(OH)_2$], phosphoric acid

(H_3PO_4), potassium chloride (KCl), and sodium carbonate (Na_2CO_3).

3. (a) Determine the number of grams of pure acid in each of the following solutions: 1 liter of 1 N hydrobromic acid (HBr), 500 ml of 1 N sulfurous acid (H_2SO_3), 1 liter of 2 N H_2SO_3, and 2 liters of 0.1 N phosphoric acid (H_3PO_4). (b) Determine the number of grams of base in each of the following solutions: 1 liter of 1 N potassium hydroxide (KOH), 500 ml of 1 N barium hydroxide [$Ba(OH)_2$], 1 liter of 2 N $Ba(OH)_2$, and 2 liters of 0.2 N $Sr(OH)_2$.

4. (a) Describe a method of preparing each of the following solutions: 1 m glucose $(C_6H_{12}O_6)$; 1 m potassium nitrate (KNO_3); 2 m potassium nitrate. (b) How does each of these molal (m) solutions differ from the corresponding 1 M solution?

CHANGES IN SOLVENT PROPERTIES

If you live in that part of the nation where winter temperatures fall below freezing, you know that a noncorrosive liquid such as ethylene glycol or methyl alcohol must be added to the car radiator to prevent the water from freezing when the car is not in use. The addition of solute particles to water can produce changes in the properties of the water; the first change concerns the heat energy resulting when the solute dissolves.

Heat of Solution

To prove for yourself that the dissolving of various substances in water causes temperature changes, *try the following:*

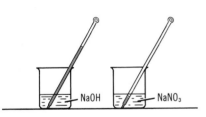

Add 100 ml of water to each of two beakers and determine the exact temperature of the water. When the temperatures are identical, add 10 grams sodium hydroxide (NaOH) to one beaker and stir the mixture *gently* with a thermometer. Observe any changes in temperature that occur. Do you notice that as the sodium hydroxide dissolves, the water in the beaker becomes warmer? Now dissolve an equal amount of sodium nitrate $(NaNO_3)$ in the water in the second beaker. Just the opposite phenomenon occurs; the beaker becomes cooler.

The increased temperature of the water in the first beaker indicates that substances such as sodium hydroxide give off heat when they dissolve in water—an exothermic reaction. On the other hand, since sodium nitrate dissolves with the *absorption* of heat, an endothermic reaction takes place. The amount of heat either given off or absorbed when sufficient solute dissolves to form a saturated solution is called the **heat of solution** of the solute.

Dissolving a solute in water involves at least two processes. The particles that make up the crystal lattice of the solid must be separated from one another. Then each of the resulting particles must become hydrated.

The first of these processes, disrupting the solid lattice, consumes energy. As you know, this energy is called lattice energy. The second process, hydration, liberates energy called hydration energy.

When the hydration supplies more energy than is needed to separate the solid particles from their lattice structure, excess heat is given off. In this type of reaction, an exothermic reaction, the heat of solution is said to be *positive*. When hydration does not supply enough energy to overcome the attractive forces between the solid particles in their lattice, additional heat must be supplied from the surroundings. In such endothermic reactions the heat of solution is said to be *negative*.

When salt (NaCl) is placed in water, very little change in temperature is observed. This is because the lattice energy of the salt and the hydration energy are nearly the same. In contrast, some compounds used in washing clothes, particularly those containing trisodium phosphate (Na_3PO_4), liberate very large quantities of energy when they are added to water.

In the chemistry laboratory, you may have had experience preparing one solution with a high positive heat of solution. You were cautioned to prepare dilute sulfuric acid by pouring the concentrated acid into the water while stirring constantly. The reaction is highly exothermic, in fact, so much heat is produced that if dilution occurs too quickly, the water may actually boil and spatter the acid.

Boiling Point and Freezing Point

For years cooks have added salt to water so that the water would boil at a higher temperature and the food would cook faster. *Is this fact or fiction?*

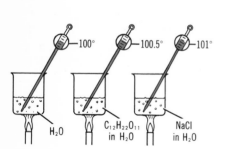

Bring some water to a boil in an uncovered beaker. Allow the water to boil a few minutes and measure the boiling temperature. Observe that if the atmospheric pressure is 760 mm, the water boils at 100° C. Now prepare 250 ml of a 1 molal solution of sucrose and allow it to boil. Does this solution boil at about 100.5° C? Prepare a similar amount of a 1 molal solution of sodium chloride. This time notice if boiling begins at about 101° C. Could the thermometers be inaccurate? Interchange them and find out.

Continue heating each of the beakers and record their boiling points at intervals. The pure water continues to boil at 100° C while the boiling temperature of both solutions rises gradually as boiling continues.

From repeated determination of the boiling points of a number of 1 *m* solutions (measured at standard pressure) it has been found that the boiling points of all 1 *m* solutions of molecular solutes, such as sugar, are about 0.52° C higher than the normal boiling point of water. The

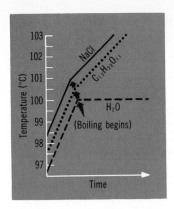

12-9 When water boils, its temperature remains constant as boiling continues. When solutions boil, their boiling temperatures increase gradually; the solutions become more concentrated as the water boils away.

Table 12-2 **FREEZING POINT DEPRESSION OF 1-MOLAL IONIC SOLUTIONS**

Compound	$^\circ C$
$Co(NO_3)_2$	5.5
$FeCl_3$	8.18
KOH	3.60
$NaCl$	3.37
$Zn(NO_3)_2$	5.83

boiling points of $1\,m$ solutions of ionic substances, such as NaCl, are higher still—usually close to some multiple of $0.52°$ C higher than the boiling point of water.

Why did the boiling temperatures gradually increase as the solutions continued to boil while the boiling temperature of the water without solute remained unchanged? The changes in the boiling temperatures of water to which sucrose or sodium chloride is added are compared on the graph in Fig. 12-9. Study the graph to find how closely your observations agree with the gradual increase of the boiling temperatures of the sugar and salt solutions determined by repeated experimentation. This gradual rise occurs because as water escapes from each solution, the solution becomes more concentrated. The relative number of solute particles, either sugar or salt, increases. As the water without solute continued boiling, it evaporated but did not, of course, become more concentrated in doing so.

Similar comparisons can be made between the freezing point of pure water and the freezing points of various solutions. These show that $1\,m$ solutions containing molecular solutes freeze at temperatures about $1.86°$ C lower than the freezing point of water. As might be expected, $1\,m$ solutions of ionic solutes have freezing points which are still lower. These freezing-point differences between pure water and $1\,m$ solutions of ionic solutes are always close to a multiple of $1.86°$ C, as shown in Table 12-2.

Why does adding a solute to water affect its boiling point and freezing point, and why do ionic solutes have greater effect than molecular solutes? Chemists have concluded that it is not the weight of the solute that affects boiling and freezing points. Instead, the determining factor is the number of solute particles in relation to the number of solvent particles. Consequently, molal solutions in which the number of solute and solvent particles can be determined are useful in such studies. We find that a $1\,m$ solution of NaCl has a lower freezing point than a $1\,m$ solution of sucrose because the salt solution contains twice as many solute particles as the sucrose solution. Each mole of solute particles added to 1,000 grams of water raises the boiling point an average of $0.52°$ C; it lowers the freezing point an average of $1.86°$ C. Sucrose, which is molecular, raises the boiling point only $0.52°$ C, while ionic sodium chloride, which provides twice the number of particles, raises the boiling point twice that amount.

Determining Molecular Weight

The effect of solutes on the freezing point of water offers a method of determining the molecular weights of covalent compounds. For example, experiments show that 90 grams of glucose dissolved in 1,000 grams of water will depress the freezing point to $-0.93°$ C. Since a solution containing 1 **GMW** of solute in 1,000 grams of water has a freezing point of $-1.86°$ C, and since 0.93 is one-half of 1.86, it can be concluded that

90 grams of sucrose represent one-half a mole of the compound. Therefore, the molecular weight of glucose is 180:

$$90 \text{ g}: -0.93° \text{ C} = x: -1.86° \text{ C}$$
$$x = 180 \text{ g (GMW)}$$
$$\textbf{MW} = 180$$

Separating Solute from Solvent by Distillation

Suppose that you want to separate the salt (NaCl) from the water in a salt solution. The salt cannot be removed by filtration; and if the solution is heated, the water will boil away. The operation can be completed if you use the apparatus shown in Fig. 12-10. If the solution is heated it will begin to boil, at standard pressure, at a temperature slightly above 100° C. The steam that forms can be cooled by passing it through the condenser. This condensed steam contains no salt. The water continues to boil away, and eventually solid salt is left. Though the remaining salt solution boils at increasingly higher temperatures as the water boils away, the salt will not vaporize because the vaporization of salt requires a temperature of 1,413° C.

This process of separating substances of different boiling points from one another by vaporization and condensation is known as **distillation.** The liquid that condenses during distillation is called the *distillate.* The condensed pure water achieved through distillation is the familiar *distilled water.* The chemist has many uses for the water which he obtains by distillation in the laboratory. Outside the laboratory distillation may eventually be of great importance in obtaining pure water from the sea. At its present stage of development, this process is too costly for large-scale use.

Now consider what happens when a solution of ethyl alcohol and water is distilled. The solution begins to boil slightly above 78° C, the temperature at which the alcohol boils. Early in the process a test of the distillate, the condensed vapor, shows that a high percentage of alcohol is present. As more alcohol vaporizes from the solution, higher and higher temperatures are needed for boiling to continue. It is not possible in your laboratory distillation to separate the components completely because the water as well as the alcohol vaporizes and then condenses.

In some cases the heat needed for distillation causes one or more of the components of a solution to decompose. To prevent decomposition, heating may be done in a partial vacuum, enabling the liquid to boil at lower temperatures.

Separating Solutes by Crystallization

It is quite easy to "grow" cubic crystals of NaCl by gradually chilling a warm saturated solution of NaCl. Crystals of pure NaCl settle to the bottom of the container. Similarly, when some of the solvent is allowed to evaporate from a solution, excess solute crystallizes out from the solu-

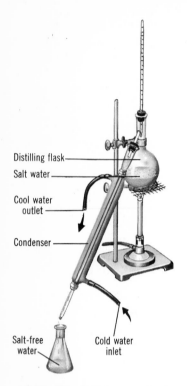

Distilling flask

Salt water

Cool water outlet

Condenser

Salt-free water

Cold water inlet

12-10 This distillation apparatus is used with aqueous solutions to separate a dissolved salt from water. The salt remains in the distilling flask; the water, as distilled water, is recovered at the lower end of the condenser.

tion that remains. The process of separating solute from solvent either by chilling or by evaporation is called **crystallization.**

In crystallization the size of the crystals is affected by the rate of evaporation. *You can demonstrate this by a simple investigation.*

> Divide a saturated solution of copper sulfate into two equal portions. Allow one portion to evaporate slowly over a number of days. Heat the other portion so that the rate of evaporation is increased. Compare the size of the crystals formed.

You will doubtless find that the crystals formed during the slower evaporation are the larger. In the same way, if the chilling of a saturated solution is gradual, the crystals produced will be larger than those produced by either rapid cooling or rapid evaporation.

Water of Hydration

If a large crystal of blue copper sulfate is placed in a Pyrex test tube and heated, large amounts of water escape from the crystal as steam. Though some of this steam condenses on the inside of the test tube, it leaves behind a powdery substance, white copper sulfate (Fig. 12-11). This simple procedure demonstrates that water plays a major role in the lattice structure of the copper sulfate crystal. In fact, water is an important constituent in the lattice structure of many crystalline substances.

Crystals, such as copper sulfate, that contain water molecules in their lattice structure, are called **hydrates.** When a chemical contains water in its structure the adjective **hydrated** is used; blue crystalline copper sulfate is called hydrated copper sulfate. The water in these hydrates is called **water of hydration** or **water of crystallization.** The substance that remains after the water of hydration has been removed from the crystal is said to be **anhydrous.** In the previous investigation the powdered white copper sulfate is *anhydrous copper sulfate.* If a few drops of water are added to the anhydrous copper sulfate, the compound regains its original blue color.

X-ray analyses of crystals of hydrated copper sulfate have revealed that each of the copper ions is surrounded by four water molecules. Each of the sulfate ions has one water molecule attached to it. To indicate the water of hydration, the formula for hydrated copper sulfate can be written in several ways. The long formula $[Cu(H_2O)_4 \cdot SO_4(H_2O)]$ shows the proportion in which the five water molecules are distributed among the ions. For convenience the shorter formula, $CuSO_4 \cdot 5 H_2O$, is more often used. In a similar manner, the formula for hydrated magnesium sulfate is usually written $MgSO_4 \cdot 7 H_2O$.

Efflorescence and Deliquescence

Crystals of hydrated copper sulfate retain their shape and structure when exposed to the air. *But what of other compounds?*

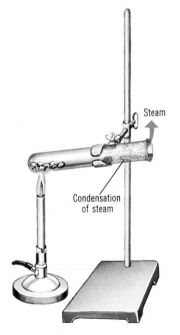

Steam

Condensation
of steam

12-11 When blue, hydrated copper sulfate crystals are heated, water is driven off and white, powdery anhydrous copper sulfate remains.

Crystals of
sodium sulfate

Powdered
sodium sulfate

a

Granules of
calcium chloride

Solution of
calcium chloride

b

Put a few crystals of hydrated sodium sulfate ($Na_2SO_4 \cdot 10\ H_2O$) on a watch glass and keep the glass in a warm place. After an hour or two, observe the watch glass. The crystals are no longer there; they have been replaced by a powder, anhydrous sodium sulfate.

Cautiously place a few grams of calcium chloride granules in a similar watch glass, and observe them after the same period of time. Have the anhydrous granules changed into a solution of calcium chloride?

The change from hydrated crystals to anhydrous powder which occurs when some solids are placed in a dry atmosphere is called **efflorescence.** The reverse change, in which a solid absorbs moisture from the air to dissolve gradually and become a liquid, is called **deliquescence.** Washing soda, or hydrated sodium carbonate ($Na_2CO_3 \cdot 10\ H_2O$), is so efflorescent that a package which has been on the grocer's shelf for some time usually weighs less than the amount printed on the label. Deliquescent calcium chloride is used to "wet down" dirt roads in many rural areas during the dry summer months. It, as well as deliquescent pellets of sodium hydroxide, are used frequently as drying agents in the chemical laboratory (Fig. 12-12).

Some substances, such as silk, wool, and leather, absorb large amounts of moisture without becoming liquids. Such substances are **hygroscopic.** Common table salt is sometimes considered to be hygroscopic. Actually, it contains as an impurity a small amount of deliquescent magnesium chloride that is responsible for the salt's "caking" in damp weather.

Particles of many substances dissolve in water to form solutions, but not all substances dissolve in the same way. Just as some substances affect a solution's freezing or boiling point more than others, so too, some solutions carry an electric current, others do not. It is foolhardy to touch an electric switch with wet hands—in the next chapter we see why.

12-12 The calcium chloride in the bottom of the desiccator is used to maintain a dry atmosphere around the substances in the upper portion of the desiccator.

QUESTIONS AND PROBLEMS

1. (a) Why does a 1 molal solution of sodium nitrate ($NaNO_3$) have a higher boiling point and lower freezing point than a 1 m solution of sucrose ($C_{12}H_{22}O_{11}$)? (b) Give the boiling and freezing points of a 1 molal solution of KNO_3, H_2SO_4, and $C_6H_{12}O_6$.
2. Eleven grams of methyl alcohol dissolved in 1,000 grams of water depress the freezing point of the solution to approximately $-0.62°$ C. Find the molecular weight of methyl alcohol.
3. Describe (a) two methods by which any salt can be removed from solution, (b) how to "grow" a crystal of sodium sulfate (Na_2SO_4).
4. (a) What fact determines whether the heat of solution of any reaction will be positive or negative? (b) Define the terms *water of hydration, efflorescence, deliquescence.*

THE CONCEPT

Solutions are homogeneous mixtures that contain two or more substances. Solids, liquids, and gases all occur in various combinations in solutions. Solids dissolved in water, or aqueous solutions, represent the most common solutions. In these the solid, or solute, dissolves in water, the solvent. Many liquids mix with one another in all proportions, or are miscible, while other liquids do not mix readily, or are immiscible. Gases also dissolve in liquids to form solutions, and solid solutions are possible.

The ability of substances to dissolve is referred to as solubility. Solubility is determined by the chemical nature of both solvent and solute particles as well as by temperature and pressure. The more alike solute and solvent particles are in their electronic structure, the greater the chance that they will form a solution.

At any given temperature there is a limit to solubility of solids dissolving in water. When the dissolved and undissolved solute are in equilibrium, the solution is saturated; a solution which contains less than the maximum amount of solute is unsaturated. Solubility curves indicate the amount of solute contained in saturated solutions at various temperatures. A solution that contains a higher concentration of solute than is normally present in a saturated solution is supersaturated.

Any solution, whether saturated or unsaturated, that contains a large amount of solute in relation to the amount of solvent is concentrated. If the amount of solute is low in relation to the amount of solvent, the solution is dilute. Concentration is expressed in many ways. Molar concentration (M) indicates the number of gram formula weights (**GFW**) or gram molecular weights (**GMW**) of solute present in each liter of a solution. Normal concentration (N) expresses the number of gram equivalent weights (**GEW**) of solute present in each liter of solution. Equal volumes of solutions having the same normality contain equivalent (not equal) amounts of solute. Molal concentration (m) expresses the number of **GFW** or **GEW** of solute in 1,000 grams of solvent. The total number of solute and solvent particles can be determined for solutions of known molality; only the number of solute particles can be determined for molar solutions.

Adding solute to solvent changes the boiling and freezing points of the solvent. Each mole of solute particles raises the boiling point of 1,000 grams of water by approximately 0.52° C and lowers its freezing point by approximately 1.86° C. The amount of heat either given off or absorbed when a solution forms is called the heat of solution.

Solute particles of a solid can be completely separated from the solvent by distillation, if the boiling point of the solute is considerably higher than that of the solvent. Crystallization can also be used to remove solute particles from solution. In some compounds, however, water becomes part of the crystal as water of hydration. Some hydrated crystals give up their water of hydration in a dry atmosphere—they effloresce to form anhydrous solids. Some anhydrous solids absorb water from a humid atmosphere to form liquids —they are deliquescent.

USING THE CONCEPT

Using the Basic Concept
   1. (a) What is a solution? (b) Give ten examples of solutions commonly used at home. (c) Name ten solutions used in your chemistry laboratory.
   2. Give three examples of each of the following: (a) solid dissolved in solid; (b) gas dissolved in liquid; (c) gas dissolved in gas; (d) solid dissolved in water; (e) solid dissolved in another liquid.
   3. In each example you have given in parts (d) and (e) of Question 2, indicate the solvent and the solute.
   4. (a) Define the terms *solubility, miscible, immiscible*. (b) Which of the following

substances are reasonably soluble in water and which are not: table salt, mercuric oxide, potassium chlorate, manganese dioxide, starch, sugar? (c) Which of the following liquids are miscible with water and which are immiscible: oil, concentrated sulfuric acid, carbon tetrachloride, ethyl alcohol?

5. (a) Give a general rule for determining the types of particles that will mix to form solutions. (b) Give two examples for which the rule holds true.

6. (a) Describe what chemists believe happens when a substance such as NaCl becomes hydrated. (b) Describe the action that occurs when a substance such as sucrose (table sugar) dissolves in water.

7. Define each of the following types of solutions: saturated solution, supersaturated solution, unsaturated solution, concentrated solution, dilute solution.

8. Describe and give an example of: a dilute saturated solution, a concentrated unsaturated solution, a dilute unsaturated solution, a concentrated saturated solution.

9. (a) What is a solubility curve? (b) How is the data for such a curve found?

10. (a) Define each of the following methods of expressing concentration: molar concentration (M); normal concentration (N); molal concentration (m). (b) Give an example of a solution whose concentration is expressed by each method. (c) What advantage is there to expressing concentration as: molar concentration, normal concentration, molal concentration?

11. (a) Describe three ways in which the properties of solvents are changed by the addition of solute. (b) Define the term heat of solution.

12. Explain in terms of lattice energy and hydration energy why heat is given off when some ionic solids dissolve in water while heat is absorbed when other ionic solids dissolve.

13. (a) Describe the process of distillation. (b) Give two examples of solutions in which the solute can be completely separated from the solvent by distillation. (c) Give two examples of solutions from which the solute cannot be completely separated by this process.

14. (a) How are hydration and crystallization related? (b) What is water of hydration?

15. (a) Under what general conditions are large crystals formed during crystallization? (b) What conditions favor the formation of small crystals from solution?

16. (a) What is an anhydrous substance? (b) Give three examples of anhydrous substances. (c) Differentiate between the processes of efflorescence and deliquescence.

17. (a) Define the term *hygroscopic*. (b) Though pure NaCl is not hygroscopic, it tends to "cake" in damp weather. Why?

Relating Terms Within the Concept

From the *italicized* terms below select the term that best completes each of the following statements. Do not use a term more than once.

anhydrous, aqueous solution, concentrated, deliquescence, dilute, distillation, efflorescence, heat of solution, hydrated, hydration energy, lattice energy, miscible, molal solution, molar solution, normal solution, saturated, solubility, water of hydration

1. A molecule of $CuSO_4 \cdot 5 H_2O$ contains _____ .

2. A solution that contains one **GEW** of solute per liter of solution is a (an) _____ .

3. A process that involves both boiling and condensation is _____ .

4. The liquids that mix to form a solution are _____ .

5. The ability of a substance to dissolve determines its _____ .

6. If you know the lattice energy and hydration energy of a compound dissolving in

water, you can determine the _____.

7. Hydrated crystals that normally lose water of hydration undergo _____.

8. The energy needed to disrupt a crystal structure is _____.

9. Any solution in which water is a solvent is a (an) _____.

10. Any solution that contains the maximum amount of solute that it can normally contain is _____.

11. A 1 M solution is a (an) _____.

12. A potassium ion surrounded by water molecules is _____.

13. Any solution containing a large amount of solute per amount of solvent is _____.

14. A solution that is prepared in terms of moles of solute per 1,000 grams of solvent is a (an) _____.

Solving Problems Within the Concept

1. (a) What is the maximum number of grams of silver nitrate ($AgNO_3$) that will dissolve in 100 grams of water at 20° C? (b) How many grams of $AgNO_3$ will be needed to saturate 1000 grams of water at this same temperature?

2. Determine the weight in grams of solute needed to make each of the following aqueous solutions; then indicate how you would make the required amount of each solution: (a) 1 liter of 1 M NaCl; (b) 1 liter of 0.01 M NaCl; (c) 500 ml of 0.01 M $AgNO_3$; (d) 1 liter of 0.02 M KCl; (e) 1 liter of 1 N NaOH; (f) 250 ml of 0.03 N $Ca(OH)_2$; (g) 2 liters of 0.1 N H_2SO_4 (assume the H_2SO_4 is 98 percent pure); (h) 500 ml of 0.05 M $NaC_2H_3O_2$; (i) 300 ml of 2 M KCl.

3. Determine the number of solute particles present in each of the following aqueous solutions: (a) 1 liter of 0.1 M sucrose ($C_{12}H_{22}O_{11}$), 0.1 M NaCl, and 0.1 M $Ca(OH)_2$; (b) 500 ml of 0.2 N NaOH, 0.2 N H_2SO_4, and 0.2 N glucose ($C_6H_{12}O_6$); (c) 1,500 ml of 0.01 M $MgSO_4$ and 0.01 M methyl alcohol (CH_3OH).

4. Indicate the *total* number of particles present in each of the following aqueous solutions: (a) 0.1 m KCl, 2 m NaBr, and 0.05 m $C_6H_{12}O_6$, each containing 1,000 grams of H_2O; (b) 180 grams of $C_6H_{12}O_6$ dissolved in 1,000 grams of H_2O; (c) 18 grams of $C_6H_{12}O_6$ dissolved in 1,000 grams of H_2O; (d) 5.85 grams of NaCl dissolved in 200 grams of H_2O.

5. Determine the normality and molarity of each of the following solutions: (a) 98 grams of pure H_2SO_4 dissolved in enough water to make 1 liter of solution; 2 liters of solution; 250 ml of solution; (b) 7.3 grams of pure HCl dissolved in enough water to make 1 liter of solution; 2 liters of solution; 250 ml of solution; (c) 3.7 grams of $Ca(OH)_2$ dissolved in enough water to make 2 liters of solution, 10 liters of solution; (d) 4.0 grams of NaOH in 100 ml of solution, in 600 ml of solution, in 2 liters of solution.

6. Determine the boiling point (at normal pressure) and freezing point of each of the following solutions: (a) 1 m $C_6H_{12}O_6$, 0.5 m $C_{12}H_{22}O_{11}$, 0.2 m NaCl, 0.3 m Na_2SO_4; (b) 50 grams of $C_6H_{12}O_6$ dissolved in 400 grams of water.

7. A solution containing 90 grams of a covalent compound dissolved in 500 grams of water boils at 100.26° C (at normal pressure). (a) What is the molecular weight of the compound? (b) At what temperature will this solution begin to freeze? (c) What is the molality (m) of this solution?

8. Determine the molecular weight of a covalent compound from the following data: the freezing point of a solution containing 68.4 grams of the compound dissolved in 500 grams of water is $-0.744°C$.

Applying the Concept

1. The mineral calcite is nearly pure crystalline calcium carbonate. Dolomite, another mineral, is a solid solution in which

some of the calcium ions of calcite have been replaced by magnesium ions. Give two reasons why magnesium ions can replace calcium ions so readily in the formation of dolomite.

2. When salt water is distilled, the water is separated from the salt. What does this information suggest about the amount of hydration energy needed to overcome the electrostatic force between Na^+ or Cl^- ions and H_2O polar molecules, and the amount of energy needed to overcome the ionic bonds between Na^+ and Cl^- ions?

3. (a) In hydrated magnesium sulfate, around which ion, an Mg^{+2} ion or an SO_4^{-2} ion, would you expect more water molecules to be attracted? (b) Give two reasons for your answer.

4. At 20° C a saturated solution of NaCl contains 32 grams of solute in 100 grams of water, while a saturated solution of sucrose ($C_{12}H_{22}O_{11}$), at this same temperature, contains 131 grams of solute per 100 grams of water. This data indicates that sucrose is more soluble than sodium chloride. On further inspection, however, it can be shown that the saturated salt solution contains more particles of solute than the saturated sucrose solution. Explain how this is possible.

5. Why would you expect all gases to mix with each other in all proportions?

Reading Further

Water: The Mirror of Science, by K. S. Davis and J. A. Day, New York, Doubleday, 1961. An introduction to the properties and uses of water.

"Water," by A. M. Buswell and W. H. Rodebush, *Scientific American,* April 1956. (Also available as an offprint.) Describes some of the more recently discovered physical and chemical properties of water.

13

Particles in Solution

During the early years of the nineteenth century great advances were made in our knowledge of solutions. In particular, scientists of the time were interested in the effects of an electric current on different solutions. It was already known that some solutions would not conduct an electric current at all, while others were excellent conductors of electricity. But why was this so? And why was it that whenever an electric current could be passed through a solution, the properties of that solution always changed?

Michael Faraday, one of the most versatile experimenters of all time, proved by 1832 that when electricity is passed through an acid or salt solution, the liquid decomposes at the two electrodes in a regular, repeatable manner. Though he first used such terms as "electrolyte," "electrode," and "ion" in relation to electrolysis experiments, these terms were devised for him by another experimenter.

ELECTRICAL PROPERTIES OF AQUEOUS SOLUTIONS

You have found that water to which sulfuric acid is added conducts an electric current. But will distilled water do likewise? *Why not find out for yourself?*

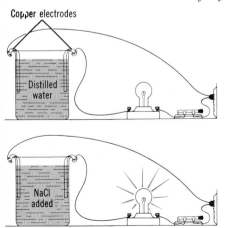

Copper electrodes

Distilled water

NaCl added

Construct the electrolysis apparatus similar to the one shown at the left, using a 25-watt bulb, a 120-volt lamp socket, some insulated wire, a plug, a switch, and two narrow strips of heavy copper. Place the two copper electrodes in a beaker of distilled water (be sure that the electrodes do not touch each other), plug the apparatus into an electrical outlet, and close the switch. Does the bulb light? Evidently, either the distilled water does not conduct electricity or it does not conduct it sufficiently to light the bulb. Add a small amount of salt (NaCl) to the distilled water; the bulb lights immediately. Add more salt gradually, and observe whether the bulb steadily glows more brightly.

Perhaps it is the salt that conducts the electric current. To find out, open the switch, dry off the electrodes, and place them in a beaker of *dry* salt. Close the switch; this time the bulb does not glow. What happens if, instead of salt, you test solid sucrose and a sucrose solution?

Though neither distilled water nor dry salt has value as an electrical conductor, a mixture of salt and water is a good conductor. However, it makes no difference whether the electrodes are placed in solid sucrose or in a sucrose solution; in neither case does the light go on. Apparently sucrose, unlike salt, does not conduct electricity, even in solution.

These procedures can be repeated with solid sodium nitrate and sodium nitrate in solution; with pure alcohol and a solution of alcohol; and with solid glucose (simple sugar) and a glucose solution. The solid sodium nitrate will not conduct electricity, but a solution of sodium nitrate will. On the other hand, neither glucose, either in its solid state or in solution, nor alcohol will conduct an electrical current.

An examination of the results of these procedures leads to some interesting conclusions. Some of the substances used, such as sodium nitrate and sodium chloride, are ionic. Others, such as sucrose, glucose, and alcohol, are covalent molecular substances. In their dry state, none of these substances conducts electricity. But as part of an aqueous solution, some of them are good conductors, others not. The substances which conduct electricity in a water solution are the ionic compounds, sodium chloride and sodium nitrate. The substances which do not conduct electricity, even in solution, are the covalent molecular compounds, sucrose, glucose, and alcohol.

Does the situation change if substances are used in their *molten* state? You can find the answer by using another, and slightly different, electrolysis apparatus, such as the model shown in Fig. 13-1. The failure of the bulb to light informs us that naphthalene, a molecular substance, does not conduct electricity. But if an *ionic* solid such as potassium chlorate ($KClO_3$) is melted in the crucible, the bulb does light when the electricity is turned on. From the similar testing of hundreds of solids, chemists have concluded that molten molecular solids do not conduct electricity while molten ionic substances do.

Molten $KClO_3$

13-1 The bulb glows because molten potassium chlorate, like other ionic solids, is conducting an electric current. Would the bulb glow if a molten molecular solid were substituted for the $KClO_3$?

Electrolytes and Nonelectrolytes

Compounds that conduct electricity when molten or in solution are called **electrolytes.** Compounds that do not conduct electricity under these same conditions are called **nonelectrolytes.** The previous procedures indicate that ionic compounds are electrolytes. Can we assume that all covalent molecular substances are nonelectrolytes?

Suppose that the electrodes of an electrolysis apparatus are cautiously placed in a small amount of 100 percent concentrated sulfuric acid, a molecular substance. As expected, the bulb does not light when the switch is closed. This molecular substance, pure sulfuric acid (acid containing no water), does not conduct electricity. But notice what happens if we add a few milliliters of the pure acid to a beaker of water, thus forming *dilute* sulfuric acid. Now the bulb glows as brilliantly as when the electrodes were placed in a dilute solution of an ionic substance. Similarly, glacial acetic acid (100 percent acetic acid) does not conduct an electric current, but dilute acetic acid will do so. Evidently some substances that seem to be molecular will, *when in solution,* conduct electricity.

Do electrolytes, whether covalent or ionic, vary in the degree to which they are conductors of electricity? *You can find out quite readily.*

Prepare aqueous 1 *M* solutions of acetic acid (HC$_2$H$_3$O$_2$), hydrochloric acid (HCl), ammonium hydroxide (NH$_4$OH), and sodium hydroxide (NaOH). Using the conductivity apparatus shown on page 201, determine whether the bulb glows brightly or dimly in each solution.

The acetic acid and the ammonium hydroxide solutions cause the light bulb to glow—but very dimly. On the other hand, a bright light is produced when the electrodes are placed in solutions of sodium hydroxide or hydrochloric acid. Substances such as acetic acid, whose solutions are poor conductors of electricity, are called *weak* electrolytes (Table 13-1). Substances such as hydrochloric acid, whose solutions readily conduct electricity, are *strong* electrolytes. There is, however, no sharp line of distinction between the two types: electrolytes vary in strength all the way from those which are extremely weak to those which are very strong.

Table 13-1   **CONDUCTIVITY OF COMPOUNDS IN 1 MOLAR SOLUTION**

Strong electrolytes	Weak electrolytes	Nonelectrolytes
Hydrochloric acid	Acetic acid	Glucose
Sulfuric acid	Ammonium hydroxide	Sucrose
Sodium hydroxide	Carbonic acid	Alcohol
Sodium chloride		
Copper sulfate		
Sodium nitrate		

Electrolytes and Ions

From the freezing points of several 1 molal aqueous solutions studied in the last chapter, you know that some 1 *m* solutions have freezing points of −1.86° C while others have freezing points that are lower. By the 1880's chemists had realized that the strength or weakness of a solution of an electrolyte is related to its freezing point. They found that 1 molal solutions of all nonelectrolytes in water have freezing points of approximately −1.86° C. While the freezing points of 1 *m* solutions of weak

−1.83°C

−2.63°C

−4.04°C

13-2 What relationship exists between the number of solute particles and the freezing points of 1 molal solutions?

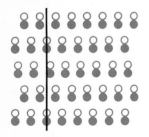

13-3 A modification of Johann Hittorf's 1853 diagrams, indicating the movement of ions during electrolysis. When he "divided" the liquid at a definite place, Hittorf found that positive ions (Na+, represented by circles) migrated in one direction, while negative ions (Cl−, represented by dots) migrated in the opposite direction.

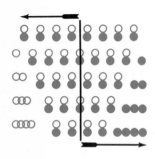

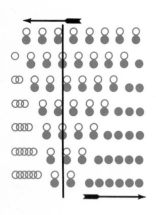

electrolytes are only slightly below this figure, 1 m solutions of many strong electrolytes have freezing points considerably below $-1.86°C$ (Fig. 13-2).

In 1883, Svante Arrhenius developed a theory to explain the nature of electrolytes and nonelectrolytes. Arrhenius reasoned that if the freezing point of a solution depends upon the number of particles it contains, and if electrolytes have lower freezing points than nonelectrolytes of equal concentration, then electrolytic solutions must contain more particles than solutions of nonelectrolytes. It might be expected that all solutions of equal concentration would contain the same number of particles, but the differences in freezing point indicated that this is not necessarily so. As an explanation, Arrhenius suggested that the process of solution must cause a breaking down or dissociation of some molecular substances into still smaller particles. Since these smaller particles were able to conduct electricity, they must be electrically charged—in short, they are ions.

In developing his ideas, Arrhenius built upon the work of Johann Hittorf, who thirty years earlier had performed numerous experiments on the nature of electrolysis. Hittorf had postulated that during the electrolysis of sodium chloride, the positive sodium ions and the negative chloride ions migrate toward different electrodes with different speeds (Fig. 13-3).

In summary, Arrhenius' original **theory of electrolytic dissociation** is based on the following five assumptions: (1) Some solutes, but not all, split apart to form ions when they are dissolved in water. (2) Each of these ions, unlike a molecule, carries an electric charge. (3) In any solution of ions, the total numbers of positive and negative charges are equal. (4) Dissolved molecules do not conduct electricity. (5) In very dilute solutions dissociation is complete; in more concentrated solutions an equilibrium exists between ions and molecules.

Although Arrhenius' theory was not received with great enthusiasm, today his theory, which is also known as the **theory of ionization,** is recognized as an important advance in chemical knowledge. It has, however, been modified in two important respects. One of these modifications concerns the difference in the way ionic and covalent substances dissolve in water (assumption 1). The other modification involves the degree of dissociation in dilute and concentrated solutions (assumption 5), a point which will be taken up later in this chapter.

QUESTIONS AND PROBLEMS

1. Differentiate between the terms in each of the following pairs: (a) *electrolyte* and *nonelectrolyte* (b) *strong electrolyte* and *weak electrolyte* (c) *ion* and *molecule.*
2. (a) On the basis of information in this section, predict whether each of the following is a strong electrolyte, weak electrolyte, or nonelec-

trolyte: Na_2SO_4, $NaOH$, $C_6H_{12}O_6$, $KClO_2$, C_8H_{18}, H_2SO_3, $KC_2H_3O_2$.
(b) Give a reason for your answer.
3. (a) Under what condition is an ionic compound a nonelectrolyte?
(b) Under what conditions are some covalent compounds electrolytes?
Give two examples. (c) Describe an experimental procedure to prove
your answers to (a) and (b).

IONIZATION AND DISSOCIATION

Arrhenius could hardly have been expected to take into account the
difference in the way ionic and covalent compounds dissolve in water,
since in his time nothing was known about the structural differences between such compounds. Yet, without this knowledge, he was able to explain electrolytic conduction, freezing point depression of electrolytes,
and certain other facts, such as colors of solutions, in terms of the
behavior of ions.

In the last chapter you were introduced to present-day explanations
of how the dissolving of ionic compounds differs from that of covalent
compounds. Let us pursue this explanation further.

Dissolving Ionic Compounds

When a crystalline solid is placed in water, some of the ions on the surfaces of the crystals become hydrated—attached to polar water molecules. If the hydration energy released is greater than the lattice energy of
the ionic solid, the solid dissolves and energy is released. Whenever this
happens, the electrostatic forces that hold together the positive and negative ions in the solid are overcome. Once this attraction between positive
and negative ions is overcome, the ions in the solid separate and move
about freely in the solution. Today this process by which ions already
present in an ionic substance separate in solution is called **dissociation.**
An ionic compound whose ions are easily separated in this manner
dissociates.

Dissolving Covalent Compounds

You have seen that a substance such as sugar, which is composed of
crystals of nonpolar covalent molecules, will dissolve in water but will
not act as an electrolyte. This is because molecules of sugar, when dissolved, do not form ions but remain as molecules. As no charged particles are produced, the molecules of sugar, although free to move about
in the solution, do not conduct electricity. The same is true of numerous
other solids and liquids which will dissolve in water. If the substances are
nonpolar compounds, they retain their molecular nature and will not
conduct electricity.

Now consider the case of hydrogen chloride. As a gas, hydrogen chloride is molecular and will not conduct electricity. Yet when this gas
is dissolved in water to form hydrochloric acid, the acid conducts elec-

13-4 Oppositely charged ends of hydrogen chloride and water molecules attract each other. When these molecules collide, the bonds of the HCl molecules break, and the H and Cl atoms become H^+ and Cl^- ions.

tricity. The hydrogen chloride molecule reacts with water to form hydrated ions. Molecules that react with water to form ions are said to **ionize.** The process by which uncharged polar molecules are changed into ions in solution is called **ionization.** The ions, once formed, are then distributed throughout the solution.

How does the dissolving of HCl gas in water produce ions? Hydrogen chloride molecules are slightly polar: the hydrogen end of each molecule has a partial positive charge, while the chlorine end has a partial negative charge. Water molecules are also polar. Thus the oppositely charged ends of the water and hydrogen chloride molecules attract each other (Fig. 13-4). When the HCl and H_2O molecules collide, the covalent bond uniting each H atom with an atom of Cl in HCl breaks, and the atoms are rearranged to form ions.

Each *positively* charged ion that forms in this way is a hydrogen ion; each *negatively* charged ion is a chloride ion. The following equation is one useful method of representing the chemical reaction that occurs when hydrochloric acid is formed from hydrogen chloride and water:

$$HCl \xrightarrow{H_2O} H^+ + Cl^-$$
hydrochloric acid

However, as we shall see immediately, this equation does not give the full picture of what happens during the ionization of HCl.

Hydronium and Other Hydrated Ions

The symbol H^+ is often used to represent hydrogen ions in solution. However, results of experiments to determine the speed with which these ions migrate through a solution indicate that hydrogen ions, or protons, never exist in a solution by themselves. Instead, they are always attached or bonded to water molecules. When a hydrogen ion is thus attached to a water molecule it is called a **hydronium ion.** The following equation represents the reaction between a hydrogen ion and a water molecule to form a hydronium ion.

$$H^+ + H_2O \longrightarrow H_3O^+$$
hydrogen   water   hydronium
ion   ion

A hydronium ion (H_3O^+) can be thought of as a *hydrated hydrogen ion* or a *hydrated proton,* as indicated in the electron dot diagrams below:

$$H^+ + \ :\!\overset{..}{\underset{..}{O}}\!:\!H \longrightarrow \left[H\!:\!\overset{..}{\underset{..}{O}}\!:\!H \right]^+$$
$$\quad\quad\ H \quad\quad\quad\quad\quad H$$

In the formation of hydronium ions, an H^+ ion—for example, one formed when hydrogen chloride is placed in water—becomes bonded to a pair of unshared electrons associated with the oxygen atom in a molecule of water. One way of showing the formation of hydronium ions when

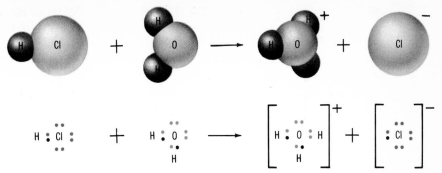

13-5 When hydrogen chloride dissolves in water, H^+ ions from HCl molecules combine with H_2O molecules to form hydronium ions (H_3O^+) and chloride ions (Cl^-), or in essence to form hydrochloric acid.

hydrogen chloride dissolves in water is indicated in Fig. 13-5. The reaction can also be represented by the equation:

$$HCl + H_2O \longrightarrow H_3O^+ + Cl^-$$

hydrochloric acid

Moreover, the polar nature of water molecules causes two, three, even four water molecules to attach to a single proton. Since we cannot specify a definite number of water molecules, the symbol, $H^+(aq)$ is sometimes used to indicate that *the proton is always hydrated.* In ionic equations, H_3O^+ may be used to emphasize a concept of acids and bases to be considered shortly.

Should we expect other ions in water solutions to be hydrated? This is indeed the case. All positive ions attract the partial negative (oxygen) end of the water molecules, while all negative ions attract the partial positive (hydrogen) end of water molecules (see Fig. 12-3a). Thus, Cl^- and Na^+ in water solutions could be written as $Cl^-(aq)$ and $Na^+(aq)$.

How Ions Conduct Electricity

The ability of a solution to conduct electricity does not depend on the source of the ions in the solution. It makes no difference whether the ions in an ionic substance dissociated in water or a polar covalent substance underwent ionization in water. For a solution to conduct electricity it need only contain ions that are free to move.

Electricity, as you know, is a flow of electrons. The role that ions play in conducting electrons through a solution can be understood *by investigating the electrolysis of 6 molar hydrochloric acid.* (CAUTION: *Do not touch the acid with your hands at any time.*)

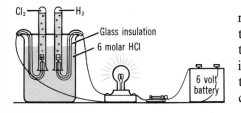

Place some 6 molar hydrochloric acid in an electrolysis apparatus. Attach the *glass insulated* wire from one electrode to the positive terminal, and the wire from the other electrode to the negative terminal of a 6-volt DC source. Cautiously immerse the electrodes in the hydrochloric acid. When the current is turned on, the electrode attached to the negative terminal becomes negatively charged: *it now has an excess of electrons.* The electrode attached to the positive terminal becomes positively charged: *it now lacks electrons.* The negatively charged electrode is called the **cathode;** the electrode with the positive charge is called the **anode.**

The bulb lights immediately, indicating that 6 *M* hydrochloric acid is an electrolyte. Within a minute or two, do you detect the pungent odor of chlorine? Open the switch and carefully invert a small acid-filled test tube over each electrode. Close the switch and observe that the green-colored gas, chlorine, is produced only at the anode. Open the switch as soon as you have collected only a very small volume of chlorine. A colorless gas collects in the tube over the cathode. By applying the burning splint test, do you find that this gas is hydrogen?

This investigation, together with what we already know about the structure of ions and atoms, suggests how the ions in a solution of hydrochloric acid conduct electricity. Hydrochloric acid contains hydrogen ions (H^+) and chloride ions (Cl^-). Before the electricity is turned on, the ions move through the solution in a random fashion. Once the direct current flows, the ions move toward the electrode that has a charge opposite to their own. The negative ions, called **anions,** are attracted toward the anode (Fig. 13-6). At the anode, each negatively charged chloride ion gives up its excess electron to become a neutral atom of chlorine. Then each pair of neutral chlorine atoms forms a chlorine molecule. This action at the anode can be denoted by the following equation which indicates that each of two chloride ions loses 1 electron (or a total of 2 electrons) to form one molecule of chlorine.

$$2\,Cl^- - 2\,e^- \longrightarrow Cl_2$$

While this is happening at the anode, the positively charged hydrogen ions, called **cations,** are moving through the solution toward the negative electrode, the cathode. Here each hydrogen ion picks up an electron, forming a neutral hydrogen atom. Then each pair of neutral hydrogen atoms bonds to form one hydrogen molecule. The equation for the action at the cathode indicates that each of two hydrogen ions gains 1 electron (or a total of 2 electrons) to form one molecule of hydrogen.

$$2\,H^+ + 2\,e^- \longrightarrow H_2$$

Thus, for each chloride ion that loses an electron at the anode, a hydrogen ion gains an electron at the cathode.

Two processes, then, that occur simultaneously, explain why electrolytes conduct electricity. First, negative ions lose electrons at the anode and positive ions gain electrons at the cathode; second, ions migrate in both directions through the solution. Whenever electricity passes through an electrolyte, chemical reactions resulting from the loss and gain of electrons occur at the two electrodes. These chemical changes usually involve the transformation of ions into atoms or molecules. In other words, electrolysis causes ionized compounds to decompose into elements.

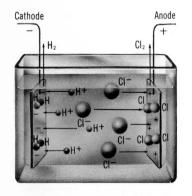

13-6 At the anode each chloride ion gives up an electron to form a chlorine atom; then two atoms combine to form a chlorine molecule. At the cathode each hydrogen ion gains an electron to form a hydrogen atom; then two atoms combine to form a hydrogen molecule.

1. Solutions of nonpolar covalent compounds are nonelectrolytes, while solutions of many polar compounds are electrolytes. Explain why.
2. Differentiate between the terms in each of the following pairs:
   (a) *anode* and *cathode*
   (b) *hydrogen* and *hydronium ion*
   (c) *ionization* and *dissociation*
3. (a) Write equations, including the hydronium ion, for (a) the ionization of sulfuric acid (b) the electrolysis of hydrogen bromide.

BEHAVIOR OF IONS IN SOLUTION

When 1 gram molecular weight of hydrogen chloride is dissolved in 1,000 grams of water, a 1 molal solution of hydrochloric acid—a good electrical conductor—is produced. On the other hand, if 1 gram molecular weight of glacial acetic acid is dissolved in 1,000 grams of water, a 1 molal solution of a very poor conductor, acetic acid, is formed (Fig. 13-7). Both of the original substances, hydrogen chloride and acetic acid, are molecular, and both ionize in water. Why, then, should the conducting ability of the two solutions be so different?

13-7 Hydrogen chloride dissolved in water is almost completely ionized, and the ions conduct electricity. Glacial acetic acid in water is only slightly ionized; the acid solution is a poor conductor of electricity.

Number of Ions

When glacial acetic acid (100 percent) dissolves in water, the following reaction occurs:

$$HC_2H_3O_2 + H_2O \rightleftharpoons H_3O^+ + C_2H_3O_2^-$$

glacial   hydronium   acetate
acetic acid   ion   ion

Notice the two arrows pointing in opposite directions. These indicate that in aqueous solutions of acetic acid, there is an equilibrium between un-ionized acetic acid and water molecules as reactants, and hydronium and acetate ions as products. At equilibrium, the hydronium and acetate ions recombine to form molecules of acetic acid and water. At the same time, an equal number of these molecules are undergoing ionization. The shorter arrow in the above equation indicates this small degree of ionization. The fact that equilibrium occurs after so few ions are produced explains why acetic acid is such a poor conductor of electricity. The ions are too few in number to yield a good conductor of electricity.

The case is very different when hydrogen chloride is dissolved in water. Essentially all of the molecules become ionized. Here there is no equilibrium between molecules and ions. For this reason, a double arrow does not appear in the equation (on page 207) which represents the ionization of HCl molecules to form a strong electrolyte.

Any strong electrolyte, such as HCl, contains a large number of ions in solution. By contrast, any weak electrolyte, such as acetic acid, con-

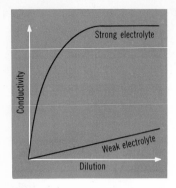

13-8 As dilution increases, the conductivity of strong electrolytes, such as most ionic compounds, hydrochloric acid, and sulfuric acid, approaches a constant value. The conductivity of weak electrolytes, such as ammonia and acetic acid, increases very slowly with increasing dilution.

tains relatively few ions in solution. The ability of an acid solution to conduct electricity is dependent upon its degree of ionization (Fig. 13-8).

When solid sodium hydroxide (NaOH) reacts with water, it also forms a strong electrolyte. The ionic NaOH dissociates:

$$NaOH \longrightarrow Na^+ + OH^-$$

Again no equilibrium exists; dissociation is virtually complete.

The very high conductivity of substances such as hydrogen chloride and sodium hydroxide in solution indicates the second important way in which Arrhenius' original theory of ionization has had to be modified. Arrhenius did not realize that *strong electrolytes consist entirely (or principally) of ions.*

Factors Affecting Ionization

Glacial acetic acid, you recall, does not conduct electricity at all, and the concentrated acid is a very poor conductor. As the acid is diluted further, it becomes a much better conductor. It must be that dilution causes a greater percentage of the available molecules in the acid to ionize. In fact, in a 1 M solution of acetic acid at 20° C only four of 1,000 molecules of the acid become ionized; but when the solution is diluted to 0.001 M at the same temperature, 150 out of every 1,000 molecules are ionized. If the solution is very dilute (10^{-5} M), 750 out of every 1,000 molecules become ionized.

You might conclude that as weak electrolytes become more and more dilute they become ever better conductors. This is true only up to a point. As more and more solvent is added, the number of solute particles, in relation to the number of solvent particles, becomes so small that the solute is no longer effective as a conductor. This failure to conduct an electric current can occur even though all of the solute has become ionized. Arrhenius was essentially correct about weak electrolytes: *the more dilute the solution, the higher the degree of dissociation into ions.*

Ionization is also affected by the nature of the solute and solvent, and by temperature. The manner in which these factors operate belongs to a more advanced study of chemistry.

Interionic Attraction in Strong Electrolytes

A 1 m solution of hydrochloric acid has a lower freezing point (−3.94° C) than a 1 m solution of NaCl (−3.37° C). Yet both substances are strong electrolytes. As NaCl is an ionic solid, no solute molecules exist in a solution of the compound; all the solute particles in both solutions must be freely moving ions. How, then, do we explain the difference in freezing point depression?

It is explained by the fact that the ions within one solute do not have the same degree of attraction for each other as the ions within another solute. In other words, **interionic attraction,** as it is known, varies from substance to substance. Though the attraction of ions for one another is

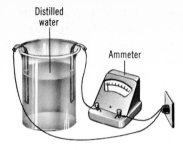

Distilled water

Ammeter

13-9 Distilled water actually does conduct an electric current, as indicated by the reading on the highly sensitive ammeter.

usually weak even when the ions are in solution, in a 1 *m* solution of NaCl the interionic attraction is greater than it is in a 1 *m* solution of HCl. Because of this greater interionic attraction, the number of ions in the NaCl solution is *apparently* less than that expected for a completely dissociated ionic solid. The ions in an NaCl solution are less free to move about; hence the higher freezing point of the solution. The less free the movement of ions in any solution, the higher its freezing point will be over that calculated on the basis of complete dissociation.

Ionization of Water

At the beginning of this chapter it was found that enough electric current could not be passed through a beaker of pure distilled water to light an ordinary light bulb. You might have assumed from this investigation that pure water has no ability whatever to conduct an electric current—but this assumption would have been wrong. If the light bulb in the original investigation is replaced by a highly sensitive ammeter, it is found that pure water, instead of being a nonelectrolyte, is simply a very, very weak electrolyte (Fig. 13-9). If this is so, pure water must contain at least a few ions. Actually, careful measurements show that at 25° C one hydrogen ion (H⁺) and one hydroxide ion (OH⁻) exist in each 556 million molecules of pure water!

This equilibrium can be shown by either of the following equations. The first equation (as well as Fig. 13-10) shows the formation of the hydronium ion; the second represents the formation of the hydrogen ion.

$$2\ H_2O \rightleftharpoons H_3O^+ + OH^-$$

water molecules   hydronium ion   hydroxide ion

$$H_2O \rightleftharpoons H^+ + OH^-$$

water molecules   hydrogen ion   hydroxide ion

13-10 A hydronium ion forms when a water molecule and a hydrogen ion from another water molecule combine. A hydroxide ion results from the loss of the hydrogen ion by the second water molecule.

One hydrogen ion and one hydroxide ion in every 556 million molecules of water is obviously an extremely low concentration of ions. For convenience, the chemist expresses this low concentration in terms of moles of H$^+$ ions or moles of OH$^-$ ions per liter of water molecules. Thus each liter of pure water at 25° C contains only 0.0000001 moles (1×10^{-7} moles) of hydrogen (or hydronium) ions and an equal number of moles of hydroxide ions. These ions in pure water, although so few in number, account for important chemical properties of water solutions.

Electrolysis of Water

If small amounts of various electrolytes such as sodium hydroxide or sulfuric acid are added to water, the solution will conduct a current. The products of the electrolysis, H$_2$ and O$_2$, are detected quite readily. Since the products are always the same, no matter what electrolyte is used, these products must come from the water and not from the electrolytes. Note particularly that the H$_2$ and O$_2$ are produced only if *small amounts* of strong electrolytes are used. In dilute solutions, the solute seems to enable the process to proceed. In concentrated solutions the solute itself may undergo electrolysis and other products may be formed. The electrolysis of a concentrated solution of NaCl, for example, is the commercial source of chlorine.

A Modern Theory

The present theory of the way in which H$_2$ and O$_2$ are formed during the electrolysis of water can be understood by considering what takes place at each of the two electrodes when sodium sulfate (Na$_2$SO$_4$) is used as the electrolyte. The solution contains sodium ions (Na$^+$), sulfate ions (SO$_4^{-2}$), H$_2$O molecules, and a *very* few H$^+$ and OH$^-$ ions. The latter are so few in number that they actually need not be given major consideration in the process. First, consider the reaction at the cathode (Fig. 13-11). Though the Na$^+$ ions migrate to the cathode, they are not affected. It is easier for the water molecules to take on electrons from this electrode to form hydrogen gas (H$_2$) and OH$^-$ ions than for the Na$^+$ ions to take on electrons and form metallic sodium. As the sodium ions are not used up, they are omitted from the following equation used to represent the reaction at the cathode:

$$4\,H_2O + 4\,e^- \longrightarrow 2\,H_2\uparrow + 4\,OH^-$$

This equation indicates that each group of four water molecules gains four electrons at the cathode to produce two molecules of hydrogen gas and four hydroxide ions. The significance of the coefficients before each formula in this equation will be clear in a moment.

Now let's turn to the reaction at the anode. The SO$_4^{-2}$ ions migrate to this electrode but they, too, are not affected. Here again, it is easier for the water molecules to give up electrons to the anode, so oxygen gas (O$_2$) and H$^+$ ions are formed. As the sulfate ions are not changed, the following equation is used to represent the reaction at the anode:

$$2\,H_2O - 4\,e^- \longrightarrow 4\,H^+ + O_2\uparrow$$

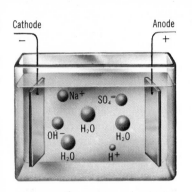

Cathode — / Anode +

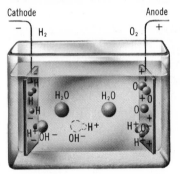

Cathode — H_2 / O_2 Anode +

13-11 When sodium sulfate serves as electrolyte for the electrolysis of water, the water contains Na^+ and SO_4^- ions, H_2O molecules, and a few H^+ and OH^- ions. At the cathode, water molecules gain electrons, and hydrogen is given off; at the anode, water molecules lose electrons, and oxygen is given off.

This equation indicates that each pair of water molecules at the anode loses 4 electrons, so that four hydrogen ions and one molecule of oxygen are produced at the anode.

Comparing the two equations above, observe that for every 4 electrons gained at the cathode, 4 electrons are released at the anode and leave the solution. Since both of these reactions occur simultaneously, they can be combined into one equation by canceling the electrons:

$$4\,H_2O + 4\,e^- \longrightarrow 2\,H_2 + 4\,OH^-$$
$$2\,H_2O - 4\,e^- \longrightarrow \quad O_2 + 4\,H^+$$
$$\overline{6\,H_2O \qquad\qquad \longrightarrow 2\,H_2 + O_2 + 4\,OH^- + 4\,H^+}$$

As soon as the H^+ ions and the OH^- ions are formed, they move away from the electrodes and recombine to produce molecules of H_2O. These molecules, in turn, undergo further electrolysis (Fig. 13-11). Hence a simplified, or net, equation for the electrolysis of water can be written:

$$2\,H_2O \longrightarrow 2\,H_2{\uparrow} + O_2{\uparrow}$$

What is the significance of the coefficients before the formulas in the above equation? The coefficients tell us that the loss of electrons at the anode, and the gain of an equal number of electrons at the cathode, result in the formation of two molecules of hydrogen ($2\,H_2$) for each single molecule of oxygen (O_2) that is formed. This is what we would expect from the observation made on page 63. By volume, twice as much hydrogen as oxygen is always produced during the electrolysis of water. The same net equation can be written for the electrolysis of water no matter what electrolyte is used. The electrolyte seems only to furnish ions needed for the process of electrolysis.

Now do you see why in the last chapter you were cautioned against touching an electric switch with wet hands? As the human body is largely water—or to be more exact, water containing dissolved electrolytes—it may, at house voltage, conduct enough electric current to give you a severe shock.

Having established that solutions of acids, bases, and salts contain ions, we shall now study in more detail how these same ions interact. Actually it is the reactions involving ions of acids, bases, and salts that account for many reactions in the laboratory as well as for many commercial processes, both familiar and unfamiliar.

QUESTIONS AND PROBLEMS

1. In terms of present-day knowledge, restate the last assumption of Arrhenius' theory of ionization (page 204).
2. Phosphoric acid is a weak electrolyte and nitric acid is a strong electrolyte. Write an equation for the dissociation of each of these acid solutions.

3. A 1 m solution of HNO_3 has a freezing point of $-3.58°$ C and a 1 m solution of $NaNO_3$ has a freezing point of $-3.02°$ C. Which compound has the higher interionic attraction? Give a reason for your answer.

4. (a) Potassium nitrate (KNO_3) is used occasionally in the electrolysis of water. Write equations for the reaction at the anode, the reaction at the cathode, and the combined reaction. (b) How would the reaction at the anode differ if potassium hydroxide (KOH) were used?

VALUE OF THE CONCEPT

THE CONCEPT

Ions in aqueous solution and in the molten state conduct electricity, while ionic solids, molecular solids, molecules in solution, and molten molecular substances are nonconductors. Compounds that conduct electricity when molten or in solution are called electrolytes; those compounds that do not conduct electricity are nonelectrolytes. Some molecular substances, when dissolved in water, become ionized. When ionic solids are dissolved in water, the ions dissociate, that is, move about freely. Depending upon their degree of ionization or dissociation, respectively, electrolytes vary in their ability to conduct electricity. Substances whose solutions are poor electrical conductors are weak electrolytes, while those whose solutions readily conduct electricity are strong electrolytes.

The original theory of Arrhenius has been revised, in part, and today the behavior of electrolytes can be summarized as follows:

1. Some molecular substances (such as acids) ionize when dissolved in water.

2. Ionic compounds, which contain ions in the solid state, simply dissociate when dissolved in water. Each ion in solution, however formed, carries an electric charge.

3. In any solution of ions, the *total* numbers of + and − charges are equal; but the numbers of positive and negative ions are not necessarily equal.

4. Dissolved molecules do not conduct electricity.

5. Strong electrolytes tend to dissociate completely. In weak electrolytes, the more dilute the solution, the higher the degree of dissociation. Some differences in conductivity of ionic substances in concentrated aqueous solutions, as well as differences in their freezing point depression, result from interionic attraction.

A number of hydrogen-containing molecular substances (acids) ionize in water to form hydrated protons or hydronium ions. Pure water, although weakly ionized, contains one hydrogen ion and one hydroxide ion per 556 million water molecules. This concentration of ions is frequently expressed in terms of moles per liter: each liter of pure water at 25° C has a concentration of 10^{-7} moles of H^+ ions and 10^{-7} moles of OH^- ions.

Electricity can be conducted through liquids by freely moving ions. Before the electricity is turned on, the ions move through the solution in a random fashion. Once direct current electricity flows, the ions move toward the electrode with a charge opposite their own. The negative ions, or anions, move toward the positive electrode, or anode, while the positive ions, or cations, move toward the negative electrode, or cathode. Anions lose electrons to the anode, and cations gain electrons from the cathode. This exchange of electrons between electrodes and ions results in chemical changes. For example, when electricity flows through water to which a small amount of electrolyte has been added, hydrogen molecules form at the cathode while oxygen molecules form at the anode. Electricity decomposes ionized compounds into elements or other substances by electrolysis.

Using the Basic Concept

1. (a) Differentiate between an electrolyte and a nonelectrolyte. (b) Describe a procedure used to determine whether substances are electrolytes or nonelectrolytes.

2. (a) What is a strong electrolyte? a weak electrolyte? (b) How do solutions of weak electrolytes differ from solutions of strong electrolytes?

3. (a) How do ionic solids form ionic aqueous solutions when they dissolve? (b) How do some molecular solids form ionic solutions when they dissolve? (c) Why don't all soluble molecular solids form ionic solutions in water?

4. Explain why molten ionic compounds can conduct electricity while solid ionic compounds cannot.

5. KCl is dissolved in NaCl to lower the melting point of the molten NaCl. Of what advantage is this in preparing NaCl for electrolysis?

6. What relationship exists between the degree to which a 1 molal aqueous solution conducts electricity and the freezing point of the solution?

7. What are the assumptions of Arrhenius' theory of ionization (or electrolytic dissociation)?

8. Describe two modifications of Arrhenius' original theory.

9. (a) Write the equation for the ionization of the following molecular substances in water: HCl, H_2SO_4, HNO_3. (b) What ion is common to each of these solutions? (c) Draw an electron dot diagram to represent this ion.

10. On what basis is it possible to predict that protons in solution must be hydrated?

11. (a) Describe the flow of ions in the electrolysis of concentrated hydrochloric acid. (b) In general terms describe how ions are conducted through any electrolyte in solution. (c) Describe the process of electrolysis.

12. (a) Draw a diagram of an electrolysis apparatus containing a solution of hydrochloric acid ready to be electrolyzed. Label the anode, cathode, anions, and cations. (b) Write an equation to indicate what happens to the cations at the cathode during the electrolysis of this acid.

13. (a) Will pure water conduct electricity? Why or why not? (b) What is the molar concentration of H^+ and OH^- ions in pure water?

14. (a) What is the difference between the degree of ionization in solution and the degree of dissociation in solution? (b) What factors affect the degree of ionization in solution?

15. (a) What is interionic attraction? (b) How does it affect the predicted freezing point of a solution?

Relating Terms Within the Concept

Select the letter of the term in Column B that is most closely related to each term in Column A. Do not use a term more than once.

COLUMN A	COLUMN B
1. dissociation	a. Arrhenius' theory
2. ionization in water	b. attracts cations
3. electrolyte	c. completely ionized liquids
4. strong electrolyte	
5. anode	d. H_3O^+
6. cathode	e. H^+ concentration in pure water
7. hydronium ion	f. hydrated electron
8. weak electrolyte	g. in the liquid state, contains ions
9. interionic attraction	h. lacks electrons
10. $10^{-7} M$	i. liquid contains both ions and molecules
	j. overcoming interionic attraction
	k. overcoming lattice energy
	l. poor conductivity of concentrated strong electrolytes

1. One hundred and eighty grams of water are decomposed by electrolysis. How many grams of hydrogen are formed? How many grams of oxygen?
2. (a) From the data in the above problem, determine how many moles of H_2 molecules are formed, and how many moles of O_2 molecules are formed. (b) How many molecules of water are decomposed? How many molecules of each element are produced?
3. (a) How many grams of H_2 form during the electrolysis of 180 grams of HCl? (b) What volume of each gas forms?
4. (a) What volume of H_2 and what volume of Cl_2 form (under normal conditions) during the electrolysis of a solution containing 36.5 grams of pure HCl? (b) What volume will the hydrogen produced during this electrolysis occupy at a temperature of 30° C and 800 mm of pressure?

Applying the Concept

1. Reread the section concerned with the dissolving of HCl gas in water. Is this a chemical or physical process? Justify your answer.

2. A concentrated solution of a weak electrolyte differs markedly from a dilute solution of a strong electrolyte. Using ammonium hydroxide and sodium hydroxide as an example, explain the reason for the difference in conductivity.
3. Show that one hydrogen ion in every 556 million molecules of water is equal to a concentration of H^+ ions of 10^{-7} M.
4. (a) Write equations to show what occurs at the anode and at the cathode during the electrolysis of water when a small amount of Na_2SO_4 is added to the water. (b) What seems to be the function of the electrolytes during this process?
5. Whether sulfuric acid or sodium hydroxide is used as the electrolyte in the electrolysis of water, the reaction is essentially the same and results in twice as much hydrogen as oxygen. Explain why the results are independent of the electrolyte.

Reading Further

"The Structure of Liquids," by J. D. Bernal, *Scientific American,* August 1960. (Also available as an offprint.) Describes the somewhat orderly arrangement of molecules in liquids.

14

Reactions Between Ions in Solution

Acids have had a long history in human affairs. Reference to vinegar appears in the records of the Babylonians and Egyptians. And hydrochloric and nitric acid were first prepared about the year A.D. 1100, but whether by Arabic or European alchemists is uncertain.

In the early days of chemistry, compounds that tasted sour were called acids. In fact, our own word acid comes from the Latin word for sour, *acidus.* But taste alone is neither a very precise test for establishing the nature of a compound, nor necessarily a safe one—many chemicals are poisonous. With the birth of modern science, chemists sought a new definition of acids that would be more practical and more accurate than the old definition relating to taste.

By 1780 Antoine Lavoisier was defining an acid as any substance that contained oxygen. This definition had to be abandoned when it was discovered that oxygen is not a component of hydrocyanic acid. In 1815 Sir Humphry Davy proposed a "hydrogen theory" of acids. Davy said that acids were "particular compounds in which the hydrogen can be replaced by metals." This remained the accepted definition of acids until almost our own time.

In 1923 a Danish chemist, J. N. Brønsted, and an Englishman, T. M. Lowry, put forward the definition of acids in use today. The Brønsted–Lowry theory, as it is called, has two great advantages over Davy's. It greatly extends the number of substances that can be considered acids. And by bringing the subject into the framework of modern atomic theory, it enables us to understand why acids behave as they do.

ACIDS

Would you like to *discover for yourself* some of the properties common to acids?

Fill three test tubes halfway with distilled water. Into the first tube bubble a small amount of hydrogen chloride (HCl) gas. Dissolve some phosphorus pentoxide (P_2O_5), produced by burning phosphorus in air, in the second test tube. Put some sulfur dioxide

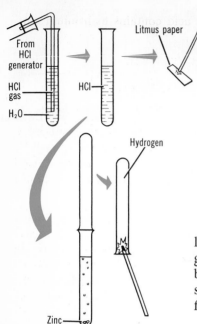

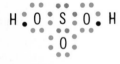
H O S O H
    O
Sulfurous acid

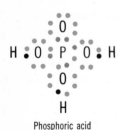
    O
H O P O H
    O
    H
Phosphoric acid

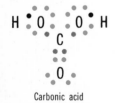
H O   O H
   C
   O
Carbonic acid

gas (SO_2), obtained by burning sulfur in air, into the third test tube.

Test each of the resulting solutions in two ways. First, remove one drop of each solution with a stirring rod and touch the rod to a small strip of blue litmus paper. Does the litmus turn pink in each case? Next, put a few small pieces of zinc in each of the first two solutions and a strip of magnesium ribbon (cleaned with fine sandpaper) in the third test tube. Bubbles of gas form on the surface of each piece of metal and eventually gas escapes from each solution. Collect the gas by inverting a test tube over each solution, and apply the burning splint test. Do you find that in each case the escaping gas is hydrogen?

Water solutions which respond in this way to these tests—which turn litmus paper pink and react with metals such as zinc to produce hydrogen gas—are called **acid solutions.** Acid solutions also have a sour taste; but because they are corrosive, you should avoid tasting them. As these solutions are often referred to by chemists simply as **acids,** we will frequently use the shorter term.

Ionization of Molecules in Acids

When each of the above acids is tested for its ability to conduct electricity, all are found to be electrolytes. As HCl, SO_2, CO_2, and P_2O_5* are all molecular compounds, and as only ions will conduct electricity, evidently these compounds ionize in water.

From the preceding chapter we already know that HCl ionizes in water to form hydronium and chloride ions. Since the other three solutions have properties similar to those of the HCl solution, and since only the HCl contains chlorine atoms, we may reasonably suspect that the similar properties of all three solutions are due to the presence of hydronium ions (H_3O^+). This, indeed, is true; all acid solutions contain hydronium or H^+ (aqueous) ions. It is, in fact, the hydronium ions that cause acids to taste sour, to turn litmus pink, and to react with metals such as zinc to produce hydrogen.

Look carefully at the formulas for each of the compounds used in the investigation. Two of them, SO_2 and P_2O_5, are covalently bonded, nonmetallic oxides. Such nonmetallic oxides that react with water to form acids are called **acid anhydrides.** These acid anhydrides form sulfurous (H_2SO_3) and phosphoric acids, respectively (Fig. 14-1).

There are several ways of writing an equation to show how an acid is formed from its acid anhydride. The equation often used to show, for example, how SO_2 reacts with water to form sulfurous acid is:

$$SO_2 + H_2O \longrightarrow H_2SO_3$$

This type of equation has one disadvantage: it does not show the ionic

14-1 Acids formed from acid anhydrides. Which ion shows resonance?

*The molecular weight of this oxide shows that P_4O_{10} is the true formula.

nature of the acid. To indicate that the acid contains hydronium ions, we can use the following equation:

$$SO_2 + 2\,H_2O \longrightarrow H_3O^+ + HSO_3^-$$

This equation can be simplified by substituting H^+ for H_3O^+:

$$SO_2 + H_2O \longrightarrow H^+ + HSO_3^-$$

In the same way, three different forms of an equation can be used to show the formation of acids from the other acid anhydrides above. Write the three similar equations which show the formation of carbonic acid from carbon dioxide and water. Remember that carbonic acid contains hydrogen ions and hydrogen carbonate (HCO_3^-) ions.

Hydrogen Halides Form Acids

Hydrogen chloride, the third substance used in these tests, is not an acid anhydride; it is a hydrogen halide. Halides are binary compounds containing a member of the halogen family of elements as the negative ion. The halogen family, as you remember from Chapter 5, consists of the elements in group VIIA of the periodic table. Each of the hydrogen halides, such as HCl, ionizes in water to form an acid.

Using HX to represent the formula for any hydrogen halide, it is possible to write a general equation to show the formation of hydrogen halide acids. Here the symbol X stands for any halogen atom and X^- for any halide ion.

$$HX + H_2O \longrightarrow H_3O^+ + X^-$$

The common hydrogen halide acids are hydrochloric acid, hydrofluoric acid, hydrobromic acid, and hydriodic acid.

Strong and Weak Acids

In previous chapters you have studied some reactions involving strong and weak acids. To help you differentiate further between such acids, *try the following.*

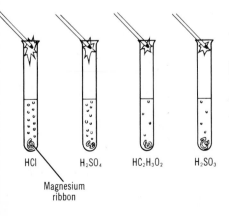

HCl H_2SO_4 $HC_2H_3O_2$ H_2SO_3

Magnesium ribbon

Secure four test tubes and fill each of them halfway with one of the following four acids: 1 M hydrochloric acid, 1 M sulfuric acid, 1 M acetic acid, and a saturated solution of sulfurous acid (H_2SO_3) [The saturated sulfurous acid can be prepared by dissolving in water as much sulfur dioxide (SO_2) gas as possible.] Now clean a strip of magnesium ribbon with fine sandpaper and cut the magnesium into four pieces of equal length. Place a strip in each of the solutions as shown at the left. Observe the bubbles of colorless gas that form on the magnesium strips and begin to escape from each of the test tubes. The burning splint test identifies the gas as hydrogen in each case. What important difference do you notice in the four reactions? In the first two test tubes, those containing hydrochloric acid and sulfuric acid, the hydrogen is produced quite rapidly. In the third and fourth test tubes, those containing acetic acid and sulfurous acid. the gas is produced more slowly.

Now use a conductivity apparatus to test a fresh solution of each acid for its ability to carry an electric current. Do you find that the hydrochloric and sulfuric acids are strong electrolytes while the acetic and sulfurous acids are weak electrolytes? Among these acids, what relationship exists between the rate with which an acid reacts with a metal to produce hydrogen and the acid's ability to conduct an electric current?

The two solutions which quickly produced hydrogen are also strong electrolytes; those which produced the gas more slowly are weaker electrolytes. The explanation for this relationship seems to be that although all acids in water solutions contain hydronium (hydrogen) ions, more hydronium ions are present in strong electrolytes than in weak electrolytes. In the stronger electrolytes—hydrochloric and sulfuric acids—ionization approaches completion; in the weaker electrolytes—acetic and sulfurous acids—there is an equilibrium between ions and molecules.

Historically, acids whose dilute solutions conduct electricity readily and react readily with metals to form hydrogen have been called strong acid solutions or simply strong acids. They include hydrochloric acid, sulfuric acid, and nitric acid (HNO_3). Dilute solutions of acids which do not conduct electricity readily and which react slowly with metals to form hydrogen are called weak acid solutions or simply weak acids. Among the weak acids are acetic acid, sulfurous acid, carbonic acid, and the complex acids found in citrus fruits.

The formation of sulfuric acid from sulfur trioxide (SO_3) and water can be represented by the equation:

$$SO_3 + H_2O \longrightarrow \underbrace{H^+ + HSO_4^-}_{\text{sulfuric acid solution}}$$

When there is an equilibrium between molecules and ions, as in weak acids, a double arrow is often used in the equations for their formation. Thus the formation of sulfurous acid from sulfur dioxide (SO_2) and water may be expressed as follows:

$$SO_2 + H_2O \rightleftharpoons \underbrace{H^+ + HSO_3^-}_{\text{sulfurous acid}}$$

Compare this to the equation for the ionization of an acetic acid solution given on page 209.

Hydrogen from Acids

The acids tested in the two previous investigations reacted with zinc or magnesium to produce hydrogen gas (H_2). Since hydronium (hydrogen) ions are the only substances common to all water solutions of acids, these

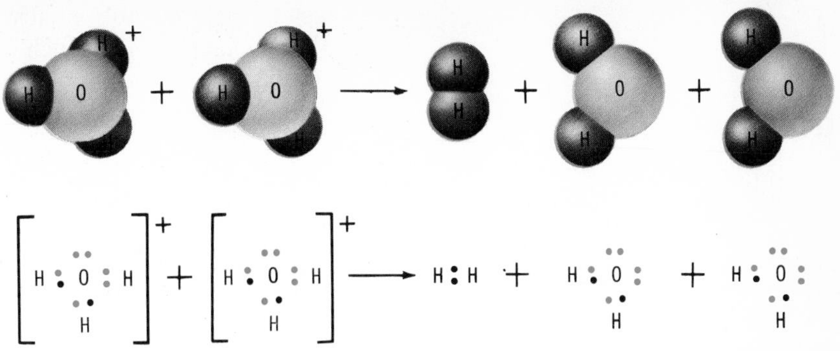

14-2 When a metal reacts with dilute acid to form hydrogen, a proton (hydrogen nucleus) from each of two hydronium ions combines with two electrons to become a molecule of hydrogen. Each of the former hydronium ions becomes a water molecule.

ions must be responsible for the formation of the hydrogen. For example, notice the similarity between the following equations:

$$Mg + 2\,HCl \longrightarrow MgCl_2 + H_2\uparrow$$
$$Mg + H_2SO_3 \longrightarrow MgSO_3 + H_2\uparrow$$

Whenever a metal such as magnesium reacts with a dilute acid, the hydrogen which is produced comes from the hydronium (or hydrogen) ions (Fig. 14-2). Hence either of the following ionic equations, showing hydronium or hydrogen ions, can be used to represent the formation of hydrogen gas from any dilute acid:

$$2\,H_3O^+ \longrightarrow H_2\uparrow + 2\,H_2O$$
$$2\,H^+ \longrightarrow H_2\uparrow$$

Can you determine in what respect these two equations are not balanced?

QUESTIONS AND PROBLEMS

1. How can you determine whether a clear, colorless solution is an acid?
2. Describe two properties that show whether an acid is strong or weak.
3. Write an equation for the formation of hydrobromic acid from hydrogen bromide.
4. Sulfur trioxide is the acid anhydride of sulfuric acid. (a) What is an acid anhydride? (b) Write three different forms of the equation to indicate the formation of sulfuric acid from its anhydride.
5. (a) Write an equation for the reaction between zinc and sulfuric acid. (b) Why may this be considered a typical equation for the production of hydrogen from an acid and a metal?

BASES

In the previous section you found that nonmetallic oxides dissolve in water to produce acid solutions. *By completing the following investigation,* determine the properties of the solutions produced when metallic oxides dissolve in water.

REACTIONS BETWEEN IONS IN SOLUTION   221

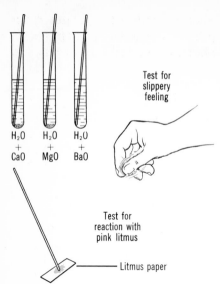

Test for
slippery
feeling

H₂0   H₂0   H₂0
+   +   +
CaO   MgO   BaO

Test for
reaction with
pink litmus

Litmus paper

Fill each of three test tubes halfway with distilled water. Into the first test tube, place a small pinch of calcium oxide (CaO); into the second, put an equal amount of magnesium oxide (MgO); and into the third put the same amount of barium oxide (BaO). Stir each solution with a clean stirring rod. Observe that only the BaO dissolves completely; in the other two solutions some of the solid solute remains in equilibrium with the dilute, saturated solution.

Now compare these three solutions by seeing how they respond to two different tests. Remove one drop of each solution with a stirring rod and touch the rod to a small strip of pink litmus paper. The paper turns blue in every case. Next, place a drop of each solution on your thumb, and rub thumb and index finger together; all the solutions have a slippery feeling. (These solutions are caustic and can blister the skin. Therefore, the hands should be washed thoroughly after this test so that no solution remains on them.) Finally, you might determine whether these solutions react with magnesium or zinc.

Water solutions that turn pink litmus paper blue and that are slippery to the touch are called **basic solutions,** or commonly, **bases.** Bases also have a bitter taste; but you were not advised to taste them since many are *caustic.* As all bases have the same properties, it is obvious that their structures must have something in common.

Dissociation of Compounds in Basic Solutions

If each of the above bases is tested with a conductivity apparatus, all are found to conduct electricity. Two of the solutions, those of calcium oxide and magnesium oxide, are fairly good conductors, while the solution of barium oxide is an extremely good conductor. As these three compounds are ionically bonded metallic oxides, the ions dissociate in water and thus conduct an electric current.

Note that each base contains positive metallic ions and negative hydroxide ions (OH^-). Since the hydroxide ion is the only ion common to all bases, it must be responsible for the properties of basic solutions. The reaction with water of each of the three metallic oxides to form calcium hydroxide [$Ca(OH)_2$], magnesium hydroxide [$Mg(OH)_2$], and barium hydroxide [$Ba(OH)_2$], respectively, is indicated below.

$$Ca^{+2} O^{-2} + H_2O \longrightarrow Ca^{+2} + 2\,OH^-$$
$$Mg^{+2} O^{-2} + H_2O \longrightarrow Mg^{+2} + 2\,OH^-$$
$$Ba^{+2} O^{-2} + H_2O \longrightarrow Ba^{+2} + 2\,OH^-$$

In these three equations, the hydroxides are shown in ionic form even though all of the hydroxides are only slightly soluble in water (20° C). Though none of the equations indicates it, all the ions freed in these reactions are hydrated. Yet, only the hydrated hydroxide ions, $OH^-(aq)$, cause solutions to taste bitter, feel slippery, and to turn litmus paper from pink to blue. Metallic oxides, such as those in the equations above, that react with water to form basic solutions are called **basic anhydrides.**

Strong and Weak Bases

Both CaO and MgO are ionic substances. Yet conductivity tests of their solutions, $Ca(OH)_2$ and $Mg(OH)_2$, show that both solutions are only fairly good conductors. You remember that CaO and MgO are only slightly soluble. Their saturated solutions are dilute. So, although saturated solutions of these two anhydrides are almost completely ionized, they do not contain sufficient ions to conduct electricity readily.

If ammonia gas (NH_3), a covalent compound, is bubbled into cold water, a tremendous amount of the gas dissolves (Fig. 14-3). A piece of pink litmus paper placed in the solution turns blue. When this ammonia solution is tested for its ability to conduct electricity, it too turns out to be a poor conductor. Yet, since very little ionization takes place when the molecules dissolve, relatively few OH^- ions are formed. The following equation represents what happens when NH_3 molecules react with water:

$$NH_3 + H_2O \rightleftharpoons NH_4^+ + OH^-$$

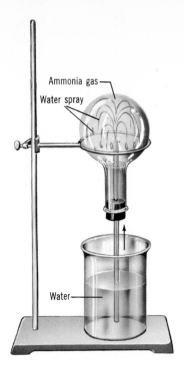

14-3 An ammonia fountain. Ammonia gas is so highly soluble that if a few drops of water are added to the flask, an ammonia water solution is formed, lowering the pressure. Water from the beaker then rushes into the inverted flask.

The arrow pointing to the right is purposely made very short to indicate that relatively few ammonium ions (NH_4^+) and hydroxide ions (OH^-) exist at equilibrium. Most of the particles present are molecules of NH_3 and molecules of H_2O. For this reason, the more accurate name for a solution of ammonia gas in water is *aqueous ammonia,* or ammonia water, written $NH_3(aq)$. However, this solution has been known for many years as ammonium hydroxide, NH_4OH.

Historically, the terms "strong" and "weak" when applied to basic solutions have referred to the number of hydroxide ions present in the solution. Basic solutions, such as NaOH, which contain many OH^- ions are called strong basic solutions or usually strong bases. They are often highly caustic and can destroy flesh. Solutions such as NH_4OH, or $NH_3(aq)$, with few OH^- ions, are called weak bases. They are safe to touch and are used for cleaning greasy surfaces. Although bases like $Ca(OH)_2$ made from slightly soluble basic anhydrides are not good conductors, they are considered to be strong because the *dissolved* hydroxide is highly dissociated. Ammonia water, a poor conductor, is a weak base since it consists of few ions in equilibrium with molecules. In recent years chemists have used the terms "strong" and "weak" to describe bases and acids in another sense. You will understand better the newer, broader meaning of these terms after learning more about H^+ and OH^- ions.

Solid Hydroxides

So far we have emphasized the hydroxide ions as they exist in solutions. But a look around your chemistry room will probably reveal a bottle containing a solid labeled SODIUM HYDROXIDE. Sodium hydroxide is one of the several useful hydroxides that exist in solid form. In the solid state, many hydroxides have an ionic lattice structure. Sodium hydroxide is one of the solid hydroxides of the alkali elements, which appear in group IA of the periodic table. All these hydroxides are highly soluble in water. They are often referred to as **alkalies.** On the other hand, the solid hydroxides of the alkaline earth or group IIA elements are markedly less soluble. An example of these latter hydroxides is calcium hydroxide.

QUESTIONS AND PROBLEMS

1. How can you determine whether or not a clear, colorless solution is a base?
2. How do strong bases differ from weak bases?
3. Define the terms *alkali* and *aqueous ammonia.*
4. Lithium oxide is the basic anhydride of lithium hydroxide. (a) What is a basic anhydride? (b) Write an equation for the formation of lithium hydroxide.
5. How do acid and basic anhydrides differ in chemical bonding?

H$^+$ AND OH$^-$ IONS

14-4 This sample of soil, being taken from a field containing corn stubble, will be analyzed for acid as well as mineral content.

Why are some red cabbages a deep purple while others are more truly red; and why do oak trees grow well in some soils and very poorly in others? The answer is largely a question of acid—the acid in the ground. The more acid there is in the soil, the more purple the cabbages will be. And oak trees will flourish only in a soil that is acid. The acidity of the soil, as of any substance, depends upon the concentration of H$^+$ ions (Fig. 14-4).

Ion Product Constant of Water

If two pieces of litmus paper, one blue and one pink, are placed in distilled water, both retain their original color. Water is neutral; the concentration of H$^+$ and OH$^-$ ions is the same. Yet if you dissolve a minute amount of acid anhydride in the water, the blue litmus turns pink, indicating an increase of H$^+$ ions. But what happens to the concentration of OH$^-$ ions?

Water contains only a few H$^+$ and OH$^-$ ions that are in equilibrium with many water molecules.

$$H_2O \rightleftharpoons H^+ + OH^-$$

In a system such as this, where there are relatively few ions in equilibrium with many molecules, the moles per liter of one ion multiplied by the moles per liter of the other ion is always equal to an unchanging value, or *constant*, at any given temperature. For water at 25° C, the moles per

pH 1
10^{-1} moles
of H$^+$ ions

0.1 M HCl

pH 2
10^{-2} moles
of H$^+$ ions

0.01 M HCl

pH 13
10^{-1} moles
of OH$^-$ ions

0.1 M NaOH

pH 12
10^{-2} moles
of OH$^-$ ions

0.01 M NaOH

14-5 The pH of any solution is the exponent of the molar concentration of H$^+$ ions expressed as a positive number.

liter of H$^+$ ions is 1×10^{-7} and the moles per liter of OH$^-$ ions is also 1×10^{-7}; therefore the value of the constant is 1×10^{-14}. This constant value of 1×10^{-14} is called the **ion product constant of water.**

$$\begin{array}{ccc} \text{moles per liter} & \times & \text{moles per liter} = & \text{ion product} \\ \text{of H}^+ \text{ ions} & & \text{of OH}^- \text{ ions} & \text{constant of water} \\ 1 \times 10^{-7} & \times & 1 \times 10^{-7} = & 1 \times 10^{-14} \end{array}$$

The symbol K_W is usually used to represent the ion product constant of water, hence K_W is equal to 1×10^{-14}. In practice, the ion product constant of water is written as:

$$K_W = [H^+] \times [OH^-] = 10^{-14}$$

The squared brackets [ ] represent the ion concentration in moles per liter.

Since this product constant applies to all water solutions, whether acidic or basic, you can now determine what happens to the OH$^-$ ion concentration in the problem posed above.

Determining [H$^+$] and [OH$^-$]

The acid added to the water caused [H$^+$] to increase. Since [H$^+$] $\times$ [OH$^-$] must always equal 10^{-14}, the concentration of OH$^-$ ions [OH$^-$] must decrease. Similarly, if a basic anhydride is added to water, causing [OH$^-$] to increase, [H$^+$] must decrease to maintain the ion product constant (K_W) at 10^{-14}. Now use this relationship to determine [H$^+$] and [OH$^-$] for solutions of 0.1 M (10^{-1}) HCl and NaOH.

As the HCl ionizes completely in water, there is 0.1 mole of H$^+$ ions in the solution—or a hydrogen ion concentration of 10^{-1} M. Therefore the concentration of OH$^-$ ions in this solution must be 10^{-13} M.

$$\begin{array}{rcl} K_W & = & [H^+] \times [OH^-] \\ 10^{-14} & = & [10^{-1}] \times [OH^-] \\ 10^{-13} & = & [OH^-] \end{array}$$

Assuming that sodium hydroxide is completely dissociated in dilute solution, we find that the concentration of OH$^-$ ions in the solution of 0.1 M (10^{-1}) NaOH is also 10^{-1} M. The concentration of H$^+$ ions in this solution must be 10^{-13} M.

$$\begin{array}{rcl} K_W & = & [H^+] \times [OH^-] \\ 10^{-14} & = & [H^+] \times [10^{-1}] \\ 10^{-14} & = & 10^{-13} \times 10^{-1} \end{array}$$

The pH Scale

In 1909 a Danish chemist, S. P. L. Sörensen, developed a scale to express the degree of concentration of hydrogen ions in solution. Called the pH scale—standing for the *power of hydrogen ions in solutions*—the scale eliminates the use of negative exponents. Sörensen based the pH scale upon the concentration of H$^+$ ions in water. The pH of any solution can be defined as the exponent, expressed as a *positive* number, of the molar concentration of H^+ ions in that solution (Fig. 14-5).

In keeping with the definition, the pH of water is 7 ($H^+ = 10^{-7}$ mole per liter). What is the pH of each solution just described? The 0.1 M solution of HCl described above has a hydrogen ion concentration of 10^{-1} mole per liter of solution; its pH is 1. Similarly, a 0.01 M solution of HCl has a hydrogen ion concentration of 10^{-2} mole per liter of solution; its pH is 2. Observe that the *more dilute acid* solution has a *higher* pH value. The 0.1 M (10^{-1} M) NaOH solution described in the last section has a hydrogen ion concentration of 10^{-13} mole per liter of solution; its pH is 13. What is the pH of a 0.01 M NaOH solution? As it has a *hydroxide* ion concentration of 10^{-2} mole per liter of solution, it has a *hydrogen* ion concentration of 10^{-12}; its pH is 12.

On the pH scale, all pH values are positive and range from 0 to 14. Water, with a pH of 7, is neutral because the concentration in moles per liter for both the H^+ and OH^- ions is equal to 10^{-7}. The neutral point (pH 7) is in the center of the pH scale as indicated below.

acids—strength increasing							neutral	bases—strength increasing						
0	1	2	3	4	5	6	7	8	9	10	11	12	13	14

Any solution with a hydrogen ion concentration greater than that of water is acid and has a pH less than 7. *The greater the H^+ ion concentration, the stronger the acid and the lower the pH.* On the other hand, any solution that has a hydrogen ion concentration less than that of water is a base and has a pH above 7. *The greater the OH^- ion concentration, the stronger the base and the higher the pH.*

A change of one unit on the pH scale, for instance, from 4 to 3, represents a tenfold increase in the concentration of hydrogen ions (10^{-3} mole per liter compared with 10^{-4} mole per liter). The pH values for a number of commonly used substances are given in Table 14-1. Observe that all acids have pH values below 7, while bases have pH values above 7.

Determining pH

Several previous investigations have made use of the different effects that acid solutions and basic solutions have upon litmus paper. In terms of the pH scale, solutions with pH values below 7 (approximately) turn litmus pink, while solutions with a pH value above 7 (approximately) turn litmus blue. Actually, litmus is purplish between pH 5.5 and pH 8. Thus the color of the litmus indicates generally whether a solution contains an excess of H^+ ions or OH^- ions. The acidic or basic nature of a solution can also be determined by using a solution of phenolphthalein. If colorless phenolphthalein is added to a sodium hydroxide solution, the solution turns red. By contrast, the phenolphthalein remains colorless in a hydrochloric acid solution.

Now use both litmus paper and phenolphthalein to *determine for yourself* the pH of a specific solution.

Table 14-1   pH VALUES OF SOME COMMON SUBSTANCES

Hydrochloric acid (0.1 N)	1.0
Sulfuric acid (0.1 N)	1.2
Soft drinks	2.4
Acetic acid (0.1 N)	2.9
Oranges	3.5
Tomatoes	4.2
Boric acid (0.1 N)	5.2
Rain water	6.2
Pure water	7.0
Sea water	8.5
Milk of magnesia	10.5
Ammonium hydroxide (0.1 N)	11.1
Sodium carbonate (0.1 N)	11.6
Sodium hydroxide (0.1 N)	13.0

Add a drop of dilute hydrochloric acid to 250 ml of boiled distilled water. Place a piece of blue litmus paper in the solution; the blue litmus turns pink. Now add two drops of phenolphthalein to the solution; no change occurs. Carefully add a dilute solution of freshly prepared calcium hydroxide drop by drop until a change occurs in either the litmus paper or the phenolphthalein. When only a few drops have been added, does the litmus return to its original blue color although the solution remains colorless? Add a few more drops of calcium hydroxide solution; the entire solution turns red. Why?

The solution changes color because the last few drops of calcium hydroxide have produced an even greater excess of OH^- ions. These visual changes show that it requires a higher concentration of hydroxide ions to change the color of phenolphthalein than to change the color of litmus. Litmus changes from pink to purplish at a pH of about 5.5, and to a definite blue color at a pH of approximately 8. Phenolphthalein changes color only as the solution reaches a pH between 8.3 and 10.

Dyes such as litmus and phenolphthalein, which are affected by changes in hydrogen ion concentration, are called *indicators* (see Colorplate I, facing page 548). They can be used with a moderate degree of accuracy to determine the pH values of solutions. Natural indicators include litmus from certain lichens and the coloring matter in red cabbage and many ripened fruits. Most other indicators, such as phenolphthalein and methyl orange, listed in Table 14-2, are synthetic.

Table 14-2   **ACID-BASE INDICATORS**

Indicator	Color at pH values more acid than transition range	pH range of color transition	Color at pH values more basic than transition range
Methyl violet	Colorless	0.2–3.2	Violet
Thymol blue	Red	1.2–2.8	Yellow
Congo red	Blue	3.0–5.0	Red
Methyl orange	Red	3.1–4.4	Yellow
Methyl red	Red	4.4–6.0	Yellow
Litmus	Red	5.5–8.0	Blue
Bromthymol blue	Yellow	6.0–7.6	Blue
Phenol red	Yellow	6.8–8.4	Red
Phenolphthalein	Colorless	8.3–10.0	Red
Thymolphthalein	Colorless	9.3–10.5	Blue
Alizarin yellow R	Yellow	10.1–12.0	Red
Indigo carmine	Blue	11.4–13.0	Yellow

14-6 pH may be determined by matching the color of Hydrion paper that has been dipped into a solution with the color scale on the container.

By combining certain indicators, chemists have developed *universal indicators* which are used to indicate a wide range of pH values. One commonly used universal indicator is Hydrion paper (Fig. 14-6). A single

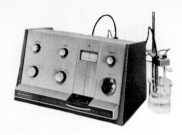

piece of Hydrion paper shows a gradual and continuous color change from pH 1 to pH 11.

Because slight changes in hydrogen ion concentration have a great effect on many chemical reactions, pH must often be determined with greater precision than can be done with indicators. Meters that indicate pH, like the one pictured in Fig. 14-7, may be used to determine hydrogen ion concentrations to the nearest 0.001 pH unit.

14-7 This pH meter can be used to determine automatically (to the nearest 0.001 pH unit) the hydrogen ion concentration of any solution.

The Neutralization Reaction

From the advertisements on television, you are only too familiar with the condition known as "acid stomach" and the so-called "neutralizing" remedies suggested for its temporary relief. But what actually occurs when an acid is neutralized? *Find out for yourself.*

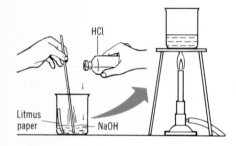

Place a piece of litmus paper in a small beaker one-fourth full of a very dilute solution of NaOH. Add dilute hydrochloric acid to the solution drop by drop and stir until the litmus begins to turn pink. Heat the beaker gently to evaporate the water completely. Then after the beaker has cooled, cautiously taste a crystal of the residue that remains. It tastes salty. A solution of NaOH tastes bitter and a solution of HCl tastes sour; the beaker must contain a new substance—common table salt.

The equation for the reaction that has taken place can be written as:

$$NaOH + HCl \longrightarrow NaCl + H_2O$$

Since NaCl, NaOH, and HCl in solution are completely ionic, a better picture of what has happened is obtained by writing these compounds in their ionic form:

$$Na^+ + OH^- + H^+ + Cl^- \longrightarrow Na^+ + Cl^- + H_2O$$

When the equations are written in this way, it is clear that Na^+, OH^-, H^+, and Cl^- ions are present as reactants. As products, the particles present are Na^+ and Cl^- ions and H_2O molecules. Notice that both the reactants and products contain Na^+ and Cl^- ions. The only chemical change that actually occurs when NaOH and HCl solutions are combined is the formation of water from the reaction between H^+ and OH^- ions.

Now consider the ionic equation for the reaction between another acid and base: potassium hydroxide and sulfuric acid.

$$2\,K^+ + 2\,OH^- + 2\,H^+ + SO_4^{-2} \longrightarrow 2\,K^+ + SO_4^{-2} + 2\,H_2O$$

By comparing the particles present as reactants with those present as products, we again find that water is the only new particle formed. The K^+ and SO_4^{-2} ions remain unchanged. Such reactions between H^+ ions of acid solutions and OH^- ions of basic solutions to form water are **neutralization reactions.** The only chemical change that occurs in any neu-

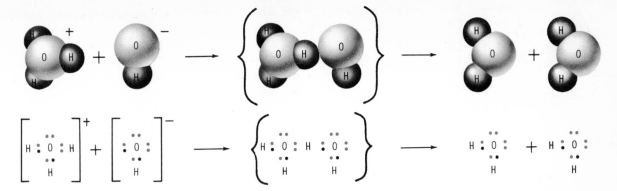

14-8 In any neutralization reaction the hydronium ion of the acid combines with the hydroxide ion of the base to form water.

tralization reaction is the combination of H^+ and OH^- ions to form H_2O.

$$H^+ + OH^- \longrightarrow H_2O \quad \text{(showing hydrogen ion)}$$
$$H_3O^+ + OH^- \longrightarrow 2\ H_2O \quad \text{(showing hydronium ion)}$$

The negative ion of the acid and the positive ion of the base are not shown in these equations since they remain unchanged during neutralization. Such ionic equations that show only the substances that actually undergo change during the reaction are called *net*, or essential, equations.

Proton Donor–Proton Acceptor Theory

When an acid and base are mixed, water forms because each H_3O^+ ion donates a proton to each OH^- ion. In turn, each OH^- ion accepts a proton from each H_3O^+ ion. This proton transfer, which is shown in Fig. 14-8, can be represented by the following pair of equations:

$$H_3O^+ - H^+ \longrightarrow H_2O$$
$$OH^- + H^+ \longrightarrow H_2O$$

This interpretation of neutralization leads to a new definition of an acid and a base. An acid is *any* substance that can *donate protons;* a base is *any* substance that can *accept protons.* Therefore, in the equations above, the *hydronium ion* is an acid because it *donates a proton;* the *hydroxide ion* is a base because it *accepts a proton.*

This theory that acids donate protons while bases accept them, *whether or not they are in aqueous solutions,* is the Brønsted–Lowry theory mentioned at the beginning of this chapter. It was advanced in 1923 by Brønsted and Lowry independently. The Brønsted–Lowry theory further states that the strength of an acid depends on its ability to donate protons, and the strength of a base on its ability to accept them. The stronger the acid, the more readily it donates protons; the stronger the base, the more readily it accepts them.

When HCl gas dissolves in water, the polar covalent hydrogen chloride molecules ionize to form hydronium and chloride ions.

$$HCl + H_2O \longrightarrow H_3O^+ + Cl^-$$

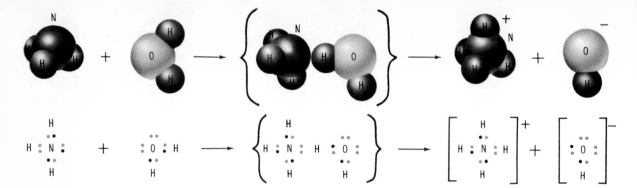

Ammonia acts as a Brønsted-Lowry base; when ammonia gas dissolves in water, a proton donated by a water molecule combines with an ammonia molecule to form an ammonium ion. Simultaneously, the former water molecule becomes a hydroxide ion.

Each HCl molecule donates a proton (H^+) to each water molecule, and each water molecule accepts a proton.

$$\text{(acid)} \quad HCl - H^+ \longrightarrow Cl^-$$

$$\text{(base)} \quad H_2O + H^+ \longrightarrow H_3O^+$$

Observe in Fig. 13-5 how a proton (that is, the hydrogen atom minus its electron) becomes attached to a water molecule to form an H_3O^+ ion. Thus, according to the Brønsted–Lowry theory, each HCl molecule is an acid, while each H_2O molecule is a base.

Consider again the reaction between NH_3 and H_2O:

$$NH_3 + H_2O \longrightarrow NH_4^+ + OH^-$$

Because each H_2O molecule donates a proton to an NH_3 molecule, the H_2O acts as an acid. Because each NH_3 molecule accepts a proton, the NH_3 acts as a base.

$$\text{(acid)} \quad H_2O - H^+ \longrightarrow OH^-$$

$$\text{(base)} \quad NH_3 + H^+ \longrightarrow NH_4^+$$

Observe in Fig. 14-9 how a proton becomes attached to the ammonia (NH_3) molecule to form an ammonium (NH_4^+) ion.

These examples indicate that familiar acids such as HCl are not the only acids; in terms of the Brønsted–Lowry theory, H_2O molecules, for example, may act as acids. Similarly, hydroxides are not the only bases; NH_3 molecules, and sometimes H_2O molecules, are Brønsted–Lowry bases. The dual nature of water is shown in the formation of hydronium and hydroxide ions.

$$\underset{\text{base}}{H_2O} + \underset{\text{acid}}{H_2O} \rightleftharpoons H_3O^+ + OH^-$$

A substance such as water, that can either accept or donate protons—depending upon the reaction—is **amphiprotic**.

Conjugate Acid-Base Pairs

Let us examine the reaction between acetic acid ($HC_2H_3O_2$) and H_2O in which hydrated H_3O^+ and $C_2H_3O_2^-$ ions are produced:

$$HC_2H_3O_2 + H_2O \rightleftharpoons H_3O^+ + C_2H_3O_2^-$$

Each hydronium ion that forms is capable of losing a proton. Therefore, the H_3O^+ ion is itself an acid. Each acetate ion that forms may gain a proton; therefore the $C_2H_3O_2^-$ ion, a product, is a base.

To indicate this acid-base relationship, each pair composed of an acid and a base related by proton transfer is called a *conjugate acid-base pair*. The conjugate acids and bases in each of the three reactions shown below are those having the same subscript (acid$_1$-base$_1$ and acid$_2$-base$_2$). The conjugate pairs are also shown connected by brackets.

	Acid$_1$		Base$_2$ $\rightleftharpoons$ Acids$_2$	Base$_1$
Equation 1	HCl	$+ H_2O$	$\longrightarrow H_3O^+$	$+ Cl^-$
Equation 2	$HC_2H_3O_2$	$+ H_2O$	$\rightleftharpoons H_3O^+$	$+ C_2H_3O_2^-$
Equation 3	H_2O	$+ NH_3$	$\rightleftharpoons NH_4^+$	$+ OH^-$

How can you determine which of the above are the stronger acids and bases in the Brønsted-Lowry sense? *The terms strong and weak pertaining to acids are used to describe the different degrees to which these compounds donate or accept protons.* Those acids that donate protons to water most completely, such as HCl, are almost completely ionized. These acids also show the greatest conductivity when tested in an apparatus similar to that in Fig. 13-7 (page 209).

If you should compare the conductivity of 100 ml of 0.1 M solutions of hydrochloric acid, acetic acid, and ammonia, you would find that the hydrochloric acid solution (HCl) caused the bulb to glow brightly, indicating its high conductivity. Calculations verify that HCl is almost 100 percent ionized. Examine the first equation above. HCl must be a better proton donor (a stronger acid) than the H_3O^+ ion because the HCl molecules have given up protons to the H_3O^+ ions. Next, you would find that the solution of acetic acid ($HC_2H_3O_2$) makes the bulb glow weakly, and calculations confirm that the solution is ionized slightly (1.3 percent). Examine equation 2 above. As most of the $HC_2H_3O_2$ remains in the molecular form, the H_3O^+ ion must be a better proton donor than $HC_2H_3O_2$. Finally you would find that the solution of ammonia, $NH_3(aq)$, also makes the bulb glow weakly. Calculations confirm its slight ionization as 1.3 percent. Now examine Equation 3 above. Most of the water remains in molecular form, so NH_4^+ must be a better proton donor than H_2O, the weakest acid.

Now how could you compare the strength of $HC_2H_3O_2$ and NH_4^+ as acids? Perhaps by testing a reaction in which both of these substances occur. Predict what would happen if you mixed 50 ml of 0.1 M $HC_2H_3O_2$ with 50 ml of 0.1 M $NH_3(aq)$ and tested the conductivity of the solution. The bulb would glow brightly; a mixture of two weak electrolytes would have produced a strong electrolyte. The equation for the reaction helps to explain this result.

$$\text{HC}_2\text{H}_3\text{O}_2 + \text{NH}_3 \longrightarrow \text{NH}_4{}^+ + \text{C}_2\text{H}_3\text{O}_2{}^-$$

| Acid₁ | Base₂ | Acid₂ | Base₁ |

Each $\text{HC}_2\text{H}_3\text{O}_2$ molecule donates a proton to an NH_3 molecule to form the completely ionic products, $\text{NH}_4{}^+$ and $\text{HC}_2\text{H}_3\text{O}_2{}^-$. Therefore, $\text{HC}_2\text{H}_3\text{O}_2$ is a stronger acid than the $\text{NH}_4{}^+$ ion. Investigations of this type enable chemists to compare the relative strengths of two acids.

The results of these and similar investigations are summarized in Table 14-3. The acids decrease in strength as you read down the table. The really strong acids include the H_3O^+ ion and those above it. The acids from the $\text{NH}_4{}^+$ ion downward are very weak acids, with water being the weakest acid. The acids from the bisulfate ion to carbonic acid are moderate in strength.

You have not considered the relative strengths of bases, but similar investigations and reasoning indicate that the strongest base in water solution is the hydroxyl ion, OH^-. The bases decrease in strength as you read up the table. Note that the strongest acid listed, perchloric acid, (HClO_4), has the weakest conjugate base, the perchlorate ion ($\text{ClO}_4{}^-$).

In each of the reactions studied in terms of the Brønsted–Lowry theory, the forward and reverse reactions are taking place at the same time. In general, of these two reactions the one that predominates, or takes place to the greatest extent, is the one that forms the *weaker acid and weaker base*. In the *conjugate acid* column of Table 14-3, the weaker acid is always *below* the stronger acid; in the *conjugate base* column, the weaker base is always *above* the stronger base. Also, any Brønsted–Lowry *acid in the column at the left can react with any base below it in the column at the right* if the concentrations are equal. In each case the forward reaction occurs to a greater extent than does the reverse reaction.

You can test and confirm these statements by applying them to the four reactions just considered. For example, in the third equation the reverse reaction of $\text{NH}_4{}^+$ (acid₂) with OH^- (base₂) predominates over the forward reaction. The reaction between H_2O, acting as a weak acid, with NH_3, the base, does not take place to any appreciable extent. You will study such slight reactions in more detail in the section on *Hydrolysis of Salts* in this chapter.

QUESTIONS AND PROBLEMS

1. (a) What indicator would you use to study a reaction that is completed at a pH of approximately 7? approximately 10? approximately 4?
   (b) Why is litmus such a widely used indicator in your laboratory?

Table 14-3 **CONJUGATE ACID-BASE STRENGTHS IN WATER SOLUTIONS**

Conjugate acid (A_1)	Formula	Strength	Conjugate base (B_1)	Formula	Strength
Perchloric acid	$HClO_4$		Perchlorate ion	ClO_4^-	
Hydrochloric acid	HCl		Chloride ion	Cl^-	
Nitric acid	HNO_3		Nitrate ion	NO_3^-	
Sulfuric acid	H_2SO_4		Hydrogen sulfate ion	HSO_4^-	
Hydronium ion	H_3O^+		Water	H_2O	
Bisulfate ion	HSO_4^-		Sulfate ion	SO_4^{-2}	
Phosphoric acid	H_3PO_4	Decreasing	Dihydrogen phosphate ion	$H_2PO_4^-$	Decreasing
Acetic acid	$HC_2H_3O_2$		Acetate ion	$C_2H_3O_2$	
Aluminum ion (hydrated)	$Al(H_2O)_6^{+3}$		Monohydroxy aluminum ion (hydrated)	$Al(H_2O)_5(OH)^{+2}$	
Carbonic acid	H_2CO_3		Hydrogen carbonate ion	HCO_3^-	
Ammonium ion	NH_4^+		Ammonia	NH_3	
Bicarbonate ion	HCO_3^-		Carbonate ion	CO_3^{-2}	
Monohydrogen phosphate ion	HPO_4^{-2}		Phosphate ion	PO_4^{-3}	
Water	H_2O		Hydroxide ion	OH^-	

2. (a) Define the term *ion product constant of water*. (b) Use K_W to determine the concentration of H^+ and OH^- ions in a 0.1 M solution of HNO_3, a 10^{-5} M solution.

3. What is the pH of 10^{-4} M HCl and of 10^{-4} M NaOH?

4. (a) Write a complete ionic equation for the reaction between sodium hydroxide and nitric acid. (b) What is the only chemical change that actually occurs during the reaction?

5. (a) In terms of the Brønsted-Lowry theory, define an acid and a base. (b) In terms of hydronium (hydrogen) and hydroxide ions, define an acid and a base. (c) Determine the conjugate acid-base pairs in the reaction between hydrogen bromide (HBr) and water.

SALTS

In the previous investigation you prepared solid sodium chloride by evaporation of a solution containing ions that do not undergo a change during neutralization. Solid ammonium acetate ($NH_4C_2H_3O_2$) can be prepared in a similar way. Such ionic substances are called **salts.** Salts are ionic compounds that can be made by combining the positive ion of a base and the negative ion of an acid.

Normal Salts

The reaction of HCl with NaOH produced only one salt, NaCl. Likewise the reaction of NH_3 with $HC_2H_3O_2$ produces only a single salt, $NH_4C_2H_3O_2$. Since each of these acids contains only a single replaceable hydrogen ion or proton per molecule, each is called a **monoprotic** (or monobasic) acid. But what kind of salt is produced when an acid such as H_2SO_4 or H_3PO_4 reacts with a base such as NaOH? Note that H_2SO_4, which contains two hydrogen atoms or protons per molecule, is a **diprotic** acid, while H_3PO_4, with three hydrogen atoms per molecule, is **triprotic.** To determine what kind of salt is produced when a diprotic acid and a base react, *try this for yourself.*

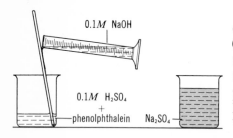

0.1M NaOH

0.1M H_2SO_4
+
phenolphthalein Na_2SO_4

Place 100 ml of 0.1 M H_2SO_4 in a 400-ml beaker and add a drop or two of phenolphthalein. The acid remains colorless. Now add 0.1 M NaOH solution, a few milliliters at a time, until the solution turns red. Did you find that about 200 ml of the 0.1 M NaOH solution are needed to effect this change? (Remember that phenolphthalein begins to turn from colorless to red at a pH of about 8.) Evaporate a portion of the solution until a crystalline solid remains. What salt forms?

The formation of sodium sulfate (Na_2SO_4) by neutralization can be represented by the following equation:

$$2\,H^+ + SO_4^{-2} + 2\,Na^+ + 2\,OH^- \longrightarrow 2\,Na^+ + SO_4^{-2} + 2\,H_2O$$

Each of the two OH^- ions has accepted a hydrogen ion from the acid to form two molecules of water. The Na^+ ions and the SO_4^{-2} ions remain unchanged.

Salts such as Na_2SO_4 whose negative ions retain no protons from the acid during neutralization are called **normal salts.** $NaNO_3$ (sodium nitrate), Na_2SO_3 (sodium sulfite), Na_3PO_4 (trisodium phosphate), and $NaC_2H_3O_2$ (sodium acetate) are other examples of normal salts.

Acid Salts

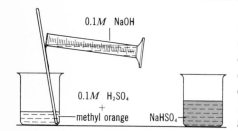

0.1M NaOH

0.1M H_2SO_4
+
methyl orange $NaHSO_4$

Again place 100 ml of 0.1 M H_2SO_4 into a 400-ml beaker. This time add a few drops of methyl orange indicator. The solution becomes red. Add 0.1 M NaOH a few milliliters at a time, until the color just changes from red to yellow. Since the methyl orange changes from red to yellow at a pH of about 4, the solution is evidently still acid. Notice that it was necessary to add only about 100 ml of 0.1 M NaOH to cause this change in color. Evaporate a portion of the solution until white crystals form. What salt is it?

This solid is the salt sodium hydrogen sulfate or sodium bisulfate ($NaHSO_4$). The ionic equation for its formation by neutralization is:

$$2\,H^+ + SO_4^{-2} + Na^+ + OH^- \longrightarrow Na^+ + HSO_4^- + H_2O$$

Notice that only one of the H^+ ions of the acid has been accepted by the OH^- ion of the base. The other hydrogen atom has remained with the sulfate ion to form a hydrogen sulfate, also called a *bisulfate,* ion.

$$\underset{\text{proton}}{H^+} + \underset{\substack{\text{sulfate} \\ \text{ion}}}{SO_4^{-2}} \longrightarrow \underset{\substack{\text{bisulfate} \\ \text{ion}}}{HSO_4^-}$$

Salts such as $NaHSO_4$ (sodium hydrogen sulfate) whose negative ions retain one or more of the hydrogen ions or protons of the acid from which they are formed are called **acid salts.**

When phosphoric acid (H_3PO_4) reacts with a base such as NaOH, three salts are possible—a normal salt and two acid salts. In the following equations observe that 3 formula weights of NaOH react with 1 formula weight of H_3PO_4 to produce normal sodium phosphate, or trisodium phosphate, Na_3PO_4. Two formula weights of NaOH react with two hydrogen ions per molecule of H_3PO_4 to form the acid salt disodium hydrogen phosphate (Na_2HPO_4). If only 1 formula weight of NaOH is used, only one of the three hydrogen ions in the phosphoric acid reacts to form another acid salt, monosodium phosphate (NaH_2PO_4).

$$3\ NaOH + H_3PO_4 \longrightarrow Na_3PO_4 + 3\ H_2O$$
$$2\ NaOH + H_3PO_4 \longrightarrow Na_2HPO_4 + 2\ H_2O$$
$$NaOH + H_3PO_4 \longrightarrow NaH_2PO_4 + H_2O$$

From such experiments it has been found that the *amount* of base used in the neutralization reaction determines the kind of salt that is produced.

Basic salts also exist, though these are not as common as acid salts. Basic salts are formed when only some of the hydroxide ions of the basic solution are neutralized. Basic lead nitrate [$Pb(OH)NO_3$] and basic bismuth nitrate [$Bi(OH)_2NO_3$] are examples of **basic salts.**

Hydrolysis of Salts

Although sodium hydroxide is extremely effective in removing dirt and grease, it cannot be used in household cleansers because it is very harmful to the skin. Instead, many household cleaning agents contain the normal salt, trisodium phosphate. When dissolved in water, this salt effectively removes dirt and grease—but why?

A solution of trisodium phosphate (Na_3PO_4) turns pink litmus paper blue. Evidently when dissolved in water this normal salt forms a basic solution. When sodium acetate is dissolved in water, it also reacts basically to litmus paper. If some ammonium chloride (NH_4Cl), another normal salt, is dissolved in distilled water, the solution turns a piece of blue litmus paper pink. Apparently when ammonium chloride dissolves in water, the solution formed is acid. Zinc chloride dissolved in water also reacts acidically.

Sodium chloride is one of the few normal salts that dissolves in water to form a neutral solution, that is, with a pH of 7. Most salts produce either an excess of H^+ ions or an excess of OH^- ions when they dissolve in water. The reaction between some salts with water to produce either acidic or basic solutions is an example of the process called **hydrolysis** (Fig. 14-10). The word hydrolysis literally means the taking apart or decomposing of water. However, any hydrolysis reaction can be considered as only an extension of the ideas expressed in the Brønsted–Lowry theory of acids and bases.

14-10 A few drops of phenolphthalein are added to solutions of sodium chloride and sodium acetate. Since NaCl does not hydrolize, the phenolphthalein remains colorless. The sodium acetate hydrolyzes to form a basic solution, indicated by a red color.

You know that solid trisodium phosphate (Na_3PO_4) dissolves in water, releasing freely moving phosphate ions (PO_4^{-3}). These PO_4^{-3} ions are strong Brønsted–Lowry bases. Since the PO_4^{-3} ion, a base, is above H_2O, an acid, in Table 14-3, you should expect little reaction to occur.

$$H_2O + PO_4^{-3} \rightleftharpoons HPO_4^{-2} + OH^-$$
$$\text{Acid}_1 \qquad \text{Base}_2 \qquad\qquad \text{Acid}_2 \qquad \text{Base}_1$$

Nevertheless, the slight forward reaction does produce a slight excess of OH^- ions. Simultaneously this causes a decrease in the concentration of hydrogen ions, H^+. Recall that in water solutions, $[H^+] \times [OH^-] = 1.0 \times 10^{-14}$. Since the value of $[H^+]$ has decreased below 10^{-7} M, the neutral point, the solution acts basic to indicators. A further reaction of HPO_4^{-2} with H_2O goes on to a smaller but negligible degree. In these reactions we have not considered the decomposition of molecules of water or the Na^+ ions from solid sodium phosphate. Actually, the sodium ions have negligible attraction for OH^- ions, as indicated by the strongly basic character of solutions containing these ions.

a. Basic reaction

b. Acidic reaction

14-11   A sodium carbonate solution (beaker a) gives a basic reaction because of the formation of an excess of OH^- ions. An ammonium chloride solution (beaker b) gives an acidic reaction because of the formation of an excess of H^+ ions.

Predicting the Approximate pH of a Salt Solution

We have just used the Brønsted–Lowry theory of conjugate acids and bases and their relative strengths to explain the basic reaction of a solution of sodium phosphate. Now we can use the same methods to predict the acidic, basic, or neutral reaction of solutions of various normal salts.

Salts of Strong Bases and Weak Acids. The sodium phosphate solution falls into this category, of course; but let us consider why another solution, that of sodium carbonate (Na_2CO_3), also gives a strongly basic reaction (Fig. 14-11a). Like most salts in water solutions, Na_2CO_3 is dissociated completely into its freely moving hydrated ions. The carbonate ion (CO_3^{-2}) reacts with water as follows:

$$H_2O + CO_3^{-2} \rightleftharpoons HCO_3^- + OH^-$$
$$\text{Acid}_1 \qquad \text{Base}_2 \qquad\qquad \text{Acid}_2 \qquad \text{Base}_1$$

Table 14-3 enables us to predict that the predominant reaction is the reverse reaction to form the weaker acid and weaker base, H_2O and CO_3^{-2} respectively. However, the slight forward reaction is enough to give an excess of OH^- ions and thus a basic solution. Any salt formed from a strong base and a weak acid gives a basic reaction (pH greater than 7) as the result of an excess of OH^- ions.

Salts of Strong Acids and Weak Bases. Recall that NH_4Cl formed an acid solution in water (Fig. 14-11b). This salt can be prepared from aqueous NH_3, a weak base, and HCl, a strong acid. Again, like most salts, NH_4Cl is dissociated completely into freely moving hydrated ions, NH_4^+

Table 14-4 HYDROLYSIS OF SALTS

Salts	*Reactions in solution*
Of strong base and weak acid	
$Ca(C_2H_3O_2)_2$	Basic
K_3PO_4	Basic
$NaC_2H_3O_2$	Basic
Na_2CO_3	Basic
Li_2CO_3	Basic
Of strong acid and weak base	
$AlCl_3$	Acidic
$CuSO_4$	Acidic
NH_4Cl	Acidic
NH_4NO_3	Acidic
$ZnCl_2$	Acidic

and Cl^-, in water solutions. The NH_4^+ reacts to a slight extent with water:

$$\underset{\text{Acid}_1}{NH_4^+} + \underset{\text{Base}_2}{H_2O} \rightleftharpoons \underset{\text{Base}_2}{H_3O^+} + \underset{\text{Acid}_1}{NH_3}$$

Table 14-3 indicates that very few NH_4^+ ions react with H_2O because the acid (NH_4^+) is far below H_2O, the base. However, the forward reaction does occur to a sufficient extent to produce an excess of H_3O^+, or H^+, ions to give an acidic solution (pH less than 7). The Cl^- ion in the solution is too weak a base to have any appreciable attraction for the H^+ ions.

Several metallic salts are listed in Table 14-4. Suppose we dissolve in water a salt whose empirical formula is $AlCl_3$. Dissociation results in freely moving hydrated ions, in this case $Al(H_2O)_6^{+3}$ and Cl^-. The hydrated aluminum ion, $Al(H_2O)_6^{+3}$, acts as a moderately weak acid:

$$\underset{\text{Acid}_1}{Al(H_2O)_6^{+3}} + \underset{\text{Base}_2}{H_2O} \rightleftharpoons \underset{\text{Acid}_2}{H_3O^+} + \underset{\text{Base}_1}{Al(H_2O)_5(OH)^{+2}}$$

Table 14-3 confirms that the forward reaction should take place only slightly. The small excess of the H_3O^+, or H^+, ion produced in this reaction accounts for the acidity of the solution. A 0.1 M solution of $AlCl_3$ or of $Al(H_2O)_6^{+3}$ ions has a pH of 3, indicating an acid solution. Further reactions with water molecules finally convert the $Al(H_2O)_5OH^{+2}$ ions to aluminum hydroxide, $Al(H_2O)_3(OH)_3$, a gelatinous solid which you may observe in any long-standing solution containing aluminum ions. Chromium and iron, both in the trivalent state, form similar hydrated ions that are also acidic in their water solutions.

In general, any salt that can be formed from a weak base and a strong acid gives an acidic reaction in water solution because of the production of an excess of H_3O^+ ions.

Salts of Weak Acids and Weak Bases. If two strips of litmus paper, one blue and one red, are placed in a solution of ammonium acetate ($NH_4C_2H_3O_2$), neither strip changes color. Since this salt is dissociated completely into hydrated NH_4^+ and $C_2H_3O_2^-$ ions, why is the solution neutral (pH 7)? Consider two possible hydrolysis reactions:

$$NH_4^+ + H_2O \rightleftharpoons H_3O^+ + NH_3$$

$$C_2H_3O_2^- + H_2O \rightleftharpoons OH^- + HC_2H_3O_2$$

As both forward reactions take place to the same small extent, neither H_3O^+ nor OH^- ions are present in excess. Water solutions of this group of salts are frequently neutral or almost so.

Salts of Strong Bases and Strong Acids. A solution of pure sodium chloride (NaCl) has a pH of 7. You know that NaCl can be prepared by neutralizing the strong base, NaOH, with the strong acid, HCl. The Na^+ ion has negligible attraction for OH^- ions and is thus a very weak acid. The Cl^- ion is too weak a base to attract protons from water molecules. No hydrolysis can occur for salts of this group. They usually form neutral solutions. Other salts which fall into this category are the nitrates and the sulfates of potassium and other IA family metals.

The next chapter deals with numerous methods by which these and other salts, as well as acids and bases, can be prepared in the laboratory.

QUESTIONS AND PROBLEMS

1. (a) Differentiate among a normal salt, an acid salt, and a basic salt. (b) How does an acid salt differ from a salt that hydrolyzes to form an acid solution? (c) Differentiate between neutralization and hydrolysis.
2. Write equations for the neutralization reactions between potassium hydroxide and phosphorous acid (H_3PO_3) to form one normal and two acid salts.
3. In terms of the Brønsted–Lowry theory, explain the hydrolysis of potassium acetate to give a basic reaction.
4. (a) Predict whether a solution of each of the following salts is acidic, basic, or neutral: NH_4NO_3, Na_2CO_3, $(NH_4)_2CO_3$, $NaNO_3$. (b) For each salt give the name and strength of the acid and base from which it is formed. (c) Which of these salts does not undergo hydrolysis?

VALUE OF THE CONCEPT

THE CONCEPT

Acid anhydrides, oxides of nonmetals, are molecular compounds that react with water to form acid solutions. These solutions react with metals such as zinc and magnesium to form hydrogen. They also turn blue litmus pink and taste sour. The properties of acid solutions result from the presence of hydronium (H_3O^+) ions. Hydrogen halides also ionize in water to form acids. Strong acid solutions, consisting almost completely of ions, are good conductors of electricity and react readily with metals. Weak acid solutions, consisting of ions and molecules in equilibrium, are poor electrical conductors and react feebly with metals to produce hydrogen.

Basic anhydrides, oxides of group IA and IIA metals, are ionic compounds that react with water to form basic solutions. These solutions, usually called bases, turn pink litmus blue, feel slippery, and taste bitter. The properties of basic solutions result from the presence of hydrated hydroxide (OH^-) ions. Strong basic solutions, consisting almost completely of ions, conduct electricity readily. Weak bases, which form when covalent compounds such as NH_3 react with water, are poor conductors.

The degree of acidity, in terms of the concentration of H^+ ions in solution, is expressed by the pH scale. Water, which is neutral, has a pH value of 7; pH values below 7 indicate an excess of H^+ ions or an acid solution, and pH values above 7 indicate an excess of OH^- ions or a basic solution. The pH of a solution is the exponent, expressed as a positive number, of the molar concentration of H^+ ions in that solution. The ion product constant of water can be used to determine the H^+ and OH^- ion concentration in a solution.

Acids and bases in solution react with one another by the process of neutralization, in which H^+ and OH^- ions combine to form water. An understanding of neutralization leads to the broader Brønsted–Lowry definition of acids and bases: acids donate protons, while bases accept protons.

During neutralization the metallic ions and other nonmetallic ions remain to produce salts. Salts are ionic compounds containing the positive ions of basic solutions and negative ions of acid solutions. Salts whose negative ions retain no protons from acids when they form during neutralization are normal salts. Salts whose negative ions retain one or more of the hydrogen ions or protons are acid salts, while basic salts form when only some of the OH^- ions of the basic solutions are neutralized.

Many salts dissolve in water to form acid or basic solutions by the process of hydrolysis. Salts of strong bases and weak acids hydrolyze to form basic solutions; salts of strong acids and weak bases hydrolyze to form acid solutions. Although salts of weak acids and weak bases hydrolyze, their solutions are neutral. Salts of strong acids and strong bases do not hydrolyze; their solutions are also neutral.

USING THE CONCEPT

Using the Basic Concept

1. (a) What properties are common to all acid solutions? (b) According to the Brønsted–Lowry definition, what property is common to all acids?
2. Write equations to represent the formation of acid solutions from each of the following molecular substances: HCl, H_2SO_4, HNO_3.
3. (a) Write equations to represent the formation of hydrogen by the reaction of the following acids with zinc: HCl, H_2SO_4, $HC_2H_3O_2$. (b) Write a net equation that truly represents the reaction between any acid solution and zinc.
4. (a) Write conventional equations to represent the formation of acids from the following acid anhydrides: N_2O_5, SO_3, CO_2, (b) Repeat, using ionic equations showing hydronium ions.
5. (a) Write an ionic equation representing the reaction between HI and H_2O. (b) Compare this chemical change with that occurring when an acid anhydride reacts with water. (c) Describe completely the process that is common to both reactions.
6. (a) Name and write the formulas for four common strong acids, two common weak acids. (b) How do strong and weak acids differ? (c) How could you distinguish experimentally between acids and bases?
7. (a) What properties are common to all basic solutions? (b) According to the Brønsted–Lowry definition, what property is common to all bases?
8. Acid solutions form from the ionization of certain covalent molecular substances. (a) Is this also true for the formation of basic solutions? (b) What single process does occur during the formation of both acid and basic solutions?
9. (a) Write conventional equations to indicate the formation of hydroxides from the following basic anhydrides: Na_2O, CaO, MgO. (b) Repeat, using ionic equations.
10. (a) What is a strong basic solution, a weak basic solution? (b) Name and give the formulas for four strong hydroxides, two weak hydroxides. (c) Are all basic solutions that do not readily conduct electricity weak bases? Explain your answer.
11. Determine the conjugate acid-base pairs formed when H_2SO_4 reacts with water.
12. (a) What is meant by pH? (b) What is the pH of pure water? (c) What is the pH range for acid solutions? basic solutions?
13. How is the ion product constant of water used to determine the pH of a basic solution?
14. (a) Define the chemical term *neutralization*. (b) Write a net equation representing any neutralization reaction.
15. (a) Show that both hydrochloric acid solution (ionic) and gaseous HCl (molecular) are acids according to the Brønsted–

Lowry theory of acids and bases. (b) What ion of hydrochloric acid truly makes it an acid? Prove your answer.

16. (a) Show that ammonia and ammonia water are both bases according to the Brønsted–Lowry theory. (b) What ion of the ammonia water (although few actually exist) makes it a base? Explain.

17. (a) What is a salt? (b) What is a normal salt? (c) Give three examples of normal salts.

18. (a) Define the terms *monoprotic acid, diprotic acid, acid salt, basic salt.* (b) Give three examples of acid salts and two examples of basic salts.

19. (a) What takes place when a salt undergoes hydrolysis? (b) Explain the difference between acid salts and salts that hydrolyze to form acid solutions.

Relating Terms Within the Concept

Each of the following statements contains two *italicized* terms. Select the italicized term that makes the statement correct.

1. The symbol K_W is used to represent the (*ion product constant of water, pH of water*).
2. According to the Brønsted–Lowry theory, an acid is a (*proton acceptor, proton donor*).
3. According to the Brønsted–Lowry theory, NH_3 is (*an acid, a base*).
4. $NaHSO_3$ is (*an acid salt, a normal salt*).
5. An example of a basic anhydride is (*SO_2, MgO*).
6. The pH scale indicates directly (*H^+ concentration, OH^- dilution*).
7. $H_3O^+ + OH^- \longrightarrow 2 H_2O$ is a net equation for (*hydrolysis, neutralization*).
8. An acid solution is characterized by the presence of (*H_3O^+ ions, HOH^+ ions*).
9. Any basic solution contains (*an excess of hydronium ions, hydrated hydroxide ions*).

Solving Problems Within the Concept

1. (a) How many moles of hydrogen gas are produced when 2 moles of magnesium completely react with dilute hydrochloric acid? (b) How many grams of hydrogen are produced? (c) How many moles of hydronium ions react to produce each mole of hydrogen gas?

2. Calculate the pH of the following solutions, using the ion product constant of water where necessary (assume ionization is complete in each case): (a) 0.1 M hydrochloric acid, (b) 0.01 M hydrochloric acid, (c) 0.1 M sulfuric acid, (d) 0.0001 M nitric acid, (e) a solution having an OH^- concentration of $10^{-7} M$, (f) a solution having an OH^- concentration of $10^{-9} M$.

3. A solution of NH_4Cl has a pH of 5. What is the H^+ concentration of this salt solution?

Applying the Concept

1. Moist NH_4Cl is often used in dry cells where it reacts with the zinc electrode of the cell to produce hydrogen. Explain the reaction that occurs.

2. (a) Why would it have been difficult to convince a chemist of the early 1800's that the ammonium ion NH_4^+ is a base, and that water can act as either an acid or a base? (b) Write three equations to represent each of these facts.

3. Prove that basic anhydrides, such as CaO and MgO, are actually bases according to the Brønsted–Lowry theory.

4. Why would you predict that for strong acids and bases the heat evolved per mole of each reactant in a neutralization reaction is always the same?

5. Explain the following statement: The concentration of very dilute hydrochloric acid is the same as its H^+ concentration, while the concentration of dilute acetic acid is greater than its H^+ concentration.

Reading Further

"Models Illustrating the Lewis Theory of Acids and Bases," by F. Y. Herron, *Journal of Chemical Education,* vol. 30, p. 199, 1953. Delves deeper into an understanding of the modern concept of acids and bases.

15

Acids, Bases, and Salts

In some areas of the world the land simply will not produce enough food for the people who depend upon it for their existence. In some places, hundreds of years of steady use have depleted the minerals necessary for good crop growth—and fertilizer is expensive. In many of these same areas, as well as others, crop yield is low because of the pH of the soil. Each crop has a pH range at which it grows best. Rice, for example, grows best at a pH between 5.0 and 6.5, definitely in an acid soil; while sugar cane grows best at a pH between 6.0 and 8.0, in a soil that is relatively neutral. Still another factor affecting crop production is the salinity of the soil. Some crops, such as corn and rice, grow in soil with a moderate amount of soluble salts. Some plants, such as barley and beans, produce only about 50 percent of their normal yield if grown in soil whose salinity is "incorrect."

Salinity and pH are important not only for plants but for animals as well. Human gastric juice normally has a pH of 0.9 to 1.5 due to the presence of HCl. By contrast, human blood is slightly alkaline, with a pH of about 7.4. The salinity of the blood is also highly critical; it must be maintained at approximately 0.9 percent (by weight). Consequently, physiological saline, a 0.9 percent NaCl solution, is used in dissolving dry glucose for blood transfusions, as the solute for glucose solutions used in intravenous feeding, and in various types of tissue study.

Thus far, we have considered acidity, alkalinity, and salinity in relation to living things. But what of industry? Truly, the industrial structure of our nation rests on the heavy chemicals industry—on acids, bases, and salts. Without acids, we would have no steel products, no explosives, little fertilizer, and no plastics. Without bases, there would be no soaps or synthetic fabrics. Without salts, construction of homes and buildings would come to a standstill and transportation could not exist as we know it today.

PREPARATION OF ACIDS

As a rocket roars into outer space, the oxygen needed to burn the fuel may well be supplied by nitric acid. But this is not the only use of an acid in the rocket. Virtually every part, from the smallest wire to the metal shell of the rocket itself, required an acid in its processing or fabrication. In these processes, the acid most widely used is not nitric acid, but rather sulfuric acid—the workhorse of the chemical industry. Concentrated strong acids and dilute solutions of acids such as these are also used in the manufacture and preparation of drugs, batteries, dyes, and synthetic fabrics. Solutions of weak acids, on the other hand, are present in the soda pop and in the fruits and salad dressings we eat. But they are also essential to many industrial processes. Even the paper on which this book was printed required a weak acid, sulfurous acid, in its preparation.

Acids from Acid Anhydrides

Waste sulfur dioxide escapes into the air from various industrial processes; once in the air it probably combines with moisture in the air to form sulfurous acid. *We can duplicate this process in the laboratory:*

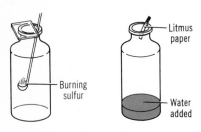

Ignite a small amount of sulfur in a deflagrating spoon and hold the spoon with the burning sulfur (as shown at the left) inside a collecting bottle for a few minutes. Remove and extinguish the burning sulfur and quickly pour a few milliliters of distilled water into the bottle. Cover the mouth of the bottle with the palm of your hand. After shaking the contents, touch the moist inside of the bottle with a piece of blue litmus paper. Does it change color?

The blue litmus turns pink, indicating that an acid is present, in this instance sulfurous acid. Here, as in Chapter 14, you have prepared an acid by reacting an acid anhydride with water.

$$SO_2 + H_2O \longrightarrow H_2SO_3$$

A general equation for a reaction to show the ionic nature of the acid is:

$$\text{acid anhydride} + H_2O \longrightarrow H_3O^+ + \text{negative ion}$$

In nonionic form, the equation is:

$$\text{acid anhydride} + H_2O \longrightarrow \text{acid}$$

Hereafter, whenever feasible, we shall write nonionic equations for the formation of acids. However, it must not be forgotten that acids ionize in water. Numerous acids are prepared from their acid anhydrides, and it would be useful to consider several methods of preparing the anhydride.

Preparing Acid Anhydrides

Sulfur and oxygen, that is, a *nonmetal and oxygen,* were combined to form SO_2, an acid anhydride. Similarly, phosphorus, another nonmetal, burns in oxygen to produce the acid anhydride, phosphorus pentoxide (Fig. 15-1).

$$P_4 + 5 O_2 \longrightarrow 2 P_2O_5$$

15-1 When phosphorus burns in a bottle of oxygen, smoky white phosphorus pentoxide quickly fills the bottle.

The general equation for this relatively simple method of producing an acid anhydride is:

$$\text{nonmetal} + \text{oxygen} \longrightarrow \text{acid anhydride}$$

Salts and oxygen also react to give acid anhydrides. For example, when the salt, zinc sulfide, is heated to a high temperature it combines with the oxygen in the air. Zinc oxide and sulfur dioxide, a nonmetallic oxide or acid anhydride, are formed:

$$2\,ZnS + 3\,O_2 \longrightarrow 2\,SO_2\uparrow + 2\,ZnO$$

The general equation for the formation of an acid anhydride from salt and oxygen is:

$$\text{salt} + \text{oxygen} \longrightarrow \text{acid anhydride} + \text{other oxide}$$

You will meet other ways of preparing specific anhydrides in your study of the individual nonmetals.

Acids from Salts and Nonvolatile Acids

It is not always necessary to prepare an acid anhydride in order to prepare an acid. Sometimes the acid is prepared by reacting a salt of the acid with another acid. The choice of the acid used in the preparation depends in large part upon its boiling point. Concentrated HNO_3 boils at about 120° C and concentrated H_2SO_4 boils at 338° C. Nitric acid, which vaporizes easily, is a *volatile acid,* while sulfuric acid is a *nonvolatile acid.* To determine whether a volatile acid is used in preparing hydrochloric acid, *try the following.*

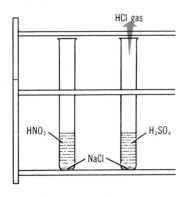

Place a small amount of dry sodium chloride into each of the two test tubes. To one test tube add a small amount of concentrated nitric acid. To the other test tube add an equally small amount of concentrated sulfuric acid. Do you distinctly detect the irritating odor of a gas coming only from the test tube containing the salt and sulfuric acid? Perhaps you can recognize the gas as hydrogen chloride.

Hydrochloric acid, which you have just demonstrated to be a volatile acid, is usually prepared in the laboratory by the reaction between sodium chloride and sulfuric acid—a salt of the acid desired and a non-volatile acid.

$$NaCl + H_2SO_4 \longrightarrow NaHSO_4 + HCl$$

The resulting hydrogen chloride gas is dissolved in water to form hydrochloric acid. Similarly, nonvolatile acids such as phosphoric acid can be used to prepare an acid like hydriodic acid (HI) from certain salts.

The general equation for these reactions is:

$$\text{salt of acid} + \text{nonvolatile acid} \longrightarrow \text{volatile acid} + \text{another salt}$$

Binary acids

$$H \cdot \overset{\cdot\cdot}{\underset{\cdot\cdot}{Cl}} \cdot$$

Hydrochloric acid

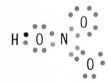

$$H \cdot \overset{\cdot\cdot}{\underset{\cdot\cdot}{S}} \cdot H$$

Hydrosulfuric acid

Ternary acids

Nitric acid

Sulfuric acid

15-2   Binary and ternary acids.

Acids from Halogens and Hydrogen

Hydrogen and fluorine combine explosively, even in the dark. Hydrogen also combines explosively with chlorine in direct sunlight. Both these reactions are examples of a halogen (represented by X in the equation below) combining directly with hydrogen to form a hydrogen halide:

$$H_2 + X_2 \longrightarrow 2\,HX$$

All hydrogen halides react with water to form solutions of halogen acids. The equation for the formation of hydrochloric acid from hydrogen chloride and water (page 229) indicates that each molecule of HCl loses a proton to a water molecule to form an H_3O^+ ion. After studying this equation, write the equation for the reaction between hydrogen fluoride and water to form hydrofluoric acid.

Naming Acids

By now you are familiar with the names of a number of acids. Some names, for instance sulfuric acid and sulfurous acid, indicate that certain acids are related to each other. Let us examine the system chemists have developed for naming the common acids.

Binary Acids. Notice the similarity between the names of the following acids:

HCl—hydrochloric acid
HBr—hydrobromic acid
H_2S—hydrosulfuric acid

Acids such as these, whose formulas contain *two* elements, are **binary acids** (Fig. 15-2). The names of all binary acids begin with the prefix *hydro-* and end in *-ic*.

Ternary Acids. Acids like the following, whose formulas contain *three* elements, are **ternary acids:**

HNO_3—nitric acid
HNO_2—nitrous acid
H_2SO_4—sulfuric acid
H_2SO_3—sulfurous acid

The common ternary acids contain hydrogen, oxygen, and one other element, usually nonmetallic. Thus nitric acid contains hydrogen, oxygen, and nitrogen; sulfuric acid contains hydrogen, oxygen, and sulfur. Some acids are related if they contain the same elements. For example, nitric acid and nitrous acid are related since both contain the same three elements: hydrogen, oxygen, and nitrogen.

As all the common ternary acids contain hydrogen and oxygen, they are named after the third element they contain. The first letters of this third element begin the name of the acid—for instance, *nitr*ic acid and *nitr*ous acid. The ending *-ic* is given to the most commonly used acid in a related group. The ending *-ous* is given to the acid whose formula contains one less oxygen atom than its *-ic* relative. Confirm this by looking

Hypobromous acid

Bromous acid

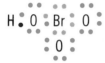

Bromic acid

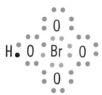

Perbromic acid

15-3 Ternary acids containing bromine.

Table 15-1 **NAMING TERNARY ACIDS**

Acid	Name
$HClO_4$	*Perchloric* acid
$HClO_3$	Chlor*ic* acid
$HClO_2$	Chlor*ous* acid
$HClO$	*Hypo*chlorous acid

back at the above list. You see that the formula for nitric acid contains three oxygen atoms, that for nitrous acid contains two. The formula for sulfuric acid contains four oxygen atoms; as expected, the formula for sulfurous acid contains one less oxygen atom, or three. The name for $HClO_3$ is chloric acid. What name would you give to the acid whose formula is $HClO_2$?

The names and formulas for several acids which contain the elements hydrogen, oxygen, and chlorine are listed in Table 15-1. Notice the formula for hypochlorous acid, $HClO$. This formula contains one less oxygen atom than the formula for the related chlorous acid, $HClO_2$. The names of such acids which contain one less atom than their related *-ous* acids begin with the prefix *hypo-*. For example, the formula for hypobromous acid, $HBrO$, contains one less oxygen atom (Fig. 15-3) than the formula for the related bromous acid, $HBrO_2$.

What if the formula contains one *more* oxygen atom than the related *-ic* acid? In that case, the prefix *per* is attached to the name of the *-ic* acid. So $HClO_3$ is chloric acid, while $HClO_4$ is perchloric acid (Table 15-1).

As noted in our study of salts, acids may also be classified according to the number of hydrogen ions they yield in solution. An acid such as HCl, which yields one hydrogen ion, is monoprotic; H_2SO_4, which yields two, is diprotic; and H_3PO_4 is triprotic.

QUESTIONS AND PROBLEMS

1. For each of the reactions described below (a) name the acid produced, (b) write a balanced equation, and (c) give the method of preparing acids which it represents.
   (1) Carbon dioxide bubbled into cold distilled water gives an acid reaction when tested with litmus paper.
   (2) Phosphorus burns to form a dense white smoke that dissolves in water to form an acid.
   (3) A few drops of concentrated sulfuric acid added to a small amount of solid sodium bromide produces a gas that gives an acid reaction with moist litmus paper.
2. Write the equation for the reaction between cupric sulfide and oxygen when heated. What acid anhydride is formed?
3. Write the name of each of the following acids: $HClO$, H_2SO_3, H_2SeO_4, HIO_2, $HBrO_2$.

PREPARATION OF BASES

Bases, like acids, find manifold applications in daily life. They are used in such varied procedures as producing photographic film, refining petroleum, making mortar and plaster, liming soil, and making soap. Soap, for example, is prepared by a chemical reaction between alkalies and fats. Today, bases used in industry are prepared in huge chemical plants, usually located near inexpensive sources of electric energy.

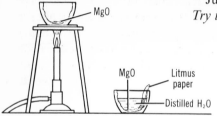

Bases from Basic Anhydrides

Just as many acids may be prepared from anhydrides, so too can bases. *Try this for yourself.*

Heat a small piece of magnesium ribbon in a crucible until the magnesium burns. Observe that a white, powdered substance, magnesium oxide, forms. After the crucible cools, add distilled water to the magnesium oxide. Is it soluble or insoluble? Test the liquid with pink paper. If it turns blue, explain why.

Evidently some of the oxide has reacted with the water to form an excess of hydroxide ions. In short, a solution of a base has been formed. Previously, you prepared magnesium hydroxide by dissolving magnesium oxide in water. Here you have done much the same thing—prepared a metallic oxide or basic anhydride and reacted it with water to form a base. The equation for this reaction may be written in ionic form to show the hydroxide ion; it is more conventionally written as:

$$MgO + H_2O \longrightarrow Mg(OH)_2$$

If you performed this investigation with other basic anhydrides, such as calcium oxide and sodium oxide, you would find that these metallic oxides also react with water to form bases. A general equation to represent the formation of bases from basic anhydrides and water can be written in the following ways:

basic anhydride + $H_2O \longrightarrow$ positive metallic ion + OH^-

basic anhydride + H^+ (from water) $\longrightarrow$ positive metallic ion + OH^-

basic anhydride + $H_2O \longrightarrow$ base

The first and second equations indicate that the reaction between basic anhydrides and water produces solutions containing the hydroxide ion. For convenience, however, chemists often use the nonionic (third) equation to represent the formation of either a base in solution or a solid base.

Preparing Basic Anhydrides from Salts

It is seldom feasible to prepare basic anhydrides by the direct combination of a metal with oxygen. However, when a metallic oxide is readily available, a base may be prepared by reacting the oxide with water. Where this approach is not practical, other methods are used.

Decomposition of metal carbonates is one such method. For example, the naturally occurring salt, calcium carbonate, decomposes when heated to form calcium oxide and carbon dioxide.

$$CaCO_3 \longrightarrow CaO + CO_2$$

The calcium oxide then reacts with water to form calcium hydroxide, as shown in Fig. 15-4.

15-4 A piece of calcium oxide placed in water forms calcium hydroxide, which causes the pink litmus paper to turn blue. At the bottom of the beaker, tiny particles of the relatively insoluble calcium hydroxide are being agitated by the rising bubbles.

Bases from Active Metals and Water

Bases are formed by reactions other than those between basic anhydrides and water. Consider the violent reaction between water and an active metal like sodium. The hydrogen gas produced (page 56) may ignite from the heat of reaction. When the reaction is complete the solution remaining in the dish can be tested with pink litmus paper. The litmus turns blue.

$$2\,Na + H_2O \longrightarrow 2\,NaOH + H_2\uparrow$$

If the liquid in the dish is evaporated, a white residue remains. This white residue is solid sodium hydroxide.

A number of the active metals listed in groups IA and IIA of the periodic chart react directly with water to form bases.

$$\text{active metal from groups IA and IIA} + H_2O \longrightarrow \text{base} + H_2\uparrow$$

Insoluble Bases from Salt and a Strong Base

Just as some acids are prepared from a salt and another acid, so some bases are prepared from a salt and another base. *Try this for yourself.*

Dissolve a small amount of magnesium chloride in a test tube half-full of distilled water. To this solution add an equal volume of saturated calcium hydroxide solution. Does a white precipitate form? What is it?

This precipitate is the relatively insoluble base, magnesium hydroxide.

$$MgCl_2 + Ca(OH)_2 \longrightarrow CaCl_2 + Mg(OH)_2\downarrow$$

The arrow placed after the $Mg(OH)_2$ indicates that although the compound is ionic, it is insoluble.

The general equation for the formation of an insoluble base by reacting a solution of a salt with a strong base is:

$$\text{a salt} + \text{strong base} \longrightarrow \text{another salt} + \text{insoluble base}$$

Electrolysis of Salt Solutions

Most of the alkali-bases that are produced commercially today are prepared by the electrolysis of solutions of soluble halogen salts. Sodium hydroxide, for example, is produced by the electrolysis of a NaCl solution. The electrolysis yields hydrogen gas at the cathode and chlorine gas at the anode. In addition, Na^+ and OH^- ions remain in solution. As the H_2 and Cl_2 escape, the concentration of H^+ and Cl^- ions in solution is reduced and the relative concentration of Na^+ and OH^- ions is increased. In time the solution gradually changes from an aqueous NaCl solution to an aqueous NaOH solution. This concentrated NaOH solution is removed and the water evaporated. The solid residue that remains is mainly sodium hydroxide.

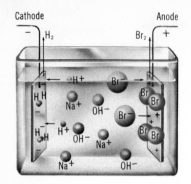

Cathode   Anode

15-5 The electrolysis of sodium bromide yields bromine at the anode and hydrogen at the cathode. The solution that remains is mainly sodium hydroxide.

$$2\,NaCl + 2\,H_2O \xrightarrow{\ DC\ } Cl_2\!\uparrow + H_2\!\uparrow + 2\,NaOH$$

The electrolysis of some halogen salt solutions, such as a concentrated bromide solution, is undertaken to obtain the halogen (Fig. 15-5). The alkali (group IA base) is a by-product. Nonetheless, the general equation for the electrolysis of halogen salts remains:

$$\begin{array}{c}\text{halogen}\\\text{salt solution}\end{array} \xrightarrow{\ DC\ } \text{hydrogen} + \text{halogen} + \begin{array}{c}\text{alkali}\\\text{base}\end{array}$$

Amphoteric Hydroxides

Most hydroxides act as bases in all reactions. However some bases, such as aluminum hydroxide [$Al(OH)_3$], may behave either as a base *or* an acid. If insoluble $Al(OH)_3$ (suspended in water) reacts with an excess of hydrochloric acid, a neutralization reaction occurs in which the soluble salt aluminum chloride ($AlCl_3$) forms.

$$Al(OH)_3 + 3\,HCl \longrightarrow AlCl_3 + 3\,H_2O$$

On the other hand, if the $Al(OH)_3$ reacts with NaOH solution, the soluble salt sodium aluminate [$NaAl(OH)_4$] is produced:

$$Al(OH)_3 + NaOH \longrightarrow NaAl(OH)_4$$

In the reaction with HCl, aluminum hydroxide reacts as a base neutralizing an acid. In the second reaction (with NaOH) aluminum hydroxide reacts as an acid neutralizing a base. Such hydroxides that behave as bases in reactions with strong acids and as acids in reactions with strong bases during neutralization reactions are called **amphoteric hydroxides.** Chromium hydroxide, another amphoteric hydroxide, reacts with acids to form water and a chromium salt, or with bases to form water and a salt with the chromite, CrO_2^-, ion. In general, elements forming amphoteric hydroxides are located near the center of the periodic table.

Naming Bases

The name of a common base, either in solid form or in solution (Fig. 15-6), consists of the name of its metallic ion followed by the word "hydroxide." The foregoing bases illustrate this practice. According to the Brønsted–Lowry theory, which defines a base as any substance that accepts protons, these compounds should properly be called *hydroxide bases.* However, since it is the OH^- ion that usually acts as the proton acceptor, the simple term "base" is commonly used to cover all hydroxide bases.

Depending upon the number of OH^- ions represented in the formula, or the number of protons they can accept, bases may be classified as *monohydroxy, dihydroxy,* or *trihydroxy.* NaOH is a monohydroxy base; while $Ca(OH)_2$ is a dihydroxy base and $Al(OH)_3$ is a trihydroxy base.

15-6 Solid sodium hydroxide is available in pellets or sticks; calcium hydroxide, in lumps.

1. For each of the reactions described below (a) name the base produced, (b) write a balanced equation, (c) give the method of preparing bases which it represents.

   (1) A small amount of sodium oxide dissolved in water gives a basic reaction to litmus.

   (2) A small piece of metallic potassium placed in an evaporating dish of distilled water produces a basic solution.

   (3) When an excess of sodium hydroxide solution is added to a calcium chloride solution, a precipitate forms.

2. Write an equation for the electrolysis of a solution of potassium bromide.

3. Write an equation for the reaction between (a) amphoteric $Cr(OH)_3$ and HCl, (b) $Cr(OH)_3$ and NaOH.

4. Write the names for the bases KOH, NH_4OH, and $Cd(OH)_2$.

5. What would happen if you placed a small piece of metallic calcium in an evaporating dish of distilled water? Write an equation for the reaction.

PREPARATION OF SALTS

15-7 A blasting agent composed mainly of ammonium nitrate and aluminum chips. It is so safe to handle that a rifle bullet won't set it off, yet it is five times more powerful by volume than the usual ammonium nitrate-fuel oil mixture.

Sodium chloride is of the greatest importance to human life. Without sufficient amounts of salt, our bodies would soon become dehydrated and the osmotic pressure of the blood and other body fluids would be disturbed. Other salts are equally important. For example, the body requires salts of calcium, the mineral present in greatest abundance, for the proper growth of bones and teeth and for the conduction of nerve impulses. Salts also yield the iodine necessary for the proper functioning of the thyroid gland and the iron vital to the formation and functioning of red blood cells. Besides being essential to the building and maintenance of the human body, salts are needed for making fertilizers, explosives (Fig. 15-7), cement, preservatives, and a host of other products.

While many of these useful salts, such as NaCl and $CaCO_3$, are found naturally in the earth's crust, others have to be prepared in the laboratory or through industrial processes. There are many laboratory methods of preparing salts. Here we shall take a brief look at some of the most common methods.

Neutralization. In the discussing of neutralization (page 228) you found that sodium hydroxide reacts with hydrochloric acid to form water which, when evaporated, leaves behind a salt, sodium chloride. Although the union of H^+ and OH^- ions to form water is the essential part of the reaction, a salt is formed as a by-product in all neutralization reactions. For example, when calcium hydroxide reacts with sulfuric acid, water and a salt, calcium sulfate ($CaSO_4$), result. When the water is evaporated away the salt remains.

ACIDS, BASES, AND SALTS   249

$$Ca(OH)_2 + H_2SO_4 \longrightarrow 2\,H_2O + CaSO_4$$

The general equation for all such neutralization reactions is:

$$\text{acid} + \text{base} \longrightarrow \text{salt} + \text{water}$$
$$\text{in solution}$$

Metallic Oxides and Acids. As metallic oxides are basic anhydrides, their combination with an acid to produce water and a salt is much like neutralization. Thus calcium oxide and hydrochloric acid react together to produce calcium chloride and water.

$$CaO + 2\,HCl \longrightarrow CaCl_2 + H_2O$$

In this reaction note that the oxide ion of the basic anyhdride accepts protons from the HCl.

Or, again, sodium oxide reacts with hydrochloric acid to produce sodium chloride and water:

$$Na_2O + 2\,HCl \longrightarrow 2\,NaCl + H_2O$$

The general equation for these reactions is:

$$\text{metallic oxide} + \text{acid} \longrightarrow \text{salt} + \text{water}$$

Nonmetallic Oxides and Bases. As nonmetallic oxides are acid anhydrides, their combination with a base to produce a salt and water is also comparable to neutralization. For example, carbon dioxide and potassium hydroxide react to yield potassium carbonate and water:

$$CO_2 + 2\,KOH \longrightarrow K_2CO_3 + H_2O$$

Here the general equation is:

$$\text{nonmetallic oxide} + \text{base} \longrightarrow \text{salt} + \text{water}$$

Active Metals and Dilute Acids. Hydrogen, as you know, is frequently produced by the action of an acid on metal. Such a reaction always produces a salt as a by-product. In the laboratory you may have obtained hydrogen by the reaction between zinc and hydrochloric acid. In addition to the hydrogen gas, the salt, zinc chloride ($ZnCl_2$), was also produced.

$$Zn + 2\,HCl \longrightarrow ZnCl_2 + H_2\uparrow$$

The general formula for such reactions is:

$$\text{active metal} + \text{dilute acid} \longrightarrow \text{salt} + \text{hydrogen}$$

Salts and Nonvolatile Acids. A general method of preparing acids (page 243) is to react a salt with a nonvolatile acid. This process always yields another salt as a by-product. Nitric acid, for example, is prepared in the laboratory by the action of sulfuric acid on potassium nitrate. The reaction yields not only nitric acid but another salt, potassium sulfate.

$$2\,KNO_3 + H_2SO_4 \longrightarrow K_2SO_4 + 2\,HNO_3$$

The general equation for this reaction is:

$$\text{a salt} + \text{nonvolatile acid} \longrightarrow \text{another salt} + \text{volatile acid}$$

Direct Combination of Elements. Some active metals combine directly with active nonmetals to produce a salt. For example, the elements sodium or copper are burned in chlorine to produce the salts sodium chloride or copper chloride respectively.

$$2\,Na + Cl_2 \longrightarrow 2\,NaCl$$
$$Cu + Cl_2 \longrightarrow CuCl_2$$

And aluminum and sulfur can be fused to form aluminum sulfide.

$$2\,Al + 3\,S \longrightarrow Al_2S_3$$

The general equation is:

$$\text{metal} + \text{nonmetal} \longrightarrow \text{salt}$$

Two Soluble Salts. If you would like to prepare an insoluble salt and a soluble salt from two soluble salts, *try the following:*

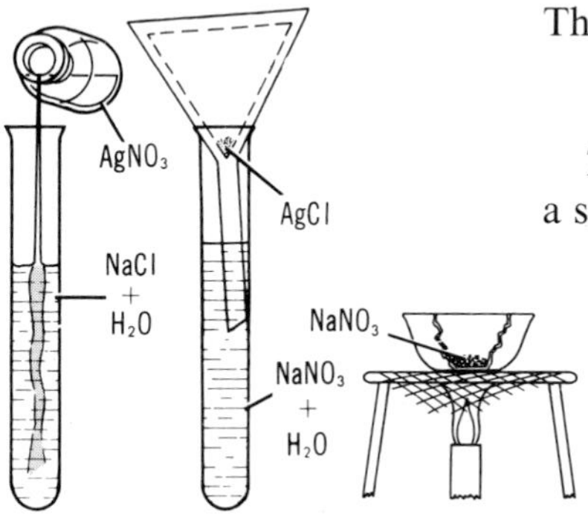

Add a few milliliters of silver nitrate ($AgNO_3$) solution to half a test tube of NaCl solution. A white, insoluble salt, silver chloride ($AgCl$), forms. Separate this solid AgCl from the liquid by filtration and evaporate the liquid filtrate in an evaporating dish. Observe that crystals form on the bottom of the dish. What are they?

These crystals are a second salt, sodium nitrate ($NaNO_3$).

$$AgNO_3 + NaCl \longrightarrow AgCl\!\downarrow + NaNO_3$$

The general equation for the double replacement type reaction between two soluble salts to form an insoluble and a soluble salt is:

$$\begin{array}{cccc} \text{soluble} & + & \text{soluble} & \longrightarrow & \text{insoluble} & + & \text{soluble} \\ \text{salt} & & \text{salt} & & \text{salt} & & \text{salt} \end{array}$$

Naming Salts

Consider the names and formulas of the following salts:

$NaCl$—sodium chloride
K_2S—potassium sulfide
CaF_2—calcium fluoride

Notice that each of these salts contains only two elements; for this reason they are called **binary salts** (Fig. 15-8). They are, of course, related to the two-element or binary acids. NaCl is related to HCl; similarly K_2S is related to H_2S. The name of a binary salt consists of the names of the two elements it contains, with the name of the second element ending in *-ide*. What name would you give to each of the following salts: NaI, K_2Se, and AlF_3?

Binary salts

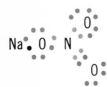

Sodium chlor*ide*

H : Cl :

Hydrochlor*ic* acid

15-8 In a binary or ternary salt related to an acid, a metal ion replaces the hydrogen ion.

Ternary salts

Sodium nit*rate*

Nit*ric* acid

Potassium chlor*ite*

H : O : Cl : O :

Chlor*ous* acid

Salts that contain three elements are called **ternary salts** (Fig. 15-8). The name of a ternary salt usually combines the names of the ions of which it is composed: the positive ion is named first, followed by the name of the negative radical. Thus $NaNO_3$ is sodium nitrate. The name of the radical is always related to the corresponding ternary acid. Sodium nitrate is related to nitric acid (HNO_3) and potassium chlorate ($KClO_3$) is related to chloric acid (Table 15-2). The names of ternary salts end in *-ate* if they are related to ternary acids whose names end in *-ic*. What is the name of Na_2SO_4, which is related to sulfuric acid?

If the names of salts end in *-ite,* they contain one less atom of oxygen in their formulas than the corresponding *-ate* salts and are related to acids whose names end in *-ous*. Thus potassium chlorite ($KClO_2$) is related to chlorous acid ($HClO_2$), and sodium sulfite (Na_2SO_3) to sulfurous acid (H_2SO_3). Salts like $NaClO$, which have one less atom of oxygen in their formulas than the *-ite* salts, are related to acids whose names begin with *hypo-*. The names of such salts begin with the prefix *hypo-* and end in *-ite*. $NaClO$ is called sodium hypochlorite, and $KBrO$, potassium hypobromite. These two salts are related, respectively, to hypochlorous acid and hypobromous acid.

The salt $NaClO_4$ is related to perchloric acid ($HClO_4$). Its name is sodium perchlorate. All salts related to acids with the prefix *per* have the same prefix in their names, which end in *-ate*. The name of $KBrO_4$, a salt related to perbromic acid, is potassium perbromate.

Related Salts. Some metals, like iron and copper, form ions of two different charges. The salts $FeCl_2$ and $FeCl_3$ are related, as are $CuSO_4$ and Cu_2SO_4. How do we distinguish between two salts whose metallic portions have two (variable) ionic valence numbers? The name of the salt whose metallic ion has the lower valence number ends in *-ous;* the name of the salt with the metallic ion of higher valence number ends in *-ic*.

Thus $FeCl_2$ is called ferrous chloride, while $FeCl_3$ is called ferric chloride. Likewise the copper salts Cu_2SO_4 and $CuSO_4$ are cuprous sulfate and cupric sulfate. As the names indicate, the latter has the higher ionic valence number ($+2$ contrasted with $+1$).

A newer system for naming related salts is gradually coming into use. In this system the charge of the metallic ion of the salt is given after the name of the metal. By this system, $FeCl_2$ becomes *iron(II) chloride,* and $FeCl_3$, *iron(III) chloride.*

Acid Salts. During neutralization to form an acid salt, the negative radicals of an acid may retain one or more protons. Such was the case with the acid salt $NaHSO_4$. The name of such an acid salt is similar to that of its related normal salt. However, with the acid salt the prefix *bi-* is added to the second word in the name of the salt. The normal salt Na_2SO_4, for example, is named sodium sulfate while its related acid salt, $NaHSO_4$, is called sodium bisulfate. Similarly, the salt $NaHSO_3$, related to Na_2SO_3, is called sodium bisulfite.

Table 15-2 **NAMING SALTS**

Salt	Related acid	Name of salt	Salt	Common name	Modified name
Ternary salts			*Related salts*		
$NaNO_3$	Nit*ric*	Sodium nit*rate*	$FeCl_2$	Ferr*ous* chloride	Iron(II) chloride
$KClO_3$	Chlor*ic*	Potassium chlor*ate*	$FeCl_3$	Ferr*ic* chloride	Iron(III) chloride
Na_2SO_4	Sulfur*ic*	Sodium sulf*ate*	Cu_2SO_4	Cupr*ous* sulfate	Copper(I) sulfate
$NaNO_2$	Nitr*ous*	Sodium nit*rite*	$CuSO_4$	Cupr*ic* sulfate	Copper(II) sulfate
$KClO_2$	Chlor*ous*	Potassium chlor*ite*	Hg_2S	Mercur*ous* sulfide	Mercury(I) sulfide
Na_2SO_3	Sulfur*ous*	Sodium sulf*ite*	HgS	Mercur*ic* sulfide	Mercury(II) sulfide
$NaClO$	Hypochlor*ous*	Sodium hypochlor*ite*	*Acid salts*		
$KBrO$	Hypobrom*ous*	Potassium hypobrom*ite*			
$NaClO_4$	*Per*chloric	Sodium *per*chlorate	$NaHSO_4$	Sodium *bi*sulfate	Sodium hydrogen sulfate
$KBrO_4$	*Per*bromic	Potassium *per*bromate	$NaHSO_3$	Sodium *bi*sulfite	Sodium hydrogen sulfite

A system that is coming into increasing use for naming acid salts substitutes the word *hydrogen* for the prefix *bi-*. In this system $NaHSO_4$ is *sodium hydrogen sulfate,* and $NaHSO_3$, *sodium hydrogen sulfite.*

QUESTIONS AND PROBLEMS

1. For each of the reactions described below (a) name the salt produced, (b) write a balanced equation, (c) give the method of preparing salts which it represents.
   (1) When a clean piece of aluminum is placed in dilute hydrochloric acid, a salt forms.
   (2) Sodium acetate reacts with concentrated sulfuric acid to produce a salt.
   (3) When a piece of potassium burns in chlorine, a salt is produced.
2. Why is the preparation of a salt from a metallic oxide and acid or from a nonmetallic oxide and base comparable to the preparation of a salt by neutralization?
3. When a few milliliters each of solutions of $BaCl_2$ and Na_2SO_4 are combined, a precipitate of $BaSO_4$ forms. What other salt is formed? Write the equation for the reaction.
4. Write the name of each of the following salts: NaI, K_2Se, AlF_3, $NaClO_3$, $Ca(ClO_4)_2$, $KClO_2$, K_2SO_3, Na_2SO_3.
5. Give two names for each of the following salts: Cu_2SO_3, $CuSO_3$, $Fe(NO_3)_2$, $Fe(NO_3)_3$, $HgCl$, $HgCl_2$, $KHSO_3$, $NaHCO_3$, $KHSO_4$.

TITRATION

Acids are an important ingredient in a variety of substances used daily. Vinegar is a dilute solution of acetic acid; ascorbic acid (vitamin C) is a health-giving ingredient in orange juice; and acetylsalicylic acid is marketed as aspirin (Fig. 15-9). To protect the public, the minimum amount of such ingredients which certain commercial products must

15-9 How can a chemist determine acid concentration in a food or drug?

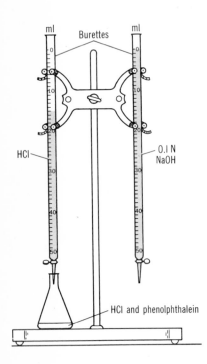

Burettes

ml   ml

HCl

0.1 N
NaOH

HCl and phenolphthalein

contain is set by law. To make sure you get what you pay for, chemists of the Food and Drug Administration continually test samples of various products sold at the drugstore or supermarket. The process they use to determine a product's acid or base concentration is **titration.**

Determining Concentration by Titration

In practice, this use of titration is based on a neutralization reaction. It depends upon using solutions in which the number of gram equivalent weights of solute are known. Recall that in normal solutions there is one gram equivalent of the solute present in 1 liter of the solution. Thus two solutions have the same normal concentration when equal volumes of the solutions contain the same number of gram equivalent weights of their respective solutes.

Suppose you want to determine by titration the concentration of a solution of hydrochloric acid of unknown strength. To do so, *try the following:*

You will need dilute hydrochloric acid of unknown normality, freshly prepared 0.1 N sodium hydroxide, and the equipment shown at the left.

Into one of the two burettes pour 50 ml of the HCl solution whose normality you are trying to determine. Into the second burette pour an equal amount of a 0.1 N solution of NaOH. Now run a measured volume, say exactly 15 ml, of the HCl into an Erlenmeyer flask. Add two drops of colorless phenolphthalein indicator to the acid; it remains colorless. Run the 0.1 N NaOH solution into the acid solution *a few drops at a time while constantly swirling the flask* until the indicator just turns faintly pink. This is the point at which the chemically equivalent amounts of the two substances have reacted. It is called the **end point** of the titration.

You may find that the amount of NaOH added to reach the end point of the titration is exactly 15 ml. If so, since 15 ml of 0.1 N NaOH are required to neutralize or completely react with the 15 ml of HCl, and since equal volumes of solutions with the same normal concentration are chemically equivalent, the concentration of the acid solution must also be 0.1 N.

Now titrate another solution of HCl, whose normality is also unknown, against the 0.1 N NaOH. With the second solution you may find that the end point of titration is reached only after 30 ml of basic solution have been added to 15 ml of the acid solution. If so, evidently 15 ml of this new acid solution contain the same number of gram equivalents as 30 ml of basic solution. Thus you reason that the acid has twice the normality of the base. Since the base is 0.1 N, the new acid solution must be 0.2 N.

In this investigation you determined that the more concentrated the acid solution the greater the volume of base needed to neutralize it. You needed 15 ml of 0.1 N NaOH to neutralize 15 ml of 0.1 N HCl. But when the acid solution was twice as concentrated, 0.2 N, you needed 30 ml of base to achieve neutralization.

At the end point of titration, the number of milliliters of basic solution multiplied by *its* normality equals the number of milliliters of the acid solution times *its* normality.

	basic solution	acid solution
first titration	15 ml $\times$ 0.1 N =	15 ml $\times$ 0.1 N
second titration	30 ml $\times$ 0.1 N =	15 ml $\times$ 0.2 N

This is a useful relationship because it enables us to find the normality of a known volume of solution, or the volume of a solution of known normality, when the solution has been titrated against a known volume of a standard solution (a solution of known concentration). A simple formula that expresses this relationship is:

$$\text{volume} \times \text{normality of acid} = \text{volume} \times \text{normality of base}$$
$$\text{ml} \times N \text{ (acid)} = \text{ml} \times N \text{ (base)}$$

Let's try out this formula. Assume that when 20 ml of HNO_3 are titrated against 0.1 N KOH, 10 ml of base are needed to reach the end point. The normality of the HNO_3 is determined as follows:

$$\text{ml} \times N \text{ (acid)} = \text{ml} \times N \text{ (base)}$$
$$20 \text{ ml} \times x = 10 \text{ ml} \times 0.1 \ N$$
$$x = \frac{10 \text{ ml} \times 0.1 \ N}{20 \text{ ml}}$$
$$x = 0.05 \ N$$

Determining Percentage by Weight of Solute in Solutions

One important use of titration is in determining the percentages by weight of the solutes in different solutions. Suppose, for example, that you want to determine the percentage by weight of the acetic acid in a sample of vinegar. Titrate the vinegar, which is a dilute solution of acetic acid in water, against a standard solution of 0.1 N NaOH. In selecting an indicator, remember that because of hydrolysis of the salt formed, a weak acid titrated against a strong base gives a basic solution, and vice versa. For this titration, phenolphthalein is a good indicator.

Assume you find that 35 ml of 0.1 N NaOH are needed to neutralize completely 5 ml of the vinegar. Now use the titration formula to determine that the concentration of the sample of vinegar is 0.7 N. Since the gram equivalent weight of acetic acid ($HC_2H_3O_2$) is 60 grams, a 1 N solution contains 60 grams of acetic acid per liter of solution. Hence a 0.7 N solution of the acid—the sample of vinegar—must contain 42 grams (0.7 $\times$ 60 grams) of acetic acid in each liter of solution. As vinegar is a very dilute aqueous solution, a liter of vinegar, like water, weighs approximately 1,000 grams. If each 1,000 grams of vinegar con-

15-10 In many university and industrial laboratories, titrations are routinely performed in various types of automatic titrators.

tains 42 grams of $HC_2H_3O_2$, the percentage by weight of acetic acid in your sample is 4.2 percent (42 grams ÷ 1,000 grams = 0.042 or 4.2%). By titration with normal solutions, the composition of many other liquids, as well as the composition of solids that dissolve to form solutions, can be determined (Fig. 15-10).

In every titration a point is reached at which a single drop of acid or base brings about a change in the color of the solution, indicating that neutralization has taken place. Once this drop is added, the color change occurs almost instantly. In contrast, potassium chlorate must be heated for some time before oxygen is released. Some reactions, such as the direct combination of hydrogen and nitrogen to produce ammonia, are never completed; they reach a state of equilibrium. This particular reaction occurs, moreover, only under specific conditions of temperature and pressure in the presence of a catalyst.

Why do the rates of reactions and the conditions under which they occur vary; how can they be altered or controlled? Chapter 17 offers several explanations.

QUESTIONS AND PROBLEMS

1. Thirty milliliters of 0.1 N HCl solution are required to neutralize exactly 60 ml of an NaOH solution whose normality is unknown. Determine the normality of the NaOH solution.
2. How many milliliters of a 0.2 N H_2SO_4 solution can be neutralized completely by 40 ml of a 0.1 N KOH solution?
3. Fifteen milliliters of 0.5 N HCl solution are required to neutralize a 20-ml sample of a $Ca(OH)_2$ solution. What is the percentage of $Ca(OH)_2$ by weight in the solution?

VALUE OF THE CONCEPT

THE CONCEPT

Acids are prepared by many methods, including reactions between acid anhydrides and water, salts and nonvolatile acids, and halogens and hydrogen. Acid anhydrides are prepared by the direct combination of nonmetals and oxygen, and by various other methods such as the reaction between salts and oxygen.

Bases are prepared by many methods, including reactions between basic anhydrides and water, active metals and water, and salts and strong bases. Usually the alkali hydroxides are produced commercially by the electrolysis of halogen salt solutions. Basic anhydrides are prepared by reactions between salts and oxygen, and by the decomposition of certain salts. The hydroxides of elements near the center of the periodic table are amphoteric, since they react as bases with strong acids, and as acids with strong bases during neutralization.

The preparation of salts includes reactions between acids and bases (neutralization), metallic oxides and acids, nonmetallic oxides and bases, metals and dilute acids, salts and nonvolatile acids, metals and nonmetals, two soluble salts.

Names of binary, or two-element, acids begin with *hydro-* and end with *-ic*. Ternary acids, containing oxygen and hydrogen besides a third element, are named after the third element they contain. The name of the related ternary acid ends in *-ic.*

The ending *-ous* is given to the acid whose formula contains one less oxygen atom than its *-ic* relative. The names of ternary acids with one less oxygen atom than the related *-ous* acids begin with *hypo-* and end in *-ous.* If the formula for the related acid contains one more oxygen atom than the related *-ic* acid, the prefix *per-* is attached to the name of the *-ic* acid.

The names of the common bases, either solid or in solution, consist of the names of their metallic ions followed by the word *hydroxide.*

Names of binary salts consist of the names of the two elements with the name of the second element ending in *-ide.* The positive ion of a ternary salt is named first followed by the name of the negative radical. The name ends in *-ate* if the ternary salt is related to the ternary acid ending in *-ic.* The ending *-ite* is used if the ternary salt is related to an acid ending in *-ous.* The prefix *hypo-* and the ending *-ite* designate ternary salts related to acids whose names begin with *hypo-.* All salts related to acids with the prefix *per-* have the same prefix and end in *-ate.*

Metals forming ions of two different charges are found in related salts. The name of the salt whose metallic ion has the lower valence number ends in *-ous;* the related salt containing the ion with the higher valence number ends in *-ic.* Sometimes the Roman numeral indicating the appropriate valence number follows the name of the positive ion. The prefix *bi,* or the name *hydrogen,* is used with the name of the negative ion to indicate an acid salt.

The process of determining the concentration of an acid or base by means of a neutralization reaction is called titration. A definite volume of the unknown acid solution is neutralized with a base solution of known normality, or vice versa. The end point, or neutralization, is determined by means of an indicator; and the concentration of the unknown is then determined mathematically.

USING THE CONCEPT

Using the Basic Concept

1. (a) Describe two methods for preparing acid anhydrides and three methods for preparing acid solutions. (b) Write an equation to represent each method described.

2. (a) Describe two methods for preparing basic anhydrides and three methods for preparing bases. (b) Write an equation to represent each method described.

3. Write equations for two reactions that produce a basic anhydride and an acid anhydride at the same time.

4. (a) Differentiate between a volatile acid and a nonvolatile acid. (b) How would you show that an acid is nonvolatile?

5. (a) What is the fundamental reaction that takes place when HCl, H_2SO_4, and other strong acids react with water? (b) What fundamental reactions take place when basic anhydrides react with water?

6. Describe the electrolysis of halide salt solutions. What products are formed, and in what part of the apparatus, during the electrolysis of halide salt solutions?

7. (a) What are amphoteric hydroxides? (b) Give an example of such a hydroxide. (c) Write an equation to show how the hydroxide you have named reacts with an acid, with a base.

8. (a) Name each of the following acids and bases: H_2SO_3, HNO_2, H_2SeO_3, HF, $Sn(OH)_2$, $Cu(OH)_2$, $Cu(OH)$, $CsOH$, $Ga(OH)_3$. (b) Write the formulas for the following acids and bases: hydriodic acid, hypobromous acid, magnesium hydroxide, strontium hydroxide, chromous hydroxide, chromic hydroxide.

9. (a) Describe briefly four methods for preparing salts. (b) Write an equation for each method described.

10. (a) Name each of the following salts: KCl, $NaClO_3$, $FeSO_4$, $Fe_2(SO_4)_3$, $Ca(HSO_3)_2$, $Ca(NO_2)_2$, $Mg(ClO)_2$. (b) Write the for-

mulas for each of the following salts: sodium nitrate, cupric sulfide, cuprous nitride, aluminum bromate, calcium hypoiodite.

11. (a) What is titration? (b) Mention three things that can be determined by titration. (c) What three factors must be known to determine the concentration of a solution by titration?

12. Why is the preparation of salts from metallic oxides and acids, as well as their preparation from nonmetallic oxides and bases, comparable to neutralization?

Relating Terms Within the Concept
Each of the following exercises consists of five terms. From the last four, select the term or terms closely related to the *italicized* term.

1. *iron(II)*: ferrous, ferric, +2, +3.
2. *volatile acid*: HNO_3, H_2SO_4, HCl, H_3PO_4.
3. *binary compound*: contains two elements, contains three elements, HCl, $AgNO_3$.
4. *hydro . . . ic*: binary acid, ternary acid, HCl, HClO.
5. *bi- or hydrogen*: Na_2CO_3, $NaHSO_3$, $Ca_3(PO_4)_2$, CH_4.
6. *hypo . . . ite*: ternary salts, ternary acids, KClO, NaBrO.
7. *titration*: end point, equivalent amounts of two substances, indicator, valence number.
8. *related salts*: -ous and -ic, $KClO_3$ and $NaClO_3$, $Ba(NO_3)_2$ and $Ba(NO_2)_2$, FeO and Fe_2O_3.

Solving Problems Within the Concept
1. (a) How many moles of basic anhydride and how many moles of acid anhydride are produced when 20 moles of ZnS react completely with oxygen? (b) How many pounds of each of the two products are formed when 97 pounds of ZnS react completely with O_2?

2. Forty-five milliliters of 0.1 N NaOH neutralize exactly 30 ml of HCl solution. What is the normality of the acid?

3. Thirty milliliters of NaOH solution are just neutralized by 41.2 ml of 0.24 N HCl. What is the normality of the NaOH solution?

4. Five milliliters of vinegar are neutralized by 33.6 ml of 0.12 N NaOH. What is the percentage of acetic acid by weight in the vinegar sample?

Applying the Concept
1. Suggest a naturally occurring substance that can be used economically as a source of NaOH.

2. Solutions of NaOH are difficult to make accurately since solid NaOH is deliquescent. Suggest a non-deliquescent base that might be used in place of NaOH in titrations. Explain your choice.

3. Why wouldn't phenolphthalein be a good indicator to use in the titration of ammonium hydroxide against hydrochloric acid? Why is methyl orange an appropriate indicator for this titration?

4. Which one of the following equations represents the reaction of $Al(OH)_3$ as an acid? as a base? Explain your choices.

$$Al(OH)_3 + 3 H^+ \longrightarrow Al^{+3} + 3 H_2O$$
$$Al(OH)_3 + OH^- \longrightarrow Al(OH)_4^-$$

Reading Further
Elementary Quantitative Analysis, 2d. ed., by W. J. Blaedel and V. M. Meloche, New York, Harper & Row, 1963. Includes a clear account of the Brønsted–Lowry theory, instructions for preparing reagent solutions, and instructions for procedures in acid-base titrations.

16

SKILLS—Types of Reactions

If we look carefully at the many equations for reactions between ions in the last few chapters, a pattern begins to emerge. The reactions can be classified into two fundamental groups: those in which some or all of the reacting substances undergo a *change in valence number* (redox reactions), and those in which the *valence numbers remain unchanged*. Redox reactions will be considered more fully in a later chapter.

The first fundamental group includes reactions illustrating *composition, decomposition,* and *single replacement*. The second group includes all *double replacement* reactions. As you study the distinguishing characteristics of these four types of reactions, note that while many composition and decomposition reactions involve ionic substances, all single and double replacement reactions are reactions among ions in solution.

All of the equations used here represent chemical changes that actually occur. However, they do not indicate the conditions of heat, pressure, concentration of reactants, pH, or catalysts that may be necessary for the reaction to proceed.

COMPOSITION REACTIONS

Historically, **composition** reactions have also been known as **combination** or **synthesis** reactions. In these reactions, two substances, either elements or compounds, combine to form a single compound.

You have already met this type of reaction in the combination of iron and sulfur to produce ionic iron sulfide and in the burning of coal in air to produce covalent carbon dioxide.

$$Fe + S \longrightarrow FeS$$
$$C + O_2 \longrightarrow CO_2 \uparrow$$

Still other composition reactions occur between two compounds:

$$CaO + H_2O \longrightarrow Ca(OH)_2$$
$$SO_3 + H_2O \longrightarrow H_2SO_4$$

DECOMPOSITION REACTIONS

Traditionally **decomposition** reactions, also known as **analysis** reactions, are reactions in which a compound is broken down into simpler substances, either elements or compounds. Priestley's heating of mercuric oxide to produce oxygen and mercury is an example of the decomposition of an ionic compound to produce two elements. The electrolysis of water is now a familiar decomposition reaction in which a covalent compound decomposes into its elements.

$$2\,HgO \xrightarrow{\Delta} 2\,Hg + O_2 \uparrow$$
$$2\,H_2O \xrightarrow[DC]{H_2SO_4} 2\,H_2 + O_2 \uparrow$$

The heating of calcium carbonate (marble chips) to produce calcium oxide and carbon dioxide is a decomposition reaction resulting in two compounds.

$$CaCO_3 \longrightarrow CaO + CO_2 \uparrow$$

PROBLEMS

1. Write a balanced equation to show the composition reactions between (a) hydrogen and oxygen, (b) zinc and sulfur, (c) magnesium and oxygen, (d) water and carbon dioxide.
2. Write a balanced equation to show the decomposition of (a) calcium chloride, (b) sugar (to produce water and carbon), (c) sulfurous acid.

SINGLE REPLACEMENT REACTIONS

In **single replacement,** or **simple replacement,** reactions, a free element replaces an element in a compound, usually in solution. The element and the compound interact to produce a different free element and a new compound. An example of a simple replacement reaction is the laboratory preparation of hydrogen by the reaction between zinc and dilute hydrochloric acid. Hydrogen is also liberated by reacting magnesium with sulfuric acid or sodium with cold water.

$$Zn + 2\,HCl \longrightarrow ZnCl_2 + H_2\uparrow$$
$$Mg + H_2SO_4 \longrightarrow MgSO_4 + H_2\uparrow$$
$$2\,Na + 2\,HOH \longrightarrow 2\,NaOH + H_2\uparrow$$

A single replacement reaction also occurs if you place a bright shiny iron nail in a solution of copper sulfate. Gradually the nail is covered with a deposit of copper.

$$Fe + CuSO_4 \longrightarrow FeSO_4 + Cu\downarrow$$

When moist chlorine is passed over solid potassium bromide, the chlorine replaces the bromine, which escapes as a gas.

$$Cl_2 + 2\,KBr \longrightarrow 2\,KCl + Br_2\uparrow$$

In these reactions observe that an insoluble gas (hydrogen or bromine) or an insoluble solid (copper) is formed. Since these products are removed from the solution, as indicated by the appropriate arrows, a reverse reaction cannot take place. Such reactions in which a reverse reaction does not occur are said to *go to completion*. Single replacement reactions ordinarily go to completion because a gas or precipitate is formed.

Ionic Equations

Since all single replacement reactions involve ions in solutions, equations for this type of reaction can be written in ionic form. This enables the determining of further data for such reactions.

$$Zn^0 + 2\,H^+ + 2\,Cl^- \longrightarrow Zn^{+2} + 2\,Cl^- + H_2{}^0\uparrow$$
$$Mg^0 + 2\,H^+ + SO_4{}^{-2} \longrightarrow$$
$$Mg^{+2} + SO_4{}^{-2} + H_2{}^0\uparrow$$
$$2\,Na^0 + 2\,H^+ + 2\,OH^- \longrightarrow$$
$$2\,Na^+ + 2\,OH^- + H_2{}^0\uparrow$$
$$Fe^0 + Cu^{+2} + SO_4{}^{-2} \longrightarrow Fe^{+2} + SO_4{}^{-2} + Cu^0\downarrow$$
$$Cl_2{}^0 + 2\,K^+ + 2\,Br^- \longrightarrow 2\,K^+ + 2\,Cl^- + Br_2{}^0\uparrow$$

A detailed inspection of the ionic equations shows that the charge on the free element in the reactants is invariably zero (0). If the free element is a metal, it replaces the positively charged portion of the compound, as in the first four equations. If the free element is a nonmetal, like chlorine, it replaces the negatively charged portion of the compound. Clearly, these single replacement reactions involve electron transfers in which there is a loss and gain of electrons by particles.

Net Equations

Occasionally chemists find it convenient to write a net (or essential) ionic equation that shows only the elements involved in the electron transfer, that is, elements which undergo a change in outer electron structure during the reaction. The net equation for the reaction between zinc and hydrochloric acid is:

$$Zn^0 + 2\,H^+ \longrightarrow Zn^{+2} + H_2{}^0\uparrow$$

Note the similarity between this net equation and that for the reaction of sodium with water.

$$2\,Na^0 + 2\,H^+ \longrightarrow 2\,Na^+ + H_2\uparrow$$

Now consider the complete ionic equations for the reactions of magnesium with steam, hydrochloric acid, and sulfuric acid, respectively.

$$Mg^0 + 2\,H^+ + 2\,OH^- \longrightarrow$$
$$Mg^{+2} + 2\,OH^- + H_2{}^0\uparrow$$
$$Mg^0 + 2\,H^+ + 2\,Cl^- \longrightarrow Mg^{+2} + 2\,Cl^- + H_2{}^0\uparrow$$
$$Mg^0 + 2\,H^+ + SO_4{}^{-2} \longrightarrow Mg^{+2} + SO_4{}^{-2} + H_2{}^0\uparrow$$

As an indication of the similarity among these reactions, the following net equation may be used to indicate any (or all) of them:

$$Mg^0 + 2\,H^+ \longrightarrow Mg^{+2} + H_2{}^0\uparrow$$

Whether the hydrogen is replaced from water or from acid is immaterial from the standpoint of electron transfer in such reactions.

PROBLEMS

1. Write complete balanced equations for reactions between: (a) zinc and sulfuric acid, (b) calcium and sulfuric acid, (c) chlorine and sodium iodide, (d) copper and silver nitrate.

2. Write complete ionic equations for reactions a, c, and d.

3. Write net equations for the following pairs of reactions: (a) iron with hydrochloric acid, and iron with sulfuric acid, (b) aluminum with hydrochloric acid, and aluminum with phosphoric acid.

4. Why do simple replacement reactions go to completion?

DOUBLE REPLACEMENT REACTIONS

While **double replacement** reactions have been known as **double displacement** or **double decomposition** reactions, the first name seems preferable since in these reactions ions or radicals of two compounds interchange to form two new compounds. Such reactions go to completion when ions in solution combine to form an insoluble product, or when a gas or water is formed.

If you have combined equal volumes of silver nitrate and sodium chloride solutions having the same concentrations, you have seen the formation of the white precipitate, silver chloride. If you then filtered the mixture and evaporated the filtrate, sodium nitrate crystallized out.

$$AgNO_3 + NaCl \longrightarrow NaNO_3 + AgCl\downarrow$$

The sodium and silver have "changed partners." The formation of insoluble silver chloride causes the reaction to go to completion. (See the Appendix for table of solubilities.)

Similarly, the reaction between lead nitrate and potassium iodide goes to completion because of the formation of a precipitate.

$$Pb(NO_3)_2 + 2\,KI \longrightarrow 2\,KNO_3 + PbI_2\downarrow$$

If concentrated sulfuric acid and sodium chloride are combined, hydrogen chloride gas escapes and sodium hydrogen sulfate remains.

$$H_2SO_4 + NaCl \longrightarrow NaHSO_4 + HCl\uparrow$$

This reaction goes to completion because the gaseous product escapes.

The qualitative test to distinguish limestone from other rocks is a variation of another double replacement reaction. If a drop of hydrochloric acid is placed on limestone, bubbles of carbon dioxide appear. Actually the reaction occurs in two steps. The first is a double replacement reaction between the carbonate and acid to form calcium chloride and carbonic acid. Then the acid undergoes decomposition to water and the insoluble gas carbon dioxide.

$$CaCO_3 + 2\,HCl \longrightarrow CaCl_2 + H_2CO_3$$
$$H_2CO_3 \longrightarrow H_2O + CO_2\uparrow$$

The first reaction produces unstable carbonic acid. This reaction goes to completion because the resulting carbon dioxide escapes.

As a final example of a double replacement reaction, recall what happens when hydrochloric acid and sodium hydroxide solutions react.

$$HCl + NaOH \longrightarrow NaCl + HOH$$

In this neutralization reaction the positive ions (H^+ and Na^+) once again appear to change partners. In reality, the only chemical change that actually occurs is between the H^+ and OH^- ions to form water. However, neutralization reactions are usually classed as double replacement reactions. The formation of water in these reactions causes them to go to completion.

Ionic Equations

As all double replacement reactions involve ions in solution, the equations just written may be shown in ionic form:

$$Na^+ + Cl^- + Ag^+ + NO_3^- \longrightarrow$$
$$Na^+ + NO_3^- + AgCl\downarrow$$
$$Pb^{+2} + 2\,NO_3^- + 2\,K^+ + 2\,I^- \longrightarrow$$
$$2\,K^+ + 2\,NO_3^- + PbI_2\downarrow$$
$$Na^+ + Cl^- + H^+ + HSO_4^- \longrightarrow$$
$$Na^+ + HSO_4^- + HCl\uparrow$$
$$Ca^{+2} + CO_3^{-2} + 2\,H^+ + 2\,Cl^- \longrightarrow$$
$$Ca^{+2} + 2\,Cl^- + H_2O + CO_2\uparrow$$
$$Na^+ + OH^- + H^+ + Cl^- \longrightarrow Na^+ + Cl^- + H_2O$$

When the equations are written in ionic form, it becomes clear that despite the ionic nature of these reactions, *there is no transfer of electrons* among any of the elements involved. There is only an interchange of positive (or negative) ions. As you have seen, the *formation of a precipitate, a gas, or slightly ionized water causes double replacement reactions to go to completion.* However, some neutralization reactions result in the reverse process of hydrolysis. Though water is a product of neutralization, a state of equilibrium occurs between the soluble products and reactants. Hence, hydrolysis reactions do *not* go to completion.

Net Equations

The reaction just discussed can be written as net equations involving only the ions which react.

$$Ag^+ + Cl^- \longrightarrow AgCl\downarrow$$
$$Pb^{+2} + 2\,I^- \longrightarrow PbI_2\downarrow$$
$$H^+ + Cl^- \longrightarrow HCl\uparrow$$

Similarly, the neutralization reaction between HCl and NaOH may be written as

$$H^+ + OH^- \longrightarrow H_2O$$

This last reaction, recall, does not show that the hydrogen ions are hydrated. If you wish to show the hydronium ion, the net equation becomes

$$H_3O^+ + OH^- \longrightarrow 2\,H_2O$$

QUESTIONS AND PROBLEMS

1. Write complete balanced equations for reactions between each of the following: (a) barium chloride and potassium sulfate, (b) magnesium nitrate and sodium carbonate, (c) nitric acid and potassium hydroxide, (d) barium hydroxide and hydrochloric acid, (e) iron sulfide and hydrogen chloride, (f) ammonium chloride and calcium nitrate. (Refer to the table of solubilities in the Appendix.)

2. (a) Write complete ionic equations for reactions a, c, and e. (b) Write net equations for reactions b, d, and f. (c) Which reactions go to completion? Why?

3. Complete each of the following equations. Then indicate which of the four main types of chemical reactions each represents.

(a) $N_2 + 3\,H_2 \longrightarrow$
(b) $Mg + H_2O \longrightarrow H_2 +$
(c) $ZnCO_3 \xrightarrow{\Delta} ZnO +$
(d) $NaI + Cl_2 \longrightarrow I_2 +$
(e) $H_2SO_4 + Ca(NO_3)_2 \longrightarrow$
(f) $CaO + H_2O \longrightarrow$

ADDITIONAL PROBLEMS

1. Write balanced equations for the following composition reactions:
(a) antimony + chlorine $\longrightarrow$
(b) nitric oxide + oxygen $\longrightarrow$
(c) barium oxide + water $\longrightarrow$

2. Write balanced equations for the following decomposition reactions:
(a) magnesium chloride $\longrightarrow$
(b) potassium chlorate $\xrightarrow{\Delta}$
(c) hydrogen peroxide $\longrightarrow$

3. Write balanced equations for the following single replacement reactions:
(a) magnesium + phosphoric acid $\longrightarrow$
(b) copper + mercurous nitrate $\longrightarrow$
(c) calcium + water $\longrightarrow$

4. Write balanced equations for the following double replacement reactions:
(a) cupric chloride + hydrogen sulfide $\longrightarrow$
(b) sodium bromide + phosphoric acid $\longrightarrow$
(c) sodium hydroxide + nitric acid $\longrightarrow$

5. Explain why each reaction in Questions 3 and 4 above goes to completion.

6. For the reactions in Questions 3 and 4, write (a) complete ionic equations, (b) net equations.

7. Complete each of the following equations. Indicate which of the four types of chemical reactions each represents.
(a) $KOH + HCl \longrightarrow$
(b) $NaClO_3 \xrightarrow{\Delta}$
(c) $Cu + S \xrightarrow{\Delta}$
(d) $CuSO_4 + NaOH \longrightarrow$
(e) $Fe + HCl \longrightarrow$
(f) $Cu + Hg(NO_3)_2 \longrightarrow$

17

Controlling Chemical Reactions

Had you been among the spectators at Lakehurst, New Jersey, late on May 6, 1937, you would have seen the *Hindenburg*, the largest dirigible ever built, move majestically into view. In the last moments, just as it was mooring, its hydrogen-filled envelope burst into flames. The cause of the explosion—perhaps an electrical discharge—is uncertain, but the fact that hydrogen and oxygen combine explosively if a single spark is present is well known. And yet a stream of dry hydrogen gas burns quietly in air.

Though the substitution of nonflammable helium for hydrogen has solved the problem for the occasional dirigible built today, the dangers resulting from highly explosive substances remain to plague the rocket designer. The liquid oxygen used for oxidizing the fuel in some rockets also needs only a single spark to combine explosively with the fuel. When the LOX (liquid oxygen) is being loaded into the rocket, every precaution is taken to prevent a spark from friction. Even the surrounding pavement is "wetted down" as a precautionary measure. And yet we light fires constantly, and they are kept burning quietly by the oxygen in the air.

In each instance, combustion or rapid oxidation occurs. In the *Hindenburg*, the combustion was extremely rapid. In a rocket the very high concentration of liquid oxygen and of a combustible fuel nearby accounts for a possible explosion—that is, each burning particle would be near enough to another particle to raise the entire volume of the fuel almost simultaneously to its kindling point. By contrast, the nitrogen in the air "dilutes" the oxygen so that the fuel of a fire, or a stream of dry hydrogen, actually burns in a limited supply of the oxygen.

Clearly, combustion reactions take place at different rates of speed depending upon the concentration and nature of the combustible substance and the amount of oxygen available. But what of other types of chemical reactions—what determines the rates at which they proceed and how can these rates be altered or controlled?

REACTIONS AND REACTION RATES

An explosion of dynamite that tears away the side of a hill occurs in a fraction of a second. The concrete foundation of a skyscraper requires days to harden. Rust, over a period of years, can eat away unpainted iron so that it crumbles to the touch. All these are chemical reactions occurring at very different rates. To determine for yourself that all reactions do not occur as quickly as most of those you have observed in the laboratory, *try the following investigation.*

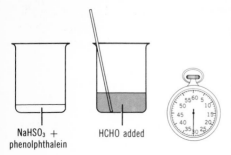

NaHSO₃ +
phenolphthalein   HCHO added

Prepare two solutions, a 0.3 M solution of formaldehyde (HCHO) and a 0.1 M solution of sodium hydrogen sulfite (NaHSO₃). Let them stand until they reach the same temperature, about 24° C. Using a pipet, measure 10 ml of the sodium bisulfite solution into a clean beaker and add one drop of phenolphthalein. Now add to this solution 10 ml of the formaldehyde, stirring the mixture as you do so. Using a watch with a second hand, find the number of seconds that pass between the time mixing starts and the time the contents of the beaker turn red. Do you find that it takes about 30 seconds for the red color to appear—an indication that a chemical reaction has taken place, producing an excess of OH⁻ ions?

Evidently an excess of OH⁻ ions was not produced the instant the two solutions were mixed. Chemists use the term **rate of reaction** to describe the time it takes for a reaction to occur under given conditions. The rate of reaction may be defined as the *mass of a reacting material* (usually measured in gram molecular or gram formula weights) *that is changed to products in a definite period of time.* The time can be expressed in any convenient unit—seconds, minutes, hours, or even days. Less precisely, reaction rates are described simply as rapid, moderate, or slow.

The collision theory, as you remember, states that particles must collide with each other before they can combine and effect a chemical change. Not every collision is effective in producing such a change, but any factor which increases the number of collisions will, in turn, increase the rate of reaction. Now let us consider several factors which do affect the rate of a chemical reaction.

Concentration Alters Reaction Rate

You can study the effect of concentration on the rate of reaction *by varying the investigation* just performed.

This time dilute the concentration of the 10-ml solution of sodium hydrogen sulfite and phenolpthalein by adding to it 20 ml of distilled water, measured at 24° C. Then add 10 ml of formaldehyde as before and again time the reaction. How does the time compare with that determined previously?

Now you probably find that it takes a full minute (instead of 30 seconds) for the red color to appear. You would judge from this that, in

Fig. 17-1 Reaction rate . . .

. . . is often increased by change
in concentration of either reactant.

certain cases at least, diluting the concentration of a solution slows down the rate of reaction. However, another investigation shows that dilution does not always have this effect. Consider, for example, the rate at which hydrogen is produced when strips of magnesium with equal surface areas are placed in sulfuric acid solutions of different concentrations. The magnesium reacts with 1 M sulfuric acid to produce hydrogen far more rapidly than with the more concentrated 6 M acid. For ionic solutions, too high a concentration of ions may reduce their mobility, causing the reaction rate to decrease. You see, then, that the effect of a change in concentration on the rate of reaction (Fig. 17-1) must be determined individually for each reaction.

Temperature and Reaction Rate

If you repeat the first investigation with the formaldehyde and sodium hydrogen sulfite solutions at a temperature of 34° C, notice that the color change occurs in about 15 seconds. By raising the temperature of the reactants 10° C, the rate of reaction is doubled. With some solutions the same temperature change increases the rate of reaction three- or fourfold.

Why does a rise in temperature increase the rate of reaction? The answer is partly that there is more motion among particles at the higher temperature. But more important is the fact that at the higher temperature a greater number of particles have acquired the activation energy necessary to insure that the collisions between them result in a chemical change (Fig. 17-2). In the investigation mentioned, a rise in temperature of 10° C doubled the number of activated particles in the reaction.

Reactants and Reaction Rate

A third factor which affects the reaction rate is the nature of the chemicals involved. When you mixed solutions of HCl and silver nitrate (AgNO$_3$), both ionic substances, there was an immediate reaction which resulted in a white precipitate of AgCl. Compare that reaction *with the results of the following investigation.*

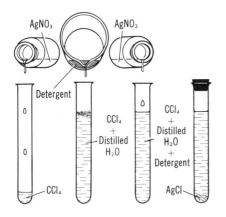

Mix a few drops of silver nitrate (AgNO$_3$) with a small amount of carbon tetrachloride (CCl$_4$). No reaction is observed even though these compounds remain in contact with each other for a long period of time. Now combine equal volumes of carbon tetrachloride and distilled water in a large test tube, adding a small amount of detergent, as shown at the left. Although shaking the test tube causes the once immiscible liquids to mix together, again no chemical reaction is apparent. Now add a few drops of the silver nitrate to this solution, stopper the test tube, and let it stand in a warm place for a day or two. Do you find that finally a slight precipitate of AgCl has formed? Given time, a chemical reaction did take place.

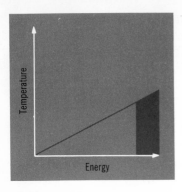

17-2 The higher the temperature, the greater is the energy of the particles undergoing reaction. Effective collisions are assured, however, only with those "activated" particles whose energies are found in the gray area at the right.

Carbon tetrachloride is a covalent, nonpolar substance. Yet the investigation shows that over a period of time a few chloride ions (Cl^-) were freed from the carbon tetrachloride. And once these ions were formed, they reacted almost instantly with the Ag^+ ions of the $AgNO_3$ to form an AgCl precipitate. As this investigation suggests, ions in solution generally react very rapidly, while molecular substances react much more slowly. The ionization of the molecular carbon tetrachloride in water was very slow; although as few as 1/10,000 mole of Cl^- ions were formed, they reacted very rapidly with the Ag^+ ions of the silver nitrate: AgCl can be produced at a rate of at least 1,000 particles per second. The rate of a chemical reaction is affected by the nature of the chemical particles—whether ionic or molecular and, if the latter, by the arrangement of atoms in the molecule.

Why Increase Surface Area?

A large lump of coal takes a long time to ignite and burns slowly. But if the coal is pulverized—so that a great many surfaces are exposed to the oxygen in the air instead of just a few—the coal catches fire with almost explosive force. Similarly, if a small iron nail is held in the flame of a Bunsen burner, the nail may glow but will not burn. If, however, you sprinkle iron filings very cautiously into the flame, they burn immediately. In certain parts of the country, sawdust, as a fuel, is blown into furnaces to increase the rate at which it burns. Since reactions take place at the surfaces of particles, increasing the surface areas of reacting substances causes chemical reactions to occur at a faster rate.

Catalysts

A solution of hydrogen peroxide kept in the medicine cabinet slowly loses its "strength" by decomposing exothermically into water and oxygen. This reaction liberates, or has a heat of reaction of, 23.5 kilocalories per mole of H_2O_2:

$$2\ H_2O_2(l) \longrightarrow 2\ H_2O(l) + O_2(g) \qquad \Delta H = -47\ kcal$$

However, the decomposition reaction can be speeded up greatly by adding a catalyst such as manganese dioxide (MnO_2). Why should the addition of the MnO_2 change the rate of the reaction?

By examining Figure 17-3, you find that the catalyzed reaction has a lower activation energy than does the uncatalyzed reaction. The lower activation energy for the catalyzed reaction indicates that *more molecules of hydrogen peroxide have at least the minimum energy necessary to begin the reaction,* and thus more molecules react within a given time. Nevertheless, *both the catalyzed and uncatalyzed reactions liberate the same energy* —a total of 47 kcal.

As you might expect, in other reactions, catalysts reduce the activation energy. But in any particular reaction, the amount of energy liberated or absorbed is the same whether the reaction takes place with or without a

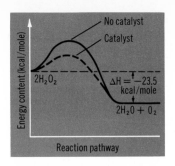

17-3 Although the reaction pathways for the catalyzed and uncatalyzed decomposition of hydrogen peroxide differ, the same energy is liberated in both reactions.

catalyst. A study of the energy changes involved in the decomposition of potassium chlorate under catalyzed and uncatalyzed conditions (page 8) would confirm this fact.

It is not yet fully known how catalysts work to vary the rate of reaction, although a possible explanation for their action was suggested in Chapter 10. A given substance acts as a catalyst only in certain reactions —finely divided platinum speeds up the production of sulfur trioxide from sulfur dioxide and oxygen; a trace of acetanilide slows down the decomposition of hydrogen peroxide. Catalysts also often act only under certain conditions. The enzyme pepsin, which catalyzes the first step in digestion of certain insoluble proteins to soluble amino acids, acts as a catalyst in an acid solution. In the presence of an excess of OH^- ions, the action of the pepsin is inhibited.

Predicting the Possibility of Chemical Reactions

In Chapter 10 you learned that the reactions that proceed most readily are those which go to a *lower* energy state—exothermic reactions. However, there are also endothermic reactions that proceed spontaneously toward a *higher* energy state. Why do such reactions occur? J. Willard Gibbs, an American physical chemist of the nineteenth century, explained the likelihood of chemical reactions using the concept of **entropy,** which is defined as *a measure of disorder, or randomness.*

Any pure crystalline substance has low entropy because the ions or molecules are in a definite array that gives a characteristic shape to the crystal. When ice, a crystalline substance, melts, the molecules of liquid water, $H_2O(l)$, reach a more random state—an increase in entropy occurs. When the liquid H_2O is heated, the bonds between some of the molecules break and vaporization occurs to form gaseous water, $H_2O(g)$. Gases have a more random motion than liquids or solids, and thus have greater entropy.

Consider the change

$$H_2O(l) \longrightarrow H_2O(g)$$

The entropy of the product is greater than that of the reactant, and the *entropy change,* represented by the symbol ΔS (delta S) is positive. The reverse change, the condensation from gas to liquid, has a negative ΔS value. In chemical reactions, *when there are more moles of products than of reactants or when the products include more moles of gases, the disorder, or entropy, is increased and ΔS is positive.*

Let us examine this statement with reference to the decomposition of mercury(II) oxide (HgO), with a heat of reaction of 21.7 kilocalories per mole of HgO:

$$2\ HgO(s) \longrightarrow 2\ Hg(l) + O_2(g) \qquad \Delta H = +43.4\ kcal$$

How did Gibbs explain the effect of increased temperature on this and other endothermic reactions?

Free Energy

For any chemical reaction, Gibbs combined the energy changes, ΔH, and the entropy changes, ΔS, into a single equation:

$$\Delta G = \Delta H - T\Delta S$$

In this equation ΔG represents the quantity called the **free energy change** for the reaction. Gibbs stated that *a reaction is possible at a given temperature, T, only if ΔG is a negative quantity.*

In the decomposition of HgO, ΔH is, of course, positive. However, when T is 500° C, the term $T\Delta S$ is large enough to make the free energy change, ΔG, negative; and when ΔG is negative, a chemical reaction can occur. When the free energy change, ΔG, is zero, the reaction is at equilibrium, and there is no tendency for the reaction to go to completion.

QUESTIONS AND PROBLEMS

1. If a piece of zinc is placed in a test tube of dilute sulfuric acid, hydrogen gas usually forms slowly. (a) Write the equation for the reaction. (b) Predict what will happen to the rate of reaction if: the acid is heated; less dilute acid is used; powdered zinc is used instead of a piece of solid zinc. (c) How else could the rate be changed?
2. Ozone (O_3), a molecular form of oxygen, is more active than O_2. Silver is not easily affected by O_2; predict the effect of O_3 on silver.
3. Why does an endothermic reaction such as the dissolving of NH_4Cl in water proceed spontaneously?
4. In a reaction ΔH and the entropy term, $T \Delta S$, are equal. (a) What is the free energy change, ΔG? (b) What conditions exist in this reaction?

REVERSIBLE AND IRREVERSIBLE REACTIONS

In industrial processes chemists are concerned not only with affecting the rates at which chemical reactions take place, but also with causing these reactions to go to completion so that as much product as possible is formed. Suppose a chemist wants to prepare some hydrogen iodide by the direct combination of gaseous hydrogen and gaseous iodine. This reaction involves the formation of the compound hydrogen iodide, which is relatively unstable.

$$H_2(g) + I_2(g) \longrightarrow 2\,HI(g)$$

Normally, hydrogen iodide is a colorless gas. Yet when prepared in this way in the laboratory, it has a faint violet color. This color indicates the presence in the gas of free iodine. The iodine is there because as soon as hydrogen iodide is formed, it begins to decompose (Fig. 17-4) into its constituent elements, H_2 and I_2:

$$2\,HI(g) \longrightarrow H_2(g) + I_2(g)$$

If the chemist starts with a closed container full of hydrogen and iodine and raises the temperature, as soon as the HI is formed, the reverse reaction, the decomposition of HI, starts to occur. True, heating the reaction increases the rate of formation of HI, but it also increases the rate of decomposition.

Such reactions in which the products, once formed, immediately react to form the original reactants are called **reversible reactions.** Usually a single equation is used to represent a reversible reaction. For example, the following equation represents both reactions described above:

$$H_2 + I_2 \rightleftharpoons 2\,HI$$

The opposite directions of the two arrows indicate that the forward and reverse reactions occur simultaneously and at the same rate. As a reversible reaction proceeds, it eventually reaches a point at which no change *seems* to be taking place. There is no increase in the amount of reactants or products. Yet chemical changes are still continuing; it is simply that the two reactions are proceeding at exactly the same rate. A state of dynamic equilibrium has been reached.

Dynamic Equilibrium

Another example of what can be considered a reversible reaction occurs when 10 ml of 1 M Na_2SO_4 and 20 ml of 1 M KCl solutions are mixed together. You might predict that this reaction would be of the following double replacement type:

$$Na_2SO_4 + 2\,KCl \longrightarrow K_2SO_4 + 2\,NaCl$$

But if you let the water evaporate from the mixture of the two solutions and analyze the solid residue carefully, you find a surprising result. The residue, which was expected to contain only crystals of K_2SO_4 and NaCl, also contains crystals of Na_2SO_4 and KCl. Four different compounds are present!

The presence of the four compounds, instead of the predicted two, can be explained in two different ways. The first explanation assumes that Na^+, SO_4^{-2}, K^+, and Cl^- ions are in solution and, therefore, are free to move about. As water evaporates from the solution, these positive and negative ions become arranged by chance into the four different lattice structures of four different salts: Na_2SO_4, KCl, K_2SO_4, and NaCl. This explanation says, in effect, that apparently no chemical reaction has taken place among the various ions present.

The second explanation is in terms of a reversible reaction. It assumes that in solution a chemical reaction does take place between the four types of ions in Na_2SO_4 and KCl to produce K_2SO_4 and NaCl. At the outset, the reactants are present in a certain concentration. As the reaction proceeds, the concentration of the reactants is reduced, new products are formed, and the reverse reaction sets in. When the concentrations of the reactants and of the products become constant, the two

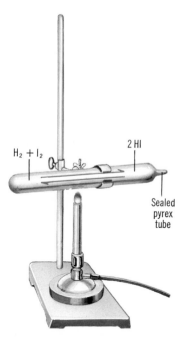

17-4 If gaseous iodine and hydrogen are sealed in a thick-walled tube and heated gently over a low flame, hydrogen iodide is formed. Some hydrogen iodide decomposes as soon as it is formed, and equilibrium is soon reached in this reversible reaction. The number of molecules remains unchanged throughout the reaction. Why?

reactions continue at the same rate. From this point on, there is no increase in the amount of reactants or products; a state of dynamic equilibrium exists.

An Incomplete Reaction

Obviously if equilibrium exists, the reaction does not go to completion. Another example of such an incomplete reaction is neutralization between a strong base, NaOH, and a weak acid, $HC_2H_3O_2$. As sodium acetate ($NaC_2H_3O_2$) is produced, the reverse reaction, hydrolysis, occurs and the reactants are re-formed. Eventually neutralization and hydrolysis occur at the same rate. Then the two reactions are in chemical equilibrium.

$$Na^+ + OH^- + H^+ + C_2H_3O_2{}^- \underset{\text{hydrolysis}}{\overset{\text{neutralization}}{\rightleftarrows}} Na^+ + C_2H_3O_2{}^- + H_2O$$

All neutralization reactions which involve hydrolysis are reversible, or incomplete, reactions.

If all the products of a reaction that occurs in solution are soluble, they react with each other and a reverse reaction takes place. It is important to remember that in these reversible reactions chemical changes still continue to occur even after a state of equilibrium has been reached. The changes are not apparent only because the forward and reverse reactions are proceeding at the same rate (Fig. 17-5).

Reactions that Go to Completion

Of course, not all chemical reactions are reversible; many go to completion. For example, consider what happens when a piece of zinc reacts with an excess of hydrochloric acid. The hydrogen gas that forms is insoluble and escapes readily. After the gas ceases to form, only the salt zinc chloride ($ZnCl_2$) remains. No zinc reappears. The reaction cannot reverse itself because one of the products, hydrogen, escapes as a gas. The reaction goes to completion.

$$Zn + 2\,HCl \longrightarrow ZnCl_2 + H_2\uparrow$$

All reactions in which one of the products is an insoluble gas are complete and irreversible.

To determine for yourself another reason why certain reactions go to completion, *try the following investigation.*

Mix together equal volumes (10 ml) of $1\,M$ solutions of $Ba(NO_3)_2$ and Na_2SO_4. A white precipitate of barium sulfate ($BaSO_4$) forms. Separate this precipitate from the liquid by filtration, then allow the liquid to evaporate. What are the white crystals that remain?

This reaction between barium nitrate and sodium sulfate goes to com-

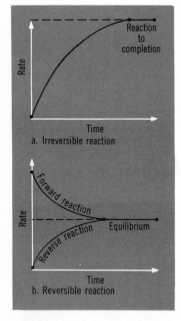

17-5 In an irreversible reaction, the forward reaction continues to completion. In a reversible reaction, when the forward and reverse reactions become equal, a state of equilibrium exists.

17-6 In the upper photograph, the lump of calcium generates bubbles of hydrogen gas that escape into the test tube. In the lower photograph, another irreversible reaction occurs when barium nitrate, added to a sodium sulfate solution, forms a white, flocculent precipitate of barium sulfate.

pletion because one of the products, $BaSO_4$, is an insoluble solid. When the $BaSO_4$ precipitates, it leaves a solution of sodium nitrate.

$$Ba(NO_3)_2 + Na_2SO_4 \longrightarrow BaSO_4\!\!\downarrow + 2\,NaNO_3$$

Recall from Chapter 15 the neutralization reaction between HCl and NaOH in which NaCl and H_2O were formed. When the water was boiled away after neutralization, only NaCl crystals were left. Neither of the reactants (NaOH nor HCl) remained. Reactions of this kind, in which water is one of the products (except neutralization reactions in which hydrolysis occurs) are irreversible and go to completion.

To sum up, we have seen that reactions in which an insoluble gas or solid is formed (Fig. 17-6), or in which water is one of the products, go to completion. These types of reactions are irreversible because the removal of ions in an *undissociated* form prevents the reverse reaction.

$$Na^+ + Cl^- + H^+ + HSO_4^- \longrightarrow HCl\!\!\uparrow + Na^+ + HSO_4^-$$

$$Ag^+ + NO_3^- + Na^+ + Cl^- \longrightarrow AgCl\!\!\downarrow + Na^+ + Cl^-$$

$$Na^+ + OH^- + H^+ + Cl^- \longrightarrow Na^+ + Cl^- + HOH$$

QUESTIONS AND PROBLEMS

1. Define *reversible reaction, irreversible reaction,* and *dynamic equilibrium.*
2. (a) List three reasons why reactions go to completion. (b) Write an equation (not in previous section) to illustrate each type of reaction.
3. (a) Complete each of the following equations. Indicate by appropriate arrows whether each of the reactions is reversible or irreversible. (Use the solubility table on page 184 where necessary.) (b) Explain why each reaction is reversible or irreversible.
   (1) $Mg + H_2SO_4 \longrightarrow$
   (2) $NaOH + HCl \longrightarrow$
   (3) $HC_2H_3O_2 + KOH \longrightarrow$
   (4) $Ba(NO_3)_2 + H_2SO_4 \longrightarrow$

CONTROLLING EQUILIBRIUM

Carbon monoxide, despite its poisonous effect, is used as a constituent in many fuel gases because it burns easily even though it does not support combustion. Consider for a moment one method of producing this gas in which carbon dioxide and hydrogen react to form water and carbon monoxide. If this reaction takes place in a closed container at a constant temperature and pressure (as a closed system), it can be shown readily that the reaction does not go to completion but reaches a state of dynamic equilibrium.

$$CO_2 + H_2 \rightleftharpoons H_2O + CO$$

How can the point of equilibrium be shifted so that a greater proportion of CO is produced? By introducing additional CO_2 into the cylinder container, a new point of equilibrium is established. At this new equilibrium point the proportion of both carbon monoxide and water increases. If we control, or shift, the point of equilibrium in a reversible reaction, we vary the proportion between the product that is formed and the reactants that are re-formed. In other words, we can get more product than reactants—and vice versa.

Concentration Affects Equilibrium

In the reaction described above, the equilibrium was shifted by changing the concentration of one of the reactants. As another example of the effect of concentration on the point of equilibrium, consider the reaction that occurs when highly concentrated sulfuric acid mixes with solid sodium chloride. You remember that one product of this reaction is hydrogen chloride gas (HCl):

$$2 \, NaCl + (conc.) \, H_2SO_4 \xrightarrow{\Delta} Na_2SO_4 + 2 \, HCl\uparrow$$

Since almost no water is present in which the hydrogen chloride can dissolve, it escapes as a gas and the reaction goes to completion. The reaction is complete because one of the products is removed. However, if instead of concentrated sulfuric acid a dilute solution of this same acid is used, the very soluble hydrogen chloride dissolves in the water and cannot escape. The reaction does not go to completion; instead, chemical equilibrium exists between the reactants (NaCl and H_2SO_4) and the products (Na_2SO_4 and HCl):

$$2 \, NaCl + (dilute) \, H_2SO_4 \rightleftharpoons Na_2SO_4 + 2 \, HCl \, (in \, solution)$$

To study the reverse reaction, mix equal volumes of saturated sodium sulfate solution and concentrated hydrochloric acid in a test tube. Filter the precipitate and wash it thoroughly with alcohol. Spread the filter paper out and let it dry completely. Carefully taste the white residue that remains. Is it sodium chloride?

The hydrochloric acid in this investigation was so concentrated that a reaction between Na_2SO_4 and HCl—the reverse of the reaction between NaCl and H_2SO_4—actually occurred:

$$Na_2SO_4 + (conc.) \, 2 \, HCl \longrightarrow H_2SO_4 + 2 \, NaCl\downarrow$$

The NaCl, which is less soluble in HCl than in water, precipitated.

The concentration of the reactants in relation to the concentration of the product determines the point of equilibrium for any chemical reaction occurring in solution. In the above investigation, increasing the concentration of one of the products (HCl) shifted the point of equilibrium toward the formation of more of the reactants. If the concentration of one of the reactants had been increased, then the point of equilibrium would have been shifted in favor of the products.

When the shift in the point of equilibrium favors the formation of the reactants, equilibrium is said to shift toward the left. When the shift favors the formation of more of the products, equilibrium is said to shift toward the right. In the reaction between concentrated H_2SO_4 and solid NaCl, the *escape* of HCl (a product) causes a shift of equilibrium toward the right. But the *addition* of concentrated HCl causes a shift of equilibrium toward the left.

Mass Action and the Equilibrium Constant

About 100 years ago, chemists realized that concentrations were important in any quantitative study of equilibrium. To express the relationship between the rate of a reaction and the concentration of the reactants, the Norwegians Cato Guldberg and Peter Waage, a mathematician and a chemist, respectively, formulated the **Law of Mass Action.** They found that for dilute solutions or for low concentrations, the *forward and reverse rates of a reaction are proportional to the concentrations of the reacting substances.*

Consider once again an equilibrium reaction for which a great deal of experimental work has been done.

$$H_2(g) + I_2(g) \rightleftharpoons 2 HI(g)$$

Table 17-1 gives the data for an investigation in which a constant quantity of hydrogen and varying amounts of iodine were heated in a closed system to a temperature of 454° C. By using the data in the "At equilibrium" column, you can determine that, depending upon the amount of iodine used, approximately 75 to 95 percent of the iodine was transformed. Thus, the equilibrium point is toward the formation of the product, HI. In the right-hand column, observe approximately the same numerical value, 50.8, for each trial. This value, designated K, is known as the **equilibrium constant.** The equilibrium constant is a numerical value derived from a relationship among the concentration of the products and the concentration of reactants at a given temperature. This relationship is, in essence, a quantitative expression of the Law of Mass Action.

The equilibrium constant expression for the production of hydrogen iodide is

$$\frac{[HI]^2}{[H_2][I_2]} = K$$

Conventionally, in this equilibrium constant expression, the products appear in the numerator and the reactants in the denominator; the square brackets designate concentration in moles per liter and the coefficients appear as exponents.

As the value of K is different for each reaction at equilibrium, how can we determine the equilibrium constant for other reactions? Assume a

Table 17-1   EQUILIBRIUM REACTION OF $H_2 + I_2 \rightleftharpoons$ 2HI

	At outset		At equilibrium			Equilibrium constant
	H_2 moles/l	I_2 moles/l	H_2 moles/l	I_2 moles/l	HI moles/l	$\dfrac{[HI]^2}{[H_2][I_2]} = K$
Trial 1	1.35	0.50	0.88	0.02	0.944	50.6
Trial 2	1.35	0.88	0.54	0.09	1.57	50.7
Trial 3	1.35	1.61	0.23	0.43	2.25	51.2
Average						50.8

generalized equation for any reversible reaction at equilibrium:

$$aA + bB \rightleftharpoons cC + dD$$

The small letters stand for coefficients and the capital letters for reactants and products. The equilibrium constant expression for this generalized reaction is

$$\frac{[C]^c \times [D]^d}{[A]^a \times [B]^b} = K$$

Now apply this expression to the reaction for the direct synthesis of ammonia from gaseous nitrogen and hydrogen:

$$N_2(g) + 3H_2(g) \rightleftharpoons 2NH_3(g)$$

The equilibrium constant expression for the synthesis of ammonia is

$$\frac{[NH_3]^2}{[N_2][H_2]^3} = K$$

Uses of the Equilibrium Constant

Once the equilibrium constant is determined for a reaction *at any given temperature,* it does not vary despite the original concentration of the substances. Consider, for example, what happens if you place only hydrogen iodide in the closed system and heat it to 454° C. For this reaction at this temperature, K is known to be 50.8; hence, we can predict confidently that hydrogen iodide will decompose into hydrogen and iodine until equilibrium is reached. It does not matter from which side of the equation equilibrium is approached; K remains the same for the reaction.

In any reaction at equilibrium, if the equilibrium constant is small, the numerator of the equilibrium expression is smaller than the denominator. Therefore, a small K, such as 1.3×10^{-5}, indicates that the reaction does not proceed far to the right. If the equilibrium constant is large, say 1.7×10^7, the reaction proceeds essentially to completion.

Now let us see how this equilibrium expression can be used to determine data about a given reaction. Consider the equilibrium reaction between hydrogen and carbon dioxide to produce water and carbon monoxide.

$$CO_2 + H_2 \rightleftharpoons H_2O + CO$$

How many moles per liter of carbon monoxide are formed at the temperature at which K is 1.6 if the concentration of the other gases in moles per liter are as follows: carbon dioxide, 0.54; hydrogen 0.34; and steam 0.46? First, write the equilibrium constant expression for the reaction.

$$\frac{[H_2O] \times [CO]}{[CO_2] \times [H_2]} = K$$

Then substitute the values for the known concentrations and solve for x.

$$\frac{[0.46] \times [x]}{[0.54] \times [0.34]} = 1.6$$

$$x = [0.64]$$

The concentration of CO at the temperature given is 0.64 moles per liter.

Application of the Equilibrium Constant

In the reactions discussed thus far, the reactants and products have been in gaseous form. An interesting application of the equilibrium constant is found in the ionization of weak electrolytes, such as acetic acid:

$$HC_2H_3O_2 \rightleftharpoons H^+ + C_2H_3O_2^-$$

This ionization may be written in the form of the equilibrium expression:

$$\frac{[H^+][C_2H_3O_2^-]}{[HC_2H_3O_2]} = K_i$$

The equilibrium constant derived from the equilibrium expression for *weak electrolytes* is often known as the **ionization constant,** K_i. Ionization constants are usually quite small; here K_i is 1.8×10^{-5} at room temperature. The smaller the value of K_i, the weaker the acid (Fig. 17-7).

With only slight modifications, this expression can be used in reactions involving solids, as well as gases and substances in aqueous solution. Consider again the formation of practically insoluble barium sulfate when sulfuric acid is added to a solution of barium chloride. In a saturated salt solution, such as $BaSO_4$, equilibrium exists between the ions in solution and the excess solid.

$$BaSO_4 \rightleftharpoons Ba^{+2} + SO_4^{-2}$$

An expression similar to that used for the equilibrium constant can be written to indicate to what extent $BaSO_4$ dissolves.

$$[Ba^{+2}][SO_4^{-2}] = K_{sp}$$

ACETIC ACID

K_i 1.8×10^{-5}

HYDRO-FLUORIC ACID

K_i 6.7×10^{-4}

SULFUROUS ACID

K_i 1.3×10^{-2}

17-7 From their ionization constants, you can determine that the weakest of these acids is acetic acid.

17-8 When silver nitrate is added to a solution of sodium chloride, white silver chloride precipitates.

—NaCl

HCl

Saturated
solution of
NaCl

Crystals of
NaCl

17-9 Although the compound being added to the two tubes differs, the compound settling to the bottom of one, and precipitating from the other, is identical. Why?

In this expression, the equilibrium constant, K_{sp}, is called the **solubility product.** Since the amount of $BaSO_4$ that dissolves at a given temperature is the same regardless of the amount of undissolved $BaSO_4$ present, the concentration of $BaSO_4$ is included in the constant and does not appear as the denominator on the left side of the equation. This procedure is used in determining the K_{sp} for any almost insoluble substance.

The solubility product constant is useful in comparing the degree of solubility of slightly soluble salts. For example, $BaSO_4$ with K_{sp} (at room temperature) of 1.5×10^{-9} is less soluble than $CaSO_4$ with a K_{sp} of 2.4×10^{-5}. The solubility product is also useful in predicting the formation of a precipitate when two solutions containing the ions of two different salts are combined. For example, when solutions of silver nitrate and sodium chloride are combined, if the concentration of Ag^+ ions times the concentration of Cl^- ions $[Ag^+][Cl^-]$ *exceeds* the K_{sp} for silver chloride (1.7×10^{-10}), a precipitate of AgCl forms (Fig. 17-8).

You have actually met the equilibrium constant previously in the ion product constant of water (page 225). Because the concentration of H_2O in very dilute solutions can be considered constant, its value is combined with K to give K_w (in effect, the denominator is omitted):

$$\frac{[H^+][OH^-]}{[H_2O]} = K \qquad becomes \qquad [H^+][OH^-] = K_w$$

The Common Ion Effect

What happens if you add solid NaCl to a saturated solution of sodium chloride from which the excess NaCl has been removed by filtration? Of course, solid crystals of NaCl settle to the bottom of the container. Now predict what will happen when hydrogen chloride is bubbled into a saturated solution of sodium chloride that has been carefully filtered (Fig. 17-9). Again, a large quantity of solid NaCl crystals settle to the bottom of the container. The precipitate in the first case resulted from adding more NaCl than the water could dissolve at a given temperature. But the explanation in the second case is quite different.

In the saturated solution, the NaCl is dissociated into Na^+ and Cl^- ions. Hydrochloric acid also contains chloride ions —the Cl^- is a common ion. When the acid is added to the salt solution, the concentration of chloride ions increases. The equation for the equilibrium and the equilibrium constant expression at a given temperature are:

$$NaCl \underset{precipitating}{\overset{dissolving}{\rightleftharpoons}} Na^+ + Cl^- \qquad K = \frac{[Na^+][Cl^-]}{[NaCl]}$$

K for this reaction must, of course, remain constant at a given temperature. Hence, you can predict that an increase in the concentration of Cl^- ions results in a decrease of Na^+ ions and causes the equilibrium to shift to the left, resulting in the formation of more crystalline NaCl. The effect produced on the point of equilibrium by increasing the concentration of a single ion in the equilibrium is the **common ion effect.**

Another example of the common ion effect *can be observed* by adding sodium acetate to a solution of acetic acid.

> Prepare 100 ml of a 1 *M* solution of acetic acid and use Hydrion paper to determine its pH. Now add 0.1 mole of solid sodium acetate to the solution and determine the pH again. Do you find that the pH increases—the solution has become less acid? What causes this change in pH?

The small ionization constant for acetic acid (1.8×10^{-5}) indicates that an acetic acid solution is only slightly ionized; it consists chiefly of $HC_2H_3O_2$ molecules.

$$HC_2H_3O_2 + HOH \rightleftharpoons H_3O^+ + C_2H_3O_2^-$$

The addition of highly ionized sodium acetate ($NaC_2H_3O_2$) increases the concentration of the acetate ions ($C_2H_3O_2^-$). Consequently, the equilibrium is shifted toward the formation of more acetic acid molecules and fewer hydrogen ions (Fig. 17-10). Because of the decrease in the concentration of hydrogen ions, the solution is less acid—in other words, its pH has increased.

In both reactions illustrating the common ion effect, an increase in the concentration of one ion on the product side of the equation is counteracted by the using up of that ion to form more of a substance on the reactant side of the equation. In fact, *in any reaction at equilibrium an increase in the concentration of any of the reacting substances causes the reaction to shift in the direction that uses up the substance.*

17-10 In which beaker does the addition of sodium acetate to acetic acid demonstrate the common ion effect?

Effect of Heat on Equilibrium

Let us consider what factors, besides concentration, can cause a shift in equilibrium. Remember that the heat of reaction can be considered as one of the products of an exothermic reaction. An example of such a reaction is the direct combination of nitrogen gas (N_2) and hydrogen gas (H_2) to form ammonia gas (NH_3). This is the reaction that occurs in the *Haber process* which is very important in the conversion of atmospheric nitrogen into ammonia, useful in producing compounds (Chapter 25).

$$N_2 + 3 H_2 \rightleftharpoons 2 NH_3 \qquad \Delta H = -22 \text{ kcal}$$

The negative value of ΔH in the above equation indicates that heat is produced when nitrogen and hydrogen combine. The sign of ΔH also indicates that heat is absorbed when the reverse reaction occurs. Putting it another way, the reaction to the right is exothermic while that to the left is endothermic.

Under normal conditions, the combination of N_2 and H_2 produces a low yield of NH_3. The point of equilibrium in this reaction is far toward the left because the heat (ΔH) that is a product of the reaction causes the NH_3 molecules, as they form, to decompose into molecules of N_2 and

H_2. Chemists increase the yield of NH_3 by removing the heat, allowing the reaction to occur at a lower temperature.

Pressure Affects Equilibrium

When the reactants and the products of a reaction are gases, any change in pressure during the reaction affects the point of equilibrium. Consider, for example, the coefficients of the substances involved in the Haber process. These coefficients indicate that for each four molecules of reactants (1 of N_2 and 3 of H_2), two molecules of product are formed. Since the product contains fewer molecules than the reactants from which it is made, the pressure inside the reaction vessel is reduced as the reaction takes place. The formation of ammonia from its elements is accompanied by a decrease in pressure, or a reduction in volume. If the pressure is increased in the Haber process, favoring a decrease in volume, the equilibrium shifts to the right so that a desired larger percentage of ammonia is produced. It has indeed been found that the yield of ammonia increases steadily as the pressure increases, as indicated in Fig. 17-11.

Catalysts and Equilibrium

Oxides of iron are often used as positive catalysts in the Haber process. Such positive catalysts cause the reaction to proceed faster at a lower temperature; that is, they increase the rate of reaction, causing equilibrium to be reached more rapidly. But *catalysts themselves do not change the point of equilibrium;* the rates of both the forward and reverse reactions are affected equally. Catalysts simply increase the rate of reaction if they are positive catalysts or decrease it if they are negative catalysts.

Controlling Stresses on Systems at Equilibrium

In 1884 a young French chemist, Henri LeChatelier, was considering the effect that changes in concentration, temperature, and pressure have on equilibrium in both chemical and physical systems. From his experimentation, he proposed a general principle to describe the effect that any change in conditions has upon any system in which equilibrium exists. This principle, called LeChatelier's Principle, can be stated as follows: *If any stress is applied to a system at equilibrium, the equilibrium will shift in such a way as to relieve the stress.*

LeChatelier's Principle is of great value in industry in determining what conditions will give the best yield of a product. For example, it is applied to increase the yield of ammonia by the Haber process. Here the problem is to find the proper compromise between temperature and pressure. Increased heat shifts the point of equilibrium to the left, while increased pressure shifts it to the right. Thus there must be a compromise between low temperature and high pressure to make the yield of ammonia as great as possible. In practice, the best conditions for the Haber

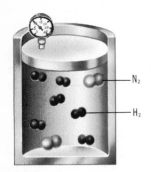

$-N_2$

$-H_2$

$-NH_3$

17-11 When the six hydrogen molecules and two nitrogen molecules in the upper diagram combine to form four molecules of ammonia, the pressure on the cylinder walls decreases.

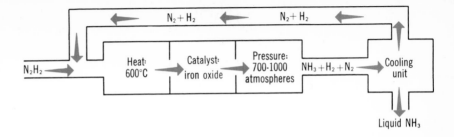

17-12 In the Haber process increased pressure increases the yield of ammonia, but the resulting heat causes the ammonia molecules to decompose. In practice, a compromise is reached between pressure and temperature to give the highest possible yield of ammonia. The catalyst, which allows the reaction to proceed faster at a lower temperature, does not affect the point of equilibrium.

process are a temperature of about 600° C and a pressure of 1,000 atmospheres, together with the presence of an improved catalyst (Fig. 17-12).

Another application of LeChatelier's Principle is seen in the equilibrium reaction between NaCl and H_2SO_4 (page 272). But if we use conditions, such as heat, that favor the escape of the HCl produced, there is a shift in equilibrium; the reaction proceeds to form more HCl. As a result, equilibrium is never reached; instead, the reaction goes to completion.

Importance of Controlling Chemical Equilibrium

As you have just seen, the control of equilibrium is important in getting maximum yield in many chemical processes. As another example, consider the reaction of sulfur dioxide with oxygen to form sulfur trioxide (SO_3), the acid anhydride of sulfuric acid.

$$2\,SO_2 + O_2 \rightleftharpoons 2\,SO_3$$

If the SO_2 and O_2 are mixed at room temperatures, there is no observable formation of SO_3. Yet when the temperature is raised slightly (in the presence of a platinum catalyst) SO_2 and O_2 molecules react. Increasing the temperature at the start of the reaction increases the rate of reaction. However, heat is also a product of the reaction. Therefore the yield of SO_3 will be increased if the reaction occurs at a lower temperature. In practice, optimum yield occurs at a temperature of about 400° C.

Consider also the reaction between hydrogen chloride and oxygen. Here the products are chlorine (Cl_2) and water (H_2O):

$$4\,HCl + O_2 \rightleftharpoons 2\,Cl_2 + H_2O$$

If equilibrium is reached at a temperature of 345° C, only 20 percent by weight of the predicted product forms. Yet if equilibrium is reached at the higher temperature of 385° C, 75 percent of the predicted weight of product is obtained! The existence of equilibrium in chemical reactions means that the yield of products of these reactions will not be identical with that calculated according to the methods learned in Chapter 11. Chemists must experiment to find the optimum set of conditions to "drive" a chemical reaction as near to completion as possible. LeChatelier's Principle is as much a tool of the industrial chemist as are the flasks, burets, and balances of his laboratory.

Many of the reactions in which equilibrium exists, as well as those which go to completion, involve the transfer or sharing of valence electrons among the elements involved. In the next chapter we shall see that there is a pattern to this electron transfer—it is not a haphazard arrangement, it is predictable.

QUESTIONS AND PROBLEMS

1. What is the effect of increasing the concentration of hydrogen in the reaction between gaseous iodine and hydrogen to produce hydrogen iodide? Explain in terms of Le Chatelier's Principle.
2. The addition of sodium citrate to citric acid, a weak acid, changes the pH of the acid. Does the pH increase or decrease? Explain.
3. Differentiate among the following terms: *equilibrium constant, ionization constant, solubility product,* and *ion product constant of water.*
4. In a closed system, the reaction $PCl_5 \rightleftharpoons PCl_3 + Cl_2$ reaches equilibrium at 230° C. The concentrations in moles per liter of the gases are: PCl_5, 0.47; PCl_3, 0.098; and Cl_2, 0.098. Determine the equilibrium constant.
5. A platinum catalyst changes the rates of the reaction between SO_2 and O_2, but it cannot shift its point of equilibrium. Explain in terms of LeChatelier's Principle.
6. What effect does adding heat have on each of the following reactions? Why?
   (a) $3\,Fe + 4\,H_2O \longrightarrow Fe_3O_4 + 4\,H_2 \quad \Delta H = +36$ kcal
   (b) $4\,NH_3 + 5\,O_2 \longrightarrow 4\,NO + 6\,H_2O \quad \Delta H = -217$ kcal

VALUE OF THE CONCEPT

THE CONCEPT

The rate of chemical reaction is a measure of the mass of a reacting material that is changed to product in a definite period of time. Changes in concentration of the reactants can either increase or decrease the rate at which the products are formed. An increase in temperature increases the reaction rate; usually ionic substances react more rapidly than do molecular substances. Since reactions occur at the surfaces of substances, increased surface area also increases reaction rate. Positive catalysts increase and negative catalysts

decrease the rate of reaction. A reaction at a constant temperature tends to proceed so that in its final state it has lower free energy and higher entropy than in its initial state.

Some chemical changes are complete; that is, all of the reactants are used up to form products. Many chemical changes, however, are reversible. In these reactions the products, once formed, immediately begin to re-form the original reactants. As a reversible reaction proceeds, it eventually reaches a point at which there is no decrease or increase in the amounts of reactants or products. Though no change seems to be occurring, the two reactions are proceeding at the same time; a state of dynamic equilibrium has been reached. Reactions go to completion whenever one of the products of the reaction is removed, either because it is an insoluble solid or an insoluble gas. Reactions also go to completion whenever water forms unless the salt that also forms in a neutralization reaction undergoes hydrolysis.

Equilibrium of a reaction is affected by changes in concentration. The Law of Mass Action states that the forward and reverse rates of a reaction are proportional to the concentration of the reacting substances. In reversible reactions involving ions, equilibrium points can be shifted by changing the concentration of a single ion—the common ion effect.

The equilibrium constant is a numerical value derived from the relationship that exists among the concentration of the products and the concentration of the reactants in a reaction at equilibrium. The equilibrium constant is, in effect, a quantitative expression of the Law of Mass Action. Two applications of the equilibrium constant are the ionization constant, which indicates the degree of ionization of weak electrolytes, and the solubility product, useful in predicting the formation of precipitates.

Since the point of equilibrium is affected by changes in temperature, the heat absorbed or released in most reactions is important in determining the equilibrium point. Finally, changes in pressure affect the point of equilibrium. These pressure changes are particularly important in determining the equilibrium point for gaseous reactions in which the number of reacting molecules differs from the number of molecules of the products. While catalysts do affect the rate of reaction, they have no influence upon the point of equilibrium in reversible reactions.

The influence that the several factors have upon the point of equilibrium within a system is summed up in LeChatelier's Principle, which says: if any stress is laid upon a system at equilibrium, the equilibrium will shift in such a way as to relieve the stress. Application of this principle is quite important to many industries as chemists attempt to increase the yield of products obtained from chemical reactions.

USING THE CONCEPT

Using the Basic Concept

1. (a) What is meant by *rate of reaction?* (b) What five factors affect the rate of reaction? (c) According to the collision theory, why does an increase in temperature increase the rate of reaction?

2. (a) Differentiate between a reversible and an irreversible reaction. (b) Give three examples, using equations, for each of the above types of chemical reactions.

3. Does dynamic equilibrium exist in a reversible reaction? in an irreversible reaction? Explain your answers.

4. Explain, in two ways, the results obtained when solutions of K_2SO_4 and NaCl are mixed, and the water is allowed to evaporate.

5. (a) What three types of chemical reactions go to completion, or are irreversible? (b) Give an equation to represent each of the three types.

6. (a) Complete each of the following equations. (b) Which of these reactions go to completion? (c) Which are reversible? Justify each answer.
   (1) $NaOH + HC_2H_3O_2 \longrightarrow$
   (2) $AgNO_3 + LiCl \longrightarrow$
   (3) $CO_2 + H_2 \xrightarrow{\Delta}$
   (4) $ZnS + O_2 \xrightarrow{\Delta}$
   (5) $Ba(NO_3)_2 + NaCl \longrightarrow$
   (6) $H_2 + O_2 \xrightarrow{\Delta}$
   (7) $HgO \xrightarrow{\Delta}$
   (8) $H_2CO_3 \longrightarrow$
   (9) $NaCl + KNO_3 \longrightarrow$

7. Why are all neutralization reactions which involve hydrolysis reversible reactions?

8. (a) Describe three factors affecting the point of equilibrium. (b) Illustrate a change in each factor affecting the point of equilibrium in a specific reaction.

9. (a) Define the terms *entropy* and *free energy change.* (b) How can the entropy and free energy change values of a reaction be used to predict whether it will take place?

10. (a) What is the common ion effect? (b) Is the common ion effect consistent with the Law of Mass Action? Explain your answer.

11. Define the terms *equilibrium constant, ionization constant, ion product constant of water, solubility constant.*

12. (a) State LeChatelier's Principle. (b) Explain how this principle encompasses the Law of Mass Action.

13. Give an example of a chemical reaction or reactions indicating how application of each of the following stresses affects the results of the reaction: addition of heat, reduction of pressure, increasing concentration of a reactant, and adding a common ion.

14. List two factors that determine whether an increase in concentration increases or decreases the rate of a particular reaction.

15. Contrast the energy and entropy changes in an exothermic reaction such as the combining of carbon and oxygen to form carbon dioxide.

16. Three reactions at 25° C have equilibrium constants of 2×10^{15}, 0.013, and 1.7×10^{-10}, respectively. (a) Which reaction yields very little product? (b) Which reaction goes to completion? (c) Explain why.

17. The ionization constant of sulfurous acid is 1.3×10^{-2}, and the K_i for nitrous acid is 4.5×10^{-4}. Which is the weaker acid? Why?

18. The solubility product constant of CuCl is 3.2×10^{-7} and that of $PbSO_4$ is 1.3×10^{-8} (at room temperature). Which is the less soluble compound? Explain why.

Relating Terms Within the Concept

Select the letter of the term in Column B that is most closely related to each term in Column A. Do not use a term more than once.

COLUMN A	COLUMN B
1. rate of reaction	a. affects point of equilibrium
2. catalyst	b. affects rate of reaction
3. reversible	c. causes a change in concentration
4. complete reaction	d. describes effect of stress on systems
5. common ion	e. describes effect on equilibrium of changes in concentration
6. Law of Mass Action	f. dissociation of weak electrolytes
7. LeChatelier's Principle	g. dynamic equilibrium
8. ionization constant	h. irreversible reaction
9. equilibrium constant	i. K_{sp}
10. solubility product	j. K_w
	k. mass of a reacting material changed to product in a definite period of time
	l. quantitative relationship between concentration of products and reactants

Solving Problems Within the Concept

1. In the Haber process, 280 tons of nitrogen react with 6 tons of hydrogen to produce ammonia. (a) Theoretically, how much ammonia should be formed? (b) What is the maximum amount of NH_3 produced from the initial reaction between the quantities of N_2 and H_2 mentioned above? (c) How many tons of N_2 and H_2 will remain?

2. (a) In the Haber process what volume will 1 mole of N_2 and 3 moles of H_2 gas occupy at 600° C and at 300 atmospheres of pressure? (This is 300 times normal

pressure.) (b) Assuming that the pressure and temperature do not change, what volume of NH_3 will form when all of the above N_2 and H_2 combine?

3. At a given temperature the equilibrium constant for the formation of hydrogen iodide is 48.88. How many moles per liter of HI are formed if the initial concentration in moles per liter of hydrogen is 0.00562, and of iodine is 0.00059?

Applying the Concepts

1. (a) In terms of the collision theory, explain how a catalyst may speed up or slow down the rate of a chemical reaction. (b) Why doesn't a catalyst affect the point of equilibrium in a chemical reaction?

2. Show by an example that the Law of Mass Action describes merely a small portion of the applications explained by LeChatelier's Principle.

3. Show that the behavior of gases described by Gay-Lussac's Law relating temperature and pressure is an application of LeChatelier's Principle applied to physical systems.

4. Explain why the equilibrium constant for a particular reaction varies with temperature.

5. Suggest two reasons why a solid paraffin or wax candle does not burn until it vaporizes, and why oil is sprayed into oil furnaces.

6. Why is a prolonged fever dangerous to the proper functioning of the human body?

Reading Further

Chemistry, by James Quagliano, 2d. ed., Englewood Cliffs, N. J., Prentice-Hall, 1963. A superior, if quite detailed, mathematical presentation of the concept of equilibrium and the Law of Mass Action.

"How Can You Tell Whether a Reaction Will Occur?" by G. E. MacWood and F. H. Verhoek, *Journal of Chemical Education,* vol. 38, 1961, page 334. An excellent presentation of factors determining whether or not reactions will occur.

18

Oxidation and Reduction

It may take all the strength of a grown man to carry a large log into a room. But once the log has been burned in the fireplace, a child can carry the ashes out. Small wonder that as late as the eighteenth century scientists believed that when a substance burned, a mysterious gas—which they called *phlogiston*—escaped from it so that the substance lost weight. Further, since metals increase in weight on burning, metals were said to contain phlogiston with a negative weight. When metals burned, the negative phlogiston escaped and the metal gained weight.

Not until 1774 was experimental evidence for refuting the theory presented by Lavoisier. By burning substances in a closed vessel, Lavoisier demonstrated that combustion was not the result of gas escaping from a substance. On the contrary, the burning substance *combined* with a gas—the oxygen of the air. Thus the weight of a substance burning in an enclosed space actually increases. According to Lavoisier, combustion is due in no case to an escape of phlogiston, but to chemical combination of the combustible substance with oxygen. But cherished theories die hard. As late as 1800 there were proponents of the theory, including Joseph Priestley.

OXIDATION—REDUCTION

Does combustion—a chemical change producing heat and light—always involve oxygen? *Try this investigation* to find out for yourself.

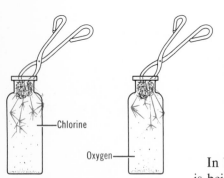
Chlorine

Oxygen

Heat a small piece of clean steel wool (iron) by holding it with tongs in the flame of a Bunsen burner. After the steel wool becomes hot, thrust it cautiously into a bottle of oxygen. Sparks fly as the steel wool combines with the oxygen to form a red-brown powder, iron oxide. Now repeat the procedure, but this time use a bottle of chlorine gas instead of oxygen. Are sparks again produced? This time the steel wool combines with the chlorine to form a yellow-orange powder, iron chloride.

In both bottles the heat and light produced indicates that something is being burned or undergoing combustion. Yet no oxygen took part in the second reaction. For many years, as an indication that oxygen combines with the substance being burned, the term "oxidation" was used as a synonym for combustion or burning. Even Lavoisier thought that a substance could burn only by combining with oxygen. Yet the second reaction shows that a substance can undergo combustion by uniting with an element other than oxygen, in this case, chlorine. As this chapter proceeds, you will discover that not only does combustion take place without oxygen but that combustion of a substance, whether in oxygen or another element, represents only one of several forms of oxidation.

Slow Oxidation

You are already familiar with another meaning of the term oxidation. In your body oxygen combines slowly with food—food undergoes oxidation. Here no light is given off, though heat is produced. Does a similar type of slow oxidation occur outside of the body? From using steel wool at home, you can probably answer the question. If not, moisten a piece of steel wool and let it stand in the air for a day or two. You will find that it has become coated with rust (Fig. 18-1). This rust is closely related to the red-brown powder, iron oxide, produced in the earlier investigation. The rust results from a combination of the iron with the oxygen in the air; rusting is a form of slow oxidation.

Although heat was not *applied* in the second of these two types of oxidation, the reaction itself produces heat. Yet because the rate of reaction is so slow, the heat has time to dissipate. The steel wool never reaches its kindling temperature. Thus, flames do not form during rusting or other forms of slow oxidation.

Oxidation and Electrons

The equations for reacting iron with oxygen and iron with chlorine are similar:

$$4\,Fe + 3\,O_2 \longrightarrow 2\,Fe_2O_3$$
$$2\,Fe + 3\,Cl_2 \longrightarrow 2\,FeCl_3$$

In both of these reactions, iron loses electrons—in one case to oxygen, in the other to chlorine.

$$Fe^0 - 3\,e^- \longrightarrow Fe^{+3}$$

At the same time, both the oxygen and the chlorine gain electrons from the iron.

In writing the formulas for the products of these two reactions, observe that *the charge is shown by placing a superscript to the right of the symbol* for each particle in the product:

$$4\,Fe^0 + 3\,O_2{}^0 \longrightarrow 2\,Fe_2{}^{+3}O_3{}^{-2}$$
$$2\,Fe^0 + 3\,Cl_2{}^0 \longrightarrow 2\,Fe^{+3}Cl_3{}^{-1}$$

18-1 Household steel wool provides an example of slow oxidation. Once moistened, it rusts readily; the rust formed is easily shaken from the steel wool.

Both ferric oxide (Fe_2O_3) and ferric chloride ($FeCl_3$) are essentially ionic compounds. Hence the superscripts after each symbol in the formulas of the compounds represent the number of electrons lost or gained by each atom involved in the reactions. When superscripts are written in this way it is easy to see that when iron reacts with either oxygen or chlorine, each atom of iron *loses* electrons to form an ion with a positive charge.

This last point is extremely important to an understanding of oxidation. *Oxidation involves a loss of electrons. Any substance,* in any chemical reaction, *that loses electrons and attains a more positive charge during the reaction* becomes *oxidized.* Both the slow and rapid oxidation of iron with oxygen or chlorine are examples of oxidation—a process in which substances lose electrons.

Can iron be oxidized by other substances, for example, an acid? To find out for yourself, *try the following:*

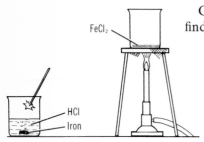

> Place a piece of iron in a beaker of hydrochloric acid. Use the burning splint test to identify the gas produced. As the reaction proceeds, observe that the acid turns yellow. Boil away the excess acid solution under a fume hood until a yellowish-green solid remains. What is it?

The solid is ferrous (iron II) chloride. It is closely related to the ferric (iron III) chloride formed when iron reacted directly with chlorine. The equation for the formation of $FeCl_2$ shows the charges on each of the particles involved. Notice that here, as in the reaction between iron and chlorine, each iron atom loses electrons. It becomes oxidized to form an ion with a charge of $+2$:

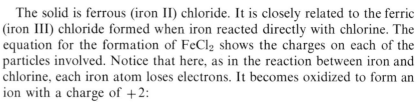

At first sight this reaction might have appeared to involve only the replacement of hydrogen from the acid. But actually it involves the oxidation of the iron by HCl, as shown by the fact that the iron atoms lose electrons. This is indeed the same process that took place when iron reacted with oxygen or chlorine.

Oxidation of Carbon

If a piece of charcoal (carbon) is heated until it glows and is thrust into a bottle of oxygen, the carbon bursts into flames and carbon dioxide is produced (Fig. 18-2). Evidently carbon, a nonmetal, burns in oxygen just as iron, a metal, burns in either oxygen or chlorine. However the carbon dioxide produced, instead of being an ionic substance, is, of course, a covalent molecular compound. Just as iron is oxidized during its reaction with oxygen or chlorine, so carbon is oxidized as it reacts with oxygen:

$$C^0 + O_2^0 \longrightarrow C^{+4}O_2^{-2}$$
$$\overset{\llcorner\quad\text{oxidized}\quad\lrcorner}{}$$

In a covalent compound such as CO_2 the superscripts represent the number of electrons shared by each atom. In the formula for carbon dioxide, the superscript 4 indicates that each carbon atom shares a total of four electrons with two oxygen atoms. The plus sign in front of the 4 indicates that these four electrons, paired with four electrons from the oxygen atoms, have become displaced as a result of the reaction. They are displaced more toward the oxygen end than toward the carbon end of the polar molecule. In this displacement, the carbon atoms have not actually *lost* electrons, as happened in the case of ionic compounds. They have, however, become *more* positive than they were before. *Chemists say that the carbon atoms in this reaction are oxidized.*

Thus far we have demonstrated that burning, or combustion—a process which produces flames—is only one of the various types of oxidation. Oxidation can take place not only in the presence of oxygen, as was thought in the time of Lavoisier, but in the presence of other substances such as chlorine and hydrochloric acid. Oxidation can occur slowly or rapidly and its products can be either ionic or covalent. Finally, the substance being oxidized always attains a more positive charge. In the case of ionic substances, this results from an actual loss of electrons. In the case of covalent substances, it results from the substance losing some of its attraction for electron pairs.

Reduction

Iron cannot burn or rust unless a substance such as oxygen, chlorine, or hydrochloric acid is present to accept the electrons lost by the iron. Likewise, carbon cannot change into carbon dioxide unless oxygen is present. In short, chemicals do not become oxidized by themselves. Together with the substance being oxidized—which loses electrons—there must be another substance that gains these same electrons. *The process by which a substance gains electrons is called reduction. Whenever a substance is reduced it gains* (or increases its attraction for) *electrons and thus increases its negative charge.* In effect, oxidation and reduction are Siamese twins: one is never found without the other. To emphasize this fact, the process as a whole is called **oxidation-reduction.**

Consider the actual gain in electrons by the oxygen in the reaction between iron and oxygen, and the displacement of the electrons toward the oxygen atoms in the formation of covalent carbon dioxide from carbon and oxygen. In both reactions the charge of the oxygen becomes more negative: the oxygen is reduced.

$$O_2^0 + 4\,e^- \longrightarrow 2\,O^{-2}$$

The following equations summarize the reduction portion of the reactions between iron and oxygen, and carbon and oxygen, respectively.

18-2 A piece of charcoal heated until it glows will burst into flame when thrust into a bottle of oxygen.

Charcoal

Charcoal

Oxygen

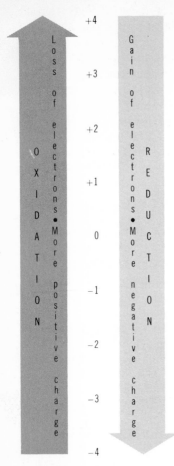

18-3 When an element is oxidized, it loses electrons and acquires a more positive charge; when reduced, it gains electrons and acquires a more negative charge.

$$4\,Fe^0 + 3\,O_2^0 \longrightarrow 2\,Fe_2^{+3}O_3^{-2}$$
$$\llcorner \text{reduced} \longrightarrow$$

$$C^0 + O_2^0 \longrightarrow C^{+4}O_2^{-2}$$
$$\llcorner \text{reduced} \longrightarrow$$

In the reaction between iron and chlorine, the chlorine gains electrons and is reduced:

$$2\,Fe^0 + 3\,Cl_2^0 \longrightarrow 2\,Fe^{+3}Cl_3^{-1}$$
$$\llcorner \text{reduced} \longrightarrow$$

When iron reacts with hydrochloric acid, the hydrogen *ions* of the acid gain electrons and are reduced:

$$Fe^0 + 2\,H^+Cl^- \longrightarrow Fe^{+2}Cl_2^{-1} + H_2^0$$
$$\llcorner \text{reduced} \longrightarrow$$

A careful study of Fig. 18-3 will help you in understanding the loss and gain of electrons in oxidation-reduction reactions.

Oxidizing and Reducing Agents

You have seen that whenever a substance is oxidized, there must be present another substance which is reduced. The agent that removes the electrons and brings about oxidation is called the **oxidizing agent**. Because it *gains* electrons, the oxidizing agent is *itself reduced.* Oxygen, chlorine, or hydrochloric acid act as oxidizing agents when they react with iron.

When iron reacts with either oxygen or chlorine, the charge on the oxygen atom and the chlorine atom is reduced from 0 to -2 and -1 respectively. When iron reacts with hydrochloric acid, each H^+ ion of the acid, the oxidizing agent, accepts 1 electron to form a hydrogen atom with a charge of zero. Once again the charge on the oxidizing agent becomes *more negative.*

$$Fe^0 + 2\,H^+Cl^- \longrightarrow Fe^{+2}Cl_2^{-1} + H_2^0$$
$$\text{oxidizing}$$
$$\text{agent}$$

Finally, when carbon reacts with oxygen to form carbon dioxide, the oxygen end of the carbon dioxide molecule becomes more negative than the oxygen atom from which it forms. Here again, oxygen acts as an oxidizing agent.

When iron reacts with oxygen, it is the electrons from the atoms of iron that cause the reduction of the oxygen. In like manner, when carbon reacts with oxygen, carbon supplies the electrons that give the oxygen in CO_2 a greater negative charge than it had before. In the one case, iron, and in the other, carbon, are the *agents* which cause the reduction of the oxygen. Hence iron and carbon are called **reducing agents.** Because it *loses* electrons, the reducing agent is *itself oxidized.*

18-4 Oxidation-reduction in a closed system—a flash bulb containing strips of aluminum foil in an atmosphere of pure oxygen. When the bulb is fired, which element is reduced, and which is oxidized? The intense heat bubbles the plastic coating of the bulb.

These observations reinforce our picture of the *oxidation-reduction* process: it always deals with a transfer of electrons. On one hand, the charge of the substance causing oxidation, the oxidizing agent, becomes more negative—it is reduced. At the same time, the charge on the substance causing reduction, the reducing agent, becomes more positive— it is oxidized.

The name oxidation-reduction is often abbreviated **redox** to indicate that the two processes always occur simultaneously. For redox reactions to take place, at least two types of substance must be present: a reducing agent which donates electrons, and an oxidizing agent which accepts these electrons (Fig. 18-4).

QUESTIONS AND PROBLEMS

1. Define the terms *oxidation, reduction,* and *redox* (be sure that your definition is applicable in all reactions).
2. Examine the information below for the reaction between sodium and water. Explain why the terms written below each reactant are correct.

$$2\,Na^0 + 2\,H^+(OH)^- \longrightarrow 2\,Na^+(OH)^- + H_2{}^0$$

<table>
<tr><td>reducing
agent
(becomes
oxidized)</td><td>oxidizing
agent
(becomes
reduced)</td></tr>
</table>

3. Write the equation for the reaction between zinc and hydrochloric acid. Label the substance that becomes oxidized and the substance that becomes reduced. Also label the oxidizing agent and reducing agent, explaining why you labeled them as you did.
4. In the partial equations below, indicate whether each element is oxidized or reduced.

   (a) $H_2{}^0 \longrightarrow 2\,H^{+1}$
   (b) $O_2{}^0 \longrightarrow 2\,O^{-2}$
   (c) $C^0 \longrightarrow C^{+4}$
   (d) $2\,Cl^{-1} \longrightarrow Cl_2{}^0$
   (e) $S^{-2} \longrightarrow S^{+4}$
   (f) $Mn^{+4} \longrightarrow Mn^{+2}$
   (g) $C^0 \longrightarrow C^{-4}$

OXIDATION NUMBERS

Among the thousands of redox reactions there are different degrees of oxidation. Chemists use **oxidation numbers** to indicate the degree to which atoms are oxidized, either in ionic or covalent compounds. The oxidation number, also called the **oxidation state,** shows the charge on an ion (if the reaction is ionic), or the charge which an atom appears to have (if the reaction is molecular).

Oxidation Numbers in Ionic Compounds

Consider the equations for the reaction between iron and chlorine and the reaction between iron and hydrochloric acid. Each reaction produced a different form of iron chloride. In the first reaction both of the reactants, iron and chlorine, consist of atoms which have no charge; they are both arbitrarily assigned an oxidation number of zero. The atoms of an element are always assigned an oxidation number of zero, no matter how they may be combined with like atoms in a molecule.

In the reaction between iron and chlorine, the product is $FeCl_3$, ferric (iron III) chloride. Ions are formed as each atom of iron loses 3 electrons, 1 to each of 3 atoms of chlorine. The ferric (iron III) ion that forms has a charge of $+3$, while each chloride ion has a charge of -1. Since oxidation numbers show the actual charges on ions, the oxidation number of each of these two types of ions is the same as its charge. Thus the oxidation number of the ferric ion is $+3$, while that of the chloride ion is -1. In the second reaction, that between iron and hydrochloric acid, the product is $FeCl_2$, ferrous (iron II) chloride. Here ions are formed as each atom of iron loses 2 electrons, one to each of 2 atoms of chlorine. The ferrous (iron II) ion that forms has a charge of $+2$, and each chloride ion has a charge of -1. Again the oxidation number of each ion is equal to its charge: that of the ferrous ion is $+2$, while that of the chloride ion is -1.

In the following equations for the reactions just described, and throughout this text, *oxidation numbers are always written above the symbol.*

$$2 \overset{0}{Fe} + 3 \overset{0}{Cl_2} \longrightarrow 2 \overset{+3 \ -1}{FeCl_3} \ [\text{iron(III) chloride}]$$

$$\overset{0}{Fe} + 2 \overset{+1-1}{HCl} \longrightarrow \overset{+2 \ -1}{FeCl_2} + \overset{0}{H_2} \ [\text{iron(II) chloride}]$$

The iron in ferric chloride, having an oxidation number of $+3$, is said to be in a **higher oxidation state** than the iron in ferrous chloride, with an oxidation number of $+2$. The more positive the oxidation number of an atom, the higher its oxidation state.

Consider the possibility of converting ferrous chloride to ferric chloride, or vice versa. Iron(II) chloride in the presence of an oxidizing agent such as chlorine becomes iron(III) chloride:

$$2 \overset{+2 \ -1}{FeCl_2} + \overset{0}{Cl_2} \longrightarrow 2 \overset{+3-1}{FeCl_3}$$

The oxidation number of iron changes from $+2$ in $FeCl_2$ to $+3$ in $FeCl_3$. It is now in a higher oxidation state. By reacting the ferric chloride with a reducing agent such as iron, ferrous chloride is again produced.

$$2 \overset{+3 \ -1}{FeCl_3} + \overset{0}{Fe} \longrightarrow 3 \overset{+2 \ -1}{FeCl_2}$$

The iron returns to its lower oxidation state.

Notice that the sum of the oxidation numbers in $FeCl_2$, like the sum of its ionic charges, is equal to zero.

$$\overset{+2}{Fe} \quad \overset{-1}{Cl_2}$$
$$+2 + 2\,(-1) = 0$$

In any compound, the total of the positive oxidation numbers must equal numerically the total of the negative oxidation numbers. Show that the sum of the oxidation numbers in $FeCl_3$ is zero.

Oxidation Numbers in Covalent Compounds

Now consider the oxidation numbers in two reactions between carbon and oxygen.

$$2\,\overset{0}{C} + \overset{0}{O_2} \longrightarrow 2\,\overset{+2-2}{CO} \text{ (carbon monoxide)}$$

$$\overset{0}{C} + \overset{0}{O_2} \longrightarrow \overset{+4-2}{CO_2} \text{ (carbon dioxide)}$$

Carbon and oxygen are elements, so each is assigned an oxidation number of zero. In each case the products formed, carbon monoxide and carbon dioxide, are covalent. Therefore, the oxidation numbers assigned to the atoms of these products indicate only their *apparent* charges.

Each oxygen atom shares two pairs of electrons to form a polar bond in which the electron pairs are attracted more toward the oxygen atom than toward the carbon atom. Therefore the oxygen atom is assigned an oxidation number of -2. As with ionic substances, the sum of the oxidation numbers in each covalent molecule must equal zero; the oxidation number of carbon in carbon monoxide is $+2$, while it is $+4$ in carbon dioxide:

$$\overset{+2}{C} \quad \overset{-2}{O} \qquad\qquad \overset{+4}{C} \quad \overset{-2}{O_2}$$
$$+2 + (-2) = 0 \qquad\qquad +4 + 2\,(-2) = 0$$

Notice that the carbon atom in each CO_2 molecule (oxidation number, $+4$) is in a higher oxidation state than the carbon atom in each molecule of carbon monoxide (oxidation number, $+2$).

18-5 Since the electrons in a molecule of CO_2 are attracted toward the oxygen atoms, the shared electrons are counted with the oxygen, as indicated by the dotted lines. The carbon atom appears to have a $+4$ charge and is assigned an oxidation number of $+4$; each oxygen atom appears to have a -2 charge and is assigned an oxidation number of -2.

Determining Oxidation Number

The relationship between the electron structures and the oxidation numbers of the carbon and oxygen atoms in carbon dioxide is shown in Fig. 18-5. As this diagram suggests, you can find the oxidation number for any atom in a compound by examining the electron dot diagram of the compound. But this method is too time consuming. It is more convenient to follow a few simple rules. We have already mentioned several of these rules but shall repeat them here along with additional ones.

1. The oxidation number for each atom of a free element is zero. For example, each atom of hydrogen in H_2 (Fig. 18-6) and each atom of

18-6 In a molecule of hydrogen the electron pair is shaped equally by two like atoms. The apparent charge of each atom is zero, and the oxidation number is 0.

18-7 In a molecule of water, the shared electrons are attracted toward the oxygen. Each hydrogen atom appears to have a charge of +1 and is assigned an oxidation number of +1. The oxygen atom appears to have a charge of −2 and is assigned an oxidation number of −2.

sodium in metallic sodium (Na) is assigned an oxidation number of zero.

2. The oxidation number of an ion consisting of a single element is the same as the charge on that ion. Thus each cuprous (copper I) ion is assigned an oxidation number of +1 ($\overset{+1}{\text{Cu}}$), while each cupric (copper II) ion is assigned an oxidation number of +2 ($\overset{+2}{\text{Cu}}$).

3. Hydrogen, in either ionic or covalent compounds (except in the case of the class of compounds called hydrides) is assigned an oxidation number of +1; oxygen is *usually* assigned an oxidation number of −2. These oxidation numbers are illustrated in the following formulas for compounds containing hydrogen or oxygen (Fig. 18-7).

$$\overset{+1\ -2}{\text{H}_2\text{O}}, \quad \overset{+1-1}{\text{HCl}}, \quad \overset{+2\ -2}{\text{CaO}}, \quad \overset{+1\ \ -2}{\text{Na}_2\text{O}}$$

4. Whether a compound is ionic or covalent, the sum of the oxidation numbers of all atoms in the formula for the compound is equal to zero. For example, in the formula for ionic calcium chloride, $\overset{+2\ -1}{\text{CaCl}_2}$,

$$[1 \times (+2)] + [2 \times (-1)] = 0$$

Or in the covalent compound water, $\overset{+1\ -2}{\text{H}_2\text{O}}$,

$$[2 \times (+1)] + [1 \times (-2)] = 0$$

5. In the formula for a radical, the sum of the oxidation numbers of all the atoms is equal to the charge on the ion. Consider, for example, the nitrate ion, NO_3^{-1}. Since each of the three oxygen atoms in one nitrate ion has an oxidation number of −2, the total apparent charge on these oxygen atoms is −6 (3 × −2). The single nitrogen atom in the ion must have an oxidation number of +5: +5 added to −6 equals −1, the charge on the radical.

$$[\overset{+5-2}{\text{NO}_3}]^{-1}$$

Now determine the oxidation number for each atom in the dichromate radical $(Cr_2O_7)^{-2}$. The total apparent charge on the seven oxygen atoms is −14. As the charge on the entire radical is −2, the two chromium atoms together must have a total apparent charge of +12; each chromium atom must have an oxidation number of +6. The characteristic oxidation numbers of the A groups of elements are shown in Table 18-1.

Although, strictly speaking, oxidation number is *not* identical with valence number, you will find that they are usually the same. An exception occurs in hydrogen peroxide, H_2O_2 (Fig. 18-8). In hydrogen peroxide the peroxide ion has a valence number of −2 (O_2^{-2}) and oxygen is in an unusual −1 oxidation state. Sometimes oxidation numbers are considered a special type of valence number. The system of oxidation numbers was developed more recently, and it is in wide use both in describing the oxidation state of an element in a compound and in balancing equations for oxidation-reduction reactions.

18-8 In the oxygen-oxygen bond in a molecule of hydrogen peroxide, the electron pair is shared equally by two like atoms. Thus the apparent charge on each oxygen atom is −1, and oxygen here, as in all peroxides, has an oxidation number of −1.

Table 18-1 OXIDATION NUMBERS BY GROUPS

The ochre dots indicate the usual oxidation numbers of group A elements in their compounds. The ochre circles indicate unusual oxidation numbers. Hydrogen, for example, has the unusual -1 oxidation number in all hydrides.

Oxidation number	Group						
	IA	IIA	IIIA	IVA	VA	VIA	VIIA
+7							○
+6						●	
+5					●		○
+4				●		●	
+3			●		●		○
+2		●		●		●	
+1	●				●		○
0			— Atoms of free elements —				
−1	○					○	●
−2						●	
−3					●		
−4				●			

Determining Oxidized and Reduced Substances

The use of oxidation numbers allows us to develop a new definition of oxidation. *Oxidation refers to any chemical change in which there is an increase in oxidation number.* The oxidation number of the substance oxidized always becomes *more* positive (Fig. 18-9). Consider, for example, the reaction of hydrogen with oxygen to form water, or of hydrogen with chlorine to form hydrogen chloride. In both cases the oxidation number of hydrogen increases from zero to $+1$.

$$2 \overset{0}{H_2} + \overset{0}{O_2} \longrightarrow 2 \overset{+1\ -2}{H_2O}$$
$$\underset{\text{oxidized}}{\rule{2cm}{0pt}}$$

$$\overset{0}{H_2} + \overset{0}{Cl_2} \longrightarrow 2 \overset{+1\ -1}{HCl}$$
$$\underset{\text{oxidized}}{\rule{2cm}{0pt}}$$

In both reactions, hydrogen is oxidized.

Similarly, we can now use the term "reduction" to refer to *any chemical change in which there is a decrease in oxidation number.* The oxidation number of the substance reduced always becomes *less* positive (Fig. 18-9). Note that the oxidation number of oxygen changes from zero to -2 when it combines with hydrogen; the oxidation number becomes less positive.

$$2 \overset{0}{H_2} + \overset{0}{O_2} \longrightarrow 2 \overset{+1\ -2}{H_2O}$$
$$\underset{\text{reduced}}{\rule{2cm}{0pt}}$$

18-9 When an element is oxidized, its oxidation number becomes more positive. When an element is reduced, its oxidation number becomes less positive.

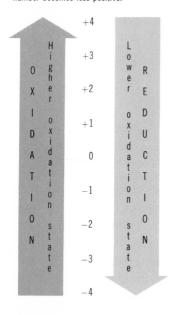

OXIDATION AND REDUCTION   293

Oxidation number, +4

Oxidation number, −2

Oxidation number, 0

18-10 In SO₂, four electrons from the sulfur atom are counted with the oxygen atoms, giving sulfur a +4 oxidation number. In H₂S the two electrons from the hydrogen atoms are counted with the sulfur atom, giving sulfur a −2 oxidation number. In a single sulfur atom, the oxidation number is 0.

Likewise, when chlorine reacts with hydrogen, there is a decrease in oxidation number. The oxidation number of chlorine changes from zero to −1. Both the oxygen and the chlorine—the substances other than hydrogen in these reactions—are reduced.

Determining Oxidizing and Reducing Agents

Sulfur dioxide and hydrogen sulfide react to form sulfur and water. In this reaction, which substance is oxidized and which reduced? We can find the answer by using oxidation numbers.

$$\overset{\text{oxidized}}{\overbrace{}}$$
$$\overset{+4-2}{SO_2} + 2\,\overset{+1-2}{H_2S} \longrightarrow 3\,\overset{0}{S} + 2\,\overset{+1-2}{H_2O}$$
$$\underset{\text{reduced}}{\underbrace{}}$$

Notice that during the reaction the oxidation number of the sulfur in sulfur dioxide (SO₂) changes from +4 to zero. This *decrease* in oxidation number shows that the sulfur in SO₂ is reduced. The H₂S must contain the reducing agent in the reaction.

On the other hand, the oxidation number of the sulfur from the hydrogen sulfide (H₂S) increases from −2 to zero. This increase in oxidation number indicates that the sulfur in H₂S becomes oxidized (Fig. 18-10). Therefore the sulfur in SO₂ is the oxidizing agent in the reaction. Such oxidation-reduction reactions in which a single element is both the reducing agent and the oxidizing agent are known as **auto oxidation-reduction reactions** or **disproportionations.**

Another interesting auto-oxidation reaction occurs between bromine and potassium hydroxide to produce potassium bromide, potassium bromate, and water.

$$\overset{\text{oxidized}}{\overbrace{}}$$
$$3\,\overset{0}{Br_2} + 6\,KOH \longrightarrow 5\,\overset{-1}{KBr} + \overset{+5}{KBrO_3} + 3\,H_2O$$
$$\underset{\text{reduced}}{\underbrace{}}$$

The bromine, which is simultaneously oxidized and reduced, is said to disproportionate.

Compounds like H₂S that contain one particular type of atom with a *low* oxidation number are usually good reducing agents. Two other examples are ammonia ($\overset{-3\,+1}{NH_3}$) and methane ($\overset{-4\,+1}{CH_4}$) with the relatively low oxidation numbers of their nitrogen and carbon atoms respectively. On the other hand, compounds like $\overset{+1+5-2}{KClO_3}$, which contain one particular type of atom (chlorine) with a relatively *high* oxidation number, are generally good oxidizing agents. Another example is potassium nitrate, $\overset{+1+5-2}{KNO_3}$, with the relatively high oxidation number of its nitrogen atom.

With experience in the use of oxidation numbers, you can determine at a glance a number of things about oxidation-reduction reactions. You can determine the oxidizing agent, the reducing agent, the substance that has been oxidized, and the substance that has been reduced. The relative degree to which substances have been oxidized or reduced can also be discerned quickly.

QUESTIONS AND PROBLEMS

1. Determine the oxidation numbers of the atoms represented in H_2S, MgO, and $(SO_4)^{-2}$.
2. Determine the substance oxidized, the substance reduced, the oxidizing agent, and the reducing agent in the reaction represented by each of the following equations:

$$2\,Na + Cl_2 \longrightarrow NaCl$$

$$NO_2 + SO_2 \longrightarrow NO + SO_3$$

Justify your answer in terms of changes in oxidation numbers.
3. In each of the following pairs of formulas, the metal is in a different oxidation state. (a) Indicate the metal's oxidation number in each compound. (b) Indicate in which compound the metal is in its higher oxidation state: $CuCl$ or $CuCl_2$, HgO or Hg_2O, $Fe(NO_3)_2$ or $Fe(NO_3)_3$.
4. (a) What is auto-oxidation? (b) Determine the substance oxidized and the substance reduced in the reaction:

$$3\,Cl_2 + 6\,NaOH \longrightarrow 5\,NaCl + NaClO_3 + 3\,H_2O$$

ACTIVITY OF METALS

If a gold ring is placed in hydrochloric acid, no reaction occurs. Yet if a small bit of potassium is placed in water, so rapid and violent a reaction occurs that the escaping hydrogen may actually burn. Gold is very inactive; potassium is extremely active. But gold is not unique in its inability to liberate hydrogen. If equal-sized strips of zinc and copper are placed in separate test tubes of dilute hydrochloric acid, bubbles of hydrogen appear on the surface of the zinc strip, but no reaction occurs between the copper and the acid.

Chemists once explained this difference in results by saying that zinc *replaces* the hydrogen from acid while copper does not. Today it is explained in terms of oxidation and reduction. Evidently zinc atoms give up electrons to the hydrogen ions of the acid, while copper atoms do not. The difference can be understood by noting the changes in oxidation numbers—or lack of change—in the equations below:

$$\overset{0}{Zn} + 2\,\overset{+1-1}{HCl} \longrightarrow \overset{+2\,-1}{ZnCl_2} + \overset{0}{H_2}$$

$$\quad\text{oxidized}\quad\text{reduced}$$

$$\overset{0}{Cu} + \overset{+1-1}{HCl} \longrightarrow \text{no reaction}$$

During the replacement reaction that does take place, the oxidation number of zinc increases from zero in the elemental form to $+2$ in zinc chloride. The oxidation number of hydrogen decreases from $+1$ in the acid to zero in molecular hydrogen. These changes in oxidation number indicate that zinc is the reducing agent and that hydrogen is the oxidizing agent.

Since no hydrogen forms when copper is placed in hydrochloric acid, we can reasonably assume that copper atoms, unlike zinc, cannot reduce hydrogen ions. Indeed copper, like gold, is relatively inactive; while zinc is between the two extremes of gold and potassium. Are there varying degrees of activity among other metals?

Activity Series

Cut out equal-sized strips of zinc, magnesium, and tin. Make sure that the surfaces of the metals are clean by rubbing them with fine sandpaper. Place each of these metal strips in a separate test tube and pour equal amounts of 3 N hydrochloric acid into each tube. Be sure that the strips are covered. Now observe the different amount of bubbling that occurs in each tube. Apply the burning splint test to the gas that escapes from each tube. What is it?

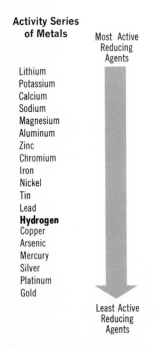

Zinc   Magnesium   Tin

Activity Series of Metals

Most Active Reducing Agents

Lithium
Potassium
Calcium
Sodium
Magnesium
Aluminum
Zinc
Chromium
Iron
Nickel
Tin
Lead
Hydrogen
Copper
Arsenic
Mercury
Silver
Platinum
Gold

Least Active Reducing Agents

You probably found that the most bubbling occurred when magnesium reacted with the acid. The zinc reacted less vigorously, while very little bubbling occurred with the tin. Repeating this procedure with various metals leads to two conclusions: first, not all metals react with acid to produce hydrogen; and second, each metal that reacts produces a different amount of hydrogen in a given time. In short, different metals have different abilities to free hydrogen from acids.

When a metal replaces hydrogen in an acid, it reduces hydrogen ions. Thus the ability of a metal to free hydrogen from an acid is a measure of that metal's activity as a reducing agent. A list of metals, arranged in order of their decreasing activity as reducing agents in water solutions, is called the **activity series,** or **replacement series,** of metals (Fig. 18-11). The activity of the metals as reducing agents *decreases* as you proceed from the top to the bottom of the list.

From previous experience with reactions involving metals and acids, you should be able to predict where some of the more common metals fall in the activity series. For example, recall that metals like sodium and potassium react violently with water, a substance which contains a low concentration of hydrogen ions. It is reasonable then to expect that these same metals react even more violently with substances that contain a higher concentration of hydrogen ions, such as dilute acids. Experiments show that of these two metals, potassium is more reactive than sodium. Hence potassium appears above sodium in the activity series.

By comparing the activities of potassium and sodium with the activities of magnesium, zinc, and tin it is clear that potassium and sodium

18-11 ... or the replacement series.

appear above these other three metals in the series. As you have already determined the rate at which magnesium, zinc, and tin free hydrogen from dilute acid, list these elements in their proper order in relation to each other. A look at the activity series in Fig. 18-11 shows that all five metals are listed correctly in order of decreasing activity.

Metals Less Active than Hydrogen

Some metals, like copper and silver, do not react with acid to liberate hydrogen. They are incapable of doing so because they do not reduce hydrogen ions. Hence these metals appear below hydrogen in the activity series. At first glance it might seem that these less active metals have no reducing ability whatever. *Test this assumption by means of a simple investigation*—remembering that both copper and silver are metals that do not react with dilute acids.

> Place a piece of thin copper wire in a test tube of colorless silver nitrate solution. After an hour or so, hold a piece of white paper behind the test tube. Has the formerly colorless solution turned a pale blue, a color that denotes the presence of cupric (copper II) ions in the solution? Do you also notice that shiny metallic crystals of silver have appeared on the copper wire as shown at the left?

You can say that many of the copper atoms in the wire replaced silver from the solution of silver nitrate. But, stated more precisely, what has happened is this: copper atoms reduced the silver ions present in the silver nitrate solution to silver atoms. At the same time the copper atoms were oxidized by the silver ions to cupric (copper II) ions.

The following equation summarizes this reaction by showing the changes that occur in oxidation numbers:

$$\overset{0}{Cu} + 2\overset{+1}{AgNO_3} \longrightarrow \overset{+2}{Cu}(NO_3)_2 + 2\overset{0}{Ag}$$

(with "reduced" arrow from Cu to Ag, "oxidized" arrow from Cu to Ag)

The loss and gain of electrons during the reaction can also be indicated in terms of charge in the following way:

$$Cu^0 - 2e \longrightarrow Cu^{+2} \quad \text{(oxidation)}$$
$$2\,Ag^{+1} + 2e \longrightarrow 2\,Ag^0 \quad \text{(reduction)}$$

The results of this investigation indicate that copper, although less active than hydrogen, does have reducing ability. It shows that copper is more active as a reducing agent than silver. Hence copper is placed above silver in the activity series although both metals are placed below hydrogen.

Once an activity series is prepared, it can be used to predict how metals will react. The metals above hydrogen can reduce hydrogen ions, that is, they react with various acids to liberate hydrogen. The metals below hydrogen cannot reduce hydrogen ions; they do not liberate hydrogen from acids. As we proceed from top to bottom of the activity, or replacement, series in Fig. 18-11, the metals become ever poorer reducing agents, but any metal in the series can replace any metal below it. In other words, a metal higher up on the series can reduce the ions in solution of a metal lower down. For example, calcium can reduce to atoms the ions of all metals below it in the activity series. Zinc can reduce ions of iron and tin to atoms; it cannot reduce potassium or magnesium ions. Lead can reduce hydrogen ions to free hydrogen although arsenic and copper cannot.

Oxidation of Metals

Thus far we have considered the abilities of metals to react with acids or with other metallic ions as evidence of their relative activity. Evidence from other sources, some of which are already familiar, confirms their relative activity.

Compare what happens when a freshly cut piece of sodium, a clean strip of magnesium, and a gold ring are exposed to the air for the same period of time. The surface of the sodium loses its luster very rapidly, while the magnesium takes a little longer. In the same period the ring doesn't tarnish at all. Sodium, a very active metal which appears near the top of the activity series, is oxidized quickly by oxygen. Magnesium, less active and further down in the series, does not react with oxygen so rapidly, while metals like gold and platinum, near the bottom of the series, do not combine with oxygen (Fig. 18-12). The rates at which different metals react with oxygen is another indication of their relative activity.

Reduction of Compounds

The ease with which the compounds of metals decompose is another measure of the metal's activity. During the decomposition of metallic compounds, the metallic ion is reduced to the metal. If we let M stand for the metal, the reduction of the metal can be indicated by:

$$M^+ + e^- \longrightarrow M^0$$

18-12 A lump of sodium exposed to the air quickly loses its luster as it reacts with oxygen. Magnesium ribbon has a soft sheen resulting from the much slower oxidation, forming magnesium oxide. The relatively unreactive gold retains its high luster.

The ease with which M^+ is reduced reflects the activity of the metal.

Certain metallic oxides, such as mercuric oxide, are decomposed simply by heating. The change in oxidation numbers in the equation below indicates that mercury is reduced when mercuric oxide is decomposed by heating:

$$2 \overset{+2\,-2}{HgO} \longrightarrow 2 \overset{0}{Hg} + \overset{0}{O_2}$$

Iron and numerous other metals cannot be obtained from their compounds simply by heating. Compounds of these metals must be placed in contact with a reducing agent, such as carbon, before they decompose. The change in oxidation numbers indicates that iron is reduced when ferric (iron III) oxide reacts with carbon:

$$\overset{\displaystyle \overbrace{\hspace{3cm}}^{\text{oxidized}}\searrow}{2\ \overset{+3}{Fe_2}O_3 + 3\ \overset{0}{C} \longrightarrow 2\ \overset{0}{Fe} + 3\ \overset{+4}{C}O_2}$$
$$\underset{\underbrace{\hspace{3cm}}_{\text{reduced}}\nearrow}{}$$

The removal of sodium and other Group IA metals from their compounds by electrolysis similarly reduces sodium ions to metallic sodium.

$$\overset{\displaystyle \overbrace{\hspace{3cm}}^{\text{oxidized}}\searrow}{2\ \overset{+1\,-1}{NaCl} \longrightarrow 2\ \overset{0}{Na} + \overset{0}{Cl_2}}$$
$$\underset{\underbrace{\hspace{2cm}}_{\text{reduced}}\nearrow}{}$$

These examples demonstrate that the ions of very active metals, those near the top of the activity series, can be reduced only by electrolysis. The ions of metals of medium activity, those near the center of the series, are reduced through chemical reactions with reducing agents. And the ions of the inactive metals can be reduced simply by heating.

QUESTIONS AND PROBLEMS

1. Which of the following elements liberates hydrogen from acid or water: tin, copper, cobalt, gold, lithium, mercury?
2. Complete the equation, including the changes in oxidation numbers, for each of the following reactions that occur in solution:

   (a) $Al + HCl \longrightarrow$ (b) $Au + CuSO_4 \longrightarrow$ (c) $Cu + Ag_2SO_4 \longrightarrow$

3. On the basis of the activity series predict what method would probably be used to remove the metal from SnO_2, KCl, HgS, $CaCl_2$, ZnO.

ELECTROCHEMICAL CELLS

An experiment first performed in 1786 by a great Italian scientist, Luigi Galvani, gives striking evidence of the activity of metals. Galvani twined together iron and copper wires and touched the ends of the wires to a frog's leg. The leg moved. Galvani attributed this effect to what he called "animal electricity." *You can repeat the essentials of Galvani's experiment* without using an animal.

Place a plate of *porous* porcelain in the center of a glass container so that the plate divides the container in half, as shown at the left. Now attach equal-sized strips of copper and of zinc to a wooden holder. Suspend the holder above the container so that the two strips are on opposite sides of the plate. Into the side of the container with the copper strip, pour enough 1 *M* copper sulfate solu-

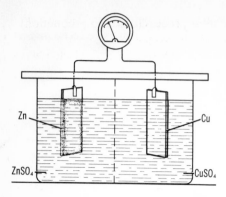

tion to partially cover the strip. On the other side of the plate, sufficient 1 _M_ zinc sulfate solution to cover the zinc strip to the same height. Attach one end of an electric wire to the copper strip and connect the other end to the _positive_ terminal of a DC voltmeter. Attach one end of a second piece of wire to the zinc strip; then connect the other end to the _negative_ terminal of the voltmeter. As soon as the circuit is completed, the needle of the meter moves: an electric current is flowing through the wire or external circuit. Does the voltmeter read 1.1 volts?

Dismantle the apparatus after about 10 minutes and observe the two metal strips carefully. Has the zinc strip begun to dissolve; has the copper strip become coated with additional copper?

The dissolving of the zinc and the deposition of the copper can be explained in terms of oxidation and reduction. Earlier you learned that zinc loses electrons more readily than copper. Hence, in this investigation the flow of electrons, which constitutes the electric current, is from the strip of zinc, through the external circuit, to the strip of copper. As the electrons flow from the zinc strip, zinc atoms lose electrons, or become oxidized, to zinc ions (Zn^{+2}). The Zn^{+2} ions migrate away from the zinc strip and go into solution, and the zinc strip slowly disappears.

The electrons that pass from the zinc strip through the external circuit to the surface of the copper strip are picked up by copper ions (Cu^{+2}) in the solution surrounding the strip. In this way the copper ions in the solution are reduced to copper atoms. These copper atoms are deposited, in turn, on the surface of the copper strip. The current can continue to flow in constantly reducing amounts until _equilibrium is reached,_ a condition in which the concentration of Zn^{+2} ions approaches but does not quite reach 2 _M_ and in which the concentration of Cu^{+2} ions approaches but does not quite reach zero.

It is the difference in the ability of atoms of copper and atoms of zinc to lose electrons, or become oxidized, that causes electrons to flow through the circuit. The numerical measurement of this difference in reducing ability is given by the voltage on a voltmeter (Fig. 18-13).

Cells and Cell Reactions

In the investigation just performed, two substances of different reducing activities were immersed in different electrolytes. Whenever this happens an **electrochemical cell,** or simply a cell, is produced. The cell just described is called a **voltaic cell.** This and other kinds of cells, such as the dry cell and the storage battery, are used as sources of direct current electricity. Every cell must contain at least one electrolyte. And every cell has two electrodes (strips or poles): an electrode where oxidation occurs, and an electrode where reduction occurs.

The chemical reaction that takes place in a cell can best be understood by considering the oxidation and reduction processes separately. Taken by itself, each process is called a **half-cell reaction,** or simply a **half-**

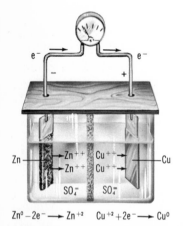

$Zn^0 - 2e^- \longrightarrow Zn^{+2}$ $Cu^{+2} + 2e^- \longrightarrow Cu^0$

18-13 In a zinc-copper electrochemical cell, the atoms of the zinc electrode lose electrons; the resulting zinc ions migrate into the solution. Simultaneously, copper ions in solution gain electrons and deposit as atoms on the copper electrode.

reaction. Each represents half of the total process (oxidation-reduction) that takes place within the cell. Consider the voltaic cell as an example. The oxidation reaction that occurs at the negative, or zinc, electrode is represented in terms of ionic charge by the following equation:

$$Zn^0 \longrightarrow Zn^{+2} + 2e^- \qquad \text{(oxidation)}$$

The reduction reaction at the positive or copper electrode is:

$$Cu^{+2} + 2\ e^- \longrightarrow Cu^0 \qquad \text{(reduction)}$$

Adding together the two half-cell reactions results in an equation for the complete oxidation-reduction reaction that occurs within the voltaic cell:

$$
\begin{aligned}
Zn^0 &\longrightarrow Zn^{+2} + 2\ e^- &\text{(oxidation)}\\
Cu^{+2} + 2\ e^- &\longrightarrow Cu^0 &\text{(reduction)}\\
\hline
Zn^0 + Cu^{+2} &\longrightarrow Zn^{+2} + Cu^0
\end{aligned}
$$

This separate consideration of the two half-cell reactions indicates that the number of the electrons lost during oxidation is exactly equal to the number of electrons gained during reduction.

Oxidation Potential

The activity of metals was originally described in terms of their ability to "replace" hydrogen from acid. Consequently, hydrogen was used as a sort of dividing line between those metals which are more active and those which are less so. Today a hydrogen half-cell, or hydrogen electrode, is used as a standard against which to measure the ability of a metal (or other element) to lose electrons. The hydrogen electrode is arbitrarily assigned a voltage of zero, and the entire voltage of the cell is attributed to the reaction at the other electrode. This voltage, called the **oxidation potential** of the metal (or other element), is designated $E°$.

Suppose a chemist wants to discover the oxidation potential of zinc. He prepares a half-cell by immersing a zinc electrode in a 1 M solution of zinc sulfate. Then he connects this electrode with a hydrogen electrode, making a complete cell in which oxidation-reduction occurs (Fig. 18-14). The voltage produced when the circuit is completed in this way is 0.76 volt; the oxidation potential, $E°$, of zinc is +0.76 volt.

By definition, substances which lose electrons more easily than hydrogen when in contact with their ions have positive oxidation potentials. The oxidation potential of zinc is positive, since the electrons flow from the metal electrode to the hydrogen electrode. On the other hand, substances which do not lose electrons as readily as hydrogen are assigned negative oxidation potentials. For example, in a hydrogen-copper cell in which the electron flow is from the hydrogen electrode to the copper electrode, the oxidation potential, $E°$, of copper is negative, −0.34 volt.

These and other oxidation potentials are given in Table 18-2. The voltage of any complete reaction can be determined by combining the voltages of its two half-reactions. Repeated experimentation has shown that the half-reaction which produces the higher voltage has the greater tend-

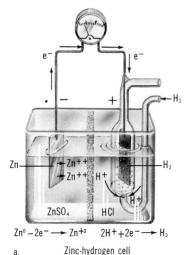

$$Zn^0 - 2e^- \longrightarrow Zn^{+2} \qquad 2H^+ + 2e^- \longrightarrow H_2$$

a. Zinc-hydrogen cell

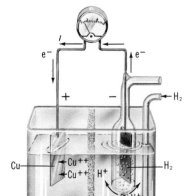

$$Cu^{+2} + 2e^- \longrightarrow Cu^0 \qquad H_2 - 2e^- \longrightarrow 2H^+$$

b. Copper-hydrogen cell

18-14 The relative position of Zn and Cu in the electrochemical series could be used to predict that in the cell in **a** hydrogen is reduced, in the cell in **b** hydrogen is oxidized.

ency to occur. In a zinc-copper cell, therefore, the zinc half-cell has the greater tendency to release electrons ($Zn^0 \longrightarrow Zn^{+2} + 2\ e^-$). These electrons are transferred to the copper electrode, forcing the reaction in the copper half-cell in the reverse direction ($Cu^{+2} + 2\ e^- \longrightarrow Cu^0$). In a zinc-copper cell, the zinc is oxidized and the copper ion is reduced. Now observe the double arrows in each reaction in Table 18-2. The voltages given apply to the reaction proceeding to the right, or to the substance being oxidized. *If the reaction proceeds in the reverse direction, or the substance is reduced, the sign of the voltage must be reversed.*

In determining the voltage of a Zn-Cu cell, for example, reverse the sign, for Cu, since the Cu^{+2} ion is reduced:

$$
\begin{array}{ll}
Zn^0 \longrightarrow Zn^{+2} + 2\ e^- & E^\circ_{Zn} = +0.76 \text{ volt} \\
\underline{Cu^{+2} + 2\ e^- \longrightarrow Cu^0} & \underline{E^\circ_{Cu} = +0.34 \text{ volt}} \\
Zn^0 + Cu^{+2} \longrightarrow Zn^{+2} + Cu^0 & E^\circ_T = +1.10 \text{ volts}
\end{array}
$$

The voltage, E°_T, of the Zn-Cu electrochemical cell is 1.10 volts. In general, *the half-reaction having the higher oxidation potential* (E°) *forces the half-reaction with the lower oxidation potential in the reverse direction so that it becomes a reduction half-reaction.*

Electrochemical Series

Once the oxidation potentials of the substances have been determined, the atoms or ions of elements can be listed in order of their decreasing activity in water solutions. The most active reducing agents are the metallic elements having the highest positive oxidation potentials. The *reactants* in the half-reactions in Table 18-2 *are listed in order of decreasing ability to act as reducing agents* as we go toward the most negative oxidation potentials. A list of this kind in which the atoms, molecules, or ions are listed in order of their decreasing ability to lose electrons, or act as

Table 18-2 **OXIDATION POTENTIALS**

Reactant	Half-reaction*	Volts	Reactant	Half-reaction*	Volts
Li $\rightleftharpoons$ Li$^+$ + e$^-$		+3.05	Sn $\rightleftharpoons$ Sn^{+2} + 2 e$^-$		+0.14
K $\rightleftharpoons$ K$^+$ + e$^-$		+2.93	Pb $\rightleftharpoons$ Pb^{+2} + 2 e$^-$		+0.13
Cs $\rightleftharpoons$ Cs$^+$ + e$^-$		+2.92	H$_2$ $\rightleftharpoons$ 2 H$^+$ + 2 e$^-$		0.00
Sr $\rightleftharpoons$ Sr^{+2} + 2 e$^-$		+2.89	Cu $\rightleftharpoons$ Cu^{+2} + 2 e$^-$		−0.34
Ca $\rightleftharpoons$ Ca^{+2} + 2 e$^-$		+2.87	2I$^-$ $\rightleftharpoons$ I$_2$ + 2 e$^-$		−0.54
Na $\rightleftharpoons$ Na$^+$ + e$^-$		+2.71	Fe^{+2} $\rightleftharpoons$ Fe^{+3} + e$^-$		−0.77
Mg $\rightleftharpoons$ Mg^{+2} + 2 e$^-$		+2.37	Ag $\rightleftharpoons$ Ag$^+$ + e$^-$		−0.80
Al $\rightleftharpoons$ Al^{+3} + 3 e$^-$		+1.66	NO + 2 H$_2$O $\rightleftharpoons$ NO$_3^-$ + 4 H$^+$ + 3 e$^-$		−0.96
H$_2$ + 2 OH$^-$ $\rightleftharpoons$ 2 H$_2$O + 2 e$^-$		+0.83	2 Br$^-$ $\rightleftharpoons$ Br$_2$ + 2 e$^-$		−1.09
Zn $\rightleftharpoons$ Zn^{+2} + 2 e$^-$		+0.76	2 H$_2$O $\rightleftharpoons$ O$_2$ + 4 H^{+2} + 4 e$^-$		−1.23
Fe $\rightleftharpoons$ Fe^{+2} + 2 e$^-$		+0.44	2 Cl$^-$ $\rightleftharpoons$ Cl$_2$ + 2 e$^-$		−1.36
Cd $\rightleftharpoons$ Cd^{+2} + 2 e$^-$		+0.40	Mn^{+2} + 4 H$_2$O $\rightleftharpoons$ MnO$_4^-$ + 8 H$^+$ + 5 e$^-$		−1.51
Ni $\rightleftharpoons$ Ni^{+2} + 2 e$^-$		+0.25	2 F$^-$ $\rightleftharpoons$ F$_2$ + 2 e$^-$		−2.87

* Ions are hydrated, at 1 M concentration in water solution at 25° C

reducing agents, is known to chemists as an **electrochemical series.**

The molecules or ions at the right of each double arrow are reduced by the gain of electrons. Thus the molecules or ions at the right in each column are oxidizing agents. The fluorine molecule, F_2, is the strongest oxidizing agent in water solutions. In fact, F_2 reacts violently with water to liberate oxygen. In the electrochemical series, the strength of the oxidizing agents *decreases as we go to higher oxidation potentials.* The permanganate ion, MnO_4^-, for example, is a strong oxidizing agent in acidic solutions; the nitrate (NO_3^-) ion is also an oxidizing agent in acidic solutions, but not as strong as the MnO_4^- ion. You can, of course, combine many of the two half-reactions listed to yield a complete reaction. But which of these predicted reactions will occur?

Predicting Reactions

You found earlier (pages 297–98) that zinc and magnesium easily reduced the H^+ ions in acidic solutions. On the other hand, copper was too weak a reducing agent to reduce H^+ ions. At equal concentrations, a reducing agent reacts with an oxidizing agent below it and at the right of the double arrow in Table 18-2. Stated in another way, if the total voltage, E_T°, obtained from the two half-reactions is a *positive* value, we can expect the reaction to occur spontaneously.

You know that the voltage of any reduction half-reaction has the reverse sign of its oxidation potential and that the hydrogen half-reaction (whether as an oxidation or a reduction reaction) has an assigned voltage of zero. Thus, a reaction between magnesium and an acid has a total voltage, E_T°, of 2.37 volts ($2.37 - 0.00$), while the zinc-acid reaction gives an E_T° of 0.76 volt ($0.76 - 0.00$). The copper-acid reaction gives an E_T° of -0.34 volt ($-0.34 - 0.00$), a value that confirms the lack of reaction you found by experimentation. *Any negative value of E_T° indicates that the reaction will not occur.*

Can we expect the ferric ion (Fe^{+3}) to oxidize the Br^- ion; or, said in another way, can we expect the Br^- ion to reduce the Fe^{+3} ion?

$$2\ Br^- \longrightarrow Br_2 + 2\ e^- \qquad E_{Br}^\circ = -1.09 \text{ volts}$$
$$2(Fe^{+3} + e^- \longrightarrow Fe^{+2}) \qquad E_{Fe}^\circ = +0.77 \text{ volt}$$
$$\overline{2\ Br^- + 2\ Fe^{+3} \longrightarrow Br_2 + 2\ Fe^{+2} \qquad E_T^\circ = -0.32 \text{ volt}}$$

The second half-reaction was reversed and the sign of its oxidation potential was changed because we are investigating the use of the Fe^{+3} ion as an oxidizing agent. The second half-reaction is multiplied by two (2) so that the two electrons lost in the oxidation half-reaction are balanced by two electrons gained in the reduction half-reaction. Note that the voltage of the second half-reaction was *not* changed by the multiplication to balance the electron loss and gain. The negative value of E_T° obtained leads us to predict that this reaction will not occur, and experimentation confirms this. Using a similar procedure, convince yourself that the Fe^{+3} ion can oxidize the iodide ion, I^-.

However, even when positive E_T° values are obtained by the addition of two half-reactions, one a reduction and the other an oxidation, nothing can be predicted about the speed of the reaction. When E_T° values are positive by only a few hundredths of a volt, the reaction may not occur.

Throughout this unit we have dealt with various substances in solution. But what of such diverse things as clouds, smoke, floating soaps, mayonnaise, and protoplasm—are they true solutions? Or perhaps they all belong to that unique group of substances known as colloids.

1. (a) Write the half-cell reactions for an electrochemical cell composed of copper sulfate and cadmium sulfate half-cells separated by a partition. (b) Indicate the positive and negative electrodes and the direction of electron flow. (c) Determine the voltage, E_T°, of the cell.
2. Use Table 18-2 of oxidation potentials to predict the direction of electron flow in each electrochemical cell containing the following pairs of electrodes and suitable electrolytes: (a) hydrogen and magnesium (b) hydrogen and nickel (c) hydrogen and silver (d) nickel and silver.
3. The half-reaction $Mn^{+2} + 4\ H_2O \rightleftharpoons MnO_4^- + 8\ H^+ + 5\ e^-$ has an oxidation potential of -1.51 volts. Is the permanganate ion (MnO_4^-) a strong oxidizing or reducing agent? Explain your answer.

VALUE OF THE CONCEPT

THE CONCEPT

Since the late eighteenth century the concept of oxidation has changed markedly. Today chemists agree that oxidation reactions do not require oxygen. Rapid oxidation or combustion may result in the formation of heat and light, while slow oxidation takes a number of forms, including rusting. In ionic reactions the substance that loses electrons, thus gaining a more positive charge, is oxidized. In reactions involving molecular substances, oxidation occurs when the change in sharing of electrons causes a particle to become more positive.

In ionic reactions, the substance that gains electrons, thus increasing its negative charge, is reduced. In reactions involving molecular substances, reduction occurs when the change in sharing of electrons causes a particle to become more negative. Reduction always occurs with oxidation. To emphasize this fact, the process as a whole is called oxidation-reduction, and the reactions are known as redox reactions.

Because the substance reduced during an oxidation-reduction reaction is the agent that removes the electrons and brings about oxidation, it is the oxidizing agent. During a redox reaction, the oxidizing agent attains a greater negative charge. Similarly, because the substance oxidized is the agent that loses the electrons and brings about reduction, it is called the reducing agent. During a redox reaction, the reducing agent attains a more positive charge.

A system of oxidation numbers is used in redox reactions to indicate the extent to which oxidation has occurred. A prescribed set of rules is followed in assigning oxidation numbers. In terms of oxidation numbers, oxidation refers to any chemical change in which there is an increase in oxidation number; conversely, reduction involves a decrease in oxidation number.

Studies of the replacement of hydrogen from acids lead to an understanding of the activity of metals. Metals are listed in order of their activities as reducing agents. This list is referred to as the activity, or replacement, series. Metals and nonmetals placed in this same order make up the electrochemical series. Metals above hydrogen in either series will replace hydrogen or reduce hydrogen ions in acids. Metals and nonmetals below hydrogen will not replace hydrogen or reduce hydrogen ions. Metals will reduce the ions in solution of metals listed below them in the series. The differences in activities (abilities to lose electrons) of metals make possible the electrochemical cell as a source of electricity. Fundamentally, such a cell consists of electrodes of two substances, each having a different ability to lose electrons, and one or more electrolytes. Half-cell reactions indicate individually the oxidation and the reduction reaction that occur at opposite electrodes. Oxidation potentials can be used to predict whether a reaction will occur.

USING THE CONCEPT

Using the Basic Concept
1. (a) Describe the changes that have occurred since the eighteenth century in scientists' understanding of the process of oxidation. (b) In early chemistry how was the term *oxidation* used? (c) Is it an appropriate term today?
2. (a) Give three examples of rapid oxidation, of slow oxidation. (b) Write an equation for each example given.
3. (a) Write equations for three oxidation reactions that *do* involve oxygen. (b) Write equations for three reactions that *do not* involve oxygen. (c) In terms of oxidation number, show that oxidation occurs in each equation.
4. Define *oxidation* and *reduction* (a) in terms of loss or gain of electrons, (b) in terms of oxidation number. (c) Show in each equation written for Question 3 that both reduction and oxidation occur.

5. (a) What does the term *oxidation-reduction,* or *redox,* indicate? (b) What is disproportionation?
6. (a) What is an oxidizing agent, a reducing agent? (b) Write three redox equations not used in Question 3. In each case, label both the oxidizing and the reducing agent.
7. (a) State the rules for determining oxidation numbers. (b) What three things do oxidation numbers help us determine?
8. (a) How is the replacement of hydrogen from acids explained in terms of oxidation and reduction? (b) Give an example to support your answer.
9. (a) What is the activity, or replacement, series of metals? (b) Compare and contrast the activity series and the electrochemical series.
10. (a) Explain the statement: Neither copper nor silver, both of which are metals, react with nonoxidizing acids; yet copper and silver do not have the same activity. (b) Give some experimental evidence to support your answer.
11. (a) From your experience (without referring to the activity series) where would you place each of the following in the series (near the top, middle, or bottom): gold, sodium, zinc, platinum, iron, lead? (b) Give evidence to support each choice.
12. Why is electric energy needed to decompose certain compounds, while heat alone will decompose others? (Explain in terms of reduction.)
13. (a) What is an electrochemical cell? (b) Draw a labeled diagram of a cell containing Cu and Sn electrodes, and appropriate electrolytes. (c) Draw a second labeled diagram showing a cell containing tin and hydrogen electrodes, with appropriate electrolytes. (d) Under ideal conditions, what is the oxidation potential, $E°$, of this second cell?
14. (a) Write the two half-cell reactions for the first cell described above. Add these half-cell reactions and obtain the com-

plete oxidation-reduction reaction. (b) Are all of the ions present involved in the cell reactions? Explain.

15. In a chemical cell with a hydrogen and a metal electrode, what is the significance of (a) a positive oxidation potential, (b) a negative oxidation potential?

Relating Terms Within the Concept

From the *italicized* terms listed select the term that best completes each statement. Do not use a term more than once.

disproportionation, electrochemical series, $\overset{+2}{Fe}$ to $\overset{+3}{Fe}$, $\overset{+2}{Hg}$ to $\overset{+1}{Hg}$, oxidation, oxidation number, oxidation potential, oxidizing agent, rapid oxidation, reducing agent, reduction, replacement, slow oxidation.

1. In an equation the oxidation state of an element is indicated by the _____.
2. In any redox reaction, the substance that is reduced is also the _____.
3. Whenever the charge or apparent charge on an atom becomes more negative, the atom undergoes _____.
4. An atom that shows an increase in oxidation number has undergone _____.
5. Combustion is a form of _____.
6. In any redox reaction, the substance that is oxidized is also the _____.
7. An example of reduction is the change of _____.
8. Metals and nonmetals listed in order of their decreasing ability to act as reducing agents form the _____.
9. In a cell containing a metal and a hydrogen electrode, the voltage attributed to the metal electrode is its _____.
10. A reactant that is oxidized and reduced in the same reaction undergoes _____.

Solving Problems Within the Concept

1. Determine the oxidation number of each element in the following: $NaBr$, $FeSO_4$, NH_3, $AlCl_3$, $Al_2(SO_4)_3$, $KSCN$, CCl_4, LiH, Na_2O_2, $(H_3O)^+$, $(Cr_2O_7)^{-2}$, $K_2S_4O_6$.

2. Write a balanced equation for each of the following reactions. Indicate the changes in oxidation number that occur in each reaction. Also indicate the substance oxidized and the substance reduced.
   (a) $FeCl_3 + H_2 \longrightarrow FeCl_2 + HCl$
   (b) $H_2O_2 \longrightarrow H_2O + O_2$
   (c) $K_2Cr_2O_7 + H_2O + S \longrightarrow$
       $SO_2 + KOH + Cr_2O_3$

3. Calculate the voltage, E_T°, obtained when each of the following standard half-cells is combined. (Assume appropriate electrolytes in each case.) (a) hydrogen and zinc, (b) hydrogen and iron, (c) hydrogen and copper, (d) hydrogen and tin.

4. Calculate the voltage, E_T°, of each of the following electrochemical cells: (a) nickel and silver, (b) tin and aluminum.

Applying the Concept

1. When sprinkled into a Bunsen burner flame, glucose chars or burns completely, emitting light; but inside the body the oxidation of glucose does not emit light. How are the two reactions similar; how do they differ?

2. A combination of Ca and Mg carbonates is found as the mineral dolomite. Why would it be incorrect to conclude that dolomite was formed by calcium atoms reducing magnesium ions present in molten magnesium carbonate?

3. Describe how the spontaneous combustion of oily rags can occur.

4. Explain why aluminum is obtained from its compounds by electrolysis rather than by replacement or reduction with metals above it on the electrochemical series.

Reading Further

Antoine Lavoisier: Scientist, Economist, Social Reformer, by Douglas McKie, New York, Abelard-Schuman, 1952. The biography of a man who, among many other accomplishments, contributed to the understanding of the theory of oxidation.

19

SKILLS—Balancing Oxidation-Reduction Reactions

From the last chapter you realize that composition, decomposition, and single replacement reactions involve oxidation and reduction. Since in these three types of reactions (studied in Skills Chapter 16) an actual or apparent gain or loss of electrons is involved, they are classified into one fundamental group: *redox reactions.* Also, many complex oxidation-reduction reactions that cannot be classified into one of these types are known simply as redox reactions.

THE NATURE OF ELECTRON EXCHANGE

The equations for some redox reactions may be "balanced" or completed simply by inspection. In other cases the balanced equation may be determined more efficiently by "balancing the electron exchange." The first two examples that follow are composition reactions. Though they are easily balanced by inspection, they serve to indicate the procedure to be used in balancing the more complex equations considered later in the chapter.

The reaction between metals and nonmetals to form salts illustrates composition reactions. For example, the "unbalanced" equation for the reaction between iron and chlorine to form ferric chloride is:

$$Fe + Cl_2 \longrightarrow FeCl_3$$

Inspection readily provides the necessary coefficients.

$$2\,Fe + 3\,Cl_2 \longrightarrow 2\,FeCl_3$$

In more complex redox reactions, such as the one between copper and nitric acid, in which cupric nitrate, nitric oxide, and water are formed, balancing by inspection is tedious and often unsuccessful. Therefore, a method of balancing the electron exchange, sometimes called the *electron transfer method,* is often used by itself or together with inspection to make certain that the final equation is balanced. To illustrate how this electron transfer method of balancing equations works, consider again the reaction between iron and chlorine in which ferric chloride is the product.

Balancing the Electron Exchange

When iron and chlorine react to form ferric chloride, each iron atom loses 3 electrons. These electrons are accepted by chlorine atoms. The electron exchange that occurs may be expressed in the form of two *half-reactions.* A half-reaction represents what happens during either the oxidation or the reduction of a substance in a chemical change. Half-reactions representing ionic changes show the actual charge on each particle that is either oxidized or reduced as indicated below:

$$Fe^0 - 3\,e^- \longrightarrow Fe^{+3} \quad \text{(half-equation for oxidation of iron atoms to ferric ions)}$$

$$Cl^0 + e^- \longrightarrow Cl^{-1} \quad \text{(half-equation for reduction of chlorine atoms to chloride ions)}$$

But chlorine exists as diatomic molecules (Cl_2) rather than as individual atoms. The reduction of a molecule of free chlorine, therefore, requires 2 electrons and results in the formation of 2 Cl^- ions. To "supply" the 2 electrons, multiply each member of the reduction half-equation by 2:

$$Cl_2^0 + 2\,e^- \longrightarrow 2\,Cl^-$$

The oxidation and reduction half-equations now become:

$$Fe^0 - 3\,e^- \longrightarrow Fe^{+3} \quad \text{(oxidation)}$$
$$Cl_2^0 + 2\,e^- \longrightarrow 2\,Cl^{-1} \quad \text{(reduction)}$$

Since the number of electrons lost does not equal the number gained, we must adjust the coefficients of the two electron equations so that the number of electrons lost by oxidation and gained by reduction is the same. By inspection, you can determine that two iron atoms lose 6 electrons to become two ferric ions, and that simultaneously six chlorine atoms gain these 6 electrons to become six chloride ions. It is not always so easy to adjust coefficients by inspection, but you can *always adjust the coefficients by determining the least common multiple of the number of electrons lost and gained.* Here the least common multiple is 6 (3×2); therefore multiply the coefficients in the first half-equation by 2 and the second half-equation by 3.

$$\begin{array}{rcl} 2\,Fe^0 - 6\,e^- & \longrightarrow & 2\,Fe^{+3} \\ 3\,Cl_2^0 + 6\,e^- & \longrightarrow & 6\,Cl^{-1} \\ \hline 2\,Fe^0 + 3\,Cl_2^0 & \longrightarrow & 2\,Fe^{+3} + 6\,Cl^{-1} \end{array}$$

Observe that the number of electrons lost and gained is equal. Therefore they are eliminated when the two half-reactions are added to determine the final electronic equation.

The next step is to transfer these coefficients from the balanced electronic equation to the original unbalanced equation:

$$Fe + Cl_2 \longrightarrow FeCl_3$$

The coefficients of the Fe^0, Fe^{+3}, and Cl_2^0 are transferred directly.

$$2\,Fe + 3\,Cl_2 \longrightarrow 2\,FeCl_3$$

The six Cl^- ions required are provided by the $2\,FeCl_3$. The equation just written is the balanced equation.

Reactions Involving Molecular Compounds

Consider, as a second example of the electron transfer method for balancing equations, the composition reaction that occurs when carbon burns incompletely in oxygen to form carbon monoxide (CO):

$$C + O_2 \longrightarrow CO\uparrow$$

Although no ions are produced during the burning process (carbon monoxide is a molecular substance), half-reactions may be written to rep-

resent the oxidation and reduction processes that occur. The charge that is shown as part of each half-reaction indicates the number of electrons that appear to be lost or gained during the reaction.

As carbon burns it is partially oxidized. Each atom appears to lose 2 electrons.

$$C^0 - 2\,e^- \longrightarrow C^{+2} \quad \text{(oxidation)}$$

At the same time each oxygen atom appears to gain 2 electrons.

$$O^0 + 2\,e^- \longrightarrow O^{-2} \quad \text{(reduction)}$$

However, as oxygen is diatomic, actually 4 electrons are gained when a molecule of oxygen is reduced:

$$O_2^0 + 4\,e^- \longrightarrow 2\,O^{-2} \quad \text{(reduction)}$$

To balance the electron exchange, determine the least common multiple of the coefficients of the electrons lost and gained. As the least common multiple is 4, multiply the oxidation half-reaction by 2.

$$2\,C^0 - 4\,e^- \longrightarrow 2\,C^{+2} \quad \text{(oxidation)}$$

The reduction half-equation remains unchanged, as it already indicates the gain of 4 electrons.

Check to make sure that the number of electrons lost equals the number of electrons gained in the final electronic equation:

$$\begin{array}{rcl} 2\,C^0 - 4\,e^- & \longrightarrow & 2\,C^{+2} \\ O_2^0 + 4\,e^- & \longrightarrow & 2\,O^{-2} \\ \hline 2\,C^0 + O_2^0 & \longrightarrow & 2\,C^{+2} + 2\,O^{-2} \end{array}$$

Then transfer the coefficients from the half-equation to the original unbalanced equation:

$$2\,C + O_2 \longrightarrow 2\,CO\uparrow$$

In the equations considered so far, each element has undergone either oxidation or reduction. In redox reactions some of the elements involved are neither oxidized nor reduced. The balancing of equations for such reactions poses no special problems, as the coefficients needed for the formulas containing these elements are obtained by inspection.

The steps to be followed when using the electron transfer method for balancing oxidation-reduction reactions can be summarized as:

Step 1: Write an "unbalanced" equation for the reaction being considered. Be sure to use correct formulas.

Step 2: Assign the correct actual or apparent charge to each element. *In more complex redox reactions,* assign oxidation numbers to each element, as illustrated in the next section.

Step 3: Determine which elements have been oxidized and which reduced. Write the half-reaction in terms of actual or apparent charge for the oxidation process that occurs, followed by the half-reaction for the reduction process.

Step 4: Balance the actual or apparent loss and gain of electrons in the two half-reactions by multiplying the coefficients of the electrons in the half-reaction by their least common multiple. Add the two half-reactions to obtain a single electronic equation for the reaction.

Step 5: Transfer the determined coefficients from the electronic equation to the original "unbalanced" equation.

Step 6: Balance by inspection any remaining formulas in the original equation.

PROBLEMS

1. The heating of copper(II) oxide with carbon produces copper and carbon dioxide. Use the electron transfer method to write the balanced equation for the reaction.

2. Oxygen is usually produced in the laboratory by heating potassium chlorate. Use the electron transfer method to write a balanced equation for this decomposition reaction.

3. Arsenic reacts with oxygen (in moist air) to produce arsenious oxide, As_4O_6. Write the equation for this reaction by balancing the electron exchange.

MORE COMPLEX REDOX EQUATIONS

Now let us apply these six steps for writing a balanced oxidation-reduction equation to a more complex redox reaction between substances in solution. Consider the reaction between copper and dilute nitric acid in which cupric nitrate, nitric oxide, and water are formed.

The first step in determining the coefficients for a completed equation is to write an "unbalanced" equation for the reaction.

$$Cu + HNO_3 \longrightarrow Cu(NO_3)_2 + NO\uparrow + H_2O$$

Examine the equation carefully to make sure that all formulas are correct.

Now write the oxidation numbers above each symbol.

$$\overset{0}{Cu} + \overset{+1+5-2}{HNO_3} \longrightarrow \overset{+2\ +5-2}{Cu(NO_3)_2} + \overset{+2-2}{NO}\uparrow + \overset{+1-2}{H_2O}$$

Next, note that the actual reaction involves only the oxidation of copper atoms to copper ions, and the reduction of *part* of the nitrogen in the nitrate ion. The nitrogen becomes reduced in forming nitric oxide. Write half-reactions in terms of actual (or apparent) charge for the electron exchanges that occur.

$$Cu^0 - 2\,e^- \longrightarrow Cu^{+2} \quad \text{(oxidation)}$$
$$N^{+5} + 3\,e^- \longrightarrow N^{+2} \quad \text{(reduction)}$$

Balance the electron transfer by multiplying the coefficient in the oxidation half-equation by 3, and in the reduction half-equation by 2.

$$3\,Cu^0 - 6\,e^- \longrightarrow 3\,Cu^{+2}$$
$$2\,N^{+5} - 6\,e^- \longrightarrow 2\,N^{+2}$$
$$\overline{3\,Cu^0 + 2\,N^{+5} \longrightarrow 3\,Cu^{+2} + 2\,N^{+2}}$$

Now transfer the determined coefficients from the final electronic equation to the "unbalanced" equation for the reaction:

$$3\,Cu + 2\,HNO_3 \longrightarrow 3\,Cu(NO_3)_2 + 2\,NO + H_2O$$

The equation is still not balanced; by inspection, adjust any coefficients that are still inappropriate. As part of the nitrate ion remains unchanged, the coefficient 2 before HNO_3 must still be altered. Since six nitrate ions appear unchanged as products, six additional nitrate ions must appear as reactants. Adding six unchanged nitrate ions to two reduced nitrate ions gives a coefficient of 8 for HNO_3. Now complete the balancing of the equation by placing the coefficient 4 before H_2O.

$$3 Cu + 8 HNO_3 \longrightarrow$$
$$3 Cu(NO_3)_2 + 2 NO + 4 H_2O$$

Finally, check the completed equation to make certain that the numbers of each type of atom represented are the same on both sides of the arrow. And indeed they are.

PROBLEMS

1. When hydrochloric acid and manganese dioxide are heated gently, chlorine gas escapes. Water and manganous chloride are also produced. Write a balanced equation for the reaction.

2. Phosphorus is obtained commercially by heating a mixture of calcium phosphate, coke, and sand in an electric furnace. Balance the equation for the reaction:

$$Ca_3(PO_4)_2 + C + SiO_2 \longrightarrow$$
$$CaSiO_3 + CO\uparrow + P_4$$

3. Following is an "unbalanced" equation for the reaction that occurs when potassium permanganate, ferrous sulfate, and sulfuric acid react. Write the balanced equation for this reaction:

$$KMnO_4 + FeSO_4 + H_2SO_4 \longrightarrow$$
$$KHSO_4 + MnSO_4 + Fe_2(SO_4)_3 + H_2O$$

ADDITIONAL PROBLEMS

1. Use the electron transfer method to write a balanced equation for each reaction at the top of the next column:

(a) $Mg + O_2 \longrightarrow MgO$
(b) $F_2 + H_2O \longrightarrow HF + O_2\uparrow$
(c) $P_4O_{10} + C \longrightarrow P_4 + CO\uparrow$
(d) $UO_3 + Al \longrightarrow U + Al_2O_3$
(e) $Fe_2O_3 + CO \longrightarrow Fe + CO_2\uparrow$
(f) $KIO \longrightarrow KI + KIO_3$

2. When equal volumes of hydrogen sulfide and oxygen react, only some of the sulfur combines with oxygen, as indicated below:

$$H_2S + O_2 \longrightarrow H_2O + SO_2 + S$$

Use the electron transfer method to balance this equation.

3. Most of the sodium hydroxide produced commercially results from the electrolysis of sodium chloride solutions. Hydrogen and chlorine are by-products of this reaction. Use the electron transfer method to write the balanced equation for this reaction.

4. Balance the equation below for the hydrolysis of iodine monochloride, ICl:

$$ICl + H_2O \longrightarrow Cl^- + IO_3^- + I_2 + H^+$$

5. Use the electron transfer method to write balanced equations for each of the following redox reactions:

(a) $Zn + HNO_3 \longrightarrow$
$$Zn(NO_3)_2 + NH_4NO_3 + H_2O$$
(b) $KMnO_4 + HCl \longrightarrow$
$$KCl + MnCl_2 + H_2O + Cl_2\uparrow$$
(c) $KI + H_2SO_4 + MnO_2 \longrightarrow$
$$K_2SO_4 + MnSO_4 + H_2O + I_2\uparrow$$
(d) $NaOH + Cl_2 \longrightarrow$
$$NaCl + NaClO_3 + H_2O$$
(e) $K_2Cr_2O_7 + HCl \longrightarrow$
$$KCl + CrCl_3 + H_2O + Cl_2\uparrow$$
(f) $Ti_2(SO_4)_3 + KMnO_4 + H_2SO_4 \longrightarrow$
$$Ti(SO_4)_2 + K_2SO_4 + MnSO_4 + H_2O$$

Colloids

No doubt you have ridden down a fog-shrouded road and found the car windshield so wet that it was necessary to turn on the windshield wipers. Fog is composed of tiny droplets of moisture dispersed in the air, but the moisture does not fall to the earth as rain. Or consider a glass of homogenized milk. The fat is broken up into tiny particles throughout the milk, and a sample taken from one portion of the glass of milk is like any other sample. Yet milk is not a liquid solution: particles can be seen in a drop under a microscope. But not until the milk sours do the particles separate. What then are fog and milk? What characteristics do they have in common?

THE NATURE OF COLLOIDS

If you shake up some finely divided clay in a cylinder of water, the clay begins to settle as soon as you put the cylinder down. If you shake the mixture thoroughly and filter it through filter paper, the clay does not pass through the filter. Evidently the clay particles are larger than the pores of the filter paper. This clay in water is an example of a **suspension,** a heterogeneous mixture of finely divided solid particles in a liquid. Upon standing, the solid particles settle to the bottom.

By contrast, a **solution** is a completely homogeneous mixture: it remains uniform throughout. In a sodium chloride solution, for example, the salt cannot be separated from the water by filtration; and on standing the salt does not settle out. If you looked at a drop of the solution under the most powerful microscope, no individual ions or other particles could be detected: solute and solvent are completely homogeneous.

Are all homogeneous mixtures true solutions? *The following investigation may supply the answer.*

Secure two medium-sized beakers. Add cold water to one, and an equal amount of boiling distilled water to the other. Shake a small amount of solid ferric chloride into both beakers and stir. In the cold water, the solution that forms is yellow-brown in color. In the boiling water the color is different—a dark reddish-brown.

Now test the contents of the two beakers to see in what ways

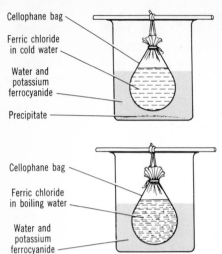

Cellophane bag

Ferric chloride in cold water

Water and potassium ferrocyanide

Precipitate

Cellophane bag

Ferric chloride in boiling water

Water and potassium ferrocyanide

they are similar. Does a precipitate appear in either of the two beakers? Try filtering the contents of the beakers. Can any particles be removed by filtration? Observe a drop from each beaker under a microscope. Are any individual particles visible? For the contents of both beakers, the answer to all three questions is no. Evidently, then, both mixtures, except for the matter of color, seem alike.

For a final test, pour the two mixtures into separate cellophane bags and place each bag in a beaker of water at room temperature, as shown at the left. After several minutes test the contents of each beaker to see if either mixture has diffused through the cellophane into the surrounding water. To do so, place a few drops of potassium ferrocyanide in the water surrounding the bags. If any ferric ions have diffused through the cellophane bags, they will form a dark blue precipitate in the presence of the potassium ferrocyanide. Does a precipitate form in either or in both beakers?

No doubt you found that the first mixture, made with cold water, diffused through the cellophane into the surrounding water. On the other hand, the second mixture, made with boiling water, did not diffuse through the cellophane bag. There is a difference between the two mixtures. The cold-water mixture is a true solution; its ions are small enough to diffuse through a membrane. The hot-water mixture is not a true solution; its particles are too large to diffuse through the membrane. In the cold water, the ferric chloride dissolved to form ferric (Fe^{+3}) and chloride (Cl^-) ions. In the boiling water, the ferric chloride hydrolyzed to form ferric hydroxide.

$$FeCl_3 + 3 H_2O \longrightarrow Fe(OH)_3 + 3 HCl$$

The particles of ferric hydroxide are larger than particles in a true solution. Although small enough to remain permanently in suspension, they are too large to diffuse through a membrane. Such particles are called **colloidal particles** and the mixtures containing colloidal particles are **colloidal systems, colloidal dispersions,** or simply **colloids.**

Dialysis

The first important work on colloids was done about 100 years ago by the Scottish scientist, Thomas Graham. Graham added various substances—sugar, salt, glue, starch, and gelatin—to water in parchment bags and suspended the bags in water. He found that while the sugar and salt passed through the membrane of the parchment easily enough, the glue, starch, and gelatin did not. For those substances which would not diffuse through a membrane, Graham coined the word *colloid* from the Greek word meaning "gluelike."

Graham's method of using a *selective* or *semipermeable* membrane to separate the smaller particles of a solution from the larger particles of a colloid is called **dialysis.** It is, of course, the process you used in the

Water

20-1 A mixture of gelatin and sugar in water can be separated completely by dialysis. The gelatin remains in the cellophane bag, and the sugar solution diffuses into the running water.

previous investigation. In the method used there, much of the colloid would remain inside the cellophane bag. To completely separate a colloid, such as gelatin, from a sugar solution, chemists use the dialysis procedure diagrammed in Fig. 20-1. When the bag containing the mixture is placed in a steady stream of water, the molecules of sugar continue to diffuse through the cellophane bag, and ultimately all are carried away. At the same time, the larger particles of the colloidal gelatin are left behind. In other words, the colloid and the solution are separated completely.

Size of Colloidal Particles

While Graham believed that the colloidal state depended upon the nature of the substance, it was later found that the colloidal state is determined by the size of the particles. In fact, almost any substance can be made into particles of colloidal size by one of the techniques to be discussed shortly. There is no sharp dividing line between the size of particles in solution and a colloid, or between those in a colloid and a suspension. There are, however, certain ranges of size into which the three types of particles usually fall, with the size increasing gradually from solutions, to colloids, to suspensions. The atoms, ions, and molecules in solutions usually have diameters of from 10^{-8} to 10^{-7} centimeters. Colloidal particles, which are *aggregates* of these smaller particles, usually have diameters of from 10^{-7} centimeters to 10^{-5} centimeters. Particles found in a suspension generally have diameters larger than 10^{-5} centimeters.

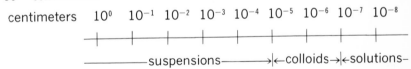

centimeters 10^0 10^{-1} 10^{-2} 10^{-3} 10^{-4} 10^{-5} 10^{-6} 10^{-7} 10^{-8}

—————————suspensions—————→|←colloids→|←solutions–

The Tyndall Effect

When a beam of sunlight enters a darkened room, the path of the beam is seen easily because the dust particles of colloidal size reflect and scatter the light. *You can use this same phenomenon* to differentiate between true solutions and colloidal dispersions.

Fill a large, rectangular glass container with a 0.01 *M* solution of hypo (sodium thiosulfate) as shown at the left. Notice that the solution appears perfectly clear. In a darkened room pass the beam of a flashlight or of a low-voltage parallel-beam light through the solution. The light is transmitted unseen through the solution. It is not reflected in any way, as the sodium and thiosulfate ions are too small to scatter light.

Now add, a milliliter at a time, dilute hydrochloric acid to the sodium thiosulfate solution. The solution gradually becomes cloudy as colloidal particles of sulfur form. Now shine a beam of light through the container. Is the path of the beam visible?

Colloidal particles of sulfur form as additional acid is added to the hypo.

$$Na_2S_2O_3 + 2\,HCl \longrightarrow 2\,NaCl + H_2SO_3 + S$$

The colloidal sulfur particles are large enough to reflect and scatter the beam of light just as do the dust particles in a room. This phenomenon of the scattering by colloidal particles is called the **Tyndall effect** after John Tyndall, the English physicist who first explained it. He reasoned that though the particles themselves were too small to be seen, he was able to detect the light reflected by them. Since the particles in a true solution are too small to reflect light, the Tyndall effect is one means of distinguishing between colloidal systems and true solutions.

If you had continued adding acid to the hypo solution, the color of the main beam of light produced by the Tyndall effect would have changed first to orange then to red, much like the light of the setting sun. On the other hand, the light reflected at right angles to the main beam is blue, like the color of the sky. Colloidal particles are the cause of some remarkably beautiful color effects. The lovely colors often seen in sunsets are due to colloidal dust particles in the earth's atmosphere. The colors of stained glass windows and birds' plumage come from the scattering of white light by particles of colloidal size.

The Tyndall effect can also be used in connection with a microscope to observe colloidal dispersions. A beam of light is focused on a colloidal dispersion which is viewed through a high-powered microscope against a black background and at right angles to the beam of light (Fig. 20-2). This arrangement is called an **ultramicroscope.** Under the ultramicroscope the colloidal particles appear as tiny, bright flashes of light darting back and forth in a zigzag type of straight-line motion. In addition, if you look carefully, you can observe a slight vibration of each particle. These effects constitute the *Brownian movement* studied in connection with the kinetic-molecular theory. Because the colloidal particles are being bombarded by molecules of the **dispersing medium,** the colloidal particles do not settle, even though they may be somewhat denser than the dispersing medium.

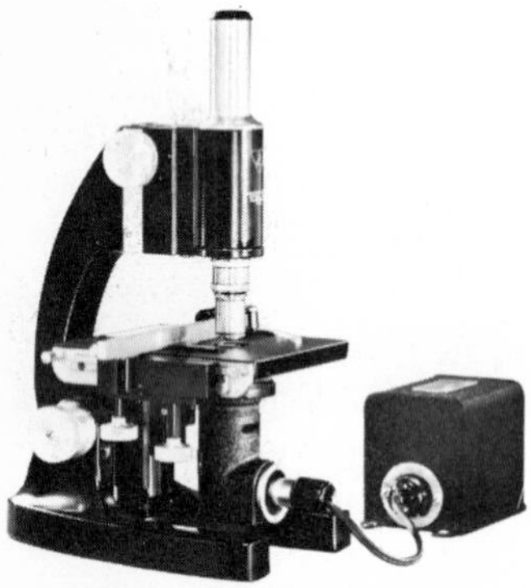

20-2 In an ultramicroscope, if all light is excluded except the diffracted light from the microscope itself, the light scattered by an individual particle can be seen.

Colloidal Systems

Colloidal particles—aggregates of atoms, molecules, or ions—are usually found to be evenly distributed throughout the dispersing medium. A *colloidal system,* then, can be defined as *colloidal particles evenly dispersed in a dispersing medium.* As you have seen, colloidal systems are homogeneous mixtures. Just as solids, liquids, and gases can be mixed together to form true solutions, so, also, can they be dispersed in one another to form different types of colloidal systems. These are

Table 20-1　TYPES OF COLLOIDAL SYSTEMS

Dispersed phase	Dispersing medium	Common names	Examples
Gas	Liquid	Foam	Whipped cream, beaten egg whites
Gas	Solid	Solid foam	Pumice, floating soap
Liquid	Gas	(Liquid) aerosol	Fog, cloud, some spray insecticides
Liquid	Liquid	Emulsion	Milk, mayonnaise
Liquid	Solid	Solid emulsion	Cheese, butter
Solid	Gas	(Solid) aerosol	Smog, dust, smoke
Solid	Liquid	{ Sol { Gel	{ Warm gelatin { Cooled gelatin
Solid	Solid	Solid sol	Colored glass, some alloys

listed in Table 20-1. Though there are nine possible combinations of solids, liquids, and gases, only eight of these are colloidal systems. The ninth combination, a gas dispersed in a gas, is always a solution, never a colloid.

Each type of colloid has a different name. Solids dispersed in liquids are called **sols;** the sulfur dispersed in water in the previous investigation was a sol. Oil paint, composed of solid pigment dispersed in oil, is also a sol. In a true sol the colloidal particles will never settle. In the London Museum there is a sol consisting of colloidal gold dispersed in water which was prepared by Michael Faraday in 1857!

If we pass a beam of light through a bowl of gelatin, the Tyndall effect is produced; gelatins are colloids. The colloidal system to which gelatins belong is called a **gel.** In a gel, a dispersing liquid medium contains a solid which extends in a fine network throughout the system. Both the solid and the liquid in the gel are continuous (Fig. 20-3). Gels can frequently be made by cooling sols. Gels can also be produced by evaporating the dispersing medium, thereby bringing the colloidal particles closer together to form a soft, semirigid mass.

No doubt you have made "an educated guess" that the fog mentioned at the beginning of this chapter is a colloid in which a liquid is dispersed in a gas. The Tyndall effect produced by the headlights of the car is an indication of the colloidal nature of fog. While ordinary fog consists of tiny droplets of water dispersed in air, certain insecticides, like DDD and DDT, are various liquids dispersed throughout gases. Closely related to fog is the colloid called *smog.* The smog which often hovers over great cities or heavily industrialized areas consists of colloidal particles of unburned fuel and ashes dispersed in the air. Fogs, smogs, insecticides, and paints in the form of sprays are all referred to as **aerosols,** a term used today to mean either solids or liquids dispersed in gases. A trip to the nearest drug or hardware store will undoubtedly reveal an array of products, ranging from hair spray to degreasing agents, in "aerosol" cans.

20-3 An electron micrograph of gelatin shows the colloidal particles brought so close together that they form a loosely arranged "network" trapping the dispersing medium.

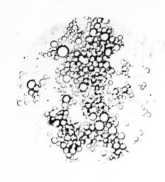

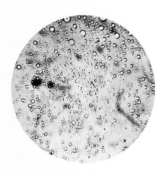

20-4 The upper photograph shows butterfat globules in whole milk. When milk is homogenized, as in the lower photograph, these globules are broken down and remain evenly spread throughout the non-fat portion of the milk.

When two ordinarily immiscible liquids are evenly dispersed in each other, an **emulsion** is formed. Homogenized milk is an emulsion; it consists of liquid butterfat dispersed in a medium which is essentially water (Fig. 20-4). If diluted sufficiently, homogenized milk produces the Tyndall effect.

Lyophobic and Lyophilic Systems

Colloids in which liquids are the dispersing media are sometimes separated into two categories on the basis of the affinity of the dispersed particles for the dispersing liquid. If there is a strong attraction between the dispersed particles and the dispersing medium, the system is called **lyophilic,** a term meaning "solvent lover." Even though the concentration of the dispersed particles in a lyophilic colloidal system may be relatively great, the dispersed particles usually do not coagulate. If coagulation does occur, the system can usually be restored by adding liquid. Gels such as gelatin, agar, and glue are examples of lyophilic colloids.

If there is only slight attraction between the colloidal particles and the dispersing medium, the system is called **lyophobic.** The term "lyophobic" is of Greek origin and means "solvent hater." Though the concentration of dispersed particles in a lyophobic colloidal system is usually relatively low, when charged particles are added the dispersed particles tend to coagulate. Once this happens, the colloidal system can seldom be restored. The ferric hydroxide you made in your investigation on page 311 is an example of a lyophobic colloid.

QUESTIONS AND PROBLEMS

1. Indicate how a colloid differs from a suspension and from a solution in each of the following: (a) particle size, (b) appearance, (c) rate of settling.
2. How would you separate a salt solution from gelatin?
3. How could you use a flashlight to differentiate between a colloidal dispersion and a true solution?
4. How are sols and gels related? How do they differ?
5. Differentiate between each of the following pairs of terms:
   (a) *lyophobic* and *lyophilic*
   (b) *colloidal particle* and *dispersing medium*
   (c) *emulsion* and *aerosol*

PREPARING AND MAINTAINING COLLOIDAL SYSTEMS

Since the dispersed particles of a sol, a gel, or an emulsion must be of colloidal size, these systems cannot be prepared in the same way as solutions. Instead, all colloidal systems must be prepared in one of two ways:

20-5 A colloid mill in which large particles are reduced to colloidal size by a shearing or tearing action.

by *dispersion,* in which larger particles of matter are *broken down* into colloidal-sized particles, or by *condensation,* in which atoms, ions, or molecules are *built up* into aggregates of colloidal size.

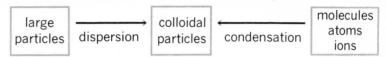

Dispersion

A number of methods have been developed to reduce larger particles to particles of colloidal size. Here we shall consider those most commonly used.

The Colloid Mill. When a solid is to be reduced to particles of colloidal size, a device called a **colloid mill** is frequently used (Fig. 20-5). The solid to be broken down is placed between two rapidly moving surfaces which, by a shearing or tearing effect, ultimately reduce the size of the particles. The pigments of most paints are prepared in this way.

Homogenization. In preparing certain emulsions, such as homogenized milk, a *homogenizing machine* is used. In preparing homogenized milk, liquid butter fat is reduced to particles of colloidal size by being forced through minute openings under tremendous pressure. When the particles are of proper size, they disperse in the watery medium.

The Bredig Arc. Suppose you wish to disperse a metal, such as gold, silver, or platinum, in water. This can be done by means of a **Bredig arc,** the operation of which is indicated in Fig. 20-6. In a Bredig arc two rods made of the metal to be dispersed are dipped into water, and an electric arc is set up between them. The heat of the arc first vaporizes the metal so that its atoms become gaseous; then these gaseous atoms combine into aggregates of colloidal size and disperse throughout the water.

Peptization. Some substances when placed in the proper media disperse spontaneously to form colloidal systems. Substances which behave in this manner undergo **peptization.** Gelatin and glue, for example, are peptized when placed in warm water.

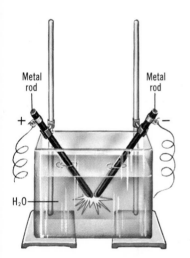

20-6 In a Bredig arc the metal of the rods vaporizes, and the gaseous atoms formed combine into colloidal particles that are dispersed throughout the water.

Emulsifying Agents

Prepare an oil and water emulsion by thoroughly shaking together 10 ml of salad oil and 50 ml of water in a stoppered bottle. Now let the oil and water mixture stand for a few minutes. The dispersed droplets coalesce quickly and the mixture separates out into two layers. Add a few drops of liquid soap to the mixture and again shake it thoroughly. Do the oil and water separate or remain mixed?

The soap added to the oil and water mixture caused the two immiscible liquids to remain suspended in each other, that is, to form an emulsion. Any substance that stabilizes an emulsion by reducing the tendency of

Grease or oil droplet in water

○---Water soluble or polar end
⧘---Oil soluble or nonpolar end

20-7 Soap is both an emulsifying agent and a wetting agent. Soap emulsifies grease and water because the polar end of a soap molecule dissolves in the water and the nonpolar end dissolves in the grease.

the droplets to coalesce is an **emulsifying agent.** Soap, of course, is an emulsifying agent for oil and water. Similarly, egg yolk serves to stabilize the vinegar and oil in mayonnaise, while in homogenized milk, the emulsifying agent is casein.

The action of soap well illustrates the way an emulsifying agent works. Grease or greasy dirt on your hands or clothes is difficult to wash off with water alone. But with soap as an emulsifying agent, the grease or dirt is easily removed. What happens is illustrated in Fig. 20-7. One end of a soap molecule is polar, while the other end is nonpolar. The polar end of the soap molecule dissolves in the water, while the nonpolar end dissolves in the grease. As a result, each colloidal-sized particle of grease or oil is surrounded by a monomolecular film of soap molecules. Not only is soap a good emulsifying agent, but also it is a good **wetting agent.** As a wetting agent, soap lowers the surface tension of the water, increasing the ability of the water to stick to, or wet, the grease or dirt particles that are to be washed away.

Condensation

The process of **condensation** is just the opposite of dispersion. During condensation, particles such as ions, atoms, and molecules that are smaller than colloidal size are built up into colloidal aggregates. Condensation is usually the result of a chemical reaction. Here we shall consider the three main types of chemical reactions by which condensation occurs.

Displacement. When you added hydrochloric acid to sodium thiosulfate in the investigation on page 313 you produced colloidal particles by *displacement.* The aggregates of sulfur grew larger and larger until they finally reached colloidal size. Similarly, an arsenious sulfide sol can be produced by adding hydrogen sulfide to a solution of arsenious oxide.

$$As_2O_3 + 3\,H_2S \longrightarrow As_2S_3 + 3\,H_2O$$

Ordinarily these procedures would cause the sulfur and arsenious sulfide, respectively, to precipitate as insoluble substances. However, if the concentration of the reactants is not too high, and if the temperature is controlled carefully, colloidal particles are formed and precipitation does not occur. Unfortunately, the formation of colloidal sulfur in reactions involving sulfur compounds frequently causes trouble, since the colloidal sulfur cannot be removed by the usual filtering techniques.

Hydrolysis. In your investigation, the colloidal ferric hydroxide resulting from the addition of ferric chloride to boiling water was formed by *hydrolysis.* The ferric hydroxide particles were larger than the particles in a true solution but still small enough to remain suspended permanently.

Oxidation-Reduction. Metallic sols can be formed by *oxidation-reduction* reactions. For example, a colloidal gold sol can be produced by reacting a very dilute solution of gold chloride with a reducing agent such as iron(II) sulfate or formaldehyde. The net equation for this reaction would be:

$$Au^{+3} + 3\,e^- \longrightarrow Au^0$$

The water of the ocean contains some colloidal gold which has been formed in this way by the reduction of soluble gold salts.

QUESTIONS AND PROBLEMS

1. Differentiate between dispersion and condensation in the preparation of colloids.
2. (a) List two mechanical devices used in producing colloids by dispersion. Under what conditions is each used? (b) Describe briefly two methods by which a gold sol can be produced. (c) How does the preparation of an arsenious sulfide sol differ from the preparation of a ferric hydroxide sol?
3. What is the function of an emulsifying agent?

CHARGED COLLOIDAL PARTICLES

The particles in any colloidal system will eventually settle if condensation is allowed to proceed far enough. Just why colloidal systems tend to destroy themselves by excessive condensation and coagulation is not completely understood. However, it is known that many colloidal particles are charged, and that the charges on all the particles within a given system are alike—either all positive, or all negative. As long as the particles retain their like charge, they repel each other and the system is maintained. Possibly coagulation results from the particles losing their charge for some reason. Uncharged, they no longer repel each other.

Precipitation of Colloids

Had you continued to add hydrochloric acid to the solution of sodium thiosulfate (page 313), the sulfur particles would finally have become so large that they would have settled to the bottom of the container. In a similar fashion, ice cream or jellies finally crystallize. This process by which colloidal particles settle is called **precipitation.**

To prevent the coagulation and ultimate precipitation of the dispersed particles, another colloid is frequently added to the system. The second colloid, called a **protective colloid,** forms a protective film around the dispersed particles and prevents their coagulation. In ice cream, gelatin prevents the formation of granular ice crystals; in mayonnaise, the protective colloid is egg yolk.

Electrophoresis

The fact that the dispersed particles in a given colloidal system all have the same electrical charge *can be illustrated readily.*

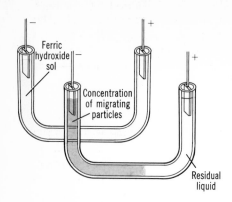

Ferric
hydroxide
sol

Concentration
of migrating
particles

Residual
liquid

Partly fill a **U**-tube with a ferric hydroxide sol (made by the hydrolysis of ferric chloride), and insert electrodes into the sol, as shown at the left. Connect the electrodes to a low-voltage source of direct current. After the current has been on for about half an hour, observe that a boundary appears between a dark-colored and light-colored portion of the liquid. While the current continues to flow, observe whether the boundary moves slightly toward the negative or positive electrode. Is the charge on the colloidal particles positive or negative? Let the current remain on for a day or more to observe increased migration of the boundary. Also observe that the migrating sol is colored while the residual liquid is now colorless.

The movement of the boundary toward the negative electrode indicates that the colored ferric hydroxide colloidal particles are positively charged. This movement of colloidal particles in an electrical field is called **electrophoresis.** If you can, repeat the electrophoresis investigation with an arsenious sulfide sol. Do you find that this particular colloid is negatively charged?

Since the speed at which different kinds of dispersed particles move in an electric field varies, two colloids can often be separated by electrophoresis. Experimentation has shown that the colloidal gamma globulin and fibrinogen proteins in the blood act differently during electrophoresis. The principle of electrophoresis is also used in industries which deal with colloidal materials. In the making of rubber gloves, for example, the charged rubber particles are made to collect upon an oppositely charged electrode shaped like a human hand.

Neutralizing Charged Particles

You have seen that in a ferric hydroxide sol all the particles of ferric hydroxide are positively charged, yet in an arsenious sulfide sol all the particles of arsenious sulfide have a negative charge. As expected, if these two sols are mixed together, the positive charge of the one cancels out the negative charge of the other. The particles are neutralized and precipitation occurs.

The addition of soluble ions to a sol may also cause precipitation. In this way deltas are formed at the mouths of great rivers, like the Mississippi. Ions present in sea water meet the oppositely charged particles of colloidal silt which are carried downriver in the fresh-water stream; the particles precipitate, building up deltas. At the mouth of the Mississippi River, the positively charged sodium ions of the waters of the Gulf of Mexico neutralize the negatively charged silt particles to build up the Mississippi Delta.

Industrial smoke contains colloidal particles of carbon, metallic oxides, and other substances. These particles can be precipitated and salvaged for use by a device known as the **Cottrell precipitator,** described

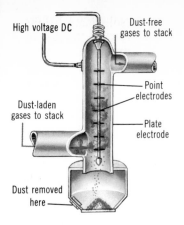

High voltage DC

Dust-free gases to stack

Dust-laden gases to stack

Point electrodes

Plate electrode

Dust removed here

20-8 A Cottrell precipitator reduces air pollution. It removes dust, composed of carbon and other substances, from dust-laden industrial gases before they escape into the atmosphere.

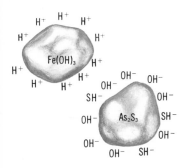

Fe(OH)₃

As₂S₃

20-9 Some colloidal particles selectively adsorb either positive or negative ions. A particular type of particle is consistently positive or consistently negative.

in Fig. 20-8. The precipitator consists of alternately charged plates through which the smoke passes before it enters the smokestack. The charged colloidal particles are attracted to plates having the opposite charge. In this way valuable substances, including the precious metals, can be recovered. Precipitators of the Cottrell type also serve to reduce air pollution.

Adsorption

Some colloidal particles demonstrate an unusual behavior; the particles attract ions or molecules of other substances to their surfaces without causing the colloid to precipitate. This process is called **adsorption.** Notice that *ad*sorption differs from *ab*sorption. Molecules that are *ab*sorbed actually enter into the pores of the absorbing substance. *Ad*sorption, on the other hand, is a phenomenon of surfaces only. Molecules that are adsorbed attach themselves to the surfaces of other particles, forming a layer which is probably no more than a few molecules thick. For example, the gelatin molecules in a gel adsorb molecules of water. These adsorbed water molecules keep the lyophilic gel from precipitating.

Adsorption is a selective process. A given colloidal particle adsorbs only certain ions. In a ferric hydroxide sol the ferric hydroxide particles are neutral when formed but they quickly adsorb many positively charged hydrogen ions (Fig. 20-9). This may well be the reason why ferric hydroxide particles are positively charged. By contrast, arsenious sulfide particles become negatively charged by adsorbing OH⁻ or SH⁻ ions (Fig. 20-9). Though the charge on these and other particles could not have been predicted, any type of charged colloidal particle is either consistently positive or consistently negative.

Adsorption by Solid Surfaces

Consider what happens to the surface area of any solid object when that object is broken down into particles of colloidal size. Imagine a cube whose original volume is 1 cubic centimeter, and whose original surface area is 6 square centimeters. When this original cube is broken down into cubes of colloidal size (10^{-5} centimeter on edge), the total surface area is enlarged to 6×10^5 square centimeters. The surface area is now 100,000 times greater than the original surface.

Since the surface area of a substance increases markedly as it is broken down into colloidal particles, the atoms on the surfaces of these colloid-sized particles represent a considerable fraction of the total number of atoms present in the substance. This fact, for example, is basic to the use of activated charcoal in adsorbing certain poison gases. Activated charcoal (charcoal from which all gases have been removed by extreme heat) contains a very high proportion of surface atoms. These exposed surface atoms have incomplete outer electron shells—their valences are unsaturated. At ordinary temperature the surface carbon atoms attract or adsorb mainly polar molecules to satisfy their unsaturated valences. These carbon atoms, for instance, adsorb polar molecules of the poisonous gas hydrogen sulfide (H_2S), while at the same time the nonpolar molecules of gases like oxygen and nitrogen are allowed to pass through. The ability to adsorb H_2S and other poisonous gases while letting others pass through accounts for the use of activated charcoal in gas masks.

Dangerous gases like H_2S, which have been adsorbed by activated charcoal, are released when the charcoal is heated. The bonds between the adsorbed polar molecules of such poisonous gas and the carbon atoms are weak; heating increases the molecular motion which overcomes these bonds. Once the adsorbed polar molecules of poison gas have been driven off, the carbon is again ready to adsorb other polar molecules.

In this unit you have studied solutions and near-solutions, or colloids. You are now familiar with most of the basic types of chemical compounds and chemical reactions. The role of water as a medium in which ionic compounds dissociate and molecular compounds ionize is central to many reactions. In your study of the individual families of elements in Unit 4, you will fully appreciate the significance of oxidation-reduction reactions. For the present, however, we will turn to a brief study of an area of chemistry unknown until the turn of the twentieth century—nuclear chemistry.

QUESTIONS AND PROBLEMS

1. Describe briefly the principle upon which the Cottrell precipitator operates.
2. (a) H_2S is adsorbed by activated carbon, but O_2 and N_2 are not. Why? (b) How is the adsorption of OH^- or SH^- ions by arsenious sulfide related to the adsorption of H_2S by activated carbon?
3. Define the terms *protective colloid, electrophoresis, adsorption,* and *precipitation* in relation to colloids.

VALUE OF THE CONCEPT

THE CONCEPT

Colloidal particles are larger than those in a true solution, but small enough to remain permanently in suspension. Mixtures containing colloidal particles are called colloidal systems, colloidal dispersions, or simply colloids.

Colloids may be separated from true solutions by dialysis, a process requiring a selective membrane. The size of colloidal particles (10^{-7} to 10^{-5} centimeters in diameter) enables them, when suspended, to reflect and scatter light. This light scattering, called the Tyndall effect, is used to distinguish colloidal systems from true solutions.

Solids, liquids, and gases can disperse in one another to form eight types of colloidal systems. A solid dispersed in a liquid, for example, produces a sol. Colloids in which liquids are the dispersing medium can be separated into two categories: lyophilic colloids in which there is a strong attraction between the dispersed particles and the dispersing medium, and lyophobic colloids in which there is little attraction between the two parts of the system.

Colloidal systems may be prepared by dispersion, a process in which larger particles are broken down into those of colloidal size. Homogenization and peptization, as well as the Bredig arc and colloid mill, are used in dispersing particles. Some immiscible liquids will form colloidal systems if emulsifying agents such as soap, egg yolk, or casein are added. Colloidal systems may also be formed by causing smaller particles to condense. Displacement and hydrolysis, as well as oxidation-reduction in some dilute solutions, cause condensation.

Colloidal particles within the same system usually have the same charge. They may be made to coagulate and eventually precipitate by the addition of oppositely charged particles. However, coagulation can sometimes be prevented by the addition of a protective colloid. The movement of charged colloidal particles within an electric field toward the electrode of opposite charge is called electrophoresis.

The surface area of a substance increases tremendously as it is broken into colloidal particles. The incomplete valence structure of certain substances in the colloidal state enables them to selectively adsorb or attract certain other substances to their surfaces.

USING THE CONCEPT

Using the Basic Concept

1. (a) Describe three ways in which colloids differ from solutions. (b) Describe one way in which colloids differ from suspensions.
2. (a) What is dialysis? (b) Describe an experiment involving dialysis.
3. (a) What is the size range of colloidal particles? (b) By what two general methods can particles of this size be prepared?
4. (a) What is the Tyndall effect? (b) Why is it observed only with colloids?
5. Prepare a table showing six types of colloidal systems. Include a *brief* description of the type of colloid and an example of each type.
6. (a) Differentiate between a lyophobic and a lyophilic colloidal system. (b) Give an example of each type of colloid.
7. (a) Describe and give one example for each of four methods of preparing colloids by dispersion. (b) Describe and give an example for each of three methods of preparing colloids by condensation.
8. (a) Name three emulsifying agents and two protective colloids. (b) What is the purpose of an emulsifying agent? (c) Why are protective colloids used?
9. (a) Describe three methods of precipitating colloids. (b) Give an example of the use of each method of precipitation described.
10. (a) What is *ad*sorption? (b) How does it differ from *ab*sorption? (c) Why are some colloidal-sized particles, and other small particles, able to selectively *ad*sorb substances?

Relating Terms Within the Concept

Each of the following exercises consists of five terms. From the last four, select the term or terms closely related to the *italicized* term.

1. *dialysis:* separating colloid, semipermeable membrane, diffusion, unsaturated valence
2. *Tyndall effect:* precipitation, ultramicroscope, electrodes, beam of light
3. *sol:* gel, red glass, smog, jelly
4. *aerosol:* paint, fog, solid dispersed in gas, liquid dispersed in gas
5. *lyophobic:* "solvent hater," "solvent lover," gelatin, lyophilic
6. *dispersion:* peptization, displacement, colloid mill, oxidation-reduction

7. *condensation:* Bredig arc, hydrolysis, displacement, homogenization
8. *emulsifying agent:* electric field, soap, mayonnaise, Cottrell precipitator
9. *electrophoresis:* Brownian movement, dispersing agent, protective colloid, migrating colloidal particles
10. *adsorption:* Mississippi Delta, surface phenomenon, charged colloidal particles, activated charcoal

Solving Problems Within the Concept
1. A given molecule has a diameter of 2.4×10^{-8} centimeter. How much larger in diameter is a colloidal particle with a diameter of 1.2×10^{-5} centimeter?
2. What is the maximum weight of sulfur that can be precipitated from 31.6 grams of $Na_2S_2O_3$ in solution by the addition of an excess of hydrochloric acid?
3. A cube whose volume is 1 cubic centimeter is dispersed into smaller cubes of colloidal size (10^{-7} centimeter is the length of each side). Determine the total surface area of the colloidal cubes.

Applying the Concept
1. At about $-183°$ C (the temperature at which oxygen liquefies) oxygen molecules *are* adsorbed by activated charcoal. Explain.

2. Many colloidal substances are colored. The color is determined by the size rather than by the chemical nature of the colloidal particle. Explain.
3. Some colloids that have become coagulated can be returned to the colloidal state by the addition of more dispersing medium. Other colloids, once they coagulate, cannot be redispersed. Explain this difference between colloids in terms of lyophilic and lyophobic properties.

Reading Further
"Electrophoresis," by George W. Gray, *Scientific American,* December 1951. Discusses the properties of particles which enable them to migrate in an electric field, with emphasis on the use of electrophoresis in studying proteins.

"How Giant Molecules are Measured," by Peter J. Debye, *Scientific American,* September 1957. The scattering of light and other effects make it possible to determine the weight and configuration of giant molecules.

"Separating Solids with Bubbles," by A. M. Gaudin, *Scientific American,* December 1956. Flotation is a technique for sorting solids with bubbles; varying the chemical solutions causes various ores to adhere to the bubbles.

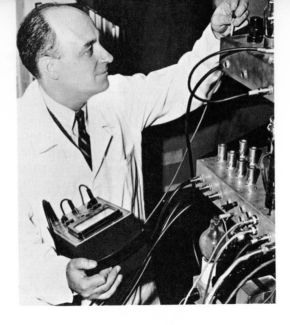

The Behavior of Nuclear Particles

On December 2, 1942, under the west stands of Stagg Field at the University of Chicago, man first initiated *and controlled* a self-sustaining nuclear chain reaction. The team assembled in the squash court at Chicago that day was an international one. It included some of America's most distinguished scientists, two Hungarians, and a Canadian. The leader of the group was an Italian, Enrico Fermi, who had already won a Nobel prize for his work with transuranic elements.

Everyone present knew that this was a fateful moment. The building of the first atomic pile, around which they were now standing, had required months of careful planning and experimenting. If successful, the operation of the pile would represent a great breakthrough for science. At 3:25 that afternoon Fermi called: Pull the control rod another foot. After a few minutes of calculating, he announced that the reaction was self-sustaining. The world's first nuclear chain reaction was in operation. Man had not only initiated a self-sustaining fission reaction but had then stopped it. He had not only released the energy of the atom's nucleus; he had controlled it.

The pile was aptly named, for it actually was a pile of bricks—bricks of graphite containing fissionable uranium. So precise were Fermi's calculations that he predicted almost to the brick when the fission reaction would become self-sustaining.

21

The Atomic Nucleus

The age of nuclear science can be dated from two "accidental discoveries" that occurred just before the turn of the century. In 1895 Wilhelm von Roentgen, a German scientist, discovered the existence of X rays; and the following year Henri Becquerel discovered natural radioactivity. By 1902 the Curies had discovered radium, and the theory of radioactive disintegration—that atoms of one element disintegrate to form atoms of another element—had been proposed. Only a year later, the Curies and Becquerel shared a Nobel prize for their work.

Reasoning with what often seemed like contradictory data resulting from careful experimentation, these scientists and others soon proved the existence of subatomic particles. Knowledge of such particles within the nucleus changed the complexion—and the complexity—not only of chemistry but of all sciences. But we are getting ahead of our story; let us return to the discovery of X rays.

DISCOVERY OF RADIOACTIVITY

Roentgen had been working in a dark room with a gas discharge (or cathode ray) tube covered with black paper. He noticed that when he passed an electric current through the tube, a glow appeared on a small screen coated with barium platinocyanide lying a few feet away. What caused the glow? There was no apparent contact between the electric current, the cathode rays, and the screen. Yet *something* was able to pass from the current, through the glass walls of the discharge tube, through the black paper, and across several feet of air to create a fluorescence on the screen (Fig. 21-1). Roentgen concluded that it must be some kind of *invisible ray*. Since the existence of such a ray was unknown to science, Roentgen called it an *X ray* after the algebraic symbol for an unknown quantity. From numerous experiments with such discharge tubes, Roentgen observed that the glass wall of the tubes fluoresced with a yellow-green glow where the cathode rays struck the glass. He finally concluded that X rays are produced when cathode rays strike the glass wall. These X rays, in turn, cause certain chemical substances to fluoresce.

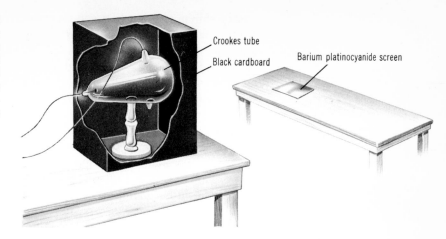

21-1 Roentgen observed that when current passed through a Crookes tube completely covered by black paper, a barium platinocyanide screen a few feet away glowed. He finally concluded that invisible X rays, produced when cathode rays struck the glass of the tube, penetrated the black paper and caused the screen to glow.

Crookes tube

Black cardboard

Barium platinocyanide screen

Roentgen's discovery caused much interest. It was taken up and pursued further not only by other research scientists but also by members of the medical profession. Roentgen reported that when he passed these mysterious rays through his hand, they left a shadow of the bone structure on a sensitized photographic plate. The short time that elapsed before X rays were used in medical diagnosis is a tribute to his work.

Radiation

Today scientists know that Roentgen's invisible X rays, like visible light, are electromagnetic radiation. Though electromagnetic radiation includes rays and waves of many different wavelengths, from short to long, our eyes can detect only the wavelengths of visible light rays. Because X rays have short wavelengths, they cannot be seen.

The wavelengths of X rays are not only shorter than those of visible light rays but they also have a great deal more energy. X rays are usually produced when electrons in the inner shells of atoms are dislodged. In Roentgen's experiments, X rays were produced by the cathode rays striking the walls of the discharge tube. Later on, the cathode rays were focused on a metal target placed inside the tube. This arrangement produced a more intense source of X rays. Today it is known that when X rays strike uranium salts and certain other compounds, such as zinc sulfide or barium platinocyanide, visible light is emitted. The screen Roentgen used in his experiments was covered with the latter compound; it fluoresced when struck by X rays. Since the glass of the tube contained small amounts of uranium salts, it too glowed.

Radioactivity

Among those most interested in Roentgen's discovery was the physicist Henri Becquerel. His father had studied certain substances, notably uranium salts, that fluoresce when exposed to sunlight. Thinking that a

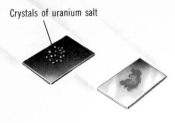

Crystals of uranium salt

Crystals of uranium salt

21-2 For Becquerel "chance favored the prepared mind." The fact that sunlight in no way affected the rate or amount of radiation emitted by a uranium salt was an early observation that along with others led to his discovery of natural radioactivity.

relationship might exist between the fluorescence of these substances and X rays, Becquerel performed numerous experiments with the fluorescent uranium salt, potassium uranyl sulfate [$K(UO)SO_4$]. He wrapped a photographic plate in black, lightproof paper, placed crystals of the uranium salt on the paper, and exposed the arrangement to sunlight for several hours (Fig. 21-2). When he developed the photograph he found a black spot at the place where the salt had rested over the plate. Evidently some form of energy other than light had been able to penetrate the envelope and produce the outline of the crystals.

On one occasion he developed several plates on which uranium salts had remained in place for several days but with only a brief exposure to sunlight. In Becquerel's own words, he was "... expecting to find very faint images. On the contrary, the silhouettes appeared with great intensity. . . . " Thus Becquerel showed that the uranium salts emitted radiation without being exposed to sunlight, and that this radiation lasted for some time.

Later Becquerel found that the radiations from his uranium compound were far more penetrating than X rays: they could pass easily through a sheet of aluminum or copper. From these experiments and others Becquerel showed that this radiation was different from Roentgen's artificially produced X rays. Becquerel had discovered that radiation is given off spontaneously from certain naturally occurring substances. This phenomenon soon became known as **natural radioactivity.**

Becquerel noticed another interesting thing about the radiation emitted by a naturally radioactive substance. In passing through the air, the radiation caused the molecular particles of air to lose electrons, so that these formerly neutral particles become charged (ions). This important property was used in determining the intensity of radioactivity and ultimately in the discovery of two radioactive elements. Today the ability of radiation to ionize gases is employed in devices for detecting radiation.

Radioactive Elements

Inspired by Becquerel's discovery, Marie Curie, a young Polish student studying in Paris, undertook a study of "uranium rays" for her doctoral thesis. By measuring the "power of ionization" of various minerals, she found that thorium was also radioactive. With the help of her husband Pierre, she undertook a study of the radioactivity of pitchblende, an ore of uranium. They found the ore to be four times more radioactive than the element uranium. From numerous experiments and calculations they could only conclude that this radioactivity resulted from a new radioactive element present in small amounts in the ore. But proving the existence of such an element was not easy.

By July 1898 they announced the existence of a new radioactive element; they called it *polonium* in honor of Madame Curie's native land. Though polonium was four hundred times more active than uranium, this minute amount still could not account for the great activity of pitch-

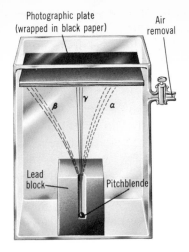

Photographic plate (wrapped in black paper)   Air removal

Lead block   Pitchblende

21-3 Rutherford found that pitchblende disintegrates to produce three types of radiation. From the location of the "spots" produced on a photographic plate in the procedure above, he determined that the elements in pitchblende give off alpha particles, beta particles, and gamma radiation.

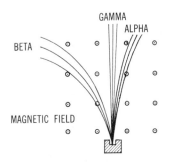

GAMMA
ALPHA
BETA

MAGNETIC FIELD

21-4 Marie Curie included this diagram of alpha, beta, and gamma radiation in a magnetic field in her doctoral dissertation published in 1903.

blende. So the search continued. In December of 1898 the Curies, together with G. Bémont, announced the discovery of a second new element. It was nine hundred times more active than an equal mass of uranium! Because of its extreme radioactivity, the Curies named the new element *radium*.

Scientists were reluctant to accept the discovery of not one, but two radioactive elements, and the Curies spent four painstaking years isolating one-tenth of a gram of radium chloride from several tons of pitchblende residue. With this small amount Marie Curie was able to confirm that radium was a new, radioactive element with an atomic weight of 225. For her contributions in the field of radioactivity Marie Curie was awarded not one, but two Nobel prizes in science—the only person ever to be so honored.

Since the Curies began their work at the turn of the century, some forty naturally radioactive elements have been found. And many of these elements have several isotopes—atoms of an element that differ in the numbers of neutrons in their nuclei. Those naturally occurring isotopes that emit radiation spontaneously from their nuclei are called **natural radioactive isotopes,** or **natural radioisotopes.**

Types of Radiation

Is the radiation from a radioactive element of only one type, or can the same element emit several kinds of radiation? In 1903 Ernest Rutherford sought to find the answer to this question by observing the effect of a magnetic field upon the radiation from a radioactive substance. Previous reactions studied by chemists had involved changes in the electron structure; in the study of radioactive elements, Rutherford was considering a new kind of change, one that occurs in the atom's nuclear core. This now classic experiment can be repeated if a piece of pitchblende is available.

A small piece of pitchblende is placed in the bottom of a deep, but narrow, cavity in a small block of lead, as in Fig. 21-3. Since the pitchblende is surrounded on three sides by the dense lead, radiation can only escape in the form of a vertical beam through the opening at the top. The lead block is placed in a chamber from which all air can be removed, and an undeveloped photographic plate (wrapped in black paper) is suspended horizontally about 6 inches above the opening in the block. A strong magnetic field is applied perpendicular to, and out of the plane of, the apparatus. After several hours, the film is developed.

On the film are three distinct spots—the result of three different types of radiation emitted from the nuclei of the uranium and other radioactive atoms in the pitchblende. One of these spots is to the *right* of a vertical line over the cavity in the lead block (Fig. 21-4). The position of this spot indicates that the rays causing it were deflected slightly by the magnetic field. From the amount and direction of deflection, scientists conclude that this type of radiation must consist of positively charged

Table 21-1 COMMON TYPES OF RADIATION

Type of radiation	Symbol	Charge	Mass
Alpha particle	α	+2	4 amu
Beta particle	β	−1	>0 amu
Gamma radiation	γ	0	0 amu

particles of considerable mass. These are called **alpha particles.** Further experimentation has shown that the mass of each positively charged alpha particle is equal to that of a helium nucleus, which has a mass number of 4. Like the helium nucleus, each alpha particle has a charge of +2. The Greek letter alpha (α), the first letter of the Greek alphabet, is often used to represent alpha particles or alpha radiation.

The second spot on the film is somewhat further to the *left* of a vertical line over the cavity in the lead block. Evidently the radiation that produced this spot consisted of negatively charged particles whose mass is only negligible. These are called *beta particles.* Further evidence showed that beta particles are extremely energetic electrons originating in the nucleus of the atom. Like all electrons, beta particles have negligible mass and a charge of −1. The name comes from the second letter of the Greek alphabet, beta (β), which is used to represent beta particles or beta radiation.

The third spot on the film indicates that the third type of radiation, called **gamma radiation,** is unaffected by the magnet: the spot lies in a direct vertical line with the slit. This position of the spot indicates that gamma radiation has no electrical charge. Gamma radiation is electromagnetic radiation with a wavelength shorter than that of X rays. As with all electromagnetic radiation, gamma radiation has no measurable mass and travels at the speed of light. The Greek letter gamma (γ) is used to represent this third type of radiation. (For a summary of these types of radiation see Table 21-1.)

These three types of radiation—alpha, beta, and gamma—are not the only types, but they are the most common. Some few radioisotopes emit all three types of radiation; others, as shown in Table 21-2, emit only one or two types. Depending on the main type of radiation they emit, isotopes are called either alpha emitters, beta emitters, or gamma emitters. Almost all radioisotopes, however, emit some gamma radiation.

Table 21-2 RADIOISOTOPES AND TYPES OF RADIATION

Radioisotope	Type of radiation		
Bismuth-212	α	β	γ
Carbon-14		β	
Chlorine-36		β	
Cobalt-60		β	γ
Iodine-131		β	γ
Iron-59		β	γ
Phosphorus-32		β	
Polonium-214	α		
Polonium-215	α	β	
Polonium-216	α		
Sodium-24		β	γ
Strontium-90		β	
Uranium-235	α		γ
Uranium-238	α		γ
Uranium-239		β	γ

QUESTIONS AND PROBLEMS

1. (a) How are X rays produced? (b) With respect to wavelengths, energy, speed, and source how do they differ from light rays; from gamma rays?
2. Define the terms *radioactivity, radioactive isotope,* and *radioisotope.*
3. Describe briefly the contribution of each of the following scientists to the field of radioactivity: Roentgen, Becquerel, Marie Curie, Rutherford.
4. (a) Name the three types of radiation most frequently emitted from radioactive elements. (b) How do these types of radiation differ from each other in mass and charge? (c) How is a beta particle similar to an orbital electron? How does it differ? (d) Which of these types of radiation is not composed of particles?

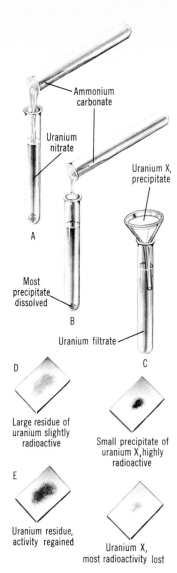

Ammonium carbonate

Uranium nitrate

A

Uranium X, precipitate

Most precipitate dissolved

B

Uranium filtrate

D

Large residue of uranium slightly radioactive

C

Small precipitate of uranium X, highly radioactive

E

Uranium residue, activity regained

Uranium X, most radioactivity lost

21-5 Crookes mistakenly concluded that regaining of radioactivity by the uranium residue and loss of activity by uranium X resulted from an impurity in the uranium—but the results were soon to be reinterpreted in light of the theory of radioactive disintegration.

In contrast to the prospector with his Geiger counter, interested only in locating radioactive ore, the scientist wants to know not only what causes radioactivity, but why one radioactive substance is different from another. Why does uranium change slowly into lead? How can one element be changed into another? The search for answers to questions such as these has greatly enlarged scientists' understanding of the nature of matter.

Radioactive Disintegration

In 1900 William Crookes, an English scientist, was studying the radioactive properties of the salt, uranium nitrate. He found that when ammonium carbonate was added to an aqueous solution of the salt, a precipitate formed. When an excess of ammonium carbonate was then added to the precipitate, most of the precipitate redissolved *but a small quantity remained* (Fig. 21-5). First, Crookes separated the small quantity of precipitate by filtration and evaporated the liquid filtrate. What remained after evaporation was a large amount of solid residue that contained most of the uranium salt. He then compared the effect on a photographic film of this large amount of residue and the small amount of precipitate. The results were startling. The residue from the filtrate, containing essentially all of the uranium, exposed the film very slightly while the precipitate exposed it intensely. From this Crookes assumed that radioactivity was not a property of uranium itself but of some *impurity* associated with it. He named this impurity uranium X. The conclusion was natural enough, but it was incorrect, as we shall soon see.

A year later Becquerel performed a similar experiment. But he allowed the substances which had separated from each other—the active precipitate and the less active residue—to stand for a period of 18 months. At the end of that time he found that the uranium salt residue had completely regained its radioactivity while the small amount of precipitate was no longer radioactive. The mysterious substance which made up the precipitate—a substance which was so very active for a time and then appeared to lose its radioactivity altogether—was Crookes' *uranium X*.

In 1902 Rutherford and Frederick Soddy, another English scientist, used the same method of precipitation and filtration to separate an extremely active precipitate from the element thorium. This substance, which behaved much like uranium X, they named *thorium X*. They noticed that as the thorium X eventually began to lose its radioactivity, the thorium started to regain radioactivity at exactly the same rate.

This experiment and others eventually led Rutherford and Soddy to propose the theory of **radioactive disintegration.** According to this theory, *atoms of radioactive elements are unstable and undergo spontaneous disintegration by emitting radiation.* This disintegration produces atoms of new elements which may themselves be radioactive and hence undergo further disintegration.

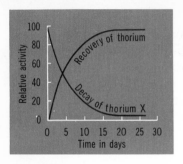

21-6 Rutherford and Soddy found that thorium X lost its radioactivity at the same rate that thorium in the residue removed from thorium X regained its activity.

Using this theory to explain the results of the experiments just described, Rutherford and Soddy stated that thorium and uranium are only weakly radioactive. They undergo spontaneous disintegration to form, respectively, thorium X and uranium X, which are strongly radioactive. The thorium X and uranium X, in turn, disintegrate to form relatively weak radioactive products.

thorium ⟶ thorium X ⟶ products
(weak   (strong   (weak
radioactivity)   radioactivity)   radioactivity)

In Rutherford and Soddy's experiments the precipitate, thorium X, gradually disintegrated to a weakly radioactive product over a period of time. Consequently, the precipitate appeared to lose its radioactivity. At the same time part of the residue, the thorium, slowly disintegrated into more thorium X, which is highly radioactive. Hence the residue seemed to regain its radioactivity. The thorium was disintegrating into thorium X at approximately the same rate as the thorium X was disintegrating to a weakly radioactive product (Fig. 21-6).

The experiments of Becquerel, Rutherford, Soddy, and others showed an important difference between reactions involving radioactive elements and ordinary chemical reactions. The rate of radioactive disintegration of unstable atoms is not affected in any way by changes in temperature, pressure, or other physical means. This was unexpected, although not surprising in the light of later knowledge, as *radioactivity results from changes within the atomic nucleus and not, as in ordinary chemical reactions, from changes in the electron structure outside the nucleus.*

Transmutation and Decay

Today scientists frequently use the term "transmutation" as well as "disintegration" to describe the change of an atom of one element into an atom of another element. When the transmutation is from an element of higher atomic number into one of lower atomic number, the term "decay" is often used. Thorium, for example, decays to thorium X (radium); and radium in turn decays to radon (Fig. 21-7) and finally, to lead. Transmutations can either occur naturally or be produced artificially. In the next chapter we shall see how elements beyond uranium in the periodic table have been produced artificially. These elements, whose atomic numbers are 93 and above, are called the **transuranic elements.**

At the beginning of this book an element was defined as a substance which could not be broken down into simpler form by ordinary chemical means. Does the information just learned about the transmutation of atoms alter that definition? It does not, because ordinary chemical means include such things as heating, electrolysis, and reactions with other chemicals—and none of these can produce transmutation. Only nuclear processes yet to be studied can produce transmutations, and these reactions are not considered "ordinary."

21-7 A small gold tube containing radon is being cut off. The radon containers or "seeds" are used in treating cancer where surgery is impractical.

Natural Radioactive Series

Many natural radioisotopes fall into one of three natural *radioactive series*. A radioactive series contains a related group of radioactive isotopes in which each is produced by the decay of the isotope immediately preceding it. A radioactive series, in a sense, represents a series of steps that some unstable (radioactive) isotopes go through to produce a stable (nonradioactive) isotope. The elements that make up the three radioactive series are the heavier elements, those that appear between thallium and uranium in the periodic table. Their atomic numbers are 81 to 92.

Table 21-3   **URANIUM DISINTEGRATION SERIES**

Radioelement	Corresponding element	Symbol	Radiation	Half life
Uranium I ↓	Uranium	^{238}U	α	4.51×10^9 years
Uranium X_1 ↓	Thorium	^{234}Th	β	24.1 days
Uranium X_2 ↓	Protactinium	^{234}Pa	β	1.18 min
Uranium II ↓	Uranium	^{234}U	α	2.48×10^6 years
Ionium ↓	Thorium	^{230}Th	α	8.0×10^4 years
Radium ↓	Radium	^{226}Ra	α	1.62×10^3 years
Ra Emanation ↓	Radon	^{222}Rn	α	3.82 days
Radium A 99.98% | 0.02%	Polonium	^{218}Po	α and β	3.05 min
Radium B	Lead	^{214}Pb	β	26.8 min
Astatine-218	Astatine	^{218}At	α	2 sec
Radium C 99.96% | 0.04%	Bismuth	^{214}Bi	α and β	19.7 min
Radium C′	Polonium	^{214}Po	α	1.6×10^{-4} sec
Radium C″	Thallium	^{210}Tl	β	1.32 min
Radium D	Lead	^{210}Pb	β	19.4 years
Radium E ~100% | 2×10^{-4}%	Bismuth	^{210}Bi	α and β	5.0 days
Radium F	Polonium	^{210}Po	α	138.4 days
Thallium-206	Thallium	^{206}Tl	β	4.20 min
Radium G (End product)	Lead	^{206}Pb	Stable	—

The first series, and the one we shall use as an example here, is called the uranium series. The uranium series includes the seventeen radioactive isotopes and the one stable isotope listed in column one of Table 21-3. The names listed in this column are those originally given to the isotopes in the series. But the nature of some of these isotopes was not known at the time. As knowledge of nuclear reactions increased, a more up-to-date list of names was drawn up; this is given in column two of the table. Column three gives the symbol for each isotope, while column four indicates the type of radiation the isotope emits. (The significance of column five, Half life, is discussed on page 338.) In connection with column three, recall that the mass number of a particular isotope of an element is shown by a superscript to the right of the symbol for the element.

The parent member of the uranium series is the isotope uranium-238. Uranium-238 decays by emitting an alpha particle to form an atom of the element thorium. These thorium atoms, which have an atomic number of 90 and a mass number of 234, are themselves radioactive. The atoms of thorium-234 each decay by emitting a beta particle to form radioactive protactinium with an atomic number of 91 and a mass number of 234. The decay process continues by the emission of alpha or beta particles until the stable isotope, lead-206, is eventually formed. As lead-206 is nonradioactive, its formation stops the process of decay and ends the series.

Artificial Transmutations

Not long after the discovery of natural transmutation, scientists attempted to transmute atoms artificially by bombarding them with charged particles. The first artificial transmutation was achieved by Rutherford in 1919. He bombarded nitrogen gas (nitrogen-14) with high-energy alpha particles from radioactive bismuth-214 (Fig. 21-8). The nuclei of a few of the nitrogen atoms were disrupted. The transmutation produced atoms of oxygen-17 and "charged atoms of hydrogen" (protons). For the first time in history man had been able to change one element into another (Table 21-4). On a limited scale, the dream of the ancient alchemists had come true!

Since Rutherford's historic transmutation, scientists have brought about hundreds of artificial transmutations. One of the most spectacular

21-8 Rutherford's apparatus had an alpha source at A, a thin absorbing disk at B, and a zinc sulfide screen at C. When the cylinder was filled with nitrogen-14, the oxygen-17 produced from it by alpha bombardment remained in the container, but the protons ejected caused scintillations of the screen.

Table 21-4 **RUTHERFORD'S FIRST ARTIFICIAL TRANSMUTATION**

	alpha particles	+	nitrogen-14	→	oxygen-17	+	proton
protons	2 amu		7 amu		8 amu		1 amu
neutrons	2 amu		7 amu		9 amu		0 amu
nucleus	4 amu	+	14 amu	=	17 amu	+	1 amu
			18 amu	=	18 amu		

was achieved by W. Bothe and H. Becker in Germany in 1930. They bombarded atoms of boron and beryllium with alpha particles from radioactive polonium. This produced transmutations—but it also produced highly penetrating radiation which had no charge at all. What was this powerful, uncharged radiation? At first it was thought to be gamma radiation. But in 1932 James Chadwick, while studying the effect of this radiation on paraffin or other material containing hydrogen, discovered that the radiation consisted of neutral particles each of which had a mass similar to that of a proton. These uncharged particles were neutrons—particles whose discovery Rutherford had actually predicted twelve years before!

In 1934 Irene Joliot-Curie, a daughter of Pierre and Marie Curie, and her husband, Frederic Joliot, also established a milestone in artificial transmutation. They bombarded a thin sheet of aluminum foil with alpha particles. Atoms of aluminum were changed to atoms of phosphorus-30, and these phosphorus atoms, in turn, decayed rapidly to produce atoms of silicon. Here was a radioactive series—the first ever produced by man.

QUESTIONS AND PROBLEMS

1. Use the theory of radioactive disintegration to explain the results of Becquerel's experiment involving uranium and uranium X.
2. Differentiate among the terms; *transmutation, disintegration, decay.*
3. How does natural transmutation differ from artificial transmutation?
4. Below are the first three and last three members of the thorium series.

First Three Elements	Symbol	Radiation	Last Three Elements	Symbol	Radiation
Thorium	^{232}Th	γ	Polonium	^{212}Po	γ
Radium	^{228}Ra	β	Thallium	^{208}Tl	β
Actinium	^{228}Ac	β	Lead	^{208}Pb	—

(a) Name the parent member of the series. (b) Name the only stable (nonradioactive) isotope in the series. (c) Which elements emit alpha particles? beta particles? (d) What are the atomic number and mass number of the thallium isotope?

DETECTING RADIATION

A small piece of pure uranium-235 looks harmless enough. Its radiation cannot be seen or perceived by any of the senses. Yet the radiation can be deadly. As radiation cannot be observed directly, it must be detected by observing the effect it has on other substances. The ability of radiation to produce ions is particularly helpful. To detect ions produced by a radioactive source, the nuclear scientist has devised a number of instruments referred to as *monitoring instruments.*

The Geiger Counter

The instrument commonly used in studying radioactivity is the Geiger counter. *To study its operation and uses* you need only a relatively simple counter and a watch with a luminous dial. The dial is luminous because it is painted with a radium salt and zinc sulfide; the latter glows when struck by radiation from the radium compound.

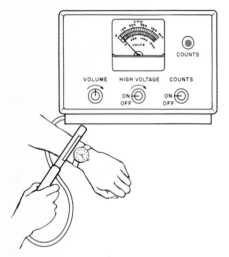

Bring the watch close to the probe of the Geiger counter, as shown at the left. Turn on the counter, and note that after a few moments it registers the presence of the radium by a sharp clicking sound or (depending on the type of counter) by the flashing of a small neon light bulb. Gradually move the watch dial away. Does the response of the counter grow fainter? Observe that as long as the counter is turned on there are intermittent clicks or flashes even though there is apparently no radioactive source at hand. You shall see the reason for that in just a moment.

If a piece of pitchblende or other radioactive ore is available, place the ore on a table and move the probe of the counter toward and away from it. What happens? (In all experimental work involving radioactive substances, handle the radioactive material as little as possible; *move the Geiger probe rather than the radioactive material.*)

Why did the counter react in this way to the radioactive face of the watch? The answer is indicated in Fig. 21-9. The probe of the Geiger counter is composed of a glass tube in which are sealed a circular metal tube with a wire through its center, and a gas under low pressure. Radiation from the watch dial or radioactive ore causes this gas to ionize. When the counter is turned on, the ionized gas permits a flow of current between the metal tube and the center wire. The electric current can manifest itself as a clicking sound, a flashing light, or a reading on a dial.

Such a counter is adequate for detecting the beta but not the alpha radiation from the radium salt and its disintegration products. To detect alpha radiation, the tube of the counter would have to be made of thin quartz: alpha radiation does not penetrate regular glass. Nor do Geiger counters detect gamma radiation as efficiently as certain other instruments, though they can be used for this purpose. The uncharged gamma radiation passes through the gas of the tube too rapidly to produce ionization effectively.

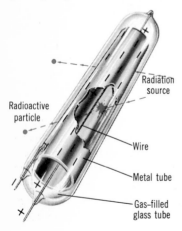

21-9 When the gas in an operating Geiger tube is ionized by radiation passing through it, current flows between the negatively charged metal tube and the positively charged center wire.

Radiation source

Radioactive particle

Wire

Metal tube

Gas–filled glass tube

The Electroscope

An electroscope is not only the oldest, but is still a commonly used instrument for detecting radiation. In fact, a simple gold-leaf electroscope was used by Marie Curie and by Rutherford in their early work on radioactivity. *You might like to try an investigation* that they must have done many times.

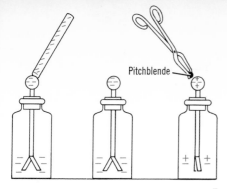

Rub a rubber rod with a piece of fur to give the rod a negative charge. Touch the charged rod to the knob of an electroscope, like the one shown at the left. Observe that the leaves of the electroscope, having the same charge, repel each other and stay apart. Remove the rod; what happens to the leaves? Now bring a radioactive substance such as pitchblende (held in long-handled tongs) close to the top of the electroscope. Why do the leaves fall together again?

In a charged electroscope, the leaves remain apart as long as the gases in the air surrounding it are un-ionized. Once something causes the gases to become ionized, the electroscope is discharged and the leaves fall together again. In the investigation, the radiation from the pitchblende ionized the air around the electroscope, thereby discharging it.

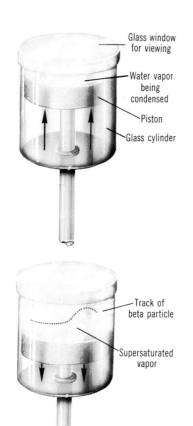

21-10 In a cloud chamber, water vapor alternately condenses and expands. Condensation around ionized particles marks the path of radiation.

The Cloud Chamber

The cloud chamber developed by C. T. R. Wilson in 1911 has one great advantage over any other detection device used previously. It makes the track of ionized particles visible. The cloud chamber is based on the principle that water vapor condenses to form visible droplets if there are nuclei of some sort around which the water vapor can collect. The construction and operation of a simple cloud chamber is indicated in Fig. 21-10. As radiation enters the cloud chamber, ions are produced and tiny droplets of water collect on these ionized particles. These droplets reflect light, marking the path of the radiation through the chamber. This path is known as a **cloud track.**

From the length and detailed structure of the cloud tracks, scientists can differentiate between alpha, beta, and other nuclear radiation. If the cloud chamber is operated between the poles of a strong magnet, the curvature of the tracks reveals to the specialist many of the properties of the radiation, such as its mass, velocity, and charge. Study the photographs of cloud tracks produced by different types of radiation in a cloud chamber in Fig. 21-11. Such photographs, together with mathematical analyses, are used by scientists to identify particles that originate in the nuclei of atoms.

Several other instruments used to detect radiation are the scintillation counter, the bubble chamber (Fig. 21-12), and the spark chamber.

Cosmic Radiation and Background

Whenever a Geiger counter is turned on, a clicking sound is heard even though no radioactive source is present. Likewise, a charged electroscope becomes discharged over a period of time without any radioactive substance being nearby. And a few tracks appear in a cloud chamber although it is far removed from any source of radiation. The reason for these changes is that small amounts of radiation are present everywhere in the earth's atmosphere. Some of this radiation comes from

21-11 The upper cloud chamber photograph shows a group of alpha particles, one of which has struck and been scattered by a fluorine nucleus. In the lower photograph, a carbon and an oxygen atom are breaking apart after being struck by high-energy neutrons.

21-12 Nuclear particles leave trails of tiny bubbles in a hydrogen bubble chamber. In a magnetic field, the slower-moving particles are deflected into spirals to the right or left according to charge.

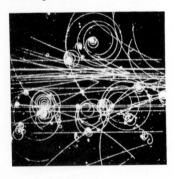

the break-up of atoms in the sun but the greater part is believed to come from the explosion of stars in outer space. For this reason it is called **cosmic radiation** from the Greek word *cosmos* meaning "universe." This primary cosmic radiation consists mainly of positively charged nuclei traveling at tremendous speed. Other cosmic radiation, called secondary radiation, is produced as the primary radiation strikes the nuclei of atoms of gases in the atmosphere.

Listen carefully to the kind of clicking that occurs as this cosmic radiation enters the probe of your Geiger counter. It is very irregular. First you may hear one click, then another, then a "shower" of clicks followed by silence for several seconds. Clearly cosmic rays enter our atmosphere in very sporadic, unpredictable fashion.

There are also minute amounts of radioactive material in many common substances. The granite walls of a building contain small amounts of radioactive materials. Even the human body contains a trace of radioactive potassium-40. These different radioactive sources, but especially cosmic radiation, together make up what is called **background radiation** or simply **background.** This background must be taken into account whenever you are trying to measure the precise amount of radiation coming from a particular source.

Half Life

Instruments such as the Geiger counter are used not only to detect radiation but also to study some of the properties of radioactive substances. One of the most important of these properties is the rate at which a radioactive substance decays. The original experiments of Becquerel, Soddy, and Rutherford showed that although radioactive substances gradually lose their ability to emit radiation, they never lose that ability completely. We cannot, therefore, speak of the time it takes for a substance to become completely nonradioactive since theoretically it never loses its radioactivity completely. No matter how infinitesimally small it may be, some radiation remains. Therefore it is more convenient and accurate to speak of the **half life** of a radioactive substance. Half life is the length of time required for any radioactive isotope to lose half its radioactivity.

Suppose you wish to measure the rate at which iodine-131 loses its radioactivity. We find that after 8 days a vial which contains 10 microcuries* (μc) of ^{131}I (as potassium iodide) solution emits just half as much radiation as it did originally. Then the half life of ^{131}I is 8 days. At the end of another 8 days the iodine-131 solution retains only one-fourth (½ × ½) of its original activity; and after 24 days only ⅛ (½ × ½ × ½) of its radioactivity remains. Regardless of the amount of ^{131}I present at the start of an investigation, after each 8-day period it possesses only one-half of its previous activity. As this relationship continues indefinitely,

*A microcurie is a unit used in measuring the activity of a radioactive substance.

Table 21-5 **RADIOISOTOPES AND HALF LIFE**

Radioisotope	Half life	Radioisotope	Half life
Bismuth-212	60.5 minutes	Polonium-215	0.0018 second
Carbon-14	5,760 years	Polonium-216	0.16 second
Chlorine-36	4×10^5 years	Radium-226	1,620 years
Cobalt-60	5.26 years	Sodium-24	15.0 hours
Iodine-131	8.14 days	Strontium-90	19.9 years
Iron-59	46.3 days	Uranium-235	7.1×10^8 years
Phosphorus-32	14.3 days	Uranium-238	4.51×10^9 years
Polonium-214	1.64×10^{-4} seconds	Uranium-239	23.5 minutes

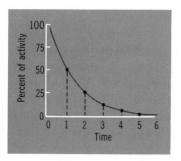

21-13 Radioactive disintegration and half life. In each successive unit of time the amount of a radioactive substance that disintegrates is less than in the preceding time unit. At the end of each time unit, half the activity present at the beginning remains.

no matter how much time passes, any radioactive substance always retains some slight radioactivity (Fig. 21-13).

The half lives of radioactive substances range from a very small fraction of a second (polonium-214 has a half life of only 1.64×10^{-4} second) to billions of years, as in the case of uranium (Table 21-5). The half life of uranium-238 is about the same as the presently accepted age of the earth, 4 to 5 billion years. This indicates that the earth today contains half as much uranium-238 as it did originally. The rest has been transmuted into the stable atoms of lead-206.

Effects of Radiation

Unfortunately the scientists who did the first experimental work with radioactive materials had no way of knowing the extent of burns and damage to body cells that could result from excessive exposure to radiation. The mechanism by which the cells are damaged is as yet not fully understood, but it is known that the harmful consequences of radiation result from the ionizing effect upon the complex molecules of the cells. The ionization of water and the possible destruction of enzymes seem to be especially important.

Of the three types of radiation discussed, alpha and beta particles produce roughly the same ionization effects. Though alpha particles travel the shortest distance, they produce high ionization because of their relatively heavy mass and double positive charge. Beta particles, being lighter and having only a single negative charge, produce less ionization per unit of length but travel further. Since the path of the beta particle is so much longer, the total number of ions produced by the two types of particle is much the same. Gamma radiation, which has no mass or charge, travels the farthest of all. Though gamma radiation usually produces only a small number of ions per unit of length, it may be extremely damaging since it travels for such a considerable distance.

Today, scientists working with radioactive sources take great care to shield themselves from radiation. You have probably seen photographs of workers manipulating radioactive solutions by means of mechanical hands behind leaded glass. Here the leaded glass is acting as **shielding**—

a substance used to reduce the amount of radiation reaching a given area. Other shielding materials include metals, such as lead, heavy water, and concrete.

Protection from Radiation

To determine for yourself the effectiveness of certain metals in shielding workers from beta and gamma radiation, complete the following investigation. Since alpha radiation is absorbed by the glass walls of most Geiger tubes, it is not studied here. If a special Geiger tube is available, you will find that a sheet of paper or a thin sheet of cardboard placed between the radioactive source and the probe absorbs practically all of the alpha radiations. Almost no radiation reaches the tube and registers on the Geiger counter.

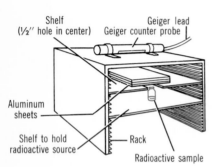

Shelf
(½″ hole in center)   Geiger counter probe   Geiger lead

Aluminum sheets

Shelf to hold radioactive source

Rack

Radioactive sample

To study the absorption of beta radiation, attach the probe of the counter in an apparatus as shown at the left. Place an open vial containing 10 microcuries of phosphorus-32 (in a sodium phosphate solution) at a measured distance from the probe. ^{32}P is used because it emits beta but not gamma radiation. Take a count, or reading, from the meter of the Geiger counter. Place one thin aluminum sheet (about 9 inches square) above the ^{32}P. Determine if it absorbs any radiation by taking another reading. Continue adding aluminum sheets and taking readings until virtually all of the beta radiation is absorbed. Some radiation always seems to remain. Could it be background radiation? How could you find out?

To determine the absorption of gamma radiation, use iodine-131 (in a potassium iodide solution) which emits both beta and gamma radiation. Absorb the beta radiation by closing the metal shield of the Geiger probe. (How else could the beta radiation be absorbed?) Now repeat the same procedure as before, but this time substitute thin sheets of lead for the aluminum sheets. Does the radiation reaching the Geiger tube decrease as the thickness of the lead increases?

Most of the beta radiation is effectively absorbed by several thin sheets of aluminum. Observe from the graph in Fig. 21-14 how beta radiation reaching the Geiger tube decreases with an increasing thickness of aluminum. Similarly, most gamma radiation is absorbed by several sheets of lead.

Numerous other investigations have also shown that alpha radiation is stopped by a thin sheet of paper, while a thin sheet of a light metal such as aluminum is sufficient protection against beta radiation. Dense metals like lead are effective shields against the more penetrating gamma radiation. Effective use is made of this knowledge to protect all individuals who work with radioisotopes and other sources of radiation.

1. (a) Describe briefly the basic operation of a Geiger counter. (b) Whenever a Geiger counter is turned on, intermittent clicks are heard. Explain. (c) Describe briefly the basic operation of a cloud chamber. (d) Why does a charged electroscope discharge after several days?
2. The half life of phosphorus-32 is approximately 14 days. How much of the original radioactivity of 20 microcuries remains after 28 days?
3. (a) Is alpha, beta, or gamma radiation the most penetrating? (b) How are individuals who work with radioisotopes protected from its effects? (c) What is a safe, simple, and inexpensive way to store a radioactive solution that emits only alpha and beta radiation? Why?

EQUATIONS FOR NUCLEAR REACTIONS

Although the atomic nucleus has been a subject for study only since the discovery of radioactivity, thousands of nuclear reactions are already known. Equations are used to represent these nuclear reactions just as they are for the ordinary reactions of chemistry. And as in the usual chemical reaction, the nuclear equation representing disintegration must show that matter is conserved during the reaction: the masses of the reactants and the products are essentially equal to each other.

Symbols in Nuclear Reactions

You know that the symbol for an isotope includes the symbol for the element preceded by a subscript showing its atomic number and followed by a superscript showing its mass number. But not all the particles which play a part in nuclear reactions are complete atoms or even complete nuclei. Protons and neutrons, for example, are only fragments of nuclei. The method used for indicating these subatomic particles is similar to the one used to indicate isotopes. Usually only a small letter is used for the subatomic fragment while a capital is used for the isotope. In the symbol for a subatomic particle, the subscript shows its positive or negative charge; the superscript shows its mass.

As the proton is assigned a charge of $+1$, and as its mass is nearly equal to 1 atomic mass unit, the symbol for the proton can be written $_1^1p$. The nucleus of a normal hydrogen atom contains a single proton. Hence, the symbol for a proton is sometimes written as $_1^1H$. A neutron has no charge but it does have a mass equal to 1 atomic mass unit. Thus the symbol for a neutron is written $_0^1n$. The Greek letter alpha (α) can be used in equations to represent alpha radiation. Since each alpha particle is the nucleus of a helium atom which contains 2 protons and 2 neutrons, the symbol $_2^4He$ may also be used for an alpha particle. A beta particle is an energetic electron that originates in the nucleus of an atom; and every electron is assigned a charge of -1. Hence instead of using the

a. Absorption of beta radiation by aluminum

b. Absorption of gamma radiation by lead

21-14 By comparing the curves of the lines on the two graphs, you can predict that it is much more difficult to completely absorb gamma radiation than beta radiation.

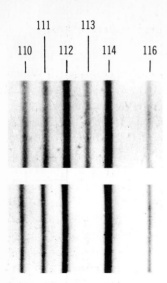

111   113
110 | 112 | 114 | 116

21-15 As indicated by the two mass spectra, when cadmium is exposed to slow neutron bombardment, the neutrons interact with cadmium-113 to form cadmium-114 and to release gamma radiation—but no significant change in mass occurs.

21-16 Cloud chamber evidence of gamma radiation producing several electron-positron pairs. The circular path is formed by an electron spinning in a magnetic field.

Greek letter beta (β) to represent a beta particle, the letter e is often used, preceded by the subscript -1 and followed by the superscript zero, $_{-1}^{0}e$. Here the zero superscript indicates that a beta particle, like an orbital electron, has no appreciable mass. Because gamma radiation has neither charge nor significant mass (Fig. 21-15), it is usually represented simply by the Greek letter gamma (γ).

Using Symbols for Radiation in Nuclear Equations

Now let us use these symbols for radiation in actual nuclear equations. Consider the first step in the natural uranium series as indicated in Table 21-3. When the uranium-238 atom decays it produces an atom of thorium-234 and an alpha particle. This nuclear reaction is represented by the following equation:

$$_{92}^{238}\text{U} \longrightarrow _{90}^{234}\text{Th} + _{2}^{4}\text{He}$$

Whenever, as here, the nucleus of the atom emits an alpha particle, the newly formed element shows a decrease in both atomic number and mass number. In the new element *the atomic number is 2 less and the mass number 4 less* than in the original element. The sum of the atomic numbers, indicated by the subscripts, is equal on both sides of the equation ($92 = 90 + 2$). Similarly, the mass numbers as indicated by the superscripts are equal ($238 = 234 + 4$). The equation indicates properly that mass is conserved in the reaction.

As another example of a nuclear equation, consider the second step in the natural uranium series. Here each thorium-234 atom disintegrates to produce an atom of protactinium-234 and a beta particle:

$$_{90}^{234}\text{Th} \longrightarrow _{91}^{234}\text{Pa} + _{-1}^{0}e$$

From this and similar equations we see that when an atom of an element emits a beta particle, a new element is formed with the *same mass number but with an atomic number one greater* than that of the original element. Each neutron in the nucleus acts *as if* it were composed of an electron and a proton. Whenever a beta particle is emitted, a neutron "disappears" while an additional proton "appears." This "appearance" of the additional proton accounts for the increase of one in the atomic number of the new element. Since a beta particle has no appreciable mass, the mass number of the new element is the same as that of the original element. In the equation above note again that the sums of the subscripts on both sides of the arrow are equal, as well as the sums of the superscripts.

Gamma radiation is emitted during many nuclear reactions (Fig. 21-16). Although the emission of gamma radiation shows that energy is being released from the nucleus, recall that this type of radiation has no mass or charge. Hence it has no effect on either the atomic number or mass number of the original radioisotope and is frequently omitted in writing nuclear reactions. However, as an example of a reaction in which gamma radiation is emitted, consider the production of hydrogen-2 from ordinary hydrogen (hydrogen-1) by bombarding it with neutrons:

$$\,^1_1H + \,^1_0n \longrightarrow \,^2_1H + \gamma$$

Again, the subscripts on both sides of the equation are equal, as are the superscripts. Mass is conserved although gamma radiation is emitted.

Equations for Artificial Transmutations

When Rutherford bombarded nitrogen-14 with energetic alpha particles, each atom of nitrogen-14 that was disrupted resulted in an atom of oxygen-17 and a proton. The long form for this equation is:

$$\,^{14}_7N + \,^4_2He \longrightarrow \,^{17}_8O + \,^1_1H$$

For artificial transmutations of this type a shorter form of the equation is sometimes used. In the shorter equation, the symbol for each isotope is written with its mass number. For the particle used in the bombardment and for the particle produced, successive abbreviated symbols are written in parenthesis. By this method the equation for Rutherford's transmutation becomes:

$$\,^{14}N\,(\alpha,p)\,\,^{17}O$$

Rutherford's artificial transmutation was among the many unprecedented advances that led to a further understanding of the nature of the atomic nucleus during the first two decades of this century. But this was only a prologue for discoveries to follow. Building upon knowledge gained by these early workers with radioactivity, scientists are using the atomic nucleus as a source of energy far greater than any previously known to man. The next chapter deals with the development of this energy.

QUESTIONS AND PROBLEMS

1. Radium changes to radon by the emission of an alpha particle. Refer to Table 21-3 for the mass numbers of radium and radon; then write a nuclear equation for the reaction.
2. Thallium-206 changes to ^{206}Pb by the emission of a beta particle. Refer to Table 21-3 for the mass numbers of the thallium and lead atoms involved, and then write the equation for the nuclear reaction that occurs during the decay.
3. When aluminum-27 is bombarded by alpha particles, each aluminum atom that is hit may change to a silicon-30 atom and a proton. (a) Write the complete equation for this nuclear reaction. (b) Rewrite the equation using the short form.
4. Carbon-14 is produced by bombarding nitrogen-14 with neutrons. (a) Write the complete equation for this reaction. (b) Rewrite the equation using the short form.

THE CONCEPT

In 1895 Wilhelm von Roentgen discovered the first type of high-energy radiation—X rays. Henri Becquerel soon discovered the phenomenon of natural radioactivity—the spontaneous emission of various types of radiation from certain naturally occurring substances. In 1898 Marie Curie and her associates discovered two new elements, polonium and radium, and proved them to be even more naturally radioactive than uranium. Today we know that about forty different elements have naturally radioactive isotopes or radioisotopes.

In 1903 Ernest Rutherford showed that three different types of radiation—alpha, beta, and gamma—are commonly emitted by radioactive substances. An alpha particle is a doubly charged particle with a mass number of 4; essentially each alpha particle is the nucleus of a helium atom. A beta particle has a single negative charge and negligible mass; essentially each beta particle is an energetic electron emitted from the nucleus. Gamma radiation is electromagnetic radiation having no mass or charge and very short wavelengths.

Rutherford and Soddy proposed the theory of radioactive disintegration, which states that atoms of radioactive elements are unstable and undergo spontaneous disintegration by emitting radiation. The disintegration of radioactive substances occurs within the nucleus and not, as in ordinary chemical reactions, from changes in the electron structure outside the nucleus. Transmutations occur whenever atoms of one element change into atoms of another element. When the transmutation is from an element higher in the periodic table into one lower down, radioactive decay is said to occur.

Many natural radioisotopes fall into one of three natural radioactive series in which each radioisotope is produced by the decay of the isotope immediately preceding it. The final member of each series is nonradioactive, or stable.

Many transmutations are induced artificially by bombarding atoms with charged particles or neutrons.

Monitoring devices, including the Geiger counter, electroscope, and cloud chamber, are used to detect radiation. The operation of these devices depends upon the ability of radiation to ionize gases through which they travel. The ever present "background" radiation detected by such instruments results from cosmic radiation. Monitoring instruments enable scientists to study many properties of radioactive substances, including the rate of decay, which is expressed in terms of half life. The half life of a radioactive isotope is the length of time required for it to lose half of its activity. In handling radioactive substances, use proper shielding as protection against harmful radiation: alpha radiation is usually stopped by paper, beta radiation by aluminum, but gamma radiation is stopped effectively only by lead and concrete.

The processes that occur during any nuclear change can be expressed by nuclear equations. In equations for transmutation or decay reactions, as in ordinary chemical equations, the masses of reactants and products must balance.

USING THE CONCEPT

Using the Basic Concept

1. Outline the major steps leading to the discovery of radioactivity.
2. Differentiate among the following terms: *radiation, radioactive isotope,* and *radioactive disintegration.*
3. (a) Describe the properties of the three types of electromagnetic radiation emitted by most radioisotopes. (b) Describe the properties of two other types of high-energy radiation.
4. (a) How do natural and artificial radioactivity differ? (b) In what ways are they similar?
5. Why is the statement, "Certain elements are radioactive," incomplete?
6. Describe Pierre and Marie Curie's con-

tributions to the understanding of radioactivity.
7. A radioactive transmutation may or may
not involve radioactive decay. Give one
example of a transmutation that involves
decay and one example that does not.
8. (a) What is a natural radioactive series?
(b) Describe the steps of the uranium-238
series. (c) Are man-made radioactive
series possible? Justify your answer.
9. (a) Describe the first artificial transmutation produced in the laboratory of Ernest
Rutherford. (b) What was the spectacular
outcome of bombarding boron atoms
with alpha particles?
10. (a) How are the atomic number and mass
number of an element affected when the
nucleus of an atom emits an alpha particle? (b) a beta particle? (c) gamma radiation?
11. (a) In general terms describe three of the
many monitoring instruments used to
detect radiation. (b) Must a radioactive
substance be present to affect these instruments? Why?
12. If polonium-214, an alpha emitter, is held
near the tube of a Geiger counter, "nothing happens." Explain why.
13. (a) Why can't the total time needed for a
radioactive substance to lose all of its
activity be determined? (b) Define the
term *half life*.
14. (a) Why should radiation, even in small
doses, be kept at a minimum? (b) How
can individuals working with radioactive
substances protect themselves?
15. Why is it preferable to use the symbols
$_1^1H$, $_2^4He$, and $_{-1}^0e$ rather than p, α, and β,
respectively, when you are writing nuclear
equations?

Relating Terms Within the Concept
Select the letter of the term in Column B
that is most closely related to each term in
Column A. Do not use a term more than
once.

COLUMN A	COLUMN B
1. cosmic radiation	a. alpha particle
2. radioactivity	b. background
3. radioactive series	c. cloud chamber
4. X ray	d. electromagnetic radiation of short wavelength
5. radioisotopes	e. elements whose atoms have un-stable nuclei
6. transmutation	f. emission of radia-tion from unstable nuclei
7. beta particle	g. energetic electron from the nucleus
8. half life	h. expresses rate of decay
9. a monitoring instrument	i. group of related isotopes, one de-caying into another
10. shielding	j. means of expres-sing nuclear re-actions
11. nuclear equation	k. $_0^1n$
	l. neutron
	m. protection from radiation
	n. type of radioactive disintegration

Solving Problems Within the Concept
1. Write a nuclear equation to represent the
bombardment of boron-11 atoms by
alpha particles to form nitrogen-14 atoms
with the emission of a neutron.
2. Show that in approximately 32 days only
one-sixteenth of the original number of
I^{131} atoms in a sample remain.
3. Each radioactive beryllium-8 atom decays to form two particles that are exactly
alike. (a) What is the type of particle
formed? (b) Write a nuclear equation to
represent this reaction.
4. When aluminum-27 nuclei are bombarded by protons, gamma radiation is
produced. Write a nuclear equation to

show what new isotope is also formed during the process.

5. The nucleus of an unstable atom of $^{65}_{30}Zn$ can disintegrate in several different ways. Write nuclear equations to indicate what happens when a $^{65}_{30}Zn$ atom emits each of the following types of radiation: alpha particle, gamma radiation, proton, neutron.

6. Write a nuclear equation for emission of a beta particle by an atom of calcium-45.

Applying the Concept

1. The age of the earth is about equal to the half life of uranium-238; therefore half the ^{238}U originally present in the earth remains today. What two assumptions must be made for the second half of the above statement to be correct?

2. In 1947 a radioactive product of the disintegration of ^{235}U atoms was proved to be an isotope of the heretofore undiscovered element technetium. (a) Where is this element in the periodic table? (b) What elements does it resemble in chemical properties?

3. Write a nuclear equation to indicate that when the nucleus of an atom emits a beta particle, a neutron is "destroyed" and a proton is "formed."

4. Give several advantages and disadvantages in the use of compounds containing radioactive carbon-14 instead of stable carbon-12 in studying the chemistry of carbon and its compounds.

Reading Further

Introduction to Nuclear Science, by Alvin Glassner, Princeton, N.J., Van Nostrand, 1961. This book includes a number of interesting experiments that can be performed if equipment is available.

The Sourcebook on Atomic Energy, 3d. ed., by Samuel Glasstone, Princeton, N.J., Van Nostrand, 1967. An excellent source of practical and historical information in the fields of atomic and nuclear science.

Laboratory Experiments with Radioisotopes for High School Demonstrations, U.S. Atomic Energy Commission, 1958. Detailed instructions for performing twenty experiments with radioactive iodine and phosphorus.

22

Energy from Nuclear Reactions

Until the discovery of nuclear energy, man was totally dependent upon the sun as his source of energy. Without sunlight he would have had no food. Coal, gas, and oil, the *fossil fuels* which have run his engines for the past two centuries, are formed from the decayed remains of once-living cells. So the sun is once again the ultimate source of this energy. But obtaining the sun's energy indirectly from food and fuels is very inefficient, and the energy supply is limited.

Today man has at his disposal two other means of obtaining energy that seem far more efficient than those just described. One means is by using solar batteries and solar furnaces to obtain energy directly from the sun. The direct use of solar energy is only now beginning to be developed. The other means, obtaining energy from the nuclei of atoms through nuclear reactions, was first harnessed for nuclear bombs. Man is only now finding it feasible to convert nuclear energy indirectly into electric energy needed to run nuclear submarines and cargo ships, as well as to supply his homes and factories with light and power. Today the only controlled source of nuclear energy is nuclear fission; tomorrow, perhaps, controlled nuclear fusion may be a reality.

ENERGY FROM NUCLEAR FISSION

Ever since Rutherford proved that artificial transmutation was possible, scientists had been searching for a way to produce transuranic elements—elements with atomic numbers higher than 92. In 1934 Fermi believed he had achieved this result when he bombarded uranium with neutrons. During natural disintegration uranium emits alpha particles. Fermi found that when bombarded with neutrons, atoms of uranium emitted beta particles. He concluded that the new elements which resulted were transuranic—and it was not until five years later that these elements were accurately identified.

Nuclear Fission

Otto Hahn and Fritz Strassmann of Germany had performed several chemical analyses which led them to conclude that some of the atoms produced by the artificial transmutation of uranium were not transuranic

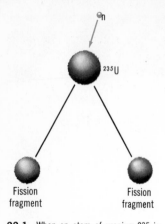

22-1 When an atom of uranium-235 is hit by a neutron, the nucleus splits or undergoes fission into two approximately equal parts, or fission fragments.

elements but a new isotope of radium. Subsequent work led them to believe that their supposed radium might actually be an isotope of the element barium. But how could this be possible? Barium, with an atomic number of 56, belongs in the middle part of the periodic table.

It remained for Lise Meitner and Otto Frisch, also working in Germany, to offer a bold explanation. In 1939 they declared that when a uranium atom is bombarded by neutrons it *splits* into two fragments of somewhat similar mass (Fig. 22-1), and these fragments are atoms of elements in the middle of the periodic table. In their own words ... "It seems possible that the uranium nucleus has only small stability of form, and may, after neutron capture, divide itself into two nuclei of roughly equal size." This process of splitting nuclei of heavy atoms, like uranium, into two approximately equal parts is **atomic,** or **nuclear, fission.**

The best-known example of nuclear fission is that which occurs when the isotope uranium-235 is bombarded with neutrons. This is the isotope that Fermi used in his historic experiment at the University of Chicago. It is the isotope used in the first atomic bomb and is still used in some bombs. Fission occurs when the ^{235}U atoms capture neutrons and then divide. The fragments created in this process are called **fission fragments.** As just seen, these fission fragments are always atoms of elements which occur near the center of the periodic table. In addition to these fragments, the fission produces neutrons and enormous quantities of energy.

Nuclear fission is extremely complex. It can occur in many ways and produce many different combinations of elements. However, the following equation may be taken as a typical reaction which occurs when an atom of ^{235}U undergoes fission by bombardment with neutrons:

$$^{235}_{92}U + ^{1}_{0}n \longrightarrow {}^{141}_{56}Ba + {}^{92}_{36}Kr + 3\,^{1}_{0}n + energy$$

22-2 In addition to fission fragments, neutrons (usually 2 or 3) and a great deal of energy are released when an atom of uranium-235 undergoes fission.

This equation indicates that the nucleus of the uranium atom splits unevenly into a barium nucleus and a krypton nucleus. In addition, 3 neutrons and a large amount of energy are released. It has been determined that the fission of each atom of uranium-235 releases 2 or 3 neutrons, an average of 2.5 neutrons (Fig. 22-2). The significance of these neutrons will become apparent shortly.

Energy from Fission

Nuclear disintegration reactions such as those studied in the last chapter do not release much energy, but nuclear *fission* reactions do. Lise Meitner predicted that nuclear fission would release at least ten times as much energy as had ever been released by any other process, chemical or nuclear, developed prior to 1939. The results have more than borne out that prediction.

The energy produced by a nuclear fission reaction results from the conversion of mass into energy. This relationship between mass and energy was set forth by Albert Einstein in the now famous equation:

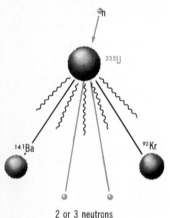

2 or 3 neutrons

$$E = mc^2$$

Here E represents energy, m stands for mass, and c represents the speed of light, which is 3×10^{10} centimeters per second. If you substitute this value for c in the equation, and express the mass (m) in grams, you find that the amount of energy that results (E) is extremely large. This E is expressed in units of energy called ergs.

$$E = 1 \text{ gram} \times (3 \times 10^{10} \text{ cm/sec})^2 = 9 \times 10^{20} \text{ ergs}$$

From Einstein's equation it can be predicted that 1 gram of matter, *if changed completely into energy,* would be sufficient to raise the temperature of 250,000 tons of water from its freezing point to its boiling point!

It *is* true that a small amount of matter is changed into energy even in ordinary chemical reactions, but the amount is so minute that it can be ignored. When 3,000 tons of coal are burned, the loss in mass per gram of coal is so slight that it cannot be measured, even with the most sensitive instruments. On the other hand, when only a single gram of matter is completely converted to energy, it gives as much heat as the burning of 3,000 tons of coal!

Mass-Energy Relationship

It must be remembered that whether a reaction is chemical or nuclear, and whether the amount of energy "created" is very small or very large, the total amount of mass and energy within a given system never changes. Energy is never "created" out of nothing; mass is never "destroyed" without the formation of energy. The total mass and energy in the reactants is always equal to the total mass and energy in the products. Before Einstein's historic equation ($E = mc^2$) and the work on nuclear fission, the laws of *Conservation of Mass* and *Conservation of Energy* were considered as two distinct laws. But even the laws of science change in the face of new evidence. Today the two laws are combined in a **Law of Conservation of Mass-Energy.** This law states that *neither mass nor energy can be created or destroyed but they can be transformed into one another.*

The nucleus of any atom provides an interesting application of this mass-energy relationship. This relationship explains two things about nuclear structure which would otherwise be baffling. First, scientists have learned that the nucleus of an atom actually has less mass than the particles of which it is composed. A helium nucleus, for instance, has slightly less mass than the combined masses of its 2 protons and 2 neutrons. There is the second puzzling fact that although the nucleus of an atom is composed of positively charged and neutral particles, the electrostatic repulsion of the positively charged particles does not cause the nucleus to fly apart.

Today it is known that the actual mass of a helium nucleus (on the carbon-12 atomic weight scale) is 4.0015 atomic mass units. This nucleus

Table 22-1 ACTUAL AND PREDICTED MASS OF AN ATOM OF HELIUM

Actual				Predicted	
2 protons	+	2 neutrons	$\longrightarrow$ 1 helium nucleus	+	energy
2 × 1.0073 amu	+	2 × 1.0086 amu	= 4.0015 amu	+	energy
2.0146 amu	+	2.0172 amu	= 4.0015 amu	+	energy
		4.0318 amu	= 4.0015 amu	+	energy*

*4.0318 amu − 4.0015 amu = 0.0303 amu Mass defect
0.0303 amu = 4.51 × 10⁻⁵ erg Binding energy

is composed of 2 protons, each with a mass of 1.0073 amu, and 2 neutrons, each with a mass of 1.0086 amu. If the masses of these protons and neutrons are combined mathematically (2 × 1.0073 amu + 2 × 1.0086 amu), the anticipated mass is 4.0318 amu or 0.0303 amu more than the actual mass of the nucleus (Table 22-1). This difference between predicted mass and actual mass is called the **mass defect** of the nucleus. Mass defect *is a measure of the amount of matter that was converted into energy* when the helium nucleus was formed.

By means of the equation $E = mc^2$, it is possible to determine the amount of energy which has resulted from this minute amount of "lost" mass; it is 4.51×10^{-5} erg. It is this energy, known as the **binding energy** of the nucleus, that holds the particles of the nucleus together. The binding energy, in effect, overcomes the electrostatic repulsion of the protons. The same amount of energy would be required to separate a nucleus into its component parts.

A Chain Reaction

A single neutron can cause the fission of a single atom of ²³⁵U—but we have seen that the fission of this one atom produces an average of 2.5 neutrons. Obviously more neutrons are produced than are needed to sustain the reaction. These extra product neutrons, if they are traveling at proper speed, can cause still more ²³⁵U atoms to split. And this fission, in turn, produces still more neutrons, as shown in Fig. 22-3. This process is called a **chain reaction.** In a chain reaction *not only does the fission sustain itself, but also the reaction increases in magnitude.*

The mass of fissionable material needed to sustain a fission reaction is called the **critical mass.** The critical mass must be such that the fission produces sufficient neutrons to compensate for neutrons that are lost. If the mass of fissionable material is less than the critical mass, no chain reaction can take place. On the other hand, if it is greater than the critical mass, there is danger of the reaction getting out of control. Hence it is vital that the reaction occur under the most exacting conditions.

Without a chain reaction there would be no atomic pile and no atomic bomb. The essential difference between an atomic pile and an atomic

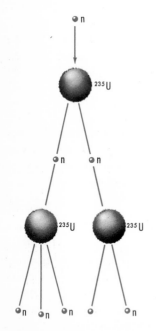

22-3 The neutrons released by the fission of one atom of uranium strike other atoms of uranium. These atoms then undergo fission, releasing neutrons that continue the "chain reaction."

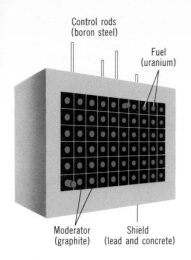

Control rods
(boron steel)

Fuel
(uranium)

Moderator
(graphite)

Shield
(lead and concrete)

22-4 The cross-section diagram shows the essential parts of a nuclear reactor. The photograph shows technicians using manual discharge rods to push "spent fuel" out of the core into a water-filled storage canal behind the shield of the Brookhaven graphite-moderated, air-cooled research reactor.

bomb is simply whether or not the chain reaction is controlled. In an atomic pile the reaction is controlled; in an atomic bomb it is uncontrolled. When a fission reaction is uncontrolled, the 2.5 neutrons resulting, on the average, from the fission of each atom split more and more atoms of ^{235}U—an atomic bomb explodes. To avoid this, Fermi used **control rods** in the first atomic pile. The control rods absorbed extra neutrons but allowed the "proper" number of neutrons from each fissioned atom to go on to produce fission in other atoms. In this way the reaction was sustained but the pile was prevented from exploding.

Nuclear Reactors

Since 1942 many atomic piles, which are frequently known as **nuclear reactors,** or simply as **reactors,** have been built. Though the design varies with the purpose for which the reactor is intended, the essential principle of controlling fission has not changed. In every nuclear reactor there is a *core* which contains the nuclear "fuel" (Fig. 22-4). The fuel is frequently uranium-238 which has been enriched (fortified) with fissionable ^{235}U, ^{233}U, or ^{239}Pu. The fissionable uranium or plutonium is required to produce and maintain a chain reaction. Stray neutrons from the air are sufficient to start the fissioning of the first few atoms.

The core itself also usually contains a **moderator** to slow down the fast neutrons and make them more effective in bringing about fission. The moderator may be a substance such as graphite, used in the original atomic pile, or it may be heavy water. The fuel and moderator may be intermingled with each other as in the first pile or the fuel may be suspended throughout the moderator in the form of rods.

The effectiveness of the slow or **thermal neutrons** is due to the greater probability of their being captured by a nucleus. When neutrons are knocked out of a radioactive nucleus they are traveling about 10,000 miles per second. But when these neutrons are made to collide with the atoms of other substances, such as water or paraffin, their speed is reduced effectively to a little more than a mile per second. It was partly for his discovery of the effect of slowing down neutrons that Fermi was awarded a Nobel prize.

The level at which a reactor operates is adjusted by controlling the number of neutrons in the reactor. This is done by varying the position of the control rods inserted in the core. The rods are made of a material that absorbs neutrons. Steel rods containing boron are often used; the control rods of the first pile were made of cadmium. When the rods are inserted completely, no chain reaction occurs; as they are pulled out farther and farther, the reaction increases. When they are at the *proper* distance, the reaction "levels off" and the pile is in operation.

The core of the reactor is surrounded by a shield which protects the operating personnel by absorbing stray neutrons, gamma rays, and other radiation. This shielding is usually made of dense lead and concrete. Finally, the reactor must have a cooling system. Air, water, and helium are the coolants most frequently used. Once the reactor has been operating for some time, problems related to removing radioactive substances, processing them, and getting rid of radioactive wastes arise. However, we shall be concerned with using the energy released in nuclear reactors.

QUESTIONS AND PROBLEMS

1. Write a nuclear equation for the fission reaction of ^{235}U which produces strontium-95 and xenon-139.
2. Explain how the equation $E = mc^2$ and the Law of Conservation of Mass-Energy are related.
3. What is the main difference between the nuclear reaction in an atomic pile and in an atomic bomb?
4. Write a short paragraph describing the operation of a nuclear reactor. Be sure to include the terms: critical mass, control rods, moderator, thermal neutrons, fuel, shielding.

ENERGY FROM NUCLEAR REACTORS

Will nuclear reactors ever become a major source of energy? This depends in great part on man's ability to obtain a continuous supply of fissionable material. Uranium-235, for instance, occurs in most uranium ores as only 1 part in 1,400! To separate this rare isotope from the other isotopes in the ore is difficult and expensive. Because isotopes of the same element have exactly the same chemical properties, they can be separated from each other only by physical means. This involves utilizing small differences in the mass of the same compound of both isotopes. The cost and difficulty of separating isotopes can be judged by the construction of the enormous **gaseous diffusion** plant at Oak Ridge, Tennessee, for that purpose. Here the U^{235} used in the first atomic bomb was separated from the more plentiful but essentially nonfissioning ^{238}U.

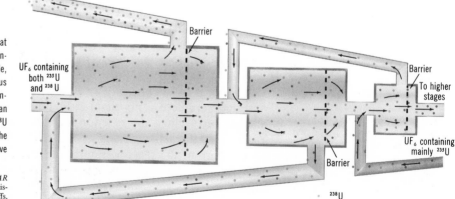

22-5 At the gaseous diffusion plant at Oak Ridge, Tennessee, uranium is converted into gaseous uranium hexafluoride, which is passed through miles of porous diffusion barriers. The molecules containing the lighter ^{235}U diffuse faster than those containing the slightly heavier ^{238}U The $_6UF$ is recirculated until almost all the molecules containing ^{235}U atoms have been isolated.

From R. E. Lapp & H. L. Andrews, *NUCLEAR RADIATION PHYSICS.* © 1954. By permission of Prentice-Hall, Inc., Englewood Cliffs, N.J.

22-6 The cloudlike mass at the bottom of the capillary "test tube" is 20 micrograms of plutonium hydroxide.

At Oak Ridge these two isotopes are separated by converting the natural uranium ore into uranium hexafluoride (UF_6), which is a gas at ordinary temperatures. This UF_6 gas, containing both isotopes of uranium, is then diffused through many thousands of porous diffusion barriers. Because the molecules containing the lighter isotope diffuse through the barriers more rapidly, the two isotopes eventually become separated almost completely (Fig. 22-5). But this is a costly and time-consuming procedure. Perhaps other reactor fuels could be produced. In fact, just such a fuel was created during World War II in the atomic pile at Hanford, Washington.

Transuranic Elements as Reactor Fuels

Suppose that a reactor contains a mixture of ^{235}U and the more common isotope ^{238}U. The ^{238}U atoms capture some neutrons produced by the splitting of the atoms of ^{235}U and are changed into atoms of ^{239}U:

$$^{238}_{92}U + ^{1}_{0}n \longrightarrow ^{239}_{92}U$$

This uranium-239 is radioactive and has a half life of only 23.5 minutes. It decays by emitting beta particles to form neptunium-239 which is also radioactive:

$$^{239}_{92}U \longrightarrow ^{239}_{93}Np + ^{0}_{-1}e$$

Neptunium-239, with a half life of 2.3 days, then decays by beta emission to form plutonium-239:

$$^{239}_{93}Np \longrightarrow ^{239}_{94}Pu + ^{0}_{-1}e$$

Neptunium has an atomic number of 93, while plutonium's atomic number is 94 (Fig. 22-6). Both of these elements are transuranic, and

22-7 When an ^{235}U atom undergoes fission in a breeder reactor, several neutrons may be released. In this diagram one neutron sustains the chain reaction; two others strike atoms of ^{238}U. These atoms are transformed into ^{239}U, ^{239}Np, and finally ^{239}Pu. Though ideally two atoms of fissionable ^{239}Pu are produced for each atom of ^{235}U that fissions, breeder reactors are complex enough for the entire procedure to require further refinements.

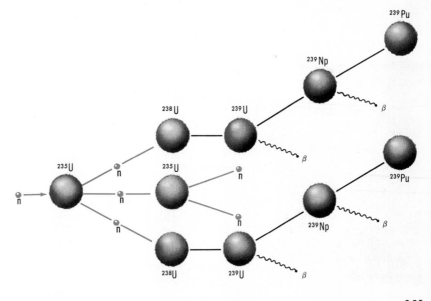

both are man-made—but the latter has an unusual property. Plutonium-239 undergoes fission when bombarded by slow-moving neutrons; it, like uranium-235, can be used as a fuel in nuclear reactors. Other man-made transuranic elements, formed by bombarding isotopes of heavy elements with neutrons, include einsteinium and fermium—names that honor two of the great pathfinders of nuclear science. At present, however, these elements have been made in such minute amounts that they are not useful as nuclear fuels.

Breeding Fissionable Material

In recent years the problem of obtaining fissionable material has been partly solved by the **breeder reactor.** As its name implies, this reactor not only releases energy through fission but actually produces more fissionable atoms than it consumes. To see how this happens, consider the situation illustrated in Fig. 22-7. Here a ^{235}U atom gives off three neutrons upon being split. Only one of these neutrons is needed to keep the chain reaction going. The other two bombard two atoms of ^{238}U, converting them ultimately into atoms of ^{239}Pu. The reaction finally ends up with two atoms of ^{239}Pu for each atom of fissionable ^{235}U consumed. But breeder reactors are not the ideal solution to the scarcity of fissionable materials. These reactors are very complex and expensive to build, maintain, and operate. Eventually, however, they may be refined to the point where they can breed fissionable fuel economically.

Types of Nuclear Reactors

Of the many nuclear reactors now in operation, most are devoted to research, power, and production. Among the substances produced are reactor fuels, transuranic elements, and isotopes. A single reactor may serve any one of these purposes or all of them. Depending upon the reactor's construction, it may even simultaneously "breed" reactor fuel. As a research aid, the reactor subjects different materials to neutrons or gamma radiation. A study is then made of the effect of radiation on the material under investigation. Gamma radiation are also used in studying the effect of radiation on experimental animals. The knowledge gained is used in treating individuals who have received excessive radiation.

Power reactors are designed to make use of excessive amounts of heat. This heat can be used to produce steam or to heat a compressed gas. The "super-heated" steam or gas then passes into turbines that drive generators to produce electricity. Thus heat from the power reactor, converted to electricity, is available for cities, industries, homes, ships, and submarines. The heat produced by the power reactors can also be used directly by the home or factory. The first full-scale nuclear power reactor in the United States began operation in 1957 at Shippingport, Pennsylvania (Fig. 22-8). Its capacity was 60,000 kilowatts of electricity. At present there are more than a dozen similar reactors in use throughout the country. The largest of these, at Indian Point, New York, can produce 255,000 kilowatts of electricity.

22-8 The core of a nuclear reactor is being lowered into position.

Some production reactors are designed to produce fissionable elements. The fissionable elements can then be used as "fuel" in other reactors, or as a source of energy in nuclear fission bombs. The reactors convert certain nonfissionable elements, such as thorium-232, into fissionable isotopes such as uranium-233. Some of the transuranic elements produced are used as reactor fuel. Uranium-238 is transformed first into ^{239}U, then into transuranic neptunium, and finally into fissionable plutonium (page 353). Various transuranic elements are used for experimental study of the structure of the nucleus.

Other production reactors, because of their intense concentration of neutrons, are used to create radioactive isotopes from stable isotopes. This occurs when a compound of phosphorus is placed in the core of a reactor. Some stable atoms of ^{31}P capture neutrons and are transformed into radioactive atoms of ^{32}P; gamma radiation is also emitted.

$$^{31}_{15}P + ^{1}_{0}n \longrightarrow ^{32}_{15}P + \gamma$$

Phosphorus-32 may also be produced in a nuclear reactor by the bombarding of sulfur-32 with neutrons.

$$^{32}_{16}S + ^{1}_{0}n \longrightarrow ^{32}_{15}P + ^{1}_{1}H$$

The latter method is preferable because the phosphorus can be separated chemically from the sulfur.

Uses of Radioactive Isotopes

The production of isotopes, both radioactive and stable, has probably been the greatest single contribution of nuclear science to humanity thus far. These isotopes have proved valuable in solving problems in the biological and physical sciences, in medicine, and in industry. Since all the isotopes of an element have the same chemical behavior, scientists can substitute one isotope for another in a chemical system. The substituted isotope serves to clearly identify or *tag* an element taking part in a particular chemical reaction. The element whose atoms are tagged is called a **tracer element.** If a radioisotope is used, the tagged element (or compound) is known as a **radioactive tracer.**

Man's life depends on the green plants which are the ultimate source of food on the earth, but until recently he has known very little about the way they carry on photosynthesis. Radioactive tracers are finally solving this mystery; and in so doing they are making possible better and more abundant crops. For example, how do green plants convert carbon dioxide into carbohydrates? To find the answer, CO_2 containing atoms of radioactive carbon-14 in addition to ordinary carbon-12 atoms is used. The tagged carbon atoms are then traced through various chemical reactions that occur during photosynthesis (Fig. 22-9).

In medicine, radioisotopes of phosphorus are used in studies of human blood. Radioactive ^{32}P is incorporated into a compound such as Na_3PO_4, which contains mainly stable ^{31}P atoms. The tagged phosphorus is readily traced. The radioisotope nitrogen-15, incorporated into amino

22-9 A leaf is exposed simultaneously to radioactive carbon dioxide and bright light. After a brief period of exposure, the leaf will be studied for the distribution of carbon-14.

22-10 A photograph taken during a study with radioactive sodium iodide of metabolism in an eight-year-old boy.

22-11 The thickness of a sheet of plastic film is being checked automatically by a radioactive gauge.

acids, enables a doctor to test the functioning of the kidneys and the liver. Radioactive iodine-131 is used to study body metabolism (Fig. 22-10) and to treat cancer of the thyroid gland.

In industry, radioactive atoms of iron incorporated into the steel of the machinery itself makes it possible to locate the slightest degree of friction. Gauges using beta radiation check the precise thickness of sheets of paper, cellophane, or plastic. The thickness is measured by determining just how much beta radiation the sheet absorbs (Fig. 22-11). In fact, there is almost no limit to the different ways man can use radioisotopes. More of these uses are listed in Table 22-2.

Nuclear Fission Bombs

On July 16, 1945, the scientists gathered at Alamogordo, New Mexico, were not interested in controlled fission, as we have just been, but rather in the first successful demonstration of uncontrolled fission—in the explosion of the first atomic bomb. On that day the conversion of a small amount of mass into a tremendous amount of energy became a reality. Though the design of fission or atomic bombs, as they are commonly known, has been improved subsequently, the essential principle of an uncontrolled chain reaction remains unchanged. The chain reaction occurs when two pieces of either fissionable uranium-235 or plutonium-239 *each of which is below the critical size* are suddenly and forcibly brought together.

The bombs produced by nuclear fission have released energy equivalent to more than 75,000 tons of TNT! The temperature of a fission explosion is believed to be about ten million degrees Celsius—approximately the temperature at the center of the sun! This tremendous heat causes the air to expand rapidly; and this expansion of air in turn creates a terrific explosive blast. It is this **blast effect** of the fission bomb that accounts for much of its destructive power.

Table 22-2   **SOME USES OF RADIOISOTOPES**

Radioisotope	Symbol	Half life	Use of isotope
Calcium-45	^{45}Ca	152 days	Studying plant nutrition
Carbon-14	^{14}C	5,760 years	Treating brain tumors, measuring age of ancient objects
Cobalt-60	^{60}Co	5.26 years	Treating cancer, irradiating food, inducing mutations
Iodine-131	^{131}I	8.14 days	Studying and treating the thyroid gland, finding leaks in water pipes
Iron-59	^{59}Fe	46.3 days	Studying the blood
Phosphorus-32	^{32}P	14.3 days	Studying plants' use of fertilizer
Sodium-24	^{24}Na	15.0 hours	Diagnosing circulatory diseases
Strontium-90	^{90}Sr	19.9 years	Treating small lesions
Sulfur-35	^{35}S	87.1 days	Studying body's use of certain amino acids

Some of the energy resulting from the loss of mass during fission is given off in the form of high-energy gamma radiation. Additional radiation, of gamma and other types, is produced by the decay of some of the fission products. It is the radioactive fission products that reach the earth as *fallout*. The heat produced by the explosion is so great that it can cause fires even at considerable distances from the explosion center.

QUESTIONS AND PROBLEMS

1. Write a series of equations for the production of fissionable plutonium from nonfissionable uranium.
2. Write a nuclear equation for the production of sulfur-35 from chlorine-35 in an atomic reactor.
3. List five radioactive tracers and give an example of how each is used.

PARTICLE ACCELERATORS

Before the days of the nuclear reactor, scientists had produced isotopes by means of the **cyclotron,** a device that accelerates positively charged nuclear particles to tremendously high speeds (Fig. 22-12). Today the cyclotron is just one of a group of devices called **particle accelerators** which cause particles to move at speeds approaching that of light. When traveling at such speeds, particles have enormous energy.

It was a particle accelerator that first enabled scientists to achieve the dream of the alchemists: to turn a base metal into gold. This was done by bombarding mercury with deuterons, the nuclei of heavy hydrogen:

$$^{200}_{80}\text{Hg} + ^{2}_{1}\text{H} \longrightarrow ^{198}_{79}\text{Au} + ^{4}_{2}\text{He}$$

Unfortunately the gold resulting from this transmutation is radioactive and has a short half life of 2.7 days. Moreover it costs far more to turn mercury into gold by this means than it would to buy the same quantity.

Accelerated Particles and Transmutation

Rutherford produced the first nuclear transmutation by bombarding nitrogen with alpha particles from radioactive bismuth-214, to produce oxygen-17 and protons (Chapter 21). To enter and be captured by nitrogen nuclei, the alpha particles had to be traveling at high speeds with great energy. They attained this speed from the energy "created" by the "destruction" of matter when the atoms of bismuth-214 decayed.

In 1928 George Gamow suggested that other charged particles, traveling at high speeds, might be even more effective than alpha particles in causing transmutations. Gamow's prediction was realized in 1932 by J. D. Cockcroft and E. T. S. Walton, two workers in Rutherford's laboratory. They first produced protons (hydrogen nuclei) by passing high-voltage electricity through hydrogen gas. Then they accelerated the speed of these protons. With the accelerated protons they bombarded a thin film of lithium oxide which contained stable atoms of lithium-7. Cloud

22-12 Lawrence's first cyclotron was only about eleven inches in diameter (the magnets are not shown). Contrast it with the huge accelerators in use today.

chamber tracks showed that some of the lithium-7 atoms captured protons and disintegrated to form two atoms of helium:

$$\mathrm{{}_3^7Li} + \mathrm{{}_1^1H} \longrightarrow \mathrm{{}_2^4He} + \mathrm{{}_2^4He}$$

This was the first time that artificially accelerated particles had been used to cause disintegration.

The Cyclotron

Soon after the experiment of Cockcroft and Walton, accelerators which were far more effective were developed. One of these was the Van de Graaff generator, invented by R. J. Van de Graaff in the United States. This machine could accelerate electrons and protons, as well as other positive ions. But the most publicized of all accelerators is the cyclotron, or "atom smasher." Developed in 1931 by Ernest O. Lawrence of the University of California, it won its inventor a Nobel prize.

In the *cyclotron,* though not in previously developed linear accelerators, positively charged particles are accelerated into a spiral path by means of a magnetic field. The cyclotron consists of a hollow cylinder containing a pair of **D**-shaped electrodes called "dees." (Fig. 22-13.) The charge on each dee is reversed rapidly by causing an electric current passing between them to alternate several million times per second. The dees are surrounded by a vessel that contains a gas such as hydrogen, deuterium, or helium at very low pressure. The vessel and dees rest between the poles of a magnet. When a beam of electrons from a sealed-in heated metallic filament bombards the atoms of gas, the atoms change to positively charged ions. The magnetic field and the reversing charge on the dees cause these positive ions to move from the center of the cyclotron outward in a spiral path. By adjusting the frequency with which the current to the dees alternates, the ions are "pulled" faster and faster in an ever-widening spiral path.

Eventually the ions reach the outer edge of the dees, where a negatively charged plate deflects them out of their spiral path. These deflected ions, now traveling at very high speed, can be used to bombard any desired material. For example, atoms of copper-63 can be hit by *deuterons,* positively charged deuterium nuclei. During this process each copper atom that is hit is transformed into an atom of zinc-64, and at the same time a neutron is emitted.

$$\mathrm{{}_{29}^{63}Cu} + \mathrm{{}_1^2D} \longrightarrow \mathrm{{}_{30}^{64}Zn} + \mathrm{{}_0^1n}$$

While neutrons in an atomic pile are most effective when traveling relatively slowly, charged particles from an accelerator are increasingly more effective the faster they travel. The purpose of increasing their speed is to give them sufficient energy to penetrate the nucleus of an atom. To be effective, a positively charged particle must be traveling with enough energy to overcome the repulsion of the positively charged nucleus. Electrons, by contrast, have to overcome the repulsion of the orbital electrons. In so doing, the accelerated electrons lose energy before reaching

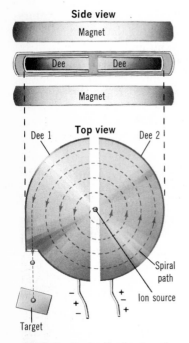

22-13 In side view, the plan of a cyclotron shows the "dees" within a hollow, gas-filled cylinder; the cylinder is positioned between the poles of a magnet. The top view shows the increasingly larger spiral path of a positive ion as it is "pulled" through the cyclotron to strike a target.

22-14 A portion of the interior cavity of a heavy-ion linear accelerator. As an indication of the large size of the accelerator, note the size of the man toward the left.

the nucleus and are generally less effective than positively charged particles in "atom smashing." Because neutrons are uncharged, they cannot be speeded up in particle accelerators.

Using Accelerators

Though Lawrence's original cyclotron produced protons with energies of only 80,000 electron volts (a unit of energy used in nuclear studies), larger cyclotrons and synchrocyclotrons can accelerate positively charged particles to energies equal to 440 million electron volts. **Linear accelerators,** which consist of a series of tubes of constantly changing electric charge arranged in a straight line, have accelerated particles to energies as high as 1 billion electron volts (Fig. 22-14). Synchrotrons have accelerated electrons to energies as high as 1.5 billion electron volts. The proton-synchroton, or cosmotron, at Brookhaven, New York, has speeded up protons until they are traveling at 178,000 miles per second—approaching the speed of light. More recent accelerators, such as the Brookhaven alternating gradient synchrotron, can produce protons that reach energies of 33 billion electron volts (Fig. 22-15).

Although the building of accelerators is extremely costly, they can be used to produce useful isotopes in small quantities, to study the nucleus, and to bring about transmutations by bombarding "target" atoms. By such bombardments two new elements, technetium and astatine, were created by accelerators in 1937 and 1940, respectively. These elements filled, as predicted, two of the four empty spaces in the periodic table.

Since the nucleus of an atom is far too small to be seen, a model of the nucleus must be built up indirectly from experimental evidence. Both in determining the forces that hold the nucleus together and in studying the structure of the nucleus, accelerators have played an important part. Experiments in which particles "bounce off," or are scattered by, the nucleus have indicated that the atomic nucleus has a radius of about 10^{-13} centimeter, or about 1/100,000 the radius of the atom as a whole. It has also been found that nuclear particles exist in shells or energy

22-15 This aerial view of the alternating gradient synchrotron at Brookhaven, New York, shows the tremendous size of the underground magnet ring (clearly outlined in the center of the photograph). In the front are the service and experimental buildings; at the right is the hydrogen bubble chamber building.

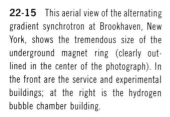

22-16 The upper photograph shows the first americium compound, isolated in January 1946. The eye of a needle indicates the degrees of magnification. The solution of curium below was photographed by its own light.

levels, just as do the electrons outside the nucleus. Experimentation on nuclear particles—now believed to be thirty-four in number—is continuing. Watch your newspaper for details of discoveries of new data about such nuclear particles as the meson, hyperon, and antineutrino.

Accelerators and Transuranic Elements

The production of transuranic elements by means of particle accelerators deserves special attention. Prior to the development of nuclear reactors the first two of these elements had been produced by particle accelerators; and of the remaining nine, only americium (Fig. 22-16) was first produced in a reactor. In 1939 E. M. McMillan, at the University of California at Berkeley, bombarded uranium-238 with slow-moving neutrons. This bombardment produced the isotope uranium-239, with a half life of 23 minutes. In addition, it produced a type of atom which emitted beta particles and has a half life of 2.3 days. At first this was thought to be an isotope of one of the already discovered members of the actinide series of elements, the elements that appear in the last horizontal row at the bottom of the periodic table. However, McMillan continued to experiment, and in 1940 he and P. H. Abelson proved that this radioactive atom, with a mass number of 239, was an isotope of a new element. This element, whose atomic number is 93, is the element we now call neptunium. It was the first transuranic element discovered.

$$^{239}_{92}U \longrightarrow {}^{239}_{93}Np + {}^{0}_{-1}e$$

Shortly after this discovery, scientists at the same laboratory produced a second isotope of neptunium with the mass number of 238 by bombarding uranium-238 with fast-moving deuterons from a cyclotron:

$$^{238}_{92}U + {}^{2}_{1}H \longrightarrow {}^{238}_{92}Np + 2\,{}^{1}_{0}n$$

Since then, the cyclotron and other accelerators have been used to produce, in small quantities, all twelve transuranic elements through atomic number 104 (Table 22-3). This has been done by bombarding atoms of the actinide series with high-energy particles. The names of two of these elements, berkelium (atomic number 97) and californium (atomic number 98), are evidence of the part the University of California has taken in these developments.

QUESTIONS AND PROBLEMS

1. (a) To be effective in "atom smashing," the particles from an accelerator must be traveling at high speed. Why? (b) How does this differ from the action of neutrons in a nuclear reactor?
2. Describe briefly the operation of a cyclotron.
3. (a) List three uses of accelerators. (b) Write an equation for the production of curium-243 by the bombardment of plutonium-239 with alpha particles.

Table 22-3   THE TRANSURANIC ELEMENTS

Name	Atomic number	Discoverers and date of discovery	Source of preparation in particle accelerator
Neptunium	93	E. M. McMillan and P. H. Abelson. 1940	Bombardment of uranium with deuterons
Plutonium	94	G. T. Seaborg, E. M. McMillan, J. W. Kennedy, and A. C. Wahl. 1941	Bombardment of uranium with deuterons
Americium	95	G. T. Seaborg, R. A. James, L. O. Morgan, and A. Ghiorso. 1944–45	Bombardment of uranium with helium ions
Curium	96	G. T. Seaborg, R. A. James, and A. Ghiorso. 1945	Bombardment of plutonium with helium ions
Berkelium	97	S. G. Thompson, A. Ghiorso, and G. T. Seaborg. 1949	Bombardment of americium with helium ions
Californium	98	S. G. Thompson, K. Street, Jr., A. Ghiorso, and G. T. Seaborg. 1950	Bombardment of curium with helium ions
Einsteinium	99	A. Ghiorso et al. 1952–53	Bombardment of uranium with nitrogen ions
Fermium	100	A. Ghiorso et al. 1952–53	Bombardment of uranium with oxygen ions
Mendelevium	101	A. Ghiorso, B. G. Harvey, G. R. Choppin, S. G. Thompson, and G. T. Seaborg. 1955	Bombardment of einsteinium with helium ions
Nobelium	102	A. Ghiorso, T. Sikkeland, J. R. Walton, and G. T. Seaborg. 1958	Bombardment of curium with carbon ions
Lawrencium	103	A. Ghiorso, T. Sikkeland, A. E. Larsh, and R. M. Latimer. 1961	Bombardment of californium with boron ions
Name undetermined	104	A. Ghiorso et al. 1969	Bombardment of californium with carbon-12 nuclei

NUCLEAR FUSION

Because relatively few atoms are involved, nuclear reactions produced by accelerators liberate only small quantities of energy. On the other hand, nuclear fission involving a much larger number of atoms can produce energy in tremendous quantities. But scientists are not pinning all their hopes on the fission process to supply man's constantly growing need for more energy. They have been investigating another source: **nuclear fusion.** Here they have taken a cue from the sun itself.

Carbon Cycle

$$^{12}_{6}C + ^{1}_{1}H \longrightarrow ^{13}_{7}N + energy$$

$$^{13}_{7}N \longrightarrow ^{13}_{6}C + ^{0}_{+1}e$$

$$^{13}_{6}C + ^{1}_{1}H \longrightarrow ^{14}_{7}N + energy$$

$$^{14}_{7}N + ^{1}_{1}H \longrightarrow ^{15}_{8}O + energy$$

$$^{15}_{8}O \longrightarrow ^{15}_{7}N + ^{0}_{+1}e$$

$$^{15}_{7}N + ^{1}_{1}H \longrightarrow ^{12}_{6}C + ^{4}_{2}He$$

Proton-proton Chain Reaction

$$^{1}_{1}H + ^{1}_{1}H \longrightarrow ^{2}_{1}D + ^{0}_{+1}e + energy$$

$$^{2}_{1}D + ^{1}_{1}H \longrightarrow ^{3}_{2}He + energy$$

$$^{3}_{2}He + ^{3}_{2}He \longrightarrow ^{4}_{2}He + 2^{1}_{1}H + energy$$

22-17 The sun's energy results from the fusion of hydrogen into helium. The result may be accounted for by either of these reactions.

Studies of the spectra of the sun and other stars indicate the presence of large quantities of hydrogen and helium. Since 1938, largely due to the work of H. A. Bethe in the United States, two reactions have been proposed to account for the presence of the helium and for the enormous quantity of energy emitted by the sun. According to either the **carbon cycle** or the **proton-proton** chain reaction (Fig. 22-17), the sun's heat results from the fusion of hydrogen nuclei to form helium. In the carbon cycle, carbon-12 seems to act as a catalyst in a six-step reaction in which 4 hydrogen-1 nuclei combine to form 1 helium-4 nucleus. But in the proton-proton chain, hydrogen nuclei combine through a three-step process involving helium-3 to produce helium-4 nuclei. The net result of both reactions is essentially the same: 4 hydrogen nuclei fuse to produce a helium nucleus and 2 positrons (positive electrons), and to release energy—44.2×10^{-6} erg from the mass "lost" in producing each helium nucleus.

$$4\,^{1}_{1}H \longrightarrow ^{4}_{2}He + 2\,^{0}_{+1}e + energy$$

Accelerators and Fusion

Consider for a moment the reaction in which lithium-7 is bombarded with protons to produce beryllium-8. Notice in the equation below that energy in the form of gamma radiation is also emitted.

$$^{7}_{3}Li + ^{1}_{1}H \longrightarrow ^{8}_{4}Be + \gamma$$

During this reaction a proton fuses with the lithium nucleus to form a more complex beryllium nucleus. In short, this reaction is not only a transmutation, it is also a fusion reaction: two simpler nuclei combine to form one that is more complex.

Other nuclear reactions of a fusion type have been produced with accelerators. But even the most powerful accelerators, those with a capacity of 33 billion electron volts, have been unable to produce a **fusion** reaction that is self-sustaining. To be self-sustaining a nuclear reaction must liberate more energy than is required to start it; and far more energy must be supplied by a particle accelerator than is released by any resulting fusion reaction.

Self-sustaining Fusion

If accelerators are unable to produce self-sustaining fusion, perhaps the method by which fusion is produced in the stars could be used here on earth. In the sun, temperatures range from 10 to 30 million degrees Celsius. The kinetic energy of atomic nuclei at these temperatures is such that instead of repelling each other as they normally would, nuclei bump into each other and fuse. If some means of obtaining such high temperatures could be found, then perhaps self-sustaining fusion reactions could be duplicated on earth. Such reactions, because of the extremely high temperatures at which they occur, are called **thermonuclear reactions.**

The fission bomb is the only presently known source of these tremendously high temperatures. The heat from a fission bomb can be used to initiate a thermonuclear reaction such as the fusion of hydrogen into

22-18 A cloud chamber photograph showing the long track of a proton and the short track of a tritium nucleus produced by the collision between two deuterons.

helium. In fact, heat from a fission bomb has been used to initiate a fusion reaction in the most deadly weapon yet exploded by man—the **hydrogen** or **fusion bomb.** Within a hydrogen bomb a fission bomb is exploded to create the heat necessary for the fusion reaction. In the fusion reaction itself, hydrogen isotopes fuse together to form helium. But there is no practical way, at present, of controlling the fusion. A fusion bomb is an uncontrolled thermonuclear reaction.

Types of Thermonuclear Reactions

If a way can be found of controlling them, three thermonuclear reactions offer hope of providing a limitless source of energy for mankind. All three involve isotopes of hydrogen: deuterium ($_1^2$H) and tritium ($_1^3$H). The equations for these three reactions are:

$$_1^2\text{H} + {_1^2}\text{H} \longrightarrow {_2^3}\text{He} + {_0^1}\text{n} + \text{energy}$$
$$_1^2\text{H} + {_1^2}\text{H} \longrightarrow {_1^3}\text{H} + {_1^1}\text{H} + \text{energy}$$
$$_1^3\text{H} + {_1^2}\text{H} \longrightarrow {_2^4}\text{He} + {_0^1}\text{n} + \text{energy}$$

Notice that helium is the product of only the first and third of the above reactions. The product of the second reaction is tritium (Fig. 22-18). Of the three reactions, the third, in which tritium fuses with deuterium, produces the greatest amount of energy—28.2×10^{-6} erg from the mass "lost" in producing each helium nucleus. The tritium for this reaction is obtained by bombarding the element lithium, which contains about 7.5 percent of the isotope lithium-6, in a nuclear reactor.

$$_3^6\text{Li} + {_0^1}\text{n} \longrightarrow {_1^3}\text{H} + {_2^4}\text{He}$$

The deuterium required for each of the thermonuclear reactions is available in almost limitless quantities in sea water. There is no problem, as with fission reactions, of obtaining the necessary materials. The only problem is that of control. If this could be solved, man would have available 100 million times as much energy as is theoretically obtainable today from all reactions of the fission type!

Controlled Fusion

At the very high temperatures necessary to maintain fusion reactions, all matter becomes vaporized and completely ionic. It then forms what scientists call a **plasma.** To achieve a controlled fusion reaction, this plasma at temperatures as high as 100 million degrees Celsius must be contained in such a way that it does not touch the walls of the container; otherwise, it loses heat. A possible answer to the problem is to place the plasma in a closed cylinder and pass an electric current through it. Once the ions in the plasma are moving in one direction, a magnetic field is created. This magnetic field is used to confine or "pinch" the plasma together. Several devices using the **pinch effect** have been developed. One type of fusion chamber is pictured in Fig. 22-19. Thus far, a temperature of over 33 million degrees Celsius has been maintained for 1/1000 of a second in such a device.

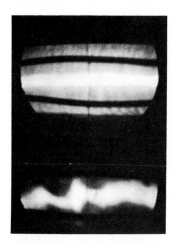

22-19 In the high speed photograph above, the bright horizontal strip in the center of the upper view shows a pinched plasma while it is stable. A few millionths of a second later, wavering reaches the tube walls, breaking down the reaction. The fusion chamber below is a dense plasma focus type being studied at the University of California.

When the problems of controlled fusion are finally solved, the deuterium and tritium in a single gallon of sea water can be used to supply energy equivalent to 300 gallons of gasoline. Not only will fusion reactions be more productive and less costly than fission reactions, they will also be much safer. Fusion creates no dangerous radioactive waste. The conquest of controlled fusion as a source of energy is one of the great challenges which scientists face today.

QUESTIONS AND PROBLEMS

1. What is the essential difference between a fusion and a fission reaction?
2. (a) Write equations for two different nuclear reactions that can be used in a fusion bomb. (b) What is the relationship of these reactions to the sun's energy?
3. What are the main problems in developing a controlled thermonuclear reaction?

VALUE OF THE CONCEPT

THE CONCEPT

Nuclear fission involves the splitting of heavy atoms, such as those of ^{235}U and ^{239}Pu, to form fission fragments, energy, and neutrons. The fission process results from bombardment with relatively slow-moving neutrons; the fission fragments produced are essentially atoms of elements listed near the middle of the periodic chart. The usefulness of fission as a source of energy depends upon man's ability to find or produce fissionable materials and to perfect means of controlling the process.

In a fission reaction, some of the neutrons produced are used to keep the fission process going—to produce a chain reaction. If too many of these neutrons are retained within the fissionable material, an explosion occurs—as in a nuclear fission bomb. In a controlled fission reaction, some of the neutrons produced must be absorbed by nonradioactive substances. Controlled fission reactions occur in nuclear reactors (or atomic piles), which are used as sources of energy, as sources of useful isotopes, to produce transuranic elements, to breed additional fissionable materials, and to study the effects of radiation. A reactor may serve one or more of these functions simultaneously.

Radioactive isotopes, produced in reactors, find many uses in industry, medicine, and the laboratory. They serve as tagged atoms useful in following the steps of chemical reactions in which they take part.

Isotopes were originally produced in the cyclotron, a type of particle accelerator. Other types of particle accelerators are the synchrotrons and the linear accelerators. These accelerators are used to speed up particles which then strike the target atoms under investigation. All of the transuranic elements have been produced by huge, high-energy accelerators, and much knowledge about the atomic nucleus has been gained by bombarding atoms in accelerators.

Whenever a chemical or nuclear reaction occurs, small amounts of matter are converted into energy. This "loss" in mass is usually too small to be detected in chemical reactions. But the great energy of the fission bomb and the even greater energy of the fusion (hydrogen) bomb result from a mass-to-energy conversion. The most common fusion, or thermonuclear, reaction is the fusion of hydrogen into helium, which occurs in the sun, the stars, and the hydrogen bomb. At present, fusion is self-sustaining only at very high temperatures; man's problem is finding a means of controlling thermonuclear reactions and developing them as a new source of controlled energy. At present the use of hydrogen isotopes in the form of a plasma held within fusion chambers by an electromagnetic field offers promise.

USING THE CONCEPT

Using the Basic Concept

1. (a) Describe the process of nuclear fission. (b) Write an equation for a nuclear fission reaction.
2. (a) Differentiate between controlled and uncontrolled nuclear fission. (b) Give a practical application of each. (c) Describe the experiment that first proved that nuclear fission could be controlled.
3. (a) Why is the fission of ^{235}U in an atomic reactor an example of a nuclear chain reaction? (b) What fission fragments generally result from such a nuclear chain reaction? (c) What is the source of the energy resulting from a fission reaction?
4. Describe briefly the contributions of the following scientists to an understanding of nuclear fission: Enrico Fermi, Otto Hahn and Fritz Strassmann, Lise Meitner and Otto Frisch.
5. (a) Describe the significance of the equation $E = mc^2$ developed by Albert Einstein. (b) Why is the conversion of matter to energy usually not considered in ordinary chemical reactions?
6. (a) State the Law of Conservation of Mass-Energy. (b) Of what significance is this law? (c) Why were the Laws of Conservation of Matter and Conservation of Energy stated as two separate laws for so many years?
7. (a) State the major purpose of a nuclear reactor. (b) Give three uses of reactors. (c) What are the major parts of any nuclear reactor?
8. (a) What particles are used as "bullets" in nuclear reactors? (b) What is the source of these particles? (c) Describe the proce-

dure by which heat energy from a nuclear reaction is eventually converted to light energy.

9. (a) Why are breeder reactors frequently more useful than ordinary reactors? (b) Give an example of a "fuel" used in a breeder reactor and the product produced from it.
10. (a) What are transuranic elements? (b) Name, in order, the last twelve transuranic elements produced. (c) Describe how transuranic elements are produced within a reactor. (d) By what other method are these elements produced?
11. (a) Give one or more uses for each isotope: ^{32}P, ^{131}I, ^{14}C, ^{235}U. (b) What is a tagged atom? a tracer element?
12. (a) Describe briefly the construction and operation of a cyclotron. (b) Name three other kinds of particle accelerators.
13. Write a nuclear equation to represent the bombarding of ^{238}U atoms with deuterons to form an equal number of ^{238}Np atoms and twice as many neutrons.
14. (a) What is nuclear fusion? (b) Give two reasons why scientists are interested in the fusion reactions.
15. (a) Write equations for two fusion reactions that have been produced experimentally. (b) Describe the method used to bring about one of the reactions.
16. (a) Describe the difficulties in using fusion reactions as a source of energy. (b) What is a self-sustaining fusion reaction?
17. (a) Where were thermonuclear reactions first detected? (b) What was the first method of supplying the tremendously high temperatures needed to start a self-sustaining thermonuclear reaction? (c) What techniques are presently being investigated?

Relating Terms Within the Concept

From the *italicized* terms on the following page, select the term that best completes each of the following statements. Do not use a term more than once.

binding energy, californium, chain reaction, critical mass, cyclotron, fallout, fission fragments, hafnium, iodine-131, moderator, neutron, nuclear fusion, plutonium-239, reactor, thermonuclear reaction.

1. A promising source of unlimited energy for the future is _____ .
2. Heavy water is used in some nuclear reactors as a _____ .
3. An accelerator in which charged particles follow a spiral path is the _____ .
4. Two transuranic elements are neptunium and _____ .
5. Self-sustaining and controlled nuclear fission take place in a _____ .
6. During the fission of ^{235}U, atoms of ^{235}U break apart into _____ .
7. The amount of fissionable material needed to sustain fission is the _____ .
8. To separate a nucleus into its component parts, apply energy equal to its _____ .
9. Two fissionable isotopes are uranium-235 and _____ .
10. An isotope used as a radioactive tracer is _____ .
11. Neutrons are both a reactant and a product in a _____ .
12. The energy of the sun results from a nuclear fusion or _____ .

Solving Problems Within the Concept
1. How much binding energy (in ergs) is produced theoretically when a helium-3 nucleus forms from 2 protons and 1 neutron? (To convert amu's to ergs multiply amu's by 1.49×10^{-3}; $^3He = 3.0161$ amu).
2. With perfect separation, what quantity (in grams) of uranium hexafluoride is needed to supply 100 grams of uranium-235 atoms? (Only seven of each 1,000 uranium atoms in the UF_6 are ^{235}U atoms.)
3. How many grams of helium-4 are produced by the fusion of 1 gram of hydrogen-3 with hydrogen-2? Assume that the reaction is 100 percent efficient.
4. How many gallons of sea water must be processed to obtain enough ^2H to supply the energy needed to run the average automobile for one year? Assume that the average automobile travels 12,000 miles yearly and that it travels 20 miles for each gallon of gasoline used.

Applying the Concept
1. Five abundant isotopes in the earth's crust and atmosphere are ^{16}O, ^{28}Si, ^{40}Ca, ^{56}Fe, and ^{24}Mg. Determine the number of protons and neutrons in each of these nuclei. Is the number odd or even in each case? Compare these results with the number of protons and neutrons in ^{235}U, ^{239}Pu, ^{131}I, and other unstable isotopes. From this comparison what relationship *might* you suggest between number of protons and neutrons and nuclear stability or instability?
2. (a) Why do slow-moving neutrons make such effective "bullets" for bombarding atoms? (b) Why are slow-moving alpha particles so ineffective?
3. Suggest several reasons why graphite is being used extensively as a moderator in nuclear reactors even though it is not quite as effective as beryllium.
4. Why is it unlikely that nuclear reactors will be used as a source of energy for automobiles? Give at least two reasons.

Reading Further
Atoms in the Family, by Laura Fermi, Chicago, University of Chicago Press, 1954. A delightfully told story of the work of Enrico Fermi. (Don't miss the anecdotes.)

The following *Scientific American* articles (also available in the Scientific American Off-prints series) are most interesting:

"Radiation and the Human Cell," by Theodore T. Puck, April 1960.

"The Synthetic Elements, Part I and Part II," by Glenn T. Seaborg, April 1950 and December 1956.

"The Omega-Minus Experiment," by W. B. Fowler and N. B. Samios, October 1964.

The Families of Elements

Fritz Haber is best remembered for the development of a process that enabled his native Germany to continue its manufacture of explosives during World War I after the Allied blockade became effective. The process, you may recall, was the synthesizing of ammonia directly from its elements.

The difficulties in preparing ammonia from nitrogen and hydrogen was that though the reaction did occur, it occurred slowly and produced a very poor yield of ammonia. Haber succeeded in overcoming these handicaps, where others had failed, by bringing to the problem his unusual knowledge of theoretical chemistry. His achievement called for a full understanding of the factors that influence the course of a chemical reaction and the ability to predict just how these factors should be modified to favor a desired reaction.

Yet his contributions were not so much to industrial chemistry as to physical chemistry. He was interested mainly in electrochemistry, and his innovations ranged from the improvement of techniques and apparatus to the chemical application of Planck's quantum theory. For his contributions to chemistry, Haber was awarded the Nobel prize in 1918.

Haber's activities ranged from a dramatic but unsuccessful attempt to secure gold from sea water, to establishing the Japan Institute in Berlin and Tokyo to promote mutual understanding and cultural interests.

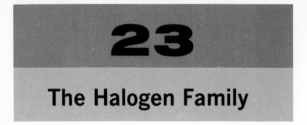

23

The Halogen Family

In 1930, the chemist could make the following sweeping statement. "We know of the existence of ninety-two elements; but four of them, of atomic numbers 43, 61, 85, and 87, have not yet been detected. We can predict that element number 85 will be a black or darkly colored solid, insoluble in water but soluble in benzene, carbon tetrachloride, and carbon disulfide to produce

Table 23-1 **PORTION OF PERIODIC TABLE OF 1930**

		O
		2 **He** 4.003
VIA	**VIIA**	
8 **O** 16.000	**9** **F** 19.00	**10** **Ne** 20.183
16 **S** 32.066	**17** **Cl** 35.457	**18** **Ar** 39.944
34 **Se** 78.96	**35** **Br** 79.916	**36** **Kr** 83.80
52 **Te** 127.61	**53** **I** 126.91	**54** **Xe** 131.30
84 **Po** [210]	**85** **?** [?]	**86** **Rn** [222]

darkly colored solutions. This element will probably vaporize readily at room temperature. It will react moderately with sodium and potassium to produce white salts that will dissolve in water to form colorless solutions." How did the chemist know that an element number 85 was yet to be discovered? On what basis could he make the predictions outlined above?

Group VIIA Elements

Let us look at a portion of the periodic table *as it was known in 1930* (Table 23-1). Polonium, element number 84, must be placed in group VIA, or the oxygen family, by virtue of the resemblance of its properties to those of oxygen, sulfur, selenium, and tellurium. But the next heaviest element, radon, can hardly be considered a member of group VIIA. Radon is an inert gas, like helium, whereas the members of group VIIA are all active nonmetals. Obviously, there is a missing element between polonium and radon, related in properties to the members of group VIIA, the **halogen** elements. Let us examine the data to see how chemists could deduce the as-yet-undiscovered existence of another member of the halogen family (Table 23-2).

To predict the existence of element number 85, the chemist had only to examine the changes in the properties of these elements as their atomic numbers (and weights) increase. As the atomic number increases, the elements pass from the gaseous to the liquid to the solid state, while the color darkens progressively and the solubility in water decreases. Hence, the chemist was superbly confident that element number 85 would be a darkly colored solid, slightly soluble in water. The halogens become progressively darker when dissolved in benzene or carbon tetrachloride, so it was anticipated that the undiscovered element would be soluble in either of these compounds to form darkly colored solutions. As the members of the family increase in atomic number and weight, their reactions with sodium or potassium become less energetic. On this basis, element number 85 should react moderately or even weakly with these metals. Since these elements usually exist in the -1 oxidation state in compounds, the same should be expected of the missing element, which must therefore have an outer orbit of 7 electrons. Further, this element, like the other members of the group VIIA family, should exist in the form of covalently bonded diatomic molecules when in the gaseous state. We may further expect it to possess a relatively high ionization potential. The missing element was discovered, in the form of one of its radioactive isotopes, as a by-product of nuclear reactions; it has been named **astatine.**

You have now met the full membership of the group VIIA elements, or *halogens*, known as the salt-formers from their reaction with metals. Large quantities of these elements (except astatine) are used yearly; from photography to antiknock gasoline, from refrigeration to medicine, these elements, in the form of their compounds, find a great variety of uses.

Harvesting the Halogens

Since these elements are not found free in nature as a result of their rather strong electron-borrowing behavior, it should be of interest to investigate the manner of their preparation and their individual properties more fully. Although naturally occurring halogen compounds usually contain the element in the -1 oxidation state ($Na\overset{-1}{Cl}$, $K\overset{-1}{Br}$), occasional compounds occur in which the halogen exists in a higher oxidation state ($Na\overset{+5}{I}O_3$, $K\overset{+7}{Cl}O_4$); but these are scarce in nature and they are usually prepared industrially.

How can the halogens be prepared from their compounds?

Whatever method of preparation is used, laboratory or commercial, the method involves changing the halogen ion, X^{-1} (also called the halide ion and represented here by X^{-1}) to the halogen atom, X^0. Since two of the latter are covalently bonded to form a molecule, the change is best represented by

$$2\,X^{-1} \longrightarrow X_2{}^0$$

Such a change requires the *loss* of 2 electrons by the pair of halide ions.

$$2\,X^{-1} - 2\,e^- \longrightarrow X_2{}^0$$

You have already learned (Chapter 18) that *any change in which electrons are lost is known as oxidation.* This brief but informative equation indicates that the preparation of the halogen elements from their halide compounds requires an agent capable of removing electrons, and therefore called *an oxidizing agent.* This removal of electrons can be achieved either with a chemical oxidizing agent, or by means of a direct current. It is important to remember that a chemical oxidizing agent, by removing electrons from another substance, is itself reduced. Let us see how this principle of oxidation is applied in producing the individual halogen elements.

CHLORINE

The first known of the halogen elements was chlorine, prepared by Scheele in 1774 but considered by him to be an oxide. In 1810 Sir Humphry

Table 23-2   **THE GROUP VIIA ELEMENTS**

Element	Atomic number	Atomic weight	Electron configuration	Density (20° C)	Melting point (°C)	Boiling point (°C)	State and color	Ionization potential (ev)	Oxidation state	Solubility in water
Fluorine	9	18.9984	2 7	1.69 g/l	-233	-188	Pale yellow gas	17.4	-1	Decomposes water
Chlorine	17	35.453	2 8 7	3.214 g/l	-103	-34.6	Greenish-yellow gas	13.0	$-1, +5, +7$	Moderate
Bromine	35	79.909	2 8 18 7	3.12 g/ml	-7.2	58.8	Reddish-brown liquid	11.8	$-1, +5$	Moderate
Iodine	53	126.9044	2 8 18 18 7	4.93 g/ml	113.5	184.4	Grayish-black solid	10.4	$-1, +5, +7$	Slight
Astatine	85	[210]	2 8 18 32 18 7	?	?	?	Dark-colored solid	?	-1	Slight

Davy proved that the choking gas was an element and named it chlorine, from the Greek meaning "greenish-yellow."

The present-day method of preparing chlorine utilizes the *electrolysis of brine,* a solution of sodium chloride. Refinements are being made continually in the process, but the fundamental reaction is the same. You can observe the course of the process by *the following investigation.*

Pour a $2\,N$ solution of sodium chloride containing a few drops of purple litmus into a **U**-tube as shown below. Insert two carbon electrodes and connect them to a source of direct current of not more than 30 volts. When the current is turned on, observe the bubbling at both electrodes. After a few

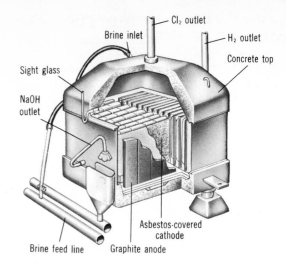

23-1 A Hooker cell for the electrolysis of brine.

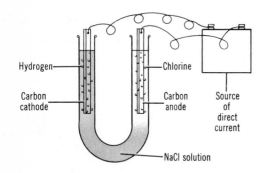

minutes, observe the color of the solution around each electrode. Bring a lighted splint to the mouth of each tube. The gas produced at the cathode ignites and burns explosively, but the gas produced at the anode does not. What do these observations tell us about the products of this reaction?

The change of neutral (purple) litmus around the cathode to a blue color indicates the formation of an excess of OH^- ions. As sodium is the only metallic element in our starting materials, it is reasonable to conclude that sodium hydroxide has been formed. The almost complete disappearance of color around the anode indicates the presence of a bleaching agent. We therefore suspect the formation of chlorine gas, which is

known to be a bleaching agent. The presence of a flammable gas at the cathode can be explained by the formation of hydrogen, the only element of those present in the reacting materials which is known to burn. Having determined the products by direct experiment, you can write the ionic equation for the reaction. Throughout this section the oxidation and reduction half-reactions and final electronic equations are also indicated below the ionic equation or the equation showing oxidation numbers.

$$2\,Na^+ + 2\,Cl^- + 2\,HOH \xrightarrow{\ DC\ }$$
$$\underbrace{2\,Na^+ + H_2{}^0 + 2\,OH^-}_{cathode} + \underbrace{Cl_2{}^0}_{anode}$$

$$
\begin{array}{lll}
2\,Cl^- - 2\,e^- & \longrightarrow Cl_2{}^0 & \text{(oxidation)} \\
2\,H_2O + 2\,e^- & \longrightarrow H_2{}^0 + 2\,OH^- & \text{(reduction)} \\
\hline
2\,Cl^- + 2\,H_2O & \longrightarrow H_2{}^0 + Cl_2{}^0 + 2\,OH^-
\end{array}
$$

The sodium ions do not appear in these equations because they do not undergo a change in oxidation number. Neither do the electrons appear in the final equation, as those removed from the chloride ions have been transferred to the water molecules. Observe that in this reaction the water molecules act as the oxidizing agent, but are themselves reduced to molecular hydrogen and hydroxide ions by removing electrons from the chloride ions. The electric current (battery or generator) serves to *transfer* electrons from one set of ions to the other.

Commercially the electrolysis of brine is performed in a number of *cells* such as the **Vorce cell** and the **Hooker cell** (Fig. 23-1), which are designed to prevent the chlorine produced from reacting with the sodium hydroxide, and to allow for convenient removal of the products. Chlorine gas is also produced in the **Downs process** by electrolyzing molten sodium chloride to produce metallic sodium.

Laboratory Preparation of Chlorine

If you would like, duplicate Scheele's method to see for yourself how chlorine is prepared. (CAUTION: *Prepare the element in a fume hood.*)

Arrange the apparatus as shown below and introduce about 5 grams of powdered manganese dioxide into the Florence flask. Replace the stopper and pour enough concentrated hydrochloric acid into the flask to cover the bottom of the thistle tube to a depth of at least $\frac{1}{4}$ inch. Arrange a train of four collecting bottles and place a cardboard cover over each. Use the first three bottles for collecting chlorine by the displacement of air. Next, partly fill the fourth bottle with water, which acts to dissolve the excess gas. *Check to be sure that the apparatus has no*

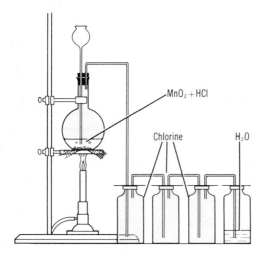
MnO₂ + HCl

Chlorine   H₂O

leaks and begin to warm the flask with a *low* flame. When the first three bottles are filled with the gas, discontinue heating. When all reaction in the flask has stopped, remove the bottles of gas, and cover each with a glass plate.

Lower a burning splint into one bottle of chlorine. Does the splint continue to burn or go out? Observe the pale greenish-yellow color of the gas; then add about 3 ml of water to the second bottle and shake it thoroughly. What is the color of the solution that forms? *Cautiously* sprinkle a small amount of antimony (from the end of a splint) into the third bottle. Does the antimony burn?

The equation for the reaction is:

$$\overset{+4}{Mn}O_2 + 4\,H\overset{-1}{Cl} \xrightarrow{\Delta} \overset{0}{Cl_2}\uparrow + \overset{+2}{Mn}Cl_2 + 2\,H_2O$$
$$2\,Cl^- - 2\,e^- \longrightarrow Cl_2{}^0 \quad \text{(oxidation)}$$
$$Mn^{+4} + 2\,e^- \longrightarrow Mn^{+2} \quad \text{(reduction)}$$
$$\overline{Mn^{+4} + 2\,Cl^- \longrightarrow Mn^{+2} + Cl_2{}^0}$$

Once again, the formation of chlorine involves *oxidation* of chloride ions to the chlorine molecule, the electrons being removed by the manganese in the +4 oxidation state. Note particularly that the $\overset{+4}{Mn}$, by removing the electrons to bring about oxidation, is itself reduced to the +2 state.

The Properties of Chlorine

Two *physical* properties indicated by the way in which the gas is collected in the laboratory are that chlorine is heavier than air (**MW** = 71*), and is probably somewhat soluble in water. Experiment shows that two volumes of chlorine dissolve in one volume of water at room temperature (20° C). Chlorine gas is choking and irritating when inhaled; even moderate amounts are poisonous.

The chemical properties of chlorine can be observed by studying its reaction with hydrogen, with metals, and with water.

* If the **MW** of a gas is above 29, the gas is denser than air.

23-2 Filter paper moistened with turpentine ($C_{10}H_{16}$) burns in a jar of chlorine, giving off a dense, black smoke rich in carbon.

Reaction with Hydrogen. If a burning wood splint is lowered into a jar of chlorine gas, the flame is extinguished; neither does the gas burn. Chlorine does not support the burning of wood. But if a jet of burning hydrogen is lowered into a bottle of chlorine gas, the flame is *not* extinguished; however, it does have a different appearance. If you now blow gently across the mouth of the bottle, a white mist will appear, just as with a bottle of concentrated hydrochloric acid. These observations *appear* to be contradictory, chlorine supporting the combustion of hydrogen but not that of wood, a compound containing hydrogen and carbon. The wood splint stops burning because oxygen is necessary for its combustion. The jet of hydrogen, however, continues to burn even in the absence of oxygen. The combination of hydrogen and chlorine to form hydrogen chloride is an example of combustion accompanied by noticeable heat and light in which oxygen is not involved.

$$H_2 + Cl_2 \longrightarrow 2\,HCl(g)$$

Fundamentally, however, the burning of hydrogen in oxygen and the burning of hydrogen in chlorine are the same, as can be seen from an examination of the electronic equations. With chlorine:

$$\overset{0}{H_2} + \overset{0}{Cl_2} \longrightarrow 2\,\overset{+1-1}{HCl}$$

$$
\begin{aligned}
H_2 - 2\,e^- &\longrightarrow 2\,H^{+1} \quad \text{(oxidation)} \\
Cl_2 + 2\,e^- &\longrightarrow 2\,Cl^{-1} \quad \text{(reduction)} \\
\hline
H_2{}^0 + Cl_2{}^0 &\longrightarrow 2\,H^{+1} + 2\,Cl^{-1}
\end{aligned}
$$

With oxygen:

$$2\,\overset{0}{H_2} + \overset{0}{O_2} \longrightarrow 2\,\overset{+1-2}{H_2O}$$

$$
\begin{aligned}
2\,H_2{}^0 - 4\,e^- &\longrightarrow 4\,H^+ \quad \text{(oxidation)} \\
O_2{}^0 + 4\,e^- &\longrightarrow 2\,O^{-2} \quad \text{(reduction)} \\
\hline
2\,H_2{}^0 + O_2{}^0 &\longrightarrow 4\,H^+ + 2\,O^{-2}
\end{aligned}
$$

In both reactions, hydrogen has been oxidized by the apparent loss of electrons; it has a *more positive* charge. Chlorine, which acquires a *more negative* charge, serves as the oxidizing agent in place of oxygen; the chlorine molecules are reduced to chloride ions. Note once again that oxidation in its broader sense does not require the presence of oxygen.

Chlorine can combine with hydrogen even when the hydrogen is part of a compound. A filter paper moistened with warm turpentine ($C_{10}H_{16}$) bursts into flame when immersed in a jar of chlorine, and a cloud of black smoke appears (Fig. 23-2). It is also possible by careful experimentation and observation to detect a white mist when the breath is blown across the jar, indicating the formation of hydrogen chloride gas.

$$C_{10}H_{16} + 8\,Cl_2 \longrightarrow 10\,C + 16\,HCl\uparrow$$

Reaction with Metals. The reaction of chlorine with metals, predicted from its atomic structure, is further proof of its ability to support combustion. When gently warmed sodium is cautiously lowered into a jar of chlorine, a *violent* reaction follows. A shower of yellow sparks is thrown off and white sodium chloride is formed.

$$2\,\overset{0}{Na} + \overset{0}{Cl_2} \longrightarrow 2\,\overset{+1-1}{NaCl} + \Delta$$

The reaction is less violent if heated steel wool is used, producing reddish-brown ferric chloride.

$$2 \overset{0}{Fe} + 3 \overset{0}{Cl_2} \longrightarrow 2 \overset{+3\ -1}{FeCl_3} + \Delta$$

Even a much less active metal such as antimony, when sprinkled into the chlorine, reacts to form a white cloud of antimony chloride, with only a modest evolution of heat and light.

$$2 \overset{0}{Sb} + 3 \overset{0}{Cl_2} \longrightarrow 2 \overset{+3\ -1}{SbCl_3} + \Delta$$

Chlorine reacts with even the most inactive metals, such as gold and platinum; but the reaction is slow, usually requiring heat.

The compounds formed in these reactions vary in their nature with the activity of the metal. The very active metals (sodium, magnesium) form ionic chlorides, but the weakly active metals (antimony, gold) form covalent compounds. Metals of intermediate activity form chlorides which are partly ionic and partly covalent.

Reactions with Water. When a greenish-yellow solution of chlorine water is stored, the color gradually fades until the liquid becomes colorless. The odor of chlorine is now faint and the solution is acid to litmus. If the solution is stored in the light, as shown in Fig. 23-3, the same results are obtained; but this time a colorless gas

23-3 In the sunlight, chlorine water slowly gives off oxygen.

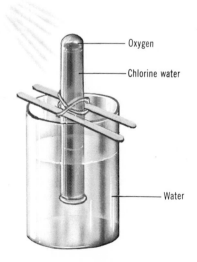

collects. The gas can be shown to be oxygen. These results occur from a reaction between chlorine and water:

$$Cl_2 + H_2O \longrightarrow HCl + HOCl$$
$$\text{(hypochlorous acid)}$$

Hypochlorous acid (which is sometimes written HClO) is unstable and decomposes to form hydrochloric acid and oxygen.

$$2\ HOCl \longrightarrow 2\ HCl + O_2\uparrow$$

Replacement of Halogens by Chlorine

As a further illustration of the oxidizing nature of chlorine, you might *try the following*.

Add a few drops of greenish-yellow chlorine water to a test tube containing a colorless solution of sodium bromide. Instead of a much weaker greenish-yellow color (be-

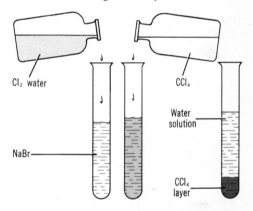

cause of dilution), you will observe a darker, brownish color in the solution. Now add a a few milliliters of carbon tetrachloride (CCl₄), shake the mixture well, and place the test tube in a test tube rack. On standing, the mixture separates into two layers. The upper layer retains a faint brownish color; the lower, or carbon tetrachloride layer, becomes distinctly reddish, the color of *bromine in this liquid* (Colorplate II, following page 548). Repeat the procedure with a colorless solution of sodium iodide. This time observe that the carbon tetrachloride is violet, *the color of iodine in this solvent.*

In the first reaction the chlorine reacted with the sodium *bromide* to produce free *bromine*. In short, chlorine oxidized bromine ions from sodium bromide.

$$2\,Na\overset{-1}{Br} + \overset{0}{Cl_2} \longrightarrow \overset{0}{Br_2} + 2\,Na\overset{-1}{Cl}$$

$$
\begin{array}{rll}
2\,Br^- - 2\,e^- & \longrightarrow Br_2{}^0 & \text{(oxidation)} \\
Cl_2{}^0 + 2\,e^- & \longrightarrow 2\,Cl^- & \text{(reduction)} \\
\hline
2\,Br^- + 2\,Cl_2{}^0 & \longrightarrow Br_2{}^0 + 2\,Cl^- &
\end{array}
$$

A similar reaction occurred in the second reaction, chlorine replacing the iodide ions in the compound.

$$2\,Na\overset{-1}{I} + \overset{0}{Cl_2} \longrightarrow \overset{0}{I_2} + 2\,Na\overset{-1}{Cl}$$

$$
\begin{array}{rll}
2\,I^{-1} - 2\,e^- & \longrightarrow I_2{}^0 & \text{(oxidation)} \\
Cl_2{}^0 + 2\,e^- & \longrightarrow 2\,Cl^- & \text{(reduction)} \\
\hline
2\,I^- + Cl_2{}^0 & \longrightarrow I_2{}^0 + 2\,Cl^- &
\end{array}
$$

These reactions illustrate *the replacement of another halogen element by chlorine*. Observe once more that oxygen is not essential to this process, and that the chlorine is itself reduced in the reaction. Note that these reactions represent reactions of chlorine with *compounds* of other halogen elements. The *replacement* by chlorine of bromine and iodine from their compounds will help you to understand one of the ways in which relationships are established in a family of elements.

Uses of Chlorine

Chlorine finds dozens of uses in the home, in the community and in industry. Hardly an hour passes in which we are not indebted to chlorine—from the water we drink to that snow-white shirt we wear.

Purifying Water. Observe from Fig. 23-4 the sharp drop in the number of deaths from typhoid fever since 1900. This decline followed the introduction of the practice of treating municipal water supplies with chlorine. Two pounds of chlorine added to one million pounds of water suffice to kill all the microorganisms present. This application is met on a small scale in swimming pools and in foot-baths designed to control "athlete's foot." Chlorine compounds which decompose in water to release the element are used for the treatment of small quantities of water when the use of chlorine as the gas may be impractical. Soldiers, campers, and others who must drink water where and how they find it employ tablets containing these compounds (Halozone, Chloramid).

Bleaching. The early nineteenth-century China clippers put to sea as spick and span as American naval ingenuity could make them, but with sails light brown in color. When the ships returned some years later, the same sails were now bone white. The intervening months of exposure to sunlight and air had bleached the cotton fiber. This method of bleaching was well known to early peoples who exposed cotton and linen fibers to the bleaching action of sunlight and air. When the pressure of time became important in the growth of the textile industry, the old-fashioned, time-consuming procedure began to disappear. In its place there appeared the first large-scale use of a relatively new process—bleaching with chlorine.

23-4 The graph shows the decline in death rate from typhoid fever after 1900. In 1911, following an outbreak among military personnel, typhoid vaccine became compulsory for members of the armed forces.

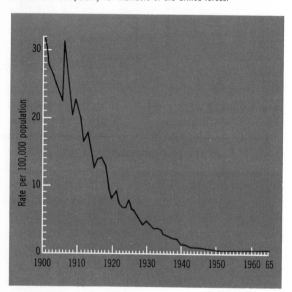

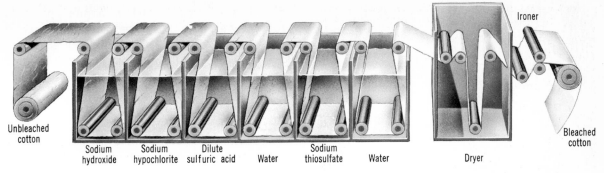

23-5 Unbleached fabric is passed continuously through a series of chemical baths. The bleached fabric is treated to remove chlorine, then rinsed, and dried, after which it is ready for immediate use or for further processing.

Let us examine this property by inserting a strip of dry colored cloth into the gas. The expected bleaching does *not* occur. Moisten the strip of cloth and repeat the procedure. Does the color disappear almost at once?

Chlorine does not bleach unless water is present. The reason lies in the reaction of chlorine with water (page 373). The hypochlorous acid formed is an oxidizing agent, releasing oxygen in the *atomic* form. The atomic oxygen is more reactive than molecular oxygen, and oxidizes the dye to a colorless substance. Chlorine will not oxidize all dyestuffs; only those dyes whose oxidation products are colorless will be bleached by chlorine.

Raw cotton and linen fibers are treated with a warm, dilute solution of sodium hydroxide to remove their natural waxy coating. They are now passed through a solution of sodium hypochlorite (NaClO) or chlorinated lime (CaOCl₂), and then through a bath of dilute sulfuric acid (Fig. 23-5). Reaction between the acid and these compounds produces hypochlorous acid which does the bleaching.

$$\text{NaClO} + \text{H}_2\text{SO}_4 \longrightarrow \text{NaHSO}_4 + \text{HOCl}$$
$$\text{CaOCl}_2 + \text{H}_2\text{SO}_4 \longrightarrow \text{CaSO}_4 + \text{HCl} + \text{HOCl}$$

The bleached fibers are washed and treated with a solution of a mild *reducing* agent such as sodium thiosulfate ($\text{Na}_2\text{S}_2\text{O}_3$) to remove any remaining chlorine. They are finally washed thoroughly to remove all chemicals, after which they are ready for further processing.

The Chemical Industry. One of the major uses of chlorine is the *preparation of chlorine compounds*. Most of these are made by direct combination of the elements, the technique followed in the preparation of metallic chlorides.

$$2\,\text{Al} + 3\,\text{Cl}_2 \longrightarrow 2\,\text{AlCl}_3$$
$$\text{Sn} + 2\,\text{Cl}_2 \longrightarrow \text{SnCl}_4$$

The bleaching agents mentioned, and the various chlorine compounds to be met shortly, are made by direct action of chlorine on various compounds.

The preparation of other halogen elements involves the use of chlorine, and will be considered later in this chapter.

Uses of Chlorine Compounds

Carbon tetrachloride, CCl₄, removes fatty, gummy, and waxy stains as well as gasoline or naphtha but offers no fire hazard. Carbon tetrachloride and related compounds are used in various *dry-cleaning practices*. While these solvents are nonflammable, *their vapors should not be inhaled.*

A number of new and efficient *insecticides* such as *chlor*dane, benzene hexa*chloride*, and DDT are chlorine compounds. Orthodi*chlor*-benzene can be used to poison the soil against termites, while wood treated with penta*chlor*-phenol is resistant to attack by the same insects (Fig. 23-6).

THE HALOGEN FAMILY 375

23-6 The cross-piece of a wooden telephone pole is being treated with pentachlor-phenol to make it resistant to attack by insects.

Bleaching liquids are as much a part of laundry operations as detergents. Many of these bleaches are dilute solutions of sodium hypochlorite.

Metallic chlorides have diverse applications. Sodium chloride is used in the preparation of metallic sodium, sodium hydroxide and chlorine, and in washing and baking soda. Calcium chloride is also used to melt snow and ice, as well as to keep down dust on roads by absorbing water vapor from the air. The latter property makes the compound useful as a drying agent in the laboratory. Considerable quantities of aluminum chloride are used in organic chemistry as a catalyst for many reactions. Silicon and titanium tetrachlorides, both liquids, combine with moisture in the air to form a white smoke containing fine particles of their respective dioxides as well as hydrogen chloride. For this reason, they are used in "sky-writing" and as a means of producing smoke screens in warfare. Titanium and zirconium are made commercially by reducing their chlorides with sodium metal.

$$\overset{+4}{Ti}Cl_4 + 4\,\overset{0}{Na} \longrightarrow \overset{0}{Ti} + 4\,\overset{+1}{Na}Cl$$

A new method of *bleaching flour* employs chlorine dioxide, ClO_2, which is a more powerful bleaching agent than chlorine gas. Since the compound is too unstable to be stored, it is generated as needed by reacting chlorine with sodium chlorite, $NaClO_2$.

$$2\,NaClO_2 + Cl_2 \longrightarrow 2\,ClO_2 + 2\,NaCl$$

QUESTIONS AND PROBLEMS

1. Draw electron orbital diagrams of the (a) chloride ion, (b) chlorine atom, and (c) chlorine molecule.

2. Write electronic half-reactions for the reactions between chlorine and (a) hydrogen, (b) potassium, (c) zinc.

3. Explain, with equations, the bleaching action of chlorine.

4. Write the ionic and electronic equations for the reaction between (a) chlorine and magnesium bromide, and (b) chlorine and zinc iodide. Label the oxidation and reduction half-reactions.

5. How are chlorine and chlorine compounds related to good health? Give examples.

HYDROCHLORIC ACID

The most important and widely used manufactured compound containing chlorine is hydrochloric acid, the muriatic acid of industry. Commercially it is prepared by burning hydrogen in chlorine and absorbing the hydrogen chloride *gas* formed in water. Some hydrogen chloride is obtained as a by-product in the reaction of chlorine with hydrocarbons (page 593). The concentrated acid of commerce contains about 37 percent by weight of the gas.

Laboratory Preparation of Hydrochloric Acid

The laboratory preparation of the acid, also used in industry, employs a double replacement reaction between a chloride (a salt of hydrochloric acid) and concentrated sulfuric acid.

$$NaCl + H_2SO_4 \longrightarrow HCl\uparrow + NaHSO_4$$

Study the following procedure to *see for yourself how hydrochloric acid is prepared.*

Arrange the apparatus as shown below. Place about 8 grams of sodium chloride in the flask, replace the thistle tube, and add sufficient concentrated sulfuric acid to cover the bottom of the thistle tube to a depth of at least ¼ inch. Prepare collecting bottles for the upward displacement of air. Insert the delivery tube through a hole in a cardboard cover into one of the bottles and warm the reaction mixture with a low flame. If the gas evolved is colorless, determine when the bottle is full of the gas by raising the cardboard lid and laying a strip of moistened blue litmus paper over the top of the bottle. If the strip changes color slowly, continue the collection for 1 minute and repeat the procedure. When the strip changes color

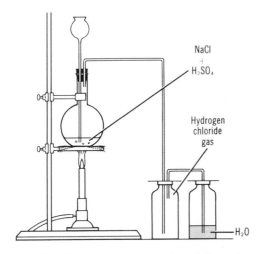

NaCl + H₂SO₄

Hydrogen chloride gas

H₂O

immediately, cover the bottle with a glass plate and proceed with the collection of another bottle of the gas in the same manner. Fill your last bottle with water to a depth of 1 inch and allow the final gas evolved to bubble through the water for at least 1 minute. Why?

Cautiously determine the odor of hydrogen chloride in the first bottle (do not breathe it directly). Blow your breath across the mouth of the second bottle of gas. Explain the results. Test the solution in the third bottle with litmus paper. What essentially is the solution?

Why was it necessary to heat the flask in the preparation of HCl? If a *cold, concentrated* solution of $NaHSO_4$ (sodium bisulfate) is added to *concentrated* hydrochloric acid, a white precipitate of sodium chloride appears. Under these conditions, the reaction between concentrated sulfuric acid and sodium chloride is reversible.

$$H^+ + HSO_4^- + Na^+ + Cl^- \rightleftharpoons$$
$$H^+ + Cl^- + Na^+ + HSO_4^-$$

But hydrogen chloride is a gas, and like all gases, it becomes less soluble in water as the temperature is raised. The volatility of hydrogen chloride under these conditions causes the reaction to go to completion.

$$Na^+ + Cl^- + H^+ + HSO_4^- \xrightarrow{\Delta}$$
$$HCl\uparrow + Na^+ + HSO_4^-$$

Properties of Hydrogen Chloride

Hydrogen chloride is a colorless gas with a choking, penetrating odor, denser than air and very soluble in water. Its water solution possesses the typical properties of acids, tasting sour, turning blue litmus red, and reacting with many metals to produce hydrogen gas. Although hydrogen chloride is a polar covalent compound and a nonconductor, it reacts with the water dipole (Chapter 13) to form a large number of hydronium ions; its water solution is a strong acid.

$$HCl + HOH \longrightarrow H_3O^+ + Cl^-$$

Uses of Hydrochloric Acid

Hydrochloric acid is used to increase the yield of petroleum from oil wells, in the manufacture of other chemicals, and in the metals industries. When iron and steel are to be protected from corrosion by coating them with another metal (tinning or galvanizing), the iron or steel must first be cleaned of all corrosion products so that the covering metal will adhere tightly. This is done by treating the metal with warm, dilute acid (pickling), usually hydrochloric or sulfuric acid (Fig. 23-7), which reacts with and dissolves any oxides or carbonates. Small quantities of hydrochloric acid are used in converting cane sugar into confectioners' sugar, used in candy-making.

QUESTIONS AND PROBLEMS

1. From your knowledge of the periodic table, suggest a substitute for NaCl in the laboratory preparation of hydrogen chloride gas.

2. Why is hydrochloric acid important to the steel industry?

3. What does the method used to collect hydrogen chloride in the laboratory indicate about hydrogen chloride's (a) density, (b) solubility in water?

4. In preparing hydrogen chloride from sodium chloride and sulfuric acid, the sodium bisulfate produced can react with additional sodium chloride in a second step to produce more hydrogen chloride. Which procedure will produce more gas from 10 pounds of NaCl: the first step alone, or a combination of both steps?

FLUORINE

Whipped cream from cans, "push-button" shaving creams, insect or paint sprays—all of these operate through the action of a gas under pressure which forces the contents out of the can when the gas is released. The propelling gas is a compound of fluorine, an element which 50 years ago was a laboratory curiosity, but today is the starting point of new, very useful compounds.

The Preparation of Fluorine

Fluorine compounds were known before the close of the eighteenth century, but the element itself was not isolated until more than 100 years later. Early attempts to oxidize hydrogen fluoride were a failure whether oxidizing agents or elec-

trolysis was used. Liquid hydrogen fluoride is a nonconductor of electricity. It was further discovered that when elemental fluorine could be produced (in small amounts), the gas reacted with the materials of the apparatus, as well as with water. Success was finally achieved in 1886 by Henri Moissan of France, who dissolved potassium fluoride in *liquid* hydrogen fluoride to form a conducting solution. He found that an apparatus made of a platinum-iridium alloy was resistant to the fluorine produced by electrolysis of the solution. This method, with minor modifications of the apparatus, is still used commercially to produce fluorine. It is not prepared in the laboratory by oxidation of the fluoride ion.

The Properties of Fluorine

Some of the first physical properties noted for fluorine were that it is a pale yellow gas with an odor resembling that of chlorine, but even more dangerous to inhale. It is denser than air (**MW = 38**); its solubility in water cannot be determined because it reacts violently with water. Other properties result from its most important chemical property—fluorine is the most active of the nonmetals by virtue of its small atomic size. The electron being borrowed to complete the outer shell of each fluorine atom can approach much closer to the positive nucleus than

23-7 In continuous pickling lines, hot rolled steel is cleaned in very dilute acid, then washed with water prior to tinning or galvanizing.

is true for any other nonmetallic element. The energy released in this transfer is great, and the ionic bond formed is very strong. Fluorine is therefore the most electronegative of the elements, and it is the strongest oxidizing agent known. Conversely, the fluoride ion, formed by the reduction of fluorine, cannot be oxidized by means of *chemical* oxidizing agents. Fluorine compounds, as expected, are very stable.

The oxidizing nature of fluorine can be observed in a number of reactions. A mixture of hydrogen and chlorine explodes when exposed to sunlight, but a mixture of hydrogen and fluorine will explode in the dark. *Hydrogen burns in fluorine* to form hydrogen fluoride, evolving more heat than when burned in chlorine.

$$H_2 + F_2 \longrightarrow 2\,HF\uparrow + \Delta$$

The *reaction of fluorine is violent with active metals* (such as sodium, potassium), and vigorous with the less active metals. Those metals (silver, copper, and gold) which are attacked slowly by chlorine react much more readily with fluorine. Here you observe the effect of electronegativity on the vigor of electron-borrowing.

$$2\,Na^0 + F_2^0 \longrightarrow 2\,Na^{+1}F^{-1}$$
$$2\,Fe^0 + 3\,F_2^0 \longrightarrow 2\,Fe^{+3}F_3^{-1}$$
$$Cu^0 + F_2^0 \longrightarrow Cu^{+2}F_2^{-1}$$

Moreover, the bonding between chlorine and some metals (aluminum, lead) is covalent rather than ionic. Because fluorine is more electronegative than chlorine, the fluorides of these metals are more ionic than covalent.

Chlorine reacts slowly with water with little evolution of heat, but *fluorine reacts violently* with water to produce hydrogen fluoride and oxygen (Fig. 23-8).

$$2\,F_2 + 2\,H_2O \longrightarrow 4\,HF\uparrow + O_2\uparrow$$

This reaction presents further evidence that fluorine is much more active than chlorine.

Uses of Fluorine and Its Compounds

The extreme reactivity between hydrogen and fluorine has been investigated as a means of

23-8 A jet of fluorine played on a crucible of water results in fire. Fluorine reacts vigorously with the hydrogen of the water.

propulsion for some rockets. Except for this possible use, all the fluorine made is converted into a variety of highly useful compounds.

An investigation of the effects of minerals in our water supply on the incidence of cavities in teeth led to the discovery that *small amounts of fluorides in water retard the development of cavities.* Some communities have adopted the practice of adding controlled amounts of fluorine compounds to their water supplies (if it does not occur naturally). Dentists have followed the practice of swabbing the teeth of small children with a 1 to 2 percent solution of sodium fluoride. At present, you are familiar with many brands of toothpastes that contain fluorine compounds (usually stannous fluoride).

Compounds of fluorine with carbon and hydrogen, known commercially as "Freons," are now used widely as refrigerants. The Freons (for example, $CHClF_2$) have replaced such materials as ammonia, sulfur dioxide, and methyl chloride in refrigeration. Many *plastics* now available cannot withstand attack by concentrated acids and oxidizing agents; this has limited their use in the chemical industry. Fluorine compounds with hydrogen and carbon (fluorinated hydrocarbons or fluorocarbons), known commercially as *Teflons,* are resistant to hot, concentrated sulfuric acid and other corrosive chemicals. Such materials now find application in pipes and containers for the transport of chemicals, as well as for mechan-

23-9 These Teflon bushings from a grand piano replace cloth bushings, which alternately swell and shrink, and ultimately rot and must be replaced. Teflon's slippery surface is an added dividend.

ical parts that come into contact with corrosive materials. Teflon, as expected, is relatively unaffected by atmospheric changes (Fig. 23-9).

One method of the *purification of uranium* for use in nuclear reactors depends on the conversion of the isotopes of the element into the hexafluoride compound (page 353). This is accomplished by reacting the metal with fluorine.

$$U + 3F_2 \longrightarrow UF_6\uparrow$$

Hydrofluoric Acid

In the laboratory you have used glass measuring cylinders and thermometers graduated (marked off) in lines and numbers. Perhaps you have seen a vase with an initial or design which seems to be cut into the glass. Each of these was prepared by *etching* ("eating away") the glass according to a pattern. The etching was done with hydrofluoric acid, a water solution of hydrogen fluoride. The glass object to be etched is coated with wax or a similar acid-resistant material. The pattern to be produced is cut through the wax to expose the glass below. When the object is dipped into or swabbed with hydrofluoric acid, the latter etches the glass by reacting with the silicates of the glass where there is no protective coating.

$$CaSiO_3 + 6HF \longrightarrow CaF_2 + SiF_4 + 3H_2O$$

The acid is now washed away and the wax removed to show a permanent design of lines,

numbers, figures, or designs. Obviously, hydrofluoric acid cannot be stored in glass bottles and was originally kept in bottles shaped from wax. Today, newer plastics, such as Teflon, are used as containers for this acid.

Hydrofluoric acid is prepared commercially by burning hydrogen in fluorine and dissolving the gaseous hydrogen fluoride in water in lead containers. In the laboratory, the acid may be prepared by the general procedure of reacting sulfuric acid with any fluoride salt; naturally occurring calcium fluoride (fluorspar) is frequently used for this purpose.

$$CaF_2 + H_2SO_4 \xrightarrow{\Delta} 2HF\uparrow + CaSO_4$$

You might like to duplicate this procedure to *see for yourself how hydrofluoric acid is prepared and used to etch glass.*

Prepare a glass plate coated with wax (paraffin) and scratch a suitable design or

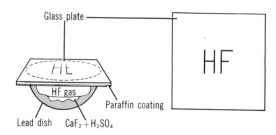

your initials through the wax. Place some powdered calcium fluoride in a lead dish, and mix enough concentrated sulfuric acid with the CaF_2 to form a paste. Cover the dish with the glass plate prepared previously (waxed side down) and set it aside, as shown below. After a few hours wash the wax off the plate with hot water and observe the etched pattern on the glass.

QUESTIONS AND PROBLEMS

1. In terms of atomic size, electronegativity, and ionization potential, explain why fluorine is the most nonmetallic element.

2. Compare the action of fluorine and chlorine with (a) water, (b) active metals, (c) less active metals, (d) hydrogen.

3. Compare and contrast the laboratory preparation of hydrogen fluoride and hydrogen chloride. Account for any differences in procedure.

4. List four uses of fluorine or fluorine compounds in the home.

BROMINE

The third member of the halogen family, bromine, is the only nonmetallic element that is liquid at room temperature. Discovered in 1826 by Antoine Balard of France, the reddish liquid with an exceedingly choking odor was named for the Greek word meaning "stench."

Commercial Preparation of Bromine

Bromine compounds, unlike those of chlorine, occur in only small amounts on the crust of the earth. For the commercial preparation of the element, we harvest the sea, where 1 pound of bromine is extracted from 7 tons of sea water (Fig. 23-10). The process is a triumph of chemical engineering ingenuity. Sea water is acidified with sulfuric acid and passed into a tower where it

23-10 Extracting bromine from sea water involves massive amounts of the latter. Each pump transports several million gallons of water per hour.

meets a current of chlorine gas. Chlorine reacts with the bromide compounds of the water to form molecular bromine.

$$2\,NaBr^- + Cl_2{}^0 \longrightarrow Br_2{}^0 + 2\,NaCl^-$$

The liberated bromine is blown out of the water by a current of air. It can be condensed directly, or it can be reacted with sulfur dioxide.

$$Br_2 + SO_2 + 2\,H_2O \longrightarrow 2\,HBr + H_2SO_4$$

The acidified mixture is now treated with chlorine to release the bromine.

$$2\,HBr^- + Cl_2{}^0 \longrightarrow Br_2{}^0 + 2\,HCl^-$$

Other methods of recovering the bromine are used, but they also apply the fundamental principle of *oxidizing* the bromide ions (Br^-) to free bromine ($Br_2{}^0$). The process is commercially practical because of the low cost of chlorine.

Laboratory Preparation of Bromine

In the laboratory, bromine can be prepared in a manner analogous to that used for chlorine—the oxidation of a solution of hydrogen bromide (hydrobromic acid) by manganese dioxide.

$$\overset{+4}{Mn}O_2 + 4\,HBr^- \longrightarrow \overset{0}{Br_2}\uparrow + \overset{+2}{Mn}Br_2 + 2\,H_2O$$

$$2\,Br^- - 2\,e^- \longrightarrow Br_2{}^0 \quad \text{(oxidation)}$$
$$Mn^{+4} + 2\,e^- \longrightarrow Mn^{+2} \quad \text{(reduction)}$$
$$\overline{Mn^{+4} + 2\,Br^- \longrightarrow Mn^{+2} + Br_2{}^0}$$

In practice, hydrobromic acid is not used because the solution changes slowly as dissolved oxygen oxidizes the bromide ion to free bromine.

$$4\,\overset{-1}{H}Br + O_2 \longrightarrow 2\,\overset{0}{Br}_2 + 2\,H_2O$$

The preparation is performed by reacting manganese dioxide with a mixture of concentrated sulfuric acid and a bromide, the hydrogen bromide being oxidized as it is formed.

$$MnO_2 + 2\,NaBr + 3\,H_2SO_4 \longrightarrow$$
$$Br_2 + 2\,NaHSO_4 + MnSO_4 + 2\,H_2O$$

The apparatus used for the preparation of chlorine cannot be used because the hot bromine vapors, being more reactive than cold chlorine gas, attack rubber and cork. The bromine must also be collected in a different manner to keep its injurious vapors out of the laboratory atmosphere. For this purpose, we use an all-glass apparatus called a *retort*. The distilled bromine is collected under water, where it first forms a reddish saturated solution; soon a layer of dark red bromine forms at the bottom of the test tube. The vapor can be condensed directly to the liquid by cooling the test tube with ice. If you wish, try the following procedure to *see for yourself how bromine is prepared.*

Prepare a mixture of 9 grams of sodium bromide and 5 grams of manganese dioxide and introduce this mixture into a retort as shown below. Through a small funnel add 10 ml of a solution of sulfuric acid made by adding 7 ml of the concentrated acid to 3 ml of water. Clamp the retort in place over a wire gauze on a tripod, insert the delivery tube of the retort into a large test tube half filled with water, and support the test tube as shown in a large beaker filled with cold water. Now begin to heat the retort *gently.*

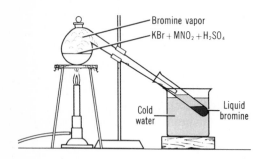

The flask fills with reddish-brown fumes of bromine which condense under the surface of the water in the test tube. When the reaction in the retort approaches completion (the fumes in the retort become much lighter), carefully raise the retort so that the tip of the delivery tube is just above the water, and discontinue heating.

Cautiously pour about 1 inch of liquid from the collecting test tube into a 6-inch test tube. Add an equal amount of carbon tetrachloride to the second test tube. Stopper this test tube, shake it thoroughly, and let it stand for 1 minute. Is bromine more soluble in carbon tetrachloride or in water?

Properties of Bromine

In physical appearance the liquid collected in this manner is black; but when viewed in thin layers it is dark red. As might be expected, the odor of bromine resembles that of chlorine, the vapors being equally dangerous to inhale. The liquid element is corrosive to the skin, causing bad burns. The vapors are very irritating to the eyes and nose. The observations made in collecting bromine tell us that it is slightly soluble in water and denser than water. Actual measurements show that only 3.2 parts of bromine dissolve in 100 parts of water at 20° C, and that the density of bromine is slightly more than three times that of water. Bromine, however, is very soluble in organic solvents such as benzene and carbon tetrachloride forming reddish solutions.

As bromine is a member of the halogen family, you anticipate that it is chemically similar to the other halogens. Predict what will happen if you lower a burning wood splint into a jar of bromine vapor. The flame is extinguished, as it was in chlorine gas; like chlorine gas, the bromine vapors do not ignite. In contrast to the wood, a jet of burning hydrogen continues to burn in bromine, forming hydrogen bromide gas.

$$H_2 + Br_2 \longrightarrow 2\ HBr\uparrow$$

Metals react with bromine as they do with chlorine, but their reactions with bromine are less vigorous. The reaction with sodium is not as energetic as that between sodium and chlorine; the reaction with antimony produces little light. Like chlorine, bromine is an oxidizing agent in its reactions with metals. In terms of oxidation numbers:

$$2\ \overset{0}{Na} + \overset{0}{Br_2} \longrightarrow 2\ \overset{+1\ -1}{NaBr}$$

$$2\ \overset{0}{Fe} + 3\ \overset{0}{Br_2} \longrightarrow 2\ \overset{+3\ -1}{FeBr_3}$$

$$2\ \overset{0}{Sb} + 3\ \overset{0}{Br_2} \longrightarrow 2\ \overset{+3\ -1}{SbBr_3}$$

Bromine also reacts with some nonmetals to form covalent compounds.

$$2 P + 3 Br_2 \longrightarrow 2 PBr_3$$

Bromine reacts with water as does chlorine, forming corresponding acids.

$$Br_2 + H_2O \longrightarrow HBr + HOBr$$
$$\text{(hypobromous acid)}$$

Like chlorine, *bromine is a bleaching agent* only when water is present; but its bleaching action is much slower. Here is another indication of lesser activity on the part of bromine.

Replacement by Bromine

Earlier you found that chlorine replaced bromine and iodine from their respective compounds. Does bromine imitate this behavior— *and if so, to what degree?*

Add a few drops of bromine water to a test tube containing a colorless solution of potassium iodide. Instead of a lighter color because of dilution, observe that a *deeper* color results. Now add a few milliliters of carbon tetrachloride to the mixture, shake it well, and place the test tube in a test tube rack. On standing, the liquid separates into two layers, the denser carbon tetrachloride settling to the bottom. What is the color of the carbon tetrachloride layer? Instead of being colored the red of bromine (Colorplate II, following page 548), it is now colored violet! Now repeat the procedure using sodium chloride instead of potassium iodide. The carbon tetrachloride is colored red, indicating that the bromine remains unchanged.

In the first test tube the bromine oxidized the iodide ions from the potassium iodide to form molecular iodine (I_2).

$$2 \overset{-1}{K}I + \overset{0}{Br_2} \longrightarrow \overset{0}{I_2} + 2 \overset{-1}{K}Br$$

$$
\begin{array}{ll}
2\,I^{-1} - 2\,e^- \longrightarrow I_2^0 & \text{(oxidation)} \\
Br_2^0 + 2\,e^- \longrightarrow 2\,Br^- & \text{(reduction)} \\
\hline
2\,I^{-1} + Br_2 \longrightarrow I_2^0 + 2\,Br^-
\end{array}
$$

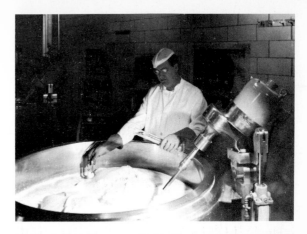

23-11 Special lighting was used to take this photograph of the production of silver bromide (from KBr, AgNO$_3$, and gelatin) for photographic film. The process normally occurs in total darkness.

In the second, the bromine did not oxidize the chloride ions in the sodium chloride, demonstrating that bromine is less active than chlorine. Bromine can oxidize the ions of the element below it in the family; it cannot oxidize the ions of the element above it.

The Uses of Bromine and Its Compounds

Every ounce of bromine produced is used to prepare bromine compounds. Today's automobile engines use *antiknock* gasoline to provide increased power. One method of producing antiknock gasoline involves the addition of tetraethyl lead [Pb(C$_2$H$_5$)$_4$] to gasoline. When such gasoline is burned in an automobile engine, deposits of lead form in the cylinders. In order to prevent these deposits, ethylene dibromide (C$_2$H$_4$Br$_2$) is added to the gasoline. This reacts with the lead to produce lead bromide, which is volatile and is therefore swept out of the cylinder with the exhaust gases. Much bromine is used in the *preparation of ethylene bromide.*

Photographic film and paper are coated with an emulsion containing light-sensitive compounds (Fig. 23-11). The silver salts of the halogen elements are widely used for this purpose, either singly or in combination. Silver bromide for these emulsions is prepared by a double replacement reaction between silver nitrate and sodium or potassium bromide.

Organic compounds of bromine (containing carbon and hydrogen) exist in great variety, with many uses other than in gasoline. Tear-gas compounds used by law-enforcement officers contain bromine. Other organic bromine compounds are used as dyes in cosmetics. Sodium, potassium, and ammonium bromides are used as mild sedatives.

Hydrobromic Acid

This acid is prepared by dissolving hydrogen bromide gas in water. An attempt to prepare this gas in a manner duplicating the preparation of hydrogen chloride—the reaction between a bromide and sulfuric acid—emphasizes a difference among the halogen compounds. When a mixture of concentrated sulfuric acid and sodium bromide is heated, hydrogen bromide gas is produced, together with some bromine. The gas first produced undergoes oxidation to free bromine by the concentrated sulfuric acid.

$$2\,HBr^- + H_2SO_4 \xrightarrow{\Delta} Br_2^0 + SO_2\uparrow + 2\,H_2O$$

For this reason, the gas is best prepared by reacting (hydrolyzing) phosphorus tribromide with water.

$$PBr_3 + 3\,H_2O \longrightarrow$$
$$3\,HBr + H_3PO_3 \text{ (phosphor}ous \text{ acid)}$$

QUESTIONS AND PROBLEMS

1. Why is bromine *not* prepared in the laboratory simply by a double replacement reaction between MnO_2 and HBr?

2. What does the method used to prepare bromine in the laboratory indicate about bromine's (a) density, (b) solubility in water?

3. Bromine replaces iodine from its compounds but does not replace chlorine from its compounds. Why?

4. (a) Chlorine is *not* found as a product when hydrogen chloride is prepared by the reaction

of a metallic chloride and sulfuric acid; but bromine is found when an analogous procedure is used. Explain why. (b) From what you have learned thus far in the chapter, predict what should be observed in the reaction between sulfuric acid and an iodide salt.

IODINE

The formation of a violet vapor when certain types of seaweed were heated led to the discovery of iodine in 1811. This vapor condensed to a grayish-black solid that was named *iodine*, from the Greek word *iodes*, meaning violetlike. It was not until three years later that iodine was shown to be another halogen element.

Commercial Preparation of Iodine

Iodine compounds are very scarce in the crust of the earth, and their concentration in sea water is even lower than that of bromine compounds. Marine organisms are able to concentrate many of the elements of sea water in their tissues. Certain types of giant seaweed (kelp) extract iodides from sea water in this way. When the seaweed is burned, some of the iodides are converted to iodine vapor and the rest forms iodide compounds found in the ash. This, the first method of producing iodine, has been superseded by two more efficient methods.

Many gas and oil wells contain brine with a moderate concentration of halogen salts. The brine of some of these wells is rich in iodide salts from which the iodine is recovered by treatment with chlorine.

$$2\,\overset{-1}{Na}I + \overset{0}{Cl_2} \longrightarrow \overset{0}{I_2} + 2\,\overset{-1}{Na}Cl$$

Sodium iodate, $NaIO_3$, is found as an impurity in Chile saltpeter, $NaNO_3$. It is separated from the nitrate when the latter is purified by fractional crystallization. Iodine is then produced by *reducing* the iodate with sodium bisulfite (in the presence of an acid).

$$2\,NaIO_3 + 5\,NaHSO_3 \longrightarrow$$
$$I_2 + 3\,NaHSO_4 + 2\,Na_2SO_4 + H_2O$$

Laboratory Preparation of Iodine

In the laboratory, iodine can be prepared in a manner related to that used in the preparation of chlorine and bromine—the oxidation of the halogen acid. However hydriodic acid, HI, is more unstable when stored than is hydrobromic acid. In practice, manganese dioxide is reacted with a mixture of concentrated sulfuric acid and an iodide salt. Why not *try this for yourself.*

Prepare a mixture of 10 grams of sodium iodide and 3 grams of manganese dioxide; then introduce this mixture into a 600-ml beaker. Pour 5 ml of concentrated sulfuric acid over the mixture to wet it with the acid. Now cover the beaker with an evaporating dish filled with cold water, as shown below.

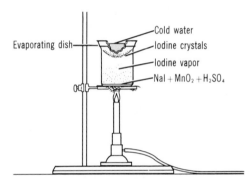

Cold water
Iodine crystals
Iodine vapor
Evaporating dish
$NaI + MnO_2 + H_2SO_4$

Heat the mixture with a *low* flame for a period of about 10 minutes. Let the apparatus cool thoroughly, remove the evaporating dish and quickly pour out the water. *Cautiously* examine the residue on the underside of the evaporating dish. How does the iodine crystal residue differ in color from the iodine vapor in the beaker?

The reaction in the beaker is indicated as:

$$\overset{+4}{Mn}O_2 + 2\,Na\overset{-1}{I} + 3\,H_2SO_4 \longrightarrow$$
$$\overset{0}{I_2} + 2\,NaHSO_4 + \overset{+2}{Mn}SO_4 + 2\,H_2O$$

$$2\,I^- - 2\,e^- \longrightarrow I_2^0 \quad \text{(oxidation)}$$
$$\underline{Mn^{+4} + 2\,e^- \longrightarrow Mn^{+2} \quad \text{(reduction)}}$$
$$Mn^{+4} + 2\,I^- \longrightarrow Mn^{+2} + I_2^0$$

As iodine at room temperature is a solid, in contrast to chlorine and bromine, different apparatus is used for its preparing and collecting it (pages 371 and 382). During the reaction, the beaker is filled with purple vapors of iodine. But when the reaction is complete, and the water poured out of the dish, the underside of the dish is found to be covered with a cluster of shiny, grayish-black crystals of iodine. An unusual property of iodine is demonstrated here, different from any of the other halogen elements (with the probable exception of astatine). On cooling, the iodine vapor "condensed" directly to a solid, without passing through the liquid state. The reverse process, which occurs on heating the solid, is known as **sublimation.** Sublimation is used to purify iodine and certain other solids when the impurities present are not volatile.

Properties of Iodine

Iodine crystals have a faint odor of chlorine that is more pronounced when the element is vaporized (but do *not* breathe the vapors). Iodine is relatively insoluble in water. It is very soluble in alcohol and forms the familiar *tincture of iodine,* which usually contains some potassium iodide and a small amount of water. Iodine also dissolves readily in benzene, carbon disulfide, and carbon tetrachloride to form violet solutions.

All the *chemical* properties of iodine are in accord with what has been learned about the halogen elements. As their atomic weight and number increase, they are progressively less reactive. For example, iodine combines slowly with hydrogen and the metals. The reaction with hydrogen *requires additional energy,* and the reaction does not go to completion, reaching an equilibrium state. Further, the product, hydrogen iodide, is not stable and undergoes slow decomposition. The reaction of iodine with metals produces relatively little heat. Similarly, there is very little reaction of iodine with water to form acids in the manner of chlorine and bromine.

You learned that chlorine replaces bromine and iodine from their compounds, and that bromine replaces iodine from iodides. Neverthe-

23-12 Unlike the tincture of iodine at the left, the iodine compounds at the right provide antiseptic action by releasing the element slowly.

less, iodine does not replace from their compounds any of the halogen elements above it in the periodic table. While all of the halogen elements are oxidizing agents, the failure of iodine to replace the other halogens (except possibly astatine) from their compounds indicates that it is a much weaker oxidizing agent than the halogens of lower atomic number.

One interesting property of iodine that differs from those of the other halogens has practical value as a test. If you place a drop of dilute tincture of iodine on a bread crumb or potato slice, a bluish spot appears. This color change indicates that starch is present in the bread or potato. As this test for starch depends on the use of iodine, starch can also be used in testing for the element.

The Uses of Iodine and Its Compounds

Tincture of iodine has long been used in the *treatment of cuts and scrapes.* All of the halogens have severe effects on body tissues and iodine is no exception. Too liberal an application of its tincture can be harmful to the skin. For this reason a freshly prepared dilute solution—about 2 percent by weight—is now used. Currently in use for the same purpose are preparations of iodine compounds which release the element slowly to provide *antiseptic action* (Fig. 23-12).

The word "iodized" appears on the labels of many brands of table salt. This term informs the consumer that about 1 to 2 percent of potassium iodide has been added to the salt. What is the reason behind this? A deficiency of iodine in the diet leads to the condition known as simple goiter. The comparative absence of simple goiter among seacoast dwellers was traced to their diets. Seacoast residents consume saltwater fish and other seafood, both good sources of iodine. Inland dwellers are not as likely to obtain this element in their diets. The addition of potassium iodide to their table salt helps to reduce the incidence of simple goiter among these people.

Iodides in the diet are concentrated by the body in the thyroxin hormone of the thyroid gland. It is for this reason that radioactive iodine, as an iodide, is used to *treat cancer of the thyroid gland* and to study the activity of this gland (Fig. 22-10).

Silver iodide is sensitive to light, as are the silver compounds of chlorine and bromine; this salt is therefore also used in the light-sensitive emulsions which coat *photographic film and paper.*

Hydriodic Acid

The combination of hydrogen and iodine demonstrates in another way the order of activity of the halogen elements. Hydrogen, recall, combines explosively with fluorine and burns readily in chlorine; its reaction with bromine is slow but its reaction with iodine is exceedingly slow at room temperature. The reaction between hydrogen and iodine is rapid at higher temperatures, particularly with catalysts such as platinum and gold, but the reaction is now reversible. Attempts to prepare the acid by a reaction between iodides and sulfuric acid give poor results; the iodide ion is oxidized to the element by the acid. Hydrogen iodide is best prepared by reacting red phosphorus and iodine with water.

$$2\,P + 3\,I_2 + 6\,H_2O \longrightarrow 6\,HI\uparrow + 2\,H_3PO_3$$

Once prepared, hydrogen iodide shows family resemblances. It is a colorless gas, very soluble in water to form a strong acid. The acid finds use in the laboratory as a reducing agent, the iodide ion being easily oxidized to the molecular form.

The many factual details of this chapter do not constitute its most important feature. Rather, it is the manner in which these details, which develop into a pattern, substantiate the basis of the periodic table. It remains to be seen whether this pattern differs as the total number of electrons in the outermost shells of atoms undergo changes. You will begin to see better if and how the pattern differs as you study the elements with six outer electron orbitals—the oxygen family.

1. The equipment used to prepare iodine in the laboratory is unlike that used for any other halogen. Why?

2. Describe three chemical reactions that establish iodine as the least active halogen (except astatine).

3. How are iodine and iodide compounds essential to good health?

4. Outline the experimental procedure you would follow to prove that iodine cannot replace the halogen elements of lower atomic number from their compounds.

5. Was your prediction in Question 4 (b) on page 384 correct? If not, explain what is observed in the reaction between sulfuric acid and an iodide salt.

VALUE OF THE CONCEPT

THE CONCEPT

The halogen elements illustrate clearly the family relationships of the periodic table. Lying immediately before the inert gases at the end of each period (except the first), the halogens are characterized by an outer shell of 7 electrons. This single feature accounts for a number of properties of these elements. First, their most common oxidation state is -1, although higher numbers, such as $+5$ ($KClO_3$) and $+7$ (KIO_4) do exist. Second, except for the inert elements, the halogen elements possess the highest ionization potentials of the elements in their respective periods. Third, the halogen elements are the most electronegative members of their respective periods. Fourth, these elements, being electron acceptors, are oxidizing agents as well as nonmetals. This oxidizing ability decreases as the atomic number increases, since the positive nucleus of the increasingly larger halogen atom is farther from the electron being attracted.

In contrast, the oxidation of the *halide ion* becomes increasingly easy with increasing atomic number; the added electron, being farther from the nucleus, is less strongly held. This greater ease of oxidation accounts for the difficulty of oxidizing the fluoride ion with chemical oxidizing agents and for the great stability of fluorine and chlorine compounds compared with those of iodine. This feature also indicates why the preparation of the halogen elements involves an oxidation process.

A tabulation of such properties as color, state, density, melting and boiling points, and solubility demonstrates an orderly progression related to the increasing atomic number of these elements. Similar progressions are observed in the properties of the halogen *compounds*. For example, a plot of the solubility of the sodium salts of the halogens against their formula weights (or atomic number of the halogen element) reveals a smooth curve.

The halogen elements, except fluorine, which is the strongest oxidizing agent known, can be prepared in the laboratory by the oxidation of a solution of hydrogen halide by manganese dioxide. Because of the instability of some hydrogen halides, and the properties of the elements, details of the preparation vary with the halogen being collected. Hydrogen chloride and hydrogen fluoride are prepared by double replacement reactions between a metallic halide and concentrated sulfuric acid. This technique cannot be employed in the preparation of hydrogen bromide and hydrogen iodide because as soon as each gas is produced, it is oxidized to the free element by the acid.

These elements and their compounds have a surprising variety of uses. In and around the home, for instance, the halogens and their compounds may appear on the kitchen table, in the refrigerator, the laundry room, the medicine cabinet, and the darkroom.

USING THE CONCEPT

Using the Basic Concept

1. Explain why different apparatus is used to prepare each of the halogen elements.
2. Write an equation to show the reaction of hydrogen bromide gas with water to form the hydronium ion.
3. What relationships among the members of the halogen family are used in preparing bromine from bromides in sea water?
4. List the observations you would make during the electrolysis of a solution of potassium bromide. Write an electronic equation for the reaction at each electrode.
5. (a) Why does the preparation of the hydrogen halides by reaction of halide salts with concentrated sulfuric acid give poor results in some instances? (b) Write an equation for the preparation of hydrogen bromide from sodium bromide.
6. (a) Outline the *commercial* methods used to prepare the halogen elements. (b) In what way are these methods alike? How do they differ?
7. Using X_2 as the formula for the element, write *one* general equation representing the laboratory preparation of chlorine, bromine, and iodine.
8. (a) Describe the chemical tests that would enable you to distinguish among the chloride, bromide, and iodide ions. (b) How would you test for the presence of the fluoride ion in an unknown solid?
9. Outline *two* procedures by which the ingredients in a mixture of sand, salt, and iodine could be *separated and recovered.*
10. Write an ionic equation for each of the following reactions: (a) the laboratory preparation of chlorine from manganese dioxide and hydrochloric acid, (b) the laboratory preparation of hydrofluoric acid from calcium fluoride and sulfuric acid, (c) the addition of silver nitrate to a solution of aluminum chloride to produce aluminum nitrate and a precipitate of silver chloride.
11. Write a conventional equation for each of the following reactions:
    (a) zinc chloride + silver nitrate $\longrightarrow$ silver chloride + zinc nitrate
    (b) sodium sulfite + bromine + water $\longrightarrow$ sodium sulfate + hydrogen bromide

Relating Terms Within the Concept

Each of the following statements contains two italicized terms. Select the *italicized* term that makes the statement correct.

1. The halide ion cannot be (*oxidized, reduced*).
2. The hydrogen halides are usually produced in the laboratory by (*decomposition, double replacement*).
3. When the halogen elements are changed to halide ions, the elements are (*reduced, oxidized*).
4. The absence of halogens in the +2 state results from their (*high ionization potentials, low ionization potentials*).
5. Bromine can be replaced from its compounds by (*chlorine, iodine*).
6. A halogen that undergoes sublimation is (*bromine, iodine*).
7. The electronegativities of the halogens are relatively (*high, low*).
8. Astatine, as was predicted, is a (*light-colored gas, dark-colored solid*).
9. Halogen compounds are (*ionic only, both ionic and covalent*).

Solving Problems Within the Concept

1. (a) What fraction of the chloride ions in hydrochloric acid becomes chlorine gas in the laboratory preparation of chlorine described on page 371? (b) Would the same fraction be obtained if a mixture of table salt and sulfuric acid were sub-

stituted? (c) Would the same fraction be obtained if the chlorine were prepared from either hydrochloric acid or sodium chloride by electrolysis? Explain.

2. Which of each of the following pairs of compounds contains the greater percent by weight of the halogen element: calcium bromide or sodium bromide, aluminum fluoride or beryllium fluoride, sodium iodate or cesium iodide?

3. (a) What volume of chlorine gas (**STP**) is needed to replace the bromine in 154.5 grams of sodium bromide? (b) What will this volume of the gas weigh?

4. If the electrolysis of brine (NaCl) produces 33.6 liters of chlorine (**STP**), how many grams of sodium hydroxide will be produced at the same time?

5. How much bromine, by weight, can be obtained by reacting 100 grams of calcium bromide with MnO_2 and H_2SO_4?

6. If 12 liters of hydrogen and 13 liters of chlorine react under the influence of an electric spark, which gas will be left in excess? How much of it?

7. What weight of calcium hydroxide will be neutralized by a solution containing 47 grams of hydrogen iodide?

8. In which reaction would the greater yield of sodium chloride be obtained from 46 grams of the metal: the reaction of the metal with hydrochloric acid or its reaction with chlorine? Explain.

Applying the Concept

1. What are the possibilities that scientists will discover a halogen element lighter than fluorine?

2. In their reactions, the halogen elements are oxidizing agents but no oxygen is present. Explain.

3. Why does the stability of the hydrogen halides vary in the same order as the activity of the halogen elements?

4. Aluminum chloride is a covalent compound but aluminum fluoride is largely ionic. Account for this difference.

5. Should we expect the halogen elements to form molecules *between themselves* (for example, BrCl, ICl_3)? Investigate this in reference texts to confirm or correct your answer.

6. Wires connected to a dry cell are attached to the ends of a moistened strip of paper containing a mixture of starch and potassium iodide. Why does a blue color develop at the positive terminal?

7. (a) In the equation: $KClO_3 + HCl \longrightarrow Cl_2 + KCl + H_2O$ which substance is the oxidizing agent? the reducing agent? (b) What unusual feature is demonstrated in this equation? How do you account for it?

8. Chlorine gas is passed through a warm tube containing dishes of chemicals as shown below. Predict the observations you would make.

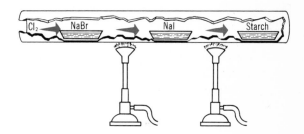

Reading Further

Modern Chemical Discoveries, by Richard Clements, New York, Dutton, 1954. Pertinent and interesting details of the discovery of the halogen elements.

The Chemistry and Fertility of Sea Water, 2d. ed., by Hildebrande Harvey, New York, Cambridge University Press, 1957. The salts of the sea serve man both as a source of elements and as a source of "food."

24

Sulfur and the Oxygen Family

Group VIA Elements

At the very outset of your study of chemistry you become acquainted with oxygen, one of the most important substances of the environment. In Chapter 1 you became familiar with its discovery, and its laboratory preparation and properties. In this chapter, you will consider the element more fully. Having gone further into chemistry, you are now well aware that oxygen is a member of group VIA in the periodic table. What are the other members of the group which includes oxygen? How do they resemble oxygen and differ from it? What are their particular properties, and to what particular uses may they be put? As a first step toward answering these questions, examine Table 24-1.

All of the elements portrayed fall into one group because each of them has an outer electron shell of 6 electrons. They achieve an oxidation state of −2 by reactions involving the incomplete p orbitals of their outer shells (Fig. 24-1). As the atomic weight and number increase, the elements pass from the gaseous to the solid state; unlike the halogen family, none of the members of the oxygen family is liquid at room temperature. The melting points, boiling points, and densities also increase with increasing atomic weight. The solid members of the family have a distinct color, and tellurium has a silvery luster typical of metals. Little has been learned about polonium since the half life of the only known

The many natural processes which consume oxygen—our breathing and slow oxidation, fires, bacterial and related actions—all depend on an atmosphere containing only about 20 percent of the element by volume. Where an oxidation process proceeds feebly or slowly (or may even be impossible) because of this "diluted" oxygen, it is advantageous to have a supply of the pure gas.

The skin diver who descends into the ocean or the mountain climber who ascends the world's tallest mountain must carry his own oxygen supply. The skin diver, though surrounded by water which contains oxygen, must have gaseous oxygen to breathe. And the mountain climber, as he ascends to higher and higher peaks, finds himself in circumstances where the available supply is much reduced.

Without oxygen, life—as we know it—would be impossible.

Table 24-1 **THE GROUP VIA ELEMENTS**

Element	Atomic number	Atomic weight	Electron configuration	Density (20° C)	Melting point (°C)	Boiling point (°C)	State and color	Ionization potential (ev)	Oxidation states
Oxygen	8	15.9994	2 6	1.429 g/l (0° C)	−218.4	−183.0	Colorless gas	13.6	−2, (−1)
Sulfur	16	32.064	2 8 6	2.07 g/ml (rhombic)	112.8 (rhombic)	444.6	Light yellow solid	10.4	−2, +4, +6
Selenium	34	78.96	2 8 18 6	4.8 g/ml	220	688	Gray solid	9.8	−2, +4, +6
Tellurium	52	127.60	2 8 18 18 6	6.24 g/ml	452	1390	Silvery solid	9.0	−2, +4, +6
Polonium	84	[210]	2 8 18 32 18 6	?	?	?	Silvery solid	?	?

( ) Indicates an infrequent oxidation state.

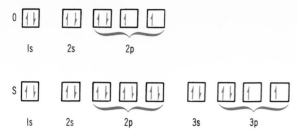

24-1 Two incomplete p orbitals in the outer shell identify oxygen and sulfur as group VIA elements, with a usual oxidation state of -2.

isotope is only 140 days. The little data collected indicates a strong resemblance to tellurium. This resemblance might have been predicted from the information considered in Chapter 5 about the families of the periodic table. As the members of a family increase in weight and number, they develop progressively more metallic features. Recall that while the halogen elements darken progressively in color, iodine possesses some degree of metallic luster.

Family relationships are demonstrated in still another way in the group VIA elements. All of them, with the possible exception of polonium, possess allotropic forms. We will meet some of these forms in detail in the course of this chapter. Let us begin the study of this family by considering in more detail its first member, oxygen.

OXYGEN

If you are interested in producing heat *quickly,* you can achieve your goal by burning a fuel more rapidly. One method of doing this is to supply air under forced draft; a better method is to supply the fuel with pure oxygen. Remember that while sulfur burns with a pale blue flame in air, it burns brightly in a bottle of oxygen. And charcoal, which burns quietly in air, burns vigorously in undiluted oxygen. Even steel wool, which burns feebly in air, burns brightly in pure oxygen.

If you have not already investigated these reactions in the laboratory, why not do so now? You could prepare oxygen by the electrolysis of water, or by heating $KClO_3$. Another method is by *the reaction between sodium peroxide and water.*

Arrange the apparatus as shown below for collecting oxygen by water displacement. Add about 5 grams of sodium peroxide to the flask and add cold water to the dropping funnel. CAUTION: *Do not allow sodium peroxide to come in contact with your skin or with paper; use only metal or glass in handling it.* Regulate the speed of the reaction by maintaining a very slow flow of water through the funnel. As the sodium peroxide and water react, observe bubbles of gas in the collecting bottle. Use

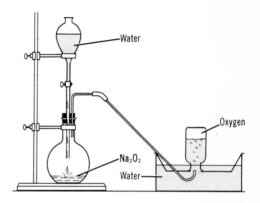

the glowing splint test to prove that the gas is oxygen. Collect three bottles of oxygen. What are its properties? Ignite some sulfur in a deflagrating spoon and a piece of charcoal in another deflagrating spoon. Thrust each into a separate bottle of oxygen. Use a pair of tongs to thrust a piece of heated steel wool into the third bottle. Do your observations confirm your predictions?

In the flask the water reacted with the sodium peroxide to yield oxygen and sodium hydroxide.

$$2\,Na_2O_2 + 2\,H_2O \longrightarrow 4\,NaOH + O_2\uparrow$$

Commercial Preparation of Oxygen

Many present-day operations require large amounts of pure oxygen; indeed, some of them would be impossible if unlimited quantities of the element were not available. How, then, is oxygen prepared for commercial uses requiring the pure element? From a number of facts you know that the gases of the air are uncombined with each other. For example, a change of temperature may cause precipitation of the water vapor of the atmosphere; neither rain, nor sleet, nor snow contains the remaining gases of the air. As the air is therefore a mixture, its constituents can be separated by relatively simple means.

Air is liquefied by first removing the water vapor and carbon dioxide. Then it is alternately compressed and cooled until liquid air is produced at a temperature below $-200°$ C (Fig. 24-2). It is important to realize that the liquid contains a number of individual elements *each of which has its own boiling point*. If the liquid air is now allowed to become warmer gradually, a temperature is reached at which the constituent of lowest boiling point begins to boil. When the temperature of the liquid air reaches $-196°$ C, the nitrogen boils away almost independently of the remaining substances. The nitrogen is collected and "bottled" in steel tanks under pressure. If the temperature of the remaining liquid is allowed to reach $-183°$ C, the oxygen begins to boil away, again almost independently of other materials. Separation of the components

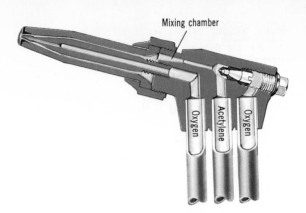

24-3 The oxyacetylene torch used in steel welding can also be used, with relatively minor modifications, as a cutting torch.

of a liquid mixture, such as liquid air, by utilizing their different boiling points is known as **fractional distillation.** By repeated fractional distillation, oxygen of better than 99 percent purity is obtained. What are the many uses which require oxygen of this purity?

Uses of Oxygen

The high temperatures needed to melt many metals in order to weld them or cut them apart cannot be reached by the combustion of fuels in air. If, however, the combustion is performed with pure oxygen, more fuel can be burned per unit of time to provide much more heat and consequently a higher temperature. This is the principle upon which the oxyacetylene torch (Fig. 24-3) and the oxyhydrogen torch (Fig. 24-4) basic to welding operations operate. Temperatures even higher than those reached by such torches have been obtained by burning aluminum powder in a stream of oxygen. The tremendous thrust necessary to propel space rockets with chemical fuels depends on the rapid combustion of the fuel. When oxygen is the oxidizing agent, it is provided as liquid oxygen, known as LOX.

In a number of applications, pure oxygen serves to provide an "artificial atmosphere." When lung tissue is damaged so that less of its area is available to utilize the oxygen of the inhaled air, or when breathing is very shallow so

24-2 Fractional distillation of liquid air—liquified as indicated here—is the chief commercial source of pure oxygen and pure nitrogen.

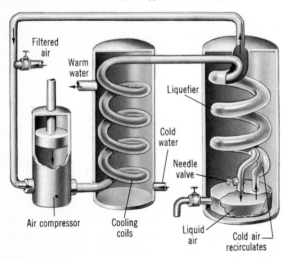

that a patient suffers from a reduced intake of air, the deficiency can usually be remedied by providing the patient with an atmosphere richer in oxygen. This technique accounts for the now-familiar oxygen tent. Those engaged in rescue work involving fires or mine accidents must enter an atmosphere in which little oxygen may be present, and in which various dangerous gases have been produced. Such workers must carry their oxygen with them in small tanks strapped to their backs.

Pure oxygen is also being used to speed up industrial processes. For example, the production of iron from its ore offers a considerable saving in time when pure oxygen, rather than air, is employed. Water purification and sewage treatment, both slow when air alone is used, are hastened by treatment with the pure gas.

Ozone

If you have ever been in the vicinity of electrical apparatus which sparks, or near a powerful source of ultraviolet light, you may have become aware of a peculiarly irritating odor. This is the odor of **ozone,** a form of oxygen. When oxygen is subjected to the forms of energy mentioned above, or a silent electric discharge, its molecules are dissociated into atoms. These usually recombine into oxygen molecules. Sometimes *three* oxygen atoms recombine into a new molecule, O_3, called ozone.

Properties and Uses of Ozone

Ozone is prepared by passing oxygen through an ozone generator like that in Fig. 24-5. An electrical discharge passing through the generator converts part of the oxygen to ozone.

$$3\,O_2 + \text{electrical energy} \longrightarrow 2\,O_3$$

Observe that ozone is still an element; it contains nothing more than oxygen atoms (Fig. 24-6). But this "triplet" differs in properties from ordinary oxygen. It is therefore called an **allotrope** of oxygen. *Allotropes are different forms of the same substance* (either element or compound) *having different physical and chemical properties.* Ozone

24-4 The oxyhydrogen torch is being operated to weld a hexagon-shaped aluminum device into place in the air-flow structure of a wind tunnel. This type of torch can also be used in underwater operations.

differs from oxygen not only in odor but in density and melting point. The chemical differences are more pronounced. Anything which oxygen does, ozone does much more energetically. Rubber becomes brittle and inelastic after slow oxidation by the air; ozone produces this result within a few hours, and in very low concentrations. This triatomic form of oxygen is unstable and changes to the ordinary form with time. The

24-5 In an ozonizer an electric discharge between the inner and outer cylindrical metal electrodes converts oxygen to ozone.

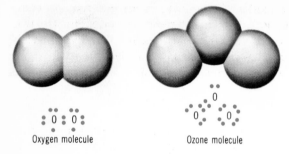

Oxygen molecule   Ozone molecule

24-6 Unpaired electrons account for the magnetic properties of diatomic oxygen. Ozone is not magnetic; its electrons are paired. The ozone molecule, with oxygen atoms arranged in a triangle, is a resonance hybrid.

change is catalyzed by many substances, such as silver, copper oxide, and platinum.

Outside of the laboratory, the gas has been used in low concentrations to deodorize and sterilize air. We are also the beneficiaries of the reaction by which ultraviolet light transforms oxygen into ozone. The intensity of the ultraviolet light of the sun which reaches our upper atmosphere is dangerous to living organisms. But the oxygen of the upper atmosphere absorbs this ultraviolet energy when the oxygen is transformed into ozone and thus reduces the intensity of this radiation on the earth below.

Hydrogen Peroxide

Oxygen and hydrogen usually combine to form hydrogen oxide—H_2O. Under special conditions they react to form hydrogen peroxide, H_2O_2 (Fig. 24-7). You are probably familiar with hydrogen peroxide as an antiseptic that must be kept in a dark bottle in a cool place—an indication of its relative instability.

Hydrogen peroxide can be prepared by reacting dilute sulfuric acid with barium peroxide.

$$H_2SO_4 + BaO_2 \longrightarrow H_2O_2 + BaSO_4\downarrow$$

When the insoluble barium sulfate is separated by filtration, a solution of hydrogen peroxide remains.

Today the commercial preparation is carried out by the electrolysis of an approximately 50 percent solution of sulfuric acid, or sulfuric acid

and ammonium sulfate, at a temperature of about 35° C. The electrolysis causes the sulfate ion to be oxidized to the *perdisulfate* ion.

$$2 SO_4^{-2} - 2 e^- \longrightarrow S_2O_8^{-2} \quad \text{(perdisulfate ion)}$$

The resulting perdisulfuric acid ($H_2S_2O_8$) hydrolyzes in warm water to form sulfuric acid and hydrogen peroxide.

$$H_2S_2O_8 + H_2O \longrightarrow H_2SO_4 + H_2O_2$$

When the products are separated by fractional distillation, the concentration of the hydrogen peroxide rises above 90 percent.

Properties and Uses of H_2O_2

In its pure form, hydrogen peroxide is a syrupy liquid that appears colorless in small amounts but bluish when viewed in bulk. It boils at 151° C, freezes at −0.9° C, and is about 1.5 times as dense as water. It decomposes readily into water and oxygen when in contact with rough surfaces, finely divided precious metals, MnO_2, and traces of alkalies. In contrast, traces of acids and certain organic compounds such as glycerine and acetanilide prevent the compound from decomposing so rapidly.

Hydrogen peroxide and other peroxides are of interest because they contain oxygen in the unusual −1 oxidation state. This is midway between the 0 oxidation state for molecular oxygen and the usual −2 oxidation state found in oxides. Hydrogen peroxide is both an oxidizing and a reducing agent. When the peroxide ion, O_2^{-2}, is converted into a pair of oxide ions, each O^{-2}, the peroxide ion is an oxidizing agent. In interpreting the equation below, note that though *each* oxygen atom in the peroxide ion is in the −1 oxidation state, the ion itself contains two atoms of oxygen and has a charge of −2.

$$O_2^{-2} + 2 e^- \longrightarrow 2 O^{-2}$$

For example, a solution of hydrogen peroxide oxidizes ferrous to ferric ions in the presence of an acid.

$$H_2O_2 + 2 HCl + 2 \overset{+2}{Fe}Cl_2 \longrightarrow 2 \overset{+3}{Fe}Cl_3 + 2 H_2O$$

24-7 In the asymmetrical hydrogen peroxide molecule, the left bond angle H-O-O is 97°. All four atoms are not in the same plane; the right hydrogen atom projects 94° from the plane of the other three atoms.

In contrast, the peroxide ion is a *reducing* agent when it is converted to molecular oxygen.

$$O_2^{-2} - 2\,e^- \longrightarrow O_2^0$$

Hydrogen peroxide solutions decolorize solutions of potassium permanganate by reducing the intensely purple-colored permanganate ions to the light pink manganous ions.

$$2\,\overset{+7}{K}MnO_4 + 5\,H_2O_2 + 3\,H_2SO_4 \longrightarrow$$
$$2\,\overset{+2}{Mn}SO_4 + 5\,O_2 + K_2SO_4 + 8\,H_2O$$

In the decomposition to water, hydrogen peroxide acts as both an oxidizing and a reducing agent, that is it undergoes *auto-oxidation*.

$$2\,H_2O_2 \longrightarrow 2\,H_2O + O_2$$
$$O_2^{-2} - 2\,e^- \longrightarrow O_2 \quad \text{(oxidation)}$$
$$O_2^{-2} + 2\,e^- \longrightarrow 2\,O^{-2} \quad \text{(reduction)}$$

Besides being used for antiseptic purposes in the form of its 3 percent solution, it is used in 85 percent concentration as an oxidant in rocket propulsion. For some years hydrogen peroxide has found extensive use as a bleaching agent for hair, fur, silk, and wool; more recently it has been used in bleaching cotton and linen.

Peroxides and Dioxides

BaO_2, Na_2O_2, and H_2O_2 are called barium *peroxide*, sodium *peroxide*, and hydrogen *peroxide*, respectively. But SiO_2, PbO_2, and CO_2 are called silicon *dioxide*, lead *dioxide*, and carbon *dioxide*. What distinction, if any, exists between *peroxides* and *dioxides*? In addition to the unusual -1 oxidation state of oxygen in peroxides, the bonding in the two types of compounds is quite different. In peroxides, the two oxygen atoms are covalently bonded to each other, as represented by the electron dot formula below for the peroxide ion.

$$\left[\ddot{\underset{..}{O}} \ddot{\underset{..}{O}} \right]^{-2}$$

By contrast, in dioxides, each oxygen atom is bonded to the second type of atom in the molecule and *not* to another oxygen atom. In carbon dioxide, for example,

$$\ddot{\underset{..}{O}} :: C :: \ddot{\underset{..}{O}}$$

Usually the oxygen-oxygen bond of peroxides is easily broken, while the bonds in dioxides are quite strong.

The study of oxygen has now provided you with a frame of reference with which to compare and contrast the remaining group VIA members. Above all, keep in mind that these elements, both through their similarities and differences, develop the concept of a family or group of elements. You continue your study by looking carefully at the next element with an outer shell of 6 electrons—sulfur.

QUESTIONS AND PROBLEMS

1. (a) Define the term *allotrope*. (b) How do the two allotropic forms of oxygen differ?

2. How does the dioxide of any element differ from the peroxide of the same element?

3. (a) List three methods by which oxygen can be prepared in the laboratory. (b) Write an equation for each method listed.

4. (a) Write oxidation and reduction half-reactions to show the reducing action of hydrogen peroxide on potassium permanganate. (b) How could you return the color of the permanganate ions to a solution?

5. Write an equation for the oxidation of aluminum by ozone.

SULFUR

The yellow solid whose symbol, S, occurs below oxygen in the periodic table is no newcomer

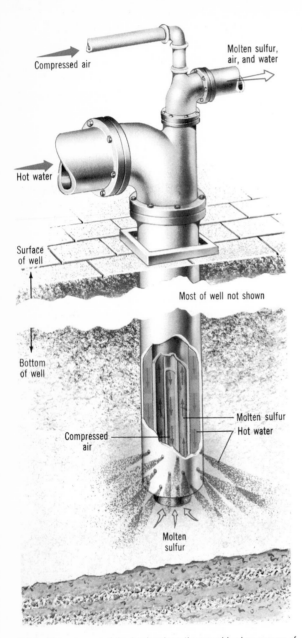

24-8 The upper part of the drawing shows the ground level appearance of a Frasch-process well. The lower section shows the concentric arrangement of pipes for compressed air, hot water, and molten sulfur.

Labels in figure:
Compressed air
Molten sulfur, air, and water
Hot water
Surface of well
Most of well not shown
Bottom of well
Molten sulfur
Hot water
Compressed air
Molten sulfur

to the chemical scene. The Biblical brimstone of Sodom and Gomorrah was this element; much later, it formed the basis of "Greek Fire" in Byzantine warfare. Not much more than a century ago, it became the vital ingredient in the vulcanization of rubber, a process that revolutionized the use of the latter material. Still later, sulfur began to be used in great quantities for the preparation of the most widely used acid of industry, sulfuric acid. But how is the element itself obtained?

The Frasch Process

Sulfur is found in the earth both as the free element and combined with metals in such minerals and ores as galena (PbS), zinc blende (ZnS), cinnabar (HgS), and iron pyrites ("fool's gold," FeS_2). As deposits of free sulfur are often associated with volcanic action, it is not surprising to learn that the island of Sicily was the main source of the world's sulfur at the beginning of the twentieth century. There sulfur is found mixed with the volcanic rock in "sulfur hills" just below the surface of the earth. By setting fire to some of these "sulfur hills," enough heat is produced to melt the remaining sulfur, which runs off from the rocks and is collected and distilled. During distillation the sulfur vaporizes. When cooled, the vapor condenses and sulfur is deposited as fine particles known as *flowers of sulfur*. This sulfur, as well as other forms, can be melted and poured into molds to form hard, crystalline *roll* sulfur.

While sulfur was being mined in Sicily, it was known that there were extensive deposits of sulfur some 500 to 700 feet below ground in Louisiana and Texas. Repeated attempts to mine this sulfur had failed because of the difficulty of raising the sulfur through beds of sand and clay which lay between the sulfur and the surface. In 1900 Herman Frasch, an immigrant pharmacist, proposed a totally new and radical scheme. Since liquids can be made to flow, why not melt the underground sulfur and bring it to the surface through pipes? The idea met with considerable ridicule; but confident of his ideas,

Frasch proceeded with his plans. And his plan was highly successful; the bulk of the sulfur consumed today is mined by his process.

In the Frasch process, a 12-inch casing is first driven through the earth to the beds of sulfur. Through this casing, a series of three concentric pipes (one within the other) is lowered to the sulfur (Fig. 24-8). A stream of *superheated* (170° C) water under pressure is forced down into the outermost pipe to melt the sulfur. When a pool of liquid sulfur has formed, a current of hot, compressed air is forced down through the innermost pipe. The high air pressure forces the frothy emulsion of melted sulfur, hot air, and water through the middle pipe to the surface, where it flows into shallow enclosures made of wood. As the sulfur cools and hardens, the wooden bin is built up and the block of sulfur grows. To ship this sulfur, it is necessary for tractors to break the sulfur loose so that it can be scooped up by power shovels and hauled away in railroad cars (Fig. 24-9). The sulfur obtained by the Frasch process is more than 99 percent pure, and it needs no further purification for most purposes.

The Properties of Sulfur

Sulfur shows the typical physical properties of the nonmetals. The light yellow, brittle solid lacks

24-9 A tremendous block of sulfur obtained by the Frasch process.

mechanical strength and is an excellent insulator against heat and electricity. It is about twice as dense as water and practically insoluble in it. By contrast, sulfur is soluble in a variety of organic solvents such as carbon disulfide, carbon tetrachloride, benzene, and a number of alcohols.

Allotropic Forms of Sulfur

It is no surprise that sulfur, like oxygen, exists in several allotropic forms. Three different allotropic forms of sulfur *can be prepared readily by simple procedures.*

Place about 2 grams of flowers of sulfur in a test tube, add 5 ml of carbon disulfide, and shake the mixture well. Filter the liquid into a watch glass or shallow dish, as shown below, and allow the solvent to evaporate

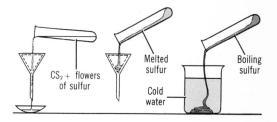

CS$_2$ + flowers of sulfur

Melted sulfur

Cold water

Boiling sulfur

slowly in a warm place. When all the solvent has evaporated, observe that the bottom of the dish is covered with pale yellow, transparent crystals. Use a magnifying glass to determine that these crystals, known as **rhombic** crystals, are eight-sided, resembling two pyramids joined base to base.

Next, *very carefully* melt about one-third of a test tube of flowers of sulfur. Pour the resulting yellowish fluid into a folded filter paper, and allow it to cool slowly until a yellow crust forms. Break the crust by unfolding the filter paper. Does your examination reveal that under these conditions sulfur forms needle-shaped crystals called **prismatic** or **monoclinic** sulfur? Prismatic sulfur is unstable below 96° C, and if left standing at room temperature, changes slowly to the rhombic form.

To obtain prismatic sulfur, you carefully heated sulfur above its melting point. Now, let us heat a similar portion of flowers of sulfur *to boiling*. If the sulfur is heated rapidly to hasten melting, its color darkens progressively. Observe that the sulfur melts but becomes so gummy that it cannot be poured. As you continue heating, the gummy sulfur becomes fluid and even darker in color; finally it begins to boil. Carefully pour the boiling sulfur into cold water. Does it form a black, rubbery mass, completely unlike the sulfur in the two preceding parts of the investigations? Because this allotropic form of sulfur has no definite shape, it is called **amorphous** sulfur. Amorphous sulfur is unstable; if you allow it to remain at room temperature, it also slowly changes to the rhombic form. From the change observed in the preparation of amorphous sulfur, explain why the sulfur in the second test tube was heated gently, and only to the melting point.

This investigation shows some of the allotropic forms of sulfur, each of which exists over a definite temperature range.

$$S_{rhombic} \xrightarrow[below\ 96°\ C]{above\ 96°\ C} S_{prismatic} \xrightarrow[below\ 119°\ C]{above\ 119°\ C} S_{liquid}$$

Since all forms eventually return to the same stable form, there can be no doubt that rhombic, prismatic, and amorphous sulfur are different solid forms of the same element (Fig. 24-10).

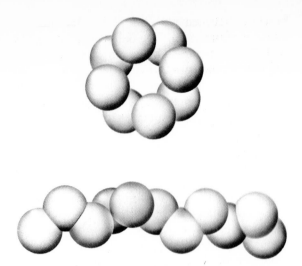

24-11 Rhombic sulfur exists in the form of a ring of eight sulfur atoms. As the sulfur is heated to higher temperatures, the ring breaks to form part of a continuous chain of sulfur atoms.

It is customary to use the symbol S to represent sulfur; but the element in the solid state exists in the form of a ring of eight sulfur atoms, S_8 (Fig. 24-11). These rings are the molecular units in the rhombic crystal. At a temperature of 96° C, the units rearrange themselves to form the prismatic crystal. Melting of the sulfur results when the binding forces among these units are broken, and the units are free to move. At higher temperatures, the eight-membered rings of sulfur are broken to form chains of sulfur atoms. On long standing, these chains rearrange themselves into rings of sulfur atoms typical of the rhombic form.

The Reactions of Sulfur

The study of oxygen acquainted you with the burning of sulfur to form sulfur dioxide. Examination of the electron structure of sulfur (Fig. 24-12) will enable you to predict two additional properties of this element. First, since its outer shell structure is like that of oxygen, sulfur should *react with metals*. Second, because like oxygen it also accepts electrons, sulfur should *act as an oxidizing agent*.

From your experience (Chapter 1) of heating a mixture of iron and sulfur, you know that the

24-10 Both the rhombic and prismatic allotropes of sulfur are crystalline in form; liquid or amorphous sulfur is not. On standing at normal temperature, all sulfur returns to the rhombic crystalline form.

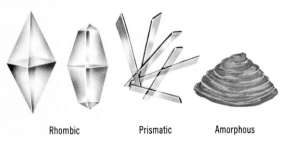

Rhombic   Prismatic   Amorphous

reaction between iron and sulfur produces its own heat and light. The *following investigations* will also show that sulfur behaves similarly to oxygen in other reactions.

Heat some powdered roll sulfur to boiling and lower a strip of bright, shiny copper into the hot sulfur vapors. The copper strip suddenly glows cherry red. Withdraw it from the test tube and observe that the strip is coated with blue-black cuprous sulfide. Once again, the reaction between sulfur and a metal has produced noticeable heat and light.

Finally, mix 5 grams of zinc *dust* and 3 grams of sulfur powder into a small heap on an asbestos pad. Ignite this mixture by using a Bunsen burner *held at arm's length*. A sudden, *semiexplosive* reaction occurs, producing a cloud of zinc sulfide and considerable heat and light.

Clearly, sulfur reacts with metals, as predicted.

$$Fe + S \xrightarrow{\Delta} FeS$$
$$2\,Cu + S \xrightarrow{\Delta} Cu_2S$$
$$Zn + S \xrightarrow{\Delta} ZnS$$

Moreover, the noticeable heat and light which accompany each of these reactions indicates that sulfur is not only an oxidizing agent but also supports combustion.

Not all the reactions of sulfur with metals require heat. If you keep a dime or quarter in contact with powdered sulfur and rub the sulfur over the coin from time to time, the coin soon takes on a blackened appearance (Fig. 24-13).

$$2\,\overset{0}{Ag} + \overset{0}{S} \longrightarrow \overset{+1}{Ag_2}\overset{-2}{S}$$
$$2\,Ag^0 - 2\,e^- \longrightarrow 2\,Ag^{+1} \quad \text{(oxidation)}$$
$$S + 2\,e^- \longrightarrow S^{-2} \quad \text{(reduction)}$$

This reaction shows further the resemblance between sulfur and oxygen. When heat is not applied, sulfur still acts as an oxidizing agent by removing electrons from the metal, but it does so more slowly. While there is hardly any free sulfur in the kitchen, many foods (such as onions, mus-

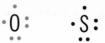

24-12 The outer electron shell of either an oxygen atom or a sulfur atom contains only six electrons—a family characteristic.

tard, and eggs) contain sulfur compounds. Industrial smoke, and even some wastes from home coal furnaces and oil burners, also contain sulfur compounds. If silver is in contact with any of these materials over a long period of time, gray-black silver sulfide will form gradually on its surface.

$$4\,Ag + 2\,H_2S + O_2 \longrightarrow 2\,Ag_2S + 2\,H_2O$$

The reaction of sulfur with metals occurred naturally long before it was studied in the laboratory. The result was the formation within the earth of numerous useful metallic ores and minerals. Besides those mentioned at the beginning of this section, we find chalcopyrites, a mixed sulfide of both iron and copper ($CuFeS_2$), and stibnite, Sb_2S_3.

Sulfur combines with various nonmetals at high temperatures to form covalent compounds. For example, in the intense heat of an electric furnace, sulfur vapor combines with coke to form carbon disulfide, CS_2. This liquid is of great value as a

24-13 Compare the two silver quarters. The coin at the right was blackened by lying for several days in contact with sulfur.

solvent and starting material in chemical synthesis, particularly in the preparation of artificial silk (Chapter 37).

The chapter thus far has dealt with sulfur as the element. Of particular importance is the close resemblance of sulfur to oxygen in chemical behavior. What can be learned further about sulfur from a study of certain of its compounds?

QUESTIONS AND PROBLEMS

1. Why must the water used in the Frasch process be superheated?

2. (a) Differentiate among the following allotropic forms of sulfur: rhombic, prismatic, amorphous. (b) How is each prepared?

3. Give an example of a reaction to prove that: (a) sulfur reacts with metal, (b) sulfur supports combustion, (c) sulfur is an oxidizing agent.

4. (a) List the chemical properties in which sulfur resembles oxygen. (b) List those in which the two elements differ.

HYDROGEN SULFIDE AND METALLIC SULFIDES

Hydrogen sulfide, the gaseous compound responsible for the extremely unpleasant odor of rotten eggs, is also noticed around sulfur springs and often near active volcanoes. The gas has many industrial uses and right now is being produced and used in many chemical laboratories. How is the gas made? What are its properties? How do chemists use it?

The Preparation of Hydrogen Sulfide

A mixture of hydrogen and oxygen combines readily and violently when a spark or flame is provided. But when hydrogen gas is passed into boiling sulfur, a poor yield of hydrogen sulfide results, the reaction being reversible.

$$H_2 + S \rightleftharpoons H_2S$$

We have here an instance of the lower reactivity of the sulfur atom; it is a weaker acceptor of electrons than oxygen because the electrons being accepted cannot approach the sulfur nucleus as closely as that of oxygen. Hydrogen sulfide is much more easily prepared in the manner used for acids in general—the reaction of its salts (sulfides) with sulfuric acid.

$$FeS + H_2SO_4 \longrightarrow H_2S\uparrow + FeSO_4$$

Hydrochloric acid can be substituted for the sulfuric acid in this reaction, which requires only moderate heating to start.

$$FeS + 2\,HCl \longrightarrow H_2S\uparrow + FeCl_2$$

Why not use this last reaction to see for yourself how hydrogen sulfide is prepared? CAUTION: *This investigation must be performed under a hood.*

Prepare the apparatus for the collection of a gas by displacement of air as shown below. Place about 10 grams of ferrous (iron II) sulfide in the generator flask, replace the stopper and thistle tube, and add about 25 ml of dilute hydrochloric acid. If no reaction occurs after about 2 minutes, *gently* warm the contents of the generator with a *low* flame. As soon as a reaction begins, discontinue heating. Collect two bottles of the gas,

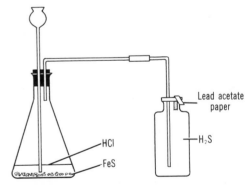

covering each with a glass plate as soon as it is full. To determine when a bottle is filled with gas, attach a strip of moist lead acetate paper inside the mouth of the bottle. When the paper turns black the bottle is full. After the last bottle has been collected, place the delivery tube in a bottle half full of ammonia water. Why?

From preparing the gas, you are aware of the color and odor of hydrogen sulfide. Insert a burning splint into the first bottle. Does hydrogen sulfide burn? Add about 5 ml of water to the second bottle of gas, cover it, and shake it well; then test the solution with litmus paper. Is it acidic or basic?

Properties of Hydrogen Sulfide

The physical properties of hydrogen sulfide are readily apparent. The colorless gas collected has the familiar odor of rotten eggs. It is moderately soluble in water and its possible collection by the upward displacement of air indicates that it is denser than air ($MW = 34$). While its odor is disagreeable, the gas does not cause any choking sensation and is therefore tolerated when *inhaled* by those exposed to it. This is unfortunate, as hydrogen sulfide is poisonous, and a continued accumulation in the body causes unconsciousness and even death.

In contrast to the decided red color produced by a drop of hydrochloric acid on blue litmus paper, water solutions of hydrogen sulfide turn blue litmus paper pink. The indicator shows that in solution hydrogen sulfide forms a weak acid, namely, hydrosulfuric acid (compare the name and formula with hydrochloric acid). Salts of this acid are called sulfides.

$$H_2S + H_2O \rightleftharpoons H_3O^+ + HS^-$$

Hydrosulfuric acid is so weakly ionized that even magnesium, an active metal, replaces the hydrogen slowly.

If you insert a burning splint into a bottle of hydrogen sulfide gas, the gas ignites with a pale blue flame which moves down into the bottle. As the gas burns, a pale yellow deposit appears on the walls of the bottle—sulfur has been produced (Fig. 24-14). Since the burning observed in this reaction involves a combination with oxygen, the remaining product is an oxide of hydrogen, water vapor. You can therefore write,

$$2 H_2S + O_2 \longrightarrow 2 H_2O + 2 S$$

Sulfur deposited

H₂S

24-14 When a burning splint is inserted into a bottle of hydrogen sulfide, the gas burns with a pale blue flame. As the flame moves slowly downward, sulfur is deposited on the walls of the bottle.

Sulfur was deposited rather than oxidized because only the oxygen at the mouth of the bottle was available for the burning; the supply of oxygen was limited—the combustion was *incomplete*. When hydrogen sulfide is burned in an abundant supply of air, the odor of sulfur dioxide is readily detected.

$$2 H_2S + 3 O_2 \longrightarrow 2 H_2O + 2 SO_2$$

A study of the half-equations for reactions from the viewpoint of apparent charge reveals some interesting features. When the supply of oxygen is limited, sulfur is produced.

$$2 S^{-2} - 4 e^- \longrightarrow 2 S^0 \quad \text{(oxidation)}$$
$$O_2{}^0 + 4 e^- \longrightarrow 2 O^{-2} \quad \text{(reduction)}$$

But when the supply of oxygen is abundant, the sulfur is transformed to sulfur dioxide.

$$2 S^{-2} - 12 e^- \longrightarrow 2 S^{+4} \quad \text{(oxidation)}$$
$$3 O_2{}^0 + 12 e^- \longrightarrow 6 O^{-2} \quad \text{(reduction)}$$

In neither case is the hydrogen in hydrogen sulfide oxidized, even though it is changed to water; it *does not undergo any loss of electrons*. In contrast, the sulfide ion is oxidized in both reactions, even though it does not combine with oxygen when the supply of air is limited. Oxidation still occurs because the sulfide ion *loses electrons*, forming elemental sulfur in the first case and sulfur in the +4 oxidation state in SO_2 in the second.

Metallic Sulfides

Of what use is this disagreeable-smelling gas? Suppose you have solutions of soluble salts such as zinc sulfate, lead acetate, cadmium nitrate, and antimony chloride, each of them clear and colorless. How can you distinguish among them and identify each? If you pass hydrogen sulfide gas into these solutions, each immediately forms a colored precipitate.

$$H_2S + Zn(SO_4) \longrightarrow H_2SO_4 + ZnS\downarrow$$
$$\text{(white)}$$

$$H_2S + Pb(C_2H_3O_2)_2 \longrightarrow 2\,HC_2H_3O_2 + PbS\downarrow$$
$$\text{(black)}$$

$$H_2S + Cd(NO_3)_2 \longrightarrow 2\,HNO_3 + CdS\downarrow$$
$$\text{(yellow)}$$

$$3\,H_2S + 2\,SbCl_3 \longrightarrow 6\,HCl + Sb_2S_3\downarrow$$
$$\text{(orange)}$$

Each metal sulfide formed in these double replacement reactions is insoluble and has a characteristic color (Plate III, following page 548). Note that salts of the alkali metals (sodium family) and the alkaline earth metals (calcium family) were not suggested for testing. The sulfides of these metals are moderately soluble in water. The insoluble sulfides find use as pigments in paint. Cadmium sulfide, for example, is known to the artist as cadmium yellow, a pigment valued for its permanence of color.

Because other metallic sulfides may have the same colors as those tested here, the chemist has devised additional tests as a means of distinguishing similarly colored sulfides. For example, he can distinguish among CuS, PbS, HgS, and Bi_2S_3, all of which are black, or between CdS and As_2S_3, which are yellow. The importance of hydrogen sulfide to the chemist stems from this use in the chemical analysis of metallic ions. You will study these tests in greater detail in Skills Chapter 32.

1. How could you demonstrate that the sulfide ion, when oxidized, may achieve different oxidation states?

2. How is hydrogen sulfide useful in identifying certain metallic ions in the laboratory?

3. (a) How is hydrogen sulfide usually prepared in the laboratory? (b) Write an equation for the reaction.

4. If hydrogen sulfide were collected by the downward displacement of air, how could you determine when the collecting bottle was full of gas?

SULFUR DIOXIDE

Paper, straw hats, preserved fruit, and sulfuric acid seem to have nothing in common, yet the preparation of each of these products involves some property of the same substance—sulfur dioxide. Let us look at the preparation and properties of this useful gas.

The Preparation of Sulfur Dioxide

The *commercial preparation of sulfur dioxide* is carried out simply by burning sulfur or roasting (heating in the presence of air) sulfide ores.

$$S + O_2 \longrightarrow SO_2\uparrow \quad \text{(burning of sulfur)}$$
$$2\,ZnS + 3\,O_2 \longrightarrow 2\,ZnO + 2\,SO_2\uparrow$$
$$\text{(roasting of sulfide)}$$

Neither of these methods is particularly well suited to the school laboratory. Here the gas is usually produced by one of the following methods.

First, SO_2 can be prepared by cautiously reacting copper with hot, *concentrated* sulfuric acid.

$$Cu + 2\,H_2SO_4 \longrightarrow SO_2\uparrow + CuSO_4 + 2\,H_2O$$

In the second method, the reaction between sulfuric acid and a sulfite or bisulfite salt yields SO_2.

$$2 H_2SO_4 + Na_2SO_3 \longrightarrow$$
$$SO_2\uparrow + 2 NaHSO_4 + H_2O$$
$$H_2SO_4 + NaHSO_3 \longrightarrow SO_2\uparrow + NaHSO_4 + H_2O$$

To observe how one of these preparations can be performed in the laboratory, *try the following.*

Introduce about 10 grams of sodium bisulfite into a Florence flask and replace the stopper fitted with a thistle tube and delivery tube. Clamp the flask over a wire gauze and ring as shown below. Now pour 20 ml of

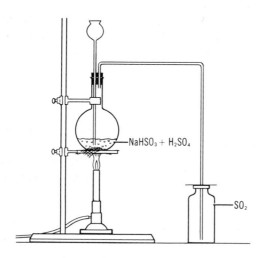

NaHSO₃ + H₂SO₄

SO₂

12 *M* sulfuric acid into the flask and begin collecting the gas evolved by upward displacement of air. When the evolution of gas dies down, heat the reaction mixture with a *small* flame; but remove the flame if the gas should be vigorously evolved. To determine when a bottle is filled with the gas, remove the cardboard cover and place a strip of moist blue litmus paper over the bottle. When the paper changes color, immediately remove the delivery tube, cover the bottle with a glass plate, and continue with the collection of the next bottle of gas. When the last bottle has been filled, insert the delivery tube into a bottle filled with water to a depth of 1 inch.

While collecting the sulfur dioxide, notice its odor and color. Insert a burning splint into one of the filled bottles. Does sulfur dioxide burn or support combustion? Add 5 ml of water to another bottle, shake the contents well, and test the solution with litmus paper. What substance forms? Next add a few milliliters of water to another bottle filled with the gas, cover the mouth of the bottle *tightly* with the palm of your hand, and shake the whole well. Do you experience a strong suction on your palm as the gas dissolves in the water?

Properties of Sulfur Dioxide

A number of *physical properties* of sulfur dioxide are easily recognized. It is a colorless gas with a sharp, choking odor. The method of collection indicates that the gas must be heavier than air and is reasonably soluble in water. You can further illustrate the solubility of sulfur dioxide by inverting a test tube filled with the gas in a pan of water. If you do so, observe that after a short time the water rises most of the way into the tube.

The *chemical properties* are equally apparent. Sulfur dioxide neither burns nor supports combustion. You will shortly discover, however, that the gas can be oxidized further under special conditions. The water solution of the gas is found to be acid to litmus paper; this simple observation recalls to mind that sulfur dioxide is an *acid anhydride* (Chapter 14).

$$SO_2 + H_2O \longrightarrow H_2SO_3 \quad \text{(sulfurous acid)}$$

This reaction is reversed on heating, partly because the solubility of the gas in water is decreased.

Bleaching by Sulfur Dioxide

If you lower a red carnation or strip of apple peel into a jar of sulfur dioxide gas, the color disappears in time. You learned in Chapter 23 that chlorine bleaches by *oxidation;* how does sulfur dioxide remove the coloring matter? If as an additional step you remove the bleached flower or apple peel, wash it, and dip it into hydrogen peroxide—the color is restored. What causes this reversal in bleaching?

When hydrogen peroxide is added to a water solution of sulfur dioxide (sulfurous acid), nothing is *seen* to happen. But it is *observed* that heat is produced; the solution is warm—a reaction occurs. If you now test the solution for the presence of the *sulfate* ion (Skills Chapter 26), you obtain a positive result.

$$\overset{-2}{H_2O_2} + \overset{+4}{H_2SO_3} \longrightarrow \overset{-2}{H_2O} + \overset{+6}{H_2SO_4}$$

$$S^{+4} - 2\,e^- \longrightarrow S^{+6} \quad \text{(oxidation)}$$
$$O_2^{-2} + 2\,e^- \longrightarrow 2\,O^{-2} \quad \text{(reduction)}$$

Sulfur in the +4 oxidation state in H_2SO_3, formed by the reaction between sulfur dioxide and water, is a *reducing agent*. In effect, SO_3^{-2} ions became oxidized to SO_4^{-2} ions. Hydrogen peroxide is the oxidizing agent in this reaction, the peroxide ion (O_2^{-2}) being reduced to oxide ions (O^{-2}). Since hydrogen peroxide, which acts as an oxidizing agent in this reaction, causes reappearance of the color in the bleached flower, we can reasonably conclude that sulfur dioxide causes bleaching (a disappearance of color) by *reducing* the coloring matter. Sulfurous acid (or a solution of sulfur dioxide in water) is therefore a reducing agent.

You can see further evidence of the reducing nature of sulfur dioxide in water *in the following investigation.*

In a collecting bottle half full of water, dissolve a few crystals of potassium permanganate ($KMnO_4$) to form a purple solution. Now "pour" a jar of sulfur dioxide into the colored solution. As the gas "falls" into the first jar, the purple solution is bleached. If you wish, prove that the colorless solution produced contains the *sulfate* ion.

Study the equation for the reaction to determine the ions reduced and oxidized:

$$2\,KMnO_4 + 5\,SO_2 + 2\,H_2O \longrightarrow$$
$$K_2SO_4 + 2\,MnSO_4 + 2\,H_2SO_4$$

The purple permanganate ion (MnO_4^-) is bleached by reduction to the pink (and therefore hardly visible) manganous ion (Mn^{+2}). The sulfur in the +4 oxidation state in SO_2 is oxidized to the +6 state in the sulfate ion.

The Uses of Sulfur Dioxide

Chlorine is an undesirable bleaching agent for silk and wool. While it removes the coloring matter, it also leaves the fiber harsh and brittle, reducing the life of the fabric. These fibers, as well as

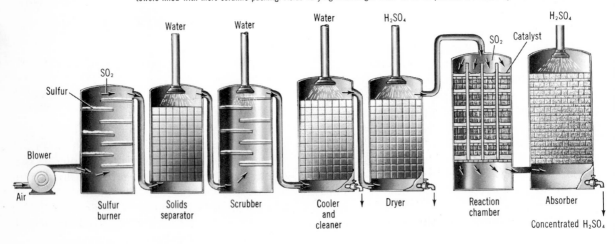

24-15 In the contact process, once sulfur dioxide is scrubbed, cleaned, and dried, the conversion to sulfuric acid occurs in towers lined with inert ceramic packing. Acids varying in strength from 40 to 98 percent are made by this method.

straw, are often bleached with sulfur dioxide. Bleaching with sulfur dioxide is likely to be temporary in nature since atmospheric oxygen may reoxidize the bleached coloring matter to form the original dye. The gas is also used to *preserve dried fruits,* such as apricots and prunes. The bulk of the sulfur dioxide produced is not used as such, but serves as a raw material for the *preparation of sulfuric acid.*

QUESTIONS AND PROBLEMS

1. Compare the bleaching of potassium permanganate by sulfur dioxide with the bleaching by hydrogen peroxide.

2. In practice, how could you differentiate most quickly between a bottle of sulfur dioxide and a bottle of hydrogen sulfide?

3. (a) Balance the equation below by the electron transfer method:

$$SO_2 + I_2 + H_2O \longrightarrow HI + H_2SO_4$$

(b) What property does the sulfur dioxide demonstrate in this reaction?

4. Contrast bleaching by chlorine with bleaching by sulfur dioxide.

SULFURIC ACID

Your study of acids revealed that one general method of preparing them is by the reaction of a salt of the acid with sulfuric acid. A moment's thought will tell you that this method cannot be used to prepare sulfuric acid. How, then, is this most important of all acids prepared?

You know that sulfur dioxide is the *acid anhydride* of sulfurous acid. What oxide might be expected to imitate this behavior and produce sulfuric acid? Since

$$SO_2 + H_2O \longrightarrow H_2SO_3$$

then we might expect

$$SO_3 + H_2O \longrightarrow H_2SO_4$$

If a way can be found to prepare sulfur trioxide,

24-16 Workmen wearing protective suits are repairing a leak in a cooler where hot sulfuric acid is cooled by 100 to 150 degrees before being pumped into receiving tanks.

and *if* SO_3 combines with water in the manner shown, our problem is solved.

When sulfur burns in air, the product is sulfur dioxide. By painstaking experiments, chemists discovered that sulfur could be oxidized further than the $+4$ oxidation state in sulfur dioxide, in the presence of a catalyst and at a suitable temperature.

$$2\,SO_2 + O_2 \xrightleftharpoons{450°\,C} 2\,SO_3$$

The first catalyst used for this step in the process of making sulfuric acid, known as the **contact process** (Fig. 24-15), was platinum. Since then, equally effective catalysts, including vanadium pentoxide, have been developed. The sulfur dioxide used, produced either by burning sulfur or by roasting iron pyrites, must be highly purified. Otherwise the efficiency of the catalyst is lowered considerably—the catalyst is "poisoned."

Contrary to the equation written earlier, sulfur trioxide is only slightly soluble in water. In practice, the gas is dissolved in concentrated sulfuric

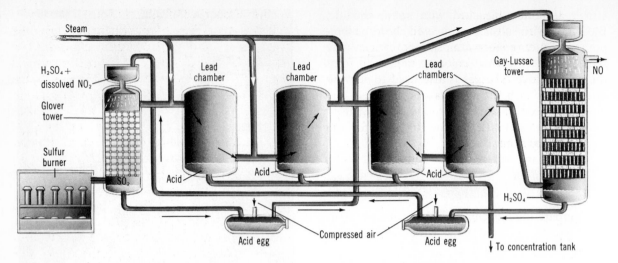

Steam

H_2SO_4 + dissolved NO_2

Glover tower

Sulfur burner

SO_2

Lead chamber

Lead chamber

Lead chambers

Gay-Lussac tower

NO

Acid

Acid

Acid

H_2SO_4

Acid egg

Compressed air

Acid egg

To concentration tank

24-17 Little sulfuric acid is currently produced by the lead chamber process, because of the cost of building and maintaining the lead chamber, and the impure nature of the acid.

acid, producing a liquid called *oleum* or *fuming sulfuric acid.*

$$H_2SO_4 + SO_3 \longrightarrow H_2SO_4 \cdot SO_3 \text{ (or } H_2S_2O_7)$$
98 percent   oleum

The necessary amount of water is then added to the oleum to react with the dissolved sulfur trioxide, and the resulting acid is cooled (Fig. 24-16) and stored.

$$H_2SO_4 \cdot SO_3 + H_2O \longrightarrow 2\,H_2SO_4$$

The contact process therefore uses one molecule of sulfuric acid to produce a second, very much as a business man invests one dollar to return two.

The Lead Chamber Process

The contact process was not the first-known commercial method of preparing the acid. Earlier, the same idea of oxidizing sulfur dioxide to sulfur trioxide was achieved by using oxides of nitrogen to supply the additional oxygen.

$$SO_2 + H_2O + NO_2 \longrightarrow H_2SO_4 + NO\uparrow$$

The resulting nitric oxide, NO, is readily oxidized by atmospheric oxygen to nitrogen dioxide, NO_2. Some of the NO_2 is dissolved in the resulting sul-

furic acid and some is reused. In this process, a current of sulfur dioxide gas is forced upward through a layer of acid-resistant crushed rock or tile. At the same time sulfuric acid containing dissolved nitrogen dioxide percolates downward, insuring intimate contact between the gas and the liquid. To insure complete reaction, the procedure is carried out through a series of towers. Because the towers in which the reaction occurs are made of lead, the process is called the **lead chamber process** (Fig. 24-17). The acid produced by this method is less concentrated and less pure than that made by the contact process; the lead chambers are also relatively expensive to build and maintain. Consequently, more than 90 percent of our sulfuric acid is made by the contact process. The impure acid made by the lead chamber process is used in making fertilizer.

Properties of Concentrated Sulfuric Acid

Suppose you had a bottle of concentrated sulfuric acid. Could you, without looking at the label, or in the absence of one, determine the contents of the bottle? The use of litmus paper is forbidden, for reasons you will appreciate shortly. Perhaps you can learn to recognize this acid *by observing its properties.*

Carefully tilt, and then turn upright, a half-filled, tightly stoppered bottle of the concentrated acid. Notice that the acid flows down the side of the bottle rather slowly. If both concentrated sulfuric acid and water are allowed to flow down an inclined glass plate, the acid flows more slowly than does the water. In these observations, the acid resembles an oil; this resemblance is reflected in a very old name for sulfuric acid—*oil of vitriol.*

Weigh equal volumes of water and concentrated acid. The acid is 1.84 times as dense as water. Now *very carefully and slowly* pour a small amount of the concentrated acid into a Pyrex test tube half filled with water and supported in a test tube rack. The acid sinks to the bottom. This is in agreement with the property just determined. Observe that while the acid appears oily when it flows, it is unlike oils in being denser than water and miscible with it.

Repeat the last procedure with a variation. Insert a thermometer in the test tube of water and note the temperature. It is about 20° C (room temperature). Now add the acid and observe the temperature. In just a few seconds the temperature rises as much as fifty to sixty degrees; your test tube very likely becomes too hot to handle. While some concentrated acids produce heat when added to water, none compares with sulfuric acid.

Earlier, you learned that concentrated sulfuric acid is a poor electrolyte, few ions being present in the liquid. Dilution with water leads to marked ionization of the acid. The temperature effect noted in this experiment arises from the heat of hydration of the hydrogen ion. In preparing dilute sulfuric acid from the concentrated acid, therefore, one must be mindful of the considerable heat produced. The proper way to dilute the concentrated acid is to *add the acid to water slowly,* with constant stirring to dissipate the heat produced (Fig. 24-18).

Further Properties of Sulfuric Acid

If you add a piece of mossy zinc to a test tube one-quarter full of cool, concentrated acid, a few bubbles of air trapped on the zinc arise—and that is all. If you now add a piece of zinc to the dilute acid (6 M), the expected rapid evolution of hydrogen results. The concentrated acid contains few hydronium ions, and the typical reaction of acids with metals does not occur. It is for this reason that the concentrated acid can be shipped in iron tank cars.

Suppose we warm the mixture of zinc and concentrated acid gently. Slowly, a reaction begins and a gas is evolved. If the gas is passed into a solution of potassium permanganate, the latter is decolorized—the gas is sulfur dioxide. Why is the hot, concentrated acid able to react with a metal which it does not attack when cold? To answer this question, examine the equation for the reaction.

$$\overset{0}{Zn} + 2\,\overset{+6}{H_2SO_4} \longrightarrow \overset{+2}{ZnSO_4} + \overset{+4}{SO_2}\uparrow + 2\,H_2O$$
$$Zn^0 - 2\,e^- \longrightarrow Zn^{+2} \quad \text{(oxidation)}$$
$$S^{+6} + 2\,e^- \longrightarrow S^{+4} \quad \text{(reduction)}$$

Each zinc atom loses electrons to become a zinc ion which combines with the sulfate ion to form the salt, zinc sulfate. At the same time, the sulfur

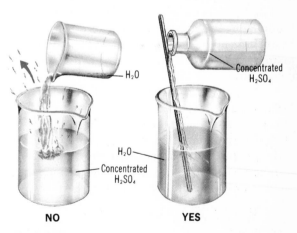

24-18 When diluting concentrated sulfuric acid, always pour the acid into the water, while stirring constantly. In the reverse procedure, the heat produced may cause the acid to bubble and splatter.

of the sulfate ion gains these electrons and is reduced to the +4 oxidation state. Thus we see that hot, concentrated sulfuric acid reacts with metals by *oxidizing* them, the sulfur of the SO_4^{-2} ion serving as the oxidizing agent. Note that while hydrogen was not a product, the reaction between a metal and an acid still produces a salt of that metal and the acid.

Copper, a metal that does not usually react with weak acids, reacts with hot, concentrated acid to yield sulfur dioxide. The hot acid is able to oxidize the copper. This reaction is another convenient laboratory method of preparing the gas.

$$\overset{0}{Cu} + 2\,\overset{+6}{H_2SO_4} \longrightarrow \overset{+4}{SO_2} + \overset{+2}{CuSO_4} + 2\,H_2O$$

Perhaps you have observed in your chemistry laboratory that a dark "ring" is found marked in the wooden shelf where a bottle of concentrated sulfuric acid has been standing. How does this "ring" arise? *Let us find out.*

> Place a wood splint in a test tube of concentrated sulfuric acid. Does the wood shortly turn black?

The concentrated acid removes the hydrogen and oxygen from the cellulose of the wood to form water and leave black carbon. The black ring you may have observed forms when any drops of the acid that remain on the *outside* of the neck of the bottle, after the acid is poured, run down to the base of the bottle and react with the wood in the manner described. The removal of hydrogen and oxygen from a compound, in the same ratio in which they exist in water, is called **dehydration.** You have just learned that concentrated sulfuric acid is a **dehydrating agent.**

This dehydrating action of concentrated sulfuric acid *can also be demonstrated* by using sugar, a compound which contains the same elements as wood—carbon, hydrogen, and oxygen.

> Spread a layer of table sugar, $C_{12}H_{22}O_{11}$, on the bottom of a beaker to a depth of ¼ inch. Add sufficient concentrated sulfuric acid to cover the sugar. Stand back and

observe the reaction carefully. The sugar first develops a brown color; in a short time,

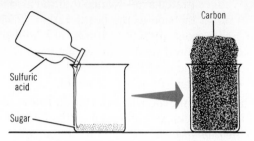

the color darkens further. Suddenly, steam arises and a black mass is pushed steadily out of the beaker. Why? (*Do not handle this mixture.*)

The black mass is brittle and porous, and consists of the element carbon. The hydrogen and oxygen of the sugar have been removed in the form of water.

$$C_{12}H_{22}O_{11} + 11\,H_2SO_4 \longrightarrow$$
$$12\,C + 11\,H_2SO_4 \cdot H_2O$$

The hydration of the concentrated acid produces sufficient heat to vaporize some of the water. Since paper is made of cellulose, which contains hydrogen and oxygen in the same ratio as in water, you can now understand why litmus paper would have been useless in testing the concentrated acid.

A summary of the properties should emphasize the many ways in which concentrated sulfuric acid differs from other concentrated acids. Because it contains so little (3–5 percent) water, it is a poorer electrolyte than other concentrated acids. The hydration of the large number of hydrogen ions provided by the acid on dilution accounts for the pronounced heat effect when this is done, a fact calling for caution in preparing the dilute acid. Unlike most acids, concentrated sulfuric acid is both an oxidizing and a dehydrating agent.

Properties of Dilute Sulfuric Acid

Dilute sulfuric acid shows all the properties typical of acids, including sour taste, effect on blue litmus paper, and the reaction with metals to yield hydrogen. When dilute sulfuric acid reacts with metals such as zinc to yield hydrogen, oxidation and reduction also occur, as they do with the concentrated acid, but the oxidizing agent is not the sulfur in the sulfate ion.

$$\overset{0}{Zn} + \overset{+1}{H_2}SO_4 \longrightarrow \overset{0}{H_2} + \overset{+2}{Zn}SO_4$$

While each zinc atom is oxidized in this reaction just as with concentrated acid, *it is the hydrogen (or hydronium) ion which is the oxidizing agent.*

$$2\,H^+ + 2\,e^- \longrightarrow H_2^0$$

Uses of Sulfuric Acid

The graph in Fig. 24-19, summarizing *the uses of sulfuric acid,* emphasizes the variety of applications of this acid, though not the great tonnage used yearly in the United States. Many of its applications relate to its specific properties.

The Preparation of Acids. Many acids, recall, are prepared by reacting salts with sulfuric acid. Such double replacement reactions are usually reversible. When concentrated sulfuric acid is added to a salt and the mixture heated, the desired acid, or its anhydride, can be removed as a gas, causing the reaction to go to completion. The use of sulfuric acid in *preparing other acids* depends on its high boiling point.

24-20 Nitrogen gas is being dried by bubbling it through concentrated sulfuric acid. The acid bottle is in the center of the photograph.

A Dehydrating Agent. The *preparation of many organic compounds,* some of which you will study later, involves reversible reactions in which water is one of the products. For example, benzene reacts with nitric acid to form nitrobenzene.

$$C_6H_6 + HNO_3 \rightleftharpoons C_6H_5NO_2 + H_2O$$
benzene   nitric   nitro-   water
acid   benzene

Concentrated sulfuric acid is added to such reaction mixtures to *remove the water formed* and lessen the extent to which the reverse reaction can occur.

This property is also employed *in providing dry atmospheres.* In the laboratory, concentrated sulfuric acid is placed in a suitable apparatus to absorb the last traces of water from gases passed through it (Fig. 24-20). Many industrial processes are carried out in atmospheres that are dry or that have controlled humidity. By adjusting the concentration of the sulfuric acid, it is possible to remove any desired portion of the water vapor.

24-19 The graph indicates that most of the sulfuric acid made in the country is used in the manufacture of fertilizers. A second major use is in the production of laboratory and industrial chemicals. There are few industries that do not use sulfuric acid in some operation.

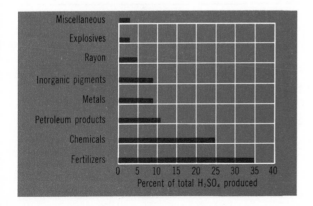

The Preparation of Fertilizers. Two of the minerals essential to plant life are phosphorus and calcium, found naturally in the form of tricalcium phosphate. This salt is very insoluble in water. By treatment with sulfuric acid, the compound is transformed into monocalcium phosphate or *superphosphate of lime* [$Ca(H_2PO_4)_2$], more soluble in water and thus more available to the plant.

$$Ca_3(PO_4)_2 + 2\,H_2SO_4 \longrightarrow$$
$$Ca(H_2PO_4)_2 + 2\,CaSO_4$$

With the constant growth of the world population and the increasing dependence on artificial fertilizers in many countries, we can understand why one third of all the sulfuric acid made annually in the United States is used for this purpose.

Refining Petroleum. The separation of petroleum into various fractions is only the first step in the production of gasoline. To *remove many of the impurities* which would interfere with the proper operation of the gasoline engine, the *petroleum is "washed" with concentrated sulfuric acid.* Our present consumption of gasoline indicates why a considerable amount of sulfuric acid is used for this purpose.

Sulfuric acid, like hydrochloric acid, is used in cleaning (pickling) the surface of iron and steel

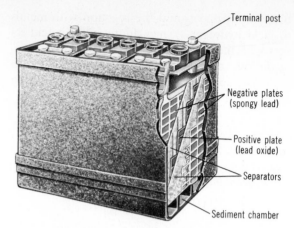

24-21 This type of lead storage battery is used as a source of direct current for automobiles and various types of small equipment. Water is added to the battery to maintain the electrolyte, moderately dilute sulfuric acid, above the level of the battery plates.

prior to coating them. Think for a moment of the large number of tin cans you can see in a single large supermarket, and you will realize how large a quantity of sulfuric acid is used *for pickling metals.* So much of the acid is used for this purpose that the disposal of the ferrous sulfate produced is often a major problem.

The Lead Storage Battery. The storage battery, which performs the vital function of starting

Table 24-2 **OXIDATION AND REDUCTION OF SULFUR**

	Oxidation state of sulfur	Substance	Example of oxidation or reduction
O X I D A T I O N / R E D U C T I O N	+6	SO_3 or H_2SO_4	
	+4	SO_2 or H_2SO_3	Reduction of MnO_4^- by SO_2 $-2\,e^-$
	0	Atomic sulfur	Burning of S $-4\,e^-$ · · · Contact process $-6\,e^-$
	−2	Sulfides	Reaction with metals $+2\,e^-$ · Incomplete combustion of H_2S $-2\,e^-$ · Complete combustion of H_2S $-6\,e^-$

trucks and cars, differs in one important respect from the dry cell customarily used in a flashlight; it can be recharged. The properties of sulfuric acid and its lead compound have made the *lead storage battery* possible (Fig. 24-21). The electrodes are made of lead and lead dioxide, the electrolyte being a moderately dilute solution of sulfuric acid. When the cell is discharged in use, both electrodes are converted to lead sulfate.

$$Pb + PbO_2 + 2\,H_2SO_4 \longrightarrow 2\,PbSO_4 + 2\,H_2O$$

This reaction is reversed, or the battery is recharged, by passing an electric current through the battery in the reverse direction to form the original electrode materials. The battery is again ready for use.

Sulfuric acid plays a prominent role in the *transformation of many raw materials into the finished product.* The first step in the preparation of some detergents is a reaction between an organic compound (for example, an alcohol) and sulfuric acid. Many of the dyes which color your surroundings are made by treating naphthalene, the same coal-tar chemical which safeguards your woolens from moths, with sulfuric acid. And all of the synthetic sulfa drugs used in medicine are made by the same starting step—the treatment of benzene with concentrated sulfuric acid.

Oxidation and Reduction Among Sulfur and Its Compounds

You have now observed instances of oxidation and reduction among the sulfur compounds. In its reaction with metals, sulfur acts as an oxidizing agent, and is itself reduced to the sulfide ion, S^{-2}. When sulfur burns, atomic sulfur ($\overset{0}{S}$) is oxidized to $\overset{+4}{S}$ in sulfur dioxide; but in the contact process, the sulfur is oxidized further to $\overset{+6}{S}$ in sulfur trioxide.

The existence of the sulfur atom in varying oxidation states, ranging from -2 to $+6$, enables sulfur, both atomic and combined, to act either as an oxidizing or a reducing agent. Table 24-2 illustrates these possibilities. The sulfur in sulfur dioxide (or sulfurous acid), being intermediate

between a state of maximum oxidation ($+6$) and maximum reduction (-2), is capable of acting either as an oxidizing or reducing agent. The behavior of sulfur as a reducing agent has been met in the bleaching of the permanganate ion (page 404). The *oxidizing* nature of sulfurous acid can be observed *by investigating the following.*

Add a piece of zinc to a test tube containing a few milliliters of dilute hydrochloric acid. When a steady evolution of hydrogen has developed, add a few milliliters of a

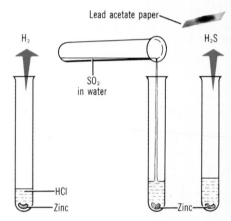

saturated solution of sulfur dioxide in water to the acid-metal mixture. Now hold a strip of moist lead acetate paper over the test tube. The paper turns black, indicating the formation of hydrogen sulfide.

In this reaction, the sulfurous acid *oxidizes* the hydrogen *gas* first produced to water; the sulfur itself is reduced to the sulfide ion.

$$\overset{+4}{H_2SO_3} + 3\,\overset{0}{H_2} \longrightarrow 3\,\overset{+1}{H_2O} + \overset{-2}{H_2S}$$

$$3\,H_2^0 - 6\,e^- \longrightarrow 6\,H^+ \quad \text{(oxidation)}$$
$$S^{+4} + 6\,e^- \longrightarrow S^{-2} \quad \text{(reduction)}$$

QUESTIONS AND PROBLEMS

1. What are the essential differences in the preparation of sulfuric acid by the contact and the lead chamber processes?

24-22 Photoelectric cells interrupt a circuit until struck by light. The three above are mounted for use in laboratory equipment, the two below at the center and right for use in cameras or barricade warning lights. The ring is similarly used when it bridges two electrodes.

2. Write a series of equations to represent the contact process of preparing sulfuric acid.

3. Why should you always pour concentrated H_2SO_4 into water—and never the reverse?

4. Suggest a reason why it may be dangerous to check the level of liquid in a storage battery with the aid of a lighted match.

5. List as many ways as you can in which sulfuric acid differs from other acids.

6. Why can it be said that the consumption of sulfuric acid is an indication of economic state of our nation?

SELENIUM, TELLURIUM, AND POLONIUM

Any treatment of the elements of group VIA must, of necessity, be devoted largely to oxygen and sulfur. These elements, by virtue of their abundance and their manifold important uses, are our most important concern. Yet, although selenium and tellurium play very minor parts in our daily lives, it is important to consider them insofar as they complete the portrait of the oxygen family of elements. Polonium, first discovered in pitchblende by the Curies, is used chiefly in experimental studies with radioactivity. Relatively little is known about the element and its compounds, but its naturally radioactive isotopes are members of the uranium disintegration series.

Both selenium and tellurium are widely distributed in nature, but they exist in few ores and minerals. They are obtained solely as by-products in the extraction of other metals, such as gold, lead, nickel, and copper, or during the refining of copper. Selenium exists in two allotropes, a red amorphous form which, on being kept somewhat below the melting point for some time, changes into a gray, crystalline form. Tellurium is silvery white in color but differs from typical metals in being brittle and a poor conductor of electricity.

Compounds of Selenium and Tellurium

Selenium and tellurium burn in oxygen (as does sulfur) to form their dioxides, which can also be produced by reacting the elements with oxidizing acids such as nitric acid. These dioxides are the anhydrides of selenous (H_2SeO_3) and tellurous (H_2TeO_3) acids, respectively. These acids, in contrast to sulfurous acid, exist as solids; like sulfurous acid, they are weak acids. Selenic (H_2SeO_4) and telluric (H_2TeO_4) acids are made by oxidizing their *-ous* acids. Except that it is a white solid at room temperature, selenic acid shows marked resemblance to sulfuric acid. It is a strong acid, absorbs water, and has a high heat of hydration when dissolved in water. Metal selenates resemble their analogous sulfates in solubility and crystal structure. Oddly enough, telluric acid and its salts do not share this family resemblance with respect to either solubility or crystal structure.

Uses of Selenium and Tellurium

Selenium and tellurium have limited uses. Selenium is used to provide a ruby color in glass. The conductivity of its gray form increases markedly on exposure to light; consequently this allotrope is used in some photoelectric cells (Fig. 24-22). Selenium is also used to make some types of rectifiers. Small amounts (0.1 percent) of tellurium are added to lead to make the latter metal more resistant to corrosion.

The oxygen family of the elements, like the halogens, has illustrated once again the generalizations that can be made from the periodic table. In both physical and chemical properties, the group VIA elements and their compounds show a reasonably ordered variation of properties as the atomic weight (or atomic number) of the family member increases. It will be interesting to note whether this trend continues as another electron is removed from the outer orbit to create another group of elements. You can judge this best by investigating the group of elements in which the outer orbit has a total of 5 electrons—the nitrogen family.

QUESTIONS AND PROBLEMS

1. What acid is present in a water solution of (a) hydrogen selenide (b) hydrogen telluride?

2. What is the most outstanding characteristic of polonium?

3. Write the formulas for silver selenide, mercuric telluride, and magnesium selenate.

4. What is the oxidation number of the group VIA element in each of the following compounds: $PbSe$, Na_2TeO_4, TeO_2, SeO_3?

VALUE OF THE CONCEPT

THE CONCEPT

The elements in group VIA show the orderly progression of properties expected in a family of elements. The atomic weights, melting points, boiling points, and densities increase with increasing atomic number. Except for oxygen, which usually has an oxidation state of -2, the remaining elements (with the possible exception of radioactive polonium) show oxidation states of -2, $+4$, and $+6$.

Family relationships are obvious in the chemical behavior of both the elements and their compounds. All the elements are nonmetallic and they serve as oxidizing agents. These activities fall off as the atomic number of the element increases; selenium and tellurium are much less reactive with metals and much weaker oxidizing agents than oxygen and sulfur. Conversely, the compounds of selenium and tellurium are more easily changed to the element than are those of oxygen and sulfur.

Both oxygen and sulfur exist in allotropic forms. Ozone, O_3, changes readily to oxygen, O_2. Allotropic rhombic, prismatic, and amorphous sulfur are formed at different temperatures. Both of the latter change gradually to the rhombic form, which exists in the form of a ring of eight atoms, S_8.

The hydrogen compounds of these elements are a good illustration of a pattern within the family. Direct combination of the element with hydrogen is vigorous only with oxygen. The reaction with hydrogen becomes less active and more reversible as the family members become increasingly heavier. Each of these hydrogen compounds forms a weak acid in water solution. Because the stability of the hydrogen compound in water solution decreases with increasing atomic number of the elements, air oxidation of the compound proceeds more readily. With the exception of water (and we do not know the facts about hydrogen polonide), the hydrogen compounds have offensive odors and are poisonous when inhaled.

Interestingly enough, the natural abundance of these elements decreases with increasing atomic number. Elemental oxygen and sulfur and their compounds have widespread and valuable applications; the remaining elements and their compounds have little application. In particular, hydrogen sulfide is used in identifying metallic ions in the laboratory, while sulfur dioxide finds use in bleaching and in the commercial preparation of sulfuric acid. Sulfuric acid, the most widely used acid, serves as an oxidizing agent or dehydrating agent in the preparation of many compounds, dyes, and drugs. It is essential to the preparation of fertilizer and the refining of petroleum.

All families show differences as well as similarities, and group VIA is no exception. Oxygen stands apart from its group in many respects. It is the only member of the family that is gaseous at room temperature; no liquid element appears in the transition to the heavier members. Oxygen demonstrates almost entirely a single oxidation state (-2) in its compounds, in contrast to its other family members. Oxygen does, however, combine with other elements to form peroxides, in which oxygen is in the -1 oxidation state. Peroxides differ from oxides in the oxidation state and the bonding of the oxygen atoms. Hydrogen peroxide decomposes readily to water and oxygen. Water is a highly stable compound and the nearest approach we know to a "universal" solvent.

USING THE CONCEPT

Using the Basic Concept

1. Why is it possible for some sulfur compounds to act as *both* oxidizing and reducing agents?

2. What natural processes would be affected, and in what manner, if our atmosphere contained 50 percent by volume of oxygen?

3. Compare and contrast the properties of ozone and oxygen.

4. Give (a) three uses of ozone and (b) five uses of oxygen.

5. (a) Write an equation for the preparation of oxygen by adding the catalyst MnO_2 to hydrogen peroxide. (b) How is oxygen usually prepared commercially?

6. (a) How do rhombic, prismatic, and amorphous sulfur differ? (b) How are they similar?

7. (a) In what allotropic form would you expect flowers of sulfur to exist? (b) How would you explain the presence of more than one form?

8. (a) Differentiate between a dioxide and a peroxide. (b) Draw electron dot diagrams of silicon dioxide and sodium peroxide.

9. Sulfur in the solid state exists as a ring of sulfur atoms. (a) Write the formula for solid sulfur. (b) Which allotrope of sulfur does this formula represent? (c) To which form does all sulfur change on long standing?

10. What chemical behavior of sulfur indicates that it belongs in the same family as oxygen?

11. (a) Explain why sulfurous and sulfuric acids form two series of salts. (b) Name one other acid that duplicates this behavior.

12. Compare and contrast the bleaching reactions of hydrogen peroxide and sulfur dioxide.

13. Compare the acids of sulfur with respect to their formulas, strength, oxidizing or reducing nature, and any special chemical properties.

14. (a) Compare and contrast the apparatus used for the laboratory preparations of sulfur dioxide and hydrogen sulfide. (b) Relate the similarities and differences among them to the properties of the substance being prepared.

15. When a lead storage battery is discharged, will the concentration of sulfuric acid increase, decrease, or remain the same? Explain.

16. (a) What are the essential details of the contact process for producing sulfuric acid? (b) the lead chamber process?

17. Write the formula for each of the following compounds: calcium sulfite, sodium selenide, ferrous telluride, lead bisulfate, antimony sulfide.

18. Determine the oxidation number of the group VIA element in each of the following compounds: SF_6, $KHSO_4$, $ZnSO_3$, H_2TeO_3, SeO_2, Fe_2O_3.

19. Indicate whether each substance is an oxidizing agent, a reducing agent, or a dehydrating agent: H_2S, SO_2, S, O_2, O_3, H_2SO_4.

20. The reaction between sulfur dioxide and oxygen in the contact process is *exothermic*. (a) What temperature range

should favor this reaction? (b) What reason might account for the use of a different temperature range in practice?

Relating Terms Within the Concept

Each of the following exercises consists of five terms. From the last four, select the term or terms closely related to the *italicized* term.

1. *Frasch process*: sulfur, ferrous sulfide, selenium, compressed air
2. *allotropes*: O_3 and O_2, oleum and ozone, sulfur, H_2O and H_2O_2
3. *H_2SO_4*: lead chamber process, contact process, dehydrating agent, reducing agent
4. *H_2O_2*: polonium, -1 oxidation state, stable in sunlight, negative catalyst
5. *SO_2*: auto-oxidation, acid anhydride, oxidizing agent, bleaching agent
6. *H_2S*: reducing agent, odor of rotten eggs, silver tarnish, colored metallic compounds
7. *prismatic sulfur*: monoclinic, allotrope, noncrystalline, changes to rhombic

Solving Problems Within the Concept

1. Which of the following ores contains the largest percentage of sulfur: $CuFeS_2$, FeS_2, ZnS, As_2S_3, HgS?
2. How many liters of SO_2 (**STP**) can be obtained by reacting 10.4 grams of sodium bisulfite with sulfuric acid?
3. How many liters of sulfur dioxide (**STP**) will react with a solution containing 1.59 grams of potassium permanganate (according to the equation on page 404)?
4. One gram of sulfur dioxide reacted completely with 25 grams of a hydrogen peroxide solution. What is the percent by weight of hydrogen peroxide in the solution?
5. Assuming complete conversion, how many liters of oxygen would be needed to produce 50 liters of ozone (**STP**)?
6. Platinum metal is introduced into a mixture of oxygen and ozone totaling 20 liters. After the complete decomposition of the ozone, the gas occupied a volume of 25 liters. What fraction of ozone did the original mixture contain?
7. Using hydrogen sulfide as the standard (equal to 1), what are the relative densities of hydrogen selenide and hydrogen telluride?
8. Determine (a) the weight of 10 liters of H_2S, 1 liter of SO_2 (**STP**), (b) the volume (**STP**) of 3.4 grams of H_2S, 16 grams of SO_2.
9. A mixture of two volumes of hydrogen sulfide and four volumes of oxygen is ignited to produce complete combustion of the former gas. (a) When the system has cooled down to its original temperature, what volume of gas will be present? (b) What composition will this gas have?
10. Fifty milliliters of a sulfuric acid solution are required to react exactly with 0.300 gram of calcium carbonate. (a) What is the normality of the acid? (b) What weight of H_2SO_4 does the solution contain?
11. What weight of sulfuric acid can be prepared from 64 kilograms of sulfur? (Can you solve this using a single equation?)

Applying the Concept

1. What properties of sulfur dioxide might have led to its replacement by the Freon gases in refrigeration?
2. Write an equation for the reaction between silver metal and hot concentrated sulfuric acid to form sulfur dioxide and silver sulfate. Balance this equation by the electron transfer method.
3. What property of concentrated sulfuric acid is involved when the acid is used to: (a) prepare hydrochloric acid, (b) dehumidify air, (c) refine gasoline?
4. In what properties does water differ from the other hydrogen compounds of the group VIA elements?
5. Write a balanced equation for the complete combustion of carbon disulfide.

6. Pigments in white paints include compounds of lead, zinc, and titanium. (a) Which of these should *not* be used in a chemical laboratory? (b) Why?
7. Write an equation illustrating the roasting of lead sulfide.
8. Why are carbon dioxide and water vapor removed from air before it is liquefied?
9. Why are you sometimes advised to collect hydrogen sulfide by displacement of warm water?
10. A pigment for white paint can be prepared by reacting solutions of barium sulfide and zinc sulfate. Write the equation for this reaction.
11. Hydrochloric acid is added to two test tubes, one containing a mixture of powdered iron and sulfur, the other containing powdered ferrous sulfide. Describe the reactions that occur.
12. Hydrogen chloride gas is evolved when concentrated hydrochloric acid is dropped into concentrated sulfuric acid. Explain why.
13. Write an equation for the reaction between calcium hydroxide and sulfur dioxide to form calcium bisulfite.
14. Carbon and sulfur form carbon disulfide by covalent bonding. Draw the orbital overlap diagram for this molecule.

Reading Further

Building Blocks of the Universe, rev. ed., by Isaac Asimov, New York, Abelard-Schuman, 1961. Chapter 8, "Sulfur—The Yellow Element," describes the discovery, uses, and problems related to sulfur.

"The Origin of the Atmosphere," by Helmut Landsberg, and "The Upper Atmosphere," by David Blemenstock, in *Scientific American* for August 1953 and January 1949, respectively, present a fascinating story of the gases in space.

25

The Nitrogen Family and the Inert Gases

In Mendeleev's original periodic table, the elements at the extreme left end of the periods (such as Na and K) were those, as we now know, whose outer orbits contain a single electron. The elements placed at the extreme right end of each period in his scheme (Cl, Br, and so forth) were those whose outer orbits contain a total of 7 electrons. No element was located between the halogen of one period and the alkali of the next. In fact, *no elements were known in Mendeleev's time whose atomic weights would have placed them in the positions described.*

Today, because of the many discoveries since Mendeleev's time, we know that each period comes to a close with an element whose outer orbit is complete. These elements, as you know, were discovered by Ramsay and Rayleigh during a study to determine accurately the density of nitrogen. By their ingenious approach, Ramsay and Rayleigh discovered the first of the inert gases, the start of a new family, group O, in the periodic table (summarized in Table 25-1).

THE INERT GASES

While determining the density of nitrogen, Ramsay prepared samples of gas in two ways as a means of checking his results. The first method involved the decomposition of ammonium nitrite, utilizing a solution containing a mixture of ammonium chloride and sodium nitrite (Fig. 25-1).

$$NH_4NO_2 \longrightarrow N_2 + 2 H_2O$$

In the second procedure, he prepared nitrogen from the atmosphere by removing all the other *known* gases from a sample of air. Oxygen was removed from the air by means of suitable reducing agents; then the carbon dioxide present was absorbed in sodium hydroxide. The nitrogen obtained in each of these preparations was dried thoroughly and weighed; the results were almost *but not* exactly the same. Nitrogen prepared from the air was always *slightly denser* than that prepared from ammonium nitrite. This difference could not be explained by errors in experimental technique.

At this point, Ramsay, assisted by Rayleigh, profited from an observation made by Sir Henry Cavendish more than a century earlier. Cavendish had noted that nitrogen would combine with oxygen when stimulated by an electric spark. The resulting oxides of nitrogen (as well as the carbon dioxide present) could be absorbed in potassium hydroxide. Cavendish noted further that despite repeated experiments, a trifling fraction of the air, 1/120 of the total volume, was not absorbed.

Table 25-1   **THE GROUP O ELEMENTS**

Element	Atomic number	Atomic weight	Electron configuration	Density g/l (0° C)	Melting point (° C)	Boiling point (° C)	Ionization potential (ev)
Helium	2	4.0026	2	0.177	−272.1 (under pressure)	−268.9	24.6
Neon	10	20.183	2 8	0.899	−248.7	−245.9	21.6
Argon	18	39.948	2 8 8	1.784	−189.2	−185.7	15.8
Krypton	36	83.80	2 8 18 8	3.708	−156.6	−152.9	14.0
Xenon	54	131.30	2 8 18 18 8	5.85	−112	−107.1	12.1
Radon	86	[222]	2 8 18 32 18 8	9.73	−71	−61.8	10.7

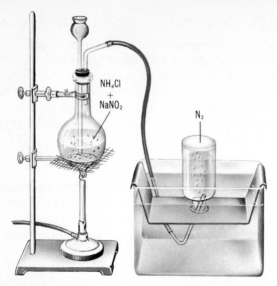

25-1 Ammonium nitrite, which decomposes to form nitrogen and water, is too unstable to store in the laboratory. The nitrite is prepared by the gentle heating of ammonium chloride and sodium nitrite.

Here was a hint for Ramsay and Rayleigh that might explain the difference in their results. If the nitrogen obtained from the air by removal of other, known gases contained an unknown gas that was denser than nitrogen, the measured density of the mixture would be greater than that of nitrogen alone. These experimenters now utilized the fact that nitrogen reacts with hot magnesium to form a solid nitride of the metal. When they passed nitrogen prepared from the air over hot magnesium, a small fraction (1.2 percent by volume) of the gas remained unchanged. This residual gas, which could not be removed by treatment with any chemical, was found to be considerably denser than nitrogen. Its presence in small amounts was sufficient to account for the original difference in density. Further study of the residual gas showed it to have properties never before observed for any gas. This gas, named argon, would not combine with any other element.

Careful separation of the gases in liquid air resulted in the discovery of much smaller amounts of neon, krypton, and xenon—relatives of argon. Later, helium was also found in liquid

air. Radon, the final member of this group of rare gases, was discovered in the study of radioactive elements. This heaviest of the inert gases is formed by the disintegration of radium, as you observed in Fig. 21-7.

Until recently these gases were thought to be completely inert. Each has a stable electron configuration with 8 electrons in the outer shell (except helium, which has only 2 electrons). But as you learned in Chapter 4, several binary compounds composed of xenon or krypton combined with fluorine have been produced. The once "noble" gases have yielded to the ingenuity of the chemist.

Helium

The first hint of the existence of these elements had come many years earlier in a study of the composition of the sun by means of the spectroscope. With this instrument, an element not yet detected on the earth was discovered in the solar atmosphere. This element was helium, second only to hydrogen in density. With the discovery in the earth's atmosphere of other inert gases, the hunt for helium was intensified. It was found to be present not only in our atmosphere but also in the earth itself, absorbed in certain uranium minerals and as a constituent in natural gas.

The relatively inert nature of helium and the other gases is not a handicap; it makes possible a number of valuable applications. When the available supply of helium was increased greatly by its discovery in natural gas in appreciable quantities (1–2 percent), the gas provided an excellent substitute for hydrogen in dirigibles (page 263). Helium has 93 percent of the lifting power of hydrogen without the dangerously flammable nature of the latter. However, relatively little helium is now used for this purpose because of the great demand for the element in various phases of the nuclear energy program. For example, helium is used as a coolant in some nuclear reactors since it does not become radioactive.

When divers and tunnel builders work at air pressure greater than normal, the gases they inhale become more soluble in the bloodstream. These workers must therefore return *slowly* to normal atmospheric pressure so that the dissolved gases can escape from solution. Unless a slow procedure is followed, the dissolved nitrogen forms gas bubbles in the muscle tissues and leads to the agonizing and dangerous condition known as the "bends." Present-day practice provides divers and tunnel workers with a mixture of helium and oxygen instead of ordinary air. Helium is much less soluble in the blood than is nitrogen and the danger of "bends" is thereby lessened.

Many metals, such as aluminum, cannot be welded in the ordinary manner (with torches) because the metal is oxidized at the same time. If an electric arc is used for this purpose and the object is surrounded by a "blanket" of helium (or argon) gas, the welding can be done successfully. Helium is also used to provide an inert atmosphere for the preparation (by reduction with sodium) of metals that combine readily with nitrogen of the air.

Argon

Unseen by you is the argon that fills an incandescent bulb. The lamp provides light when a tungsten filament is heated white-hot by an electric current. The first incandescent lamps had the air evacuated from them to prevent oxidation and destruction of the hot filament. Under this condition the hot tungsten evaporated, blackening the inner surface of the bulb and making the

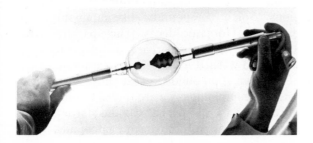

25-2 This 5000-watt xenon arc lamp provides light three times as intense as the sunlight that reaches us. Designed for searchlights, it was first used in a solar simulator for space vehicle investigation.

filament weak. These bulbs were therefore filled with nitrogen to retard evaporation of the filament. Although nitrogen is not a reactive element, the high temperature caused slow reaction between the gas and the tungsten. Both difficulties, that of evaporation of the filament and its reaction with a surrounding atmosphere, have been overcome by filling incandescent bulbs with argon.

Argon, like helium, can be used in welding metals that oxidize and in preparing certain metals that react with nitrogen. Argon is also used to fill many Geiger-counter tubes.

Neon, Krypton, and Xenon

The use of neon in advertising signs is well known. Neon, as well as helium and argon, singly or in combination, is used in mercury vapor lamps to provide a variety of colors.

Both neon and krypton are used in lamps at airports because their brilliant glow can penetrate the fog. For similar reasons, xenon is used in high-speed photographic lamps and in extremely powerful arc lamps (Fig. 25-2). It also finds use in radio and television tubes.

QUESTIONS AND PROBLEMS

1. What is the main source of each of the inert gases?

2. Although helium has an atomic weight of 4, it is only twice as dense as hydrogen. Explain why.

3. What is the chief use of each of the inert gases (except radon)?

4. How can the helium present in natural gas be separated from it?

NITROGEN AND THE GROUP VA ELEMENTS

About four fifths of the ocean of air consists of the element nitrogen, neighbor to oxygen in the periodic table and, like oxygen, important to our lives in many ways. The nitrogen family of ele-

Table 25-2 THE GROUP VA ELEMENTS

Element	Atomic number	Atomic weight	Electron configuration	Density (20° C)	Melting point (°C)	Boiling point (°C)	State and color	Ionization potential	Oxidation states
Nitrogen	7	14.0067	2 5	1.2506 g/l	−209.86	−195.8	Colorless gas	14.5	−3, +3, +5
Phosphorus	15	30.9738	2 8 5	2.20 g/ml (red)	44.1	280	Yellow-white solid	11.0	(−3), +3, +5
Arsenic	33	74.9216	2 8 18 5	5.73 g/ml	814 (under pressure)	615 (sublimes)	Gray solid	10	(−3), +3, +5-
Antimony	51	121.75	2 8 18 18 5	6.691 g/ml	630.5	1380	Blue-white solid	8.6	(−3), +3, +5
Bismuth	83	208.980	2 8 18 32 18 5	9.747 g/ml	271.3	1560	Pinkish-white solid	8	(−3), +3, (+5)

( ) indicates an infrequent oxidation state.

ments, characterized by an outer electron shell of 5 electrons, is summarized in Table 25-2. All of the family members show a variety of oxidation states, the most common being −3, +3, and +5. The heavier members of the family possess increasingly metallic characteristics. Nitrogen is a gas, and phosphorus is a typical nonmetallic element in all its features; but arsenic, antimony, and bismuth, the three remaining metals in group VA, are progressively more lustrous and dense (Fig. 25-3). The binary compounds of these elements are, with few exceptions, covalent and becoming more polar as the group VA elements increase in atomic number; bismuth compounds show partial ionic character. The oxides of these elements are acid anhydrides, but this property becomes less marked as the element increases in atomic weight, bismuth forming a *hydroxide*. All of these elements exist in the form of negative

radicals, but the prevalence of this feature diminishes with increasing atomic number. Having looked at these elements as a group, let us examine the individual elements more closely.

Nitrogen and Its Compounds

Nitrogen or, more precisely, the compounds of nitrogen are important in many ways. Two of their widespread applications are in explosives and fertilizers. At home, nitrogen compounds are found in the form of ammonia water, dyes, and plastics. Important to us in another way are nitrogen compounds associated with living organisms —the proteins. These nitrogen compounds are present in all tissue and are essential to the constant rebuilding and repair of our body cells. Recent investigations into the chemistry of the genetic process have revealed that nitrogen compounds play a key role (Chapter 38).

Nitrogen compounds occur naturally in organic (living or once-living) matter such as proteins, as well as in inorganic matter such as sodium and potassium nitrates, which are often found as extensive deposits in hot, dry desert regions. Some compounds, like ammonia, are products of organic decay. They pass into the atmosphere as gases or are dissolved by rain water and washed into the soil. Natural deposits of nitrogen compounds fall far short of the need for such compounds; we are forced to turn to the nitrogen of the atmosphere as the starting point in the preparation of nitrogen compounds.

25-3 Phosphorus is a waxy, translucent, nonmetal of little luster. Steel-gray arsenic and blue-white antimony are progressively more lustrous metalloids. Bismuth is a lustrous metal with a pink tinge.

25-4 The bottles contain nitrogen. A burning wooden splint is extinguished by immersion in the bottle at the left. Burning magnesium flares brightly when immersed in the other bottle of nitrogen.

Nitrogen Fixation

All the elements you have studied thus far, except the inert gases, are reactive at room temperature or higher. But nitrogen is unreactive unless the temperature is raised very high—considerable energy is required to make nitrogen react with other elements. Burning wood splints, for example, are extinguished by this gas. In contrast, burning magnesium continues to burn in nitrogen to form magnesium nitride (Fig. 25-4).

$$3 \, Mg + N_2 \longrightarrow Mg_3N_2$$

The reason for this difference lies in the structure of the nitrogen molecule. The triple covalent bond between the two nitrogen atoms is very strong, and considerable energy is required to break the bond so that the nitrogen molecule can break apart into the more reactive nitrogen atoms. Burning magnesium provides a temperature high enough to break the triple bond.

We know of only two natural processes that convert molecular nitrogen into compounds. Lightning flashes supply enough energy to break apart both nitrogen and oxygen molecules in the atmosphere into atoms. These nitrogen and oxygen atoms may combine to form nitrogen oxides, which combine with water vapor to form nitric acid. The acid is then washed down on the earth where it reacts with minerals in the soil to form nitrates that can be utilized by plant life.

Have you ever removed from the soil such plants as beans, peas, or clover? You may have noticed small nodules attached to the plant roots (Fig. 25-5). These nodules contain a type of bacterium that transforms nitrogen of the air into nitrates, which the plants then absorb as food. Plants of the type mentioned are often used as a cover crop for land deficient in nitrates. At the end of the growing season, the crop may be plowed under to provide a more nourishing soil for other crops planted the following season.

Both processes just discussed—the action of lightning in forming nitric acid and the work of bacteria in producing nitrates—are examples of the **fixation of nitrogen,** the conversion of atmospheric nitrogen into useful nitrogen compounds. How man has learned to duplicate this action of bacteria and lightning is our next concern.

Nitric Acid

Explosives are not always used destructively. Highways are now built through hills and mountains by using explosives and machines. Rock layers, as well as tree stumps, are loosened from the earth with dynamite, which is essentially nitroglycerin in an absorbent material. Nitroglyc-

25-5 Nitrogen-fixing bacteria in nodules on the roots of clover plants bind free nitrogen into nitrates, which are useful to the plants.

erine and some other explosives like TNT and gunpowder, as well as many synthetic dyes and fertilizers, are nitrogen-containing compounds made from nitric acid. Let us look at the preparation and properties of this all-important acid, which finds its greatest use in making explosives.

The Commercial Preparation of Nitric Acid

For many years nitric acid was prepared by the general method of making an acid, *the reaction between a salt of the acid and sulfuric acid.* Chile saltpeter ($NaNO_3$) served as the nitrate salt.

$$NaNO_3 + H_2SO_4 \xrightarrow{\Delta} HNO_3\uparrow + NaHSO_4$$

The reaction, which is reversible at room temperature, reaches an equilibrium. However, nitric acid has a relatively low boiling point and can be removed from the reaction mixture by gentle heating, causing the reaction to go to completion. At a higher temperature, the sodium bisulfate formed reacts with additional sodium nitrate to yield more nitric acid.

$$NaHSO_4 + NaNO_3 \xrightarrow{\Delta} HNO_3\uparrow + Na_2SO_4$$

Theoretically, more nitric acid could be prepared in this manner, but the higher temperature decomposes some of the nitric acid into oxides of nitrogen that dissolve in the condensed acid.

$$4\,HNO_3 \xrightarrow{\Delta} 4\,NO_2\uparrow + 2\,H_2O + O_2\uparrow$$

Nitrogen dioxide is reddish brown and colors the acid solution yellow.

Because the supply of naturally occurring nitrates is limited, chemists very early turned their efforts to the preparation of the acid from atmospheric nitrogen. One of these early attempts imitated the formation of nitric acid in nature. But here the energy is supplied not by a lightning bolt, but by an *electric arc* passed between two electrodes. When air is passed between the electrodes, the very high temperature of the electric arc results in oxidation of the nitrogen to nitric oxide.

$$N_2 + O_2 \rightleftharpoons 2\,NO$$

Even at 3,000° C only a very small amount of

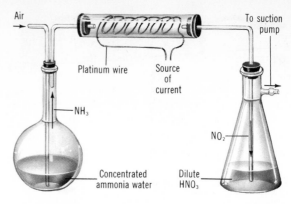

25-6 Oxygen in the air drawn into the system, and ammonia gas released in the Florence flask react near charged platinum wire to produce nitrogen dioxide. This oxide, passed into water, forms dilute nitric acid.

nitric oxide is formed, about 5 percent by volume. Before it cools, the nitric oxide is oxidized by additional oxygen in the air to form nitrogen dioxide.

$$2\,NO + O_2 \longrightarrow 2\,NO_2$$

The nitrogen dioxide reacts with water to form nitric acid and nitric oxide.

$$3\,NO_2 + H_2O \longrightarrow 2\,HNO_3 + NO$$

The nitric oxide formed is again oxidized by air to nitrogen dioxide, which reenters the reaction. This **arc process** did not come into widespread use because of the low yield of the desired product. Except where electric power was inexpensive, the arc process fell into disuse when a more efficient and less costly method of oxidizing nitrogen was developed.

You have learned that it is possible to oxidize atmospheric nitrogen directly, but it is easier and more efficient to oxidize a nitrogen compound to form the oxide. Such a method became commercially possible when the *Haber process* (page 279) made ammonia inexpensive and abundant.

In the **Ostwald process** for the preparation of nitric acid, ammonia is mixed with air and the mixture is heated to 600° C. The mixture of gases is then passed over heated platinum gauze, which serves as a catalyst. The ammonia gas is oxidized to nitric oxide.

$$4\,NH_3 + 5\,O_2 \longrightarrow 4\,NO + 6\,H_2O$$

As in the arc process, the nitric oxide becomes oxidized further to form brown fumes of nitrogen dioxide. The gases are now passed through water which absorbs the dioxide, forming nitric acid. The Ostwald process is currently the leading method for the preparation of the acid. For a procedure you can use in the laboratory to demonstrate this process, see Fig. 25-6.

The Laboratory Preparation of Nitric Acid

The laboratory preparation of nitric acid employs the general method of preparing an acid. The reaction vessel used is an all-glass retort because the hot vapors of the product attack both cork and rubber. Try the following procedure if you wish to *see for yourself how nitric acid is prepared.*

Introduce into a retort 17 grams of sodium nitrate and 15 ml of concentrated sulfuric acid. Clamp the retort over a tripod and wire gauze. Arrange the retort so that its long neck dips into a large Pyrex test tube which is surrounded by cold water in a battery jar, as shown below. Now heat the mixture with a small flame until about 10 ml of the product have been collected. Discontinue heating at this point and allow the retort to cool before proceeding to test the product.

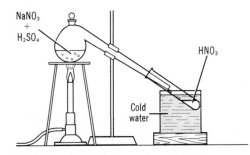

NaNO₃ + H₂SO₄

HNO₃

Cold water

Place 3 ml of the concentrated nitric acid into a test tube and add a very small piece of metallic copper. What is the color of the gas produced? Fumes of the same color may have appeared when you started heating the retort. Identify the gas. Pour 2 ml of the con-

centrated acid into a test tube and heat it *cautiously.* While heating the tube, hold a glowing splint above the acid. Explain the results.

The Properties of Nitric Acid

Prepared in this way, the acid contains about 68 percent by weight of HNO_3, boils at 120° C, and is somewhat denser than water. This 68 percent acid is a colorless liquid which, like concentrated hydrochloric acid, fumes in moist air. Its effect on litmus and its ability to neutralize bases brand the product an acid. Yet in the preparation of hydrogen from a metal and an acid, nitric acid is not used. Even when dilute, nitric acid rarely yields hydrogen when reacted with metals. You may well inquire whether this acid possesses any other chemical properties not common to acids. Let us find out.

Nitric Acid and Metals

If a piece of copper metal is dropped into *concentrated* nitric acid, a reaction occurs immediately. Brownish nitrogen dioxide (NO_2), but no hydrogen, is produced. The solution, which turns blue-green at the same time, can be evaporated to leave a mass of blue crystals typical of copper compounds.

$$Cu + 4\,HNO_3 \longrightarrow Cu(NO_3)_2 + 2\,NO_2\uparrow + 2\,H_2O$$

The reaction demonstrates an important chemical property of concentrated nitric acid; it is a strong *oxidizing agent.* It oxidizes copper, a relatively nonreactive metal.

$$Cu^0 - 2\,e^- \longrightarrow Cu^{+2} \quad \text{(oxidation)}$$
$$N^{+5} + 1\,e^- \longrightarrow N^{+4} \quad \text{(reduction)}$$

Metals more active than copper (magnesium, zinc) react with the concentrated acid in similar fashion to produce nitrogen dioxide. However, gold and the platinum metals are unaffected by the concentrated acid.

The products of the reaction between metals and *dilute* nitric acid vary with the metal and the concentration of the acid. This can be observed *in the following investigation.*

Prepare a very dilute (1 percent) solution of the acid by adding 1 ml of concentrated nitric acid to 50 ml of water. Place some of this very dilute acid in a test tube and drop a strip of magnesium into it as shown below. Test the gas evolved with a burning splint. Is the popping sound of a hydrogen explosion heard?

Now prepare a second dilute solution of the acid by mixing one volume of the concentrated acid with eight volumes of water. Drop a strip of magnesium or lump of zinc into a portion of this acid. This time, no gas is evolved. But test a portion of the resulting solution for the presence of the ammonium ion (Skills Chapter 32) by neutralizing it with concentrated NaOH and heating the test tube gently. Ammonia gas is liberated and easily identified by its odor.

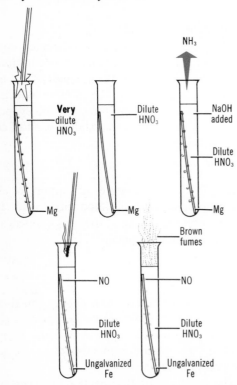

Take a second portion of this dilute (1:8) acid and drop a strip of ungalvanized iron into it. Observe that a gas is evolved. Test

the gas with a burning splint. This time, there is no popping sound. Although the gas is colorless, it is not hydrogen. However you note that when this colorless gas leaves the test tube and meets the air, it turns brown. The colorless gas produced is nitric oxide.

With the *very* dilute acid in the first test tube, the reaction with the magnesium to liberate hydrogen is:

$$\overset{0}{Mg} + 2\,\overset{+1+5}{HNO_3} \longrightarrow \overset{0}{H_2}\uparrow + \overset{+2\ +5}{Mg(NO_3)_2}$$

In this reaction, *it is the hydrogen (hydronium) ion of* the acid which is the oxidizing agent.

$$Mg^0 - 2\,e^- \longrightarrow Mg^{+2} \quad \text{(oxidation)}$$
$$2\,H^+ + 2\,e^- \longrightarrow H_2^0 \quad \text{(reduction)}$$

When metals such as magnesium and zinc react with dilute nitric acid, the $\overset{+5}{N}$ of the dilute acid is reduced to NH_3. The ammonia then reacts with excess nitric acid to form ammonium nitrate. No hydrogen is liberated.

$$4\,\overset{0}{Zn} + 10\,\overset{+5}{HNO_3} \longrightarrow$$
$$4\,\overset{+2}{Zn(NO_3)_2} + \overset{-3}{NH_4}NO_3 + 3\,H_2O$$

In the last test tube, the less active iron reduces the nitrogen of the dilute acid to nitric oxide.

$$Fe + 4\,HNO_3 \longrightarrow Fe(NO_3)_3 + NO\uparrow + 2\,H_2O$$

To summarize our findings, active metals such as magnesium and zinc react with *very dilute* acid to yield hydrogen. They react with *dilute* acid to yield ammonia. Metals less active than magnesium and zinc (for example, iron) and some which do not replace hydrogen from acids (copper and silver) react slowly with the *dilute* acid at room temperature to yield nitric oxide. When the acid is concentrated, reaction with most metals, including copper and silver, yields nitrogen dioxide. In almost all of its reactions with metals, nitric acid acts as an oxidizing agent. This property accounts for the reaction of the acid with metals such as copper and silver, which are unaffected by other acids.

One additional property of the acid is of note. When *active* metals such as iron, chromium, nickel, and aluminum are dipped into the cold, concentrated acid, the metals no longer react (for example, with acids) in their usual manner; they are said to be "passive." This is believed to result from the formation by the acid of a thin, protective layer of their oxides. The condition is temporary, however. Striking the metal or scratching the surface destroys the passive condition.

Nitric Acid and Nonmetals

Nitric acid, unlike most other acids, is a strong oxidizing agent. This property, already evident in its reaction with metals, is further demonstrated in its reaction with nonmetals and nonmetallic substances. The hot, concentrated acid converts phosphorus to phosphorous and phosphoric acids, H_3PO_3 and H_3PO_4, and arsenious oxide, As_2O_3, to arsenic acid, H_3AsO_4. Similarly, iodine is oxidized to iodic acid, HIO_3, while sulfur is oxidized to sulfur dioxide:

$$4 HNO_3 + 3 S \longrightarrow 3 SO_2\uparrow + 2 H_2O + 4 NO\uparrow$$

The sulfur dioxide can be oxidized further to the sulfate ion.

The hot vapors of the acid can ignite straw; the oxygen necessary for the combustion is provided by the decomposition of the acid molecules:

$$4 HNO_3 \longrightarrow 4 NO_2 + 2 H_2O + O_2\uparrow$$

Glowing charcoal continues to burn when surrounded by hot vapors of the acid:

$$4 HNO_3 + 3 C \longrightarrow 2 H_2O + 3 CO_2\uparrow + 4 NO\uparrow$$

And the cold, concentrated acid reacts violently with carbon compounds such as turpentine.

Nitrogen dioxide dissolves in concentrated nitric acid to form red, fuming nitric acid, an even more powerful oxidizing agent. This serves as an oxidant in some rocket engines in which the fuels are carbon compounds such as aniline or hydrazine (p. 627). The concentrated acid therefore differs from typical acids because the concentrated acid can also oxidize nonmetallic substances.

Proteins and Nitric Acid

With a forceps, dip a strand of white wool or pure silk into colorless concentrated nitric acid. After about 30 seconds, remove the strand and wash it well. Is it now colored yellow?

The same observation can be made by the chemist whose fingers come into contact with the acid. Perhaps you have learned, by chance, that such a yellow stain on the skin will not wash off. The similarity of the two results indicates that wool and silk, as well as skin cells, are of animal origin and contain proteins. Many *proteins combine with nitric acid to form complex organic compounds that are yellow*. These compounds, in turn, are made orange by treatment with ammonia water, $NH_3(aq)$.

Aqua Regia

If hot concentrated nitric acid does not react with either gold or platinum, how then can these metals be dissolved? The alchemists, seeking to dissolve gold for their experiments, found an answer; *you can also; but do so with caution.*

Drop small pieces of gold leaf into each of two test tubes containing concentrated hydrochloric and nitric acids, respectively. Warm the acids *gently*. Still no reaction is observed. Now prepare a mixture of three volumes of concentrated hydrochloric acid and one volume of concentrated nitric acid, and drop a small piece of gold leaf into a test tube of this mixture. Observe that in a short time the gold leaf begins to dissolve and the color of the solution changes to orange. How does this mixture of acids, which is known as **aqua regia** (because it dissolves metals associated with royalty) succeed in dissolving the metal when the individual acids have failed?

In a mixture of concentrated hydrochloric and nitric acids, the nitric acid slowly oxidizes the hydrochloric acid to form chlorine.

25-7 Nitric acid is used to etch copper plates. The blank plate is covered with wax, and the item to be etched is scraped into the wax. When the plate is dipped into acid, only the exposed metal is etched.

$$3\,HCl + HNO_3 \longrightarrow$$
$$Cl_2 + 2\,H_2O + NOCl \quad \text{(nitrosyl chloride)}$$

The metal is oxidized by the chlorine as the gas is generated. The gold or auric chloride formed combines with hydrochloric acid to form stable chlorauric acid ($HAuCl_4$).

$$2\,Au + 3\,Cl_2 + 2\,HCl \longrightarrow 2\,HAuCl_4$$

The Uses of Nitric Acid

Many uses of nitric acid, including its major use in the preparation of fertilizers and explosives, have been indicated in the previous pages. For example, glycerine can be nitrated to yield the explosive nitroglycerine.

$$C_3H_5(OH)_3 + 3\,HNO_3 \rightleftharpoons C_3H_5(NO_3)_3 + 3\,HOH$$
glycerine $\qquad\qquad$ glyceryl nitrate

And cellulose can be nitrated to form nitrocellulose. By carrying out the nitration of cellulose only partway, the chemist produces cellulose nitrate, which is used as a plastic material (Celluloid) or dissolves in a number of organic solvents to form lacquers.

The reaction of nitric acid with metals provides a means of preparing metallic nitrates not found

naturally. An interesting application of the metal-acid reaction is found in the preparation of copper (or other metal) plates used in *etching* (Fig. 25-7).

The Uses of Nitrates

Nitrate salts, particularly sodium, potassium, calcium, and ammonium nitrates, are used extensively in fertilizer mixtures. Almost all of the silver nitrate made is used in the preparation of the silver salts of the halogen elements for photographic purposes (Chapter 23).

Because nitrates (as well as nitric acid) are good oxidizing agents, they are often used in explosives. An explosion is an exceedingly fast oxidation reaction, requiring a trifling fraction of a second for a complete reaction. Explosions are possible because the necessary oxygen is "built into" the explosive molecule, as in the nitro-compounds (nitrocellulose, nitroglycerine), or added in the form of one of the metallic nitrates or ammonium nitrate. Not only do nitrates provide a rich store of oxygen, but also they release this oxygen readily.

Nitric Oxide and Nitrogen Dioxide

Recall that concentrated nitric acid differs from most other acids in reacting with copper. What substance is produced when copper and fairly dilute nitric acid react? If you try this in the apparatus like that shown in Fig. 25-8 you will notice that the flask fills with brownish fumes, but that the gas which you collect is colorless. How can you reconcile these two observations? No sooner do you remove the cover from the bottle of colorless gas (in order to smell the gas or test its combustibility) than the gas within turns brown. Your previous experience tells you that the gas first produced in the generator is colorless nitric oxide, NO. The NO produced combines with the oxygen of the air to form a second substance, nitrogen dioxide, NO_2. But why wasn't this second substance collected? If you add a small amount of water to a bottle of the brown NO_2, the brown gas dissolves completely. The NO_2 is very soluble in water.

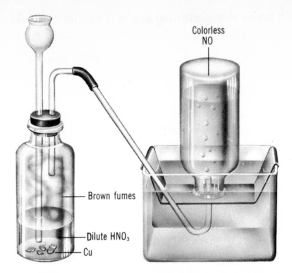

25-8 Dilute nitric acid and copper react to produce colorless nitric oxide, which combines with the oxygen of the air in the generating bottle to produce brown fumes of nitrogen dioxide. The latter reacts with water to reform nitric acid, releasing nitric oxide.

When copper reacts with dilute nitric acid, the mixture of nitric oxide and nitrogen dioxide enters the collecting bottle; the nitrogen dioxide dissolves in the water while the nitric oxide passes through unchanged. The first product of the reaction between copper and *dilute* nitric acid is nitric oxide, NO.

$$3\,Cu + 8\,HNO_3 \longrightarrow$$
$$2\,NO\uparrow + 3\,Cu(NO_3)_2 + 4\,H_2O$$

The nitric oxide reacts immediately with additional oxygen to form reddish-brown nitrogen dioxide, NO_2.

$$2\,NO + O_2 \longrightarrow 2\,NO_2$$

And the latter reacts with water to form nitric acid and nitric oxide.

$$3\,NO_2 + H_2O \longrightarrow 2\,HNO_3 + NO\uparrow$$

Nitrous Oxide

Neither nitric oxide nor nitrogen dioxide has any practical value outside of the chemical industry. But there is a third oxide of nitrogen that has become useful in medicine. In 1772 Joseph Priest-

ley reported the preparation of a new gas, nitrous oxide (N_2O). Soon thereafter, it was obtained by *gentle* heating of ammonium nitrate.

$$NH_4NO_3 \xrightarrow{\Delta} N_2O + 2\,H_2O$$

Inhalation of a small quantity of this sweet-smelling gas produced a sensation of light-headedness, resulting in fits of laughter (Fig. 25-9). Hence the name, "laughing gas." But a more practical use arose as further inhalation of the gas produced unconsciousness. The possibilities in surgery were not overlooked, for until this time it had been a dreaded event. Though the discovery of ether was soon to stimulate the search for new and better anesthetics, the history of man's "triumph over pain" had received a tremendous push forward. Look closely at the tanks of gas in a dentist's office; one of them bears the label NITROUS OXIDE, the other, OXYGEN. A mixture of these two gases is used to produce unconsciousness.

25-9 This late 18th-century cartoon was entitled "New Discoveries in Pneumaticks." The actual demonstration of nitrous oxide inhalation took place at the (British) Royal Institute. The cartoon satirizes the demonstration because of the humorous effects produced by the gas.

Nitrous Acid and Nitrites

Remove one atom of oxygen from the formula for sulfuric acid; you now have the formula for sulfurous acid, H_2SO_3, salts of which are called sulfites. Remove one atom of oxygen from the formula for nitric acid; you now have the formula for nitrous acid, HNO_2, salts of which are called *nitrites*. Nitrous acid is never found on the laboratory shelves because it is highly unstable, yet we are indebted to it for beautifying our lives. Many dyes in everyday use require nitrous acid in their preparation. Because the acid is so unstable, it is made when needed by combining sodium nitrite with hydrochloric acid at or below room temperature. Sodium nitrite is made by heating sodium nitrate strongly to remove one atom of oxygen, or by reduction with lead.

$$2\,NaNO_3 \longrightarrow 2\,NaNO_2 + O_2\uparrow$$
$$NaNO_3 + Pb \longrightarrow NaNO_2 + PbO$$

The nitrogen compounds studied so far have been either oxides, acids, or salts in which the nitrogen exists in a *positive* oxidation state. But the introduction to this chapter revealed that nitrogen and its family members may also exist in negative oxidation states. The next section will consider examples of compounds where nitrogen has an oxidation number of -3, its most common negative oxidation state.

QUESTIONS AND PROBLEMS

1. (a) What two processes are employed in the commercial preparation of nitric acid? (b) Compare and contrast the two processes.

2. If you were given unlabeled samples of concentrated nitric and concentrated sulfuric acids, how could you distinguish between them *chemically?*

3. Describe briefly the two natural means of fixation of nitrogen.

4. What are the major uses of nitric acid and nitrates?

5. What relationship exists between nitrous acid and nitrites?

6. (a) Why does a bottle of colorless nitric oxide turn brown when exposed to the air? (b) Differentiate among NO, NO_2, and N_2O.

7. Write an equation to demonstrate each of the following reactions: (a) zinc and very dilute nitric acid, (b) zinc and dilute nitric acid, (c) zinc and concentrated nitric acid, (d) copper and dilute nitric acid, (e) copper and concentrated nitric acid.

AMMONIA AND ITS COMPOUNDS

Ammonia, a gas whose odor is familiar, is a product of the decay of animal matter, especially proteins. Just as certain bacteria transform nitrogen of the air into nitrates (page 421), other bacteria transform nitrogenous waste into ammonia gas. Prior to this century, ammonia was not used as the pure liquid or gaseous NH_3, but it was used in water solution as a cleansing agent or transformed into ammonium compounds. The ammonia produced at that time was made by two methods. One was the destructive distillation of soft coal, which yields only a small amount of the gas. The other was the **cyanamide** process. In this process nitrogen is passed over calcium carbide (CaC_2) at a high temperature to form calcium cyanamide ($CaCN_2$).

$$CaC_2 + N_2 \longrightarrow CaCN_2 + C$$

Steam is then passed over the calcium cyanamide to form ammonia gas.

$$CaCN_2 + 3\,H_2O \longrightarrow CaCO_3 + 2\,NH_3\uparrow$$

When the world's supply of naturally occurring nitrates proved to be insufficient for the growing demand in fertilizers and explosives, ammonia proved to be an excellent substitute. Ammonia readily forms salts which serve as fertilizers. It can also be transformed into the nitric acid used to make explosives. But elementary nitrogen is rather inactive; how was it made to combine directly with hydrogen?

The Haber Process

The reaction between nitrogen and hydrogen was known to be reversible and exothermic. Under normal conditions, less than one percent of the nitrogen used is converted to ammonia under the influence of an electric spark. In seeking ways to increase the efficiency of this reaction, Fritz Haber, a German chemist, applied to the problem a principle which had been stated some twenty-five years earlier by the French scientist, Le Chatelier. Let us review quickly from Chapter 17 how the application of Le Chatelier's Principle proved to be the means of producing ammonia efficiently. First examine the equation below for the reaction.

$$N_2 + 3 H_2 \rightleftharpoons 2 NH_3 + heat$$

one   three   two
volume   volumes   volumes

A high temperature does enable the reaction to reach an equilibrium *more rapidly*. Yet, since the reaction between nitrogen and hydrogen is *exothermic*, the addition of heat also causes the point of equilibrium to shift far to the left—little ammonia will be produced. Le Chatelier's Principle also indicates that the reaction to the right (formation of ammonia) is favored by an *increase* in pressure, which causes a *decrease* in volume. Haber found that a temperature of 550° C and a pressure of 250 atmospheres would increase the yield of ammonia to 10 percent when a platinum catalyst was used. When equilibrium has been reached, the ammonia formed is removed by chilling the reaction mixture suddenly and separating the ammonia either by liquefaction or by dissolving the gas in water. The uncombined nitrogen and hydrogen pass back to the reaction chamber to be reacted once more (Fig. 25-10).

Since Haber's time, technical advances in the production of ammonia have enabled engineers to shift the equilibrium in the direction of higher yields. This is done chiefly through the use of temperatures around 600° C and higher pressures which range from 700 to 1,000 atmospheres. Today yields of 55 to 60 percent are not uncommon. Newer and better catalysts, such as iron

25-10   From this control room, the entire, complex Haber process is regulated. A tall purification tower appears in the background.

oxide containing small amounts of potassium and aluminum oxides, have enabled equilibrium to be reached sooner.

Laboratory Preparation of Ammonia

If you dip a strip of red litmus paper into some household ammonia water, the paper turns blue, indicating that ammonia water contains hydroxide ions—it is a base. This base, ammon*ium* hydroxide, results from a very slight reaction between ammonia gas and water.

$$NH_3 + H_2O \rightleftharpoons NH_4^+ + OH^-$$

If you hold a strip of *moistened* red litmus paper just above an open bottle of ammonia water, the paper turns blue, indicating again the presence of hydroxide ions. What is the source of these ions? If you *very cautiously* waft some of the air above the bottle toward your nose and *sniff it gently,* the odor of ammonia is unmistakable. The explanation for the change in color of the litmus paper is at once apparent. Ammonium hydroxide is unstable and decomposes into water and ammonia.

$$NH_4^+ + OH^- \longrightarrow NH_3\uparrow + H_2O$$

The gas escaping from the bottle reacts with the water of the moist litmus paper to form excess hydroxide ions.

THE NITROGEN FAMILY AND THE INERT GASES   **429**

These observations suggest a means of preparing ammonia gas. If we first prepare ammonium hydroxide, it can be decomposed to form ammonia. You can *test this idea in the following way.*

Mix together small quantities of powdered calcium hydroxide and ammonium chloride. Rub a small portion of this mixture between your fingers and smell the mixture; the odor of ammonia is unmistakable.

In general, when any base (except ammonium hydroxide) reacts with an ammonium salt, ammonium hydroxide is produced. Gentle heating decomposes the base and yields ammonia gas. Thus:

$$\left.\begin{array}{l} 2\,NH_4Cl + Ca(OH)_2 \\ (NH_4)_2SO_4 + 2\,NaOH \\ 2\,NH_4NO_3 + Ba(OH)_2 \end{array}\right\} \longrightarrow 2\,NH_4OH + \text{a salt}$$

$$NH_4OH \xrightarrow{\Delta} NH_3\uparrow + H_2O$$

Use the first of these reactions to *see for yourself how ammonia is prepared.*

Mix together on a sheet of paper 10 grams of ammonium chloride and 7 grams of powdered calcium hydroxide. Introduce this mixture into a 6-inch Pyrex test tube and clamp the tube as shown below. Insert a one-

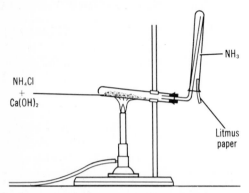

holed rubber stopper fitted with the delivery tube shown and place a small test tube over the delivery tube. Heat the reaction mixture with a *small* flame; if white vapors are ob-

served in the collecting tube, discontinue heating for 1 minute and resume with more gentle heating. To determine when the collecting tube is filled with ammonia gas, place a strip of moistened red litmus paper at the mouth of the tube. If the paper turns blue immediately, remove the collecting tube and place it mouth down on the table for future use. Replace it with a second tube and continue the preparation and collection.

Insert a glowing splint into the first tube of gas. Does ammonia burn or support combustion *in air?* Add about 10 ml of water to the second tube, shake it, and test the solution with red and blue litmus paper, and with phenolphthalein. Explain the results.

The Properties of Ammonia

Two immediately obvious physical properties of ammonia gas are that it is colorless and has a strong, pungent odor. If a test tube full of the gas is inverted in a dish of water, the water rises rapidly into the tube. Careful measurement has shown that at room temperature, one volume of water dissolves about 1,000 volumes of ammonia gas. The collection of ammonia by displacement of air differs from that of other gases collected in this way because the air is displaced *downward.* The molecular weight of ammonia is 17; the gas is only little more than half as dense as air.

Nitrogen and hydrogen are combined in ammonia by polar covalent bonds. Because the orbitals of the nitrogen atom are at right angles to each other, the ammonia molecule has a pyramidal shape, with the nitrogen atom at the apex and the hydrogen atoms at the vertices of the base (Fig. 25-11). Hydrogen bonding occurs among the molecules in liquid ammonia but not as strongly as among water molecules.

When ammonia gas is tested with a burning splint, it neither burns nor supports combustion. But this observation is somewhat misleading; the flame of a burning splint is not hot enough to reach the kindling temperature of ammonia. The gas does burn in pure oxygen; and mixtures of ammonia and oxygen are explosive. In the pres-

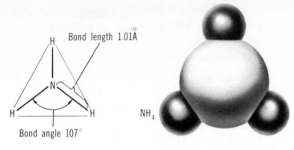

Bond length 1.01Å

Bond angle 107°

NH_3

25-11 The ammonia molecule, as represented by the solid model, is an excellent example of a pyramidal, polar, covalently bonded compound.

ence of a catalyst, ammonia will burn in air if the temperature is high enough. The Ostwald process makes practical use of this reaction in the commercial preparation of nitric acid.

Assume for the moment that red litmus paper is unavailable and that the gas should not be smelled to identify it. A third method of recognizing ammonia gas is available, *as you can determine.*

Moisten the interior of a test tube with one drop of concentrated hydrochloric acid. Then hold the inverted tube over the delivery

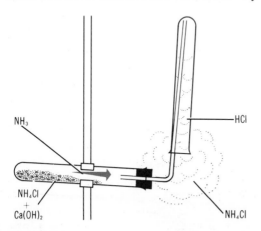

NH_3

HCl

NH_4Cl

NH_4Cl
+
$Ca(OH)_2$

NH_4Cl

tube of the ammonia apparatus. Does a white cloud or smoke form immediately in and around the tube?

This cloud consists of fine crystals of ammonium chloride (sal ammoniac) formed by the reaction

between ammonia and hydrogen chloride gas from the acid vapors.

$$NH_3 + HCl \longrightarrow NH_4Cl$$

The Ammonium Radical

The reactions of ammonia with water and hydrogen chloride are fundamentally the same; both represent the combination of ammonia gas with polar compounds containing hydrogen. A comparison of these reactions with others in which ammonia reacts with acids highlights a basic resemblance among them.

$$NH_3 + HOH \rightleftharpoons NH_4OH$$
$$NH_3 + HCl \longrightarrow NH_4Cl$$
$$NH_3 + HNO_3 \longrightarrow NH_4NO_3$$
$$2\,NH_3 + H_2SO_4 \longrightarrow (NH_4)_2SO_4$$

In general: $NH_3 + H^+ \longrightarrow NH_4^+$

The more negative (nitrogen) end of each molecule of *ammonia* combines with the hydrogen end of a polar molecule to form an *ammonium* radical. If the hydrogen is provided by water, the product is ammonium hydroxide; if the hydrogen is donated by an acid, the product is an ammonium salt.

It is necessary to distinguish carefully between the compound ammonia and the ammon*ium* radical. Study Table 25-3, which summarizes the data learned about these substances thus far.

Table 25-3 AMMONIA AND AMMONIUM RADICAL

Name	Formula	Charge	Nature	Physical properties
Ammonia molecule	NH_3	Neutral	A gaseous molecule, existing independently.	A colorless gas, with a sharp, penetrating odor, very soluble in water and lighter than air.
Ammonium radical	NH_4^+	+1	A radical, never found alone; always part of a compound.	The radical exists only in ammonium compounds, each of which has different and specific properties.

The Uses of Ammonia and Ammonium Compounds

The greatest single use of ammonia is in the preparation of other nitrogen compounds. It is the starting material for the preparation of all ammonium salts and most nitric acid. The acid in turn serves for the preparation of nitrates. Ammonia is also used in the manufacture of other useful compounds which do not contain nitrogen. In a later chapter, you will learn how it is used in the preparation of sodium carbonate (Na_2CO_3) and sodium bicarbonate ($NaHCO_3$).

Ammonia gas, which is easily liquefied by only moderate cooling and pressure, is still the mainstay in railroad refrigerator cars and the commercial preparation of ice. In the latter process, tanks containing the water to be frozen are surrounded by brine (a solution of sodium or calcium chloride), through which passes a series of coils. When liquid ammonia evaporates inside these coils, the resulting drop in temperature cools the brine below the freezing point of water. The water in the tanks freezes, the cakes of ice are removed, and the freezing cycle is repeated.

Ammonium nitrate, sulfate, and phosphate have been widely used as fertilizers. Recently however, a technique has been developed to introduce gaseous ammonia directly into the soil as a fertilizer (Fig. 25-12). Ammonium nitrate is also a component in certain explosive mixtures. The latter property was shown vividly some years ago when a shipload of this salt, anchored off the coast of Texas, blew up and destroyed much of nearby Texas City.

It is not likely that your home is without an ammonium compound. Ammonia has long been used for cleansing purposes. It is ideal for the removal of greasy spots and stains, since it is weakly basic and does not affect the fibers. It also evaporates completely when its job is done. Your flashlight contains dry cells which use ammonium chloride as the electrolyte. If you ever work with radios and similar devices, you probably use solder. Before applying the solder to the wires to be connected, you may clean the wires with a flux containing ammonium chloride.

The compound diammonium hydrogen phosphate [$(NH_4)_2HPO_4$] may be employed to fireproof cloth. It is also sprayed as a foam from airplanes to put out forest and grass fires. In contrast to boron compounds used for this purpose, residues of the phosphate are beneficial to the soil.

25-12 When this photograph was taken, the chinks of the applicator were raised while ammonia was expelled at the usual rate, indicating what happens underground. In actual operation, the chinks are underground and no ammonia is seen.

The chapter thus far has dealt almost exclusively with the inert gases and nitrogen and nitrogen compounds. But you are also concerned about the other members of group VA, and with the broad relationships among these elements and nitrogen. It is now time to look at these elements more closely and to examine these relationships in some detail.

QUESTIONS AND PROBLEMS

1. By what three techniques can you identify ammonia gas?

2. Differentiate between ammonia gas and the ammonium radical.

3. (a) What properties of ammonia make it useful as a refrigerant? (b) What property may have led to a decline in this application? (c) List several other important uses of ammonia and ammonium compounds.

4. How does the sucessful production of ammonia by the Haber process demonstrate Le Chatelier's Principle?

5. (a) Write an equation for the reaction between ammonia and phosphoric acid. (b) Write a net ionic equation for the reaction of ammonia with acids.

PHOSPHORUS, ARSENIC, ANTIMONY, AND BISMUTH

Antimony and arsenic are the oldest of the remaining group VA elements. Women in the ancient Near East used antimony compounds to beautify their eyes, and a Chaldean vase of metallic antimony dates back to 4000 B.C. In the Middle Ages compounds of antimony were used in medicinal preparations and in the fifteenth century the metal was used in making type, mirrors, and bells. The earliest known arsenic compounds, the sulfides, were referred to by Aristotle in the fourth century B.C. Arsenic's use as a poison is well known, but perhaps not so well known is the fact that the inhabitants of a small area of central Europe take minute amounts of arsenic compounds as a tonic for a variety of ailments, including anemia, rheumatism, malaria, and trypanosome infections.

Bismuth was known in the Middle Ages, but was not recognized as a distinct element and was often confused with tin and antimony. It was not until the end of the sixteenth century that bismuth was found to be a distinct metal. Phosphorus has been known for only about three centuries, and for most of that time it was only a curiosity. It was discovered comparatively recently that phosphorus compounds, necessary to plant life and the growth of bones and teeth, also play a vital role in body metabolism.

With the exception of phosphorus, only limited amounts of the last four group VA elements are found in the crust of the earth. Nevertheless, each is a constituent of one or more alloys, in addition to its other specific uses.

Phosphorus: Its Occurrence and Preparation

The main sources of phosphorus are phosphate minerals, notably calcium phosphate, found in our country chiefly in Florida and Tennessee. This compound serves for the preparation of superphosphate of lime (Chapter 24), as well as for the preparation of the element. Whatever means of preparing phosphorus from calcium phosphate is used, the phosphorus must be changed from the $+5$ oxidation state in this salt to that of zero for the element. A reduction process is thereby indicated. The reduction is achieved by heating the phosphate rock in an electric furnace with a mixture of sand (SiO_2) and coke (Fig. 25-13).

$$2\,Ca_3(PO_4)_2 + 6\,SiO_2 + 10\,C \longrightarrow P_4\uparrow + 6\,CaSiO_3 + 10\,CO\uparrow$$

The calcium silicate produced forms a molten slag which is tapped from the furnace. The carbon monoxide and the phosphorus, a gas at the operating temperature, pass into a condenser. The phosphorus is condensed *under* water and run into molds (still under water) to form sticks of the solid element.

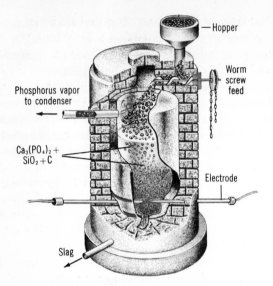

25-13 In the electric furnace, phosphorus vapor is extracted from crushed calcium phosphate that is fed into the hopper. The phosphorus vapor is conducted away and condensed into sticks under water.

Labels on figure:
- Hopper
- Worm screw feed
- Phosphorus vapor to condenser
- $Ca_3(PO_4)_2 + SiO_2 + C$
- Electrode
- Slag

The Properties of Phosphorus

The properties of phosphorus cannot be appreciated without considering the markedly different properties of its allotropic forms. The phosphorus produced commercially is white or yellowish, consisting of P_4 molecules. This form is insoluble in water but soluble in carbon disulfide. It has a slight, garlicey odor and is poisonous. White phosphorus has a very low kindling temperature (35° C) and must therefore be both kept and handled under water to avoid the danger of spontaneous combustion. When white phosphorus is kept at a temperature of 250° C, a trace of iodine being added as a catalyst, it changes slowly to the red form. This allotrope contains many more atoms of phosphorus per molecule than does the white form. Red phosphorus is insoluble in both water and carbon disulfide, has no odor, and is nonpoisonous when pure. It differs markedly from the white form in having a much higher kindling temperature; therefore, it is safe to handle when exposed to air. The red form is the stabler form of the element at room temperature.

Both forms of phosphorus undergo the same chemical reactions; there is a difference only in the rate of reaction. Phosphorus burns readily to form oxides; the trioxide (P_4O_6) is formed in insufficient oxygen and the pentoxide (P_4O_{10}) in an abundant supply of air. (The molecular weights of these oxides show that P_4O_6 and P_4O_{10} are the true formulas rather than P_2O_3 and P_2O_5, respectively.) Like nitrogen, phosphorus combines with active metals when heated. It forms phosphides, for example calcium phosphide, Ca_3P_2. Like nitrogen, phosphorus also forms *covalent* binary compounds with hydrogen, the halogens, and other nonmetals. Though the compound phosphine, PH_3, exists, it is not made by direct combination of the elements. Unlike ammonia (and here is a difference in the family), phosphine does not react with water to form even a weak base.

The Uses of Phosphorus

Elemental phosphorus is a constituent of phosphor bronze, an alloy so highly resistant to corrosion that it is used in ships' propellers and fittings. Much phosphorus is consumed by the match industry. A compound with sulfur, phosphorus sesquisulfide (P_4S_3), appears in the heads of friction or "strike anywhere" matches, while red phosphorus is present in the striking surface of a book of safety matches (Fig. 25-14). Most phosphorus is used to prepare phosphorus compounds.

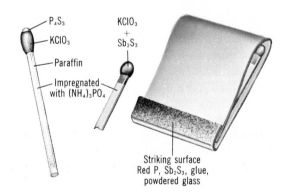

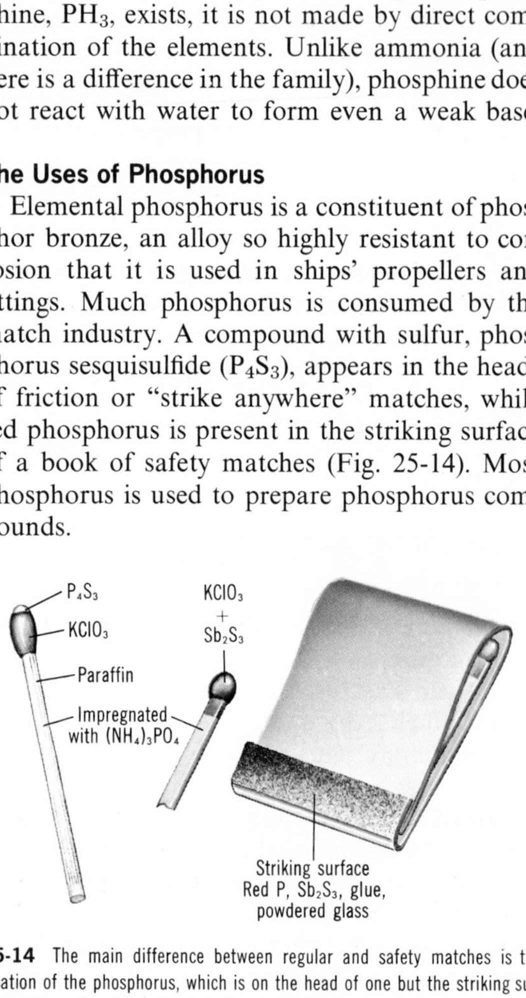

Labels on figure:
- P_4S_3
- $KClO_3$
- Paraffin
- Impregnated with $(NH_4)_3PO_4$
- $KClO_3 + Sb_2S_3$
- Striking surface Red P, Sb_2S_3, glue, powdered glass

25-14 The main difference between regular and safety matches is the location of the phosphorus, which is on the head of one but the striking surface of the other. Upon friction, the phosphorus ignites the head.

The Oxides and Acids of Phosphorus

Both oxides of phosphorus (P_4O_6 and P_4O_{10}) are acid anhydrides.

$$P_4O_6 + 6\,H_2O \longrightarrow 4\,\overset{+3}{H_3}PO_3 \quad \text{(phosphor\textit{ous} acid)}$$

$$P_4O_{10} + 6\,H_2O \longrightarrow 4\,\overset{+5}{H_3}PO_4 \quad \text{(phosphor\textit{ic} acid)}$$

The latter reaction finds considerable use in the chemical laboratory where phosphorus pentoxide is used as a drying agent. The pentoxide is also one constituent of special chemical glassware.

The major phosphorus acid of industry is orthophosphoric acid, H_3PO_4, which is usually known simply as phosphoric acid. It is prepared from the anhydride as indicated above, or by reacting calcium phosphate with sulfuric acid.

$$Ca_3(PO_4)_2 + 3\,H_2SO_4 \longrightarrow 2\,H_3PO_4 + 3\,CaSO_4\downarrow$$

The precipitated calcium sulfate is removed by filtration and the acid is then concentrated by evaporation.

Commercial phosphoric acid is a syrupy liquid containing 85 percent (by weight) of H_3PO_4. It differs significantly from hot, concentrated sulfuric acid in that H_3PO_4 is not an oxidizing agent. Thus, while the preparation of HBr or HI by reaction of the appropriate halide salt and concentrated sulfuric acids leads to some oxidation of the hydrogen halide, the use of phosphoric acid in place of sulfuric acid provides a straightforward double replacement reaction.

Phosphoric acid is a triprotic acid, ionizing in stages to make three hydrogen ions available for reaction.

$$H_3PO_4 \rightleftharpoons H^+ + H_2PO_4^{-1}$$
$$H_2PO_4^{-1} \rightleftharpoons H^+ + HPO_4^{-2}$$
$$HPO_4^{-2} \rightleftharpoons H^+ + PO_4^{-3}$$

Consequently, three types of phosphate salts are known, depending on the number of hydrogen ions replaced from the acid. Hypophosphorus acid, H_3PO_2, is made by a reaction between phosphorus and strong bases. The phosphorus in this acid exists in an oxidation state of $+1$, which is different from that ($+3$, $+5$) of the other acids.

The Uses of Phosphoric Acid and Its Salts

Phosphoric acid is used as a flavoring agent in the food industries, in pharmaceutical products, and for the preparation of phosphates and fertilizers. Its salts have diverse uses. Trisodium phosphate is a constituent of cleansing powders in which it acts as a water softener and detergent. This salt is effective in removing grease. Monocalcium phosphate, $Ca(H_2PO_4)_2$, is present in some baking powders. Ammonium phosphates are used as fertilizers or fireproofing agents. Hypophosphite salts (for example NaH_2PO_2), in which phosphorus exists in the $+1$ oxidation state, are used in a chemical method of nickel-plating metals.

Arsenic: Its Occurrence and Preparation

Occasionally arsenic is found free as the element, but more often it is found in the form of its sulfide ore, realgar (As_2S_3). The metal can be obtained from the ore by roasting (heating an ore in an excess of air to form an oxide) followed by reduction. Arsenic is also obtained as a by-product in the roasting of other metal ores (Cu, Pb, Zn). It is extracted from the dust collected from the chimney flues of the smelters used to process these ores.

Properties of Arsenic

Physically, arsenic shows the more metallic properties expected of a family member lower in the periodic table. It has a metallic luster and density typical of the metals. In contrast, its strength and electrical conductivity are well below those of the usual metals. Like phosphorus, the vapors of the element consist of clusters of four atoms, As_4. Chemically, the element is far from metallic. Its compounds with the nonmetals and hydrogen are polar covalent in nature rather than ionic. It neither replaces hydrogen from acids nor forms bases. Arsenic also combines with oxygen to form negative radicals. The hydrogen compound, arsine, AsH_3, is gaseous like NH_3 and PH_3. Unlike ammonia, arsine does not react with water. Unlike both ammonia and phosphine, it does not react with acids to form salts.

25-15 A compositor has set the metal type by hand and is adjusting it with metal blocks that do not print. Antimony in the alloy for the type causes it to expand after being cast, sharpening the type impression.

Unlike the oxides of nitrogen and phosphorus, the oxides of arsenic react with acids or bases.

Uses of Arsenic and Its Compounds

The metal is alloyed (in small quantities) with lead to make lead shot. The alloy is harder and assumes a more nearly spherical shape than molten lead when formed into shot. Most of the metal is used to make arsenic compounds. Arsenic and its compounds are poisonous; arsenates of lead and calcium are therefore used as insecticides in fruit sprays. This fact explains why it is wise to wash fruits before they are eaten.

Antimony

This element is closely akin to arsenic in its natural occurrence. Only limited amounts of antimony are found, chiefly in the form of its sulfide ore, stibnite (Sb_2S_3). Reduction with iron, or roasting followed by reduction, is used to extract the metal.

Physically, the element resembles arsenic. Its metallic properties are more marked, as shown by its higher melting and boiling points and by its greater density. Chemically, antimony is also much like arsenic. It forms related compounds with nonmetals, oxygen, and hydrogen, and it reacts with concentrated sulfuric acid, nitric acid, and aqua regia. Stibine, SbH_3, is much like arsine, but it is more readily decomposed on heating.

The Uses of Antimony and Its Compounds

Elemental antimony finds good application in the field of alloys. Combined with lead and tin, it forms the low-melting alloy known as type metal (Fig. 25-15). Antimony provides the molten alloy with the unusual property of *expanding as it solidifies.* This produces the sharp edges of type necessary for good impressions. Lead alloyed with 6 percent antimony produces a harder product that is more resistant to acids. This lead-antimony alloy is used to make the lead plates of the storage battery.

Antimony sulfide is used as a red pigment in rubber. Tarter emetic, potassium antimonyl tartrate ($KSbOC_4H_4O_6$), is used as a *mordant* in dyeing cotton. Fibers treated with mordants can be dyed with dyes which otherwise do not adhere to the fiber. The mordant forms a chemical combination with both the fiber and the dye.

Bismuth

Bismuth ores occur mixed in small amounts with ores of other metals, chiefly lead, zinc, and copper. The metal is extracted from the flue dusts obtained in the smelting of these ores and is refined by electrolysis.

Both physically and chemically, bismuth, with outer electrons farther from the nucleus than in any of its family members, is decidedly metallic in nature. The element, which has a high melting point, boiling point, and density, has a bright metallic luster and is a fair conductor of electricity.

Compounds composed of bismuth and nonmetals are more ionic than are the corresponding compounds of arsenic and antimony. In contrast to the latter oxides, bismuth oxide is somewhat soluble in water to give a basic reaction. The element is rarely found in a negative radical. The hydrogen compound BiH_3 is difficult to prepare and is very unstable. This follows the pattern within any family—proceeding down each column of elements, the hydrogen compounds become progressively less stable.

The Uses of Bismuth and Its Compounds

The major use of bismuth is as a constituent in alloys. Best known of these are the fusible alloys, capable of melting at temperatures below that of boiling water. Such alloys find good use in the mechanisms of automatic fire sprinklers like those in Fig. 25-16.

Soluble bismuth salts, such as bismuth nitrate, hydrolyze in water to form basic (or hydroxy) salts.

$$Bi(NO_3)_3 + H_2O \rightleftharpoons Bi(OH)(NO_3)_2 + HNO_3$$

The basic nitrate and carbonate are used in the form of suspensions to treat disturbances of the digestive system.

This and the previous two chapters have shown the pattern among the families of elements whose members each have more than 4 electrons in their outer shell. Now for comparison we will turn to those families of elements whose members each have less than 4 valence electrons. Before doing so, you might wish to try several laboratory procedures described in the next skills chapter to test for some of the negative ions of the elements in the groups we have been studying—groups VA, VIA, and VIIA.

25-16 A fusible alloy plug has melted and separated from the sprinkler head at the right. A plug from another sprinkler head appears in the lower left of the photograph. Water has begun to spray from the head.

5. Write the formulas for three different sodium salts of phosphoric acid.

6. How could you separate a gaseous mixture containing ammonia, phosphine, and arsine?

7. Write an equation for the reaction between bismuth chloride and water to form basic bismuth chloride.

VALUE OF THE CONCEPT

THE CONCEPT

The inert gases, or the group O family of elements, are unique in having their valence electron shells complete. Helium, the lightest, is found as a constituent of natural gas as well as in the atmosphere. Neon, argon, krypton, and xenon are separated from liquid air. Radon, the heaviest, is radioactive and results from the disintegration of radium. The increasing atomic numbers of the inert gases are accompanied by an anticipated increase in atomic weight and density. Recently it has been found that under special conditions xenon or krypton will combine with fluorine and certain other elements.

QUESTIONS AND PROBLEMS

1. Differentiate between the red and white allotropic forms of phosphorus.

2. What properties of bismuth indicate that it is the most metallic of the group VA elements?

3. Write a balanced equation for the reaction between potassium iodide and phosphoric acid.

4. List two uses of each of the following: phosphorus, arsenic, antimony, bismuth.

The properties of the members of group VA emphasize their family relationship. With increasing atomic number, the elements, at first completely nonmetallic in nature, develop more and more the physical properties of metals; the densities, luster, melting and boiling points, and electrical conductivity increase to the point where bismuth is indistinguishable from any other metal.

Chemically, the same trend appears. The early members of the family form mainly covalent compounds, and their oxides are acid anhydrides. These elements usually occur in negative radicals. With increasing atomic number, the elements form partially ionic compounds. While these elements still occur in the form of negative radicals, their oxides have a dual nature and react with both acids and bases. The last member of the family emphasizes the trend toward a metallic nature. Bismuth compounds are more ionic than those of its family members; the element is rarely found in a negative radical, and it forms a base. While all of these elements form compounds with hydrogen, the compounds become less stable as the atomic number of the element increases.

These elements all have more than one oxidation state, but they vary considerably in the occurrence of these states. Nitrogen exists in a wide range of oxidation states from -3 to $+5$, while phosphorus is most often found in the $+3$ and $+5$ states. Though arsenic and antimony occur almost entirely in the $+3$ and $+5$ states, bismuth is usually found in the $+3$ state.

The two most important compounds of nitrogen are nitric acid and ammonia. Not only does each of these have manifold uses but their compounds—nitrates and ammonium salts—are also very useful. Ammonia and nitric acid illustrate nitrogen in its extreme oxidation states, -3 for the former and $+5$ for the latter compound. Ammonia can, therefore, act as a reducing agent, while nitric acid is almost always an oxidizing agent. In its reactions with metals, the degree to which the nitrogen is reduced varies with the nature of the metal, the concentration of the acid, and other factors, such as temperature. In the preparation of nitric acid, the arc process, which simulates nitrogen fixation by lightning, gave way to the Ostwald process. The preparation of ammonia by the Haber process is a brilliant example of the use of Le Chatelier's Principle in shifting an equilibrium reaction to a point where the product can be obtained efficiently. Manufactured ammonia has made us independent of the supply of natural nitrates. The ammonia can be oxidized to nitric oxide, which is oxidized further to nitrogen dioxide, the anhydride of nitric acid.

Phosphorus occurs in two allotropic forms, and its oxides form numerous acids. Among their diverse uses, phosphorus and its compounds are important in preparing fertilizers. In addition to the specific uses of arsenic, antimony, bismuth and their compounds, each of the elements is a constituent of one or more alloys.

USING THE CONCEPT

Using the Basic Concept

1. Nitrogen and chlorine form the covalent compound NCl_3. Draw an orbital overlap diagram for a molecule of NCl_3.
2. (a) If a new inert element were discovered, what atomic number would it have? (b) Why?
3. Nitrogen and oxygen are both diatomic gases. Why is oxygen much more reactive than nitrogen?
4. (a) Describe the Ostwald process for preparing nitric acid. (b) Why has it replaced the arc process in most places?
5. Contrast the reaction of copper with dilute and concentrated nitric acid.
6. (a) In what respects does bismuth differ from the other group VA elements? (b) Account for the fact that bismuth is rarely found in the -3 oxidation state, in contrast to nitrogen and phosphorus.
7. Nitric acid is not usually suggested in the preparation of hydrogen from a metal and and acid. Why?
8. Write an equation to indicate the reaction between magnesium and each of the fol-

lowing strengths of nitric acid: (a) concentrated, (b) dilute, (c) very dilute.

9. (a) Why is nitrous acid not found in your chemistry laboratory? (b) How could you prepare it?

10. What properties of nitric acid and nitrates make them particularly important in the production of (a) fertilizers, (b) explosives?

11. (a) Prove that concentrated nitric acid differs from typical acids in reacting with nonmetals. (b) Describe a test for protein.

12. What is nitrogen fixation?

13. How can you prepare a bottle of each of the following oxides: nitric oxide, nitrogen dioxide, and nitrous oxide?

14. Describe briefly the details of the Haber process for producing ammonia. (b) How does it illustrate the importance of Le Chatelier's Principle?

15. (a) By what general process can ammonia be produced in the laboratory? (b) What is the simplest means of identifying ammonia?

16. How does ammonia gas differ from the ammonium radical in (a) charge, (b) electron structure, (c) physical properties?

17. (a) Write an equation for the reaction that occurs when ammonia dissolves in water. (b) Compare and contrast this reaction with the reaction between ammonia and an acid.

18. (a) What is the unique property of type metal, of lead shot, of fusible alloys? (b) Of what metals is each of these alloys composed?

19. In the reaction:

$$P + KOH + H_2O \longrightarrow PH_3 + KH_2PO_2$$

which element is (a) the oxidizing agent, (b) the reducing agent? (c) Balance this equation by the electron transfer method.

20. Compare and contrast the method of preparation and properties of the allotropic forms of oxygen, sulfur, and phosphorus.

21. Determine the oxidation number of each group VA element in the following compounds: $NaNH_2$, $K_4P_2O_7$, H_3AsO_3, $NaNH_4HPO_4$, $NaBiO_3$, KPF_6, N_2H_4, NH_4NO_3.

22. (a) Write an equation for the reaction between sodium bromide and phosphoric acid. (b) Why is phosphoric rather than sulfuric acid used in the preparation of hydrogen bromide?

23. Give the names and formulas for the most common binary compounds formed between hydrogen and each of the following elements: nitrogen, phosphorus, arsenic, and antimony. (b) What is the oxidation state of the group VA element in each compound?

Relating Terms Within the Concept

Each of the following statements contains two italicized terms. Select the *italicized* term that makes the statement correct.

1. The ionization potential of the inert gases is very (*low, high*).

2. Nitrogen fixation is illustrated by the (*cyanamide process, arc process*).

3. A substance that cannot exist independently is (*ammonia gas, the ammonium radical*).

4. Le Chatelier's Principle is important in determining the yield of ammonia by the (*cyanamide process, Haber process*).

5. Gold and platinum can be dissolved by (*concentrated nitric acid, aqua regia*).

6. The oxidation number of nitrogen in $NaNO_3$ is (+5, +3).

7. Copper reacts with concentrated nitric acid to produce (*NO, NO₂*).

8. Arsenic, antimony, and bismuth are important constituents of (*alloys, dyes*).

9. Nitric acid is a good (*reducing agent, oxidizing agent*).

10. The Ostwald process is an efficient substitute for the (*Haber process, arc process*).

11. Phosphorus and arsenic are obtained from their ores by (*oxidation, reduction*).

12. When exposed to the air, nitric oxide changes to (*nitrogen dioxide, nitrous oxide*).

13. A triprotic acid that ionizes to make three hydrogen ions available is (*HNO_3, H_3PO_4*).

14. Magnesium reacts with very dilute nitric acid to yield (*NH_3, H_2*).

15. The binary compounds of both nitrogen and phosphorus with hydrogen are (*covalent, ionic*).

Solving Problems Within the Concept

1. Which will neutralize a greater weight of sodium hydroxide, 100 grams of ortho-phosphoric acid (H_3PO_4) or 100 grams of metaphosphoric acid (HPO_3)?

2. What is the percent by weight of: (a) phosphorus in phosphine, (b) arsenic in arsenic acid (H_3AsO_4), (c) nitrogen in ammonium chloride, (d) bismuth in bismuth trioxide?

3. Calculate (a) the weight of 33.6 liters (**STP**) of argon, (b) the volume (**STP**) occupied by 10 grams of neon.

4. Which of the following compounds has the largest percent (by weight) of nitrogen: NH_4NO_3, HNO_3, NO_2, NCl_3, NO?

5. What weight of arsenic can be obtained from 2 tons of realgar ore containing 38 percent of the sulfide by weight?

6. What weight of calcium hydroxide can be neutralized by a solution containing 42 grams of HNO_3?

7. An alloy of copper and gold weighing 2.107 grams is treated with concentrated nitric acid. The undissolved metal, when washed and dried, weighs 0.2493 gram. What is the percentage of gold in the alloy?

8. What volume of oxygen is necessary for the complete oxidation of 14 liters of ammonia (at **STP**)?

9. What weight of silver nitrate can be prepared by reacting 5.4 grams of the metal with nitric acid?

Applying the Concept

1. Which will dissolve more copper metal, a given weight of nitric acid in concentrated solution, or the same weight of acid in dilute solution?

2. If the reaction between nitrogen and hydrogen *were* endothermic, what effect would an increased temperature have on the equilibrium? Why?

3. Magnesium nitride reacts with water to form ammonia and magnesium hydroxide. Write an equation for the reaction.

4. How could you collect ammonia gas if you were forbidden to use displacement of air?

5. (a) Which of the gases studied thus far could *not* be dried by passing over phosphorus pentoxide? (b) Why?

6. (a) In what property does concentrated nitric acid resemble concentrated sulfuric acid? (b) In what properties do they differ?

7. From the information in this chapter, devise a test for the ammonium ion.

8. In the ammonia fountain in Fig. 14-3, what would happen if the flask were inverted over water containing phenolphthalein?

Reading Further

The World of Nitrogen, by Isaac Asimov, New York, Abelard-Schuman, 1958. A highly readable account of the many organic compounds that contain nitrogen.

"Chemical Agriculture," by Francis Weiss, and "Discoveries in Nitrogen Fixation," by Martin Kamen in *Scientific American* for August 1952 and March 1953, respectively. Both articles present a new outlook on the topic they present. You can get ideas for experimentation in the first article.

"The Noble Gas Compounds" by C. L. Chernick in *Chemistry* for January 1964. The article presents an excellent account, starting with the pioneer experimental work, of the production of compounds of the inert gases.

26

SKILLS—Testing for Negative Ions

"It looks like table salt but it *may* be potassium cyanide, a deadly poison; it looks very much like sugar but it *is* arsenic trioxide, another deadly poison." Things are not always what they seem. Appearances are deceiving and labels have been known to be incorrect. In many circumstances, particularly in some fields of chemistry, we must deal with materials whose contents are unknown. A sample of an unknown metallic substance may represent a single metal or a combination of two or more metals. Spring water may be better than 99.999 percent pure or it may contain a variety of dissolved minerals. The problem of identifying unknown materials gave rise to the development in chemistry of methods of **analysis,** a procedure for the identification of materials. Analysis frequently involves separating the individual ingredients of substances before they can be identified. The chemist, for example, may be faced with the problem of determining the *kind* of fibers in a piece of cloth, the particular metals present in an ancient coin, the ingredients in a cosmetic cream, or the ions present in a sample of mineral water.

For convenience, chemical analysis is usually divided into two main categories. In **qualitative analysis** we seek to *identify* the individual substance or substances present. In **quantitative analysis** we seek to measure the *quantity* of a given substance or substances present. The labels on many present-day fabrics illustrate both branches of chemical analysis. The chemist must not only determine whether a sample of cloth contains cotton, linen, wool, silk, rayon, Dacron, or nylon (qualitative analysis) but also must ascertain *how much* or what percentage of each is present (quantitative analysis). Both of these types of analysis can be applied to all types of chemical substances, whether they be ionic or covalent. Besides acids, bases, and salts, many petroleum compounds, starches, sugars, and proteins, as well as a great number of industrial products such as paints and varnishes, plastics and textiles, are subjected to chemical analysis. In our introduction to chemical analysis, we will concentrate on the *qualitative* analysis of some of the negative ions with which you are familiar. We shall, as far as possible, follow the pattern of recent chapters by studying the elements as they occur in families.

A word before we begin. The qualitative analysis of positive and negative ions usually requires that these ions be in solution. Many common ionic compounds in your study are soluble in water, or can be dissolved by the action of dilute acids. We shall simply assume in the following procedures that the unknown material to be analyzed has been brought into solution.

THE HYDROXIDE ION

An unknown solution is smooth and slippery to the touch—does it contain an excess of the hydroxide ion? The answer happens to be *no*—the unknown is a solution of glycerine, a substance which, like basic solutions, is slippery to the touch. How, then, can we recognize an excess of the hydroxide ion? In numerous investigations you have tested for the presence of the hydroxide ion, characteristic of bases, by using indicators such as litmus and phenolphthalein. This test has two noteworthy, and often unrecognized, features. First, indicators are sensitive to *particular* concentrations of the hydroxide ion, and it is not possible to use all indicators to test for an excess of OH^- ions. (Refer to Table 14-2 on page 227 for the pH range of various indicators.) You can observe this feature for yourself *by trying the following.*

Prepare a series of test tubes containing respectively 0.1, 0.01, 0.001, and 0.0001 N NaOH. (These can be prepared by repeated tenfold dilution of 1 N NaOH. If 10 ml of 1.0 N NaOH are diluted to 100 ml and mixed thoroughly, the resulting solution will be 0.1 N. Further dilution following this formula reduces the concentration by one-tenth of its original value at each step.) To each solution add two drops of litmus solution. Each solution turns blue, indicating an excess of hydroxide ion. Now repeat this

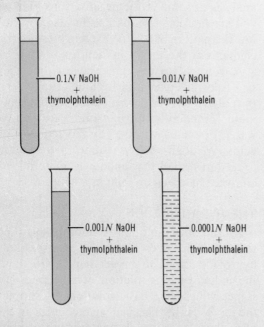

procedure, using thymolphthalein as the indicator. Why do the first three solutions turn blue while the fourth solution remains unchanged?

A very dilute solution of sodium hydroxide, which contains only a slight excess of OH⁻ ions, changes the color of pink litmus to blue, since litmus changes color at a pH of about 8. The thymolphthalein, however, does not change color until a pH of about 10.5 is reached. Therefore the thymolphthalein added to the 0.0001 N NaOH solution was not affected, since the pH of that solution is approximately 10.

Many indicators undergo a change in color even when the solution is in the acid pH range.

You can study one of these indicators *by conducting the following simple tests.*

Add two drops of Congo red solution to test tubes containing dilute HCl and dilute NaOH respectively. The acid turns the indicator blue while the base makes it deep red. Now prepare a series of test tubes containing, respectively, 0.1 N acetic acid, 0.1 N lactic acid, 0.1 N tannic acid and 0.1 N boric acid. Add two drops of the indicator to each. The first two solutions turn the indicator blue, but the last two have no effect—the indicator remains red even though the solution is acidic.

Congo red remains red even in an acid solution until a pH below 5 is reached. Therefore its color is the same in acid solutions with pH values above 5 as in basic solutions. Actually Congo red is blue below a pH of 3, changes color gradually between pH 3 to 5, and is red above a pH of 5. The color change of such indicators reminds us that hydroxide ions are still present in acid solutions, although at a lower concentration than hydrogen ions.

A second feature of the use of indicators is that a positive test for the hydroxide ion does not identify the source of the ion. A solution of sodium acetate is basic to litmus and phenolphthalein because *hydrolysis* of the salt produces an excess of hydroxide over hydrogen ions. Other salts which are formed from the neutralization of weak acids by strong bases behave similarly. To summarize, a positive reaction to such indicators as litmus, phenolphthalein, and thymolphthalein is evidence that the solution *contains hydroxide ions at a particular concentration.* For the indicators mentioned, this would mean a pH of about 8 for litmus, above 10 for phenolphthalein, and above 10.5 for thymolphthalein. Congo red is, of course, red in part of the acid range as well as in the basic range. Colorplate I (facing page 548) shows the color range for these and several other indicators. Use the information there and in Table 14-2 (page 227) to solve the following problems.

1. You are given concentrated solutions of calcium acetate, potassium carbonate, potassium nitrate, zinc chloride, and ammonium sulfate as well as litmus. (a) State the color of the indicator in each of the solutions. (b) Explain how you determined each color stated.

2. (a) In a particular hydroxide solution, litmus and thymolphthalein are blue, while phenolphthalein and Congo red are red. What is the lowest possible pH of the solution? (b) In a given salt solution, Congo red remains red and litmus turns red. What pH range is possible?

THE HALOGEN IONS

How would you recognize sodium chloride, a most commonplace substance? The most obvious answer—taste it—is risky; many white solids are poisonous. What other properties of sodium chloride might be employed? We know that it is a white solid with a cubic crystalline structure and that it dissolves in water to yield colorless solutions. But since a great many substances possess these same properties, we cannot depend on the physical properties alone as a means of identifying substances. What chemical behavior of sodium chloride can be employed? Assuming for the moment that the solid is a sodium compound, and you will be able to determine this for yourself after studying Skills Chapter 32, how could you demonstrate that it is sodium *chloride?*

Set up a series of test tubes one-third full of dilute solutions of sodium chloride, potassium chloride, calcium chloride, and magnesium chloride. To each of these, add 2 ml of a solution of silver nitrate. If a white insoluble substance that remains in suspension forms, stopper the tubes and shake their contents vigorously. A white substance coagulates and settles to the bottom. What is it?

In each test tube the white material that settles is silver chloride:

$$AgNO_3 + NaCl \longrightarrow AgCl\downarrow + NaNO_3$$
$$2\,AgNO_3 + MgCl_2 \longrightarrow 2\,AgCl\downarrow + Mg(NO_3)_2$$

Thus far, you have learned that the chloride ion forms a white precipitate in combination with the silver ion. But the appearance of a white precipitate is *insufficient* proof of the chloride ion because other negative ions duplicate this behavior. If you were to treat solutions of sodium carbonate, sodium sulfate, and sodium oxalate with silver nitrate, similar white precipitates would be formed. *How can you distinguish* between silver chloride and these other white insoluble silver salts?

Set up a series of test tubes one-third full of solutions of sodium carbonate, sodium sulfate, and sodium oxalate. Add 2 ml of

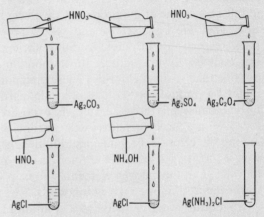

silver nitrate solution to each. White precipitates of silver carbonate, sulfate, and oxalate form. Add 3 ml of dilute nitric acid to each of these test tubes and to each test tube used in the previous investigation. Again shake the contents of each tube. The precipitates of silver chloride are unaffected by the acid. Do the precipitates of silver carbonate, sulfate, and oxalate *dissolve* in the acid?

One further step remains to prove the presence of silver chloride. Pour off as much of the liquid in each test tube containing silver chloride as possible. Now add 5 ml of dilute ammonium hydroxide. Observe that the silver chloride in each tube dissolves.

The silver chloride dissolves to form soluble silver *ammonia* chloride.

$$AgCl + 2\,NH_3 \longrightarrow Ag(NH_3)_2Cl$$

In testing for the chloride ion, therefore, *acidify the solution to be tested with dilute nitric acid and then add a solution of silver nitrate. If a white precipitate that is soluble in ammonium hydroxide appears, the chloride ion is present.*

Differentiating Among Halogen Ions

If the chloride ion forms a precipitate of silver chloride with the properties described, what should we expect of the remaining ions of the halogen family? Here we find both resemblance and difference. The fluoride ion forms no precipitate with silver nitrate; silver fluoride is *very soluble* in water. But silver bromide and silver iodide show some of the properties of silver chloride. They are light yellow and yellow precipitates, respectively, insoluble in dilute nitric acid, but increasingly less soluble in ammonium hydroxide than is silver chloride. These precipitates might be confused with silver chloride, particularly because all three darken on exposure to light. We are faced therefore with distinguishing among the chloride, bromide, and iodide ions, as well as devising a test for the fluoride ion. Your knowledge of the halogen elements will help you to distinguish among their compounds.

If chlorine water is added to a solution of an unknown halogen compound, four possibilities exist.

If unknown is: | This will happen:

a fluoride
$$NaF + Cl_2 \longrightarrow \text{no change}$$

a chloride
$$NaCl + Cl_2 \longrightarrow \text{no change}$$

a bromide
$$2\,NaBr + Cl_2 \longrightarrow Br_2 + 2\,NaCl$$

an iodide
$$2\,NaI + Cl_2 \longrightarrow I_2 + 2\,NaCl$$

If the unknown is a chloride or fluoride, the color of the solution changes to that of the added chlorine water; if either a bromide or iodide is present, the color darkens because of the formation of a new and darker halogen element. To distinguish between the latter two, carbon tetrachloride is added and the mixture shaken well. The formation of an orange or reddish-colored layer of carbon tetrachloride, on standing, indicates that the unknown is a bromide. A violet color in the carbon tetrachloride layer labels the unknown an iodide. Table 26-1 summarizes the procedure.

Table 26-1　TESTING FOR THE HALOGENS

Type of solution	Substance added	Color of CCl_4 layer
Fluoride	Cl_2 water and CCl_4	Very pale green
Chloride	Cl_2 water and CCl_4	Very pale green
Bromide	Cl_2 water and CCl_4	Orange-red
Iodide	Cl_2 water and CCl_4	Violet

Neither of the foregoing tests, the formation of a precipitate with silver nitrate and the replacement of the halide ion by chlorine, is applicable to the fluoride ion. To test for the latter, we employ the fact that when a fluoride reacts with sulfuric acid the fluoride ion is converted to hydrogen fluoride, which can be detected by its effect on glass (page 380).

In testing for the halide ions, then, we employ three procedures. If the addition of silver nitrate to a solution of unknown yields a *white* precipitate, insoluble in dilute nitric acid but soluble in dilute ammonium hydroxide, the chloride ion is present. This test is conclusive in the absence of bromide and iodide ions. *The bromide and iodide ions can be detected by replacing them with chlorine. The liberated halogens can be recognized by extracting them from the water solution with carbon tetrachloride, in which they show their characteristic colors of orange-red and violet* (Colorplate II following page 548). *The fluoride ion*, which does not respond to either of these procedures, *is transformed to hydrogen fluoride, which can be recognized by the etching of glass.*

The test for the sodium ion in sodium chloride awaits the study of positive ions in Chapter 32.

1. Devise a procedure for detecting *both* ions in solutions containing mixtures of the following ions: (a) fluoride and chloride, (b) fluoride and bromide, (c) chloride and iodide.

2. In a handbook of chemistry, find the solubility, in grams per liter, of silver chloride, silver bromide, and silver iodide. From this data, predict whether silver astatide should be soluble or insoluble in water.

THE IONS OF SULFUR

Given a sodium compound containing sulfur: How can one tell if it is sodium sulfide, sodium sulfite (or bisulfite), or sodium sulfate? (Other sulfur-containing ions are known, but they are unusual.) Add dilute hydrochloric acid to the sample to be tested and observe the products (if any) that form.

If unknown is: This will happen:

a sulfide
$$Na_2S + 2 HCl \longrightarrow$$
$$H_2S\uparrow + 2 NaCl$$

a sulfite
$$Na_2SO_3 + 2 HCl \longrightarrow$$
$$SO_2\uparrow + H_2O + 2 NaCl$$

a sulfate
$$Na_2SO_4 + 2 HCl \longrightarrow$$
no apparent change

Though a rotten egg odor immediately stamps the unknown as a sulfide, expose a strip of paper moistened with lead acetate solution [$Pb(C_2H_3O_2)_2$] to the gas to confirm your results. A darkening of the paper, resulting from the formation of lead sulfide, indicates the presence of hydrogen sulfide. The unknown must be a sulfide. *The darkening of lead acetate paper by a gas produced when dilute hydrochloric acid is added to an unknown labels the unknown a sulfide.*

Suppose, however, that the unknown is a sulfite. Here we employ the fact that the sulfurous acid formed by reaction of the hydrochloric acid with a sulfite decomposes on gentle heating to produce sulfur dioxide, whose odor is very unlike

that of hydrogen sulfide. We may confirm the presence of this gas by bubbling it into a very weak solution of potassium permanganate. The sulfur dioxide decolorizes the permanganate ion. *The production of sulfur dioxide when dilute hydrochloric acid is added to an unknown is evidence that the sulfite (or bisulfite) ion is present.*

But how does the chemist recognize a sulfate compound that shows no apparent reaction with hydrochloric acid? *Try the following.*

Prepare dilute solutions of sodium sulfide, sodium sulfite, and sodium sulfate. Add 2 ml of a dilute solution of barium chloride to each of these solutions. Nothing happens in

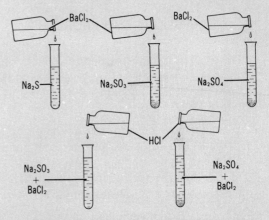

the first solution but white precipitates form in the remaining test tubes. Now add dilute hydrochloric acid to the latter tubes until the liquid is acid when tested with litmus paper. Observe that the white precipitate disappears in the test tube originally containing the sulfite ion, but remains unchanged in that containing the sodium sulfate.

The white precipitate formed is barium sulfate.

$$Na_2SO_4 + BaCl_2 \longrightarrow 2 NaCl + BaSO_4\downarrow$$

Other barium compounds such as $BaCO_3$ and $Ba_3(PO_4)_2$ are white and insoluble in water but these, unlike the barium sulfate, dissolve in dilute hydrochloric acid. *The formation of a white precipitate, insoluble in hydrochloric acid, when barium chloride is added to an unknown indicates the presence of the sulfate ion.*

In testing for ions containing sulfur, the ion was changed to a sulfur compound with characteristic properties. Sulfides are converted to hydrogen sulfide, whose distinctive odor and effect on lead acetate paper are unmistakable. Sulfites are converted to the readily decomposable sulfurous acid to yield sulfur dioxide, whose odor, acid anhydride property, and bleaching action again make it easy to identify. Sulfates are converted to insoluble barium sulfate, distinguishable from other insoluble barium compounds by its insolubility in dilute hydrochloric acid.

QUESTIONS AND PROBLEMS

1. Devise a procedure for detecting *both* ions in solutions containing mixtures of the following ions: (a) sulfide and sulfite, (b) sulfide and sulfate, (c) sulfite and sulfate.

2. What member or members of the group VIB elements should be expected to form an insoluble barium compound? Why? Check your answer against the tables of solubility in a handbook of chemistry and physics.

IONS OF THE GROUP VA ELEMENTS

Except for ammonium ions, nitrogen is usually found in negative ions or radicals, as is phosphorus. Arsenic and antimony occur in negative radicals; but they, as well as bismuth, also exist in the form of hydrated positive ions. Tests for these three ions are being reserved for a later skills chapter. Here we will consider the metals as they are found in negative ions.

Nitrides

Recall that with active metals, nitrogen forms ionic nitrides.

$$3\,Mg + N_2 \longrightarrow Mg_3N_2$$

The presence of nitrides can be detected easily, because the unstable nitrides are decomposed

completely in water to form a hydroxide of the metal and ammonia gas.

$$Mg_3N_2 + 6\,H_2O \longrightarrow 3\,Mg(OH)_2 + 2\,NH_3\uparrow$$

The ammonia gas can be recognized by any one of the methods described in Chapter 25; its odor, its effect on moist pink litmus paper, or its reaction with hydrogen chloride vapors to form a white smoke of ammonium chloride. *The formation of ammonia gas when an unknown solid is added to water indicates the presence of the nitride ion.*

Nitrates

Since some nitrates, like copper nitrate, are blue while other nitrates, like sodium nitrate, are colorless, color itself cannot be used to identify nitrates. Further, as practically all nitrate compounds are soluble in water, the nitrate ion cannot be detected by the formation of a precipitate. The nitrate ion can be identified however, even when it is present in extremely small amounts, *by the following procedure.*

To a dilute nitrate solution add a few milliliters of a *freshly prepared* fer*rous* sulfate solution. Incline the test tube and slowly add concentrated sulfuric acid so that it forms a separate layer at the bottom of the test tube, as shown below. A brown ring forms between the layers indicating that the nitrate ion is present.

Brown ring — Concentrated H_2SO_4 — $FeSO_4$ + NO_3^- — Concentrated H_2SO_4

In this test the ferrous sulfate reduces the nitrate ion to nitric oxide, NO, which forms a colored compound, $FeSO_4 \cdot NO$, with the excess ferrous sulfate. *The formation of a brown ring when concentrated sulfuric acid is added slowly to a solution to which a ferrous sulfate solution also has been added indicates the presence of the nitrate ion.*

Phosphates

Given a solution containing sodium carbonate and sodium phosphate, how could you recognize each of the negative ions? You know that carbonates and phosphates react with barium chloride solution to form insoluble precipitates, both of which are insoluble in excess hydrochloric acid. Therefore the phosphate ion cannot be recognized simply by adding a solution of barium chloride.

Instead *phosphates are identified by acidifying a solution with nitric acid and then adding a solution of ammonium molybdate* [(NH₄)₂MoO₄]. *A yellow precipitate* (ammonium phosphomolybdate) *forms slowly if the phosphate ion is present.* A similar yellow precipitate is formed with solutions of arsenates (AsO_4^{-3}) and antimonates (SbO_4^{-3}), but the means used to distinguish among these three ions must await more advanced work in qualitative analysis.

It now remains to identify the carbonate ion present in the original mixture. You will do so momentarily.

QUESTIONS AND PROBLEMS

1. How could you prove the presence of nitrogen in sodium nitride?

2. How could you demonstrate that a solution labeled $NaNO_3$ actually is a nitrate solution?

3. Devise a procedure for detecting *both* of the ions in solutions containing the following ions: (a) phosphate and bromide, (b) phosphate and sulfate.

CARBONATES

Though compounds containing the carbonate ion will be studied in detail shortly, the procedure used in testing for this ion is profitably included with those for other negative ions. The test for the carbonate ion is based upon the reaction between any carbonate and an acid. Observe *this in the following investigation.*

Place 10 ml of a solution of sodium carbonate in a large Pyrex test tube. Have ready a one-hole rubber stopper fitted with a bent glass tube as shown below. Now add 5 ml

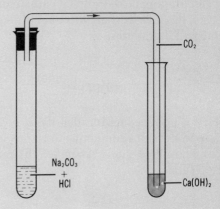

of dilute hydrochloric acid to the solution in the test tube; quickly insert the stopper and insert the delivery tube into another test tube containing 5 ml of limewater (a solution of calcium hydroxide). The gas that bubbles out of the first tube turns the limewater milky. On standing, the white suspension settles to reveal a white precipitate. Repeat this procedure to determine if other carbonates and other acids react in a similar way.

You conclude that carbonates react with acids to form carbonic acid, which decomposes readily to yield carbon dioxide and water.

$$Na_2CO_3 + 2\,HCl \longrightarrow$$
$$2\,NaCl + H_2CO_3 \longrightarrow CO_2{\uparrow} + H_2O$$

The carbon dioxide reacts with limewater to form white, insoluble calcium carbonate.

$$Ca(OH)_2 + CO_2 \longrightarrow CaCO_3{\downarrow} + H_2O$$

In testing for the carbonate ion, therefore, add dilute hydrochloric acid to the unknown, whether in solution or in the solid form. If a gas is evolved and bubbled into limewater, the formation of a white suspension that settles to form a white precipitate reveals the presence of the carbonate ion.

Many other tests for many other negative ions exist. We have introduced you to only a few of the more common chemical tests. The field of qualitative analysis is an ever changing, broadening, and exciting field. Coupled with quantitative analysis, it is an essential procedure in all types of chemistry laboratories.

PROBLEM

Devise a procedure for identifying *both* of the ions in solutions containing the following ions: (a) phosphate and carbonate, (b) carbonate and sulfate.

ADDITIONAL PROBLEMS

1. In a particular acid solution, litmus and Congo red are red, thymolphthalein and phenolphthalein are colorless. What is the highest possible pH of the acid solution? Why?

2. In a given salt solution, litmus is blue, thymolphthalein and phenolphthalein are colorless, and Congo red is red. What is the pH range of the solution? Explain your answer.

3. You have concentrated solutions of potassium acetate, sodium carbonate, sodium nitrate, and ammonium chloride as well as the indicator litmus. State the color of the indicator in each of the solutions.

4. Devise a procedure for detecting *both* ions in solutions containing mixtures of the following ions: (a) fluoride and iodide, (b) bromide and chloride, (c) chloride and iodide.

5. Devise a technique for detecting the three negative ions in a solution containing potassium sulfide, sodium sulfite, and magnesium sulfate.

6. If you were given two colorless sodium salts, how could you prove that one was a nitride while the other was a nitrate?

7. Devise a procedure for detecting *both* ions in a solution containing the following ions: (a) phosphate and chloride, (b) phosphate and sulfite, (c) carbonate and bromide, (d) carbonate and nitrate.

8. You are given a solution containing sodium nitrate, sodium chloride, sodium sulfate, sodium hydroxide, sodium sulfide, and sodium carbonate. How can you determine the presence of each negative ion in the solution?

27

The Alkali Metals and Hydrogen

Bridges, skyscraper frames, and automobile bodies all require metals—metals characterized by great hardness and strength. But your experience also tells you that these materials are rather dense; this property makes the finished article heavy. If a metal were known that was both strong and light, many metallic objects would function more efficiently. Thus trucks of light weight could utilize their power to move loads rather than the weight of the vehicle. But are there any metals that are not much denser than water, or possibly even less dense? Such metals do exist. They are found among the elements listed at the left side of the periodic table.

THE METALS OF GROUP IA

Of all the metals, those in group IA are truly unique. The single electron in the outer shell of each of their atoms makes them behave chemically like metals—but in physical properties they are far from what we usually think of as metals. Some of the properties of these metals, which are also known as the **alkali** metals, are presented in Table 27-1.

You might at first not suspect that compounds of the group IA metals are more abundant in the earth's crust than are those of iron, copper, and other common metals. In the history of chemistry, the uncombined forms of the metals of group IA are late-comers, even though some of their compounds have been known and used for thousands of years. Their late discovery is supported by their positions in the electrochemical series of metals. Since the alkali metals are among the most active of the elements, their compounds are highly stable and difficult to decompose; even high temperatures are ineffective for this purpose. The necessary reduction of alkali metal compounds to the elements can be achieved efficiently only by electrical means.

Preparation of the Alkali Metals

Though the electrolysis of a solution of sodium chloride (Chapter 23) oxidizes the chloride ions to chlorine gas, the hydrogen ions in the solution are more easily reduced than the sodium ions. Therefore these sodium ions remain unchanged. The solution which remains contains sodium ions

Table 27-1 THE GROUP IA ELEMENTS

Element	Atomic number	Atomic weight	Electron configuration	Density (g/ml, 20° C)	Melting point (°C)	Boiling point (°C)	State and color	Ionization potential	Oxidation states
Hydrogen	1	1.00797	1	0.08988 (g/l, 0° C)	−259.14	−252.8	Colorless gas	13.6	+1, (−1)
Lithium	3	6.939	2 1	0.534	186	1336	White solid	5.4	+1
Sodium	11	22.9898	2 8 1	0.971	97.5	880	Silvery solid	5.1	+1
Potassium	19	39.102	2 8 8 1	0.87	62.3	760	Silvery solid	4.3	+1
Rubidium	37	85.47	2 8 18 8 1	1.53	38.5	700	White solid	4.2	+1
Cesium	55	132.905	2 8 18 18 8 1	1.873	28.5	670	Silvery solid	3.9	+1
Francium	87	[223]	2 8 18 32 18 8 1	?	?	?	?	?	+1

( ) Indicates an infrequent oxidation state.

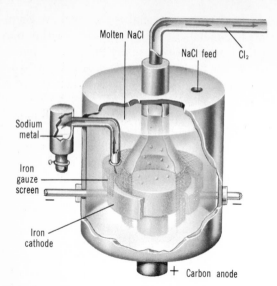

27-1 During the electrolysis of molten sodium chloride in a Downs cell, the sodium (of low density) rises to the surface of the circular iron cathode and is withdrawn. Chlorine is liberated at the carbon anode.

and hydroxide ions; but no sodium metal is produced.

$$2 H_2O + 2 e^- \longrightarrow H_2^0 + 2 OH^-$$
$$2 Cl^- - 2 e^- \longrightarrow Cl_2^0$$

Since metallic sodium cannot be produced by this process, some other method had to be found.

Sir Humphry Davy, in 1807, applied a powerful direct current of electricity to *molten* sodium hydroxide. The compound decomposed, releasing oxygen at the anode and depositing soft, silvery sodium on the cathode. This was the first isolation of sodium metal.

$$2 NaOH \xrightarrow{\text{DC}} 2 Na + O_2\uparrow + H_2\uparrow$$
$$\text{(molten)}$$

Davy also discovered potassium, barium, and calcium by electrolyzing their hydroxides in a similar way.

For a time, Davy's procedure was the basis for the commercial preparation of these elements. Today, the preparation of sodium, potassium, and lithium usually employs the molten, or fused, naturally occurring chlorides in place of the hydroxides. Because of a high melting point of

800° C, the electrolysis of sodium chloride is carried out using a mixture of sodium and calcium chlorides. The latter serves to lower the melting point. The apparatus used in the **Downs process** for preparing sodium (Fig. 27-1) is designed to prevent mixing of the hot products.

Two remaining members of the alkali metals, rubidium and cesium, occur as compounds in minute amounts in the earth's crust. Cesium and rubidium are constituents of rather rare minerals; details of their separation from other alkali metals and from each other await more advanced study. These elements, like the other family members, are prepared from their compounds by electrolysis. Francium results from the emission of alpha particles from radioactive actinium, and not enough of the element has been collected to permit its detailed study.

Properties of the Alkali Metals

Although the alkali metals are typically metallic in luster, and in electrical and thermal conductivities, they are distinguished from all other metals by three unique *physical properties*. First, these metals are very soft, capable of being cut readily with a knife. Second, they possess unusually low densities, less than twice that of water

27-2 In packaging cesium, the desired amount is drawn off the "porcupine" container into glass ampules that are cut off without the torch contaminating the remaining metal.

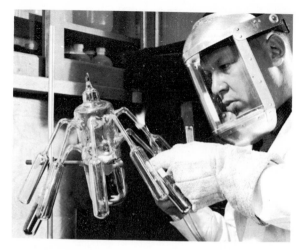

as a maximum. So low is the density of lithium, the lightest metal known, that it floats in liquids (kerosene, benzene) usually employed to keep most active metals out of contact with air and water. Finally, these metals melt (and boil) at temperatures far below the melting (and boiling) points of other metals. The melting point of cesium is so low that the metal liquefies at body temperature or in a very warm room (Fig. 27-2). Such unusual properties result from a relatively weak bonding among the atoms of the element in the solid state.

The alkali metals form a typically metallic lattice. The structural members of the lattice are the alkali metal *ions,* which are surrounded by a cloud of valence electrons. The latter are free to move when the temperature is raised or a voltage is applied across a piece of the metal. The atomic structure of the alkali metals accounts for their excellent thermal and electrical conductivities. Lithium, sodium, and potassium form cubic crystals but cesium and rubidium, whose ions are much larger than those of the former metals, crystallize in the hexagonal form.

Alkali Metals as Reducing Agents

Every reaction in which an alkali metal takes part involves the *reduction* of the other element or compound involved, and the *oxidation* of the alkali metal to its ion. A brief glance at the *ionization potentials* of these elements (Table 27-1) explains why they are the most powerful reducing agents known. *Each alkali metal has the lowest ionization potential of any element in its period.* With increasing atomic size, the outermost electron can be stripped away more easily. Except for little-known francium, cesium has the largest atoms and the lowest ionization potential of any member of this group.

All the alkali metals are silvery bright when freshly cut, but this condition is short-lived (Fig. 27-3). The exposed metal becomes oxidized almost immediately by oxygen in the air, and in the presence of moisture, the oxides formed react with carbon dioxide in the atmosphere to form carbonates.

27-3 Compare the luster of the freshly cut piece of sodium at the left with the dull surface of a piece of similar size exposed to the air.

$$4 \, Li + O_2 \longrightarrow 2 \, Li_2O$$
$$Li_2O + CO_2 \longrightarrow Li_2CO_3$$

Slow reaction of the metals with water vapor in the air liberates hydrogen and forms the hydroxide, which may also be converted to the carbonate by further reaction with carbon dioxide. Very rapid reactions occur when the metals react with water. A small piece of sodium (potassium or lithium) floated on water reacts vigorously to liberate hydrogen and produce sodium hydroxide (Fig. 27-4). The energy produced by the reaction may even ignite the hydrogen.

$$2 \, Na + 2 \, H_2O \longrightarrow H_2\uparrow + 2 \, NaOH$$

The alkali metals react readily and vigorously with nonmetals such as the halogens and sulfur.

$$2 \, K + Cl_2 \longrightarrow 2 \, KCl$$
$$2 \, Na + S \longrightarrow Na_2S$$
$$2 \, Cs + F_2 \longrightarrow 2 \, CsF$$

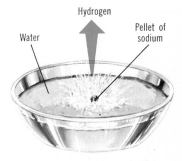

27-4 A sodium pellet reacts vigorously with water to liberate hydrogen.

27-5 The technician in both views is operating an enlarger in a photographic "darkroom." Sodium vapor light can be used at a greater intensity than light from an ordinary bulb without damaging the emulsion of the printing paper.

The reducing activity of these metals is demonstrated strikingly by their reduction of hydrogen to its rather rare *negative* oxidation state.

$$\overset{0}{2\,Na} + \overset{0}{H_2} \longrightarrow \overset{+1\,-1}{2\,NaH}$$

Sodium hydride is saltlike in appearance and ionic in nature. It has a cubic crystal structure like that of sodium chloride. When the molten hydride is electrolyzed, hydrogen gas is evolved by loss of electrons at the *anode.*

Because of their activity, the pure alkali metals are best kept under vacuum, or in an atmosphere of inert gases.

Uses of the Alkali Metals

For many decades the alkali metals represented curiosities among the metals. Reacting readily with water and oxygen, deficient in the mechanical properties associated with metals, they were seemingly without use. Today these elements are important to chemical industry because of their special properties.

The strong reducing properties of the alkali metals makes them useful in the preparation of other metals, notably titanium and zirconium.

$$TiCl_4 + 4\,Na \longrightarrow Ti + 4\,NaCl$$

This process is feasible because of the relatively low cost of the sodium in the preparation of a scarce and expensive metal. The reducing nature of sodium also makes it useful in the preparation of some types of synthetic rubber.

Because of their low melting points and excellent ability to conduct heat, sodium and potassium, in the form of an alloy which is liquid at room temperature, are used as cooling agents in certain types of nuclear reactors. In sodium vapor lamps, now being used in photographic darkrooms (Fig. 27-5) and to light foggy sections of highways, an electric current is conducted through the lamp by ionized sodium. The heated sodium vapor produces an intense yellow light.

About one-third of the more than 100,000 tons of sodium used in the United States every year is used in the manufacture of ethyl gasoline. In the process, a sodium-lead alloy reacts with ethyl bromide to form tetraethyl lead, an added ingredient in antiknock gasoline.

$$Na_4Pb + 4\,C_2H_5Br \longrightarrow 4\,NaBr + Pb(C_2H_5)_4$$

ethyl bromide   tetraethyl lead

Large quantities of sodium are used in the preparation of sodium compounds not made directly from sodium chloride. For example, sodium peroxide (Na_2O_2) and sodium cyanide ($NaCN$). The balance of the sodium produced is used as a reducing agent in the production of various organic products, ranging from alcohols to insecticides, from dyes to drugs.

The successful operation of a radio or television tube depends on the high vacuum that results when all the air is removed from inside the tube. But even the best of pumps will not remove all the air. The residual air can be removed almost entirely by coating the filament of the tube with cesium metal. When the filament is heated by an electric current flowing through it, the hot cesium metal evaporates and combines with any remaining oxygen and nitrogen. Most metals under these conditions combine with the oxygen, but only the most active combine with nitrogen. Any cesium metal that does not combine with oxygen or nitrogen forms deposits on the inner surface of the tube, giving the tube a silvery appearance. Rubidium can also be used to remove the last traces of air in high-vacuum tubes.

The next time you leave a supermarket in which the door opens automatically, stop to determine if you have just walked through a beam of light. If so, the automatic door mechanism is triggered by a photoelectric cell or "electric eye." The ease with which cesium loses electrons makes it useful in constructing electric eyes. Ordinarily, metals lose their valence electrons when heated to high temperatures. In the electric eye, this loss occurs when *light* energy strikes the cesium. When the photoelectric cell is connected in a circuit with a source of voltage, the electrons which are ejected from the metal by the light flow through the circuit.

Radioactive cesium-137 is a powerful gamma ray emitter and can be used like X rays for both therapy and photography.

QUESTIONS AND PROBLEMS

1. Describe briefly the properties in which the alkali metals differ from most other metals.

2. Why are the alkali metals the most powerful reducing agents known?

3. Why are the alkali metals usually prepared by the reduction of their hydroxides and chlorides by electricity?

27-6 This salt bed was formed by the evaporation of an ancient sea and is so internally deep that it is worked as an underground "salt mine." Compare the tunnel size and the exposed salt deposits with the size of the large trucks.

4. Why are sodium, potassium, and lithium stored in vacuum containers rather than in jars (exposed to the air) or under water?

5. Write a balanced equation for the electrolysis of (a) a solution of rubidium chloride, (b) molten cesium hydroxide.

6. Write the formulas for: lithium phosphate, cesium carbonate, rubidium nitrate, potassium hydride, cesium nitride.

COMPOUNDS OF THE ALKALI METALS

Compounds of the alkali metals, particularly those of sodium, have been part of your everyday world from infancy. These compounds are among the workhorses of the chemical industry. In your home they are found in the form of table salt in the kitchen, washing and baking soda in the pantry, lye in the basement, and soap in the bathroom. With few exceptions, all the sodium compounds in use are made from the most abundant compound of them all—sodium chloride.

Halide Salts

Most of our salt is mined from beds of salt which were formed by the evaporation of prehistoric seas (Fig. 27-6). In some mining operations extraction of salt from the earth is carried out by a process resembling that used for sulfur; fresh water is used to dissolve the salt. This underground salt often approaches 99.5 percent in purity, but even the small amount of impurity present interferes with special uses of the salt. The salt is usually purified by recrystallization.

Where no deposits of salt are found in the earth, coastal nations can obtain salt by evaporation of sea water. Careful evaporation causes the solution to become saturated first with sodium chloride, the most abundant solute. The process is stopped when a second solute approaches its point of saturation; then the precipitated salt is separated by filtration. Crystals of salt produced in this way are likely to contain small amounts of other sea water ingredients trapped within the crystals. Such salt can be purified by a series of recrystallizations. Although pure sodium chlo-

ride is not deliquescent, recall that impurities such as magnesium chloride do absorb moisture from the air and cause the familiar caking of table salt in damp weather.

The salt used in food not only serves as flavoring but also provides sodium ions essential to life. Salt is also used in preserving meat, glazing clay and stoneware, and melting ice. Fig. 27-7 illustrates some of the many uses of sodium chloride, including its use as a raw material for the preparation of other sodium compounds.

Of the remaining alkali metal compounds, only potassium chloride is found in abundance in the earth. It occurs in combination with other salts (for example, $KCl \cdot MgCl_2 \cdot 6 H_2O$) in the Stassfurt deposits in Germany or the beds of dried-up lakes in our California desert region. The remaining alkali metal halides are relatively rare in nature.

The halide salts of sodium and potassium are used in preparing silver salts for photography, while the nitrates and phosphates of these metals are important constituents of fertilizers.

Hydroxides

The hydroxides of the alkali metals are all strong bases, and, as you know, are referred to as *alkalies*. They are white solids, highly soluble in water, and strongly deliquescent. Because of the ability of concentrated alkali solutions to attack and disintegrate animal and vegetable tissues, they are also described as *caustic*. These hydroxides are made commercially by electrolysis of solutions of the metal chlorides. (In the equation below, M represents an alkali metal ion.)

$$2 MCl + 2 HOH \longrightarrow 2 MOH + H_2\uparrow + Cl_2\uparrow$$

Sodium hydroxide can also be prepared by the reaction between inexpensive and naturally abundant sodium carbonate and calcium hydroxide.

$$Na_2CO_3 + Ca(OH)_2 \longrightarrow 2 NaOH + CaCO_3\downarrow$$

The precipitated calcium carbonate that forms is filtered off, and the sodium hydroxide is recovered by evaporation of the filtrate. The proc-

The workmen above are using sodium chloride in the curing of hams. How does it retard spoilage?

Salt applied to ice-covered streets lowers the freezing point of the water surrounding it. The salt adheres to the melting ice and increases traction for cars.

This infrared spectrophotometer is invaluable in identifying organic compounds. Its prism is made of sodium chloride.

In these rows of cells, sodium chloride solution is electrolyzed to produce caustic soda (NaOH) and chlorine gas.

The unusual "pimpled" appearance on this ceramic ware is obtained by using a sodium chloride glaze.

455

ess utilizing the reaction between Na_2CO_3 and $Ca(OH)_2$ to form NaOH is called the **soda-lime process.**

Sodium hydroxide, the most widely used alkali, is also known in its impure form as *caustic soda,* or *lye.* Originally, its major use was in the manufacture of soap. While this use of the hydroxide is still of major importance, interest has shifted to its role in the manufacture of rayon. Large quantities of caustic soda are also used in neutralizing the sulfuric acid used in refining petroleum; lesser amounts are employed in the manufacture of paper pulp. In the laboratory, good use is made of the deliquescence of this compound to dry certain gases, such as oxygen, hydrogen, and ammonia.

Potassium hydroxide (KOH), *caustic potash,* has much the same properties as its sister compound, NaOH. Except for its use in the manufacture of soft soaps, potassium hydroxide finds limited use beyond the preparation of potassium compounds. It is more expensive than sodium hydroxide and, weight for weight, provides less hydroxide ion. The same differences hold true for all related potassium compounds because potassium chloride, the starting point for most of them, is more costly than common table salt. Weight for weight, the potassium compound contains less of the negative ion than does the related sodium compound.

The hydroxides of the remaining alkali metals once had no practical applications, but this is no longer true, especially for lithium hydroxide. This compound is now used in the preparation of newer types of wet cells, pharmaceutical chemicals, and multipurpose greases.

Carbonates and Bicarbonates

Cakes, soda-acid fire extinguishers and glass seem to have nothing in common; yet the soluble carbonates of sodium play a part in making each of them. Sodium bicarbonate, known also as baking soda, has spared the housewife the long hours needed to leaven dough with yeast. This compound is an ingredient in baking powders. The same compound also makes possible the soda-acid type of portable fire extinguisher, which will be studied later. Both of these uses depend on the reaction of the bicarbonate with an acid to produce carbon dioxide. (In the equation below, X stands for any negative ion.)

$$NaHCO_3 + HX \longrightarrow NaX + H_2O + CO_2\uparrow$$

The escape of CO_2 causes dough to rise; in the fire extinguisher it provides pressure to force a stream of water out of the tank.

Sodium carbonate, familiarly known as *washing soda* (and not to be confused with baking soda!) exists in the form of an efflorescent hydrate, $Na_2CO_3 \cdot 10\,H_2O$, as well as in the anhydrous form. It is an essential ingredient in the manufacture of ordinary lime glass, where it is melted together with sand and limestone. Large quantities of washing soda are also used in the manufacture of soap. Since solutions of sodium carbonate are strongly basic by hydrolysis, the carbonate ion is a strong Brønsted–Lowry base.

$$CO_3^{-2} + HOH \rightleftharpoons HCO_3^- + OH^-$$

The basic property of sodium carbonate solution makes it useful in removing grease and dirt, and accounts for its common name, washing soda. Because natural deposits of sodium carbonate and sodium bicarbonate are limited, these compounds are manufactured by an efficient and inexpensive process devised by Ernest Solvay, a Belgian chemist.

The Solvay Process

You can easily *simulate Solvay's process in the laboratory.*

Place 250 ml of concentrated ammonium hydroxide in a wide-mouthed bottle and saturate it with sodium chloride. *With a forceps* drop several small pieces of dry ice (solid CO_2) into the flask. Does a white precipitate form? If so, filter out the precipitate, blot it dry, and heat it. Bubble through limewater any gas that forms. What compound is present in the precipitate? Now evaporate the filtrate and heat it with solid calcium

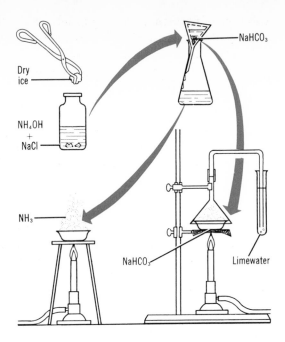

Dry ice

NH₄OH + NaCl

NaHCO₃

NH₃

NaHCO₃

Limewater

$$NaCl + NH_4HCO_3 \longrightarrow NaHCO_3\downarrow + NH_4Cl$$

Ordinarily, *the reaction is reversible,* but at the temperature employed, the sodium bicarbonate is almost insoluble in the reaction medium and precipitates out of the solution, shifting the equilibrium to the right. This shift is further aided by keeping the gaseous ingredients under pressure (Le Chatelier's Principle).

Washing soda can be prepared from the sodium bicarbonate by gentle heating, which drives off carbon dioxide and water vapor. The gas is recovered and reused in the process.

$$2\,NaHCO_3 \xrightarrow{\Delta} Na_2CO_3 + H_2O + CO_2\uparrow$$

Industrial sodium carbonate is known as *soda ash.* The pure material can be obtained as a hydrate by recrystallizing the sodium carbonate from a water solution.

The Solvay process (Fig. 27-8) is efficient in its utilization of by-products and inexpensive raw materials. Carbon dioxide is provided by the decomposition of limestone.

$$CaCO_3 \xrightarrow{\Delta} CaO + CO_2\uparrow$$
$$\text{(lime)}$$

The lime formed is reacted with the by-product ammonium chloride to produce ammonia gas, which is returned to the process.

$$CaO + 2\,NH_4Cl \longrightarrow CaCl_2 + 2\,H_2O + 2\,NH_3\uparrow$$

Only the calcium chloride cannot be returned to the process, but it finds applications in other directions.

Potassium bicarbonate and carbonate, which have very limited uses, cannot be made by imitating the Solvay process since potassium bicarbonate is too soluble in water. Its preparation must await your more advanced study.

Nitrates

Both sodium nitrate and potassium nitrate occur naturally in arid regions; sodium nitrate also exists in large deposits on the coasts of Chile and Peru. The demand for sodium nitrate decreased when it was no longer needed as a raw

hydroxide. Is ammonia given off? If so, what compound was present in the filtrate?

The ammonium hydroxide, sodium chloride, and carbon dioxide react to form sodium bicarbonate and ammonium chloride.

$$NH_4OH + NaCl + CO_2 \longrightarrow NH_4Cl + NaHCO_3\downarrow$$

The sodium bicarbonate, when heated, releases carbon dioxide which turns the limewater milky. The odor of ammonia indicates that the product in the filtrate is ammonium chloride.

The **Solvay process** for making Na_2CO_3 utilizes essentially the same compounds you used, water, sodium chloride, carbon dioxide, and ammonia—inexpensive and plentiful raw materials. A concentrated solution of sodium chloride, at about 15° C, is saturated with carbon dioxide and ammonia gas *under pressure.* The *gaseous* ingredients combine to form ammonium bicarbonate.

$$NH_3 + CO_2 + H_2O \longrightarrow NH_4HCO_3$$

This reacts with the sodium chloride to form sodium bicarbonate and ammonium chloride.

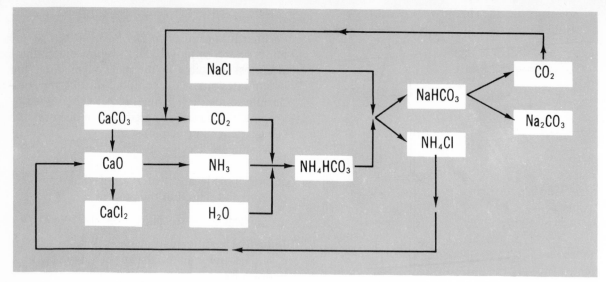

27-8 The flow chart of the Solvay process indicates that when sodium carbonate (far right) is produced from sodium chloride, carbon dioxide, ammonia, and water, the only by-product not returned to the reaction is calcium chloride.

material for the preparation of nitric acid. When it was discovered that the soil could be fertilized with the aid of chemicals alone, the demand for the nitrates of sodium and potassium again increased. Today sodium nitrate is produced by reacting sodium carbonate with nitric acid.

$$Na_2CO_3 + 2\,HNO_3 \longrightarrow$$
$$2\,NaNO_3 + H_2O + CO_2\uparrow$$

Potassium nitrate is manufactured by reacting sodium nitrate and potassium chloride, both of which are inexpensive and abundant. Potassium nitrate is used to pickle meats and as an ingredient in fertilizers and some explosive mixtures.

Compounds of Other Alkali Metals

Compounds of the remaining alkali metals were once known and used only in the laboratory. While this is still largely true for compounds of cesium and rubidium, the picture has changed greatly for lithium compounds. Lithium chloride solutions are used in air conditioning, where the amount of water vapor absorbed from the air varies with the concentration of the solutions. The tempering of metals may be performed by dipping the hot metal into molten lithium chlo-

ride, nitrate, or carbonate instead of into oil or water. Many compounds of the metal are being used as constituents of new and improved materials in the glazing of porcelain and ceramics. Certain lithium soaps are incorporated into new types of lubricating greases. Some lithium compounds, for example, lithium aluminum hydride, are, like the metal, powerful reducing agents in the synthesis of organic compounds.

QUESTIONS AND PROBLEMS

1. Give the chemical formula for each of the following: caustic soda, caustic potash, lye, baking soda, washing soda, soda ash.

2. Write a balanced equation for the (a) commercial preparation of potassium hydroxide, (b) reaction between sodium bicarbonate and sulfuric acid.

3. Describe the preparation of sodium carbonate by the Solvay process. Include equations, where useful.

4. (a) Write an equation to indicate what happens when hydrated sodium carbonate remains ex-

posed to the air. (b) What process is demonstrated by this reaction?

5. What are the main uses of (a) sodium and potassium nitrates, (b) lithium compounds?

HYDROGEN

As you know, all the elements with a single electron in their outermost shells are metals, except hydrogen. Although the latter is often placed in the alkali metal group because of its lone electron, there has as yet been devised *no* form of the periodic table in which hydrogen has been placed satisfactorily. In fact, some workers have devised forms of the table in which hydrogen is set apart from all other elements. In a sense, there is justification for this practice, since hydrogen is uniquely different from all other elements. Recall that an atom of hydrogen-1 is the only atom without a neutron in its nucleus.

Hydrogen in Compounds

Although the nuclear charge in the hydrogen atom is smaller than that of the alkali metals, its lone electron is very close to the nucleus and is not screened from it by intervening shells of electrons. As a result, the attractive force on this electron is much greater than that on the single electron in the outermost orbits of the alkali metals. This is readily observed by comparing the ionization potential of hydrogen with the ionization potentials of the alkali metals. Further study of Tables 27-1 and 23-2 reveals that the ionization potential of hydrogen is similar to those of the halogens.

Hydrogen is found combined with many elements. When it combines with elements more electronegative than itself, such as oxygen, polar covalent compounds are always formed. In forming compounds with the halogens, hydrogen acts in a manner similar to that of an alkali metal—but the compounds are covalent rather than ionic (Fig. 27-9). In most compounds hydrogen forms covalent bonds, but it may combine with the alkali and alkaline earth metals to form ionic hydrides, such as NaH and CaH_2. In these com-

27-9 In covalently bonded hydrogen chloride, hydrogen is in the $+1$ oxidation state. When hydrogen reacts with sodium to form ionic sodium hydride, hydrogen is in the unusual -1 oxidation state.

pounds in which hydrogen is combined with elements of lower electronegativities, hydrogen exists as a *negative* ion. In hydrides, hydrogen duplicates a property of the halogens; it gains 1 electron to complete its electron shell. These hydrides form ionic crystals and conduct electricity when melted, hydrogen being evolved at the anode. Hydrogen is indeed a unique element.

The Preparation of Hydrogen

You probably remember that hydrogen gas, which was first prepared in 1766, is a colorless, odorless gas that burns, but does not support combustion. If you have not already investigated these properties in the laboratory, you may want to do so now. You could prepare hydrogen by the electrolysis of water or by adding dilute sulfuric or hydrochloric acid to zinc. Very pure hydrogen can be prepared by reacting calcium hydride with water, but the hydride is expensive. *A method you might try* is the reaction between aluminum (or zinc) and concentrated sodium hydroxide. (*Handle concentrated NaOH cautiously.*)

Arrange the apparatus as shown below to collect hydrogen by water displacement. Place about ten lumps of aluminum in the flask and very carefully cover it with 25 ml of concentrated sodium hydroxide solution.

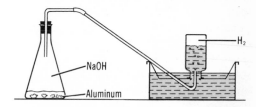

When the reaction becomes steady, collect two bottles of the gas. Use the burning splint test to prove that the gas in the first bottle is hydrogen. How can you use the second bottle to prove that hydrogen burns but does not support combustion?

The aluminum reacts with the sodium hydroxide to yield hydrogen and the complex salt, sodium aluminate.

$$2\,Al + 2\,NaOH + 6\,H_2O \longrightarrow$$
$$3\,H_2\uparrow + 2\,NaAl(OH)_4$$

Commercially, hydrogen is prepared by the electrolysis of water, or as a by-product in the electrolysis of brine. It is also made by the cracking (splitting at high temperatures) of gaseous compounds of carbon and hydrogen. Large quantities of hydrogen have been prepared for some years by reacting steam with hot coke (carbon) or carbon compounds, such as methane (CH_4). In these reactions hydrogen and carbon monoxide are produced. The carbon monoxide reacts with additional steam to produce more hydrogen and carbon dioxide. This mixture is passed through water. The carbon dioxide is dissolved in the water under pressure; the hydrogen bubbles through the water and is collected.

27-10 When a bit of lithium is placed in a beaker of water, "sparks" fly in all directions. The highly reactive lithium acts as a reducing agent, releasing hydrogen from water and producing lithium hydroxide.

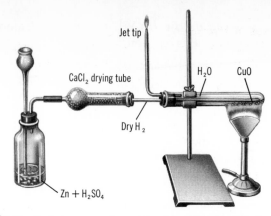

27-11 Dry hydrogen passed over hot copper oxide reduces the copper oxide to free copper and combines with oxygen from the oxide to form water.

Hydrogen and Reduction

When hydrogen is prepared by reacting metals and acids, or active metals and water, the metal acts as a *reducing agent,* reducing the hydrogen *ions* to molecules. As an example, consider the reaction between zinc and hydrochloric acid.

$$\overset{0}{Zn} + 2\,\overset{+1}{HCl} \longrightarrow \overset{+2}{ZnCl_2} + \overset{0}{H_2}$$
$$Zn^0 - 2\,e^- \longrightarrow Zn^{+2} \quad \text{(oxidation)}$$
$$2\,H^+ + 2\,e^- \longrightarrow H_2^0 \quad \text{(reduction)}$$

Active metals such as lithium (Fig. 27-10) and sodium replace hydrogen in water to yield the element and a hydroxide of the metal. Here the metal serves as a reducing agent.

$$2\,\overset{0}{Li} + 2\,\overset{+1}{HOH} \longrightarrow \overset{0}{H_2}\uparrow + 2\,\overset{+1}{LiOH}$$

Hydrogen *molecules* can be demonstrated to be reducing agents by the procedure indicated in Fig. 27-11. When hydrogen is passed over cold cupric oxide, no change is noted. But shortly after heating is begun, two observations can be made. The first is that a mist which forms on the wall of the tube finally collects into droplets; these are droplets of water. At the same time, the black copper oxide is transformed into a shiny red solid —copper oxide is reduced to copper.

$$\overset{+2}{Cu}O + \overset{0}{H_2} \longrightarrow \overset{0}{Cu} + \overset{+1}{H_2}O$$

$$H_2^0 + 2\,e^- \longrightarrow 2\,H^+ \quad \text{(oxidation)}$$
$$Cu^{+2} + 2\,e^- \longrightarrow Cu^0 \quad \text{(reduction)}$$

Uses of Hydrogen

Hydrogen finds considerable use as a fuel, whether alone or in gaseous mixtures. Its use in the oxyhydrogen welding torches is well known. In the atomic hydrogen torch (Fig. 27-12) some molecules of hydrogen are split into atoms that recombine and give an intense heat of about 5000° C. With the advent of the fusion bomb, deuterium and tritium, two isotopes of hydrogen, have taken on added importance. They are fused together in various thermonuclear reactions to release the tremendous energy of the hydrogen bomb (page 363).

A major use of the element is in **hydrogenation** reactions in which hydrogen is added to compounds of carbon. The best-known illustration involves a reaction with vegetable oils, such as cottonseed oil. Hydrogenation changes cottonseed oil, a liquid by-product of once limited use, into a solid material used widely as a shortening.

Your study of the group IA elements reveals that its first member, hydrogen, is a unique element within the group. The remaining members are the alkali family of metals. Though the alkali metals are much less dense than typical metals, these same metals have other unusual properties that render them unfit for the usual applications of metals. The alkali metals are comparatively soft and react with water; we could not therefore

take advantage of their low densities in constructing either buildings or ships. The sodium family of metals is only the first group of metals to be studied. Do the group IIA metals overcome the shortcomings of the group IA metals? We shall pursue this possibility in the next chapter.

QUESTIONS AND PROBLEMS

1. (a) Justify the placing of hydrogen in group IA. (b) In what properties is hydrogen similar to the halogens?

2. Under what circumstances does hydrogen form (a) covalent compounds, (b) ionic compounds?

3. Write an equation for the preparation of hydrogen by the reaction of zinc with concentrated sodium hydroxide.

4. Demonstrate that hydrogen molecules can act as (a) reducing agents, (b) oxidizing agents.

VALUE OF THE CONCEPT

THE CONCEPT

The alkali metals, which represent the first family of metallic elements to be studied, are atypical metals. Physically, these metals are different from other metals; in particular, they are much less dense and considerably softer. Chemically, the alkali metals react much more vigorously than do most other metals, whether it be with water, acids, oxygen, or nonmetals. The reason for this unusual behavior lies in the low ionization potentials of these elements. Each has the lowest ionization potential of all the elements in the period of which it is the first member. As a family, these elements have substantially lower ionization potentials than any other family in the periodic table. In consequence, all the reactions of the alkali metals involve their action as reducing agents; these elements are the most vigorous reducing agents known. This property explains

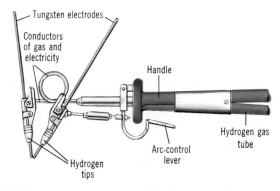

27-12 In an atomic hydrogen torch, diatomic molecules of hydrogen gas are split into atoms of hydrogen by an electric arc. The combining of atomic hydrogen with oxygen from the air produces the extremely high temperatures needed for high-speed welding and cutting.

why these metals can be prepared only by electrolysis of their molten hydroxides and chlorides.

The alkali metals cannot be used as most other metals are because they lack such properties as hardness, strength, and high melting point; nevertheless, they do find special applications. The only alkali metal compounds that are abundant in nature are the chlorides of sodium and potassium; even the nitrates of these two elements are much less plentiful. The chlorides, are, therefore, the usual starting point in the preparation of the other compounds of these elements. Particularly important in this connection is the preparation of sodium bicarbonate and sodium carbonate from table salt by the Solvay process. This process, utilizing, in addition to water, carbon dioxide and ammonia as raw materials, demonstrates the application of chemical principles in guiding the course of a chemical reaction. The main alkali metal compounds in industrial use are the halides, hydroxides, nitrates, carbonates, and phosphates.

Although hydrogen is a nonmetal, it is included in group IA by virtue of its single orbital electron. But here the similarity ends, for there is a marked contrast between the other properties of hydrogen and the alkali metals. The dominant principle in the reactions of hydrogen is its covalent bonding, which leads to diatomic molecules (unlike the alkali metals) as well as covalent compounds. Hydrogen forms compounds with members of all the periodic groups except the "inert" gases. When it combines with the strongly electron-lending metals of groups IA and IIA, hydrogen enters into its rare ionic (-1) state. Though hydrogen compounds of the remaining elements are covalent, compounds of the halogen elements exhibit marked polar covalence.

Hydrogen is prepared commercially by splitting hydrogen compounds either electrically, as in the electrolysis of water (or brine), or thermally, as with certain carbon-hydrogen compounds. In the laboratory the gas is prepared by the replacement of hydrogen from nonoxidizing acids by active metals (Zn, Mg), or from strong bases by elements such as aluminum or silicon.

USING THE CONCEPT

Using the Basic Concept

1. (a) In the commercial preparation of sodium metal, why is the sodium chloride molten? (b) Write oxidation-reduction half-reactions for the electrode reactions in this process.

2. (a) What properties prevent the use of the alkali metals in construction work? (b) List the chief uses of each alkali metal.

3. (a) What members of the alkali metals and halogen families should react together most vigorously? (b) Why?

4. (a) Why is hydrogen frequently set apart from all other elements in the periodic table?

5. (a) Why is sodium bicarbonate used in baking cakes? (b) Would sodium carbonate be a good substitute? Why?

6. How does the Solvay process apply equilibrium principles to the preparation of sodium bicarbonate and carbonate?

7. Why is cesium used in (a) electric eyes, (b) television tubes?

8. (a) In what compounds does hydrogen have an oxidation number of -1? (b) In terms of electronegativity, when does hydrogen form ionic compounds? covalent compounds?

9. Why are lithium, sodium, and potassium not used in photoelectric cells as is cesium?

10. (a) List one or more common (or commercial) names for each of the following compounds: Na_2CO_3, $NaHCO_3$, $NaOH$, KOH. (b) Give an important commercial use of each of these compounds.

11. (a) How does the crystal structure of lithium, sodium, and potassium differ from that of cesium and rubidium? (b) Account for this difference.

12. Write equations to illustrate the preparation of hydrogen by four different methods.

13. In the halogen family, activity decreases

with increasing atomic number, but in the alkali metal family, activity *increases* with increasing atomic number. Account for this difference.

Relating Terms Within the Concept

From the terms below select the *italicized* term that best completes each of the following statements. Do not use a term more than once.

baking soda, chlorides, electrons, hydrides, hydroxides, ionization potentials, lye, oxidizing agents, reducing agents, soda-lime process, Solvay process, washing soda.

1. When exposed to light, cesium emits _____.
2. Hydrogen is in the −1 oxidation state in _____.
3. The alkali metals have low _____.
4. The alkali metals are excellent _____.
5. Sodium hydroxide is also known as caustic soda or _____.
6. Sodium carbonate is prepared by the _____.
7. Sodium, potassium, and lithium are prepared commercially by electrolysis of their molten _____.
8. Efflorescent $Na_2CO_3 \cdot 10 H_2O$ is known as _____.

Solving Problems Within the Concept

1. How many grams of chromium oxide (Cr_2O_3) can be reduced to the metal by the use of 10 grams of sodium?
2. What volume of carbon dioxide (**STP**) will be produced when a solution containing 10 grams of hydrogen chloride is reacted with sodium bicarbonate?
3. Calculate the percent by weight of (a) sodium in sodium nitrate, (b) potassium in potassium hydride.
4. How many grams of sodium carbonate will be produced when 21 grams of sodium bicarbonate are heated?
5. What volume (**STP**) of ammonia gas is used to produce 1,000 grams of sodium

bicarbonate through the Solvay process?
6. What weight of calcium hydride is used to produce 6 liters of hydrogen (**STP**)?
7. What weight of potassium nitrate will contain the same weight of nitrate *ion* as 850 grams of sodium nitrate?
8. What is the percent of water of crystallization in hydrated sodium carbonate?

Applying the Concept

1. Write an equation for the reaction between (a) cesium and nitrogen, (b) potassium hydride and water.
2. Why is hydrogen, a nonmetal, included in the activity series of metals?
3. As the atomic weights of the alkali metals increase, their densities increase, but not in the same ratio. Why?
4. Although cesium has a smaller ionization potential than does lithium, their electrode potentials are close in value. What factors might account for this condition?
5. Neither concentrated nitric nor sulfuric acid can be used in the preparation of hydrogen from a metal and an acid. Why?
6. (a) What gases already studied could *not* be dried by passing them over solid sodium hydroxide? (b) Why? (c) What drying agents could be used?
7. The chlorides of the alkali metals from lithium to rubidium crystallize in the same form (face-centered cubic), but cesium chloride crystallizes in the body-centered cubic form. How might this difference be explained?

Reading Further

Crystals and Crystal Growing, by Alan Holden and Phylis Singer, Garden City, N.Y., Doubleday, 1960. Information about crystal structure and the way crystals form, including "recipes" for growing them.

"Humphry Davy," by L. P. Williams, *Scientific American*, June 1960. Davy's isolation of the alkali metals was only one of many accomplishments.

28

The Alkaline Earth Metals

Both marble and limestone have had a long history as building materials. The Roman Coliseum was faced with travertine marble which, unfortunately, was stolen during the Renaissance and used in the interior of villas. The Romans also built with limestone and developed a type of lime mortar and even a concrete made from lime and volcanic ash. After Roman times the skill required to make concrete fell into disuse and not until the 1840's did the first concrete structures reappear in England. High quality concrete construction began in the United States when the process for making Portland cement was introduced from England.

Limestone, marble, concrete, and cement contain compounds of calcium, a member of the group IIA elements. Are all the elements of this group used in the building trades? If not, how are they used?

THE ALKALINE EARTHS

The elements in the group following the alkali metals in the periodic table are known collectively as the **alkaline earth metals** (Table 28-1). Though they have an outermost shell of 2 electrons, they show a marked similarity to the alkali metals. With the exception of beryllium, these elements are silvery bright and have lower melting and boiling points than most metals. Although denser than water, these metals (except radium) are much less dense than typical metals such as iron, copper, and lead. They are harder than the alkali metals but, once again excluding beryllium, are not as hard as typical metals.

Most of them react readily with water to yield hydrogen and a hydroxide of the metal, but this reaction is less vigorous than that between the alkali metals and water. The ionization potentials of these group IIA metals, while higher than those of the group IA elements, are still relatively low. We should expect the group IIA elements to be strong reducing agents and to react readily with oxygen, other nonmetals, and acids. This is indeed the case; the alkaline earth elements, like the alkali metals, react with nitrogen to form nitrides and with hydrogen to form ionic hydrides. The low ionization potentials of the group IIA elements result in vigorous reactions forming quite stable compounds. Because of their stability, these compounds can be efficiently reduced to the metal only by electrolysis of their molten compounds. These elements rank high in

Table 28-1 **THE GROUP IIA ELEMENTS**

Element	Atomic number	Atomic weight	Electron configuration	Density (g/ml, 20° C)	Melting point (°C)	Boiling point (°C)	State and color	Ionization potential	Oxidation state
Beryllium	4	9.0122	2 2	1.8	1278	2970	White solid	9.3	+2
Magnesium	12	24.312	2 8 2	1.74	651	1107	Silvery solid	7.6	+2
Calcium	20	40.08	2 8 8 2	1.55	842	1240	Silvery solid	6.1	+2
Strontium	38	87.62	2 8 18 8 2	2.54	800	1150	Silvery solid	5.7	+2
Barium	56	137.34	2 8 18 18 8 2	3.5	850	1140	Silvery solid	5.2	+2
Radium	88	[226]	2 8 18 32 18 8 2	5 (?)	700	1140	Silvery solid	5.3	+2

the electrochemical series. Calcium, strontium, barium, and radium are on a par with the alkali metals in this respect.

Beryllium and magnesium differ from the other members of group IIA in several ways. For example, they are harder, the hardness of beryllium equaling that of iron or nickel. Ordinarily both of these metals decompose water only if the metal is powdered and the water is boiling, or if steam is passed over the heated metal. If the surface of magnesium is freed of its usual oxide coating (by treatment with mercuric chloride solution), the metal reacts with cold water as do all the other family members. Beryllium shows considerable resemblance to aluminum, a member of the group IIIA elements, while magnesium bears some resemblance to zinc in the group IIB elements. Because of a special property, radioactivity, radium was considered separately in Unit 3. Chemically, however, radium is typical of the family, being silvery bright, tarnishing readily in air to form a nitride. Like the other metals of the group, radium reacts with water and the nonmetals. Compounds of the group IIA metals are often hydrated. The alkaline earth metal ions are *smaller* than those of the group IA family, and also bear a greater nuclear charge. Thus, a greater charge is concentrated in a smaller volume, and the negative end of the water dipole is more readily attracted to the ions, forming hydrates.

Occurrence and Preparation of the Alkaline Earth Metals

The compounds of the alkaline earth metals, unlike those of the group IA elements, are usually insoluble in water. Consequently, the alkaline earth metals are found in the crust of the earth in the form of sulfates, carbonates, and phosphates. Since magnesium sulfate is a soluble compound, it is sometimes a constituent of mineral spring water. Although beryllium is widely distributed, its main source is the mineral beryl, a complex beryllium aluminum silicate. Transparent forms of this mineral occur as emeralds and aquamarine (Fig. 28-1). Radium, a product of the radioactive decay of uranium, is found in pitch-

28-1 When expertly cut and polished, these two transparent forms of beryl —an emerald on the left and an aquamarine on the right—will become a number of beautiful, if relatively expensive, gems.

blende and carnotite, minerals of the latter element. The ocean is a vast reservoir of the relatively few soluble compounds of these elements.

The commercial preparation of group IIA elements utilizes both of these sources, the crust of the earth and the sea. Whatever compound or process is used, the final step usually involves electrolytic reduction. Each of the metals can be prepared by the electrolysis of its molten chloride. The chlorides are prepared by reacting naturally occurring carbonates, oxides, or hydroxides of these metals with hydrochloric acid.

$$MgCO_3 + 2\,HCl \longrightarrow MgCl_2 + H_2O + CO_2\uparrow$$
$$BeO + 2\,HCl \longrightarrow BeCl_2 + H_2O$$
$$Ca(OH)_2 + 2\,HCl \longrightarrow CaCl_2 + 2\,H_2O$$

As an example of the preparation of these metals, consider two processes for isolating magnesium from its compounds. Magnesium is harvested from sea water by a process which owes its efficiency to the low cost of the materials involved as well as to the virtually unlimited amount of ocean water available (Fig. 28-2). To obtain magnesium, sea water is treated with a solution of calcium hydroxide made by roasting oyster shells and limestone, rich in calcium carbonate, and reacting the oxide produced with water.

28-2 Magnesium is recovered from sea water in these huge Dorr tanks. Treatment with calcium hydroxide causes the magnesium to settle as magnesium hydroxide, which imparts a milky appearance to the water. The hydroxide is drawn off from the base of the tank.

$$CaCO_3 \xrightarrow{\Delta} CaO + CO_2\uparrow$$
$$CaO + H_2O \longrightarrow Ca(OH)_2$$

The magnesium ions in the sea water are precipitated in the form of magnesium hydroxide by a reaction with calcium hydroxide.

$$Ca^{+2} + 2\,OH^- + Mg^{+2} \longrightarrow Mg(OH)_2\downarrow + Ca^{+2}$$

The precipitated hydroxide is filtered, washed, and treated with hydrochloric acid to yield the chloride, which is then dried. The chloride is then electrolyzed in the molten state.

$$MgCl_2 \xrightarrow{DC} Mg + Cl_2\uparrow$$

Another method of producing magnesium utilizes dolomite, the most abundant magnesium compound in the earth's crust. Dolomite is a carbonate of both magnesium and calcium ($CaCO_3$, $MgCO_3$). The rock is ground and roasted to form the mixed oxides. When the mixed oxides are combined with ferrosilicon (an alloy of iron and silicon), and the mixture is heated in a vacuum to a temperature of $1150°$ C or higher, the calcium oxide combines with the ferrosilicon to form a slag. Simultaneously, the magnesium is vaporized and condensed.

Uses of the Alkaline Earth Metals

Magnesium and beryllium find their greatest use in the preparation of **alloys.** *An alloy is a combination of two or more elements, at least one of which is a metal, which has metallic properties.* Such combinations are made in order to eliminate an undesirable property of one metal or to improve another. Both aluminum and magnesium are light metals, but neither alone is mechanically very strong. Alloys of the two, containing from 10 to 30 percent magnesium, are known as *magnalium* alloys. These alloys are not only light but are also much stronger than the individual metals of which they are composed. Such alloys are used for airplane parts, extension ladders, and lightweight garden furniture. Even lighter alloys serving the same purposes are made by alloying 90 to 95 percent magnesium with aluminum and small amounts of copper and zinc. The addition of small amounts of manganese increases the resistance of these alloys to corrosion.

Beryllium metal is transparent to X rays (a property of atoms of low atomic number) and is therefore used for "windows" in X-ray tubes. The major use of beryllium today is in the preparation of alloys with copper and nickel. Beryllium equals magnesium in density, but it is much harder and tougher. The addition of 4 percent of beryllium to copper produces a bronze that acquires, by heat treatment, strength and hardness far beyond those of any other copper alloy. Beryllium bronze is noteworthy for its elastic properties, in which it exceeds those of steel (Fig. 28-3). The alloy also has a "fatigue limit" far beyond that of steel. Hand tools made from this alloy are unusual in that they do not spark when dropped or struck, a fine safety feature when fire and explosion must be prevented. Such tools find good use in the chemical, explosive, and petroleum industries. Beryllium-nickel alloys, besides being strong and tough, are resistant to the action of sea water. They are used to make ships' propellers and engine parts.

The remaining alkaline earth metals have limited use. Calcium, active enough to combine with nitrogen as well as with oxygen, is used to remove dissolved air from molten metals. Because of their great affinity for oxygen, strontium and barium are also used. For the same reason, calcium and barium are used to provide the very high vacuum needed in a radio or television tube by removing final traces of air. A small amount of calcium alloyed with lead increases the hardness of the latter. The use of radium in therapy has already been considered. Traces of radium compounds mixed with zinc sulfide provide the luminous coating for the hands and numerals of clocks and watches. The radiation from the radium strikes the zinc sulfide, which emits tiny flashes of light.

The alkaline earth elements find their greatest use in the form of their compounds, those of calcium being most important because of their great abundance in nature. Let us consider therefore the compounds of the group IIA elements most involved in industrial processes and in daily life.

28-3 Beryllium-bronze was selected for these underwater components of the transoceanic cable system because of the high strength and corrosion resistance of this beryllium-copper alloy.

QUESTIONS AND PROBLEMS

1. (a) In what one important respect do compounds of the alkaline earth metals differ from compounds of the alkali metals? (b) What is the importance of each of the following minerals: beryl, carnotite, pitchblende, dolomite?

2. (a) Describe briefly the preparation of magnesium from sea water. (b) Why are calcium and beryllium prepared by the electrolytic reduction of their compounds?

3. (a) What are the main uses of magnesium and beryllium? (b) What common property of calcium, strontium, and barium accounts for many of their uses?

4. Write electron equations for the reactions between: (a) strontium and water, (b) magnesium and bromine.

THE COMPOUNDS OF CALCIUM

The most abundant calcium compound in the earth is calcium carbonate ($CaCO_3$) which occurs in a number of forms such as calcite, aragonite, and limestone. The shells of most marine animals consist of calcium carbonate. When the animals die their shells slowly sink to the bottom of the ocean. Here, in time, the calcium carbonate in the accumulated shell deposits is changed into beds of *limestone*, a sedimentary rock. These beds are shaped into mountain ranges by the uplift of the ocean bottom. Some layers of limestone are also subjected to intense heat and pressure which transforms (metamorphoses) the limestone into marble. Calcite, a crystalline form of calcium carbonate, is shown in Fig. 28-4. Calcite, which is transparent, is unusual because it produces a double image of objects seen through it.

Properties and Uses of Calcium Carbonate

Both marble and limestone, quarried in many of our states, are employed for the facing of many modern buildings. Limestone also enters into construction indirectly since it is used in making glass and cement. Its greatest contribution to modern building comes in another way—the metallurgy of iron ore. In the extraction of iron, limestone is added to the blast furnace to remove any silicious (silicon-bearing) materials present in the concentrated ore.

Carbonates react with hydronium ions to form carbonic acid which decomposes into carbon dioxide and water.

$$2\,H_3O^+ + CO_3^{-2} \longrightarrow H_2CO_3 + 2\,H_2O$$
$$H_2CO_3 \longrightarrow H_2O + CO_2\uparrow$$

This reaction makes powdered limestone useful in neutralizing acid soils because it transforms the hydronium ions of the soil acid into neutral water.

$$CaCO_3 + \underbrace{2\,H_3O^+ + 2\,X^-}_{\text{soil acid}} \longrightarrow$$
$$Ca^{+2} + 2\,X^- + 3\,H_2O + CO_2\uparrow$$

Any carbonate will effectively neutralize the soil. But while an excess of sodium carbonate is injurious to the soil (being strongly basic by hydrolysis), an excess of *insoluble* calcium carbonate has no harmful effect.

Another important application of calcium carbonate is as the starting point for the preparation of most other calcium compounds. For example, reaction with acids such as nitric or hydrobromic produces the corresponding salt.

$$CaCO_3 + 2\,HNO_3 \longrightarrow Ca(NO_3)_2 + H_2O + CO_2\uparrow$$
$$CaCO_3 + 2\,HBr \longrightarrow Ca(Br)_2 + H_2O + CO_2\uparrow$$

28-4 Calcite, a crystalline form of calcium carbonate, is the chief mineral in limestone and marble. In its crystals it has the unusual property of double refraction. Observe also the flat surface of the cleavage planes.

the limestone into ... Calcite, a ... form of calcium ... nate, is shown in Calcite, which ... transparent, is ... unusua it produce ... double image ... obj through it.

The Decomposition of Calcium Carbonate

Limestone or marble serves as the starting point for the preparation of calcium compounds in still another way. *A simple investigation* will serve to make clear the chemistry behind this method.

> Wash thoroughly a marble chip and allow it to stand in distilled water for 10 minutes.

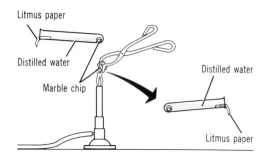

Test the liquid with pink litmus paper. Is any change observed? Wash another marble chip, hold it in a pair of tongs, and heat it intensely for 15–30 minutes. Now drop the hot chip into a test tube one-quarter full of distilled water. Shake the contents briefly and test this liquid with pink litmus paper. This time, the paper turns blue. What ion is formed?

Calcium carbonate decomposes when heated to form calcium oxide. The calcium oxide then reacts with water to form calcium hydroxide.

$$CaCO_3 \longrightarrow CaO + CO_2\uparrow$$
$$CaO + H_2O \longrightarrow Ca(OH)_2$$

The calcium oxide made in this manner is known as *lime*.

The Preparation of Cement

In the manufacture of cement, a mixture of limestone and clay (an aluminum silicate) is heated in a rotary kiln (Fig. 28-5). The reaction between these materials forms small, pebble-sized lumps of calcium aluminum silicates, called *clinkers*. When cool, the clinkers are ground into a fine powder and mixed with about 2 percent

28-5 In a cement kiln, ground limestone and clay are fed into the upper end of the inclined, rotating cylinder. When these compounds meet the flame from the fuel gas at the opposite end, clinkers are formed.

of powdered gypsum (calcium sulfate). The latter helps to control the speed with which the cement sets.

In use, cement is mixed with water and sand, the latter providing bulk. The changes which occur when cement sets or hardens are complex, involving a series of hydrations of the compounds in the cement. These changes occur in slow stages, so that cement does not reach its full strength until many months after the initial setting. Concrete is made by mixing cement with water, sand, and crushed rock or gravel. Where great strength is required, steel bars and wire mesh are used to form *reinforced concrete.* Since the setting of cement involves reaction with water, cement and concrete will harden under water. This unusual property accounts for its widespread use in underwater construction, such as bridge supports.

Glass

Glass for windows, tumblers, mirrors, ashtrays, and other household articles is made by heating a mixture of sand (SiO_2), limestone, and washing soda (Na_2CO_3) in the type of furnace shown in Fig. 28-6. The raw materials are fed in at one end of the furnace, melted together for a period of days, and withdrawn at the other end when reactions are complete. The reactions produce a mixture of calcium and sodium silicates.

$$CaCO_3 + SiO_2 \longrightarrow CaSiO_3 + CO_2\uparrow$$
$$Na_2CO_3 + SiO_2 \longrightarrow Na_2SiO_3 + CO_2\uparrow$$

In the making of bottles, molten glass is placed in molds having the shape of the bottle desired. A stream of compressed air then forces the glass against the surface of the mold. This air pressure is maintained until the glass has cooled to a solid in the shape desired; then the mold is opened and the bottle removed. To make plate glass, a horizontal iron bar is lowered into the molten glass and slowly withdrawn, carrying with it a thin sheet of viscous material which hardens as it cools. The sheet is then laid flat on a polishing table where both sides are made smooth (Fig. 28-7). Since uneven cooling produces strains which make the glass brittle and likely to shatter, all finished glass articles must be cooled slowly to room temperature. Slow, even cooling is achieved by moving the finished glass through ovens (called lehrs) in which the temperature is reduced gradually. This treatment is known as **annealing.**

Special glass is made by variations in the formula. The more lustrous glass desired for cut

28-6 The technician is removing from the test furnace a glass "melt" contained in a platinum crucible. Note the visual and body protection.

28-7 A continuous sheet of plate glass emerges with a clear, jewellike finish from this massive polishing machine. The trick is not so much in making the continuous sheet, or polishing it, as in cutting it afterward without breakage—then storing or shipping it safely.

introducing a blast of steam or air. This technique insures that the reaction will be essentially complete. Small quantities of quicklime of lower quality are produced in vertical kilns (Fig. 28-8).

The manufacture of paper pulp, dehairing of hides before tanning in leather manufacture, water-softening, recovery of by-product ammonia in the Solvay process (Chapter 27), and the manufacture of rubber, varnish, and soda-lime brick require an annual production of eight million tons of lime. Mixed with sulfur powder, lime is used as an insecticide in the form of a lime-sulfur spray. Alone, it is used to neutralize acid soils quickly. It is also used as a dehydrating agent.

Calcium Hydroxide

If a lump of calcium metal is cut into small pieces, the exposed surface, similar to that of the

glass is made by replacing the lime and washing soda of ordinary window glass with lead oxide and potassium carbonate. Glassware that is designed to withstand heat, such as that used in the laboratory and in the kitchen, is made by combining aluminum and boron oxides with the sand. Colored glass is made by the addition of various metals or their oxides. The addition of selenium produces the red glass for auto taillights and traffic signals; the addition of cobalt oxide produces a blue glass.

Calcium Oxide

In the rotary kiln used in the commercial preparation of **lime** (CaO), limestone is introduced into the top of the long, inclined cylinder, which may be about 10 feet in diameter and 250 feet in length. It is heated at the bottom by means of burning gas or oil. As the kiln rotates, the limestone moves downward, becoming increasingly hotter as it meets the hot, gaseous products of combustion. Decomposition is complete by the time the material reaches the bottom of the kiln, where the lime, also known as **quicklime,** is removed. The reaction occurring in the kiln is reversible, so the carbon dioxide is removed by

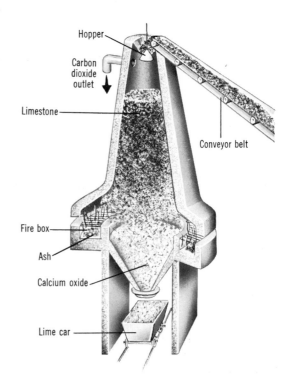

28-8 In a vertical lime kiln, lumps of calcium carbonate are heated to drive off carbon dioxide. The remaining calcium oxide, or lime, moves slowly downward and is loaded into lime cars waiting beneath the kiln.

alkali metals, is silvery bright and tarnishes rapidly on exposure to air. If a piece of calcium the size of a match head is dropped into water, hydrogen is evolved immediately; however, the reaction is not as vigorous as with the alkali metals. During the reaction between calcium and water, a white precipitate also forms. The precipitate is calcium hydroxide, which is only slightly soluble in water.

$$Ca + 2\,H_2O \longrightarrow Ca(OH)_2\downarrow + H_2\uparrow$$

Commercially, calcium hydroxide is much more easily, and inexpensively, prepared by reacting calcium oxide with water. *You can duplicate the process.*

> Place a lump of calcium oxide (about the size of a marble) in a watch glass. Add five to ten drops of water to the lump. At first, nothing appears to be happening, but continue your observation. Soon the lump swells, splits and crumbles into a powder, and a mist rises. Carefully feel the underside of the watch glass. Is it warm or even hot?

The exothermic process you initiated is known as the **slaking of lime.** The product formed is calcium hydroxide or **slaked lime,** $Ca(OH)_2$.

$$CaO + H_2O \longrightarrow Ca(OH)_2$$

The heat of hydration is sufficient to vaporize some of the water, producing the mist you saw.

In dilute, saturated solution, calcium hydroxide is the familiar *limewater* of the laboratory. In suspension, it is whitewash or **milk of lime,** sometimes used to paint fences, chicken coops, and cellar walls. By reaction with sulfur dioxide, calcium hydroxide forms calcium bisulfite, $Ca(HSO_3)_2$, used to separate cellulose fibers from wood pulp in paper making.

$$Ca(OH)_2 + 2\,SO_2 \longrightarrow Ca(HSO_3)_2$$

Calcium Sulfate

Have you ever observed a plasterer at work? He prepares a paste of water and white powder, **plaster of Paris;** he then applies this paste to a

28-9 The well-known sculptor Henry Moore applies plaster of Paris to a wire mesh to construct the framework for his model of a large statue.

wall or ceiling to make a smooth surface. Within a few hours the paste sets or hardens. The plaster of Paris used is made by heating the mineral **gypsum,** $CaSO_4 \cdot 2\,H_2O$, to a temperature of $125°$ C. Three-quarters of the water of hydration is driven off to form the plaster of Paris.

$$2\,(CaSO_4 \cdot 2\,H_2O) \longrightarrow 3\,H_2O\uparrow + (CaSO_4)_2 \cdot H_2O$$

When water is added to plaster of Paris, $(CaSO_4)_2 \cdot H_2O$, the reverse reaction occurs to form an interlocking network of gypsum crystals.

Plaster of Paris is used by dentists and sculptors to make molds because it expands slightly when it sets, moving into the fine lines on the surface of the object being used to make an impression. The work of the sculptor requires faithful reproduction of detail in the preparation of statuary (Fig. 28-9). The dentist, who must make accurate reproductions in preparing dentures and bridgework, also uses plaster of Paris for the same reason.

Compounds of Calcium and Chlorine

Two compounds of calcium and chlorine are widely used. One of these, calcium chloride, is a low-cost by-product of the Solvay process. Be-

28-10 Liquid soap combines with the calcium sulfate of hard water to form a gray precipitate, some of which adheres to the wall of the upper tube. The same amount of soap in distilled water cleans the lower tube.

cause $CaCl_2$ is deliquescent, it is used to absorb moisture in damp cellars and closets. Sprinkled on dirt roads, it absorbs moisture from the air to wet the surface, preventing windblown dust. In the laboratory it is used to dry gases or provide a dry atmosphere.

The second compound, bleaching powder $(CaOCl_2)$, used as a disinfectant as well as a bleach, is made by passing chlorine over either lime or slaked lime.

$$CaO + Cl_2 \longrightarrow CaOCl_2$$
$$Ca(OH)_2 + Cl_2 \longrightarrow CaOCl_2 + H_2O$$

Chlorine is liberated from bleaching powder by reaction with an acid.

$$CaOCl_2 + 2 H_3O^+ \longrightarrow Ca^{+2} + 3 H_2O + Cl_2\uparrow$$

Even the weak carbonic acid formed by the reaction of carbon dioxide and moisture of the air is sufficient to liberate chlorine from the powder in a can open to the air.

$$CaOCl_2 + H_2CO_3 \longrightarrow Cl_2\uparrow + H_2O + CaCO_3$$

QUESTIONS AND PROBLEMS

1. Differentiate among the following pairs of terms: (a) *slaked lime* and *quicklime*, (b) *marble* and *limestone,* (c) *lime* and *limestone.*

2. Describe briefly the (a) preparation of cement, (b) preparation of lime.

3. (a) Why is calcium carbonate used in neutralizing acid soil? (b) What are the chief uses of $Ca(OH)_2$, $CaCl_2$, $CaOCl_2$?

4. (a) How does the making of plate glass differ from the making of heat-resistant laboratory glassware?

5. What is the percentage of water of hydration in: (a) gypsum, (b) plaster of Paris?

HARD WATER

It is a common experience to observe a "ring" of insoluble material around the side of the tub after you take a bath. To determine the origin of this "ring," *try the following.*

Prepare two test tubes half filled with distilled water. Add three to five drops of a saturated solution of calcium sulfate to the first test tube and mix the solution well. Now add a single drop of liquid soap to each test tube and shake both tubes. A lather develops immediately in the distilled water but not in the calcium sulfate solution. Instead, observe the formation of a gray, insoluble substance floating in the first tube. Continue adding soap to each tube, shaking the contents after the addition of each drop. How many drops of soap are needed before the tube containing the calcium sulfate forms a lather? When this occurs, empty the tubes. The inside of the tube which contained the calcium sulfate solution is coated with the insoluble material observed earlier. Except for some lather, the other tube is perfectly clean inside.

The water containing calcium sulfate is **hard water,** so-called because it does not lather readily with soap; it can be recognized by the insoluble material formed as soap is added (Fig. 28-10).

These observations emphasize two disadvantages of hard water. First, it forms a lather only when an excessive amount of soap is used. Second, the sticky, insoluble material adheres to articles being washed and makes dried fabrics and glassware look dull and dingy.

The Formation of Hard Water

Hard water is produced in nature when water flows over or through beds of calcium sulfate. It is also produced in another interesting way. Water dissolves small amounts of carbon dioxide from the air and from decaying vegetation. Some of this surface water seeps into the earth through surface cracks or porous rock. What is the effect of such water on the widely present limestone? To answer this question, *try the following.*

Bubble some carbon dioxide through lime-water. The liquid becomes milky from the formation of insoluble calcium carbonate, which remains suspended in the liquid. Continue to bubble the carbon dioxide into the liquid. Observe that the milkiness diminishes and that the solution finally clears. Why?

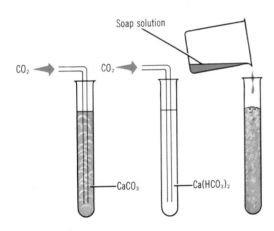

Treat some of the clear liquid with a soap solution. The scum that forms indicates that the water is hard. What compound caused the hardness?

When carbon dioxide is bubbled into lime-water, insoluble calcium carbonate forms.

$$Ca(OH)_2 + CO_2 \longrightarrow CaCO_3\downarrow + H_2O$$

28-11 One of the two boiler tubes is badly clogged with boiler scale—mainly calcium carbonate formed and deposited when hard water is heated.

Further bubbling of CO_2 results in the formation of soluble calcium bicarbonate—one cause of hard water.

$$\begin{array}{ccc} CaCO_3\downarrow + H_2O + CO_2 & \longrightarrow & Ca(HCO_3)_2 \\ \text{insoluble} & & \text{soluble} \end{array}$$

If you boil some of the clear liquid containing $Ca(HCO_3)_2$ for a few minutes, you can observe that bubbles of gas form and that the liquid becomes cloudy, forming a precipitate on standing. This precipitate is calcium carbonate.

$$Ca(HCO_3)_2 \longrightarrow CaCO_3\downarrow + H_2O + CO_2\uparrow$$

The reaction between $CaCO_3$, H_2O, and CO_2 that produced hard water is reversible when the temperature is raised. If you filter the boiled liquid and test the clear filtrate with soap solution, no scum forms. The water is no longer hard; we say that it is **soft water.**

These procedures provide a means of softening hard water containing calcium bicarbonate, and they also point out an additional disadvantage of using hard water. The calcium carbonate formed on heating deposits on the walls of boilers and hot-water pipes to form *boiler scale* (Fig. 28-11). These deposits reduce the flow of water through the pipes. They also act as insulators and interfere with the passage of heat through the boiler.

Formation of Limestone Caves

The reactions just discussed occur often in nature. When underground limestone is dissolved

28-12 The Lehman Caves of Nevada were hollowed out as water containing carbon dioxide dissolved the limestone. The "interior decorator" was calcium carbonate, slowly redeposited as stalactites, stalagmites, and even columns.

by water containing carbon dioxide, the rock is hollowed out to form caves (Fig. 28-12). If the reaction is reversed by the escape of carbon dioxide, insoluble calcium carbonate is redeposited. The deposited calcium carbonate may accumulate on the roof of the cave to form icicle-like stalactites; or it may accumulate on the floor of the cave to build deposits known as stalagmites. Water from these caves eventually finds its way into streams and lakes that serve as our source of water. Many water-supply systems located in limestone regions therefore contain calcium bicarbonate, which causes the water to be hard.

What Causes "Hard Water"

What determines whether water is hard or soft? You have already learned that water containing either calcium sulfate or calcium bicarbonate is hard. Yet if the procedure on page 472 were repeated with dilute solutions of calcium chloride, magnesium sulfate, magnesium chloride, sodium bicarbonate and sodium sulfate, all but the last two solutions would show the signs of hard water. Clearly then, soluble compounds of calcium and magnesium produce hardness in water.

One final check remains. If you shake a test tube containing a single marble chip and half-full of distilled water, and add ten drops of soap solution, a copious lather results. The marble chip fails to make the water hard because it is insoluble and does not furnish any calcium ions to the solution. In general, we can conclude that the ions of calcium and magnesium cause hardness in water. It is these ions (and sometimes other group IIA and ferrous ions) that react with soap to prevent lathering.

Softening Hard Water

The problem of softening hard water becomes very simply and logically the problem of removing the calcium and magnesium ions which make water hard. When water containing the bicarbonates of calcium or magnesium is boiled, the hardness disappears. Boiling causes the *soluble* metal bicarbonates to form *insoluble* carbonates, and therefore removes the metal ions from solution.

$$Ca^{+2} + 2\,HCO_3^- \xrightarrow{\Delta} CaCO_3\downarrow + H_2O + CO_2\uparrow$$

In contrast, boiling has no effect on solutions of calcium or magnesium sulfate. The metal ions of the compounds are still present to react with the soap.

Water containing calcium or magnesium bicarbonate can be softened by boiling; it is known as **temporary hard water.** Water containing calcium or magnesium sulfate is unaffected by boiling; it is known as **permanent hard water.** These terms *temporary* and *permanent* refer only to the effect of boiling on the hardness of the water.

Temporary hard water is softened by another method on a commercial scale. If a solution of calcium hydroxide is added to water containing calcium bicarbonate, calcium carbonate forms.

$$Ca^{+2} + 2\,HCO_3^- + Ca^{+2} + 2\,OH^- \longrightarrow$$
$$2\,CaCO_3\downarrow + 2\,H_2O$$

In this reaction the two soluble compounds react to form insoluble $CaCO_3$, leaving the water soft.

The interfering ions can also be removed from permanent hard water containing calcium sulfate by treatment with sodium carbonate. The soluble calcium ions are converted to insoluble calcium carbonate, while the sodium ions remain in solution.

$$Ca^{+2} + SO_4^{-2} + 2\,Na^+ + CO_3^{-2} \longrightarrow$$
$$CaCO_3\downarrow + 2\,Na^+ + SO_4^{-2}$$

For years Na_2CO_3, washing soda, and Na_3PO_4, trisodium phosphate, have been used to soften water inside washing machines. Write the equation for the reaction between soluble calcium ions and trisodium phosphate.

Ion Exchange and Hard Water

Some 30 years ago a completely new method of removing calcium and other group IIA ions from solution was developed. This method, called the **ion exchange method,** involves the use of a group of naturally occurring silicates known as *zeolites*. These zeolites are complex sodium aluminum silicate compounds related to clay. Zeolites may be represented by the formula Na_2Ze. When water containing calcium ions is passed through a bed of zeolites, an *exchange* occurs between the calcium ions in solution and the sodium ions in the zeolite (Fig. 28-13). This process re-

moves the calcium ions in the form of an insoluble calcium zeolite.

$$Na_2Ze + Ca^{+2} + SO_4^{-2} \longrightarrow$$
$$2\,Na^+ + SO_4^{-2} + CaZe\downarrow$$

The sodium ions, now in solution, do not make the water hard. When the zeolite has lost its capacity to remove calcium ions, it is washed with a concentrated solution of sodium chloride, causing a reaction which regenerates the original zeolite.

$$CaZe + 2\,Na^+ + 2\,Cl^- \longrightarrow$$
$$Na_2Ze + Ca^{+2} + 2\,Cl^-$$

The calcium chloride solution is washed out, and the zeolite is ready to soften more hard water.

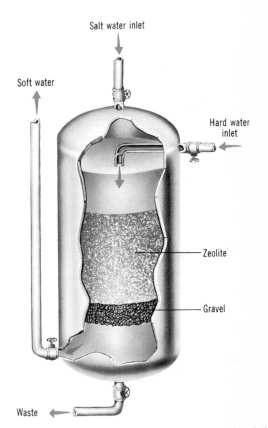

28-13 Hard water enters the ion-exchanger at the top, runs through the bed of zeolite, and emerges as soft water. At intervals, the salt water inlet and waste outlet are opened and the zeolite is regenerated.

Table 28-2 SOFTENING HARD WATER

Type of hard water	Contents	Method of softening	Reaction
Temporary	Ca Mg $\Big\}(HCO_3)_2$	Heating	$Ca^{+2} + 2\,HCO_3^{-} \xrightarrow{\Delta} CaCO_3\downarrow + H_2O + CO_2$
		Adding $Ca(OH)_2$	$Ca^{+2} + 2\,HCO_3^{-} + Ca^{+2} + 2\,OH^{-} \longrightarrow 2\,CaCO_3\downarrow + 2\,H_2O$
Permanent	$CaSO_4$	Adding Na_2CO_3	$Ca^{+2} + SO_4^{-2} + 2\,Na^{+} + CO_3^{-2} \longrightarrow CaCO_3\downarrow + 2\,Na^{+} + SO_4^{-2}$
Temporary or permanent	Ca Mg $\Big\}(HCO_3)_2$ $CaSO_4$	Ion exchange: zeolites or resins	$Na_2Ze + Ca^{+2} + SO_4^{-2} \longrightarrow CaZe + 2\,Na^{+} + SO_4^{-2}$

This principle of **ion exchange** as a means of removing metallic ions from water has been amplified with the development of synthetic *ion exchange resins* (related to the plastics) which duplicate the action of zeolites. These resins have been designed to remove *either positive or negative ions*. In practice, the water to be purified passes through a cation exchanger, or acid exchange resin, which removes positive metallic ions by exchanging them for hydrogen ions. The water then flows through a second anion exchanger, or base exchange resin, which exchanges the negative ions, such as chloride and sulfate ions, for hydroxide ions. The combined treatment results in completely demineralized water. Each of these types of resins can be regenerated by treatment with an acid or basic solution, respectively. The technique of ion exchange is being used both in industry and in the laboratory to prepare water almost as free of other materials as that prepared by distillation.

Let us review by means of Table 28-2 what we have learned about hard water.

QUESTIONS AND PROBLEMS

1. What compounds cause (a) temporary hardness in water, (b) permanent hardness?

2. (a) How does the softening of temporary hard water differ from the softening of permanent hard water? (b) Explain the reasons for this difference.

3. Describe briefly the softening of water by ion exchange with zeolites or resins.

4. How could you determine whether a sample of boiler scale consists of calcium sulfate or calcium carbonate?

COMPOUNDS OF OTHER ALKALINE EARTH METALS

Attention has been focused on the compounds of calcium because these are the most abundant and most widely used of the alkaline earth metals. The compounds of its sister elements, while not as widespread, are also of value to us in numerous ways.

Magnesium Compounds

Other than in dolomite, magnesium occurs naturally in a number of silicates, such as soapstone, talc, and asbestos. Soapstone is used to make laboratory table tops, finely ground talc is a constituent in face and talcum powders, and asbestos is well known as a heat insulator. Pipe (Fig. 28-14) and furnace insulation is made by mixing asbestos fibers with magnesium hydroxide, magnesium carbonate or magnesium silicate.

Roasting of the carbonate produces magnesium oxide, which, like all the oxides of the group IA and IIA metals, is highly stable. Shaped in the

28-14 This molded insulation is composed of asbestos and calcium silicate. Because of its light weight, low thermal conductivity, and insolubility in water, it is widely used in outdoor insulation.

form of bricks, magnesium oxide is used to line high-temperature furnaces, where it may also act to counteract the effects of acidic impurities. The oxide reacts with water to form magnesium hydroxide, a mild base that is insoluble in water. Its suspension in water—milk of magnesia—is used as a laxative and antacid.

Epsom salts, hydrated magnesium sulfate ($MgSO_4 \cdot 7 H_2O$), finds use as a laxative. It is also used in a hot bath to reduce the swelling from bruises or sprains.

Barium, Beryllium, and Strontium Compounds

Barium sulfate serves as a pigment in some types of white paint. It is also used as a filler in paper, making the paper heavier and less translucent. Suspensions of this opaque compound in water are useful in X-ray studies of the internal organs, such as the stomach, which are otherwise transparent to X rays.

Most of the compounds of the group IA and group IIA elements impart a distinctive color to a flame. The nitrates of strontium and barium, as well as the peroxide and chlorate of the latter, are therefore used in fireworks and flares; strontium compounds provide a scarlet color,

while barium compounds color the flame yellow-green. Such characteristic colors can be used to identify these and other metals, as you will learn in Chapter 32.

Although beryllium compounds have limited use, beryllium silicates are fluorescent when exposed to ultraviolet rays and are used to coat the inner walls of some fluorescent tubes. But *all beryllium compounds are poisonous.* Therefore, when a fluorescent tube is broken, its fragments should be handled with great care; and care should be exercised not to inhale any dust that may have resulted from the breakage.

Since nuclear explosions have become a reality, one of the alkaline earth elements—strontium—has achieved a new and significant prominence. Among the particles found in the debris of a nuclear explosion is the isotope strontium-90, with a half life of approximately 27 years. This isotope is a strong beta emitter. Strontium compounds, like those of calcium, are taken up from the soil by a variety of plants which serve as food for animals. The strontium, like the calcium, is in turn incorporated into the animals' bone tissue and can be present in milk. If this milk is part of the human diet, the isotope is incorporated into human bone tissue. Here its radiation may affect white blood cell formation. Research continues in order to determine the maximum amount of this isotope that can be present in our bones without causing possible danger. Further research is being aimed at methods of removing strontium-90 from milk, principally by means of ion exchange.

The previous discussions make it clear that the members of the group IIA family, like those of group IA, are decidedly metallic in their chemical behavior. But physically, the elements of both groups are very unlike typical metals. Because of their extreme activity, we normally meet their compounds rather than the metals themselves in our everyday experience. Now our attention turns to the more familiar metals—the transition metals. How do these metals differ from those already studied; what are their properties; how are they used?

1. What is the chief use of barium sulfate, strontium nitrate, beryllium silicate?

2. (a) What do soapstone, talc, and asbestos have in common? (b) milk of magnesia and epsom salts?

3. Why are scientists concerned about the strontium-90 produced during nuclear explosions?

VALUE OF THE CONCEPT

THE CONCEPT

The family relationships of the alkaline earth metals, those with 2 orbital electrons, are unmistakable from a study of their physical and chemical properties. The trend in the periodic table as you move from the alkali metals to the alkaline earth metals reinforces the general pattern of the table. The group IIA elements show marked resemblance, physically and chemically, to the group IA elements. Their densities, melting points, and boiling points are, for the most part, unusually low for metals; the vigor of their chemical reactions is again outstanding. The group IIA metals are powerful reducing agents, and they stand high in the electrochemical series. Consequently, like the alkali metals, they are prepared by electrolytic reduction. But there are differences between the two families; the densities, melting points, boiling points, and hardness of the group IIA elements are distinctly greater than those of the alkali metals. Except for density, beryllium differs markedly from its family members in these properties. Beryllium and magnesium are widely used in alloys, but the remaining group IIA elements find limited use.

In contrast to the alkali metal compounds, many of the compounds of these alkaline earth metals are insoluble in water. Abundant deposits of these compounds occur in the crust of the earth. Yet, the compounds of these elements, except calcium, find mainly specialized uses—ranging from fireworks for strontium, to X-ray studies for barium, to the valuable radioactivity of radium. Calcium carbonate, as limestone, is the starting point for the production of cement, glass, lime (quicklime), and slaked lime—all widely used in the building trades.

The widespread occurrence of these metal compounds in nature gives rise to the important phenomenon of hard water. The reaction between the ions of certain metals and soaps forms an insoluble material incapable of producing a lather. The problems of hard water encountered in laundering and hot water systems are solved by removing the causative ions—those of calcium, magnesium, and to a lesser extent, iron (ferrous). Whatever method is used to remove these ions, whether by boiling, precipitation, or ion exchange, we employ the principles of chemical equilibrium—notably that of making a reaction go to completion. In temporary hard water, soluble compounds such as calcium and magnesium carbonate are converted to insoluble calcium or magnesium carbonate, either by boiling or by precipitation. The calcium sulfate in permanent hard water is removed by precipitation. All hard water can be softened by the ion exchange method, in which the soluble compounds are changed to a form in which they are no longer ionized. The ion exchange method is used not only to soften hard water but to remove all ions, both positive and negative, from water. The now deionized or demineralized water is a substitute for distilled water.

USING THE CONCEPT

Using the Basic Concept
1. Explain why compounds of the group IIA elements are best reduced to the metal by electrolysis.
2. (a) List the properties in which the elements of group IIA and their compounds closely resemble those of group IA. (b) List the properties in which there is a marked difference.

3. Why is it difficult to make precise measurements of the physical properties of radium?

4. Magnesium has an atomic weight about two and one-half times that of beryllium, yet its density is slightly less. What factor might account for the lower density of magnesium?

5. (a) What is the chief commercial source of magnesium? (b) How is this source unlike the chief sources of the remaining alkaline earth elements?

6. What are the chief advantages of (a) magnesium alloys (b) beryllium alloys?

7. Compare and contrast each of the following substances with respect to physical and chemical properties: (a) limestone and calcite, (b) milk of magnesia and Epsom salts, (c) strontium-90 and radium.

8. Give the formula for each of the following compounds: lime, slaked lime, quicklime, limestone.

9. (a) How is plaster of Paris prepared from gypsum? (b) How do these compounds differ chemically?

10. By what three methods can temporary hard water be softened?

11. Water containing dissolved calcium sulfate can be softened by the addition of sodium carbonate; the same treatment cannot be used to soften water containing magnesium sulfate. (a) Account for this difference. (b) What treatment, other than ion exchange, could be used to soften this type of hard water?

12. Why are *concentrated* solutions of sodium chloride used to regenerate zeolites?

13. Give the general composition and origin of each of the following: marble, boiler scale, stalactite.

14. Describe briefly the formation of a limestone cave.

15. (a) Describe briefly the manufacturing of glass. (b) Why is glass annealed?

16. Tabulate the group IIA elements according to those known to be: (a) essential to our well-being (b) harmful to man (c) helpful to man.

17. Why are the alkaline earth metal ions much smaller than those of the alkali metals of the same period?

18. Explain why barium sulfate can be taken internally for X-ray examinations without harm even though many barium salts are poisonous.

Relating Terms Within the Concept

Select the letter of the term in Column B that is most closely related to each term in Column A. Do not use a term more than once.

COLUMN A	COLUMN B
1. plaster of Paris	a. beryllium and magnesium
2. gypsum	b. calcite
3. limestone	c. calcium and magnesium bicarbonate
4. temporary hard water	d. calcium oxide
5. permanent hard water	e. calcium sulfate
6. quicklime	f. clay and calcium carbonate
7. cement	g. complex ions
8. ion exchange resins	h. $(CaSO_4)_2 \cdot H_2O$
9. alloys	i. $MgCl_2 \longrightarrow Mg + Cl_2$
10. electrolytic reduction.	j. positive and negative ions
	k. shells and caves
	l. strontium and barium
	m. water of hydration

Solving Problems Within the Concept

1. (a) How many liters of carbon dioxide (**STP**) could be obtained by the decomposition of 50 grams of calcium carbonate? (b) How much would this volume of the gas weigh? (c) How would these results be influenced by the manner in which the calcium carbonate is decomposed (whether by heat or by treatment with an acid)?

2. The solubility of calcium hydroxide is 0.162 grams per liter of solution at 20° C. Assuming that the base is completely dissociated at this concentration, what is the pH of the solution?

3. A sample of calcite (pure $CaCO_3$) weighing 0.400 gram reacts with exactly 40.0 ml of hydrochloric acid. What is the normality of the acid?

4. What weight of lime will result from the decomposition of 2 tons of limestone containing 96 percent calcium carbonate?

5. The half life of radium-226 is 1,620 years. How many years will be required for the element to decay from 1,028 grams to 1 gram?

6. What weight of calcium hydroxide would be needed to soften 1 million gallons of water containing 8 milligrams of calcium bicarbonate per gallon?

7. How many pounds of magnesium hydroxide can be prepared by reacting with water the magnesium oxide obtained by roasting 2 tons of magnesium carbonate (which is 98 percent pure)?

8. A hydrate of calcium chloride contains 39.3 percent by weight of water. What is its formula?

Applying the Concept

1. Why would water containing calcium hydroxide be considered hard water?

2. Natural water supplies sometimes contain the ions of metals other than those described in this chapter. What information would you need in order to predict whether such water would be hard or soft?

3. What impurities removed from water by distillation might still be present in deionized water? Why?

4. In the absence of distilled water to serve as a standard for soft water, what *natural* substitute could be used? Why?

5. Why are solutions of calcium compounds often made more rapidly by using cold water rather than hot water?

6. Is there any gas previously studied which could *not* be dried by passing it over calcium chloride? (*Hint:* Find out whether any of these gases combine with calcium chloride.)

7. How does the weathering of limestone in a dry climate differ from that in a moist climate?

8. A solution containing magnesium sulfate, potassium nitrate, and aluminum chloride is passed through a cation exchanger. (a) What ions will be present in the resulting liquid? (b) How would the results differ if an anion exchanger were to be used?

9. Why is it recommended that cement work be kept damp for about one week after the cement has hardened?

Reading Further

A Field Guide to Rocks and Minerals, by Frederick Pough, Boston, Houghton Mifflin, 1955. A comprehensive manual for identifying rocks and minerals—for the beginner or the serious collector.

You will find the following three articles in *Scientific American* particularly interesting: "Calcium and Life," by L. V. Heilibrunn, June 1951. "Ion Exchange," by Harold Walton, November 1950. "Glass," by Charles Greene, January 1961.

29

The Transition Elements

The discovery of the first known metals, copper and gold, brought to a close the New Stone Age and opened up a new era in man's cultural development. Both copper and gold occur "free," or uncombined in metallic form, as well as in compounds. The free elements can be beaten, rubbed, and cut. Heat, which is essential to the processing of most metals, is unnecessary for the fashioning of some gold and copper articles. But copper is soft and of little value in making axes and knives; gold is both soft and scarce. Soon men learned to melt tin with copper to make bronze—and the art of metallurgy had begun to develop.

Oddly enough neither copper nor gold exhibits the typical silvery-gray color of most metals. What of their compounds? Most copper compounds are colored; many are blue. And almost without exception the compounds of gold are colored. Is their color unique? Of course not. Though many compounds you have used thus far are white solids, forming colorless solutions, others are colored solids that dissolve to form similarly colored solutions. Is there any data that enables us to predict which elements form colored compounds and also to explain why these elements do so?

TRANSITION HEAVY METALS

Examine the chemicals on your laboratory and stockroom shelves and note the names of the

Fig. 29-1   THE TRANSITION ELEMENTS

IIA	IIIB	IVB	VB	VIB	VIIB	VIII			IB	IIB	IIIA
	21 Sc Scandium	22 Ti Titanium	23 V Vanadium	24 Cr Chromium	25 Mn Manganese	26 Fe Iron	27 Co Cobalt	28 Ni Nickel	29 Cu Copper	30 Zn Zinc	
	39 Y Yttrium	40 Zr Zirconium	41 Nb Niobium	42 Mo Molybdenum	43 Tc Technetium	44 Ru Ruthenium	45 Rh Rhodium	46 Pd Palladium	47 Ag Silver	48 Cd Cadmium	
	57 LA Lanthanum Lanthanide Series 58–71	Hf 72 Hafnium	Ta 73 Tantalum	W 74 Tungsten	Re 75 Rhenium	Os 76 Osmium	Ir 77 Iridium	Pt 78 Platinum	Au 79 Gold	Hg 80 Mercury	
	89 Ac Actinium Actinide Series 90–103	— 104 —									

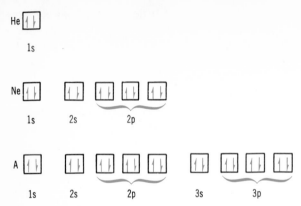

He [↑↓]
   1s

Ne [↑↓] [↑↓] [↑↓][↑↓][↑↓]
   1s   2s   2p

A [↑↓] [↑↓] [↑↓][↑↓][↑↓] [↑↓] [↑↓][↑↓][↑↓]
  1s   2s   2p   3s   3p

29-2 With each of their orbitals containing the maximum of 2 electrons, helium, neon, and argon complete their respective periods.

colored compounds. Besides cupric compounds, you will have on your list such compounds as ferric chloride and nitrate, chromium chloride and nitrate, sodium chromate and potassium dichromate, manganese chloride and potassium permanganate, cobalt nitrate, nickel chloride, and possibly compounds of titanium and vanadium. Now locate the symbols of the metallic elements of these compounds in the periodic table. Immediately, a pattern begins to emerge. The symbols for all of these metals (as well as others whose ions are colored) lie in the middle portions of the long periods (Fig. 29-1), between those elements which are strongly metallic (groups IA and IIA) and those which are strongly nonmetallic (groups VIA and VIIA). As you can observe, not all of the elements in the table possess colored ions. These middle portions of the long periods comprise the **transition elements,** many of which have colored ions, especially when hydrated. Also, these metallic elements exist in several oxidation states. In what fundamental manner do these transition elements differ from other elements to give rise to the particular properties mentioned?

We can best answer this question by reviewing the manner in which successive electrons are added to the atomic orbitals in developing each of the periods of the periodic table. The first period is complete with only two elements (H and He) because the K shell of electrons, containing only an s orbital, holds a maximum of 2 electrons (Fig. 29-2). In the second period the L shell of electrons now contains two types of orbitals, an s orbital again providing for a maximum of 2 electrons, and three p orbitals with a maximum of 6 electrons. This period is therefore complete with neon, the eighth element after helium.

In the third period, this pattern of two s electrons and six p electrons is again developed from sodium to argon. The M shell in the third period elements also includes five d orbitals, each capable of containing 2 electrons. We should expect that this period would develop to a maximum of eighteen elements. But this is not the case. In Chapter 3, you learned that as successive electrons are added in building the elements, each electron *occupies a position of lowest energy. The energies of the 4s electrons of the N shell are lower than those of the 3d orbitals of the M shell.* Therefore, when an electron is added to build the next element (potassium) after argon, this electron enters a 4s rather than a 3d orbital and the fourth period begins, as shown in the energy level diagram in Fig. 29-3. The 4s orbital is complete with the addition of a second electron in calcium.

It would seem logical that the electrons added for the successive elements in this period would occupy the p orbitals in the fourth (N) shell. *But the next orbitals to be filled are now the 3d (M shell) orbitals, so far unfilled, because these have a lower energy than the 4p orbitals.* When we pass from calcium to scandium, which has one additional electron, this electron occupies a 3d orbital in the M shell rather than a 4p orbital in the N shell. Successive electrons added for each of the elements which follow scandium go to fill the remaining 3d orbitals before any electrons enter the 4p orbitals. As the five 3d orbitals provide for a total of 10 electrons, this process is not complete until we reach zinc, the tenth element (inclusive) after scandium. At this point, further electrons added to the atom enter the 4p orbitals. The series of elements from scandium to zinc, in which the added electrons fill an incomplete set of orbitals *in a shell other than the outermost,* is the first series of transition elements.

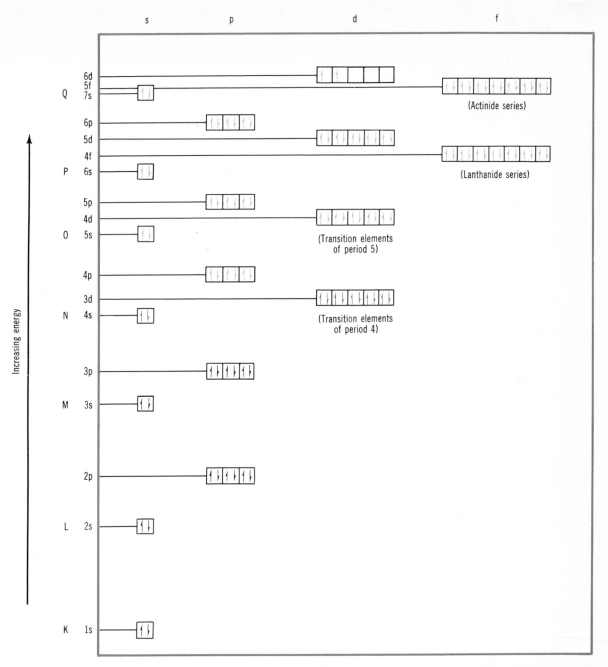

29-3 An energy level diagram. Beginning with the N shell, the energies of the subshells and their respective orbitals overlap and do not follow the straightforward order of the principal quantum numbers. When an electron enters the 4s orbital, period 4 begins; as successive electrons enter the 3d orbitals the first transition elements occur. Electrons of the transition elements of period 5 enter the 4d orbitals. In the lanthanide and actinide series, electrons enter the 4f and 5f orbitals, respectively; differences here are two shells removed from the outer shell.

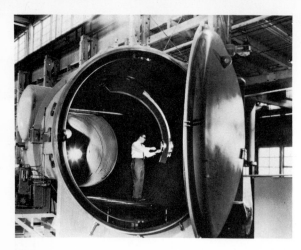

29-4 In this satellite test chamber, the use of rare earth cores for carbon arc electrodes increases light intensity tenfold. The arc produces an almost continuous spectrum identical with that of sunlight.

Period 5, 6, and 7 Transition Elements

The difference in energy between the orbitals of the same and succeeding shells becomes smaller as the principal quantum numbers (period numbers) increase. As a result, a similar pattern of development is followed in each of the succeeding periods of the table. Thus, in period 5, successive electrons added from yttrium to cadmium fill the 4d rather than the 5p orbitals. These ten elements form the second series of transition elements. The atomic number continues to increase, but the transition series that develop in periods 6 and 7 differ in one further respect.

In periods 6 and 7, the energy differences among the d, p, and f electrons of the N, O, and P shells are very small. The energy level diagram shows that the energies of these orbitals overlap and do not follow the straightforward order of the principal quantum numbers. After the s orbitals are filled in the first two elements of these periods, the next electron enters the d orbital of the preceding shell (Table 29-1). Thereafter, the succeeding electrons enter the 4f orbitals in the sixth period and the 5f orbitals in the seventh period. As a result, the sixth period contains a transition series of *fourteen* elements in which the fourteen f orbitals are being filled to form the

lanthanide series of transition elements; these fourteen elements following lanthanum are also known as the **rare earth elements** (Fig. 29-4).

The seventh period contains a very similar series of fourteen elements following actinium in which the 5f orbitals are being filled to form the **actinide series** of elements. In both the lanthanide and actinide series, the incomplete shell being filled is not next to the outer shell as it was in the earlier periods, but lies one step nearer the nucleus. The difference in atomic structure between successive elements in the lanthanides and actinides is buried deep within the atom. The outermost shells are essentially alike throughout these series. This similarity of outer electron shells accounts for the similarity in physical and chemical properties for the members of these series. Did you notice that this series includes the transuranic elements?

Color and Electron Structure

How do these facts of atomic structure account for the properties of the transition elements noted earlier? You know that the difference in energies between successive electrons in the transition elements is very small. Since the difference in energy between the 4s and 3d orbitals is small, a transition element in the fourth period will lose its two 4s (valence) electrons to exhibit an oxidation state of $+2$; but only a small additional amount of energy is needed to remove its 3d electrons. For example, in the presence of oxidizing agents, scandium may lose its 3d electron and exhibit a higher oxidation state ($+3$). In the same manner cerium, in period 6, loses the two s electrons of its P shell to form the cerous ($+2$) ion; but in the presence of oxidizing agents, it loses two f electrons from its N shell to form the ceric ($+4$) ion.

The energy for removal of these electrons *may* be provided by light energy in the visible range, as well as by oxidizing agents. White light is composed of various colors, each of which has a definite energy value. And the energy of a particular color may be exactly equal to the energy required to raise an electron to the next higher energy level. When white light strikes a transition

Atomic number	Name	Symbol	K or 1 — s	L or 2 — s p	M or 3 — s p d	N or 4 — s p d f	O or 5 — s p d f	P or 6 — s p d f	Q or 7 — s	
55	Cesium	Cs	2	2 6	2 6 10	2 6 10	2 6	1		
56	Barium	Ba	2	2 6	2 6 10	2 6 10	2 6	2		L
57	Lanthanum	La	2	2 6	2 6 10	2 6 10	2 6 1	2		A
58	Cerium	Ce	2	2 6	2 6 10	2 6 10 2	2 6	2		N
59	Praseodymium	Pr	2	2 6	2 6 10	2 6 10 3	2 6	2		T
60	Neodymium	Nd	2	2 6	2 6 10	2 6 10 4	2 6	2		H
61	Promethium	Pm	2	2 6	2 6 10	2 6 10 5	2 6	2		A
62	Samarium	Sm	2	2 6	2 6 10	2 6 10 6	2 6	2		N
63	Europium	Eu	2	2 6	2 6 10	2 6 10 7	2 6	2		I
64	Gadolinium	Gd	2	2 6	2 6 10	2 6 10 7	2 6 1	2		D
65	Terbium	Tb	2	2 6	2 6 10	2 6 10 9	2 6	2		E
66	Dysprosium	Dy	2	2 6	2 6 10	2 6 10 10	2 6	2		
67	Holmium	Ho	2	2 6	2 6 10	2 6 10 11	2 6	2		S
68	Erbium	Er	2	2 6	2 6 10	2 6 10 12	2 6	2		E
69	Thulium	Tm	2	2 6	2 6 10	2 6 10 13	2 6	2		R
70	Ytterbium	Yb	2	2 6	2 6 10	2 6 10 14	2 6	2		I
71	Lutetium	Lu	2	2 6	2 6 10	2 6 10 14	2 6 1	2		E S
87	Francium	Fr	2	2 6	2 6 10	2 6 10 14	2 6 10	2 6	1	
88	Radium	Ra	2	2 6	2 6 10	2 6 10 14	2 6 10	2 6	2	
89	Actinium	Ac	2	2 6	2 6 10	2 6 10 14	2 6 10	2 6 1	2	A
90	Thorium	Th	2	2 6	2 6 10	2 6 10 14	2 6 10	2 6 2	2	C
91	Protactinium	Pa	2	2 6	2 6 10	2 6 10 14	2 6 10 2	2 6 1	2	T
92	Uranium	U	2	2 6	2 6 10	2 6 10 14	2 6 10 3	2 6 1	2	I
93	Neptunium	Np	2	2 6	2 6 10	2 6 10 14	2 6 10 4	2 6 1	2	N
94	Plutonium	Pu	2	2 6	2 6 10	2 6 10 14	2 6 10 5	2 6 1	2	I
95	Americium	Am	2	2 6	2 6 10	2 6 10 14	2 6 10 6	2 6 1	2	D
96	Curium	Cm	2	2 6	2 6 10	2 6 10 14	2 6 10 7	2 6 1	2	E
97	Berkelium	Bk	2	2 6	2 6 10	2 6 10 14	2 6 10 8	2 6 1	2	
98	Californium	Cf	2	2 6	2 6 10	2 6 10 14	2 6 10 9	2 6 1	2	S
99	Einsteinium	Es	2	2 6	2 6 10	2 6 10 14	2 6 10 10	2 6 1	2	E
100	Fermium	Fm	2	2 6	2 6 10	2 6 10 14	2 6 10 11	2 6 1	2	R
101	Mendelevium	Md	2	2 6	2 6 10	2 6 10 14	2 6 10 12	2 6 1	2	I
102	Nobelium	No	2	2 6	2 6 10	2 6 10 14	2 6 10 13	2 6 1	2	E
103	Lawrencium	Lw	2	2 6	2 6 10	2 6 10 14	2 6 10 14	2 6 1	2	S

element compound, particular colors may be absorbed in exciting electrons to higher energy levels, and the remaining colors reflected or transmitted. Hydrated cupric ions, for example, absorb energy in the red end of the spectrum and transmit or reflect the blue.

A and B Subgroups

When Mendeleev developed his periodic table, (page 77) he found that elements falling into the same group by virtue of valence alone were markedly dissimilar in other respects. The first group contained the alkali metals as well as copper, silver, and gold. To avoid this and similar discrepancies in his table, Mendeleev divided each group further into subgroups containing related elements. The alkali metals were placed in group IA while the copper group fell into group IB. Why such dissimilar groups of elements should fall into the same group was a mystery in Mendeleev's

29-5 Pellets of copper (group IB) sink to the bottom of a beaker of carbon tetrachloride, while a piece of potassium (group IA) floats because of its lower density. Why was water not used in the beaker?

The Copper Family

Copper, silver, and gold, the members of group IB (Table 29-2), have 1 electron in their outer shells, as do the alkali metals; but there all resemblance ends, both physically and chemically. Physically, there is marked contrast between the two subgroups in density (Fig. 29-5), hardness, melting and boiling points. The chemical differences are equally pronounced. While the alkali metals possess only one oxidation state (+1), copper and the precious metals exhibit more than one oxidation state. The variable oxidation state arises because one or two of the d orbital electrons in the next-to-the-last shell of these atoms may be removed easily by oxidizing agents. Silver compounds in which the metal has an oxidation state of +2 are infrequent and usually unstable.

Further, the alkali metals are very high in the electrochemical series (page 303), whereas copper, silver, and gold lie below hydrogen in the series. The latter metals do not replace hydrogen from water under any conditions, and they do not react with dilute acids to yield hydrogen. Reactions of these metals with oxygen and the nonmetals are much slower than those of the alkali metals, usually requiring elevated temperatures. Conversely, the compounds of copper, silver, and gold are far less stable than those of the alkali metals and are often decomposed at relatively low temperatures. Because of the relative inactivity of the group IB metals, they are often found uncombined in nature, especially silver and gold. When these elements are found naturally in the form of compounds, their extraction from the ore usually involves only the use of heat

time; the arrangement was maintained because the elements which followed in order of atomic weight (the basis then used) continued the pattern of repetition of properties. Today, elements such as copper, silver, and gold are separated from the other members of a group because they represent transition elements. Chemists have avoided the difficulty of the original table by arranging the elements not only in the order of increasing atomic number, but also in the order in which their electron shells develop. Although the present-day table is far different in appearance from the original, we still retain the designation of the subgroups, for example, IA and IB, and VIA and VIB.

Table 29-2 **THE GROUP IB ELEMENTS**

Element	Atomic number	Atomic weight	Electron configuration	Density (g/ml 20° C)	Melting point (° C)	Boiling point (° C)	State and color	Ionization potential	Oxidation states
Copper	29	63.54	2 8 18 1	8.9	1083	2236	Reddish solid	7.7	+1, +2
Silver	47	107.870	2 8 18 18 1	10.5	961	1950	White solid	7.6	+1, +2
Gold	79	196.967	2 8 18 32 18 1	19.32	1603	2600	Yellow solid	9.2	+1, +3

to bring about a simple decomposition of the compound.

Most alkali metal compounds are soluble in water, exceptions being rather few in number. In contrast, many of the compounds of the group IB metals are insoluble in water. Alkali metal compounds are white in the solid form, unless the negative ions are colored, as in potassium permanganate or sodium chromate. Compounds of copper, silver, and gold in their higher oxidation states are usually colored, both as solids and in solution.

You have now been introduced to an overall picture of the transition elements and to a comparison of the group IA and IB elements. What can be learned further about them individually?

QUESTIONS AND PROBLEMS

1. What properties are most characteristic of the transition elements?

2. What is unusual in the electron configuration of the (a) period 4 and period 5 transition elements, (b) period 6 and period 7 transition elements?

3. How does the electron structure of mercury account for its variable oxidation states?

4. (a) How does each A subgroup differ from its corresponding B subgroup? (b) Give three specific examples for subgroups IA and IB.

5. Why are similar properties found among the members of the (a) lanthanide series, (b) actinide series?

COPPER

Although our mechanized world today employs "skeletons" and "muscles" of steel, and "skins" of aluminum, we still rely on copper. Copper is vital to the operation of our electrical devices because it transmits the electrical energy needed to move the steel "muscles."

The low activity of copper explains its being found uncombined; however, copper also occurs

29-6 This underground ore train, although small (see engineer), can carry tons of copper ore from deep within this copper mine in Montana.

in many minerals. Whatever the nature of the metal compound in these minerals, whether oxide, carbonate, or sulfide, the metal must ultimately be extracted by *reduction*.

$$Cu^{+2} + 2\,e^- \longrightarrow Cu^0$$
ions in   free metal
compound

Copper can be extracted from cuprite (Cu_2O) and other oxide ores by reduction with carbon. Sulfide and carbonate ores are first roasted, and the resulting oxide then reduced to the metal.

$$2\,Cu_2S + 3\,O_2 \longrightarrow 2\,Cu_2O + 2\,SO_2\uparrow$$
$$Cu_2O + C \longrightarrow 2\,Cu + CO$$

Our most common copper ores are mixed sulfides of copper and iron, such as $CuFeS_2$ (Fig. 29-6), containing small amounts of lead, nickel, zinc, silver, and gold.

The Metallurgy of Copper

The extraction of any metal from its ore involves more than merely the reduction of the metal compound in the ore to the free metal. Before this can be achieved, the ore must undergo a

29-7 In the froth flotation machine, copper ore is ground to a fine powder and mixed with oils and chemical wetting agents. With agitation, the metallic copper is trapped in a froth of bubbles and floated away.

number of treatments designed to remove impurities of many types and concentrate the metal-bearing materials. The science dealing with the processes whereby a metal is finally extracted from an ore is known as **metallurgy.**

Since copper ores contain on the average only about 5 percent of the metal, a figure too low for efficient and economical extraction, they are first concentrated by an ingenious process known as **froth flotation** (Fig. 29-7). The ore is first pulverized and the powder added to a mixture of water, certain oils (for example, pine oil), and special chemicals known as wetting agents. The mixture is now agitated vigorously to beat air into it. Metal-bearing particles in the ore are wetted by the oil which has trapped the air bubbles. As a result, these oil-coated particles rise to the top of the mixing tank in the form of a froth. The ore's earthy, nonmetal-bearing material, called *gangue,* is not wetted by the oil and sinks to the bottom of the tank. The metal-bearing froth is skimmed off the surface and its useful solid material separated by filtration.

The concentrated ore is now roasted at a red heat. Some sulfur is removed in the form of sulfur dioxide, while some of the iron combines with the silica (in the ore) to form iron silicate.

$$2\,CuFeS_2 + 4\,O_2 \longrightarrow Cu_2S + 2\,FeO + 3\,SO_2\uparrow$$
$$FeO + SiO_2 \longrightarrow FeSiO_3$$

The roasted ore is then transferred to a reverberatory (heat-resistant) furnace (Fig. 29-8), where it is fused with limestone and silica. The resulting calcium silicate slag serves to remove more of the iron. A layer of cuprous sulfide mixed with ferrous sulfide, called *matte,* is formed under the slag. The matte is transferred to a converter, a silica flux is added, and a blast of air is blown through the charge. Metals such as arsenic, which form volatile impurities, are removed by the blast, and iron and other metallic impurities enter the slag which is poured off at intervals. Some of the copper is reduced directly to the metal, but some is first converted to oxides. The latter then reacts with the remaining sulfide to form metallic copper.

$$Cu_2S + O_2 \longrightarrow 2\,Cu + SO_2\uparrow$$
$$2\,Cu_2S + 3\,O_2 \longrightarrow 2\,Cu_2O + 2\,SO_2\uparrow$$
$$2\,Cu_2O + Cu_2S \longrightarrow 6\,Cu + SO_2\uparrow$$

The metallic copper then melts and sinks to the bottom of the converter from which it is poured. The molten copper is stirred with poles of green wood which decompose into carbon and reducing gases. These gases convert to copper any copper oxide remaining.

29-8 In this reverberatory furnace the fire is not in contact with the charge. Intermediary hot gases maintain a steady, controlled heat.

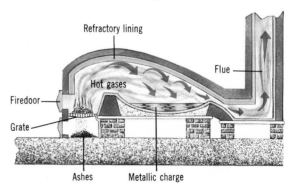

Refractory lining
Flue
Hot gases
Firedoor
Grate
Ashes
Metallic charge

When the copper is cast into slabs, the escaping gases form blisters on the surface of the metal as it cools and hardens. The product is called "blister copper." Although blister copper is about 99 percent pure, it is highly unsatisfactory for many uses. The presence of as little as *one-tenth of one percent* of arsenic, for example, reduces the electrical conductivity of copper by thirty percent. In addition, it makes the copper unsatisfactory for the preparation of copper alloys.

Refining by Electrolysis

Blister copper is further refined by electrolysis, using the apparatus illustrated in Fig. 29-9. The impure copper which has been cast into a slab serves as the anode. The cathode is a thin sheet of pure copper, and the electrolyte is a solution of cupric sulfate acidified with sulfuric acid. When a direct current passes through the electrolyte, cupric ions in solution migrate to the cathode. Here, each ion receives two electrons to become copper atoms which deposit on the cathode.

$$Cu^{+2} + 2\,e^- \longrightarrow Cu^0 \quad \text{(reduction)}$$

This removal of cupric ions from the solution leaves the liquid with more negative ions than positive ions. The charge is balanced as copper atoms from the impure anode lose 2 electrons and enter the solution as cupric ions.

$$Cu^0 - 2\,e^- \longrightarrow Cu^{+2} \quad \text{(oxidation)}$$

While the process continues, copper atoms are "peeled off" the anode by being oxidized to cupric ions; these migrate through the solution to the cathode, where they are reduced to copper atoms which are deposited on the electrode. As a result the anode shrinks in size; in contrast, the cathode becomes larger as pure copper is deposited.

How does this process separate the copper from the impurities present in the anode slab? The metallic impurities present are of two types: those which are more active than copper (Zn, Pb, Ni) and those which are less active (Ag, Au). The latter elements are not as easily converted to their

29-9 Copper cathodes of 99.98 percent purity are being lifted from electrolysis refining tanks. The workman is standing on rows of alternating impure copper anodes (suspended by lugs) and pure copper cathodes (suspended from horizontal cross bars).

ions as is the copper. When the copper atoms are oxidized to their ions at the anode, the gold and silver remain as atoms which drop to the bottom to form the "anode mud." By the same token, the metals more active than copper are converted to their ions at the same time. How are they separated? Ions of metals low in the activity series *are more easily reduced* to their atoms than are ions of the active metals. At the cathode, therefore, copper ions are reduced to the metal while ions of zinc and nickel remain in solution.

Electrorefining of copper is not expensive, since it requires only small amounts of electric power. Furthermore, the anode mud is not wasted. It is washed out of the tanks, dried, and sent to refineries for the recovery of its gold and silver content. The value of these metals often pays for the cost of electricity used in refining the copper.

The Properties of Copper

Pure copper is 8.9 times as dense as water, and melts at 1,083° C. The metal is very *malleable* and *ductile,* and therefore finds extensive use in sheets and wire (Fig. 29-10).

Copper oxidizes slowly in moist air. After a time, the oxide combines with carbon dioxide and water vapor to form a greenish-blue basic copper carbonate.

$$2\,CuO + CO_2 + H_2O \longrightarrow Cu(OH)_2 \cdot CuCO_3$$

The metal does not replace hydrogen in acids; but in the presence of oxygen, copper reacts slowly with nonoxidizing acids to form water and the corresponding cupric salt.

$$2\,Cu + 4\,HCl + O_2 \longrightarrow 2\,CuCl_2 + 2\,H_2O$$
$$2\,Cu + 2\,H_2SO_4 + O_2 \longrightarrow 2\,CuSO_4 + 2\,H_2O$$

Oxidizing acids (nitric and hot, concentrated sulfuric) also react with copper to form the corresponding salts.

$$\underset{\text{(conc.)}}{Cu + 4\,HNO_3} \longrightarrow Cu(NO_3)_2 + 2\,H_2O + 2\,NO_2\uparrow$$

29-10 Individual strands of thin copper wire (center) are being drawn into a copper cable of wider diameter (emerging from the topmost unit).

The Uses of Copper

Because it is not attacked by water or dilute acids, metallic copper is used for piping, roofing materials, and making coins. Because of its superior electrical conductivity (exceeded only by silver), the metal finds great use in electrical wiring. Another major application of the metal is in the preparation of alloys.

The widespread use of copper alloys arises out of qualities that make them superior to copper alone. Their ductility, malleability, and resistance to corrosion are often superior to those of copper, while their toughness, strength, and tensile qualities are comparable to those of steel.

The Alloys of Copper

The most common copper alloy is *brass,* in which zinc is the alloying element. The typical yellow brass of your experience consists of about two-thirds copper. An increase in this proportion makes the brass reddish. The melting point of brass is lower than that of pure copper; this property makes the alloy suitable for castings. Brass has the further advantage of being harder than copper; brass is also machined easily into screws, nuts and bolts, hinges, chains, gears, and piping.

Known to the ancients and still used today for statuary is *bronze,* an alloy of copper and tin. The recovery from the earth of bronze statuary many centuries old testifies to this alloy's excellent resistance to corrosion. This property makes bronze useful in propeller blades, laundry machines, and similar devices where even traces of rust are undesirable. Bronze, much harder than copper, is an ideal metal for pennies, which are subject to constant use and contact with the corrosive chemicals of perspiration.

The proportion of copper and tin in bronze may vary. Some of the tin may even be replaced by other metals without any loss in desirable properties of the alloy, but with a saving of the more expensive and less plentiful tin. Coinage and medal bronze contain copper, tin, and zinc. The addition of a small amount of phosphorus produces phosphor bronze; substitution of silicon and manganese for the tin produces the bronze known as Everdur. Phosphor bronze and Everdur are highly resistant to the corrosive action of salt water, and are much used in ships' propellers and fittings.

Close inspection of old coins or antique jewelry reveals signs of wear. The edges and features of the coins are worn smooth; fine detail in the jewelry has become indistinct. Each of these objects is an alloy. Had the article been made of the pure metal, this wear would have progressed more rapidly. For gold coins (not used as currency in the United States since 1933), this wearing away of metal lowers the value of a coin. Copper is therefore added to gold and silver to increase their hardness, and to prevent wear as well as reduce cost.

Copper and Printing

Copper is used in the printing of books which require a fairly large number of copies. The *type metal* used to cast type which gives a sharp impression of letters is not hard enough to withstand the wear of making many thousands of copies. After the type has been set in pages, a plastic impression is made of the page. The plastic mold is then sprayed with a solution of silver nitrate; the chemicals of the plastic act as reducing agents to convert the silver ions to free silver. This is deposited on the surface of the mold, and provides electrical conductivity. The mold is then made the cathode, and electroplated with copper (Fig. 29-11). When a sufficient thickness of copper has been deposited, the thin plating of copper is removed, and filled with molten lead to provide a firm base. We now have an *electrotype* of a page, capable of producing two or three hundred thousand copies. This electrotype is often plated with much harder metals such as chromium or nickel, and is then capable of being used to print many thousands of additional copies.

Copper Sulfate

The most used copper compound is *copper sulfate* (blue vitriol), made by reacting copper with hot, concentrated sulfuric acid, or by treating the oxide with dilute sulfuric acid.

29-11 A plastic mold, treated chemically so that copper will adhere to it, is being inserted in the solution as the cathode for copper plating.

$$CuO + H_2SO_4 \longrightarrow CuSO_4 + H_2O$$

The salt crystallizes from water as the blue pentahydrate $CuSO_4 \cdot 5\,H_2O$. It is used as the electrolyte in copper plating and in certain types of electric cells. Small amounts are added to reservoirs to control the growth of algae. A mixture of the solutions of copper sulfate and calcium hydroxide is used as a spray to control the growth of fungi on fruit trees. The copper content of such sprays makes them poisonous.

Copper Halides

The copper halides, except for the iodide, are made by reacting the heated metal with the halogen vapors. The chloride is yellow when anhydrous and blue-green in the form of the dihydrate; the bromide is a black solid. If an attempt is made to prepare cupric iodide by double replacement reactions between solutions of a cupric salt and potassium iodide, the mixture turns brown and a white precipitate of cuprous iodide settles out. The cupric ion *oxidizes* the iodide to free iodine and is itself reduced to the cuprous form.

$$2\,Cu^{+2} + 2\,SO_4^{-2} + 4\,K^+ + 4\,I^- \longrightarrow$$
$$4\,K^+ + 2\,SO_4^{-2} + 2\,\underset{+1}{Cu}I\downarrow + I_2^0$$

Copper Hydroxide

Copper hydroxide precipitates as a pale blue material when solutions of bases are added to solutions of cupric salts. The compound possesses an unusual and useful property which you can *observe for yourself.*

> Add 5 ml of a *dilute* solution of ammonia to 5 ml of a dilute solution of cupric sulfate. Note the pale blue cupric hydroxide that precipitates. Now carefully add to the mixture 5 ml of *concentrated* ammonia water. Observe that the precipitated cupric hydroxide dissolves to yield a deep blue solution.

The first reaction forms cupric hydroxide:

$$Cu^{+2} + SO_4^{-2} + 2\,NH_4 + 2\,OH^- \longrightarrow$$
$$Cu(OH)_2 + 2\,NH_4^+ + SO_4^{-2}$$

The deep blue solution results from a reaction between the cupric hydroxide and *excess ammonia* to form the soluble **complex ion,** $Cu(NH_3)_4^{+2}$. In this complex cupric-ammonia ion the ammonia molecules are combined with the cupric *ion* by *covalent bonds,* very much as water molecules in hydrates are attached to the metal ion.

$$Cu(OH)_2 + 4\,NH_3 \longrightarrow Cu(NH_3)_4^{+2} + 2\,OH^-$$

The color of the cupric-ammonia complex is so intense that this reaction can be used to detect a minute quantity of copper ions in solution.

Complex Ions

The formation of complex ions, illustrated by the solubility of cupric hydroxide in excess ammonia water, occurs frequently in chemistry. It involves a competition between two equilibria for a given ion, usually metallic, that is common to both. Copper hydroxide is slightly soluble in water, and the very small amount of dissolved material may be considered to be practically entirely dissociated.

$$Cu(OH)_2 \rightleftharpoons Cu^{+2} + 2\,OH^-$$

In the presence of *ammonia* molecules, a second reaction occurs.

$$Cu^{+2} + 4\,NH_3 \rightleftharpoons Cu(NH_3)_4^{+2}$$

The equilibrium position in this reaction can be pushed far to the right by the use of *concentrated* ammonia. The cupric ions originally provided by the dissociation of the dissolved cupric hydroxide are changed into a new substance by the excess NH_3.

$$Cu(OH)_2 \longrightarrow Cu^{+2} + 2\,OH^-$$
insoluble $+$
                4 NH_3
                $\downarrow$
            $Cu(NH_3)_4^{+2}$
                soluble

The cupric hydroxide equilibrium is therefore unbalanced, and more cupric hydroxide goes into solution and dissociates in order to maintain an equilibrium concentration of cupric ions. But if these are also removed by conversion into the cupric-ammonia complex ion, the first equilibrium will again be unbalanced and the process will be repeated. If sufficient ammonia is present, all of the copper hydroxide goes into solution. Numerous other transition elements, such as silver, iron, zinc, and cobalt, also form complex ions (Table 29-3).

QUESTIONS AND PROBLEMS

1. What properties of copper account for its use in pipes, wire, roofing, and coins?

2. Describe briefly the process of extracting relatively pure copper from its ore. Include such terms as *froth flotation, gangue,* and *matte,* as well as essential equations.

3. How is "blister copper" refined?

4. Differentiate between bronze and brass.

5. What reaction occurs when concentrated ammonia water is added to insoluble cupric hydroxide?

SILVER AND GOLD

The origin of gold jewelry is lost in antiquity. The early Babylonians used gold jewelry and

Table 29-3   DISSOCIATION OF COMPLEX IONS

Complex ion	Dissociation reaction
Cobaltous-ammonia	$Co(NH_3)_6^{+2} \rightleftharpoons Co^{+2} + 6\,NH_3$
Cobaltic-ammonia	$Co(NH_3)_6^{+3} \rightleftharpoons Co^{+3} + 6\,NH_3$
Chromic-ammonia	$Cr(NH_3)_6^{+3} \rightleftharpoons Cr^{+3} + 6\,NH_3$
Cupric-ammonia	$Cu(NH_3)_4^{+2} \rightleftharpoons Cu^{+2} + 4\,NH_3$
Ferrocyanide	$Fe(CN)_6^{-4} \rightleftharpoons Fe^{+2} + 6\,CN^{-1}$
Ferricyanide	$Fe(CN)_6^{-3} \rightleftharpoons Fe^{+3} + 6\,CN^{-1}$
Gold-cyanide	$Au(CN)_2^{-1} \rightleftharpoons Au^{+1} + 2\,CN^{-1}$
Mercuric-cyanide	$Hg(CN)_4^{-2} \rightleftharpoons Hg^{+2} + 4\,CN^{-1}$
Silver-ammonia	$Ag(NH_3)_2^{+1} \rightleftharpoons Ag^{+1} + 2\,NH_3$
Silver-cyanide	$Ag(CN)_2^{-1} \rightleftharpoons Ag^{+1} + 2\,CN^{-1}$
Zinc-ammonia	$Zn(NH_3)_4^{+2} \rightleftharpoons Zn^{+2} + 4\,NH_3$
Zinc-cyanide	$Zn(CN)_4^{-2} \rightleftharpoons Zn^{+2} + 4\,CN^{-1}$

fashioned small gold figures. In Egypt, tools used in mining gold and descriptions of the recovery process date from around 4000 B.C. In 3600 B.C. the Code of Menes set the value of gold "as equal to 2½ parts of silver"—an indication that silver, as well as gold, was mined at that time.

As gold and silver often occur free, they require only physical separation from the rock and earth with which they are mixed. The lure of gold helped to open our West during the Gold Rush of 1849 and the Klondike region in 1897. The prospector "panned" for gold by shaking the gold-bearing sand or earth with water in a shallow pan. The heavy particles of gold settled quickly to the bottom of the pan; particles of lighter sand and earth remained suspended and were poured off with the water. For present-day, large-scale production, the same principle is applied. Gold-bearing quartz is crushed and then washed with a stream of water which carries away the lighter particles of rock. The channels, or sluices, through which the water flows have barriers (riffle plates) which trap the heavier gold particles. In hydraulic mining, a variation of this method, the earth is washed away by means of powerful streams of water.

Chemical Extraction of Gold and Silver

Where mechanical methods cannot be used efficiently to separate the free metals from earth

and rock, a number of chemical processsses can be applied. In the **amalgamation process,** finely crushed gold or silver ore is washed with a stream of water which flows over a layer of mercury. The lighter rock particles are washed away, while the gold or silver dissolves in the mercury to form an **amalgam.** The amalgam, an alloy of mercury and other metals, is then heated. The gold and silver remain behind as the mercury distills away, to be used again.

In the **cyanide process,** powdered silver or gold ore is mixed with a solution of sodium cyanide. After being exposed to warm air for several days, these metals form soluble complex cyanides (Fig. 29-12). After filtration, the solution is treated with metallic zinc; the more active zinc replaces the gold or silver in the cyanide complex. The precious metals can then be filtered off and melted down.

The formation of the complex cyanide ions as a means of dissolving the gold and silver is once again an application of equilibrium principles. When gold and silver react with sodium cyanide to form soluble *complex* cyanides, the metallic atoms are changed into *ions.*

$$4\,Au^0 + O_2 + 8\,Na^+ + 8\,CN^- + 2\,H_2O \longrightarrow$$
$$4\,Na^+ + 4\,Au(CN)_2^- + 4\,Na^+ + 4\,OH^-$$

$$4\,Ag^0 + O_2 + 8\,Na^+ + 8\,CN^- + 2\,H_2O \longrightarrow$$
$$4\,Na^+ + 4\,Ag(CN)_2^- + 4\,Na^+ + 4\,OH^-$$

The low position of gold and silver in the electrochemical series indicates that these metals show little tendency to change to the ionic form.

$$Ag^0 - 1\,e^- \rightleftharpoons Ag^+$$
$$Au^0 - 1\,e^- \rightleftharpoons Au^+$$

The equilibrium position lies far to the left, but this position can be shifted to the right by removing the product. This is the function of the cyanide ion, which removes the metal ion from the above equilibria in the form of stable, complex ions. In turn, more gold or silver is ionized, and goes into solution to maintain the equilibrium.

Other reactions which form soluble compounds of gold and silver can also be used to separate

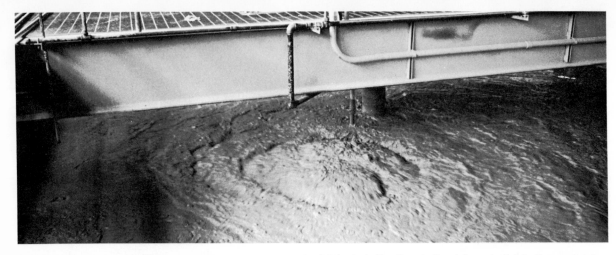

29-12 After gold ore is crushed and powdered, it is mixed with sodium cyanide solution and agitated with warm air to form soluble gold cyanide. Eventually zinc is added to displace the gold, which is filtered off and melted.

these metals from rock and earth. Gold is sometimes extracted by reaction with chlorine to form the soluble, *stable* complex acid, $HAuCl_4$.

$$2\,Au + 2\,HCl + 3\,Cl_2 \longrightarrow 2\,HAuCl_4$$

Treatment of the solution with a reducing agent such as ferrous sulfate transforms the ionic gold complex to the free metal.

Silver, when dissolved out of its ores by treatment with dilute sulfuric acid in the presence of air, forms somewhat soluble silver sulfate.

$$4\,Ag^0 + 4\,H^+ + 2\,SO_4^{-2} + O_2 \longrightarrow$$
$$4\,Ag^+ + 2\,SO_4^{-2} + 2\,H_2O$$

The silver ions are then replaced by the more active copper.

$$Cu^0 + 2\,Ag^+ + SO_4^{-2} \longrightarrow$$
$$2\,Ag^0 + Cu^{+2} + SO_4^{-2}$$

By-product Gold and Silver

Because of their high price, it is profitable to recover even small amounts of gold and silver that may be present in the ores of other metals. Several major industries help to increase our supply of gold and silver by yielding these metals as by-products. The gold and silver recovered from the sludge of the electrorefining of copper

are separated by treatment with concentrated nitric acid. The acid oxidizes the silver to silver nitrate but does not affect the gold.

Gold and silver are also often obtained in the metallurgy of lead. To separate these metals from the lead, 1 to 2 percent of zinc metal is added to the molten lead. The zinc acts as a solvent for the gold and silver. However, as the zinc is less dense than the lead and not miscible with it, the zinc-silver and zinc-gold alloys float to the surface, cool and harden. The crust formed is skimmed off, and the zinc is removed by distillation to leave the precious metals. This procedure is the **Parkes process.**

Finally, wherever gold and silver articles are fabricated or tooled, the sweepings and dust are collected for their gold and silver content and sold to refineries. Considerable silver is also reclaimed from processing tanks in photographic establishments. A related source of silver is old photographic film.

The Properties of Gold and Silver

Gold and silver are typical metals, as they are much denser than water, excellent reflectors of light, and good conductors of heat and electricity. Silver is superior to copper in the latter respects.

These metals are soft, a property that makes them easy to tool but unable to withstand wear. Gold is the most ductile and malleable metal known.

Silver and gold, which appear near the bottom of the electrochemical series, show the least tendency of all metals to form compounds. Conversely, combined gold and silver are readily reduced to the metallic form either by chemical reduction or simply by heating their compounds.

Very few chemicals react with gold and silver, even at higher temperatures. These metals are not affected by atmospheric oxygen; and their oxides, when formed by other chemical reactions, are decomposed readily at temperatures not much above that of boiling water. Aqua regia (and chlorine water) oxidizes them to the chlorides.

$$5\,Au + \underbrace{23\,HCl + 6\,HNO_3}_{\text{aqua regia}} \longrightarrow$$
$$5\,HAuCl_4 + 3\,NO\uparrow + 3\,NOCl + 12\,H_2O$$

Oxidizing agents such as concentrated nitric acid and hot, concentrated sulfuric acid will oxidize silver but will not affect gold.

The Uses of Gold and Silver

Most of the gold and silver is used today as it has been for thousands of years—for jewelry and coinage. The metals, as a rule, are not used in the pure form. The designations of **karat** for gold and **fine** for silver indicate the percentage of these metals present in alloys. Pure gold is designated 24 karat, while pure silver is labeled 1000 fine. A 14 k gold ring contains 14 parts (by weight) of gold and 10 parts of the alloying metal or metals. *Sterling silver* is sometimes marked *925 fine*, the silver representing 92.5 percent of the alloy. Table 29-4 tabulates the composition of some common jewelry and coinage alloys.

The relative inactivity of gold and silver compared to most metals makes them ideal for dental work. Combined with mercury to form amalgams, they withstand the chemical action of both body and food. Both silver and gold amalgams are employed as tooth-filling materials; gold also

Table 29-4   **COMMON SILVER AND GOLD ALLOYS**

Alloy	Composition (percent)
U.S. silver coinage*	Ag (90), Cu (10)
Former U.S. gold coins	Au (90), Cu (10)
Sterling silver	Ag (92.5), Cu (7.5)
18 k gold (yellow)	Au (75), Ag (12.5), Cu (12.5)

* Prior to late 1965.

serves to make caps (that are usually not seen) and bridges for teeth.

Articles are often electroplated with gold or silver to provide the appearance of these metals at a greatly reduced cost. Silver plate is familiar in tableware (Fig. 29-13), candlesticks, and jewelry; watch cases are often gold-plated.

The thin layers produced by electroplating can also be produced mechanically. Gold can be beaten into foil so thin that it transmits light. This

29-13 The forks being silver plated are attached to the cathode in each section of the tank. A bar of pure silver serves as the anode; the electrolyte is a solution of silver potassium cyanide. The silver must be polished after being electroplated.

gold leaf, usually about 0.0001 millimeter in thickness, is used for decorative purposes, as in bookbinding or lettering signs on glass.

The film of silver which reflects light from a mirror is produced by chemical reduction of a silver compound.

Silver and the Photographic Process

One of the most important uses of silver depends on the properties of its compounds, particularly those of the silver halides. *Observe this for yourself.*

Working in dim light, mix solutions of silver nitrate and sodium chloride. Filter the precipitated silver chloride and spread the filter paper on a watch glass. Place a coin on top of part of the paper; then expose the watch glass to direct sunlight. Within a few

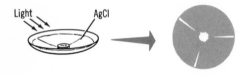

minutes the silver chloride on the filter paper darkens, first developing violet tints and then becoming gray-black. Quickly lift the coin. The silver chloride under the coin is unchanged.

The color change observed results from the formation of finely divided silver, light energy having initiated the decomposition.

$$2\,AgCl \xrightarrow[\text{energy}]{\text{light}} 2\,Ag + Cl_2$$

Silver bromide and silver iodide are also light sensitive, responding even more rapidly than silver chloride.

Repeat the preparation of silver chloride and shake the contents of the tube to cause coagulation of the precipitate. Pour off as much liquid as possible, and add a solution of sodium thiosulfate ($Na_2S_2O_3 \cdot 5\,H_2O$) to the precipitate. Does it dissolve?

These two reactions of the silver halides—their decomposition by light and their solubility in sodium thiosulfate ("hypo")—are fundamental to the chemistry of photography.

Photographic films and plates consist of cellulose acetate or glass, respectively, coated with an emulsion of the silver halides (singly or in combination) in gelatin. When the film is exposed to light, decomposition of the silver halide is *initiated,* but the reaction does not proceed further *in the dry state.* Therefore, the film is placed (in the dark or under a weak red or sodium vapor light) into a solution of a *developer,* a combination of chemicals which completes the decomposition. Since the decomposition of the silver halide represents a process of reduction ($Ag^+ + e^- \longrightarrow Ag^0$), the developing solution always contains reducing agents.

The amount of silver deposited on the different parts of the film depends on the amount of light reflected *by various objects* to the film. Where much light is reflected (as from a white shirt), more of the silver halide in the emulsion decomposes and the film appears black. A dark object (such as a blue jacket) reflects less light to the film, and that area of the film is lighter. Thus, the developed film shows a series of light and dark areas that are the *reverse of the actual object.* It is, therefore, called a **negative** (Fig. 29-14).

The unchanged silver halide in the negative (unchanged because it was not struck by light) is removed before the negative can be exposed to light by placing the film in a solution of sodium thiosulfate. This treatment dissolves any remaining silver salts. After the hypo solution has been poured off and washed from the film, the negative is dried. It is now ready for the preparation (printing) of the final picture.

In the printing process, the negative is placed on a sheet of paper coated with a silver halide emulsion. It is then exposed to light which *passes through the negative* to the *emulsion on the paper.* Where the negative is dark (much silver deposited), the light which strikes the emulsion is weak. Conversely, where the negative is light (little silver deposited), the light passing through

29-14 In the positive print at the right exposed Alpine surfaces appear dark. "Rivers of snow" that flow on either side of the exposed areas appear white. In the negative at the left the exposed surfaces appear to be snow-covered.

is strong. As a result, when the paper is developed, *the shades are opposite to those on the negative.* It is for this reason that the final picture (called a print) is known as a **positive** (Fig. 29-14). The positive, like the negative, must be washed in hypo to remove any unchanged silver halide before exposure to light. The positive, washed free of hypo and dried, is the finished picture for your album or wallet. The negative can be used repeatedly to make more prints.

Two features are foremost in this chapter. First, it indicates how scientists have improved on Mendeleev's original periodic table by arranging the elements on the basis of their orbital electron devolopment. And second, it explains how the elements formerly placed in Mendeleev's B groups represent a systematic pattern of development of electron shells within each of the long periods. The properties of the transition elements, as demonstrated by the group IB elements, are peculiarly different from those of the other elements. In the next chapter, you will study another of these elements in some detail.

QUESTIONS AND PROBLEMS

1. How does the amalgamation process for extracting gold and silver differ from the cyanide process?

2. Describe briefly the Parkes process for recovering gold and silver from the metallurgy of lead.

3. (a) What is the percent by weight of gold in 14 k and in 22 k gold? (b) What is the percent by weight of silver in those U.S. coins that are 900 *fine?*

4. Copper and silver have oxidation states of $+1$ and $+2$, but gold exists as either $+1$ or $+3$. Account for this difference.

5. Describe briefly the chemical reactions that occur when a picture is taken, the film developed, and the negative printed.

VALUE OF THE CONCEPT

THE CONCEPT

In Mendeleev's original periodic table the elements which fell into groups had to be subdivided further into subgroups A and B. Thus oxygen, sulfur, selenium, and tellurium fell into the same group as chromium, molybdenum, and tungsten. But the first four, showing strong family resemblances, were distinctly different from the latter, which in themselves constitute another family of elements. On the basis of the electron configuration of the atoms, new forms of the table have replaced that of Mendeleev. Each of the B groups of the elements represents a family of transition elements. In modern periodic tables the group VIB elements listed above are transition elements, in contrast to the members of the group VIA family whose electron configurations follow a normal development.

The pattern of the transition elements develops because electrons in orbitals of a lower quantum number electron shell may have higher energy levels than electrons in orbitals of high quantum number electron shells. For example, the 3d orbitals have a higher energy level than the 4s orbitals. In the transition elements, which occur in the middle of a period, electrons enter into shells other than the outermost because an orbital of the inner shell has a lower energy than the next orbital in the outer shell. The filling of the 3d and 4d orbitals in the next to the outer shell occurs in periods 4 and 5, respectively. Since the d orbitals provide for 10 electrons, the transition series in the fourth and fifth periods each contain ten elements. In the sixth and seventh periods, the transition series develop as the 4f and 5f orbitals, respectively, are filled. As these f orbitals provide for 14 electrons, the lanthanide and actinide series (periods 6 and 7) each contain fourteen elements. Because the f orbitals which are being filled in these series are two shells removed from the outer shell, differences among succeeding elements in these series are very minor. All the members of these series show pronounced resemblances to each other.

The transition elements are characterized by two main features, variable oxidation states and colored ions. As an example of A and B subgroups, the copper family of transition elements was contrasted with the alkali metals, similarly characterized by a single outermost electron. The two groups are far apart in other respects. The IB group of elements, including silver and gold in addition to copper, are typically metallic, although their hardness is well below that of most metals. They are the most malleable and ductile elements known. While the group IA metals are high in the electrochemical series, the copper group metals lie at the opposite end. This difference is reflected in the occurrence, extraction, and uses of copper and the precious metals. The metallurgy of pure copper demonstrates both the froth flotation process and electrolytic refining. Gold and silver are extracted by the amalgamation, cyanide, and Parkes processes. All group IB metals find wide use in alloys; the precious metals are important in jewelry-making. While the compounds of the IA elements are highly stable, those of the copper group of metals are very often easily decomposed.

USING THE CONCEPT

Using the Basic Concept

1. How can the knowledge of the lanthanides and actinides enable the scientist to predict the properties of the new elements which are being created by nuclear reactions?

2. (a) How does the electron structure of the transition elements account for their variable oxidation states? (b) What other property is characteristic of the transition elements?

3. Contrast the alkali metals and their compounds with the group IB elements and their compounds in as many ways as possible.

4. How are the facts of the electrochemical series of the metals applied in the electrorefining of group IB metals?

5. What is the essential difference in electron configuration between the period 4 and 5 transition elements, and the period 6 and 7 transition elements?

6. The atomic radii of the elements in the lanthanide series change remarkably little from one end of the series to the other. Explain why.

7. (a) How does the position of the B subgroups in the modern periodic table differ from their position in Mendeleev's table? (b) Why is their position in the modern table preferable?

8. Explain the basis for the terms *positive* and *negative* in photography.
9. How does the cyanide process for refining gold and silver make use of equilibrium principles?
10. Cupric nitrate decomposes on heating to yield cupric oxide, oxygen, and nitric oxide. Write a balanced equation for the reaction.
11. (a) How does an amalgam differ from other alloys? (b) What are the chief alloys of each of the group IB elements? (c) Of what elements is each of these alloys composed?
12. What properties of copper, silver, gold, and their compounds can be related to the position of these metals in the electrochemical series?
13. Explain why copper and its alloys are resistant to corrosion by the atmosphere.
14. Relate the main uses of copper, silver, and gold to their particular properties.
15. Describe the metallurgy of pure copper from an ore such as $CuFeS_2$.
16. (a) If enough heavier elements could be synthesized to complete the seventh period of the periodic table, how many elements would this period contain? (b) Give a reason for your answer.
17. In the froth flotation process, if the oil used were to wet particles of the gangue, but not those bearing the metal, could a concentration of the ore be effected? Explain why.
18. How could you remove a thin layer of copper which had been plated on another metal without affecting the underlying metal?

Relating Terms Within the Concept

Each of the following exercises consists of five terms. From the last four, select the term or terms closely related to the *italicized* term.

1. *gold:* malleable, ductile, 925 *fine*, +2 oxidation state
2. *lanthanide:* 4f orbitals, variable oxidation states, rare earth elements, rare gases
3. *froth flotation:* matte, gangue, copper, metallurgy
4. *copper:* blue vitriol, cyanide process, Parkes process, complex ions
5. *alloy:* amalgam, brass, sterling silver, bronze
6. *silver:* aqua regia, thermal conductivity, karat, electroplating
7. *actinide:* 5f orbitals, period 5, 3d electrons, transuranic elements
8. *group IB:* transition elements, cesium, period 1, period 7

Solving Problems Within the Concept

1. What is the percentage by weight of (a) gold in 18 k gold? (b) silver in 800 *fine* silver?
2. How many grams of copper sulfate pentahydrate, $CuSO_4 \cdot 5\,H_2O$, are needed to prepare 400 ml of a 2 M solution of the salt?
3. If an electric cell were made up of a silver electrode in a 1 M silver nitrate solution connected to a zinc electrode in a 1 M zinc nitrate solution, what would the voltage of the cell be?
4. If equal *volumes* of copper and gold were melted together and there were no expansion or contraction of the added volumes, what would the density of the alloy be at room temperature?
5. A compound contains 73.7 percent by weight of silver and 26.3 percent by weight of fluorine. (a) What is the formula of the compound? (b) What is the oxidation state of the silver?
6. What weight of silver chloride could be precipitated from 40.00 ml of a 2 N solution of silver nitrate?
7. A newly minted 1960 dime weighs 2.50 grams. If the dime were dissolved in concentrated nitric acid and the solution diluted to a volume of 100 ml, what would the molarity of the solution be with respect to (a) the copper (b) the silver?

8. Copper has two naturally occurring isotopes of weights 63 and 65. The former represents 69.09 percent of the atoms, the latter 30.91 percent. On this basis, what should the atomic weight of copper be?

Applying the Concept
1. What advantages does copper or brass have over iron when used in plumbing?
2. Cupric ions oxidize iodide ions to the element. Why doesn't the same type of reaction occur when cupric ions are added to bromides and chlorides?
3. Though the oxidation state of +3 is known for gold, it is a great rarity among silver compounds. Why?
4. How could you identify the metallic ions in a solution containing compounds of copper, silver, and gold?
5. Write a series of equations showing how copper can be extracted from an ore containing copper carbonate.
6. Silver sulfide reacts with concentrated nitric acid to form silver nitrate, water, sulfur, and nitrogen dioxide. Balance the equation by the electron-transfer method.
7. Write a balanced electronic equation for the replacement of: (a) silver in silver nitrate by iron (b) copper in copper sulfate by aluminum (c) gold in auric chloride by zinc.
8. What other chemical industry might be established near plants in which copper sulfide ores are being roasted? Why?
9. In the absence of chemical tests, what properties could be used to distinguish between a solid gold or silver article from one which is plated with these metals?
10. Why does silver nitrate produce dark or black stains in contact with such materials as paper, cloth, and flesh? What practical use can be made of this fact?

Reading Further
Discovery of the Elements, 7th ed., by Mary E. Weeks, Washington, D.C., Journal of Chemical Education, 1968. An account of the patient investigation which led to the discovery of each of the elements.
"Photographic Development," by T. H. James, *Scientific American,* November 1952. Of interest to both the experienced photographer and the novice.
"Separating Solids with Bubbles," by A. M. Guadin, *Scientific American,* December 1956. Some newly developed metallurgical processes are increasing yield and saving time.

30

The Iron Triad

Pictured below is the most impressive sight on the skyline of industrial America—the blast furnace (Fig. 30-1). In these furnaces iron is extracted from its ore; later it is made into steel. The steel, in turn, forms the skeletons of buildings and bridges, bank vaults, knives, and minute watch springs. The discovery and processing of iron marked a turning point in history; its present-day fabrication has brought about a change in our way of life.

The Triads of Group VIII

Though iron is the best known of the transition elements, we are familiar with it as a specific metal; our experience rarely tells us anything of its relationship to other elements. Let us investi-gate this relationship by studying the element as a member of a particular group of elements in the periodic table.

Midway through each of the long periods (4, 5, and 6), there occurs a horizontal sequence of three elements: Fe-Co-Ni, Ru-Rh-Pd, and Os-Ir-Pt. The members of each of these horizontal sequences, or **triads,** are closely alike in their properties—so close, in fact, that the nine elements, rather than the anticipated three in a vertical arrangement, constitute group VIII of the long form of the periodic table. In long periods 4, 5, and 6, the transition elements develop as the d orbitals of the next to the outer electron shell are filled. Each of the three horizontal triads develops just after the d orbitals in their respective periods are half-filled. Since elements whose atoms have half-filled or completely filled d orbitals possess unusual stability, the elements in the three triads of group VIII are quite stable.

Inspection of Table 30-1 shows that the members of the *iron triad* are remarkably alike in their properties. Iron, cobalt, and nickel show a greater resemblance to each other than to the transition elements on either side in period 4, or to their analogous triads in periods 5 and 6. But variations

30-1 When in operation at night, the ten-story tall blast furnaces and their accompanying "stoves" in the giant steel mills on both banks of the Monongahela River light up the sky over Pittsburgh to form a truly distinctive landmark.

Table 30-1 **THE IRON TRIAD**

Element	Atomic number	Atomic weight	Electron configuration	Density (g/ml, 20° C)	Melting point (° C)	Boiling point (° C)	State and color	Ionization potential	Oxidation states
Iron	26	55.847	2 8 14 2	7.86	1535	3000	Silver-white solid	7.9	+2, +3
Cobalt	27	58.9332	2 8 15 2	8.9	1495	2900	Reddish-gray solid	7.9	+2, +3
Nickel	28	58.71	2 8 16 2	8.9	1455	2900	White solid	7.6	+2, +3

do exist. Iron is the most magnetic substance known, even more than cobalt and nickel; these, in turn, are much more magnetic than other elements. In compounds, iron, cobalt, and nickel exist in a number of oxidation states. Ferrous (+2) salts, except in special circumstances, are readily oxidized to the ferric (+3) form, which is the most stable oxidation state. In contrast, the lower oxidation state (+2) is stable in cobalt and nickel compounds. These elements may exist in the higher state when the element forms a complex compound [as in cobaltic-ammonia chloride, $Co(NH_3)_6Cl_3$] or a highly insoluble substance (as in nickelic oxide, Ni_2O_3).

IRON AND STEEL

Iron is the second most abundant metallic element in the crust of the earth. It is extracted fairly easily from its compounds and can be worked without difficulty when heated. Although iron is soft and corrodes easily, many workers in iron and steel mills discovered by trial and error that its properties could be modified by alloying the metal with other metallic elements.

Pure iron is a rarity, even in the laboratory. Iron, like all metals, is found in minerals of the earth's crust. The chief minerals include iron oxides, sulfides, and carbonates. These, combined with clays, sand, and other metallic compounds, form iron **ores,** the most common of which are *hematite,* Fe_2O_3; *limonite,* a hydrated ferric oxide; *siderite,* $FeCO_3$; and *pyrites,* FeS_2. The chief ore in the United States is hematite, major deposits of which are found in the Lake Superior region of Minnesota, Wisconsin, and Michigan, as well as in Alabama.

Eighty percent of the steel-making plants in the United States are located in the Great Lakes area. Industry came, as it often does, to the source of raw materials. Most of the ore used is supplied by open-pit mining from the Mesabi range in Minnesota (Fig. 30-2). It is transported by ship to the lake ports and stockpiled to provide supplies for the winter months when shipping is ice-bound. This location is also convenient to deposits of limestone and soft coal, used in producing steel. As the deposits in the Mesabi range show signs of approaching exhaustion, the steel industry has developed methods for magnetically separating the iron oxide particles in

30-2 An open-pit mine in the Mesabi range in Minnesota. It is hard to imagine the vast size of these pits, which are interlaced with roadways.

low-grade iron ores, called *taconite*. The industry is also importing ore from Venezuela and from newly opened deposits in Canada's Labrador region.

The **metallurgy** of iron, the process of extracting the metal from its ores, depends upon the composition of the ores as well as the nature and amount of impurities present. Usually iron is extracted from its ore and converted into steel in the same plant; therefore, we will consider the two processes together.

The Blast Furnace

Iron is extracted from its ore in huge blast furnaces by **smelting,** the reduction of an ore with carbon. Higher than a ten-story building, and 30 feet in diameter at its base, the furnace is made of a steel shell, lined with a layer of fire-resistant brick. Next to it are several tall cylinders called "stoves," also lined with firebrick and equipped with gas burners at the bottom. Pipes (tuyères) lead from these stoves, designed to heat the air, to a series of openings in the lower portion of the furnace (Fig. 30-3).

Charges of iron ore, limestone, and coke (carbon) are fed into the furnace through openings at the top. These openings, called *airlocks,* are designed to prevent the escape of the hot gases when the charge is introduced. The proportions of materials in the charge depend on the composition of the ore, which formerly was determined by experience but now is determined by accurate chemical analysis. The percentage of iron oxide in the ore determines the amount of coke necessary, while the amount of silicates (and phosphates) present determines the amount of limestone needed. On the average, 1¾ tons of ore, 1 ton of coke, ½ ton of limestone, and *4 tons of air* are needed to produce 1 ton of iron.

Coke is a desirable fuel for mechanical reasons as well as for its low cost. It is strong enough to support the weight of very heavy layers of material above it, and porous enough to allow the blast of air to pass through it readily. The coke burns in the air blast to produce heat and gaseous products of combustion.

As the *charge* moves down inside the furnace, its temperature increases; the limestone acts as a flux by reacting with the impurities in the ore and coke to form a slag. At the same time, the iron in the ore is reduced to molten metallic iron. Both the molten iron and the molten slag move to the bottom of the furnace, where the slag floats on top of the iron and shields it from being

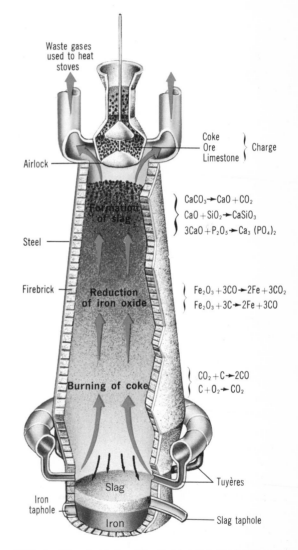

$$CaCO_3 \rightarrow CaO + CO_2$$
$$CaO + SiO_2 \rightarrow CaSiO_3$$
$$3CaO + P_2O_5 \rightarrow Ca_3(PO_4)_2$$

$$Fe_2O_3 + 3CO \rightarrow 2Fe + 3CO_2$$
$$Fe_2O_3 + 3C \rightarrow 2Fe + 3CO$$

$$CO_2 + C \rightarrow 2CO$$
$$C + O_2 \rightarrow CO_2$$

30-3 An all-important feature of the blast furnace is that it operates continuously, molten iron and slag being drawn off at intervals, and the charge (consisting of coke, iron ore, and limestone) periodically renewed.

30-4 A "submarine" ladle is being filled with molten iron from a blast furnace. The ladle is used to carry 165 tons of molten metal from the blast furnace to the open-hearth furnace, where it rolls on its axis to pour from above.

oxidized by the incoming air. This iron is far from pure. Silicon from the ore and carbon from the coke are mixed with the molten metal. In addition, small amounts of other impurities, such as phosphorus and sulfur, also remain in the molten iron.

If the iron is to be used at any considerable distance from the furnace, it is cast (poured) into moving chains of molds where it solidifies into blocks called "pigs." The iron in this form is called *pig iron,* a name that arose from the resemblance of early castings of this type to a litter of pigs.

Reactions in the Blast Furnace

Although it is impossible to write an equation for every reaction that occurs within the blast furnace to produce metallic iron, let us consider in slow motion the major reactions. The burning of coke in excess air or oxygen results in the formation of carbon dioxide and the production of the high temperature needed for the furnace reactions.

$$C + O_2 \xrightarrow{\Delta} CO_2\uparrow + \Delta$$

The hot carbon dioxide is reduced to carbon monoxide almost immediately as it comes into contact with the hot coke above it.

$$CO_2 + C \xrightarrow{\Delta} 2\,CO\uparrow$$

The carbon monoxide moves up through the furnace under the pressure of the incoming air blast and reduces the iron oxide.

$$Fe_2O_3 + 3\,CO \xrightarrow{\Delta} 2\,Fe + 3\,CO_2\uparrow$$

This reaction is reversible; the point of equilibrium is pushed to the right by maintaining an excess of carbon monoxide.

In the lower portion of the furnace, where the temperature is higher, some of the iron oxide is reduced directly by the hot coke.

$$Fe_2O_3 + 3\,C \xrightarrow{\Delta} 2\,Fe + 3\,CO\uparrow$$

The limestone is decomposed to carbon dioxide and calcium oxide, which removes sandy matter and silicates from the ore by converting them to insoluble calcium silicate. At the same time, phosphate impurities are removed as calcium phosphate by a similar reaction with calcium oxide. The calcium silicate and phosphate melt at the high temperature of the furnace and sink to the bottom as a layer of slag.

$$CaCO_3 \xrightarrow{\Delta} CaO + CO_2\uparrow$$
$$CaO + SiO_2 \xrightarrow{\Delta} CaSiO_3 \text{ (slag)}$$
$$3\,CaO + P_2O_5 \xrightarrow{\Delta} Ca_3(PO_4)_2 \text{ (slag)}$$

The blast furnace is one of the many examples of an efficient chemical plant. It operates continuously, being shut down only when repairs are needed or the demand for the product falls off. Excess gases coming from the furnace do not pass directly into the air. First, dust is removed to recover unchanged iron oxide, as well as potassium compounds which are valuable in fertilizers. The gas itself, containing combustible carbon monoxide, is used as a fuel to preheat the air which is forced into the furnace. A recent modification in the process has led to much greater efficiency. Instead of an air blast, 80 percent of which is inactive nitrogen, some furnaces utilize pure oxygen. Although its initial cost is greater, pure oxygen provides higher operating temperatures and consequently a more rapid process.

Products of the Blast Furnace

The liquid nature of both the slag and iron makes "tapping" the blast furnace a relatively simple matter. The clay plugs near the bottom of the furnace are burned out and the molten material is conducted through appropriate channels to large ladles or specially designed hot-metal cars (Fig. 30-4). Slag is often poured and cooled under jets of water to produce stony lumps useful in making concrete or as a bed for railroad ties. It may also be dumped when hot (Fig. 30-5) and crushed. Slag can be made into a fluffy-fibered insulating material called *mineral wool* by blowing jets of steam through it as it cools.

Cast Iron

About 10 percent of the pig iron produced goes to foundries where the metal is melted and cast into a variety of shapes. This form of iron, called *cast iron*, is the material of which stoves, radiators, and bathtubs are made. More extensive use of cast iron is prevented by a number of shortcomings. The metal cannot be welded (except in special circumstances); nor is it either malleable or ductile. Although strong, it is brittle and fractures easily. It cannot therefore be used for girders, plates, and springs. The need for these and related items in the expanding economy of the nineteenth century stimulated the search

for a product free of these defects. The result—now commonplace in refrigerators, automobiles, bridges, wire, and springs—is steel.

Steel

It would be incorrect to speak of *a* steel, for there are many kinds of steel. Each steel is chiefly iron, but steels vary in the small amount of carbon and various other metals present. Even when two different steels contain the same ingredients, a difference in their proportions gives each product totally different properties (Table 30-2). Even when the composition of steel remains constant, its properties can be varied by heat treating the steel in different ways (page 509). Steel making is a twofold process. The first process removes from the pig iron the impurities which give the metal undesirable properties. The second con-

30-5 In terms of the steelmaker, "slag is being dumped from thimbles at the skullcracker." When cooled, the slag is crushed into stony lumps and used in railroad beds or in place of stone chips in concrete.

trols the quantity of added elements which provide special properties in the finished product. Both of these processes are accomplished in one of three types of furnaces: the Bessemer converter, the open-hearth furnace, or the electric furnace.

The Bessemer Converter

The first successful process of making steel was developed independently by William Kelly, an American, and Henry Bessemer, an Englishman, who later bought out Kelly's company. In this process, impurities are removed from the molten iron by oxidation with air.

The Bessemer converter, in which the oxidation is performed, is an egg-shaped steel shell having a double bottom enclosing an air space (Fig. 30-6). This air space leads to one of the sup-porting arms of the converter. The upper part of this air space is perforated with holes. The converter is lined with heat-resisting (refractory) bricks in its upper portion. Molten iron is introduced into the converter by turning it on its side. A blast of cold air at a pressure of about 20 pounds per square inch is blown through the charge as the converter is tipped upright again. Although a blast of cold air is used, the heat developed by the oxidation of the impurities raises the temperature and makes the iron even hotter than it was at the beginning. The flame from the heated charge becomes yellow as the silicon impurities in the iron are oxidized. After about 5 minutes the flame becomes whiter and longer (Fig. 30-7), a sign that carbon is being oxidized. This continues for about 8 to 10 minutes. When the flames die down, a sign that oxidation

Table 30-2 **STEEL ALLOYS**

Name	Composition* (percent)	Properties	Uses
Stainless steel	Fe, Cr (10–20), Ni (8), C (0.1–0.3)	Corrosion-resistant	Cutlery, machinery for the food and chemical industries
Chrome steel	Fe, Cr (2–5), C (0.5–0.7)	Very hard and tough	Armor plate, auto parts (gears, axles, bearings)
Chrome-vanadium steel	Fe, Cr (3–10), V (0.5–5), C (0.7)	Great tensile strength	Automobile parts, springs
High-speed tool steel	Fe, W (12–20), Cr (2–5), V (1–3), C (0.7)	Maintains hardness at high temperatures	Cutting and grinding tools
Molybdenum steel	Fe, Mo (5)	Strong and tough	Automobile parts, drive shafts and gears
Manganese steel	Fe, Mn (12–14), C (1)	Exceedingly hard	Safes, teeth for power scoops, crushing and grinding machinery
Duriron	Fe, Si (12–15), Mn (0.35), C (0.85)	Acid resistant	Laboratory drains and piping
Invar	Fe, Ni (36)	Low coefficient of expansion	Instruments, clock pendulums, surveyors' tapes
Silicon steel	Fe, Si (2), C (0.4)	Easily magnetized and demagnetized	Cores of motors and transformers

* The percentages given are in addition to iron.

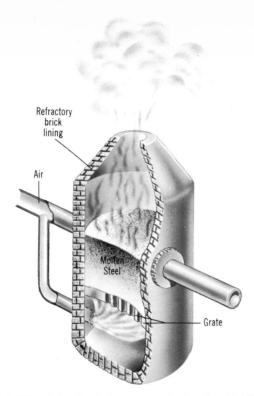

Refractory
brick
lining

Air

Molten
Steel

Grate

30-6 This vertical section of a Bessemer converter shows the cold air blast passing through the grate and up through the molten steel.

30-7 The white flame coming from the top of the Bessemer converter indicates that unwanted carbon in the molten charge is being oxidized.

is complete, the air blast is stopped, and the charge is ready for pouring after 15 to 18 minutes. However, the very speed of the process does not enable the carbon content of the finished product to be controlled. The element is oxidized almost entirely.

The product of the Bessemer process is not yet ready for rolling into various shapes, since the presence of sulfur and dissolved air from the blast makes the product brittle when hot. The rolling process becomes practical only when *small* amounts of manganese combine with the sulfur and dissolved air. Hot castings made by cooling the molten metal in molds can now be rolled. The manganese is usually added in the form of *ferromanganese* or *spiegeleisen*, alloys of iron, manganese, and carbon. The addition of these alloys also provides the steel with the desired percentage of carbon.

Although the Bessemer process is inexpensive and quick, the lack of control over the composition of the product does not enable the production of "tailor-made" steels so necessary in many applications. This process does not remove phosphorus satisfactorily unless the lining of the converter is made of dolomite bricks. Replacing the bricks as they are used up necessitates shutting down the converter for relining; the Bessemer process thus becomes discontinuous. Only about 5 percent of the total steel production is Bessemer steel. It finds use in pipes, wire, and hardware. Most of the Bessemer steel produced must be refined further in the open-hearth or electric furnaces.

The Open-Hearth Process

The time necessary for careful control of the composition of the steel is provided by the open-

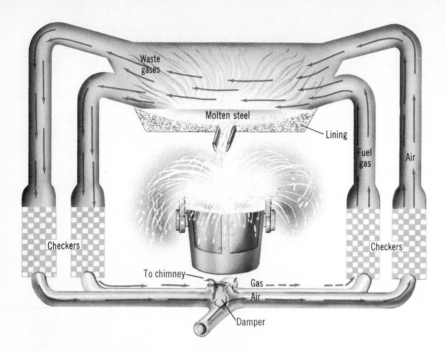

Waste gases

Molten steel

Lining

Fuel gas

Air

Checkers

Checkers

To chimney

Gas

Air

Damper

30-8 An open-hearth furnace is aptly named, since the molten steel is exposed to the flames passing over it. When chemical analysis of a sample of steel drawn from the furnace shows that the steel has the composition desired, it is tapped into a large ladle, as indicated here.

hearth process, which accounts for about 90 percent of our steel production. Picture a large, shallow basin about 40 feet long, 16 feet wide, lined with fire-resistant brick, and sloping to a depth of about 2 feet in the center (Fig. 30-8). The charge is introduced through doors in one side of the furnace, and refined steel and slag are removed on the other side. The furnace and process are named *open-hearth* because raw materials are open to the flame that keeps the mass molten. Heat is provided by burning fuel gas (or oil) in a stream of hot air. Both are fed through a system of brick "checkerwork" supporting the furnace from below. The hot products of combustion are deflected down across the charge, and then pass out through a similar system of brickwork. When the latter becomes hot, the flow of fuel and air is reversed, so that these gases become hot as they pass over the brickwork just heated. The process thus operates efficiently by conserving the heat of the waste gases.

Limestone and steel scrap are dumped or charged into the furnace. The scrap, including old automobile bodies, boilers, cans, and the like, represents about half the total charge. The charge

melts in about 5 hours, at which time molten pig iron is poured in from a large ladle. In the next 6 to 7 hours, the "melt" heaves and bubbles much like a boiling liquid, as the impurities are being removed. Carbon is removed as carbon dioxide by combining with oxygen in the air, or with iron oxide added to provide oxygen for this purpose. Sulfur and phosphorus combine with limestone and are removed as slag. While the time required for the process seems lengthy, it allows the contents of the furnace to be analyzed frequently. These analyses enable the operator to control the amounts of materials present and to make necessary adjustments. When the steel has reached the desired composition, it is tapped into a ladle—a truly spectacular process. Alloying materials may now be added to make special steels. From 150 to 200 tons of steel can be made in one "heat" by the open-hearth method, in contrast to the 15- to 25-ton capacity of the Bessemer converter.

The Electric Furnace

For the rigid control needed in the preparation of very special alloys, the steel-maker turns to the electric furnace like that pictured in Fig. 30-9.

The electric furnace produces a more carefully controlled and higher temperature than that reached in the Bessemer or open-hearth processes. Moreover, since the electric furnace does not depend on the combustion of a fuel, it requires no oxygen.

These furnaces consist of a steel shell lined with firebrick. Large carbon electrodes, as tall as a six-foot man, extend from the roof of the furnace to within a few inches of the charge. When the current is turned on, an electric arc jumps from the electrode to the charge, providing heat to melt the ingredients and bring about a reaction.

The charge may consist entirely of scrap iron and steel, or of Bessemer or open-hearth steel which is to be refined further. The metals to be alloyed are added as elements or as alloys of iron. Iron oxide is often added early in the melting to oxidize carbon and other impurities. Calcium oxide is used to remove sulfur, while ferrosilicon alloys serve to remove dissolved oxygen. When the steel with the desired properties has been produced, the furnace is tilted to pour out the steel.

30-9 In the electric furnace the three large carbon electrodes (top center) pass through the roof of the furnace to the charge, or to within a few inches of it. The electrodes are independent of one another, contacting or arcing to the charge, which acts as a common electrode.

The Fabrication of Steel

Whatever its ultimate purpose, all steel is made by one of the three processes just described. When the finished molten steel is tapped into a ladle, only the first half of the story has been completed. This steel must still be fabricated into a variety of shapes and sizes. Whatever the final product, the fabrication of steel begins with a block known as an *ingot*. Steel tapped into a ladle is poured into a series of molds. When the exterior of the ingot has become solid, the mold, which has now been inverted, is removed from the ingot by a crane. To insure that the temperature and composition are uniform throughout, the ingots are placed in "soaking pits," gas-fired furnaces which bring the temperature of the ingots to 2200° F.

Once the ingot has reached the desired temperature, it is transferred to a *rolling mill*. The mill operates on the principle of a series of clothes-wringers, the ingot being fed into a pair of rollers revolving in opposite directions. These rollers shape the original ingot into steel plates, rails, beams, girders, bars, or rods. Figure 30-10 illustrates the fabrication of steel—from the hot ingots through the rolling operation.

When the carbon content of steel is below 0.2 percent, the product is called low-carbon or mild steel. It is used to make fence wire, nuts, and bolts. Medium carbon steel contains 0.2 to 0.6 percent of carbon; it is used to make rails and structural shapes such as girders. When the carbon content ranges from 0.6 to 1.6 percent, the product is high carbon steel. This steel, which can be made very hard by tempering, is used to make razor blades, surgical instruments, and drills.

Improving Steel

Our journey through steel-making has emphasized the effect of various ingredients on the properties of steel. Yet some steel does not meet the specifications required by the manufacturer of certain products. There is still another trick up the steel-maker's sleeve—that of altering properties by heat treatment of the finished product. The process of influencing the properties of a

a The six-ton ingot (left) is being hoisted from the soaking pit where it has been heated for several hours to bring it to rolling temperature.

a

b

b The slabbing mill (above) forces the hot ingot back and forth between rollers, squeezing it out into a hot slab of longer, thinner dimensions.

c Hot slabs up to 130 feet long are reduced within minutes to thin strips a quarter of a mile long in the hot strip mill (left).

c

d Cooled, coiled steel strip is uncoiled and fed into the hot dip galvanizing line (right). The steel is pickled, galvanized, and recoiled in a continuous operation.

d

510

metal through heat treatment is known as **tempering.** *You can observe* the effects of tempering quite readily.

> Open a bobby pin. Is this easy or difficult? Now use tongs to hold a bobby pin in a flame. When the bobby pin becomes red-hot, lay it on an asbestos square to cool slowly. Heat a second bobby pin in the same manner, but this time plunge it into a beaker of cold water. Open these pins when they are cool. Is there any difference in their behavior? If so, why?

When steel is made red-hot ($500°$ to $550°$ C), the small amount of carbon present unites with the iron to form iron carbide, Fe_3C, which dissolves in the steel. This renders the steel harder but also imparts to it a brittle quality. Cooling the steel *quickly* by plunging it into oil, water, or molten salts "freezes" the high-temperature condition into the steel. However, if the temperature is reduced *slowly,* this change is reversed, and the steel becomes softer and tougher. Properties between these extremes can be obtained by tempering—heating the steel to temperatures of $220°$ to $350°$ C, and then cooling it quickly.

If a steel that is both tough and hard—capable of withstanding shock and hard wear—is desired, the tempering process will provide the toughness. To achieve the second quality, which depends on the formation of iron carbide, the article is packed in charcoal (or carbon-containing material) and heated for a number of hours. The carbon slowly diffuses into the surface of the steel and reacts to form iron carbide. This process, which is called **case hardening,** makes the surface of the object very hard. A similar method of hardening the surface depends on the formation of metal nitrides which, like carbides, are hard. These are formed by exposing the hot metal to an atmosphere of ammonia gas which decomposes into its elements at high temperatures. The nitrogen formed reacts with the metal to form the nitride. This variation of case hardening is known as **nitriding.** Steel can indeed be "made to order."

1. List the ingredients which go into a blast furnace and state the purpose of each.

2. (a) Why is the air which is forced into the furnace preheated? (b) What particular advantages result from the use of a blast of pure oxygen instead of air?

3. Contrast the Bessemer and the open-hearth processes with respect to the (a) charge used, (b) method of removing impurities, (c) time required, and (d) quality of the product.

4. Explain how it is possible for the same composition of ingredients to provide the steelmaker with a variety of steels.

5. Under what conditions is steel produced in the electric furnace?

6. Define each of the following terms as related to the production of steel: *ingot, rolling mill, tempering, case hardening, nitriding.*

IRON—THE ELEMENT

Highly pure iron, a rarity outside of the laboratory, is a comparatively soft, silvery white, malleable, and ductile metal. Two allotropes of the metal are known at elevated temperatures; they differ from the room-temperature form in crystal structure and magnetic properties. Iron can be magnetized more easily than any other metal. This behavior of the metal is known as *ferromagnetism.* Ferromagnetism is a property of the iron triad elements, but neither cobalt nor nickel approaches iron in this respect.

Chemically, iron demonstrates the typical reactions of metals in moderate fashion. It replaces hydrogen in hydrochloric acid and other nonoxidizing acids. It reduces sulfuric acid and oxidizing acids to oxides of their central elements. You have found that it reacts somewhat vigorously with nonmetals such as chlorine, oxygen, and sulfur, but the reactions are best initiated above room temperature. The most widely known reaction of iron is observed as the rusting of iron. Although rusting is an oxidation process, studies have shown that it is far from simple.

The Rusting of Iron

The rusting of iron is an example of **corrosion,** the *chemical* attack of the constituents of the atmosphere on a metal. Corrosion has been studied intensively because this process results in a considerable waste of our most widely used metal—whether exposed to moist air or sea water, or embedded in the earth. A thorough knowledge of the chemistry of corrosion is necessary before we can successfully prevent it. You can determine at least three factors that are favorable to the rusting process *through a simple investigation.* In the procedures which follow, it is essential that all samples of iron used—nails and strips—*not* be galvanized, tinned, or in any way covered by protective coatings.

Procure a 250-ml flask fitted with a tight-fitting cork stopper. Drive a long, clean nail through the stopper so that part of the nail protrudes above and part below the cork (as shown below). Add calcium chloride (or any other suitable dehydrating agent) to the flask to provide a layer at least ¼ inch thick so that any water vapor in the flask is removed. Stopper the flask with the cork containing the nail and set it aside for observation. Over a period of a week, observe the set-up. The portion of the nail exposed to air shows signs of rust. The portion inside the flask is still bright. Although air is inside the flask, the

air is now exceedingly dry. You conclude that water vapor is favorable to the rusting process.

Now boil some distilled water, let it cool, and divide it equally between two test tubes. Drop a clean nail into the first test tube. Saturate the water in the second test tube with oxygen, and place a similar nail into it. Stopper both test tubes and observe them for several days. Rusting soon occurs in the second tube, in which the water contains dissolved oxygen. But in the first tube, in which oxygen and other gases were driven out of the water by boiling, the nail remains unchanged. Evidently oxygen is favorable to rusting.

Finally, fill two test tubes half full of distilled water, and dissolve a few crystals of table salt in one of them. Place a clean iron nail in each tube, stopper the test tubes, and set them aside for several days. Rusting occurs in both tubes, but it proceeds faster in that containing the dissolved sodium chloride. You may tentatively conclude that the presence of an electrolyte favors the rusting process.

From this investigation you have learned that three factors are favorable to the rusting of iron: *the presence of oxygen, the presence of water vapor,* and *the presence of an electrolyte.* Do not be misled into thinking that a nail placed in a sealed test tube of boiled, distilled water will not in time undergo corrosion. Electrolytes in one form or another are always present in water, unless the water is highly purified. Even distilled water, if kept long enough, will contain electrolytes. Dissolved carbon dioxide will form the weak electrolyte, carbonic acid, and any constituents of glass dissolved by the water, slight though they may be, will also provide electrolytes.

Electrolysis in Corrosion

But why are electrolytes favorable to the rusting process? *The investigation which follows will provide an answer.*

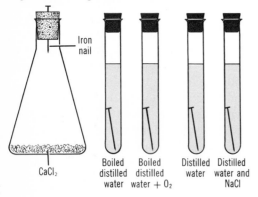

Iron nail

CaCl₂

Boiled distilled water

Boiled distilled water + O₂

Distilled water

Distilled water and NaCl

Mix 1 ml of a dilute solution of potassium chloride with 100 ml of water, and divide the solution among three beakers. In one beaker, place an iron nail. In the second place a similar nail that has been wrapped tightly with copper wire. In the third beaker place a nail that has been wrapped similarly with magnesium ribbon. Observe these beakers

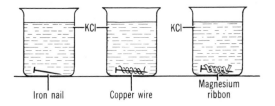

over a period of days. After the first day remove a 5-ml portion of each solution daily, and test the liquid for the presence of iron (ferrous) compounds by adding a few drops of potassium ferricyanide solution. If ferrous compounds are present, a deep blue precipitate forms.

The iron in contact with copper is the first to corrode; the liquid becomes yellowish and shows a positive test for ferrous ions. The iron nail alone is the next to corrode, but the iron in contact with magnesium shows no corrosion for many days. If after a week or two, you add a few drops of phenolphthalein to the beaker containing the iron nail wrapped in magnesium, you find that the solution has become basic. What is the reason for the difference in behavior among the three beakers?

When iron rusts, iron atoms are oxidized.

$$Fe^0 - 2\,e^- \rightleftharpoons Fe^{+2}$$

This reaction is reversible. If conditions favor the loss of electrons by the iron atoms, ferrous ions are formed readily and rusting is promoted. But if there is any interference with the loss of these electrons, the formation of ferrous ions is hindered and corrosion is prevented or delayed.

An iron nail in contact with another metal in the presence of an electrolyte produces an *electro-*

chemical cell. The electrons lost by the iron atoms *may* then flow away from the iron nail, thus favoring the reaction to the right and resulting in the formation of ferrous ions. This will be true if the metal in contact with the iron *is a poorer lender of electrons than is the iron.* For example, when copper is in contact with iron, electrons lost by the iron atoms flow from the nail to the copper (Fig. 30-11). At the copper "electrode," hydrogen ions in solution are reduced to hydrogen atoms that are then oxidized to form water. The solution now contains an excess of hydroxide ions, which combine with the ferrous ions to form insoluble ferrous hydroxide. This, in turn, undergoes air oxidation to form ferric hydroxide.

When, however, the iron is in contact with a more active metal such as magnesium, the reverse is true. Magnesium atoms lose electrons and go into solution as magnesium ions. The electrons lost by the magnesium move toward the iron. The accumulation of electrons on the iron shifts the equilibrium far to the left, almost completely preventing the oxidation of the iron atoms. As long as magnesium is in contact with the iron, rusting of the iron is prevented. Once again, reduction of the hydrogen ions to atoms leaves an excess of hydroxide ions. The presence of these ions explains why phenolphthalein turned red in the last test tube in the previous investigation.

30-11 An iron nail encircled with copper wire and placed in an electrolyte forms an electrochemical cell, in which electrons flow from iron to copper. Reactions result in the formation of ferric hydroxide.

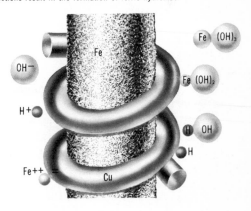

These reactions explain why it is not good practice to join copper piping with iron fittings. They will also help to explain some of the methods used to prevent the corrosion of iron and steel.

Prevention of Corrosion

If corrosion results from the attack on metals by their surroundings (whether gaseous, liquid, or solid), the answer to the problem of preventing corrosion is obvious—eliminate contact between the metal and its surroundings. This is the basis of the oldest known means of preventing rusting —coating the metal. Three types of coatings are used, nonmetallic, metallic, and, for some metals, a coating resulting from the oxidation of the metal. Each type of coating serves to prevent further oxidation.

Nonmetallic coatings are illustrated by oil paints (over a base of red lead) and enamels. The latter are mixtures of silicates baked onto an iron or steel object; for example, the porcelain finishes on sinks and bathtubs. Where the metal is a moving part that cannot be painted or enameled,

oils are used as a protective coating. Plastic coatings have come into use to protect buried pipelines made of steel.

Metals like copper and aluminum are used without protective coatings in the form of sheets of roofing and flashing, gutters, and downspouts, or in pots and pans. Copper metal that has seen outside use for a period of years becomes coated with a greenish deposit of copper hydroxide and copper carbonate which protects the metal underneath from further corrosion. Nickel, chromium, and aluminum form exceedingly thin, skintight protective coatings of their respective oxides. This is why aluminum, an active metal, can be used in pots and pans which are constantly exposed to the atmosphere at high temperatures. Not all corrosion products prevent further destruction of the underlying metal. The rust on iron, for example, is porous and allows further penetration of oxygen and water vapor from the atmosphere.

While the materials used for nonmetallic coatings protect an underlying metal, they also conceal its appearance. It is sometimes necessary

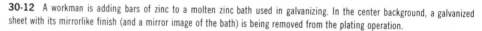

30-12 A workman is adding bars of zinc to a molten zinc bath used in galvanizing. In the center background, a galvanized sheet with its mirrorlike finish (and a mirror image of the bath) is being removed from the plating operation.

or desirable to maintain a metallic appearance. Since not all metals are readily attacked by the atmosphere, metals which are easily corroded are coated with a metal that is not readily attacked. Such protective coatings can be applied in a number of ways.

Applying Metallic Coatings

Inexpensive metals of low or moderate melting points can be used as protective coatings by melting them and then dipping the metal to be protected into the molten metal. In this procedure, known as **hot dipping,** the base metal must be perfectly clean before passage through the molten metal. Oxide (or other) coatings are first removed from the base metal by **pickling** (dipping it in dilute hydrochloric or sulfuric acid). The pickling is followed by washing, scrubbing with rotating brushes, and drying. Hot dipping was the original method of protecting iron. If the coating metal is tin, the product is **tin plate,** which serves as the start of a tin can. If zinc is used as the protective metal (Fig. 30-12), the product is **galvanized iron,** used for garbage cans, gutters and rainspouts, and hardware.

In the more recent **electroplating** technique, the object which is to be plated is made the cathode, while the anode consists of the metal which is to be the protective coating. The electrolyte is a solution of a salt of the metal to be deposited as the protective coating. When a direct current is applied, zinc (or tin) ions in the solution gain electrons at the cathode to become atoms which are deposited on that electrode.

$$Zn^{+2} + 2e^- \longrightarrow Zn^0$$

The reduction removes metallic ions from the solution. The anode (of the coating metal) serves as the source from which these ions are replenished. Here, metal atoms lose electrons to become ions which enter the solution.

$$Zn^0 - 2e^- \longrightarrow Zn^{+2}$$

These ions migrate through the solution to the cathode, where they, in turn, are deposited as zinc atoms.

30-13 When blocks of magnesium are bolted to the hull of a ship below the water line, an electrochemical cell is set up. The steel hull is protected from corrosion by the slow conversion of the more active magnesium "sacrificial electrode" to magnesium ions.

Since the *rate* at which atoms are deposited can be controlled very accurately, electroplating permits the deposition of coatings less than 0.001 inch in thickness. This technique is used to provide coatings of nickel, cadmium, or chromium on hardware, as well as rhodium or gold for jewelry.

A newer process, known as **cladding,** has done much to utilize expensive stainless steel and nickel more efficiently. The cladding process makes a metal "sandwich" consisting of very thin layers of rust-resistant metal on either side of the core of metal to be protected. The three layers are bonded permanently by rolling the metal sandwich when hot.

The Protection of Metals

When iron in contact with magnesium is exposed to corrosive conditions (page 513), the magnesium is oxidized while the iron remains unchanged. This is the basis of a method of preventing the corrosion of pipelines buried in the earth and of protecting ships' hulls immersed in sea water. Magnesium cylinders or plates are attached to the metal to be protected (Fig. 30-13). Since dissolved electrolytes are always present

30-14 These six coins from Turkey, France, Italy, and Costa Rica were die-stamped from stainless steel. As stainless steel is relatively unaffected by the atmosphere, these coins remain brilliant and durable.

in water, an electrochemical cell is set up in which magnesium atoms are oxidized to ions. The slow conversion of magnesium atoms to ions continues, but as *long as magnesium atoms are present,* the iron atoms will not be oxidized. The *magnesium* can be replaced at intervals to provide continuous protection. Results obtained by preventing rusting by the use of "sacrificial electrodes" have been highly satisfactory. This method is particularly effective in preventing the corrosion of steel.

The ultimate in protection, a metallic substance that undergoes no corrosion at all, was achieved with the development of stainless steel alloys. The best known of these contain chromium and nickel alloyed with the iron. These steel alloys are resistant to the action of most laboratory chemicals as well as the atmosphere (Fig. 30-14).

QUESTIONS AND PROBLEMS

1. (a) What is corrosion? (b) Name three factors favorable to the corrosion of iron.

2. (a) By what three methods can corrosion of iron and steel be prevented? (b) For each method, list several examples found in and around your home.

3. Define each of the following terms: *hot dipping, tin plating, galvanizing, electroplating, cladding, sacrificial electrodes.*

4. (a) Why is copper used without a protective coating in roofs and gutters? (b) Why can nickel and aluminum also be exposed to the atmosphere without a protective coating?

5. Though iron and nickel are very much alike in properties, a coating of nickel can protect iron and steel from corrosion. Why?

IRON COMPOUNDS

Though most of the iron ore mined in this country is used at iron and steel mills, the various compounds of iron deserve our attention. Like compounds of other transition elements, these compounds are often colored—the color varying with the oxidation state of the iron. These various oxidation states increase the number of iron compounds and account for certain of their properties and uses.

Oxidation-Reduction in Iron Compounds

The relationship between ferrous (+2) and ferric (+3) compounds *can be observed in the following investigations.*

Fill a large test tube half full of 3 M HCl and boil for 1 minute to remove dissolved air. Add 1 gram of iron filings, plug the test tube loosely with absorbent cotton, and set it aside. When the reaction has stopped, divide the clear liquid among four test tubes, and note the color of the solution of ferrous chloride. Stopper one tube to serve as a control. To the remaining test tubes, add respectively 5 ml of chlorine water, 5 ml of

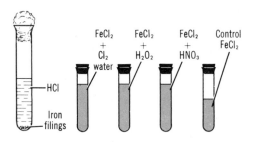

hydrogen peroxide, and a few drops of concentrated nitric acid. Let the test tubes stand for 1 minute, and then compare the colors of their contents with that of the control. In each of the treated test tubes, the color has changed from the almost colorless solution of the control tube to the red-brown of a ferric chloride solution.

Now remove the stopper from the control tube, and expose the ferrous chloride solution to the air. At intervals replace the stopper, shake the contents of the tube well, and remove the stopper once more. Note the very slow appearance of the red-brown color in the tube. What effect has the oxygen of the air had on the ferrous ion?

In the test tubes containing the chlorine water, hydrogen peroxide, and nitric acid, the ferrous ions (produced by the reaction between Fe and HCl) are *oxidized* to ferric ions.

$$2\overset{+2}{\text{FeCl}_2} + \text{Cl}_2 \longrightarrow 2\overset{+3}{\text{FeCl}_3}$$
$$2\overset{+2}{\text{FeCl}_2} + 2\,\text{HCl} + \text{H}_2\text{O}_2 \longrightarrow 2\overset{+3}{\text{FeCl}_3} + 2\,\text{H}_2\text{O}$$
$$3\overset{+2}{\text{FeCl}_2} + 3\,\text{HCl} + \text{HNO}_3 \longrightarrow$$
$$3\overset{+3}{\text{FeCl}_3} + 2\,\text{H}_2\text{O} + \text{NO}\uparrow$$

When the control tube is opened, the oxygen of the air oxidizes ferrous ions to ferric ions.

$$4\overset{+2}{\text{FeCl}_2} + 4\,\text{HCl} + \text{O}_2 \longrightarrow 4\overset{+3}{\text{FeCl}_3} + 2\,\text{H}_2\text{O}$$

You might have tested for the presence of the ferric ion by adding a solution of potassium *ferro*cyanide. If ferric ions are present, a dark blue precipitate forms. Compare this test with that for the ferrous ion (page 513).

The ferric ion can also be *reduced* to the ferrous ion, as you can see *by trying the following.*

Add 1 ml of a dilute solution of ferric chloride to a test tube containing 5 ml of dilute hydrochloric acid. Now add 1 gram of iron filings, and heat the mixture gently for 2 minutes. Filter the hot liquid quickly into a small test tube, and plug the tube loosely with absorbent cotton while the liquid cools. Observe any color change.

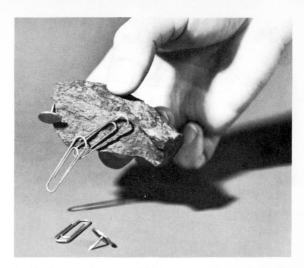

30-15 The magnetic property of lodestone or natural magnetite was discovered by the shepherd Magnes approximately 2,500 years ago.

This time, the original red-brown color of the ferric chloride has disappeared to leave an almost colorless solution. The ferric ion has been *reduced* to the ferrous form.

$$2\overset{+3}{\text{FeCl}_3} + 3\,\text{Fe} + 4\,\text{HCl} \longrightarrow 5\overset{+2}{\text{FeCl}_2} + 2\,\text{H}_2$$

Iron Oxides

Three oxides of iron are known. Ferrous (iron II) oxide, FeO, is difficult to prepare because it oxidizes readily. Ferric (iron III) oxide, Fe_2O_3, is found naturally in a variety of forms whose colors vary with the size of the oxide particle, as well as the presence or absence of water of hydration. Many of these forms are used as mineral pigments, the ochers and umbers being prime examples. Rouge is a specially prepared form of ferric oxide which is used to polish metals and grind lenses. Magnetite, Fe_3O_4, is a magnetic oxide in which the metal exhibits both its oxidation states. Natural magnetite, known for many centuries, is commonly called *lodestone* (Fig. 30-15).

Other Compounds of Iron

When iron reacts with hydrochloric acid, the salt formed is ferrous chloride.

$$\text{Fe} + 2\,\text{HCl} \longrightarrow \text{FeCl}_2 + \text{H}_2\uparrow$$

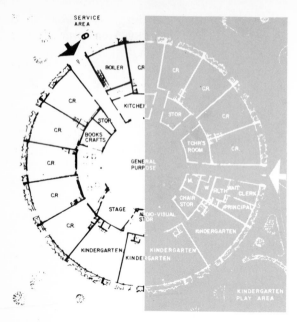

30-16 The left portion of the diagram shows half of an architect's plan for a school. The right portion is a blueprint of the other half. In the blueprint, the lines are white on a blue background.

Prepared in this way, the salt forms hydrated molecules. The anhydrous form, a pale green solid, is formed by passing dry hydrogen chloride gas over the heated metal. Ferrous chloride, as you determined, oxidizes to the ferric form.

Ferric chloride is made commercially by passing chlorine gas over hot iron.

$$2\,Fe + 3\,Cl_2 \longrightarrow 2\,FeCl_3$$

The anhydrous salt is a yellowish, deliquescent solid which forms a series of hydrates. In solution, ferric chloride is strongly hydrolyzed to form ferric hydroxide, a reddish-brown substance.

Insoluble ferrous hydroxide results when solutions of bases are added to solutions of ferrous salts.

$$FeCl_2 + 2\,NaOH \longrightarrow Fe(OH)_2\downarrow + 2\,NaCl$$

Ferrous hydroxide is colorless when pure but turns green immediately on exposure to air. It is readily oxidized to the ferric compound by oxi-

dizing agents. The latter compound, $Fe(OH)_3$, characterized by its reddish-brown color, is highly insoluble in water. It is made by double replacement between a base and a solution of a ferric salt.

$$FeCl_3 + 3\,NaOH \longrightarrow Fe(OH)_3\downarrow + 3\,NaCl$$

Large quantities of ferrous sulfate are a by-product of the pickling of metals.

$$Fe + H_2SO_4 \longrightarrow H_2\uparrow + FeSO_4$$

On concentration of the pickling liquid, the salt crystallizes in the form of hydrated ferrous sulfate, $FeSO_4 \cdot 7\,H_2O$, which undergoes slow oxidation in air or in water solution to the ferric form.

Iron Compounds in Inks and Blueprints

Two of the major uses of iron compounds are dependent on the ease with which oxidation-reduction of iron ions is accomplished. They involve permanent inks and blueprints. Ordinary blue inks contain a solution of nearly *colorless ferrous* tannate and a blue dye that enables you to observe what you have written. During its exposure to air, the soluble, almost colorless ferrous tannate is oxidized to blue, insoluble ferric tannate which produces a permanent mark that cannot be washed out with water. Reducing agents such as oxalic acid, which reverse the change, transform the insoluble ink to a colorless, soluble substance. Ink eradicators therefore contain one or more reducing agents.

To observe how oxidation-reduction applies to blueprints, *try this procedure.*

Mix equal volumes of solutions of ferric citrate (or ferric ammonium citrate) and potassium *ferri*cyanide in dim light. The mixture is yellowish-brown. Now expose the mixture to bright light or ultraviolet light. Observe the blue precipitate that begins to form shortly.

On exposure to light, the ferric citrate is reduced to ferrous citrate, which reacts with the potassium ferricyanide to form an insoluble blue substance (Turnbull's blue). This behavior of ferric citrate on exposure to light is fundamental to blueprinting.

Blueprint paper is treated *in the dark* with a solution containing ferric citrate and potassium ferricyanide, and is allowed to dry. When the paper is to be used, a drawing on transparent paper is placed over the dry blueprint paper. The combination is then exposed to bright light. Where the light passes through the drawing to strike the blueprint paper, reduction of the ferric citrate occurs; where the light is blocked from the paper, no change results (Fig. 30-16). The chemistry of blueprints, like that of inks, is an application of oxidation and reduction of iron compounds.

QUESTIONS AND PROBLEMS

1. Differentiate among the three oxides of iron.

2. (a) How can you convert a ferrous compound to its related ferric compound? (b) How could you reverse the change just produced?

3. Ferric chloride hydrolyzes to form an acid solution. Write an ionic equation to account for this reaction.

4. Explain how the principles of oxidation and reduction are applied in (a) blueprinting, (b) ink making.

5. The reaction between iron and hydrochloric acid produces ferr*ous* chloride, while that between the metal and chlorine gas produces ferr*ic* chloride. Explain why.

COBALT AND NICKEL

The restricted use of cobalt and nickel, the remaining members of the iron triad, stems in part from the very small amounts of cobalt and nickel ores that occur in the earth. Fortunately these metals are often present in small amounts in ores of other metals from which they are obtained as by-products. Methods of extraction usually involve concentrating the ores, roasting, and reduction by carbon of the oxide formed. The metals

are usually purified by electrolysis. One method of purifying nickel, called the **Mond process,** is of interest because of its application of the principles of equilibrium. At elevated temperatures, the metal reacts with carbon monoxide to form nickel carbonyl, the reaction being reversible.

$$Ni + 4\,CO \overset{\Delta}{\rightleftharpoons} Ni(CO)_4$$

The formation of the carbonyl is favored by providing the carbon monoxide under high pressure (Le Chatelier's Principle). When the carbonyl is heated under normal pressure, decomposition results to form nickel metal.

Properties of Cobalt and Nickel

Both cobalt and nickel are hard, bright metals having high melting and boiling points. The metals are magnetic, but far less so than is iron. They are somewhat less reactive than iron but will undergo the same reactions with acids, both oxidizing and nonoxidizing, and with nonmetals.

30-17 The alternating nickelic oxide anodes and metallic cadmium cathodes appear at the left with the insulation (in the right model) removed. The potassium hydroxide electrolyte is not shown.

Table 30-3 ALLOYS OF COBALT AND NICKEL

Name	Composition (percent)	Properties	Uses
Alnico	Co, Ni, Fe, Al*	Highly magnetic	Small but very powerful magnets
Stellite	Co, Cr, and W*	Retains its cutting edge at high temperatures	High-speed cutting and grinding tools
Carboloy	Tungsten carbide embedded in cobalt	Very hard	High-speed cutting tools
Nickel coinage	Ni (25) and Cu (75)	Resistant to wear	American nickel coinage
Monel metal	Ni (about 67), Cu (about 28) with small amounts of Fe and Mn	Strong, tough, and corrosion-resistant	Equipment in the food trades, sinks
Nichrome	Ni (60–80), Cr (15–20), Fe (12–15)	Offers a high resistance to an electric current	Heating coils in toasters, heaters
Permalloy	Ni (78), Fe (22)	Retains magnetism	Permanent magnets
Invar	Ni (36), Fe (64)	Low coefficient of expansion	Instruments, clock pendulums, surveyors' tapes

* Present in varying amounts.

Corrosion of these metals by atmospheric oxygen is not pronounced because the oxides formed are protective to the metals. Although these metals exhibit the same oxidation states as does iron (+2, +3), the lower oxidation state is stable and therefore common. All these elements form complex compounds such as $Co(NH_3)_6(NO_3)_2$, $Ni(NH_3)_6Cl_2$, and $K_3Fe(CN)_6$. In these complex compounds cobalt and nickel are easily oxidized to the +3 state. The compounds of these metals form hydrates very readily.

Uses of Cobalt, Nickel, and Their Compounds

Cobalt and its compounds have acquired two values unknown 30 years ago. Cobalt-60, a radioactive isotope of the element, is made by bombarding cobalt with slow neutrons. The isotope is a powerful gamma emitter and, therefore, has become a valuable substitute for the much more expensive and rare radium. Only in recent years has it been discovered that *traces* of cobalt are essential to nutrition. The element is part of the vitamin B-12 molecule which is important in red blood cell formation.

Nickel is used extensively in two types of storage batteries. In both the Edison cell and the nickel-cadmium battery, one electrode consists of nickelous oxide (Fig. 30-17). On charging the battery, this compound is oxidized to nickelic oxide; the reaction is reversed on discharge of the battery.

In keeping with the properties of the transition elements, the hydrated ions of both metals are colored. Those of cobalt are pink, while those of nickel are green. Hydrated cobaltous chloride, $CoCl_2 \cdot 6 H_2O$, is pink, but it becomes blue on loss of water. Paper cloth soaked in a solution of this compound and then dried serves to indicate changes in relative humidity. The color changes from blue to pink as the humidity and hence the degree of hydration increases. Outside of the laboratory, salts of nickel and cobalt find use in electrodeposition of these metals, or as catalysts in organic reactions. Cobalt salts of organic acids find use as dryers (catalysts) in oil paints.

The metals themselves are rarely used alone, except for plating, in which nickel finds wide use. Their greatest application is in the field of alloys, a summary of which is presented in Table 30-3.

The metals studied thus far might very easily be placed in two broad groups. In the first, we have the group IA and IIA metals which are extremely vigorous in their chemical reactions but unlike most metals in their physical properties. The metals in the second or transition group, including copper and iron, vary widely in chemical behavior but illustrate those physical properties usually associated with metals. But these latter metals are a good deal denser than water; objects made of them must of necessity be heavy. If there existed a metal that was both hard and strong but with low density, many construction problems could be solved. In the next chapter you will ascertain whether such a combination of properties exists for a metallic element or its alloys.

1. Compare and contrast the members of the iron triad with respect to (a) most common oxidation state, (b) ferromagnetism.

2. List the principal uses of (a) cobalt and cobalt compounds, (b) nickel and nickel compounds.

3. How can hydrated cobaltous chloride be used in predicting the weather?

4. How does the Mond process demonstrate Le Chatelier's Principle?

VALUE OF THE CONCEPT

THE CONCEPT

The elements in the iron triad—iron, cobalt, and nickel—are examples of the group VIII elements. This group differs in one important respect from the transition elements of the copper group. Iron, cobalt, and nickel follow each other in a horizontal progression in the periodic table, rather than in a vertical arrangement. A similar phenomenon occurs in the succeeding periods, giving rise to two triads of closely related elements. Each of these sequences of three elements occurs midway in its period. Prior to the triad in each period, the d orbitals which are being filled to create the transition elements are half-filled. In these triads, the remaining half of these orbitals begins to be filled. The stability of half-filled orbitals is the most significant factor accounting for the similarity of the elements in each triad.

Iron, cobalt, and nickel, very closely alike in physical properties, exhibit the colored ions and variable oxidation states of the transition elements. Also, they are closely alike in their ionization potentials and positions in the electrochemical series. All three are outstanding in their magnetic properties, though iron is far superior to its neighbors. A marked difference appears in the stability of their oxidation states. Iron appears most often in the higher ($+3$) form, while cobalt and nickel are most stable in the $+2$ state. As a result, oxidation-reduction reactions are typical of iron and its compounds; such reactions are not of frequent occurrence in cobalt and nickel compounds.

The metallurgy of iron, our most useful metal, involves reduction of oxide ores with carbon in the form of coke. Since most oxide ores contain silicious impurities, limestone is also a necessary ingredient in the blast furnace. Calcium oxide, the basic anhydride formed when limestone is decomposed in the furnace, combines with silica and with silicates or phosphates present in the ore to form slag. Pig iron, the product of the furnace, may be cast into finished shapes to form cast iron. Because impurities still present in this iron produce severe shortcomings in the product, the impurities must be substantially eliminated before the product is sufficiently strong to support buildings, bridges, and dams.

The production of steel, which has the necessary strength and hardness, requires the decreasing or removing of impurities from ion. The process also requires the addition of various alloying elements to confer further desirable properties on the finished product. The steel may be produced by the Bessemer process, by the open-hearth process, or in an electric furnace, depending upon the properties needed. The steel is then rolled, tempered, and hardened as required.

Unfortunately, iron and steel corrode badly when in contact with air, water, and electrolytes. Corrosion may be prevented by coating the metal with either a nonmetallic or metallic substance. Metallic coatings are applied by hot dipping, tin plating, galvanizing, and electroplating. Other metals, such as nickel, are protected from corrosion by a skintight coating of their oxides.

USING THE CONCEPT

Using the Basic Concept

1. If you were going to establish a blast furnace in a new location, what particular features would you look for before selecting an area of operation? Why?
2. How does the data of Table 30-1 support the practice of studying iron, cobalt, and nickel as one group?
3. Draw electron orbital diagrams of (a) metallic iron, cobalt, and nickel (b) of the ion of each element in its $+2$ oxidation state.
4. Explain how various features of the operation of the blast furnace help to make the process efficient.
5. (a) Under what conditions would you use each of the three processes for making steel? (b) Compare and contrast the open hearth and the electric furnace with respect to charge, the removal of impurities, and the quality of steel produced.
6. (a) Why is tempering so important in producing steel? (b) How is the desired hardness produced in steel?
7. A piece of iron pipe resting on the ground rusts rapidly. What three factors favor its rusting?
8. Describe briefly the various ways in which metallic coatings are applied to metal to prevent corrosion.

9. Differentiate between the terms *pig iron* and *cast iron.*
10. When chlorine gas reacts with iron, why does ferric chloride form rather than ferrous chloride?
11. Although cobalt and nickel are very much like iron, they are remarkably resistant to atmospheric corrosion. Account for this difference.
12. (a) In the changing of ferric chloride to ferrous chloride, is the ferric chloride oxidized or reduced? (b) What agent can be used to reverse the change?
13. Describe the major chemical changes in (a) blueprinting, (b) ink-making.
14. (a) Why is cobalt-60 important to man? (b) Why is nickelous oxide used in certain batteries? (c) What is the major use of both cobalt and nickel?
15. Write a balanced equation to show the hydrolysis of ferric chloride.

Relating Terms Within the Concept

Select the letter of the term in Column B that is most closely related to each term in Column A. Do not use a term more than once.

COLUMN A	COLUMN B
1. corrosion	a. carbon monoxide
2. ferrous ions	b. discontinuous process
3. cobalt	c. ferromagnetism
4. Mond process	d. heat treatment
5. electric furnace	e. impurities
6. blast furnace	f. most steel production
7. Bessemer converter	g. nickel
8. open-hearth process	h. nitriding
9. tempering	i. oxidized to ferric ions
10. galvanizing	j. oxidized to free iron
11. slag	k. platinum metals
	l. sacrificial electrodes
	m. special alloys
	n. zinc

Solving Problems Within the Concept

1. How many grams of ferric chloride will be produced when 1.11 grams of iron are reacted with chlorine?

2. What volume of chlorine gas (**STP**) will convert 6.34 grams of ferrous chloride to the ferric salt?

3. How many grams of $FeSO_4 \cdot 7 H_2O$ are needed to prepare 400 ml of a 2 *M* solution of this salt?

4. A newly minted nickel piece weighs 5.00 grams. (a) What weight of nickel is present in the coin? (b) On reaction with hydrochloric acid, how much nickel chloride would be produced? (c) If this weight of nickel chloride were dissolved to form a total volume of 10 ml, what would the molarity of the solution be?

5. If 11.74 grams of nickel are deposited by the decomposition of nickel carbonyl in the Mond process, what volume of carbon monoxide (**STP**) is released?

6. What is the percent of water of hydration in $CoCl_2 \cdot 6 H_2O$?

7. A compound contains 56.1 percent of nickel, 13.4 percent of nitrogen, and 30.5 percent by weight of oxygen. What is its formula?

Applying the Concept

1. If an iron ore contained iron in the form of magnetite, what scheme would you use to concentrate (enrich) the ore?

2. Draw a labeled diagram of the apparatus that would be needed to electroplate an iron nail with cadmium.

3. Ferrous nitrate reacts with nitric acid according to the following equation:

$$Fe(NO_3)_2 + HNO_3 \longrightarrow$$
$$Fe(NO_3)_3 + NO + H_2O$$

Balance this equation by the electron transfer method.

4. What *two* values do scrap metals have when added to the charge in steel-making?

5. When a solution of a ferric salt is added to one of an iodide salt, iodine is liberated. The analogous reaction does not occur with bromides and chlorides. Account for the difference.

6. Other things being equal (for example, cost) should iron and steel be electroplated with a metal more or less active than iron? Explain.

7. Write a balanced equation for the reactions necessary to extract iron from a ferrous carbonate ore.

8. Why are dehydrating agents often present in the packaging of steel objects?

9. What reaction to litmus do you predict for solutions of ferric nitrate and ferric sulfate? Why?

10. Explain whether a solution of ferrous chloride could be used in place of a solution of ferrous tannate to make a permanent ink.

11. Write balanced equations for the reactions between: (a) iron and hydrochloric acid to yield ferrous chloride, (b) nickel and copper sulfate solution, (c) heated cobalt and bromine.

Reading Further

History of American Technology, by John Oliver, New York, Ronald Press, 1956. Chapter 39 deals with metallurgy since 1920, but the book describes advances in science and technology in our country since the days of Jamestown and Plymouth.

The following *Scientific American* articles are well worth your time: "The Geography of Steel," by George Kimble, January 1952; "Ferrites," by C. Hester Hogan, June 1960; "The Origin of Ores," by H. C. Bachmann, June 1960.

31

The Aluminum Family

In the middle of the last century, aluminum was very costly—90 dollars a pound. Today, aluminum is inexpensive and plentiful because a young college student, Charles Martin Hall, was inspired by his chemistry professor's account of the possibilities that lay in the successful production of a new and lightweight metal. In 1866 the application of a direct current provided Hall, then 22 years old, with the first easily obtained aluminum (Fig. 31-1). A new era opened in the history of metals—providing man with an unusual metal, less than three times as dense as water. Oddly enough, 3,000 miles away in France, Paul Héroult conceived of the same process at about the same time.

Why does aluminum, the third most abundant element in the earth's crust and the most abundant metal, have so short a history compared to other less abundant metals? You can best answer this question by investigating the element in detail—its individual properties, the nature of the aluminum family, and the relation of the family to the other groups of elements.

Group IIIA Elements

Although aluminum comprises some 8 percent of the earth's crust by weight, the remaining group IIIA members occur in exceedingly small amounts. Boron compounds are readily obtainable only because deposits of these compounds, such as colemanite and borax, are concentrated in particular localities. In contrast, those of gallium, indium, and thallium occur in small amounts in ores of other metals, particularly zinc, lead, copper, and iron. There are no definite

ores of these group IIIA metals; they are recovered as by-products in the metallurgy and refining of the metals mentioned.

What properties should be expected of the group of elements that lies just to the right of the transition elements? The members of this group (Table 31-1) contrast sharply with those of groups IA and IIA. Boron, its first member, shows more resemblance to beryllium (group IIA) and carbon (group IVA) than it does to its own family members. This element *is never found in the ionic state,* but the succeeding members of the family, with the possible exception of thallium, are found in both ionic and covalent compounds. Aluminum fluoride is ionic, while its lower halides are covalent. Variable oxidation states occur in the aluminum family but not in a coherent pattern. All of its members exist in the $+3$ form, this being the *only* state for boron and aluminum. The members below aluminum usually exist in either the $+1$ or $+3$ states. The latter is the more stable state for thallium.

Of these elements, only thallium forms a purely basic hydroxide. A hydroxide of boron is nonexistent, while those of aluminum, gallium, and indium exhibit a dual behavior, sometimes be-

31-1 The "Crown Jewels." The small aluminum globules were made by Hall in 1886; the largest one is the first commercial aluminum produced.

Table 31-1 **THE GROUP IIIA ELEMENTS**

Element	Atomic number	Atomic weight	Electron configuration	Density (g/ml, 20° C)	Melting point (° C)	Boiling point (° C)	State and color	Ionization potential	Oxidation states
Boron	5	10.811	2 3	2.53	2300	2550	Colorless to brown solid	8.3	+3
Aluminum	13	26.9815	2 8 3	2.70	659.7	2057	Silver-white solid	6.0	+3
Gallium	31	69.72	2 8 18 3	5.91	29.78	1983	Grayish-white solid	6.0	+1, +3
Indium	49	114.82	2 8 18 18 3	7.28	156.4	2000	Soft silvery solid	5.8	+1, +3
Thallium	81	204.37	2 8 18 32 18 3	11.85	302	1457	Blue-white solid	6.1	+1, +3

having like acids. Except for thallium, these elements are often found as part of a negative radical. If you examine the electrochemical series, you find that the group IIIA elements are located well below the alkali and alkaline earth metals. Aluminum lies close to magnesium in activity, but the succeeding elements are akin to zinc and iron in electron-lending ability. None of the group IIIA elements combines directly with hydrogen, a reaction typical of the metals of groups IA and IIA.

Effects of Electron Structure

Thus far, the members of group IIIA have shown considerable differences among themselves. This is in contrast to the members of groups IA, IIA, VIA, and VIIA, where you observed a continuity of properties. And two further features distinguish these elements. The first ionization potentials of each of the first three members of this group are *lower* than those of the group IIA elements immediately preceding them. This is in contrast to the trend of increasing values as we move from the first to the last element of a new period. These exceptions occur because in the group IIIA elements, the third electron in the outer electron shell of each atom occupies a *p orbital*, from which it is more easily removed than are the *s* electrons in the outer shells of the group IIA or even group IA elements (Fig. 31-2).

The second feature is even more significant. Because atoms of these metallic elements have 3 valence electrons, compound formation through covalent bonding results in an incomplete outer shell of 6 electrons. For example, in BF_3 and $AlCl_3$, involving three pairs of shared electrons, the outer shell is incomplete. In consequence, covalent compounds of these elements are usually found in a form in which further covalent bonding occurs. This may occur between the individual molecules, or the additional electrons may be provided through coordinate covalence. Thus boron fluoride, BF_3, readily forms the fluoborate ion (BF_4^-) by bonding covalently with a fluoride *ion* as indicated in Fig. 31-3. Also, at temperatures below 400° C, aluminum chloride exists as Al_2Cl_6 (Fig. 31-3).

It is evident that the aluminum family of elements is markedly different from the groups which immediately precede it. The smooth continuity of properties characteristic of groups IA and IIA as well as group VIIA is lacking. Further, a study of the individual members and their compounds should serve to reinforce these differences.

31-2 Sodium and other group IA elements have one electron in the s orbital of their valence shell. Aluminum and other group IIIA elements have three valence electrons, two in an s orbital and one in a p orbital.

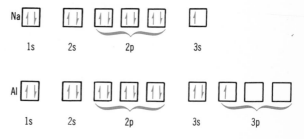

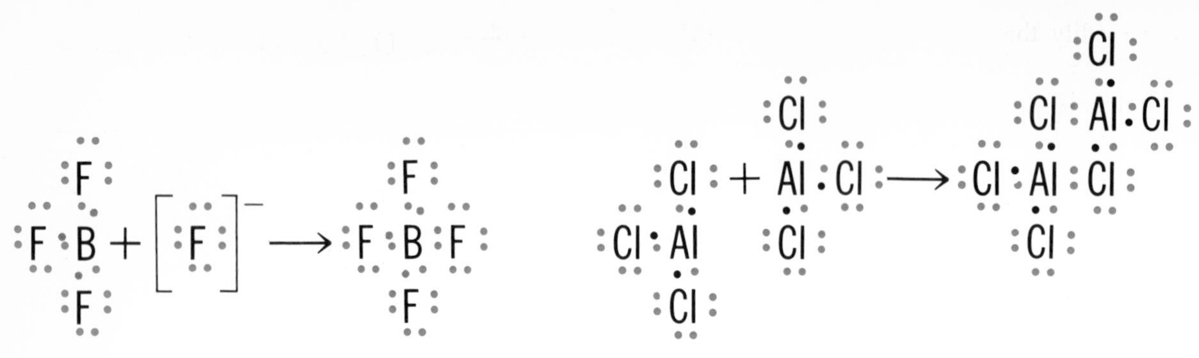

31-3 The boron atom in BF₃ and the aluminum atom in AlCl₃ each has only six valence electrons. The boron bonds covalently with the F⁻ ion to yield BF₄⁻ and complete its outer shell. At temperatures below 400°C, two AlCl₃ molecules bond to form a molecule of Al₂Cl₆ in which both aluminum valence shells are complete.

ALUMINUM AND ITS METALLURGY

Aluminum is a constituent of granite and clay, both widespread in nature, but neither is presently used for the commercial extraction of the metal, although research toward this end has been in progress for many years. Our source of aluminum is bauxite, a yellowish or reddish ore found in Arkansas, France, British Guiana, and Surinam. Bauxite consists chiefly of hydrated aluminum oxide, $Al_2O_3 \cdot 2\,H_2O$, which is mixed with silica (SiO_2) and iron oxide (as impurities). The ore is first dried and pulverized, and then heated with a concentrated solution of sodium hydroxide. The caustic soda reacts with the aluminum oxide to form soluble sodium aluminate, $NaAl(OH)_4$, but the impurities are not affected and are filtered off. A seed of crystalline aluminum hydroxide is added to the aluminate solution, which is kept warm for a period of one to three days. During this time, aluminum hydroxide precipitates (Fig. 31-4), after which it is filtered and washed. Heating in long kilns drives off water and transforms the hydroxide into aluminum oxide, known as **alumina.**

$$2\,Al(OH)_3 \xrightarrow{\Delta} Al_2O_3 + 3\,H_2O\uparrow$$

Early attempts to extract aluminum from alumina by reduction with carbon were unsuccessful because aluminum is a better reducing agent than carbon. At very high temperatures, the reaction is more favorable to production of the metal; but the process, which was employed for a time, becomes increasingly expensive. In either event, the reaction was complicated by the formation of aluminum carbides.

Reduction of aluminum oxide to the metal therefore requires consideration of the relatively high oxidation potential of the metal (page 302). Thus, only very powerful reducing agents, such as the alkali (group I) or alkaline earth (group II) metals could be used. In fact, the oxide was reduced with sodium metal to produce the first small quantities of aluminum. However, the first reasonably successful isolation of the metal was achieved in 1825 by reacting aluminum chloride with potassium.

$$AlCl_3 + 3K \xrightarrow{\Delta} Al + 3\,KCl$$

The aluminum produced by this procedure was necessarily expensive because of the high cost of obtaining potassium and preparing aluminum chloride.

Since reduction is impractical when reducing agents are used, perhaps separation can be achieved by electrolysis. Any attempt to reduce aluminum ions from its compounds in water solution is doomed to failure. By referring to Table 18-2 (page 302), you note that H_2O is reduced more readily than Al^{+3} ions. The possibility of electrolyzing melted aluminum oxide is impractical because of the very high melting point of the compound. In fact, alumina itself, unaffected by most acids and bases, is often shaped into crucibles in which these and other materials can be heated to high temperatures.

The Hall Héroult Process

By trial and error involving experiments with hundreds of materials, Charles Hall tried to find a solvent in which alumina would not only dissolve but also ionize. The mineral **cryolite,** a fluoride of sodium and aluminum (Na_3AlF_6), proved to be the sought-for solvent. When cryolite is melted and heated to approximately 1000° C, the liquid dissolves alumina to form a solution that readily conducts electricity. The apparatus for the commercial production of aluminum by the Hall-Héroult process is shown in Fig. 31-5. It consists of an iron box lined with graphite which serves as the cathode. A series of graphite blocks that extend into the box serve as the anodes. Cryolite is introduced, and then melted by passing a current of electricity through it. Next, the purified alumina is added and is dis-

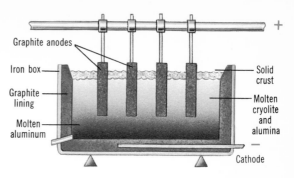

31-5 In the Hall-Heroult process purified alumina is dissolved in molten cryolite. When the reaction is complete, aluminum is withdrawn from the bottom of the tank, where it collects adjacent to the cathode.

solved in the molten cryolite. Decomposition of the solute now begins. Since the process requires huge quantities of electric power, it is economically feasible only near inexpensive sources of such power.

Although the reactions that occur are quite complex and not understood completely, essentially, aluminum ions in the liquid receive electrons from the cathode and become aluminum atoms. The molten aluminum sinks to the bottom as a separate layer. From here, the metal is tapped into molds at intervals to form ingots, which can then be fashioned into other shapes. Meanwhile, oxide ions in the solution become oxygen atoms by losing 2 electrons to the anode. The oxygen atoms readily combine with the hot graphite to form carbon monoxide, which burns on contact with the air. The oxidation of the graphite electrode necessitates its constant replacement as the process continues. The important reactions are summarized as follows:

$$4\ (Al^{+3} + 3\ e^- \longrightarrow Al^0)\ (\text{cathode})$$
$$\underline{3\ (2\ O^{-2} - 4\ e^- \longrightarrow O_2^0)\ (\text{anode})}$$
$$4\ Al^{+3} + 6\ O^{-2} \longrightarrow 4\ Al^0 + 3\ O_2^0$$

Though most uses of aluminum require that the metal be very pure, impurities are often difficult to remove. Therefore, the alumina used in the Hall-Héroult process must be highly purified. As a result, the **Hoopes process** has been developed to purify aluminum after it is isolated (Fig. 31-6). The process involves three layers of

31-4 In the precipitating tanks, which are as high as a six-story building, aluminum hydroxide precipitates out slowly.

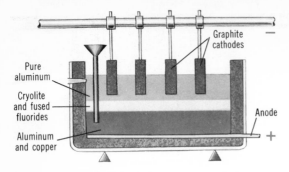

31-6 In the Hoopes process, in contrast with the Hall-Héroult process (Figure 31-5), the top electrodes that extend into the molten material are the cathodes and the pure aluminum is tapped from the top of the tank. In both processes the desired aluminum collects at the cathode.

molten, immiscible materials. The upper layer of pure aluminum serves as the cathode. The middle layer consists of a mixture of cryolite with barium and calcium fluorides. The lower layer, consisting of 30 percent copper and 70 percent impure aluminum, serves as the anode. Aluminum ions produced in this lower layer where impurities are present migrate through the middle layer to the cathode layer where they are discharged. The purified aluminum is drawn off from time to time. Impurities collect in the anode layer which is drawn off and replenished with a fresh supply of aluminum to be purified.

Properties of Aluminum

Pure aluminum is silver-white in color and 2.7 times as dense as water. It possesses all the typical physical properties of metals, ranking high in luster and in its ability to conduct heat and electricity. Freed of its oxide coating, aluminum reacts vigorously with nonoxidizing acids to yield hydrogen and the corresponding salt.

$$2\,Al + 6\,HCl \longrightarrow 3\,H_2\uparrow + 2\,AlCl_3$$

When warmed, the metal reacts vigorously with nonmetals; heat and light are often produced.

$$2\,Al + 3\,Br_2 \xrightarrow{\Delta} 2\,AlBr_3$$
$$2\,Al + 3\,S \xrightarrow{\Delta} Al_2S_3$$

Aluminum is unusual in that it reacts with solutions of strong bases to release *hydrogen*.

$$2\,Al + 2\,NaOH + 6\,H_2O \longrightarrow$$
$$3\,H_2\uparrow + 2\,NaAl\,(OH)_4$$
sodium aluminate

This reaction explains why aluminum containers should not be used to store or prepare solutions of bases.

The vigorous behavior of aluminum, anticipated from its high position in the electrochemical series, causes the surface to become oxidized immediately on exposure to air. The oxide, as you know, acts as a coating to protect the underlying metal from oxidation. As a result, although aluminum is far more active than iron, it can be used in kitchen utensils that are subjected to high temperatures.

What happens if the oxide coating is removed? *Why not find out for yourself?*

Polish a strip of aluminum with steel wool, and immerse the strip in dilute hydrochloric acid for 30 seconds to remove any additional surface oxide. Quickly rinse the strip with distilled water, then dip it into a solution of mercuric chloride. Observe that the metal becomes coated with a film of

mercury. Now suspend the coated strip over a watch glass, and observe the strip carefully. A white coating forms on the metal, peels away, and drops into the watch glass, as shown below. This process is repeated a number of times. Why?

When the aluminum strip is dipped into the mercuric chloride, mercury is replaced from the salt solution by the more active aluminum.

$$2\,Al + 3\,HgCl_2 \longrightarrow 2\,AlCl_3 + 3\,Hg$$

In the presence of the mercury amalgam coating, any oxide formed does not stick to the aluminum, and the underlying metal oxidizes further.

Similarly, aluminum metal placed in hydrochloric acid appears to be unaffected until the acid has eaten through the protective oxide. But if the metal is first amalgamated, the reaction starts immediately and proceeds vigorously to produce hydrogen and aluminum chloride.

Uses of Aluminum

The many uses of aluminum are the direct result of its properties—low density, good thermal and electrical conductivity, malleability, ductility, high luster, resistance to corrosion, and vigorous reducing action.

Containers and truck bodies of aluminum (or aluminum alloys) provide necessary strength with a reduction in dead weight and an increase in payload. Decorative panels and metalwork of aluminum now grace the interiors and exteriors of our skyscrapers. Their weight is less than that of the brick and stone they replace. Outdoor furniture of aluminum is a weight-saving improvement over its heavy and cumbersome iron and steel counterparts; and aluminum telescope tubes are a reality (Fig. 31-7). Astronomical mirrors, like those in household use, once reflected light from a film of silver deposited on the glass. But silver tarnishes and it must be tediously replaced. Today, most mirrors are coated with aluminum, the metal being deposited on the glass by evaporation from a hot filament in a vacuum.

Aluminum's electrical conductivity is not employed in house wiring, but it finds large-scale commercial applications. Production of electric power is only half the story; equally important is the efficient transmission of this power. Witness the many miles of electric cable, supported by towers, that span our countryside. By substituting aluminum (wrapped around a steel core) for

31-7 The engineer seen through the aluminum telescope tube is attaching gold-plated contact wires to the mirror of an ultraviolet telescope, for possible use in space in an Orbiting Astronomical Observatory.

the much denser copper, the weight of the electric cables is reduced considerably and fewer towers are needed. Since aluminum does not conduct electricity as well as copper, thicker cables are needed, but the weight of the aluminum cable is still far less than that of the copper.

Aluminum foil has replaced the less abundant tinfoil for wrapping candy bars, as well as providing the roll of wrapping material now commonplace in the kitchen. Household items ranging from toothpaste to ointments are packaged in aluminum tubes. Fine aluminum wire surrounded by an atmosphere of oxygen is used in flashbulbs. The electric current in the wire generates enough heat to raise the metal to its kindling temperature; rapid oxidation of the metal then produces the brilliant light.

The protective layer of aluminum oxide over the metal (and its alloys) makes possible the use of aluminum in utensils, outdoor furniture, airplanes, trains, as well as in screws and nails. Use of the latter in exterior work has eliminated the unsightly appearance of rust-stained woodwork.

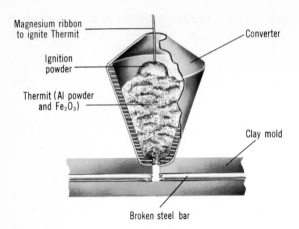

Magnesium ribbon
to ignite Thermit

Converter

Ignition
powder

Thermit (Al powder
and Fe_2O_3)

Clay mold

Broken steel bar

31-8 In the Thermit process, a piece of magnesium ribbon is used as a fuse. The molten iron produced drops through the opening in the bottom of the converter and flows into the break between two pieces of iron or steel, where it solidifies and joins the metal pieces.

The Thermit Process

The welding of metals is a common practice. If the material to be repaired cannot be moved, it is possible to carry out the welding "on the spot" by making use of aluminum's vigorous reducing action. The apparatus which is assembled above and around the broken part is shown in Fig. 31-8. In this process, known as the **Thermit process,** a prepared mixture of powdered aluminum and iron oxide is placed in the crucible. When the mixture is ignited by a fuse, the resulting reaction produces metallic iron and *sufficient heat to melt the iron.* The liquid metal flows into the break where it solidifies to produce one continuous piece of metal.

$$2\,Al + Fe_2O_3 \xrightarrow{\Delta} Al_2O_3 + 2\,Fe + 202 \text{ kcal}$$

This powerful reducing action of aluminum has also been used to extract certain metals from their oxides. Chromium and manganese were originally prepared in this way.

$$Cr_2O_3 + 2\,Al \xrightarrow{\Delta} Al_2O_3 + 2\,Cr$$

Aluminum Alloys

One of the major uses of aluminum is in the preparation of alloys, particularly those of low density. The metal is neither as hard nor as strong as steel. The use of greater thicknesses of aluminum will increase its strength, but some of the weight advantage is then lost. The addition of modest amounts of other elements can effect marked improvement in the hardness and strength of aluminum without much change in density. *Duralumin,* first developed to serve as the framework of dirigibles, contains about 4 percent copper and 0.5 percent each of manganese and magnesium. The *magnalium* alloys used largely for airplane parts are 10 to 30 percent magnesium; the balance is aluminum. The light-weight magnesium alloys known as *Dowmetals* contain from 5 to 10 percent aluminum. They are used in airplanes and automobile engines.

In bronze, the replacement of the tin by aluminum results in gold-colored aluminum bronze. This is often ground into powder and suspended in volatile liquids to form the familiar bronze paint for radiators and pipes.

Iron, cobalt, and nickel exhibit magnetic properties. If aluminum, which is nonmagnetic, is combined with these metals, the resulting alloys, instead of showing a reduction in magnetic properties, are highly magnetic. These alloys, called **alnico** alloys, can lift five hundred times their own weight. Portable and pocket-sized radios

31-9 The green line encircles the alnico magnet portion of the small speaker in a pocket radio. The round metal object at the right of the battery is the protective cover removed from the magnet.

depend on alnico for the small, yet powerful magnets which permit the design of smaller speakers (Fig. 31-9).

QUESTIONS AND PROBLEMS

1. List the essential differences between the elements of group IIIA and those of groups IA and IIA.

2. Compare and contrast the Hoopes process and the Hall-Héroult process for aluminum.

3. (a) Why are aluminum containers not used to prepare solutions of bases? (b) Why is aluminum unaffected by cold, concentrated solutions of oxidizing acids?

4. Describe briefly the Thermit process.

5. (a) List the various uses of aluminum and aluminum alloys in and around your house. (b) State the property of the aluminum or alloy on which each use depends.

ALUMINUM COMPOUNDS

Aluminum compounds were known and used long before the metal itself was isolated. The Romans, Greeks, and Egyptians used combinations of sulfates of aluminum, potassium, and iron in medicine. In later times, aluminum sulfate was used in dyeing. Some aluminum compounds that do not occur naturally are made directly from the metal. Others are produced from the oxide or hydroxide. Their uses range from water purification and dyeing, to catalysts, to the manufacture of paper products.

Aluminum Oxide

Aluminum oxide serves as more than the ore of the metal. It occurs naturally in a variety of forms, each with different properties. Besides appearing in bauxite, the oxide also occurs as *emery* and *corundum*, both noted for their hardness. They are used as abrasives in the form of paper, cloth, and grinding wheels.

Corundum, when transparent, forms gems. Rubies and sapphires consist of this mineral, the colors being produced by the presence of small amounts of different metallic oxides. Synthetic rubies and sapphires are prepared by fusing aluminum oxide with small amounts of other metallic oxides (Fig. 31-10). Chromium oxide yields a ruby-colored product, while iron and titanium oxides are used to imitate the sapphire. The synthetic products not only compete with the natural gems, but supply us with "jewels" for bearings in watches.

Alundum, also an abrasive, is produced by fusing powdered alumina. Because this material is hard, resists attack by most chemicals, withstands shock, and possesses a very high melting point, it is used for mortars and pestles, and for special crucibles in the laboratory. In industry, it shows better performance when made into parts for acid pumps than does customary cast iron. Alumina's variety of special properties make it useful as a drying agent.

The properties of many articles may be improved by incorporating aluminum oxide in their manufacture. The presence of alumina increases the strength of rubber, makes glass brighter, and ceramic glazes whiter.

An exciting new use of purified alumina is in analyzing mixtures of molecular substances by **chromatography.** In **gas chromatography** a mix-

31-10 These synthetic rubies, garnets, and emeralds are used as gems. The rubies were grown from solutions containing aluminum oxide.

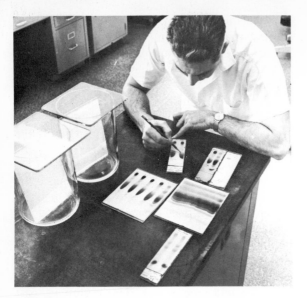

31-11 Small amounts of material to be analyzed are placed at one end of a glass plate covered with alumina, and a solvent is allowed to move up the plate (in the jar). As various components move at their own rates up the plate with the advancing solvent, they can be identified.

ture of gases is passed slowly through a tube containing alumina beads. The surface of the beads adsorbs the various gases at different rates, causing them to separate. Each gaseous component is then identified readily. In **liquid chromatography** a liquid mixture passes by capillary action along a thin layer of alumina. The various components rise to different heights, forming a *chromatogram* (Fig. 31-11). Frequently paper, rather than alumina, is used in preparing chromatograms.

Aluminum Salts

Aluminum chloride, one of the most widely used of aluminum compounds, is a white, deliquescent solid. It is made by reacting chlorine with warm aluminum metal, or passing the gas over a hot mixture of bauxite and coke.

$$2\,Al + 3\,Cl_2 \xrightarrow{\Delta} 2\,AlCl_3$$
$$Al_2O_3 + 3\,C + 3\,Cl_2 \xrightarrow{\Delta} 2\,AlCl_3 + 3\,CO\uparrow$$

The anhydrous compound sublimes on moderate heating and is very soluble in organic liquids

such as benzene and carbon tetrachloride. These properties are indicative of the covalent nature of the compound. It is used extensively as a catalyst for many reactions in organic chemistry.

Most aluminum salts form hydrates. The small, highly positive aluminum nucleus exerts a strong attraction for the negative end of the water dipole. As a result, the hydrated salts often contain six molecules of water or some multiple of this number.

Aluminum sulfate is made by reacting sulfuric acid with bauxite or aluminum hydroxide.

$$2\,Al(OH)_3 + 3\,H_2SO_4 \longrightarrow Al_2(SO_4)_3 + 6\,H_2O$$

The salt forms several hydrates; the most common contains eighteen molecules of water.

When a solution containing aluminum sulfate and a sulfate of a metal with an oxidation state of $+1$ is concentrated by evaporation, a **double salt** of these compounds will crystallize. Such salts, illustrated by $K_2SO_4 \cdot Al_2(SO_4)_3 \cdot 24\,H_2O$, or in simpler form $KAl(SO_4)_2 \cdot 12\,H_2O$, are known as **alums.** The preceding compound is commonly known as potassium alum. Replacement of the aluminum sulfate by sulfates of other metals having a $+3$ oxidation state produces other alums such as potassium chrome alum, $K_2SO_4 \cdot Cr_2(SO_4)_3 \cdot 24\,H_2O$, and ferric ammonium alum, $(NH_4)_2SO_4 \cdot Fe_2(SO_4)_3 \cdot 24\,H_2O$. Potassium alum or aluminum sulfate is an ingredient in the foam fire extinguisher. Sodium alum is present in some types of baking powders.

The Dual Nature of Aluminum Hydroxide

White, highly insoluble aluminum hydroxide is always prepared by a double replacement reaction between an aluminum salt and a mild or weak base.

$$AlCl_3 + 3\,NH_4OH \longrightarrow Al(OH)_3 + 3\,NH_4Cl$$

It is a slimy, gelatinous (jellylike) material used in water purification to coagulate suspended particles which do not settle readily. Some of the unusual chemical properties of aluminum hydroxide *can be observed by completing the following investigation.*

To 5 ml of a dilute solution of aluminum chloride add a few drops of concentrated ammonia water. Notice the white precipitate of aluminum hydroxide which floats or remains suspended in the liquid. Shake the liquid well, and divide the suspension into two parts. To one of these add 5 ml of dilute hydrochloric acid. The suspension disappears as the insoluble base is neutralized to form a soluble aluminum salt.

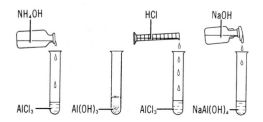

To the second portion, add drop by drop a 0.1 N solution of sodium hydroxide, shaking the mixture after each addition. The suspended aluminum hydroxide again dissolves. Apparently aluminum hydroxide has a dual nature.

When the acid is added, a typical neutralization reaction forming soluble aluminum chloride occurs.

$$3\,HCl + Al(OH)_3 \longrightarrow AlCl_3 + 3\,HOH$$

When the base is added, soluble sodium aluminate forms.

$$NaOH + Al(OH)_3 \longrightarrow NaAl(OH)_4$$

Aluminum hydroxide therefore displays amphoteric behavior (page 248). It reacts with acids in the manner of normal bases, but also reacts as an acid with *strong* bases, to form soluble compounds in which the metal becomes part of a negative ion.

Aluminum Hydroxide in Dyeing

The simplest and most direct method of dyeing a fabric is to soak the cloth in a solution of a dye, usually hot. When a particular dye does not "take" to the cloth, an *indirect* method of dyeing is used. It involves the use of an intermediate agent to help "fix" the dye on the cloth.

When dilute solutions of ammonium hydroxide and aluminum chloride are mixed with a solution of logwood, a brown, gelatinous precipitate of aluminum hydroxide forms. The liquid which remains is colorless. Aluminum hydroxide has the property of *adsorbing* dyestuffs to yield a colored precipitate. If this reaction occurs *within the body of a fiber,* a colored cloth is produced. This procedure, which is known as **mordanting,** permits the dyeing of fibers with dyes that do not ordinarily "take" to the fiber. In this process, the aluminum hydroxide acts as a **mordant.**

QUESTIONS AND PROBLEMS

1. (a) Write the formula for chrome alum and ammonium chrome alum. (b) How are these double salts formed?

2. (a) What are the main uses of emery, corundum, and alundum? (b) How are synthetic rubies produced?

3. How would you prove that aluminum hydroxide is amphoteric?

4. How is aluminum hydroxide used in dyeing cloth?

5. How can alumina be used to identify the components in a mixture of (a) hydrogen, oxygen, and carbon dioxide, (b) boric acid and sugar?

BORON, GALLIUM, INDIUM, AND THALLIUM

Though boron is the first element in group IIIA, the group is commonly known as the aluminum family—an indication of the relative unimportance of boron compared with aluminum. Even so, in comparison with gallium, indium, and thallium, boron and boron compounds have numerous uses.

Boron: Its Preparation and Properties

Our major sources of boron compounds are the beds of dried-up lakes, such as Searle Lake in the Mojave Desert (Fig. 31-12), and the Death Valley area of California. The two chief compounds in these deposits are borax (sodium tetraborate), $Na_2B_4O_7 \cdot 10\,H_2O$, and colemanite, $Ca_2B_6O_{11} \cdot 5\,H_2O$.

The element was originally prepared by reducing the oxide with sodium, potassium, or iron.

$$B_2O_3 + Fe \xrightarrow{\Delta} 2\,B + Fe_2O_3$$

This procedure yields an *amorphous* allotrope of boron which is usually contaminated with borides of the reducing metal. The borides are usually removed by washing the metal with dilute acids, but the remaining element is undoubtedly not of high purity. Boron can also be prepared by electrolysis of potassium fluoborate (KBF_4) in molten KCl or B_2O_3. A *crystalline* form of the element can be prepared by reducing boron tribromide vapor with hydrogen over a hot tungsten filament.

The chemical behavior of the element varies markedly with these two forms. Amorphous boron burns in air to form the oxide and nitride, and it reacts with the halogen elements. It is not attacked by the binary acids but reacts vigorously with the oxidizing acids and molten sodium hydroxide. The crystalline form is relatively inactive; it is unaffected by these acids or by NaOH even at high temperatures.

Borax and Boric Acid

Borax, a hydrated borate of sodium ($Na_2B_4O_7 \cdot 10\,H_2O$), is the best-known compound of boron. Not only is it obtained from brine wells and the crust of certain ancient lakes, but also it can be produced by treating similarly found colemanite with sodium carbonate solution. *Kernite* ($Na_2B_4O_7 \cdot 4\,H_2O$), another hydrate of sodium tetraborate found in California, can be transformed into borax by dissolving it in water and recovering it by recrystallization. Borax is a constituent of some hard-water soaps and cleansing

31-12 This is the world's only open pit borate mine. The pit is already over 400 feet deep, 3000 feet long, and 2000 feet wide. Ore is removed from the pit to the adjacent processing plant by a 1300-foot conveyor belt system.

powders; it is also used alone as a water softener. It is an important ingredient in some glass.

Borax can be treated with hot solutions of hydrochloric acid to yield colorless, lustrous, slightly soluble scales of boric acid, which is often used as an eyewash.

$$Na_2B_4O_7 + 2\,HCl + 5\,H_2O \xrightarrow{\Delta}$$
$$2\,NaCl + 4\,H_3BO_3\downarrow$$

When boric acid is dehydrated at elevated temperatures, it loses water in a series of steps to form other boric acids (*meta-* and *pyro*boric acids), which are finally completely dehydrated to yield boric oxide, B_2O_3.

$$H_3BO_3 \xrightarrow{\Delta} HBO_2 + H_2O$$
$$\text{metaboric acid}$$

$$4\,HBO_2 \xrightarrow{\Delta} H_2B_4O_7 + H_2O$$
$$\text{pyroboric acid}$$

$$H_2B_4O_7 \xrightarrow{\Delta} 2\,B_2O_3 + H_2O$$

Both boric acid and borax melt and then fuse with metallic oxides to form borates, glassy solids of characteristic colors. These colored compounds are used as the basis of the borax bead test for various metals (Chapter 32). Boric acid, like borax, is a constituent of laboratory glassware (Fig. 31-13). Glass made with boric acid has a lower coefficient of expansion than does ordinary soda-lime glass. It is therefore less susceptible to strain at extreme temperature changes. It is also mechanically stronger than ordinary glass and more resistant to chemical attack.

Some Compounds of Boron

Many hydrogen compounds of boron are known; all of them are made by indirect methods. Quite recently several *boranes,* compounds of boron and hydrogen, have been investigated as rocket fuels. The cost of boron liquid fuels is prohibitive, but decaborane ($B_{10}H_{18}$) is being considered as a solid propellant. As a group, boron compounds present a peculiarity—none of them possesses a sufficient number of electrons to provide the usual number of shared electron

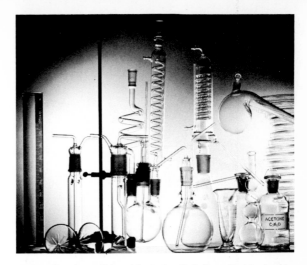

31-13 This glass, which contains boric acid, is Pyrex. Used in chemistry laboratories, it has a relatively low coefficient of expansion and is not easily broken by sudden changes in temperature.

pairs for a complete covalent shell. Their existence and stability has led chemists to consider the possibility of a *single-electron* bond—a type of bond not considered previously.

Several carbides, for example, silicon carbide and tungsten carbide, have been found to possess great hardness. Formerly boron carbide, B_4C, was the hardest synthetic substance known, approaching the diamond in hardness. Now boron nitride (BN) known as *borazon,* has been prepared with a hardness equal to that of diamond. The extremely high pressure under which it is prepared produces giant covalent molecules, imitating the structure of diamond.

Gallium, Indium, and Thallium

The remaining elements of group IIIA and their compounds have limited use. Gallium, unusual among the metals in being liquid at body temperature (Fig. 31-14), has been used in special quartz glass thermometers capable of measuring temperatures approaching 1000° C. Indium has been suggested as a reflecting surface in mirrors, and as a constituent in dental amalgams. Scarcity and consequent high prices have limited the use of these elements. Thallium compounds, being

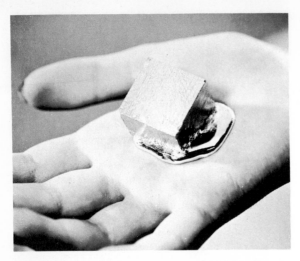

31-14 A cube of solid gallium metal melts in your hand. Its melting point is only 86° F, but it does not boil until heated to 3600° F or higher.

poisonous, are used to destroy rodents. Some thallium compounds are used in optical glass.

The aluminum metals, while generally more metallic than the sodium and calcium families in physical properties, exhibit a number of important chemical differences. Perhaps the most significant of these is that the group IIIA metals form covalent as well as ionic bonds, a property almost entirely lacking in groups IA and IIA. Since the aluminum family of metals possesses outer electron shells that are just short of being half full, it will be of interest to observe in the next chapter whether the element that follows the group IIIA metal in each period continues the trend observed in the aluminum family.

QUESTIONS AND PROBLEMS

1. Differentiate between each of the following pairs of terms: (a) *borax* and *kernite,* (b) *amorphous boron* and *crystalline boron.*

2. List a use for each of the following boron compounds: decaborane, borazon, boric acid, boron nitride.

3. Write the formula for each of the following

compounds: (a) thallous iodide, (b) gallium sulfate, (c) calcium fluoborate, (d) indous bromide, (e) boron astatide.

VALUE OF THE CONCEPT

THE CONCEPT

The group IIIA elements are not as closely knit a family as the elements of groups IA, IIA, VIA, and VIIA. Boron, the first member of this family, is markedly different from the rest; it is essentially nonmetallic and forms only covalent compounds. Though the remaining elements are metallic in physical qualities, they are increasingly less metallic in chemical behavior; they exhibit considerable covalent bonding as well as ionic bonding. Variable oxidation states occur with some of the members of this family, but the stability of these states is not consistent. In contrast to the members of the preceding A groups, the metals of group IIIA are not close together in the electrochemical series. Aluminum is about as active as magnesium, but the remaining metals are considerably less active. Direct combination of metals with hydrogen does not occur in the aluminum family. Though hydrogen compounds of these elements are known, they are covalent, in contrast to the hydrides of sodium, potassium, and calcium. In passing from the first two elements of each period to the element in group IIIA, we observe a marked change in the purely metallic behavior previously encountered.

Aluminum metal is prepared commercially by the electrolysis of alumina in the Hall-Héroult process. Low density, high thermal and electrical conductivity, ductility, and resistance to corrosion account for its many applications—ladders and lawn furniture, electrical wires, pots and pans, and alloys. The uses of aluminum compounds range from aluminum oxide in synthetic gems to alum in fire extinguishers; amphoteric aluminum hydroxide is used in dyeing cloth. In addition to borax and boric acid, the compounds of boron include the extremely hard carbides and nitrides, and the potentially useful borane fuels.

USING THE CONCEPT

Using the Basic Concept

1. Why were early attempts to extract aluminum from alumina relatively unsuccessful?
2. Why must the lowest layer of copper and aluminum be constantly replenished in the Hoopes process?
3. What is the chief danger in using Thermit welding?
4. (a) Why is aluminum widely used in alloys? (b) What is the chief advantage of most alloys containing aluminum? (c) Why are alnico magnets valuable?
5. Aluminum oxide cannot be reduced efficiently with carbon, yet it is reduced easily by sodium or potassium. Why?
6. How are artificial sapphires produced?
7. (a) What is a double salt? (b) Write the formula for sodium alum.
8. Why is aluminum hydroxide used in mordant dyeing?
9. Write equations for the reactions between (a) aluminum hydroxide and sulfuric acid, (b) aluminum hydroxide and potassium hydroxide. (c) What property of aluminum hydroxide is demonstrated by these reactions?
10. How does the small size of the boron atom explain the fact that the element does not form ionic compounds?
11. What properties, other than that of being liquid, must gallium possess to be suitable for use in thermometers?
12. What procedure could be used to prove that an aluminum compound is covalent rather than ionic?
13. Write the formula for: thallous bromide, gallium carbonate, indous iodide, magnesium fluoborate, aluminum astatide, sodium aluminate.
14. (a) Give two common names for hydrated sodium tetraborate. (b) How does crystalline boric acid differ from borax?
15. (a) Differentiate between boron carbide and boron nitride with respect to formula and chief property. (b) For what are some boranes being used experimentally?

Relating Terms Within the Concept

Each of the following statements contains two italicized terms. Select the *italicized* term that makes the statement correct.

1. Boron, unlike the other group IIIA elements, never forms (*covalent compounds, ionic compounds*).
2. The three electrons in the valence shell of an atom of a group IIIA element occupy the s orbitals and the (*d orbital, p orbital*).
3. The aluminum ore used in the Hall-Héroult process is (*cryolite, bauxite*).
4. Aluminum occurs in the form of a negative radical in (*alums, aluminates*).
5. The Thermit process is used in welding because it produces liquid (*aluminum, iron*).
6. The aluminum alloy used in airplane parts is (*Duralumin, magnalium*).
7. The aluminum oxide abrasive that is also used in special crucibles and pumps is (*corundum, alundum*).
8. Aluminum oxide fused with small amounts of other oxides produces (*artificial gems, kernite*).
9. An example of a double salt is (*potassium alum, alumina*).
10. Aluminum hydroxide is used as a mordant in dyeing cloth because it is (*amphoteric, adsorbent*).
11. The Hall-Héroult process requires continual replacement of the (*anode, cathode*).
12. An element that is liquid at body temperature is (*gallium, indium*).
13. A boron compound that is mild enough to be used as an eyewash is (*borax, boric acid*).
14. Boron compounds that are being studied as possible rocket fuels are (*borazons, boranes*).

Solving Problems Within the Concept

1. (a) How many grams of aluminum are needed to reduce 14.1 grams of manganese dioxide which is 78 percent pure? (b) How many grams of manganese will be produced?

2. Determine the percent of (a) water of hydration in borax, (b) boron in colemanite, (c) aluminum in cryolite, (d) chromium in potassium chrome alum.

3. (a) What volume of hydrogen will be obtained (**STP**) when 40.5 grams of aluminum react with a solution of sodium hydroxide? (b) What weight of sodium hydroxide will be needed?

4. An unweighed sample of aluminum is reacted with dilute hydrochloric acid to yield 1 liter of hydrogen gas (**STP**). (a) What was the weight of the metal? (b) If the resulting solution is diluted to a volume of 50 ml, what is its molarity with respect to aluminum chloride?

5. Which will yield the greater quantity of hydrogen: the reaction of 54 grams of aluminum with dilute hydrochloric acid, or the reaction of the same weight of metal with sodium hydroxide solution?

6. A compound contains 75 percent by weight of aluminum and 25 percent of carbon. Determine its formula.

7. An alloy is made by combining 9 parts of aluminum and 1 part of magnesium *by volume*. Assuming that the final volume is the sum of these parts, what is the density of the resulting alloy?

8. What weight of boron carbide will be formed when 30 grams of boron trioxide are reacted with carbon?

9. How many liters of chlorine gas (**STP**) are needed to react completely with 100 grams of gallium metal?

Applying the Concept

1. Why should solutions of washing soda not be prepared or stored in aluminum utensils?

2. Why are the group IIIA elements *not* transition elements?

3. Aluminum or aluminum bronze is ground into exceedingly fine powders for use in metallic paints. What extreme danger may result if either of these powders is thrown into the air and suspended as a dust? Why?

4. By what methods could the chemist determine that the true formula for aluminum chloride is Al_2Cl_6?

5. A flashbulb is weighed and then "fired." What change in weight will occur? A pinhole is then made in the bulb. Will any change in weight occur? Explain your answers.

6. Aluminum reacts with dilute nitric acid according to the following equation:

$$Al + HNO_3 \longrightarrow Al(NO_3)_3 + NH_4NO_3 + H_2O$$

Balance this equation by the electron-transfer method.

7. Write balanced equations for the reactions between: (a) indium and sulfur when heated, (b) aluminum hydroxide and nitric acid, (c) aluminum hydroxide and potassium hydroxide, (d) thallium and chlorine to form thallic chloride.

8. Describe *two* methods by which you could separate a mixture of *solid* aluminum chloride and sodium chloride.

9. Explain how certain dyes could be used in testing for the presence of aluminum compounds in solution.

Reading Further

The Elements: Builders of the Universe, by Jerome Meyer, Cleveland, World Publishing, 1957. A highly readable account of the history and present-day utilization of the elements from hydrogen to nobelium.

Man and the Chemical Elements, rev. ed. by J. N. Friend, New York, Scribner, 1961. A history of each family of elements—from the discovery of its first element to present uses of these elements.

32

SKILLS—Testing for Positive Ions

"All is not gold that glitters." Such was the lesson taught by "fool's gold." But how *are* these bright yellow lumps distinguished from real gold? Other metals may be equally deceptive. The kitchen faucet or bathroom towel rack may be chromium-plated—or is it nickel? How can the operator of the steel furnace know whether the scrap steel contains tungsten, molybdenum, or other metals, in order to adjust operating conditions? Many communities forbid the use of lead paint on toys or childrens' furniture—how does a chemist for the department of health analyze paints for their lead content?

In an age of metals and metal products, these are only a few of the many situations that require chemical testing for metallic elements. The tests you have learned thus far are almost entirely for the nonmetals. The only tests made for positive ions were those for the ammonium and hydrogen (hydronium) ions, and these are hardly metallic.

The preceding chapters on the families of metals have already provided many instances of reactions suitable for detecting individual metal ions. The detection of a metallic ion becomes more complicated when more than one ion responds in the same way to a particular chemical test. In the succeeding pages, you will learn some of the methods the chemist uses to distinguish a single metallic ion from all others. Since our purpose will be to *identify* a metallic ion, rather than measure its quantity, the procedures we will follow are within the area of *qualitative analysis*.

QUALITATIVE ANALYSIS OF METALLIC IONS

The first step in the chemical analysis of an unknown metal-containing substance, whether an ore, a coin, scrap metal, or a compound, is to dissolve the sample. This is done because the reactions which are used in analysis are those of the metallic ions in solution. Once the unknown substance has been dissolved, analysis may proceed. In your previous experience, the tests you performed dealt with single ions; but in actual practice, ions of more than one metal are usually present in solution. They must be separated before conclusive tests can be made. How will you proceed?

Separation of Metallic Ions

The existence of groups of metals makes rare indeed the single test that detects one metallic ion alone. From their position in the periodic table, we should expect calcium, strontium, and barium to respond similarly in some reactions;

Table 32-1 ANALYTICAL GROUPS OF METALLIC IONS

Group I	Group II	Group III	Group IV	Group V
Lead	Antimony	Aluminum	Barium	Ammonium*
Mercury(I)	Arsenic	Chromium	Calcium	Lithium
Silver	Bismuth	Cobalt	Strontium	Potassium
	Cadmium	Iron		Sodium
	Copper(II)	Manganese		
	Mercury(II)	Nickel		
	Tin(II, IV)	Zinc		

*A nonmetallic ion commonly included in this group.

also zinc, cadmium, and mercury should act alike. But this very similarity among some metals is turned into an advantage. It provides a means of separating the various metallic ions which may be present into small groups of related ions. Indeed, this is the technique by which metallic ions are separated into groups and ultimately identified. Let us see *how this separation is accomplished.*

Prepare a series of test tubes containing respectively 10 ml of a 0.1 M solution of the nitrates of lead, silver, mercury I (mercurous), mercury II (mercuric), copper II (cupric), zinc, and iron II (ferrous). Now add 1 ml of dilute HCl to each test tube. If any precipitate appears, continue adding the acid, dropwise, until precipitation is complete. Stopper each of the tubes in which a precipitate appears and shake the contents to promote coagulation of the precipitate.

Only the solutions containing the lead, silver, and mercurous ions produce precipitates. These metal ions are therefore separated, as a group, from a solution containing a number of metallic ions simply by adding HCl and filtering off the insoluble chlorides formed. The ions that precipitate as chlorides in our scheme of analysis are known collectively as *analytical group I* (shown in Table 32-1 and not to be confused with group I of the periodic table). There now remains *the problem of distinguishing among the three white precipitates* of lead, silver, and mercury(I), as shown in the diagram below.

Heat each tube containing a precipitate and observe whether there is any pronounced change in the solubility of the precipitate. Let the liquids cool and filter them, keeping the precipitate, but discarding the filtrate in each instance. Place a test tube under each funnel, pour 5 ml of dilute ammonium hydroxide over each precipitate, and collect the new filtrate. Is any change observed in the residue on the filter paper? Now add dilute nitric acid to each filtrate until the liquid is acid to litmus paper. What do you observe?

The lead chloride is quite soluble in hot water and insoluble in NH_4OH; the silver chloride dissolves in the NH_4OH but reprecipitates when HNO_3 is added. When the NH_4OH is added to the white mercurous chloride, the latter changes to a gray-black color.

Identification of the Metallic Ions of Analytical Group I

Here is a tabulation of the properties of the insoluble chlorides of Pb^{+2}, Ag^+, and Hg^+ as established in the preceding investigation.

For lead chloride:

1. The solubility in hot water is three times that in cold water.
2. The compound is not soluble in ammonium hydroxide.

For silver chloride:

1. Hot water has no observable effect on its solubility.

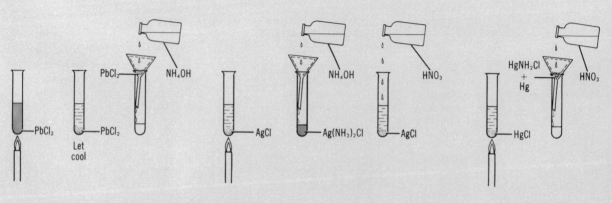

2. It dissolves in ammonium hydroxide to form soluble silver ammonia chloride.

$$AgCl + 2\,NH_3 \rightleftharpoons Ag(NH_3)_2{}^+ + Cl^-$$

This reaction is reversible. If hydrogen ions are added to this solution, they combine with the ammonia to form ammonium ions, shifting the equilibrium to the left. The silver ions reprecipitate as silver chloride.

$$Ag(NH_3)_2{}^+ + Cl^- + 2\,H^+ + 2\,NO_3{}^- \longrightarrow$$
$$AgCl\downarrow + 2\,NH_4{}^+ + 2\,NO_3$$

For mercurous chloride:

1. A rise in temperature has no observable effect on its solubility.
2. It reacts with ammonia to undergo *auto-oxidation-reduction* to form insoluble mercuric amino chloride ($HgNH_2Cl$).

$$2\,\overset{+1}{Hg}Cl + 2\,NH_3 \longrightarrow$$
$$\overset{+2}{Hg}NH_2Cl\downarrow + NH_4Cl + \overset{0}{Hg}$$

Although the insoluble mercuric amino chloride formed is white, the finely divided mercury produced is dark and colors the whole precipitate gray-black.

As a result of these reactions, we are able to separate the metallic ions of analytical group I from all other ions and then identify them. A summary scheme for identifying these metals is shown in Fig. 32-1 below. Study the arrangement carefully so that you understand the procedure and reactions involved.

Observe that in proving the presence of the lead ion, we employed two reactions that produced lead compounds of distinctive properties, rather than simply attempting to judge the solubility of an insoluble residue in hot water. Throughout any future work in analytical chemistry, you will discover that the chemist makes use of **confirmatory tests** to double-check the presence of a particular ion. Thus, the appearance of a gray-black material when ammonia is poured through the filter paper in the foregoing scheme of analysis is a *necessary* observation in proving the presence of the Hg^+ ion, but is not yet a

Fig. 32-1 SEPARATION AND IDENTIFICATION OF THE ANALYTICAL GROUP I METALLIC IONS

PROCEDURE: To precipitate the ions of analytical group I from an unknown solution (containing many metallic ions) add dilute HCl to the solution drop by drop, with stirring, until no further precipitate is formed. Add 2 ml of the acid in excess.

PRECIPITATE: May consist of $AgCl$, $PbCl_2$, and $HgCl$. Filter the liquid and set the filtrate aside for further study. Wash the residue on the filter paper with 3 ml of dilute HCl and discard the washings. Wash the residue with hot water, and retain both the filtrate and the residue.

FILTRATE: May contain Pb^{+2} ions. Divide the solution into two parts. To one, add dilute H_2SO_4; a white precipitate of $PbSO_4$ confirms the presence of Pb^{+2} ions. Acidify the other part with dilute acetic acid and add 2 ml of potassium chromate. A yellow precipitate of lead chromate confirms the presence of Pb^{+2} ions.	**RESIDUE:** $AgCl$, $HgCl$, and any undissolved $PbCl_2$. If lead ions are found in the filtrate, continue washing the residue with hot water until no further test for lead is obtained. Pour 10 ml of dilute ammonia water over the residue on the filter paper, and catch the liquid which passes through.

RESIDUE: A gray-black mixture of Hg and $HgNH_2Cl$ indicates the presence of Hg^+ ions.	**FILTRATE:** Add dilute HNO_3, while stirring constantly until the solution is definitely acid to litmus. A white precipitate or cloudiness indicates the presence of Ag^+ ions.

sufficient proof that the ion is present. Analytical chemistry textbooks will indicate to you several confirmatory tests for this and other ions.

Metallic Ions of Analytical Group II

The procedure described thus far has enabled us to identify a total of only three metallic ions. Another group of metallic ions, comprising analytical group II, can be precipitated as sulfides and identified. We already know that some metallic ions form insoluble, colored sulfides. *Let us examine* this type of reaction in more detail.

Prepare a series of test tubes containing respectively 1 ml of 1 *M* solutions of salts of cadmium, bismuth, copper(II), tin(II) and (IV), arsenic, antimony, mercury(II), iron (III), aluminum, chromium, manganese, cobalt, zinc, and nickel. To each, add 1 ml of 3 *M* HCl and 8 ml of water. This procedure makes each of the solutions about 0.3 *M* with respect to HCl. Now *in a hood* saturate

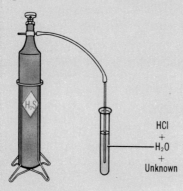

HCl
+
H$_2$O
+
Unknown

each solution with H$_2$S by placing a delivery tube from a supply of H$_2$S into each test tube. Colored precipitates (illustrated in Colorplate III, following page 548) appear in some, but not all, of the test tubes.

The precipitated sulfides of cadmium, bismuth, copper(II), tin(II) and (IV), arsenic, antimony, and mercury(II) can be tentatively identified by their colors, which are given in Table 32-2.

These reactions provide a further step in separating certain metallic ions into a second analyti-

Table 32-2   SULFIDES PRECIPITATED IN 0.3 *M* HCl

Sulfide		Color
As$_2$S$_3$	(arsenic sulfide)	Yellow
Bi$_2$S$_3$	(bismuth sulfide)	Dark brown
CdS	(cadmium sulfide)	Yellow
CuS	(cupric sulfide)	Black
HgS	(mercuric sulfide)	Black
Sb$_2$S$_3$	(antimony sulfide)	Orange
SnS	(stannous sulfide)	Brown
SnS$_2$	(stannic sulfide)	Light yellow

cal group—group II. Once the analytical group II ions precipitate as sulfides, filtration separates them from the remaining ions. Treatment with hot potassium hydroxide divides the sulfides into two subgroups. Hot KOH solution, for example, dissolves the sulfides of arsenic, antimony, and tin, but leaves the remaining sulfides unaffected. Still other reactions may be used to separate these subgroups into even smaller groups, until the individual metallic ions are completely separated from each other. Individual confirmatory tests are employed as the final step. The details of these procedures must be left for a more advanced study of qualitative analysis, where charts similar to those on the previous page indicate appropriate procedures for separating and identifying all metallic ions.

Metallic Ions of Analytical Group III

Not all the metallic ions tested in the preceding investigation yield insoluble sulfides; for example, Co^{+2}, Zn^{+2}, and Ni^{+2} solutions remain unchanged. This fact enables us to divide a large group of ions into smaller, more easily handled subgroups. *What can we learn* about these remaining metallic ions that do not form insoluble sulfides in acid solution?

Neutralize the solutions of Co^{+2}, Zn^{+2}, Ni^{+2}, Fe^{+3}, Mn^{+2}, Cr^{+3}, Al^{+3} ions with concentrated ammonium hydroxide and add 1 ml in excess. Now again saturate the solutions with H$_2$S. The sulfides of cobalt, zinc, nickel, iron, and manganese precipitate. Chromium and aluminum precipitate in the form of their hydroxides, since sulfides of these two metals hydrolyze completely in water.

This series of metallic ions that form precipitates in basic solutions when hydrogen sulfide is bubbled through their solutions comprise group III in the *analytical* scheme. Some of these sulfides have characteristic color; zinc sulfide, for example, is pure white. However, once again various chemical reactions can be used to separate the ions of analytical group III into smaller and smaller subgroups until a single element can be identified. For example, the hydroxides of Co^{+2}, Zn^{+2}, and Ni^{+2} are soluble in excess ammonium hydroxide.

The pattern of chemical analysis might be summarized as "divide and identify." The large number of metallic ions which might be present in an unknown solution is separated into analytical groups which, thus far, may contain anywhere from three to eight ions. Each of these groups is then divided further into smaller subgroups, and these in turn separated further into individual substances whose properties identify the metallic ion. Where the properties of several ions are identical, we use confirmatory tests for positive identification.

QUESTIONS AND PROBLEMS

1. If mercury is detected in analytical group I, should the analyst expect to find it in analytical group II? Why?

2. How could you identify each of the following analytical group II metals: antimony, copper, arsenic, tin(II)?

3. How could you separate cobalt, nickel, and zinc ions from the remaining metallic ions in analytical group III?

4. On the basis of what single characteristic are analytical group II sulfides separated from

analytical group III sulfides (and hydroxides)?

5. (a) List the metallic ions found in *analytical* groups I, II, and III; next to each ion, indicate its group *in the periodic table.* (b) How often do members of the same periodic group fall together in the scheme of analysis?

ANALYTICAL GROUPS IV AND V, AND SPECIFIC TESTS

After the removal of the analytical group I, II, and III ions, only a relatively small number of ions remains. These are the members of the alkali metal and alkaline earth metal groups, plus the ammonium ion. Since alkali metal ions form very few insoluble compounds, these ions are left to constitute the last group (analytical group V) in our scheme of analysis.

Group IV in the Analytical Scheme

Calcium, strontium, and barium ions are separated from the remaining group V ions by precipitating them as carbonates. This is usually done by the addition of an aqueous ammonia solution containing ammonium carbonate (Fig. 32-2). The carbonates are filtered, washed, and

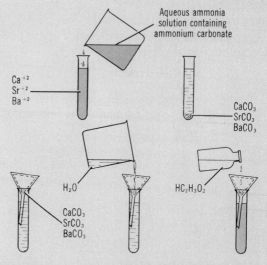

32-2 Ammonium carbonate reacts with each of these group IIA ions to form its carbonate. Since each carbonate dissolves in dilute acetic acid, flame tests are often used to differentiate among group IIA ions.

dissolved in dilute acetic acid. Adding a solution of potassium chromate (K_2CrO_4) to the acid solution causes yellow barium chromate to precipitate; the strontium and calcium ions remain in solution. Other reactions are used to separate these latter ions. Specific confirmatory tests (on the opposite page) are now used to detect or double-check each of the analytical group IV ions.

Group V in the Analytical Scheme

If a solution containing as many as twenty-five metallic ions is treated by the procedures described thus far, we are finally left with a solution containing only those metals that do not form insoluble chlorides, sulfides, hydroxides, or carbonates. The only ions present at this point, therefore, are the ammonium ions and those of the alkali metals (see Table 32-1). Because the analytical procedure described often requires the addition of ammonium hydroxide, it is necessary to perform the test for the ammonium ion on a portion of the original unknown solution. How is this done?

Add an excess of a base, such as NaOH, to a small portion of the original sample, warm the solution, and determine if ammonia gas forms. A positive test results because, as you know, the reaction between an ammonium salt and any base (except ammonium hydroxide) *must* produce ammonium hydroxide.

$$NH_4X + MOH \longrightarrow MX + NH_4OH$$

On gentle warming, the ammonium hydroxide is decomposed to yield ammonia gas and water.

$$NH_4OH \longrightarrow NH_3\uparrow + HOH$$

Ammonia gas can be identified in the three ways discussed in Chapter 25: first, it has a characteristic odor; second, it turns moist red litmus paper blue; and third, it reacts with hydrogen chloride vapors (from the concentrated acid) to yield a white smoke of ammonium chloride.

Testing for the Alkali Metals

Since alkali metals form very few insoluble compounds, the alkali metal ions of analytical group V are detected in a totally different manner. *Investigate the following* to see how they are identified.

Light a Bunsen burner and carefully observe the color of the flame. Now carefully sprinkle a pinch of table salt over the flame. Dissolve a few crystals of the salt in one-half a glass of water and sprinkle a few drops of the solution over the flame. Dilute the solution several times, repeating the test after each dilution.

The continued appearance of a yellow flame stamps this procedure as an exceedingly sensitive test for the presence of sodium ions. The small quantity of sodium ions in water accounts for the yellow color imparted to the flame when water spatters or boils over from a pot.

The procedure of determining the color produced when salts of certain metals are sprinkled into a flame is referred to as a **flame test.** This test can be used to identify the members of the alkali family, as well as the alkaline earth metals and a few metals and their ions not in analytical group V.

To perform a flame test, hold a platinum wire attached to a glass rod in a Bunsen burner flame until no color is evident beyond the normal blue color of the flame, as shown below. Then touch the wire to a sample of

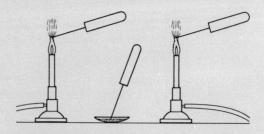

the unknown, whether solid or in solution, and again heat the wire in the flame. The colors of the flames obtained with various metals or metallic ions are listed in Table 32-3 and Colorplate IV (following page 548).

Table 32-3 FLAME TESTS

Element	Color
Barium	Yellowish green
Calcium	Orange-red
Copper	Emerald green (except for the halides which produce a bluish green)
Lithium	Crimson
Potassium	Violet
Sodium	Yellow
Strontium	Scarlet

You may encounter some difficulty with flame tests when more than one type of ion is present; traces of sodium often blot out the colors produced by other metallic ions, even when the latter are present in much larger quantities than the sodium. Observing flames through different colored glass may help, since certain colors can be filtered out by different colors of glass. For example, the violet-colored flame of potassium can be detected in the presence of sodium by viewing the flame through blue cobalt glass. The glass filters out the yellow sodium light but transmits the violet potassium light.

If the light produced in the flame test of an element is passed through a spectroscope, a bright-line spectrum forms. No two elements have the same spectrum when this is done (facing page 84). Hence, once the spectrum of each element has been determined, the "fingerprints" of any unknown can be matched against it.

Specific Tests for Some Metallic Ions

The assumption that substances in a mixture always behave as they do when they occur singly may not be justified. A very small amount of a material may be "protected" by a large amount of another substance and prevented from reacting as expected. Or a very small amount of an ion may not show the same color or precipitate as would a larger quantity of that ion. Wherever possible, we seek to double-check first impressions. A number of confirmatory tests can be used to substantiate the observations made dur-

ing the analytical procedure. The flame test described previously is one example; the **borax bead test** and the **cobalt nitrate test** are also used for this purpose.

The Borax Bead Test

Not all metallic ions color the Bunsen flame. A test for some of these ions is based on the experience gathered in the manufacture of colored glass. The borax bead test depends upon the ability of *small quantities* of metallic ions of *transition* elements to color borate glass.

You can perform a borax bead test as follows:

Make a loop in the end of a platinum wire. Clean the wire in concentrated HCl, and dip the moistened loop into a small pile of powdered borax, as shown below. Heat the borax until it melts and fuses to form a *borax bead.* Upon heating the water of hydration is

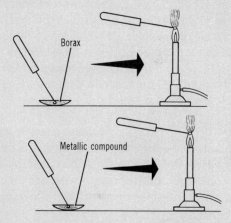

driven from the borax and the anhydrous compound melts to form a colorless, glassy solid. Now touch the borax bead to a speck of the unknown substance and reheat the bead. The two substances combine to form a borate of the unknown metal.

Salts of most of the common transition elements form *colored* borates. Too large a quantity of the unknown material tested in this way results in dark, opaque borax beads whose colors are difficult to judge. The colors produced by certain metallic ions when the bead is heated in an

Table 32-4 BORAX BEAD TEST

Element	Color
Chromium	Green
Cobalt	Blue
Copper	Greenish blue
Iron	Yellowish to brownish
Manganese	Violet
Nickel	Reddish brown

oxidizing flame are summarized in Table 32-4 and shown in Colorplate V (following page 548).

The Cobalt Nitrate Test

Some metallic ions neither impart color to a flame nor color the borax bead. To identify some of these ions, we employ the interesting observation that *mixtures* of certain metallic oxides have distinctive colors. *Cobalt oxide,* for example, is *brownish black,* while the oxides of zinc, aluminum, and magnesium are white. However, a combination of cobalt oxide with each of these oxides produces a different color. The use of cobalt nitrate to obtain a colored mixture of cobalt oxide and certain metallic compounds is called the cobalt nitrate test.

To perform a cobalt nitrate test, place a drop of cobalt nitrate solution in a cavity on a plaster of Paris (or charcoal) block and heat the drop strongly with a blowpipe, as shown below. The nitrate decomposes to

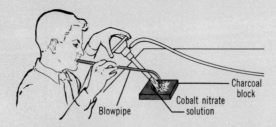

Charcoal block
Cobalt nitrate solution
Blowpipe

form cobalt oxide. Now add a drop of solution of the unknown and heat again to form the mixed oxides. The color observed on cooling reveals the metallic ion of the unknown.

The characteristic colors obtained with several oxides in the cobalt nitrate tests are listed in Table 32-5 and illustrated in Colorplate VI (facing page 549).

Table 32-5 COBALT NITRATE TEST

Element	Color
Zinc	Green
Aluminum	Blue
Magnesium	Pinkish red

QUESTIONS AND PROBLEMS

1. Devise a procedure for detecting both ions in a solution containing the following pairs of metallic ions: (a) sodium and barium, (b) manganese and chromium, (c) aluminum and zinc.

2. Give *two* confirmatory tests for copper.

3. Why are the alkali metals not easily identified by a procedure analogous to that for the other analytical groups?

4. What confirmatory tests could be used to identify the two elements in analytical group IV that are not precipitated by the addition of potassium chromate?

ANALYZING AN UNKNOWN

Let us review the total scheme of qualitative analysis for the metallic ions by examining the procedure as it would be applied to a solution containing one ion from each of the analytical groups. We shall introduce into 25 ml of distilled water ions of silver, antimony, zinc, barium, and potassium.

Procedure 1. Test the unknown with litmus paper; if it is basic, neutralize the solution with dilute nitric acid and add one drop in excess (an additional drop). Now add a few drops of dilute hydrochloric acid; a white precipitate appears. Continue addition of the acid until precipitation is complete. Stir the mixture to coagulate the precipitate and filter it, saving the filtrate for future work. Pour 5 ml of boiling water over the residue on the filter paper, catching the filtrate in a clean test tube. In the absence of lead, there will be no change in the residue; confirmatory tests for lead in the filtrate will be negative. Now place another test tube under the funnel and pour 5 ml of dilute ammonium hydroxide over the precipitate. In the absence of the mercurous ion, there will be no blackening of the residue. But this precipitate, consisting of silver chloride, will dissolve. If the filtrate is neutralized with dilute nitric acid, the white precipitate of silver chloride reappears.

Procedure 2. Neutralize the filtrate from procedure 1 with dilute ammonium hydroxide. Add 5 ml of 3 M HCl and dilute the solution to 50 ml. The solution is now 0.3 M with respect to HCl. Saturate the solution with H_2S; an orange precipitate appears. Filter this precipitate and set the filtrate aside for further work. The orange residue on the filter is probably antimony sulfide. It can be distinguished from yellow cadmium sulfide by its solubility in hot KOH solution. Antimony sulfide is distinguished from yellow arsenic sulfide by its solubility in hot, concentrated HCl.

Procedure 3. Make the filtrate from procedure 2 alkaline with ammonium hydroxide and again saturate it with H_2S. Since zinc is the only member of analytical group III present, a white precipitate forms. Filter this precipitate and reserve the filtrate for procedure 4. The presence of zinc can be confirmed by testing a portion of the precipitate by the cobalt nitrate test; a green color appears.

Procedure 4. Acidify the filtrate from procedure 3 with dilute acetic acid and boil the resulting solution to remove hydrogen sulfide. Make the solution basic with ammonium hydroxide and add 1 gram of ammonium chloride. Warm the solution, add 10 ml of ammonium carbonate solution, and stir it frequently for a period of 10 minutes. This procedure yields a white precipitate which is filtered and washed. Keep the filtrate for the analysis of the final group (V) in the scheme.

Now pour 5 to 10 ml of dilute acetic acid over the filter paper, collecting the filtrate and pouring it over the paper at least twice more. The precipitate(s) of the alkaline earth metal carbonate(s) will dissolve in the acid. Add 5 ml of a solution of potassium chromate to the filtrate. A yellow precipitate of barium chromate forms. As explained on page 544, the remaining alkaline earth metal ions would not form insoluble chromates in the acid solution. However, the presence of barium is still confirmed by dissolving the precipitate in 1:1 hydrochloric acid and applying the flame test (page 544) for barium; a greenish flame results.

Procedure 5. The filtrate from the precipitation of the carbonates of group IV can now be tested for the alkali metal ions by means of the flame test. Because the original unknown was treated with many reagents in the course of the analysis, each of which might have added traces of sodium to the solution, it is imperative to examine the flame through a cobalt blue glass. The violet of potassium is unmistakable.

The simple analysis described in this chapter helps to summarize the fundamentals behind any scheme of analysis for ions, whether metallic or nonmetallic. Because many ions may be present in an unknown solution, and because more than one of the ions reacts in the same or similar way with a given reagent, we divide our initial group of ions into smaller groups on the basis of a single reaction; for example, the precipitation of sulfides in an acid solution. We are now at liberty to separate each group into smaller groups, utilizing *differences* in reaction with a given reagent. Finally we arrive at a solution that should contain only a single ion. Although this ion may be identified by a particular reaction, we are always mindful of the variations that may occur when any given ion is in the presence of other ions. Toward that end, we employ confirmatory tests to substantiate the tentative conclusions drawn from other sources. The flame test, borax bead test, and cobalt nitrate test are some of the better-known procedures used for this purpose.

1. Outline the procedure of analysis you would follow if a solution were suspected of containing ions of mercury(I), arsenic, and aluminum.

2. What analytical procedures and confirmatory tests would you use to prove that a solution contains ions of cobalt, copper, and barium?

ADDITIONAL PROBLEMS

1. Outline the analytical procedure you would follow to prove that a solution contains ions of silver, tin, and nickel.

2. How could you confirm the identity of the metallic ions in a solution containing sodium, potassium, iron, and magnesium?

3. If a black sulfide were precipitated by adding H_2S during the analytical group II procedure, how could you determine what metallic ion was actually present?

4. Devise a procedure for detecting the silver and ammonium ions in the same solution.

5. What analytical procedures and confirmatory tests could be used to determine that a solution contains ions of zinc, nickel, and strontium?

6. Describe fully the tests you would perform to prove that an unknown substance is: (a) calcium carbonate, (b) magnesium bromide, (c) chromium sulfate, (d) lead nitrate.

7. How would you apply the reactions of the silver and barium ions to identify the negative ions in a solution containing sodium chloride and sodium sulfate?

Acid–Base Indicators

For each of the acid–base indicators, the vial at the left shows the color of the indicator at pH values more acid than the transition range. The vial at the right shows the indicator at more basic pH values. The values following the name of each indicator give the pH range of color transition.

Methyl violet   0.2–3.2

Methyl orange   3.1–4.4

Methyl red   4.4–6.0

Litmus   5.5–8.0

Bromthymol blue   6.0–7.6

Phenol red   6.8–8.4

Phenolphthalein   8.3–10.0

Thymolphthalein   9.3–10.5

Plate I

Differentiating Among Halogen Ions

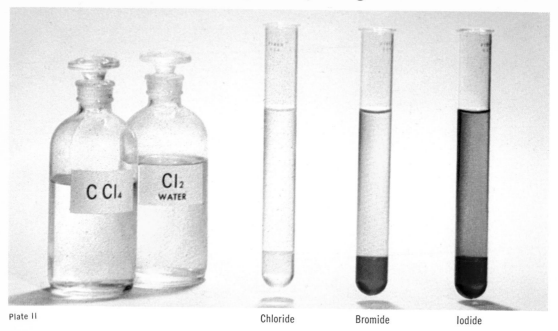

Plate II   Chloride   Bromide   Iodide

Precipitated Sulfides

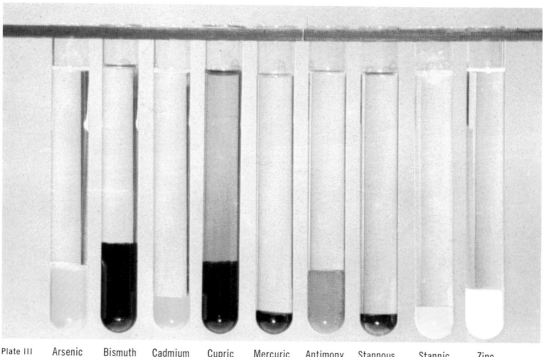

Plate III   Arsenic   Bismuth   Cadmium   Cupric   Mercuric   Antimony   Stannous   Stannic   Zinc
            sulfide   sulfide   sulfide   sulfide   sulfide   sulfide   sulfide   sulfide   sulfide

Flame Tests

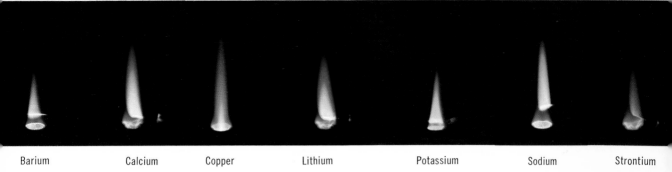

| Barium | Calcium | Copper | Lithium | Potassium | Sodium | Strontium |

Numerous procedures are used to determine the presence of ions in solids or in aqueous solutions. *Differentiating among halogen ions* requires that chlorine water and carbon tetrachloride be added to the unknown solution; the color of the carbon tetrachloride layer differs for each halogen ion. Metallic ions of analytic groups II and III can be identified by adding hydrogen sulfide gas and observing the color of the *precipitated sulfide*. In a *flame test,* a platinum wire that has been dipped into a bit of an unknown is held in a flame. The color of the flame identifies certain metallic ions. In a *borax bead test* a platinum loop is dipped into borax and heated. The bead formed is dipped into the unknown solid and reheated; the color of the bead differs with the transition element.

Borax Bead Tests

Powdered borax

Copper sulfate

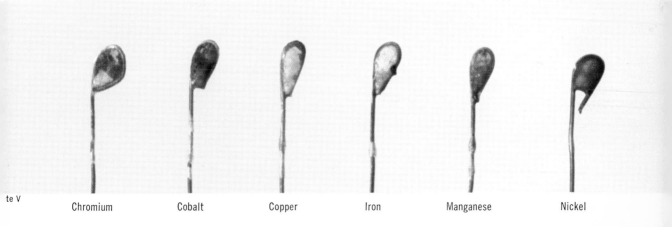

| Chromium | Cobalt | Copper | Iron | Manganese | Nickel |

Plate VI

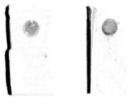

Zinc   Aluminum   Magnesium

COBALT NITRATE TESTS

To perform a *cobalt nitrate test,* this young lady has placed a drop of cobalt nitrate solution in the depression of a block of plaster of Paris. She is heating the solution by directing the flame of a burner against it with a blowpipe, producing a "hot spot." Next she will add a drop of zinc nitrate solution and heat the area again. When the area cools, a green spot will appear in the block, as at the left above. The procedure is repeated with aluminum sulfide and magnesium chloride to produce the other two samples.

33

The Carbon Family

How does an archaeologist know the age of the ruins he is excavating? Until 20 years ago, this could be determined only by using data from geology and biology, together with evidence of tools and pottery found in the ruins. Today, the archaeologist has a new and much more accurate means of measuring time—radiocarbon dating.

Carbon-14, a radioactive isotope of carbon, is produced when nitrogen in the upper atmosphere is bombarded by neutrons.

$$^{14}_{7}N + ^{1}_{0}n \longrightarrow ^{14}_{6}C + ^{1}_{1}H$$

This isotope, in the form of radioactive carbon dioxide, is soon taken in by a plant and incorporated into its tissues. Although the isotope undergoes decay, it is constantly being replenished as additional carbon dioxide is taken in by the plant. *While the plant is alive* an equilibrium is established in which the intake of carbon-14 and its decay are balanced; the concentration of the isotope in the plant tissue is constant.

When the plant dies or is cut down, this equilibrium is upset. The carbon-14 in the plant continues to decay but no further intake of the isotope occurs to replace it. The amount of carbon-14 in the plant changes in accordance with its half life. By measuring the proportion of ^{14}C to ^{12}C in a sample of wood, charcoal, or cloth found in ancient ruins (Fig. 33-1), scientists can determine the age of the sample and presumably that of the ruins. Since the half life of carbon-14 is about 5,760 years, and since sensitive instruments for detecting small amounts of low energy radiation have been developed, it is possible to date objects back 80,000 years quite accurately.

Radiocarbon dating is a recent application of carbon. Let us examine other uses of carbon, its place in the periodic table, its family relationships, and the nature of its compounds.

Group IVA Elements

The physical properties of the elements of group IVA (Table 33-1) vary with increasing atomic weight and number, as do the elements of all groups studied thus far. It is in chemical behavior that we observe the relationship of this group to the other groups of the periodic table. The families at the extreme ends of the table (groups IA, IIA, VIA, and VIIA) show strongly metallic or nonmetallic properties, respectively. As we move inward from these extremes to groups IIIA and VA, the metallic or nonmetallic nature, respectively, is still present. Here, in group IVA, the metallic or nonmetallic nature has become minimal. To a large extent, the elements form covalent compounds.

This behavior is strongest with carbon and with silicon, which, though metallic in appearance, generally behaves chemically more like a nonmetal. As we proceed down the group, tin and lead show somewhat metallic characteristics; they have a much higher electrical conductivity than do the other members of the family, possess

33-1 Carbon-14 dating of some of the recently discovered Dead Sea Scrolls has revealed that they were written around 33 A.D., ±200 years.

Table 33-1 **THE GROUP IVA ELEMENTS**

Element	Atomic number	Atomic weight	Electron configuration	Density (g/ml)	Melting point (° C)	Boiling point (° C)	State and color	Ionization potential	Oxidation states
Carbon	6	12.01115	2 4	2.25* 3.55†	3550	4200	Colorless to black solid	11.32	+4
Silicon	14	28.086	2 8 4	2.42	1420	2355	Colorless to brown solid	8.1	+4
Germanium	32	72.59	2 8 18 4	5.36	958.5	2700 (sublimes)	Gray-white solid	8.1	+2, +4
Tin	50	118.69	2 8 18 18 4	6.55	231.9	2270	Silver-white solid	7.3	+2, +4
Lead	82	207.19	2 8 18 32 18 4	11.35	327.4	1620	Bluish-white solid	7.4	+2, +4

* Graphite   † Diamond

metallic luster, and form some ionic compounds. All of the group IVA elements form covalent, volatile tetrachlorides, and they combine with hydrogen to form *covalent* hydrides. This is in marked contrast to the group IA and IIA elements, which form *ionic* hydrides. The ease with which the hydrides are formed, and their stability, decreases with increasing atomic number.

The oxides, like CO_2, of the lighter members of the family are covalent in nature, partial ionic character developing as the element increases in atomic number. The more metallic tin and lead form amphoteric hydroxides which behave chemically much like aluminum hydroxide. Carbon and silicon are usually found in the +4 oxidation state, but the remaining members of the family commonly occur in more than one oxidation state. Tin and lead occur commonly in the +2 state. This trend is reminiscent of the oxidation states in group IIIA. All of the group IVA elements are characterized by an outer electron shell containing two s and two p electrons, an electron structure accounting for the possible oxidation states.

CARBON

On first glance, the carbon atom would be expected to exist in the +4 oxidation state, but from careful research it becomes evident that the 4 electrons in its outer orbit are not equivalent. Two of the electrons are paired together in the 2s orbital while the remaining two electrons occupy separate 2p orbitals (Fig. 33-2). The expectation that these electrons might show different bonding is borne out by the existence of two oxides, carbon monoxide and carbon dioxide. In carbon monoxide only two pairs of shared electrons are involved, while in carbon dioxide there are four pairs of shared electrons. Yet carbon rarely exhibits a +2 oxidation state; the +4 state in carbon dioxide predominates. In view of its electron configuration, how can this be explained?

If sufficient energy is supplied to a carbon atom, one of its 2s electrons moves to a higher energy level and occupies one of the vacant p orbitals. This change provides four *unpaired* electrons, each of which is capable of forming a covalent bond. Theoretically, the three bonds formed by the 2p electrons should be distinctly different from that formed by the one 2s electron. But such is *never* the case. When carbon combines with four atoms of the same element, as in

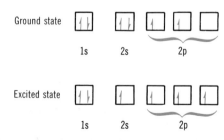

33-2 In the ground state a carbon atom contains two electrons in the 2s orbital and one electron in each of two different 2p orbitals; however, one of the 2s electrons may be energized to the vacant 2p orbital.

methane (CH$_4$), it is impossible to distinguish one covalent bond from another; all four bonds are equivalent. At present, the best explanation for the unexpected formation of equivalent bonds is that once an s orbital electron moves into the vacant p orbital a resonance hybrid is formed, and the available energy resonates equally among all of the unpaired electrons.

This equivalence of energy among its bonding electrons helps to explain a significant feature of the shape of many molecules containing carbon atoms. The four valence electrons repel each other with equal strength. The only configuration consistent with this repulsion is that of a regular tetrahedron in which the four covalent bonds are directed toward the four vertices with the carbon atom at its center (Fig. 33-3). X-ray analysis has confirmed this three-dimensional, regular tetrahedron, in which there is an equal angle between any two of the bonds.

Allotropic Forms of Carbon

Carbon, like oxygen and sulfur, exists in allotropic forms, each of which has special properties. You are acquainted with carbon in the form of soft and hard coals, and as soot, charcoal, the "lead" in a pencil, graphite, and yes—a diamond. Let us review some of the experiences that have familiarized you with these allotropes.

Light a wax candle and hold a cold saucer or dish over the flame. Very shortly, a black deposit appears on the plate, as shown below. Compare this deposit with that pro-

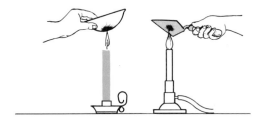

duced when the yellow flame of a Bunsen burner, caused by an insufficient supply of air, strikes a cold object.

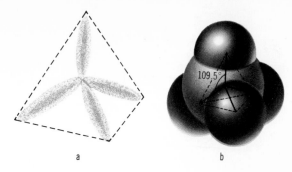

33-3 The four p orbitals of the carbon atom in a molecule of methane prescribe a regular tetrahedron. Each bond angle H—C—H measures 109.5°.

In both instances, the deposit is the same. It is commonly called *soot*, but has a variety of other names. Soot represents free carbon released by the incomplete combustion of hydrocarbons.

Examine the "lead" refill from a mechanical pencil, or cut the wood of an ordinary pencil lengthwise to remove the grayish-black rod inside. This material is **graphite,** an allotrope of carbon. The varying degrees of hardness of pencil "lead" are produced by mixing different amounts of powdered clay with powdered graphite, shaping the mixture into rods, and baking them.

Anyone would agree that a diamond does not look like coal, soot, or graphite. Yet, like soot or graphite, a diamond is composed of carbon in a highly pure form. Scientists have proved the composition of diamonds by burning them in pure oxygen. The only product is carbon dioxide —which is also the product when soot or pure graphite is burned.

Coal, which is not pure carbon, is used chiefly as a fuel. Similarly, coke, another form of impure carbon, is employed as a fuel. Coke does not occur naturally, but is made from soft coal. Both these allotropes will be considered in detail in Chapter 36, which deals with fuels.

Crystalline Carbon

All the forms of carbon possess a crystal structure. Except in diamond and graphite, however, this structure is not evident. The microc̲ structure of carbon has been determ̲

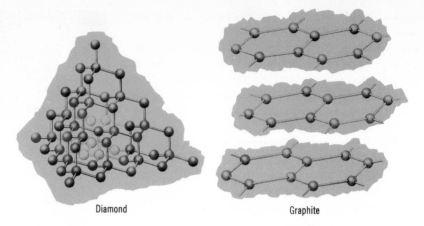

33-4 The chief structural difference between diamond and graphite is the number of near neighbors of each carbon atom. In diamond each carbon atom is bonded to four other carbon atoms at the corner of a tetrahedron, forming a giant molecule in which the atoms are rigidly held. Graphite consists of layers of carbon atoms in hexagons, in which each carbon atom is bonded to three other carbon atoms. The fourth valence electron of each carbon atom seems to weakly bond the layers together.

Diamond   Graphite

after detailed X-ray study. All of the apparently amorphous forms of carbon are found to possess the graphite structure. Though both diamonds and graphite are crystalline, each has a different structure. In the diamond crystal (Fig. 33-4) each carbon atom is surrounded by four other carbon atoms to form a tetrahedron. Examination shows that any diamond crystal must be considered as a giant molecule, or macromolecule, of an enormously large number of carbon atoms. In contrast, the carbon atoms in a graphite crystal are arranged in the form of joined hexagons which are combined layer by layer in a honeycomb effect. In graphite each carbon atom is equidistant from three other carbon atoms *in the same plane,* but farther (more than twice the distance) from the carbon atoms in adjacent planes.

Diamonds and graphite differ in two major properties as a result of their different crystal structures. The more compact arrangement of atoms in the diamond crystal makes diamond more dense than graphite. The covalent forces between carbon atoms in the different planes of graphite are much weaker than the covalent bonds between carbon atoms in the same plane. Therefore, when graphite is subjected to forces parallel to the planes, the bonds between the planes are easily broken, and one plane of carbon atoms slides over another. In this weakness lies the basis for some of the uses of graphite.

Two further differences between diamond and graphite are very striking. When pure, diamond is colorless and transparent; however, graphite is gray-black and opaque. In optical properties, therefore, the two lie at opposite ends of the scale, illustrating dramatically the meaning of allotropic forms. Being transparent, the diamond displays one further property not evident in opaque materials—refraction (bending) of the light which passes through it. The extent to which a diamond refracts light accounts for the brilliance it displays. Rough diamonds are cut into shapes to bring out this property to the fullest.

A diamond is harder than any other natural substance known, a property which can be traced back to its crystal structure. Only recently has its hardness been equaled by the newly synthesized borazon. It is significant that many of the very hard materials known, the nitrides and carbides, like diamond, consist of covalently bonded atoms of relatively small size. Badly discolored diamonds (bort and carbonado), which have no use as jewels, find a ready market for industrial cutting and drilling devices, as well as in phonograph needle tips. Diamond-tipped grinding and cutting wheels are shown at work in Fig. 33-5.

Graphite

The use of graphite in "lead" pencils depends on its extreme softness. When the pencil "lead" is rubbed on paper, the soft graphite leaves dark-colored particles behind in the path of your writing. If you rub some powdered graphite between your fingers, it is soft, smooth, and greasy. Because of these properties, graphite makes an ideal lubricant. It may be that you have lubricated bicycle parts or locks with the powdered material; it is also supplied as a suspension in oil or water for the same purpose.

Since graphite is unaffected by most chemicals, has good electrical conductivity, and oxidizes with difficulty even at high temperature, it can be used where operating conditions do not permit the use of metals. This combination of properties serves to make graphite useful for electrodes in special industrial furnaces. Its excellent heat conductivity and resistance to thermal shock also make graphite desirable for crucibles. Since graphite can be shaped into bricks, blocks, and piping, it is used for the construction of towers and tanks in which dilute solutions of strong acids are to be concentrated.

Graphite has also been used to make artificial diamonds. In 1955 at the General Electric laboratories, the crystalline structure of graphite was rearranged by keeping powdered graphite at a temperature of 3500° C under a pressure of 1½ million pounds per square inch—a pressure equal to that at the depth at which diamonds are believed to have been formed naturally. At first,

33-6 This group of carat-sized diamonds are the largest yet synthesized. Unfortunately they are dark in color and do not share the strength of countless smaller synthetic diamonds in industrial use.

the expense of the process and the small size of the diamonds obtained made the production of artificial diamonds economically unsound. Today, however, a "diamond mine" in Detroit is a large source of industrial diamonds (Fig. 33-6).

"Amorphous" Carbon

The impure forms of carbon find many useful applications. The forms vary in color from gray-black, through blue-black, to deep black. Most of them are characterized by a large surface area, either because of small particle size or a porous nature. This property has much to do with their uses.

Charcoal. Charcoal is made by the **destructive distillation** of wood. In this process wood is heated in the absence of air. During destructive distillation gases and other volatile substances are driven out of the wood. The origin of charcoal is evident on close examination; the grainy structure of wood remains visible. The porous product possesses an enormous internal surface which allows the *adsorption* of small particles and gases. The great adsorbency of charcoal (and other forms of carbon) lies behind its use in removing materials of objectionable taste from water supplies, the decolorization of various food and industrial products, the recovery of solvent

33-5 The carbide tip of this circular saw blade is so hard that its final accurate grinding requires diamond-tipped grinding wheels.

vapors, and the purification of streptomycin, as well as its use in respirators (Fig. 33-7), and as a filtering agent in the laboratory.

Animal Charcoal. More widely used in purification in industry and the laboratory is animal charcoal or **boneblack,** made by the destructive distillation of bones. The carbon resulting from this process is deposited on the surface of the calcium phosphate of the bone, thus providing a large surface area for adsorption of impurities. Boneblack finds its greatest use in decolorizing raw sugar solutions in the final stages of sugar purification and in the processing of industrial oils. After a period of time, both wood charcoal and boneblack become covered with the adsorbed impurities and begin to lose their effectiveness. Their surfaces can be reactivated by heating them in a current of steam, air, or other oxidizing gases. If you wish to observe this adsorption by boneblack, *try the following.*

33-7 The respirator is equipped with a chemical cartridge that is filled with activated coconut charcoal for filtering any organic gases from the air passing through the cartridge.

Dissolve about 10 grams of *brown* sugar in a beaker of warm water, and filter a portion of this solution. What is the nature of

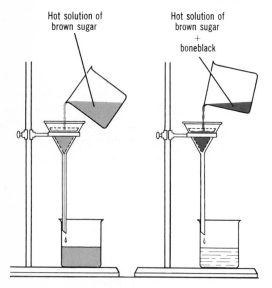

Hot solution of brown sugar

Hot solution of brown sugar + boneblack

the filtrate? Add about 5 grams of boneblack to the remaining solution, and filter the liquid after stirring it well. What is the nature of the filtrate now?

Lampblack and Carbon Black. Fuels such as candles, kerosene, and oil are mixtures of **hydrocarbons,** compounds of hydrogen and carbon. These compounds require an abundance of air for their complete combustion. Thus, when the hydrocarbon propane (C_3H_8), a constituent of liquefied petroleum gases, is burned completely, five volumes of oxygen, or twenty-five volumes of air, are needed for every volume of propane gas.

$$C_3H_8 + 5\,O_2 \xrightarrow{\Delta} 3\,CO_2 + 4\,H_2O$$

If the supply of air is insufficient, the complete combustion does not occur. Instead, only the hydrogen is oxidized to water vapor, while the carbon may be oxidized partially or not at all. Notice the products if only two volumes of oxygen are available for each volume of propane.

$$C_3H_8 + 2\,O_2 \longrightarrow 3\,C + 4\,H_2O$$

The small particles of unburned carbon produce a smoky flame. You have deposited them as soot on a cold surface (page 551).

This form of carbon, consisting of very fine particles, is known as **lampblack.** It is produced commercially by burning hydrocarbon oils in a limited supply of air. The flame is directed against revolving metal plates which are cooled internally by running water. At intervals the unburned carbon collected on these plates is scraped off and collected in bags. Because of its fine nature, lampblack finds use as a pigment in polishes. When mixed with pitch, molded, and baked, it provides carbon rods for arc lamps.

Carbon black, a related form, is made by burning natural gas in a limited supply of air. This form of carbon (Fig. 38-8), even finer than lampblack, finds use in printing inks. Its greatest use is in rubber compositions (as in tires), to which it imparts greater toughness and longer wear. Carbon black is also made by another process. When methane (CH_4) from natural gas is passed over hot brickwork, its molecules split (crack) to yield the elements.

QUESTIONS AND PROBLEMS

1. (a) Draw an orbital diagram of a carbon atom. (b) Draw a three-dimensional model consistent with the formation of compounds such as CH_4. (c) Explain how all four bonds in a carbon atom can be equivalent.

2. (a) Name as many allotropes of carbon as you can. (b) How is each allotrope usually formed? (c) Give one or more uses for each allotrope.

3. Graphite is made into containers that are used to melt materials with very high melting points. Why is graphite used?

4. Compare and contrast the crystalline structure of diamond and graphite.

CHEMICAL BEHAVIOR OF CARBON

The discussion of the allotropic forms of carbon has stressed the differences in their physical properties. Chemically, all forms of carbon behave similarly except for small differences, such as in the rate of reaction with another substance, or in the amount of heat produced during the reaction. The outstanding chemical behavior of allotropes is their combination with oxygen—or

as a reducing agent. Recall, for example, the use of coke in extracting iron from its ore.

$$Fe_2O_3 + 3\,C \xrightarrow{\Delta} 2\,Fe + 3\,CO\uparrow$$

It is in the extraction of metals from their oxide ores that carbon finds one of its most important uses. A similar reduction reaction produces highly useful metal *carbides,* compounds of metal and carbon. Carbides are very hard substances with very high melting points. Some carbides are now being molded into nose cones for re-entry rockets because they withstand the extremely high temperature produced as the rocket speeds back into our atmosphere. From this specific use you might properly predict that carbides are formed only at extremely high temperatures. Such temperatures are provided by special electric furnaces.

Electric Furnaces

Two types of electric furnaces are in widespread use today. The first, called a *resistance* furnace, depends upon the heat produced when

33-8 A handful of carbon black is a handful of the finest amorphous carbon —and the blackest substance—known to man.

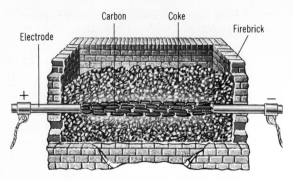

Carbon   Coke
Electrode   Firebrick

33-9 A resistance furnance gets its name from the use of a high resistance material to carry the electric current between two electrodes.

an electric current is passed through high-resistance materials (Fig. 33-9). The material to be transformed, usually a poor conductor, is placed between the carbon electrodes of the furnace. When a current is passed through the material, the high temperature produced brings about a reaction. The entire unit is enclosed in a *refractory* (or extremely high melting point) material such as firebrick.

The second type, known as the *arc* furnace, also employs carbon electrodes but operates on a different principle (Fig. 33-10). Two carbon electrodes are brought together, and the current turned on. If the electrodes are now separated, an intense arc jumps between them, vaporizing some

33-10 In an electric arc furnace, the extremely high temperature of the arc conducted between the electrodes by vaporized carbon causes chemicals that do not easily react to combine to form compounds.

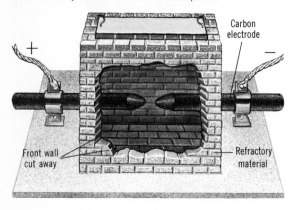

Carbon electrode

Front wall cut away

Refractory material

of the carbon, which now serves to conduct the current. Temperatures as high as 3500° C are produced in such furnaces and retained by a surrounding refractory material.

The Production of Carbides

In preparing carbides, the resistance furnace is packed with a mixture of coke and the oxide of the desired metal. Reduction of the metallic oxide occurs first; the free metal element then combines with excess carbon.

Silicon Carbide. If a mixture of sand (silicon dioxide), crushed coke, salt, and sawdust is treated in the resistance furnace, the product is silicon carbide, SiC.

$$SiO_2 + 3\,C \xrightarrow{\Delta} SiC + 2\,CO\uparrow$$

The sawdust makes the mass porous and allows the gases produced to escape freely. The dark-colored, iridescent crystals find a ready market as a synthetic *abrasive,* commonly known as carborundum. It is especially useful in machining metals and is employed largely in the form of grinding wheels (Fig. 33-11) and abrasive paper. Silicon carbide, which is extremely resistant to the effects of heat, is often used as a lining in high-temperature furnaces.

Other carbides, notably those of tungsten, tantalum, and boron, are even better abrasives. These are made in the electric furnace by reacting coke and the respective metal oxides. Boron carbide (B_4C) is the hardest synthetic carbide thus far produced.

Calcium Carbide. When calcium oxide (lime) is heated with coke in a resistance furnace, calcium carbide is produced.

$$CaO + 3\,C \xrightarrow{\Delta} CaC_2 + CO\uparrow$$

This compound is one of the most valuable products of the electric furnace. It reacts with water to produce acetylene, the starting point in the synthesis of many carbon compounds.

Carbon Disulfide

Another product of the electric arc furnace is the liquid carbon disulfide. The high tempera-

33-11 The visible evidence notwithstanding, experimentation has demonstrated that cutting of metals with carborundum grinding wheels at temperatures over 1500° F is both practical and extremely efficient.

ture brings about a reaction between charcoal and sulfur vapor to produce this strong-smelling compound.

$$C + 2S \xrightarrow{\Delta} CS_2$$

Carbon disulfide is a colorless, very volatile liquid. Because its vapor is poisonous, it is used as a fumigant for moths in furs, and for rodents and insects in grain elevators. The liquid mixed with alcohol is used as a solvent for oils and waxes. Developments in synthetic fibers have made carbon disulfide an essential material for the preparation of one type of synthetic silk.

Carbon disulfide reacts with chlorine to form carbon tetrachloride, a liquid used in certain types of fire extinguishers for putting out oil fires and fires in electrical equipment.

$$CS_2 + 3Cl_2 \longrightarrow CCl_4 + S_2Cl_2$$

Production of Graphite

Natural graphite is neither abundant nor pure. The growing demand for graphite stimulated the preparation of artificial graphite by the Acheson process in a special type of electric furnace. The furnace is charged with anthracite coal or coke and surrounded by a layer of sand or sawdust which acts as an insulator. A core of granulated carbon, a better conductor than coal, connects the electrodes. An electric current passed through the material generates a temperature of 3000° C. Five or six days of this treatment converts the coal or coke to graphite. The furnace is then cooled over a period of twenty-five days after which it is dismantled for removal of the product. The artificial graphite is crushed, mixed with pitch (as a binder), and molded into desired shapes that are baked into final form (Fig. 33-12).

Here we have been concerned mainly with the preparation and use of only a few of the many useful synthetic carbon compounds prepared by the chemist. Yet the majority of known compounds, whether natural or synthetic, contain this element. Because their number is so great, the major types of these compounds, those in which carbon bonds with hydrogen—and frequently with one or more other elements—will be considered separately in the next unit on organic chemistry. For the moment, we shall devote our attention to the two most important common compounds of the element—its oxides, carbon dioxide and carbon monoxide.

33-12 A giant-sized carbon electrode is emerging from an extrusion press. The electrode must be baked or further processed before use.

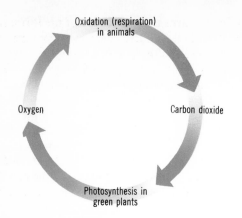

Oxidation (respiration)
in animals

Oxygen

Carbon dioxide

Photosynthesis in
green plants

33-13 In the carbon dioxide-oxygen cycle, green plants take in carbon dioxide and give off oxygen, while animals take in oxygen and give off carbon dioxide. This self-restoring pattern also exists for other materials.

QUESTIONS AND PROBLEMS

1. Why is carbon often used in extracting a metal from its oxide ore?

2. (a) What is a carbide? (b) Why can't you produce most carbides in your chemistry laboratory?

3. Compare and contrast the production of silicon and calcium carbide.

4. Describe briefly the production of graphite.

CARBON DIOXIDE

During the past two centuries the world population has increased fivefold. Our society has become highly industrialized, with an ever-expanding fuel consumption and utilization of oxygen. But our atmospheric oxygen, so necessary for breathing, has shown no sign of diminishing. Yet, if the seemingly trifling 0.04 percent of carbon dioxide in the air were removed, life would come to a standstill. As you remember from biology, carbon dioxide is essential for photosynthesis—the process by which green plants use light energy to transform carbon dioxide and water into glucose and release oxygen. Glucose molecules then combine to form more complex sugars and starch. Animals oxidize these sugars and starches

to release the chemical energy stored in them. At the same time, carbon dioxide is returned to the atmosphere for plant use. This carbon dioxide–oxygen cycle is pictured in Fig. 33-13.

Preparation of Carbon Dioxide

Carbon dioxide was first recognized in 1630, but it was not studied in detail until more than a century later by Dr. Joseph Black of Edinburgh. The gas now ranks as a major industrial chemical, a tribute to the many uses we have found for it. Its many uses could hardly depend on the atmosphere as the only source of the gas.

Carbon dioxide is produced by the combustion of coke, coal, and petroleum fuels; but it must be separated from the nitrogen present in the air and other gases resulting from the combustion of the fuel. Another method of preparing this gas commercially is by the thermal decomposition of certain metallic carbonates under heat. Many chemical industries produce this gas as a by-product of their operations, for instance, during the manufacture of lime from calcium carbonate. Such operations may serve as a commercial source of the gas if it is economically practical to separate and recover the carbon dioxide. If you have not yet prepared it in the laboratory, you may wish to *see for yourself how carbon dioxide is prepared.*

Place twelve to fifteen marble chips in a generator, as shown below. Add about 40 ml of dilute hydrochloric acid to the generator, and allow the gas produced at first to escape into the air for about 30 seconds. Now, by water displacement fill two collecting bottles with the carbon dioxide being produced.

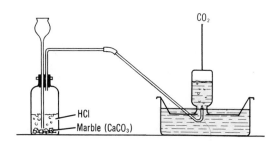

CO₂

HCl
Marble (CaCO₃)

558   FAMILIES OF ELEMENTS

To the first bottle add about 5 ml of lime-water. What change occurs? Attach a short candle to the bottom of a small battery jar and light the candle. Pour the second bottle of carbon dioxide over the lighted candle inside the jar. What happens to the flame? Explain the results.

The reaction between calcium carbonate and hydrochloric acid produces carbonic acid, which decomposes readily to produce carbon dioxide gas and water.

$$CaCO_3 + 2 H^+ + 2 Cl^- \longrightarrow$$
$$Ca^{+2} + 2 Cl^- + H_2O + CO_2\uparrow$$

Carbon dioxide can be prepared by adding various acids to any carbonate or bicarbonate; for example, by adding dilute sulfuric acid to sodium carbonate.

$$2 Na^+ + CO_3^{+2} + 2 H^+ + SO_4^{-2} \longrightarrow$$
$$2 Na^+ + SO_4^{-2} + H_2O + CO_2\uparrow$$

Properties of Carbon Dioxide

Carbon dioxide is a colorless, odorless gas, 1.5 times as dense as air (**MW** = 44). Its slight solubility in water is suggested by the method of collection; less than one volume of the gas dissolves in one volume of water at 20° C. Carbon dioxide neither burns nor supports combustion of typical fuels. However, burning magnesium, sodium, and potassium continue to burn when lowered into the gas, carbon being formed at the same time. These metals are sufficiently active to remove the oxygen from carbon dioxide.

$$2 Mg + CO_2 \xrightarrow{\Delta} 2 MgO + C$$
$$4 K + 3 CO_2 \xrightarrow{\Delta} 2 K_2CO_3 + C$$

When carbon dioxide is bubbled into water, the resulting liquid acquires a slightly sour taste and turns blue litmus faintly pink. These observations show that carbonic acid is a weak acid and that carbon dioxide is an acid anhydride.

$$CO_2 + H_2O \rightleftharpoons H_2CO_3 \rightleftharpoons H^+ + HCO_3^-$$

When carbon dioxide is passed into limewater,

the solution turns milky because of the formation of insoluble, suspended calcium carbonate, the substance present in the marble chips used to prepare the gas. Observe the very close resemblance of this reaction to neutralization.

$$\underset{\substack{\text{acid}\\\text{anhydride}}}{CO_2} + \underset{\text{base}}{Ca(OH)_2} \longrightarrow \underset{\text{a salt}}{CaCO_3\downarrow} + \underset{\text{water}}{H_2O}$$

Recall that when an *excess* of carbon dioxide is passed into calcium carbonate in water, the precipitate dissolves to form soluble calcium *bi*carbonate.

$$CaCO_3^{-2} + H_2O + CO_2 \longrightarrow Ca^{+2} + 2 HCO_3^{-1}$$

Here the carbonate ion acts as a base, accepting protons from the water. The reaction of carbon dioxide with limewater and the reaction of a carbonate (or a bicarbonate) with an acid have already been put to use in testing for these radicals.

Carbon Dioxide and Food

You have, perhaps unconsciously, enjoyed the benefits of carbon dioxide in a variety of ways. Hot dogs and soda pop are a pleasant part of your experience. For the soda and other carbonated beverages, recall that you are indebted to Joseph Priestley, who first suggested that the slightly acid water solution of the gas be bottled and sold commercially. Because of the low solubility of the gas, carbonated beverages must be prepared under pressure. Originally the carbon dioxide used to add the sparkling effervescence was produced by reacting acids with washing soda, hence the name "soda water."

A slice of bread is pitted with a multitude of small holes which make the bread porous and light. These are produced by carbon dioxide gas which "raises" the dough in the pan. In this function, the gas is known as a *leavening agent*. When your grandmother baked rolls, yeast was among the ingredients. The mixture was set aside under warm conditions for a number of hours, during which time enzymes (organic catalysts) in the yeast broke down the starch and sugar, filling

33-14 Carbon dioxide "snow" is being pressed into a large block of dry ice. Note that some of the excess "snow" has collected on the machinery. Dry ice is so called because it does not melt as does ordinary ice.

the doughy mass with minute bubbles of carbon dioxide. When this dough was placed in the oven, the gas bubbles expanded at the higher temperature and caused the dough to rise even further. As the dough hardened into its final shape, the enzymes were destroyed by heat and the expansion of the bubbles stopped, leaving a firm mass riddled with holes.

The carbon dioxide which leavens today's muffins, rolls, and cakes is produced much more readily by including a **baking powder** in the recipe. Although the ingredients in different brands may vary, every baking powder contains three fundamental ingredients—starch, baking *soda* (sodium bicarbonate), and a nonpoisonous acid salt in *solid* form. The dry acid salt may be cream of tartar ($KHC_4H_4O_6$), calcium dihydrogen phosphate [$Ca(H_2PO_4)_2$], or sodium aluminum sulfate [$NaAl(SO_4)_2 \cdot 12\ H_2O$]. The starch is a filler used to keep the chemicals dry. As long as the baking powder remains dry, no reaction takes place. But when water is added, the acid salt hydrolyzes to yield hydronium ions which react with the baking soda to produce the carbon dioxide needed for leavening.

Sodium aluminum sulfate, while containing no hydrogen ions, develops acid properties in water solution because of hydrolysis. For a cream of tartar baking powder, the reaction resulting is:

$$\underbrace{Na^+ + HCO_3^-}_{\text{baking soda}} + \underbrace{K^+ + HC_4H_4O_6^-}_{\text{cream of tartar}} \longrightarrow$$

$$CO_2\uparrow + H_2O + \underbrace{K^+ + Na^+\ C_4H_4O_6^{-2}}_{\text{Rochelle salt}}$$

Dry Ice

Though carbon dioxide usually occurs as a gas, you are probably familiar with solid carbon dioxide, commonly known as dry ice. Since gaseous carbon dioxide becomes a solid at $-78.5°$ C, dry ice can produce temperatures much lower than those produced by ice. At normal atmospheric pressure, carbon dioxide cannot exist as a liquid. Rather, upon warming, solid carbon dioxide changes directly to the gaseous state by sublimation. The heat required for the process is removed from the surrounding material. When it sublimes, dry ice leaves no liquid residue as does ordinary ice which melts into water as it cools its surroundings.

Dry ice is manufactured by liquefying under pressure carbon dioxide gas freed of dust, water vapor, and other gases. The liquid is allowed to expand under controlled conditions, and the cooling effect of evaporation solidifies some of the gas into a carbon dioxide "snow." This solid is collected and compressed into blocks (Fig. 33-14). The demand for dry ice has had a unique effect on many chemical industries. Those industries whose operations produce considerable carbon dioxide as a by-product have found it profitable to separate and purify the gas for conversion into this refrigerant.

Carbon Dioxide Fire Extinguishers

Look around your chemistry room. Undoubtedly there is a fire extinguisher available as a quick means of fighting fire should one start. Designed for on-the-spot handling of small-scale fires is the **soda-acid fire extinguisher,** a vertical section of which is shown in Fig. 33-15. The tank contains a concentrated solution of sodium bicarbonate. A receptacle at the top of the tank holds a loosely stoppered bottle of concentrated sulfuric acid. When the tank is grasped by a handle at the bottom, lifted, and inverted, the acid spills from its container and reacts with the sodium bicarbonate solution.

$$Na^+ + HCO_3^- + H^+ + HSO_4^- \longrightarrow$$
$$H_2O\uparrow + CO_2\uparrow + Na^+ + HSO_4^-$$

So much carbon dioxide is produced so quickly that it cannot be contained in the tank. As a result the gas is under pressure, and it forces the liquid contents out of the hose, often to a distance of 25 to 35 feet. This liquid, together with the carbon dioxide that escapes, extinguishes the fire.

The soda-acid extinguisher should *never* be used on fires involving electrical equipment. The liquid contains electrolytes and is thus a conductor of electricity; it may cause a short circuit in any electrical apparatus in or near a fire, possibly starting another fire. A soda-acid extinguisher will not put out oil fires. As oil is less dense than

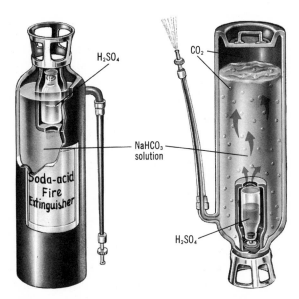

H_2SO_4

CO_2

NaHCO$_3$ solution

Soda-acid Fire Extinguisher

H_2SO_4

33-15 When a soda-acid fire extinguisher is inverted, the sulfuric acid reacts with the concentrated sodium bicarbonate solution to produce carbon dioxide, which forces the liquid out of the hose.

water, the blazing oil floats and spreads on the liquid directed at it. How then can oil fires be extinguished? For a possible answer, *investigate the following.*

Set up two tall glass cylinders, each one-quarter full of a solution of baking soda. Add approximately 5 to 7 ml of liquid detergent to one cylinder and mix the contents well. Now add about 25 ml of dilute hydrochloric acid to each cylinder. How do the resulting reactions in the cylinders compare?

In the cylinder containing only baking soda and acid, a vigorous frothing that dies down when the reaction is over results. The same frothing occurs in the cylinder to which the detergent is added, but the frothing does not die down. Instead, the entire solution is whipped into a foam which rises in the cylinder. The detergent traps the carbon dioxide produced to form millions of bubbles. Commercial **foam extinguishers,** designed particularly to combat oil fires, operate on this principle but use different materials. A solution of aluminum sulfate is used in place of sulfuric acid; the sodium bicarbonate solution contains a licorice extract that serves to trap the liquid and gas to create the foam. When this extinguisher is used, the reaction between the aluminum sulfate and the baking soda produces sticky, insoluble aluminum hydroxide.

$$6\,Na^+ + 6\,HCO_3^- + 2\,Al^{+3} + 3\,SO_4^{-2} \longrightarrow$$
$$2\,Al(OH)_3\downarrow + 6\,CO_2\uparrow + 6\,Na^+ + 3\,SO_4^{-2}$$

Oil refineries and industries which must store large quantities of flammable liquids are equipped with a system of pipes designed to carry these foam-producing chemicals to the scene of a fire. Airports have a portable supply readily available for emergencies (Fig. 33-16).

Since electrolytes are among the products of the foam extinguisher reaction, this type of extinguisher is still unsuited for fires involving electrical installations. Neither can the foam extinguisher be used in the presence of chemicals which react with water (for example, alkali metals

33-16 After a collision of two planes on the ground at New York's Kennedy Airport, firemen extinguished the flames with foam from special fire hoses. The foam is effective but leaves a sticky residue that must be cleaned up.

or calcium carbide). Lastly, the foam leaves a sticky residue which must be cleaned up after the fire is extinguished.

Liquid carbon dioxide is now used as the extinguishing agent for electrical and all other types of fires. Pure carbon dioxide has the advantages of not supporting combustion, of not leaving a residue to be cleaned up, of not damaging valuable materials, and of not conducting electricity. Being heavier than air, the gas forms a blanket around the fire. An extinguisher filled only with liquid carbon dioxide is shown in Fig. 33-17. When the nozzle is aimed at the fire and the trigger is pulled, the sudden expansion of the escaping liquid lowers its temperature and causes some of the escaping material to solidify into carbon dioxide "snow." The dry ice readily sublimes in the heat of the fire, surrounding the burning material with a blanket of carbon dioxide gas.

Some industrial plants are now equipped with piping systems which, in event of a fire, automatically discharge carbon dioxide, much in the manner of a sprinkling system.

Other Uses of Carbon Dioxide

Carbon dioxide under pressure is also used in another life-saving device—the rubber raft used by aviators forced down at sea. These rafts are now designed with cylinders of the compressed gas which inflates the raft when the gas is released.

Experiments which have been conducted with a view toward producing rainfall artificially have sometimes employed dry ice as a means of freezing the water vapor in the upper atmosphere. The ice crystals that form when clouds are seeded with dry ice serve as nuclei on which the water vapor can condense to form drops of rain.

1. What property of carbon dioxide is indicated by (a) its method of collection in the laboratory, (b) its use in fire extinguishers?

2. List several ways in which carbon dioxide is prepared commercially.

3. (a) List three uses of carbon dioxide in your home. (b) Describe briefly the action of baking powder.

4. (a) Compare and contrast a soda-acid and a foam fire extinguisher. (b) On what type of fire is each used?

5. (a) Why do many chemists prefer a carbon dioxide fire extinguisher in their laboratories? (b) Why are such extinguishers usually used on electrical fires?

CARBON MONOXIDE

Never run an automobile in a closed garage. Why? The carbon monoxide fumes produced by the burning gasoline are colorless, odorless, and tasteless, but deadly. When a car engine is run in a closed garage, a lack of adequate ventilation causes this carbon monoxide gas to accumulate. When carbon or carbon-containing materials,

33-17 A carbon dioxide extinguisher putting out a flammable liquid fire.

such as those in gasoline, are burned in a limited supply of air, the oxidation may proceed only far enough to form carbon monoxide, rather than carbon dioxide. In the car engine the carburetor, which controls the amount of air in which the gasoline is burned, is not always adjusted properly. Thus carbon monoxide is bound to be one of the materials in the exhaust gas. Carbon monoxide is very poisonous. It is all the more dangerous because it is not easily detected when inhaled.

Among the many properties in which carbon monoxide differs from carbon dioxide is its behavior in the bloodstream. In ordinary breathing the inhaled oxygen is transported to the body cells in the form of a "loose" combination with hemoglobin, a constituent of the red blood cells. When carbon monoxide is inhaled, it forms a much more stable combination with hemoglobin. Consequently, only a small amount of carbon monoxide in inhaled air prevents the available oxygen from reaching the cells. Continued inhalation of air containing less than 1 percent carbon monoxide will cause death. Carbon monoxide poisoning also often results from the use of defective coal stoves.

Preparation of Carbon Monoxide

Although carbon monoxide is dangerous, it finds significant use in chemistry. Carbon monoxide can be made by reducing carbon dioxide with hot carbon.

$$CO_2 + C \xrightarrow{\Delta} 2\,CO$$

A more convenient method of preparing the gas in the laboratory (CAUTION: *A hood must be used.*) is described below. Why not *see for yourself how carbon monoxide is prepared.*

Arrange the apparatus as shown in the diagram and place 20 ml of concentrated sulfuric acid in the flask. Begin warming the acid with *a very small flame.* Meanwhile, prepare two bottles to collect the gas by water displacement. Now, introduce formic acid from the dropping funnel into the flask at a rate of about one drop per 5 seconds, and start collecting any gas evolved. Continue with the collection, *cautiously* removing the burner from under the flask if the liquid shows any sign of boiling. When the two bottles are filled with carbon monoxide, allow the generator and its contents to cool

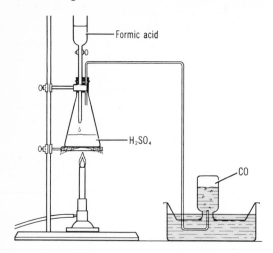

to room temperature before dismantling the set-up.

Thrust a burning splint into an inverted bottle of carbon monoxide and observe the color of the flame. To the second bottle of the gas, add about 5 ml of limewater. Does any change occur?

In this reaction, warm, concentrated sulfuric acid serves to dehydrate formic acid, leaving carbon monoxide.

$$HCOOH + H_2SO_4 \longrightarrow CO + H_2SO_4 \cdot H_2O$$
formic
acid

Properties of Carbon Monoxide

Colorless and odorless carbon monoxide ($MW = 28$) is almost as dense as air—in a closed garage it tends to stay close to the ground where it is released from a car exhaust. Its method of collection indicates that it is insoluble in water.

You can anticipate two chemical behaviors of carbon monoxide. Because the complete combustion of carbon results in the formation of carbon

dioxide, you should expect carbon monoxide to be able to combine with more oxygen. By investigation it can be shown that carbon monoxide combines with oxygen in two ways: first, by burning (with a pale blue flame) to form carbon dioxide; and second, by removing oxygen from other compounds, that is, by acting as a reducing agent.

$$2\,CO + O_2 \xrightarrow{\Delta} 2\,CO_2\uparrow$$
$$Fe_2O_3 + 3\,CO \xrightarrow{\Delta} 2\,Fe + 3\,CO_2\uparrow$$

The gas differs from carbon dioxide in the second respect. And it differs in still another. When carbon monoxide is passed into limewater, no change occurs. A white precipitate forms only with carbon dioxide which, being an acid anhydride, reacts with the base (the limewater). Carbon monoxide shows no acid properties in water.

The Uses of Carbon Monoxide

As a reducing agent the gas is an important constituent of fuel gases, both in industry and in the kitchen. It also serves as a reducing agent in metallurgical processes. The combination of carbon monoxide with the transition metals to form volatile carbonyls [$M_x(CO)_y$] was referred to in the extraction of nickel. The gas has also found increasing use in the synthesis of many organic compounds.

To complete the story of this most interesting group of elements, we will devote our attention next to the remaining members of group IVA.

QUESTIONS AND PROBLEMS

1. Write equations for the complete and incomplete combustion of ethane (C_2H_6).

2. Why is carbon monoxide such a deadly poison?

3. (a) How could you determine whether a bottle filled with gas contained carbon monoxide or carbon dioxide? (b) Describe a difference in behavior between carbon dioxide and carbon monoxide [other than that used in (a)].

SILICON, GERMANIUM, TIN, AND LEAD

Anthropologists are uncertain about when our ancestors first used tin; that it was known in 3000 B.C. is certain. Once man understood the metallurgy of tin, lead soon appeared. In contrast, germanium was not discovered until 1886. Silicon, unlike germanium, tin, and lead, is a nonmetal. Fragments of vessels made of clay, which contains silicon, have been found with the remains of early men.

Silicon

Silicon, the second most abundant element in the earth's crust, is widespread in the form of silica (SiO_2) in sand, quartz, and some gemstones (amethyst) (Fig. 33-18). It is also found in many rocks and minerals in the form of silicates, both simple and complex. Granite, containing, among other minerals, large amounts of quartz and mica, is an example of an abundant silicate rock that weathers slowly to produce the equally abundant clay.

Reduction of silicon dioxide provides an impure form of the element. A purer material is obtained by the reduction of silicon tetrachloride vapor with sodium or potassium. In contrast to carbon, silicon, which is pale brown to black in color, has no well-defined allotropes. It is rather inactive at room temperature, being attacked

33-18 Silicon dioxide is found throughout the world in many forms, here as sand, as quartz (the commonest of all solid materials), and as amethyst, a purple or blue-violet variety of crystallized quartz.

33-19 In a molecule of silicon dioxide, each silicon atom is bonded to four oxygen atoms to form a tetrahedron. Since each oxygen atom is common to two tetrahedrons a giant molecule is formed.

only by hydrofluoric acid, concentrated nitric acid, and concentrated solutions of the alkalies. The reaction was once used as a convenient, but expensive, way of generating hydrogen.

$$Si + 2\,NaOH + H_2O \longrightarrow H_2\uparrow + Na_2SiO_3$$

At elevated temperatures, silicon burns brilliantly in air and reacts vigorously with chlorine and bromine.

Silicon Compounds

Silicon dioxide in the form of quartz, like diamond and silicon carbide, exists in the form of a giant molecule. In these molecules, each silicon atom is linked covalently to four oxygen atoms at the corners of a tetrahedron; each oxygen atom, in turn, is common to two tetrahedra (Fig. 33-19). In the complex mineral silicates such as *feldspar* ($KAlSi_3O_8$), the oxygen atoms may be common to more than two tetrahedra; and some of the silicon atoms in oxidation state $+4$ may be replaced by aluminum atoms in oxidation state $+3$. This substitution alters the total ionic charge of the tetrahedron, so that other positive ions (Na^+, K^+) are added outside of the tetrahedron to maintain electrical neutrality.

The properties of natural silicates are closely related to their crystal structures; three main types exist (Fig. 33-20). When the silicon-oxygen crystal lattice develops in three dimensions (as in quartz) the resulting silicate is hard. Feldspar is such a silicate. When the tetrahedrons are linked to form sheets or layers, the layers can be separated (cleaved) with little force. An example of this type of silicate structure is *mica*, which is split readily into thin sheets that are used as electric insulators that must withstand high temperatures. In a third form, the tetrahedra are joined in chains or fibers that can be separated easily from one another. The best-known example of this type of silicate structure is the mineral *asbestos,* which can be shredded into fibers with remarkable ease. Asbestos fibers are used as a fireproofing material and in roofing and siding shingles.

Quartz is a valuable material to the scientist. Because it is transparent to ultraviolet rays, it finds use in special glass. Because of its low coefficient of thermal expansion, it is fashioned into laboratory glassware capable of withstanding temperature extremes without breaking. When a quartz crystal is cut at an angle to its major axis, the resulting quartz plate can be used as a crystal oscillator in radio transmission.

Hydrated forms of silicon dioxide are prepared by reacting solutions of sodium silicate ("water glass") with acids.

$$Na_2SiO_3 + 2\,H^+ + (n-1)\,H_2O \longrightarrow$$
$$2\,Na^+ + SiO_2 \cdot n\,H_2O$$

The hydrated silica, when washed and dried, forms a semitransparent, glassy mass known as *silica gel.* Silica gel has a porous structure and serves as a drying agent for laboratory gases, for packaging under dry conditions, and in air conditioning. It is also used as a catalyst and for the adsorption of gases.

Silicon dioxide, alone or in glass, is unaffected by most chemicals except molten or concentrated alkalies and hydrofluoric acid. Its reaction with hydrofluoric acid is used in the etching of glass, essentially a sodium calcium silicate.

$$SiO_2 + 4\,HF \longrightarrow SiF_4 + 2\,H_2O$$

Silanes

You have learned that bonding occurs between carbon atoms to form an enormous number and

33-20 In silicates, the silicon-oxygen crystal develops in three patterns: a three-dimensional solid network as in feldspar, sheets or layers as in mica, and chains or fibers as in asbestos. Hardness decreases left to right.

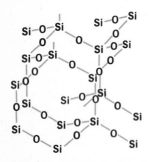

Silicate solid network

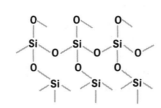

Silicate sheet

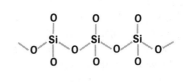

Silicate chain

Feldspar

Mica

Asbestos

variety of carbon compounds. Does silicon, a member of the same family, duplicate this behavior? Indeed it does, and the story of silicon compounds in which this type of bonding occurs is less than forty years old.

When silicon dioxide is reacted with an excess of a powerful reducing agent, such as an alkali or an alkaline earth metal, the silicon combines with the alkali metal to form a metal **silicide.**

$$SiO_2 + 4\,Mg \xrightarrow{\Delta} \underset{\text{silicide}}{Mg_2Si} + 2\,MgO$$

If the silicide is treated with an acid, gaseous compounds of silicon and hydrogen are formed; these are known as **silanes.** The equation below represents the formation of the simplest of many silanes.

$$Mg_2Si + 4\,HCl \longrightarrow 2\,MgCl_2 + \underset{\text{silane}}{SiH_4}$$

Other metal silicides react similarly to yield silanes with different numbers of Si and H atoms (Si_nH_{2n+2}). These compounds are very reactive and become increasingly unstable with increasing molecular weight. They ignite spontaneously in air and explode on contact with halogen gases. Consequently, the silanes do not form a large family of compounds analogous to the hydrocarbons. Silanes are the basis for the preparation of **silicones,** an important new class of compounds which will be considered with other synthetic materials in Chapter 37.

Germanium

Of the remaining elements of the group, germanium, which is relatively scarce, is obtained as a by-product of the metallurgy of other metals, chiefly lead and zinc. Germanium is only partly metallic. Although lustrous, it is grayish-white, brittle, and a poor conductor of electricity. However, traces of impurities increase its conductivity to such an extent that the element finds considerable use today in transistors (Fig. 33-21).

Tin

Neither tin nor lead is abundant in the earth. Tin occurs in the form of its oxide, *cassiterite,*

33-21 The die is used to cut germanium wafers used in transistors. At the right (top to bottom) are a germanium wafer, a diced wafer still attached to the glass mounting base, and individual germanium chips.

SnO_2. The earthy material (gangue) found in the ore can be separated from the much denser tin oxide by a stream of water, as well as by froth flotation. The remaining tin oxide is easily reduced with carbon.

$$SnO_2 + 2\,C \xrightarrow{\Delta} Sn + 2\,CO\uparrow$$

The metal is purified further by electrolysis.

At ordinary temperatures, tin is a silvery-bright, malleable, *but not ductile,* metal. It finds great use in the production of tin plate, commonly shaped into "tin" cans. It can be recovered from the plate by treating the warm scrap metal with chlorine gas, which transforms the metal into the easily volatile stannic chloride.

$$Sn + 2\,Cl_2 \xrightarrow{\Delta} SnCl_4$$

A major use of tin (and lead) is in alloys, which are summarized in Table 33-2.

The Compounds of Tin

Tin reacts slowly with dilute nonoxidizing acids at room temperatures.

$$Sn + 2\,HCl \longrightarrow SnCl_2 + H_2\uparrow$$

Table 33-2 **ALLOYS OF TIN AND LEAD**

Name	Composition (percent)	Properties	Uses
Solder (plumber's)	Pb (67), Sn (33)	Low melting point, remains plastic before solidifying completely	"Wiped" into joints in plumbing
Solder (soft)	Pb (50), Sn (50)	Low melting point, adheres to metal	Electrical connections in radios and electronic equipment
Pewter	Sn (85), Cu (7), Bi (6), Sb (2); this proportion may be varied, Pb and Zn being added	Soft, dull sheen	Tableware—plates, pitchers, bowls, coffeepots
Babbitt metal	Sn (90), Sb (7), Cu (3)	Very low coefficient of friction	Bearings for shafts, where roller bearings are not employed
Type metal	Pb (56–60), Sn (10–40), Sb (15–30), Cu (1)	Expands when solidified	Printers' type
Fusible alloys	Varying compositions; typically, Bi (50), Pb (25), the balance Sn alone, or Sn and Sb	Low melting points	Plugs in automatic sprinklers, ties in fire doors
Battery plate	Pb (94), Sb (6)	Not highly affected by acid	Plates for lead storage batteries

The metal reacts slowly with dilute nitric acid to yield stannous and ammonium nitrates and water.

$$4\,Sn + \underset{\text{cold dilute}}{10\,HNO_3} \longrightarrow$$
$$4\,Sn(NO_3)_2 + NH_4NO_3 + 3\,H_2O$$

The concentrated acid reacts violently to form oxides of nitrogen and an insoluble, hydrated metastannic acid.

$$Sn + 4\,HNO_3 + (x - 1)\,H_2O \longrightarrow$$
$$4\,NO_2\uparrow + H_2SnO_3 \cdot x\,H_2O$$

Tin, like aluminum and silicon, is unusual in that it reacts with strong bases like sodium hydroxide to yield hydrogen and a negative ion containing the metal.

$$Sn + 2\,NaOH + 2\,H_2O \longrightarrow H_2\uparrow + Na_2Sn(OH)_4$$

The hydroxides, in which tin occurs in both the $+2$ (stannous) and $+4$ (stannic) oxidation states, are amphoteric. They dissolve in an excess of strong base to form the complex compounds,

sodium stann*ite* $[Na_2Sn(OH)_4]$ and sodium stann*ate* $[Na_2Sn(OH)_6]$. These complex compounds, as well as those produced with acids, are used in weighting silk, as mordants in dyeing, and in fireproofing cloth.

Lead

Lead is usually found in the form of its sulfide ore, *galena* (PbS). The ore is concentrated by the froth flotation process, and the metal is obtained by partial roasting of the ore followed by an oxidation-reduction reaction between the resulting lead compounds. The roasting results in a mixture of lead oxide and lead sulfate.

$$2\,PbS + 3\,O_2 \xrightarrow{\Delta} 2\,PbO + 2\,SO_2\uparrow$$
$$PbS + 2\,O_2 \xrightarrow{\Delta} PbSO_4\uparrow$$

When the roasting has proceeded far enough, the air supply is shut off and the mixture is heated at a higher temperature. Oxidation-reduction now occurs between the lead sulfide and either the lead oxide or lead sulfate to produce the metal.

$$PbS + 2\,PbO \xrightarrow{\Delta} 3\,Pb + SO_2\uparrow$$
$$PbS + PbSO_4 \xrightarrow{\Delta} 2\,Pb + 2\,SO_2\uparrow$$

Lead is a relatively soft but dense metal of comparatively low melting point, a property which finds use in several low-melting-point alloys, such as solder (Fig. 33-22). As we may expect from its position in the electrochemical series, the metal reacts slowly with nonoxidizing acids. Nitric acid, whether dilute or concentrated, attacks the metal readily.

$$Pb + 4\,\underset{\text{conc.}}{HNO_3} \longrightarrow Pb(NO_3)_2 + 2\,NO_2\uparrow + 2\,H_2O$$

The once widespread use of lead in water pipes has been discontinued. Although the lead compounds formed by the action of water and oxygen are only slightly soluble, the metal is a cumulative poison. One of the most important uses of lead is the cathode of the lead storage battery.

Lead Compounds

Other than lead tetraethyl, $Pb(C_2H_5)_4$, an ingredient in antiknock gasoline, the major lead compounds used are the oxides. Lead oxide, PbO (litharge), is a yellowish solid used in preparing lead glass and lead compounds. Lead oxide is soluble in strong bases to form the plumbite ion.

$$PbO + H_2O + 2\,NaOH \longrightarrow Na_2Pb(OH)_4$$

The plumbous (Pb^{+2}) oxide may be oxidized, either electrolytically or chemically, to another oxide of lead, reddish-brown lead dioxide, PbO_2. This plumbic (Pb^{+4}) compound forms part of the positive plate of the lead storage battery (Chapter 24) and is employed in the laboratory as an oxidizing agent. If lead dioxide is maintained at a temperature of 450° C, it undergoes a change into a third oxide of lead.

$$3\,PbO_2 \underset{450°}{\rightleftharpoons} Pb_3O_4 + O_2\uparrow$$

This oxide, commonly known as red lead, is the well-known primer used to prevent corrosion of iron and steel.

An equally well-known white lead paint pigment is $2\,Pb(OH)_2 \cdot PbCO_3$, a basic lead carbon-

33-22 The technician is performing a precise soldering operation on an electronic subassembly from the TV system of a Mariner space probe.

ate. Though white lead pigments are widely used, they darken on exposure to an atmosphere with even small amounts of hydrogen sulfide.

In this chapter, we have dealt briefly with silicon, germanium, tin, and lead, as well as with the forms of carbon, its carbides and its oxides. But there are many other compounds of carbon with different characteristics from those we have encountered. The next unit opens the door into this fascinating branch of chemistry—the world of organic chemistry.

QUESTIONS AND PROBLEMS

1. (a) Contrast the three crystal structures of the natural silicates. (b) Give an example of each crystal type.

2. Differentiate between each of the following pairs of terms: (a) *silicide* and *silane* (b) *silica* and *silica gel* (c) *quartz* and *granite* (d) *sand* and *feldspar*.

3. Compare and contrast the extraction of tin and lead from their ores.

4. What are the major uses of each of the following: (a) germanium, (b) tin, (c) tin compounds, (d) lead?

5. Write the formula for each of the following compounds: potassium plumbite, calcium stannite, magnesium stannate.

VALUE OF THE CONCEPT

THE CONCEPT

The members of the group IVA family show little of the electron-losing or gaining characteristics of the elements at either end of their periods; instead, they exhibit marked covalency in their combinations. This is true of combinations between atoms of the same element, as in diamond or graphite. The covalent bonding may also occur between atoms of elements within the group, as in silicon carbide, or between atoms of a group IVA element and an element from another group, as in silicon dioxide. The result is the formation of giant, covalent molecules, whether natural or synthesized at very high temperatures. Despite the formation of covalent compounds, the group IVA elements imitate the trend already observed in other groups—the elements of greater atomic number show increasingly metallic properties. But this trend is only partial: tin and lead, both as elements and in compound formation, still possess covalent features.

Allotropic forms are emphasized in this family. Because of the startling contrast in structure between diamonds and graphite, and the numerous uses to which these forms are put, artificial production of these forms has been pursued intensively. Other forms of carbon, such as lampblack, are far from pure. They were once thought to be amorphous, but have been shown to be graphitic in nature. The unusually large surface area of many of these forms, such as charcoal, accounts for their great adsorbency.

Most of the group IVA compounds, whether natural or synthetic, have widespread industrial application. The carbonates and bicarbonates are widely utilized—in baking and washing powders, fire extinguishers, soap and glassmaking. Carbon dioxide has manifold uses, from fire extinguishers to refrigeration. Even the deadly carbon monoxide is of value in the purification of certain metals. As a result of recent discoveries, silicon and germanium are now utilized in electronics. Silicon dioxide appears as sand or quartz, both useful in glassmaking, either in combination or alone. Quartz also occurs in the form of many semiprecious stones. Silicates are widespread in rocks and minerals, some of which have great industrial application. Structurally different clay, talc, and asbestos are just a few examples. Tin and lead are best known as plating metals and as constituents in alloys such as solder and bronze.

USING THE CONCEPT

Using the Basic Concept

1. Contrast the structures and properties of the following allotropes of carbon: charcoal, animal charcoal, lampblack, boneblack. (b) Give one important use of each allotrope.

2. (a) In terms of crystalline structure, explain why graphite is very soft and diamond very hard. (b) How are the chief uses of these allotropes related to their structures?

3. (a) How are the valence bonds of the carbon atom arranged in space? (b) What evidence indicates that the shape you stated is correct?

4. Account for the fact that diamonds, silicon carbide, and silicon dioxide are alike in being hard and having high melting points.

5. (a) Compare and contrast the production of carbides in refractory furnaces and arc furnaces. (b) What is the chief use of carbides?

6. How could you use one or more properties of carbon dioxide and carbon monox-

ide to separate a mixture of these gases?

7. (a) Why should you use a foam-type fire extinguisher on an oil fire? (b) Why should a soda-acid fire extinguisher never be used on an electrical fire? (c) What type of extinguisher should be used on such a fire?

8. Why are very high pressures needed to transform graphite into diamonds?

9. If the electrolysis of water is performed with graphite electrodes, the volumes of gases obtained do not agree with those obtained when platinum electrodes are used. Account for the difference.

10. Give the chemical formula for each of the following substances: dry ice, carborundum, carbon tetrachloride, carbon disulfide.

11. (a) What is the function of each substance in baking powder? (b) How is baking powder related to soda water?

12. Why do solutions of stannous chloride and lead nitrate give an acid reaction to litmus paper?

13. What conclusions can be drawn from the fact that the majority of carbon compounds are soluble in liquids such as benzene, alcohol, and carbon tetrachloride, and have relatively low melting and boiling points?

14. Why it is impossible to extinguish burning magnesium by means of a carbon dioxide extinguisher?

15. (a) Differentiate among the structures of quartz, mica, and asbestos. (b) What do these three substances have in common?

16. What properties of tin and lead explain the fact that these metals have been known for a long time?

17. (a) What element is extracted from galena and cassiterite? (b) List two uses for each metal.

18. Explain why lead reacts much more slowly with hydrochloric acid than does tin.

19. (a) Write the formula for each of the following: potassium stannite, barium stannate, plumbous oxide, calcium plumbite. (b) Write a possible formula for a silicide, a silane.

Relating Terms Within the Concept

Each of the following exercises consists of five terms. From the last four, select the term or terms closely related to the *italicized* term.

1. *graphite:* ionic bonds, pencil "lead," opaque, electric furnace
2. *lampblack:* evident crystalline structure, hydrocarbon, propane, arc furnace
3. *boneblack:* destructive distillation, resistance furnace, allotrope, animal charcoal
4. *carbon's p electrons:* L shell, unpaired, resonance, third shell
5. *adsorption:* absorption, charcoal, decolorizer, surface phenomenon
6. *CO:* complete combustion, carbonic acid, odorless, limewater
7. *diamond:* hexagonal crystal, covalent bonds, transparent, giant molecule
8. *CO_2:* +2 oxidation state, dry ice, sublimation, electrical fires
9. *soda-acid extinguisher:* H_2SO_4, Na_2CO_3, oil fires, carbon disulfide
10. *baking powder:* CO_2, solid acid, calcium carbide, baking soda
11. *carborundum:* abrasive, silicon carbide, borazon, silane
12. *tin:* amphoteric hydroxide, storage battery, +2 and +4 oxidation states, froth flotation
13. *silica:* quartz, mica, silicide, asbestos

Solving Problems Within the Concept

1. (a) What weight of silicon carbide can be obtained from 1 ton of sand which is 99 percent SiO_2? (b) What weight of coke, 90 percent carbon, would be required?

2. Lead dioxide (PbO_2) reacts with concentrated hydrochloric acid as follows:

$$PbO_2 + 4\,HCl \longrightarrow Cl_2 + PbCl_2 + 2\,H_2O$$

(a) What weight of lead dioxide is needed to react with 365 grams of hydrogen chloride? (b) What volume (**STP**) of chlorine gas would be produced?

3. When carbon dioxide was bubbled into 1 liter of a solution of calcium hydroxide, the precipitate formed weighed 1.75 grams after filtration and drying. (a) What weight of calcium hydroxide was present in the solution? (b) What was the molarity of this solution?

4. If 10 grams of C_5H_{12} are burned in a limited supply of air, how many grams of carbon will be formed (assuming 100 percent efficiency)?

5. How many liters of carbon dioxide (**STP**) will have the same weight as 10 liters of methane, CH_4?

6. What volume of carbon monoxide (**STP**) can be produced by reducing carbon dioxide with 2.4 grams of carbon?

7. What is the percent by weight of: (a) silicon in silicon dioxide, (b) lead in lead nitrate, (c) tin in stannous chloride?

8. Iodine pentoxide, I_2O_5, reacts with carbon monoxide in the following manner:

$$I_2O_5 + 5\,CO \longrightarrow I_2 + 5\,CO_2$$

How many liters of carbon monoxide will react with 16.7 grams of the pentoxide?

9. A compound contains 45.5 percent tin and 54.5 percent chlorine by weight. What is the oxidation number of the tin?

Applying the Concept

1. In what respects do tin and lead resemble zirconium and titanium? In what respects do they differ?

2. Lead ores sometimes contain silver and gold, which appear in the crude lead produced in the smelting process. How could these metals be separated from the lead?

3. How can sodium hydroxide be used to separate the tin from iron in "tin cans"?

4. Write equations to show how carbon dioxide can be made from magnesium carbonate by: (a) reaction with nitric acid (b) heating to a high temperature.

5. While carbon monoxide combines readily with hemoglobin, carbon dioxide does not imitate this behavior. Why?

6. Why can powdered sodium bicarbonate be used to extinguish small fires?

7. Why must soda-acid and foam-type extinguishers be recharged after use, even if the fire on which they are used is extinguished within 5 seconds?

8. Describe two *chemical* methods by which you could distinguish between powdered charcoal and manganese dioxide.

9. Why should the generator used to prepare carbon monoxide be allowed to cool to room temperature before its contents are discarded?

10. Carbon monoxide and hydrogen are very much alike in physical and chemical properties. How could you distinguish between them by chemical means?

11. Draw electron dot diagrams of CCl_4, CS_2, and CH_4, all of which are covalent molecules.

12. Write balanced equations for the reaction between: (a) lead acetate and sodium sulfide, (b) carbon dioxide and potassium hydroxide, (c) germanium and chlorine.

13. If a container of activated charcoal is left open to the laboratory air, why does the charcoal lose its effectiveness?

Reading Further

The Chemical History of a Candle, by Michael Faraday, New York, T. Y. Crowell, 1957. The 1860 Christmas Lectures to the Royal Society in London as reported by a great figure in the history of chemistry.

"Radiocarbon Dating," by Edward Deevey, Jr., *Scientific American,* February 1952. A description of this valuable new technique in determining with great accuracy the age of carbon-containing substances.

"Synthetic Diamonds," by P. W. Bridgman, *Scientific American,* November 1955. With enough pressure and heat you can make your own.

UNIT

5

The Chemistry of Carbon Compounds

Robert Woodward, a professor of chemistry at Harvard University, is both a detective and an architect, as well as a chemist. Here he is holding a model of a molecule of chlorophyll, the substance that is essential to green plants for the process of photosynthesis. Were it not for chlorophyll, green plants could not synthesize carbohydrates, nor could they return to the atmosphere the oxygen vital to life. The green plant synthesizes its chlorophyll. Woodward received the Nobel prize in chemistry in 1965 for duplicating this process in the laboratory—for determining the exact positions of the 137 atoms making up this complex molecule and placing each atom in its proper position.

To synthesize chlorophyll, as well as other organic compounds, Woodward not only determined the actual formula of the compound but more important, its structure—the manner in which its atoms are arranged. This "detective" work called upon the analytical techniques of the chemist to establish the blueprint of the molecule. The greater task remained. Assembling the necessary kinds and numbers of atoms into an arrangement that duplicated that of a natural substance required a superb knowledge of chemical reactions. But in this "architectural" proceeding, Woodward was faced with the necessity of pioneering—developing a totally new approach. The Nobel Prize is recognition that he indeed *blazed a new trail*.

34

The Hydrocarbons

In ancient times it was recognized that alcohols, fats, and sugars were formed by living processes, while clay, gem stones, and ores were obtained directly from the crust of the earth. The compounds of "life" were later referred to as **organic,** while compounds similar to the minerals of the earth, not directly related to life, were called **inorganic.**

The term *organic chemistry* is inherited from the day when the science of chemistry was comparatively primitive. Coal was classed as an organic compound because it is formed by the decay of plant life. Urea was classed as organic because it is formed as a waste product in the metabolism of animals. Not until the nineteenth century was it discovered that organic compounds can be created artificially in the laboratory from substances which do not arise from life processes. Since then our knowledge of organic chemistry has grown until today more than a million different organic compounds have been identified. By contrast, the inorganic compounds in the world number a mere 50,000!

DEVELOPMENT OF MODERN ORGANIC THEORY

Oxalic acid is an organic compound formerly thought to be obtainable chiefly from the leaves of rhubarb or from wood sorrel. But in 1776 Karl Scheele, a German chemist, prepared oxalic acid by reacting the sugar from sugar cane with nitric acid. Scheele's experiment showed that an organic compound could be created artificially. Yet it was still assumed that a "vital force" related to life was necessary for the creation of such compounds. In the case of Scheele's experiment, this vital force was thought to come from the sugar cane that had once been a living plant. In 1828 another German chemist, Friedrich Wöhler, prepared the organic compound urea from ammonia and hydrocyanic acid. Yet here again advocates of the vital force theory were ready with an explanation. Since the ammonia Wöhler used had been obtained by distilling animal horns, it was assumed that these had supplied the necessary vital force.

Not until 1845 was the idea of a vital force finally discarded. In that year Adolf Kolbe, a German scientist, synthesized acetic acid. Since acetic acid had been prepared previously by the fermentation of sugar, it was considered an organic compound. But Kolbe had now produced acetic acid by reacting acetylene with water. Acetylene, you recall, is made from water and calcium carbide, both inorganic compounds in no way related to life; there was no possibility here for injecting the idea of a "vital force." Obviously a new definition of organic substances was called for.

Organic Compounds

It has been found that nearly all compounds related to living substances are compounds of carbon. Hence today we simply say that *organic chemistry* is the chemistry of carbon compounds. Only a few carbon compounds, such as sodium carbonate (Na_2CO_3), carbon dioxide (CO_2), and carbon monoxide (CO), are still considered inorganic. On the other hand, rubber, vitamins, hormones, natural dyes, proteins, fats, and carbohydrates are all carbon compounds and all are considered to be organic. Not only has the chemist been able to reproduce many natural organic compounds in the laboratory, but also he has been able to create many organic substances which are not found in nature. These include synthetic detergents, nylon, and many fibers and plastics (Fig. 34-1).

You may wonder why so many carbon compounds exist. Since carbon atoms have four valence electrons, each carbon atom can form a total of four covalent bonds with atoms of other elements. Closely related to its electron structure is the carbon atom's unusual ability to link covalently with other carbon atoms. Carbon atoms can link covalently with one another by sharing one, two, or three valence electron pairs —by forming single, double, or triple bonds:

$$\cdot \overset{..}{C} \colon \overset{..}{C} \cdot \qquad \colon \overset{..}{C} \colon\colon \overset{..}{C} \colon \qquad \overset{..}{C} \colon\colon\colon \overset{..}{C}$$

| single bond | double bond | triple bond |

Organic molecules containing as many as seventy carbon atoms in a carbon-to-carbon linkage are known. Finally, many organic compounds exist which have the same number and type of atoms per molecule but which have different properties because of a difference in the arrangement of their atoms. Such compounds are called **isomers.** For example, glucose (grape sugar) and fructose (fruit sugar) are isomers that you studied in biology. Both have the same formula, $C_6H_{12}O_6$; but the molecules of these two sugars differ in structural arrangement. Count the carbon, hydrogen, and oxygen atoms in each formula below to satisfy yourself that both compounds do have the same molecular formula. (In the formulas each dash (−) represents a covalent bond, as described further on page 578.)

34-1 The skydiver is almost completely outfitted in synthetic materials—from his nylon parachute to his plastic crash helmet.

glucose

fructose

Comparing Organic and Inorganic Compounds

How do the properties of organic and inorganic substances differ? We can see the difference by comparing table sugar ($C_{12}H_{22}O_{11}$), an organic compound, with inorganic table salt (NaCl). Table salt melts at a very high tempera-

ture (800° C). Sugar, on the other hand, melts at a much lower temperature (170° C). Again, when salt is heated to high temperature, it vaporizes; when sugar is heated sufficiently, it decomposes, forming carbon and water vapor. Both sugar and salt dissolve in water, but a salt solution is an electrolyte while a sugar solution is a nonelectrolyte. Organic compounds, such as fats, paper, and gasoline, are combustible. Yet—except when burning occurs—reactions between organic substances usually proceed more slowly than inorganic reactions. Catalysts are often needed to increase the rate at which organic reactions occur. The many reactions between organic compounds that take place inside living organisms require enzymes as catalysts. To sum up: most organic compounds are insoluble in water, they are combustible, they melt at relatively low temperatures and decompose at higher temperatures, and they react slowly with each other.

A Brief Classification of the Hydrocarbons

Organic compounds are made up of atoms of other elements covalently bonded to carbon atoms. More often than not the carbon atoms form the skeleton of the organic molecule while the other atoms, those covalently bonded to this carbon skeleton, are atoms of hydrogen, oxygen, or both. There are also many other types of organic molecules in which some or all of the hydrogen and oxygen atoms are replaced by nitrogen, sulfur, phosphorus, chlorine, and other atoms. These more complex organic compounds await further study. Here we will consider the simplest of organic compounds: the **hydrocarbons,** compounds in which only carbon and hydrogen atoms are bonded together.

The hydrocarbons are divided into two main groups according to the way the carbon atoms in the hydrocarbon molecule are bonded together. If the bonding of the carbon atoms is of the "open-chain" type, the hydrocarbons are called **aliphatic.** In an open chain, as in the formulas below for ethane (C_2H_6) and butene (C_4H_8), the carbon atoms at the two ends of the chain are not attached to each other. If the bonding is of the "ring" type, the hydrocarbons are usually **aromatic.** In a ring hydrocarbon, such as benzene (C_6H_6), all the carbon atoms of the chain are bonded together.

ethane   butene

ALIPHATIC

benzene
AROMATIC

Each of these two main groups of hydrocarbons is subdivided into different series. The members of each series have formulas that show a mathematical relationship. The aromatic group will be considered later. In the aliphatic, or open-chain, division of hydrocarbons, there are three main series: the **alkanes,** the **alkenes,** and the **alkynes.** Let us consider the alkanes first.

QUESTIONS AND PROBLEMS

1. (a) What are the main characteristics of organic compounds? (b) What are the main differences between organic and inorganic compounds?

2. Define each of the following terms: *hydrocarbon, isomer, aliphatic compound, aromatic compound.*

THE ALKANES—SATURATED HYDROCARBONS

You have read of explosions that occur in coal mines when a mixture of coal gas and air is accidentally ignited by a spark or flame. Coal gas is 40 percent **methane,** created as plant cells decay in the formation of coal. In addition to being a major constituent of coal gas, methane (CH_4) also makes up about 90 percent of all natural gas. *You can prepare* a small amount of methane quite readily. (*Handle the NaOH carefully.*)

Grind together in a *clean* mortar about 2 grams of anhydrous sodium acetate and 6 grams of sodium hydroxide. Work quickly, because any moisture absorbed by the base will slow down the reaction. Place the mixture in a Pyrex test tube, as shown below.

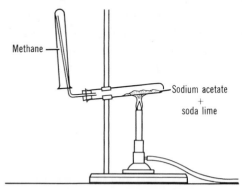

Heat the tube *gently* at first, then strongly. Collect a test tube of the methane by displacement of air. The gas has no color. Smell it carefully; it has the same odor you may have noticed in marshy or swampy regions.

In preparing methane, you have prepared the simplest hydrocarbon.

$$NaC_2H_3O_2 + NaOH \xrightarrow{\Delta} Na_2CO_3 + CH_4\uparrow$$

Each molecule of the gas consists of four hydrogen atoms bonded to one carbon atom by single covalent bonds. The formula is conveniently represented as:

$$\begin{array}{c} H \\ | \\ H-C-H \\ | \\ H \end{array}$$

methane

Actually the methane molecule, as you recall from the last chapter (Fig. 33-3), has the shape of a regular tetrahedron.

Methane is the first member of the **alkane series.** The alkane series is sometimes also called the **paraffin series.** The word *paraffin* means "having little affinity or reactivity," and, like methane, all alkanes are relatively inactive except at high temperatures. Like methane, none of the alkanes (or paraffins) reacts with hydrogen. Because the carbon atoms of these molecules have no further valence electrons to form bonds with additional atoms, such organic molecules are said to be **saturated.**

Other Alkanes

The second member of the alkane series can be prepared in the laboratory by electrolyzing a solution of sodium acetate with direct current. Bubbles of gas collect at the anode (Fig. 34-2). An analysis of the gas shows that it is a mixture of molecules of carbon dioxide and other molecules which contain *two* carbon atoms and six hydrogen atoms—molecules of **ethane.**

$$\begin{array}{c} H \quad H \\ | \quad | \\ H-C-C-H \\ | \quad | \\ H \quad H \end{array}$$

ethane

In an ethane molecule the two carbon atoms are bonded together by a single covalent bond. These

carbon atoms are said to form a two-carbon **chain.** To each of the two carbon atoms in the chain, three hydrogen atoms are bonded. Therefore, the formula for ethane, the second member of the saturated alkane series of hydrocarbons, is C_2H_6.

The third alkane, **propane,** is a gaseous hydrocarbon that can be prepared by the reaction between sodium butyrate ($NaC_4H_7O_2$) and sodium hydroxide.

$$NaC_4H_7O_2 + NaOH \longrightarrow Na_2CO_3 + C_3H_8\uparrow$$
sodium butyrate

The structure of a propane molecule is:

$$\begin{array}{c} H \quad H \quad H \\ | \quad | \quad | \\ H-C-C-C-H \\ | \quad | \quad | \\ H \quad H \quad H \end{array}$$

propane

Notice that each molecule of propane consists of *three* carbon atoms bonded together by single bonds to form a chain. Each of the end carbon atoms is bonded to three hydrogen atoms, while the middle carbon atom is bonded to only two hydrogen atoms. The formula for propane is C_3H_8.

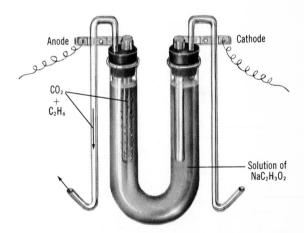

34-2 To produce ethane, a large U tube is attached by metal brackets to a vertical wooden surface. The metal electrodes in the arms of the U tube are attached to one end of the brackets and a source of direct current to the other. Electrolysis of a sodium acetate solution releases the gases carbon dioxide and ethane at the anode.

Table 34-1 THE ALKANE SERIES

Name	Molecular formula	Boiling point (° C)*	State (20° C)
Methane	CH_4	−161.7	Gas
Ethane	C_2H_6	−88.6	Gas
Propane	C_3H_8	−42.2	Gas
Butane	C_4H_{10}	−0.5	Gas
Pentane	C_5H_{12}	36.1	Liquid
Hexane	C_6H_{14}	68.7	Liquid
Heptane	C_7H_{16}	98.4	Liquid
Octane	C_8H_{18}	125.6	Liquid
Nonane	C_9H_{20}	150.7	Liquid
Decane	$C_{10}H_{22}$	174.0	Liquid

* Value for the normal isomer.

Other alkanes can be prepared. In all cases they consist of carbon atoms connected by single covalent bonds to form open-chain hydrocarbons in which each of the carbon atoms has bonded to it the maximum possible number of hydrogen atoms.

Relating Alkane Formulas

The common names and formulas for the first ten members of the alkane series containing progressively from one to ten carbon atoms per molecule are listed in Table 34-1. Study these formulas to discover any relationships among them; you will probably find two relationships at once. First, the formula for each alkane differs from the one preceding it by the same number of atoms—by one carbon atom and two hydrogen atoms. Adding CH_2 to methane, for example, gives the formula for ethane, C_2H_6. Adding CH_2 to the formula for ethane gives the formula for propane, C_3H_8. The addition of CH_2 to the formula for propane gives the formula for butane, C_4H_{10}, and so on. Such a series of compounds in which each member differs from the next by the same number and kind of atoms is called a **homologous series.**

By comparing the ten formulas in this homologous series, you probably also observe that for every carbon atom in an alkane molecule there are twice as many hydrogen atoms plus two. A

methane molecule, for instance, contains one carbon atom; it also has four $[(2 \times 1) + 2]$ hydrogen atoms. Ethane (C_2H_6), which has two carbon atoms, has six $[(2 \times 2) + 2]$ hydrogen atoms. A decane molecule ($C_{10}H_{22}$), with ten carbon atoms, has twenty-two $[(2 \times 10) + 2]$ hydrogen atoms.

The alkane series is sometimes defined as the series of hydrocarbons with the general formula C_nH_{2n+2}. Here the letter n represents the number of carbon atoms in a given alkane molecule. If the alkane molecule contains n number of carbon atoms, then it will also have $2n + 2$ hydrogen atoms.

Representing Alkane Molecules

The formulas CH_4, C_2H_6, and C_3H_8 are **molecular formulas** which convey little information about the structures of the molecules they represent. For this purpose we can use electron dot diagrams.

methane   ethane   propane

They represent more clearly the electron pairs by which the carbon and hydrogen atoms are bonded in each alkane.

Historically, however, dashes have been used to represent covalent bonds, and today chemists usually prefer to represent the structure of organic molecules by **graphic formulas** containing dashes. The graphic formulas for the first three alkanes are as you have seen:

methane   ethane   propane

In these graphic formulas observe that each carbon atom has attached to it four dashes, representing four covalent bonds. Each hydrogen atom shares one dash, representing a single covalent bond, with a carbon atom.

34-3 Propane and butane are straight-chain or open-chain hydrocarbons; the carbon atoms form a continuous chain. The bonding angles between adjacent carbon atoms (gray) and between carbon atoms and hydrogen atoms (dark ochre) are accurate as they appear in these solid models.

Propane

Butane

Compare the graphic formulas for ethane and propane. The CH_2 group by which these formulas differ is shown as

$$-\overset{\displaystyle H}{\underset{\displaystyle H}{C}}-.$$

Adding

$$-\overset{\displaystyle H}{\underset{\displaystyle H}{C}}-$$

to the graphic formula for any alkane gives the formula for the alkane next higher in the series.

The necessity for drawing dashes can be eliminated by writing in a horizontal row the appropriate symbols and subscripts for the groups of carbon and hydrogen atoms which appear in a molecule. In this abbreviated form, called a **structural formula,** the formula for ethane is written CH_3CH_3, and that for propane is $CH_3CH_2CH_3$. Though structural formulas give more information than molecular formulas, they are often not as useful as graphic formulas.

From their graphic formulas it might seem that the carbon chains of alkane molecules are straight. Actually this is true only of ethane. In other hydrocarbons, the chains of carbon atoms are usually not straight. The actual angles that exist between adjacent carbon atoms in propane and butane are shown in the solid models of Fig. 34-3. Traditionally, however, the term *straight chain* has been used to describe open-chain molecules, those in which the carbon atoms are in a continuous chain.

Isomers

The boiling points of several alkanes are listed in Table 34-2. Notice particularly the boiling points and the molecular formulas of the last two compounds in the table. Although the two formulas are identical, C_4H_{10}, the two boiling points are markedly different ($-0.5°$ C and $-10°$ C).

We conclude that there are two types of butane. Though the number of carbon and hydrogen atoms in each butane molecule is the same, the arrangement of the carbon atoms is different.

normal butane

isobutane

In the first type, called **normal butane,** the chain of carbon atoms is straight or, more correctly, *unbranched.* That is, the carbon atoms are in a continuous chain. In the second, the chain of carbon atoms is *branched* or discontinuous. This is a molecule of **isobutane.** In normal butane (*n*-butane) observe that no carbon atom is bonded to more than two other carbon atoms; in the branched chain of isobutane, the central carbon atom has three carbon atoms bonded to it. This difference between the structures of normal butane and isobutane can be represented by different structural formulas. The formula

Table 34-2   **BOILING POINTS OF SOME ALKANES**

Name	Molecular formula	Structural formula	Boiling point (°C)
Methane	CH_4	CH_4	-161.7
Ethane	C_2H_6	CH_3CH_3	-88.6
Propane	C_3H_8	$CH_3CH_2CH_3$	-42.2
n-Butane	C_4H_{10}	$CH_3CH_2CH_2CH_3$	-0.5
Isobutane	C_4H_{10}	$CH_3CHCH_3CH_3$	-10.0

$CH_3CH_2CH_2CH_3$ represents the unbranched chain of carbon atoms in normal butane. The formula $CH_3CHCH_3CH_3$ indicates the branched chain of carbon atoms that exists in isobutane. Compounds such as these, which have the same molecular formulas but different arrangements of atoms, are **isomers.** Normal butane and isobutane are examples of isomers, solid models of which are shown in Figures 34-3 and 34-4.

The different arrangements of atoms in isomers can be shown by structural formulas, graphic formulas, or solid models. It is this structural difference among isomers that accounts for their different physical properties, such as boiling points, and for differences in chemical activity.

Isomers of Other Alkanes

The only two isomers for butane are the two represented in Figures 34-3 and 34-4. However, pentane has three isomers: **normal pentane, isopentane,** and **neopentane.**

normal pentane

isopentane

neopentane

As you proceed to the higher members of the alkane series, the number of possible isomers increases greatly. While not all the isomers have been discovered, seventy-five isomers are possible for decane ($C_{10}H_{22}$). For eicosane ($C_{20}H_{42}$)

Isobutane

34-4 Comparison of an isobutane molecule with a normal butane molecule (Figure 34-3) reveals that spatial arrangement of the atoms differs.

there are 366,319 possible isomers! And other types of organic compounds exist as isomers.

Naming Alkanes

The existence of so many isomers creates a problem in naming them. It is easy enough when there are only three possible isomers of a compound, as with pentane. Then the prefixes normal (*n*-), iso-, and neo- will suffice. But what prefixes can we find to distinguish among the seventy-five isomers of decane?

Because of the importance of differentiating among isomers other systems of naming organic compounds have developed. The older of two widely used naming systems is the **derived system.**

The Derived System

According to the derived system, an alkane is considered to consist of a methane molecule to which **alkyl groups,** or **alkyl radicals,** are attached. Alkyl radicals are radicals that contain one less hydrogen atom than the corresponding alkane. An alkyl radical containing one carbon atom, for example, is called *methyl* (CH_3); two carbon atoms, *ethyl* (written as C_2H_5 or CH_3CH_2); three carbon atoms, *propyl* (written as C_3H_7 or $CH_3CH_2CH_2$), and so on.

methyl   ethyl   propyl

In naming an alkane according to the derived system, consider the carbon atom closest to the center of the formula as the core of a methane molecule. The compound is then named by first naming, in order of increasing number of carbon atoms, the alkyl radicals attached to this central atom. The names of the alkyl radicals are followed by the name methane. As an example, the derived name for ethane is methylmethane, while *n*-butane becomes methylethylmethane.

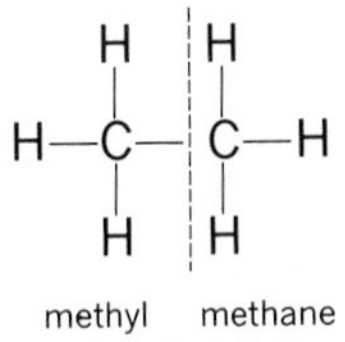

methyl   methane
methylmethane

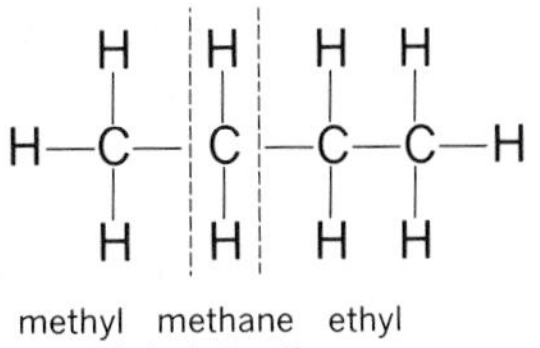

methyl   methane   ethyl
methylethylmethane

The Geneva or I.U.C. System

The I.U.C. system of naming was first considered at an international meeting of chemists at Geneva, Switzerland, in 1892, and was later improved upon in 1930 by a committee of the International Union of Chemistry; hence the names Geneva or I.U.C. system. In using the I.U.C. system, the carbon atoms in the longest chain are numbered consecutively from right to left, or left to right, to indicate on which atom or atoms individual alkyl radicals are attached. The numbering is done in the direction that will allow the smallest possible numbers to be used in indicating the position of each alkyl radical. In using the I.U.C. system, assume that a compound is derived from the alkane whose name corresponds to that with the number of carbon atoms in the longest possible chain.

Observe in the graphic formula for isopentane shown below that the longest possible chain in this alkane contains four carbon atoms.

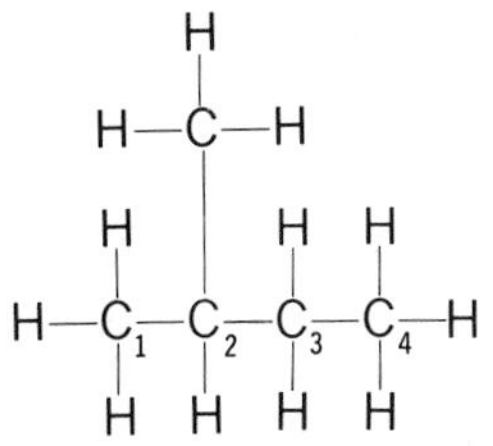

The pentane isomer appears to be derived from butane. Also notice that a methyl group is attached to the number two carbon. The I.U.C. name for this alkane, therefore, is 2-methylbutane. Though all organic compounds can be named by the I.U.C. system, details must await your more comprehensive study of organic chemistry.

Sources and Uses of Alkanes

Alkanes that contain few carbon atoms are obtained commercially by cooling and compressing natural gas. The general composition of natural gas is a mixture of alkanes and other organic compounds, together with hydrogen sulfide and helium. Though the composition varies with the area in which natural gas is found, it is usually about 90 percent methane, as noted earlier. As the natural gas begins to liquefy under pressure, methane, ethane, and helium remain in the gaseous state. Propane and butane isomers are obtained by *fractional distillation,* that is, gradually heating the liquefied natural gas and allowing each of these alkanes to boil off at its own boiling temperature. The details of this process will be studied in the chapter on fuels.

Petroleum (crude oil) is the other main source of alkanes. In fact the name *aliphatic,* the hydrocarbon group to which the alkanes belong, is derived from the Greek word for oil. Petroleum is a mixture of hydrocarbons, chiefly of the methane series. The mixture is very complex, and it is extremely difficult to separate the hydrocarbons completely from one another. When alkanes that are not found in either natural gas or petroleum are needed in their pure form, they are usually prepared in the laboratory through a series of reactions.

Natural gas and petroleum, both so important as fuels, contain large quantities of alkanes; thus a major use of alkanes must be to supply energy as fuels. Liquefied alkanes, such as propane and butane, are sold in steel containers as portable sources of heat (Fig. 34-5). Pure alkanes also serve as raw materials from which alcohols and other organic substances are produced.

34-5 Bottled propane is a convenient fuel for cooking in rural areas where there is no access to natural gas pipelines.

1. (a) Write the graphic and structural formulas for alkanes with molecular formulas C_6H_{14} and $C_{12}H_{26}$. (b) Write the graphic formulas for three other isomers of C_6H_{14}.

2. Write the molecular formula for the alkane that contains (a) eleven carbon atoms, (b) thirty hydrogen atoms.

3. Define *open-chain hydrocarbon, saturated hydrocarbon, homologous series.*

UNSATURATED OPEN-CHAIN HYDROCARBONS

In recent advertisements the term *polyunsaturated* has appeared frequently. As applied to organic molecules, the term *unsaturated* means that some of the carbon atoms are joined by double or triple covalent bonds.

$$-\overset{|}{C}=\overset{|}{C}- \qquad -C\equiv C-$$

double bond   triple bond

When hydrogen atoms are added to these unsaturated molecules, they break the double or triple bonds and convert them into single covalent bonds (Fig. 34-6). Hydrogen atoms cannot, of course, be added to alkane molecules because alkanes have only single bonds; they are *saturated.* But hydrogen atoms can be added to the alkenes or alkynes—the two *unsaturated* homologous series of the aliphatic group of hydrocarbons. The degree of saturation is different in the two series. Molecules of alkenes, or olefins, contain double bonds, while those of the alkynes contain triple bonds.

Alkenes

The simplest *alkene,* and the only one we shall consider in detail here, is **ethylene** (C_2H_4). It is the first member of the most important series of alkenes, the **ethylene series.** A colorless gas, ethylene is valuable for illumination since it burns with a particularly bright flame. If you wished to prepare the gas, you could do so by heating ethyl alcohol and then passing the hot alcohol vapor over alumina. The vapor becomes dehydrated, and the gaseous substance that forms has quite different properties from the alcohol

$$H-\underset{\underset{H}{|}}{\overset{\overset{H}{|}}{C}}-\underset{\underset{H}{|}}{\overset{\overset{H}{|}}{C}}-H \;+\; H_2 \longrightarrow \text{No reaction}$$

Saturated

$$H-\underset{\underset{}{}}{\overset{\overset{H}{|}}{C}}=\underset{\underset{}{}}{\overset{\overset{H}{|}}{C}}-H \;+\; H_2 \longrightarrow H-\underset{\underset{H}{|}}{\overset{\overset{H}{|}}{C}}-\underset{\underset{H}{|}}{\overset{\overset{H}{|}}{C}}-H$$

Unsaturated   Saturated

$$H-C\equiv C-H \;+\; 2H_2 \longrightarrow H-\underset{\underset{H}{|}}{\overset{\overset{H}{|}}{C}}-\underset{\underset{H}{|}}{\overset{\overset{H}{|}}{C}}-H$$

Unsaturated   Saturated

34-6 Double and triple bonds in the unsaturated alkene and alkyne series, respectively, are indicated in ochre in the equations. Replacements of these bonds by hydrogen bonds creates saturated products.

itself. This new substance is *ethylene*—or *ethene* to use its I.U.C. name.

$$C_2H_5OH \xrightarrow[\Delta]{alumina} H_2O + C_2H_4$$

ethyl
alcohol   ethene

If the mixture of hot ethene is reacted with hydrogen, ethane is produced.

$$C_2H_4 + H_2 \xrightarrow[\Delta]{catalyst} C_2H_6$$

ethene   ethane

This reaction demonstrates that ethene, unlike ethane, is unsaturated (Fig. 34-7).

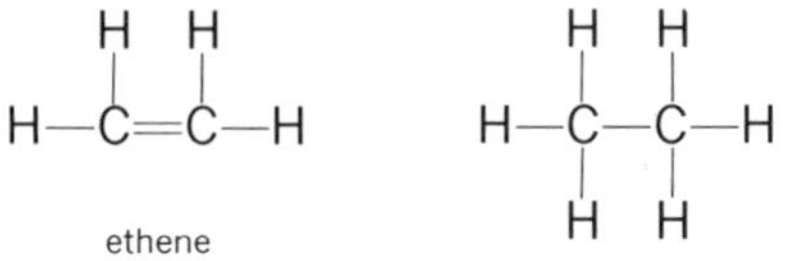

Ethane   Ethene

34-7 Ethane is saturated, ethene unsaturated. Find the double bond.

ethene
(ethylene)
unsaturated

ethane
saturated

If the ethene had been saturated, the addition of hydrogen would have been impossible. Observe in the graphic formula above that in the unsaturated hydrocarbon two covalent bonds, called a double bond, exist between the two atoms of carbon.

Formulas for Alkenes

The names and molecular formulas for the first six members of the ethylene or **ethene series** are listed in Table 34-3. Compare the ratio of carbon atoms to hydrogen atoms in each formula. In every case the ratio is one atom of carbon to two of hydrogen. In addition to having one double bond in the carbon chain, the members of the ethene series are alike in having the same general formula: C_nH_{2n}. For example, propene contains three carbon atoms and six (3×2) hydrogen atoms; butene contains four carbon atoms and eight (4×2) hydrogen atoms.

Further study shows that the formula for each succeeding member of the ethene series can be found by adding CH_2 to the formula before it. Thus, adding CH_2 to C_2H_4 (the formula for ethene) gives the formula for propene, C_3H_6. And the formula for butene, C_4H_8, is obtained by adding CH_2 to the formula for propene.

A study of Tables 34-1 and 34-3 also reveals a quick method for remembering the more recent I.U.C. name of each alkene. Simply change the *ane* ending of each corresponding alkane to *ene*. For example, but*ane*, with four carbon atoms, becomes but*ene*, and hex*ane* becomes hex*ene*.

Graphic Formulas and Isomers

The graphic formulas for the first four members of the ethene series (ethene, propene, butene, and pentene) are:

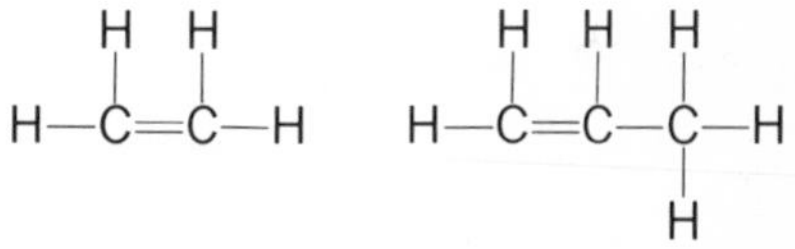

ethene
(ethylene)

propene

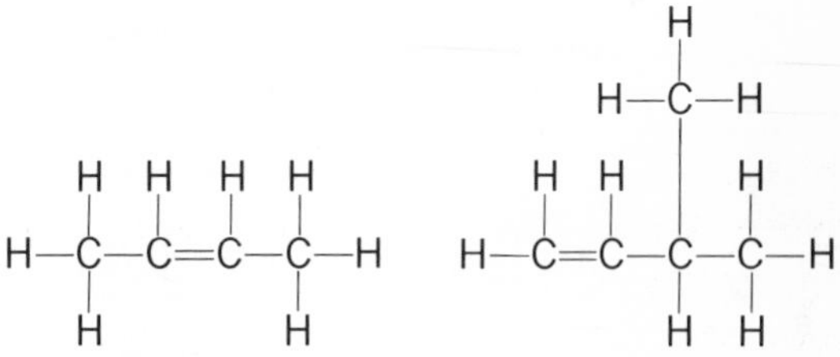

butene

pentene

Table 34-3   **THE ETHENE (ETHYLENE) SERIES**

Name	Molecular formula	Boiling point (°C)
Ethene (ethylene)	C_2H_4	−102.4
Propene	C_3H_6	−47.7
Butene	C_4H_8	−6.5
Pentene	C_5H_{10}	−3.7
Hexene	C_6H_{12}	63.5
Heptene	C_7H_{14}	93.1

THE HYDROCARBONS   583

These graphic formulas indicate several important things about alkenes. First, there is no alkene that contains only one carbon atom per molecule. Next, beginning with the alkenes that contain four carbon atoms, the double bond can appear at different places in the carbon chain. This effectively increases the number of isomers possible. Finally, the carbon atoms in the chain can be either branched or unbranched.

Many alkene isomers are known; many others are possible. These isomers can be named by their common names, derived names, or I.U.C. names. Today the derived names are used infrequently, but the I.U.C. names are increasingly important. Using the I.U.C. system, the butene isomer below is 1-butene.

$$
\begin{array}{ccccc}
 & H & H & H & H \\
 & | & | & | & | \\
H- & C & = C - & C - & C - H \\
 & & & | & | \\
 & & & H & H
\end{array}
$$

Had the double bond been between the second and third carbon atoms (as on page 583) the isomer would be 2-butene, since the number preceding the name indicates the position of the double bond.

Sources and Uses of Alkenes

Alkenes are usually obtained by the **catalytic cracking** of alkanes. Catalytic cracking is a process by which the atoms and bonds of the larger organic molecules are rearranged in the presence of suitable catalysts. In hydrocarbons this rearrangement is usually accompanied by the loss of hydrogen atoms and by the breaking down of the larger carbon chains into smaller chains.

Because alkenes are unsaturated, they are very active chemically. They react readily with hydrogen or with halogens and other alkenes to form saturated molecules or molecules that are more complex than themselves. Alkenes thus serve as the raw material from which many useful organic

34-8 The spherical tanks store large quantities of butadiene, an alkene used in GS-R (Buna) synthetic rubber.

compounds such as synthetic rubber (Fig. 34-8), polyethylene plastic, and benzene are produced.

Of particular interest is buta*diene* (C_4H_6) or 1,3-butadiene, used in the manufacture of GR-S rubber, a common synthetic rubber. Observe that butadiene contains two double bonds:

$$H-\underset{\underset{H}{|}}{C}=\underset{\underset{H}{|}}{C}-\underset{\underset{H}{|}}{C}=\underset{\underset{H}{|}}{C}-H$$

Such alkenes are called **alkadienes,** with the suffix-*diene* indicating two double bonds. Another example of an alkadiene is pentadiene, C_5H_8, or 1,4-pentadiene.

$$H-\underset{\underset{H}{|}}{C}=\underset{\underset{H}{|}}{C}-\underset{\underset{\underset{H}{|}}{\overset{H}{|}}}{C}-\underset{\underset{H}{|}}{C}=\underset{\underset{H}{|}}{C}-H$$

Alkynes

In 1836 Edmund Davy added water to some very impure potassium carbide; a chemical reaction occurred, producing a colorless gas found to have extremely useful chemical properties. The gas was **acetylene,** one of the first organic substances to be prepared from inorganic materials. Acetylene (C_2H_2) is the simplest of the third group of open-chain hydrocarbons, the group known as **alkynes.** Within this group, acetylene (Fig. 34-9) constitutes the first member of the **acetylene series.**

The graphic formula for acetylene, or *ethyne,* to use its I.U.C. name, is:

$$H-C\equiv C-H$$

Observe the triple bond between the two carbon atoms. A triple bond between two adjacent carbon atoms is characteristic of all alkynes.

Formulas for Alkynes

The molecular formula for ethyne is C_2H_2, corresponding to ethene, the simplest alkene. Compare the graphic formulas shown below for the two compounds. Notice that a molecule of eth*yne,* which has a triple bond, contains two less atoms of hydrogen than a molecule of eth*ene.*

Ethyne

34-9 Ethyne, or by its common name, acetylene, is the simplest member of the acetylene series of unsaturated alkynes. From the presence of only two hydrogen atoms in the molecule, you can reasonably predict that the two carbon atoms must be joined by a triple bond.

$$H-C\equiv C-H \qquad H-\underset{\underset{H}{|}}{\overset{\overset{H}{|}}{C}}=\underset{\underset{H}{|}}{\overset{\overset{H}{|}}{C}}-H$$

ethyne (acetylene)   ethene

The names and formulas for the first six members of the acetylene or **ethyne series** are given in Table 34-4. As with the alkanes and the alkenes, each of these formulas differs from the one preceding it in the series by CH_2. A general formula for the ethyne series can be determined from this list. Acetylene contains two carbon atoms and two $[(2 \times 2) - 2]$ hydrogen atoms; propyne, containing three carbon atoms, has four $[(3 \times 2) - 2]$ hydrogen atoms. In short, each member of the series contains twice as many hydrogen atoms, minus two, as it has carbon atoms. The general formula for the ethyne series is C_nH_{2n-2}.

Refer again to Table 34-4 to find the I.U.C. names for the alkynes. To remember them, simply change the *ane* ending of each corresponding alkane to *yne.* Prop*ane,* for example, becomes prop*yne,* and pent*ane* becomes pent*yne.*

Table 34-4   **THE ETHYNE (ACETYLENE) SERIES**

Name	Molecular formula	Boiling point (° C)
Ethyne (acetylene)	C_2H_2	−83.4
Propyne	C_3H_4	−23.3
Butyne	C_4H_6	8.6
Pentyne	C_5H_8	39.7
Hexyne	C_6H_{10}	71
Heptyne	C_7H_{12}	99.8

Graphic Formulas and Isomers

Graphic formulas for the first four members of the ethyne series (ethyne, propyne, butyne, and pentyne) are:

$$H-C\equiv C-H$$

ethyne
(acetylene)

$$H-\underset{\underset{H}{|}}{\overset{\overset{H}{|}}{C}}-C\equiv C-H$$

propyne

$$H-\underset{\underset{H}{|}}{\overset{\overset{H}{|}}{C}}-C\equiv C-\underset{\underset{H}{|}}{\overset{\overset{H}{|}}{C}}-H$$

butyne

$$H-C\equiv C-\underset{\underset{H}{|}}{\overset{\overset{H}{|}\!-\!\overset{|}{C}\!-\!H}{C}}\;\underset{\underset{H}{|}}{\overset{\overset{H}{|}}{C}}-H$$

pentyne

From graphic formulas you can determine three important facts about the alkynes. First, no alkyne containing one carbon atom per molecule exists. Second, starting with the alkynes containing four carbon atoms per molecule, the triple bond can occur at different places in the carbon chain. Finally, the atoms in the carbon chain can be branched or unbranched.

Many alkyne isomers are known and many more are theoretically possible. The I.U.C. name for the butyne isomer shown below is 1-butyne.

$$H-C\equiv C-\underset{\underset{H}{|}}{\overset{\overset{H}{|}}{C}}-\underset{\underset{H}{|}}{\overset{\overset{H}{|}}{C}}-H$$

Had the triple bond been between the second and third carbon atoms, the isomer would be 2-butyne, the number preceding the dash indicating the position of the triple bond.

Sources and Uses of Alkynes

Ethyne is the only alkyne prepared commercially in large quantities. It can be prepared by reacting water with calcium carbide. It is also obtained by cracking methane at the high temperatures of an electric arc.

$$2\,CH_4 \xrightarrow[\text{electricity}]{\Delta} C_2H_2 + 3\,H_2$$

The most important commercial use of ethyne is as a source of thousands of more complex organic compounds. The ethyne molecule is so unsaturated that it reacts with many substances, including hydrogen, halogen acids, and other alkynes. Ethyne is thus an excellent starting material for the preparation of acetic acid, ethyl and other alcohols, as well as several types of synthetic rubber and plastics (Fig. 34-10). It is also widely used in welding because of its high heat of combustion.

QUESTIONS AND PROBLEMS

1. (a) How does a saturated hydrocarbon differ from an unsaturated hydrocarbon? (b) Differentiate among the alkane, alkene, and alkyne series of hydrocarbons.

2. Write the graphic formula for (a) an alkene that contains ten carbon atoms, (b) an alkyne that contains twenty-two hydrogen atoms.

3. (a) Write graphic formulas for the isomers of the alkene C_5H_{10} and the alkyne C_5H_8. (b) Indicate whether each isomer is branched or unbranched, and give its I.U.C. name.

34-10 Without ethyne there might be no plastic coating on the record albums, no transparent wrapping—and even no unbreakable record.

4. (a) What is the common name for ethene? for ethyne? (b) What is an alkadiene?

5. Give the I.U.C. name for an (a) alkene with a molecular formula of $C_{10}H_{20}$, (b) alkyne with a molecular formula of C_9H_{16}.

RING HYDROCARBONS

In 1825 Michael Faraday began to study an oily, aromatic liquid he had detected in pipelines that carried illuminating gas. This oily substance, called **benzene,** has the molecular formula C_6H_6. From this formula you might predict that benzene would have the same chemical properties as unsaturated aliphatic hydrocarbons. For example, it might be expected to react readily with hydrogen to form a number of compounds. But this does not happen. Benzene and hydrogen react with difficulty; and when they do react they do so only under the influence of a catalyst at high temperature. From such observations it is clear to the chemist that the structure of benzene differs from that of the aliphatic hydrocarbons.

The question of just how the benzene molecule is constructed remained a mystery for more than 40 years. One of the scientists most concerned with determining its structure was Friedrich Kekulé von Stradonitz, a professor at the University of Bonn. In 1865, while dozing before the fire in his study at Ghent, Kekulé "visualized" the benzene molecule as a snake coiled back upon itself. In a flash of insight, he decided that benzene, instead of being an open chain like an aliphatic molecule, might be closed with the two ends of the molecule joined together to form a hexagonal ring. A great many chemical experiments and studies with X-ray diffraction have since confirmed that Kekulé's inspiration was correct. The benzene molecule does have the form of a hexagon, or a **benzene ring** (Fig. 34-11).

Aromatic Compounds—Benzene

All the organic compounds you have studied so far belong to the first of the two main divisions of hydrocarbons. All of them were aliphatic, or open-chain, hydrocarbons. Benzene is

Benzene

34-11 The structure of this simplest of all ring hydrocarbons eluded chemists for many years. Once the idea of a ring was established for benzene, the structure of thousands of related compounds derived from coal tar was readily determined.

the most important compound in the second of the two main divisions, the **ring hydrocarbons.** Most hydrocarbons with the ring structure are known as *aromatic compounds,* an indication that many of the compounds have a characteristic odor.

The structure of the benzene molecule is represented by either of the graphic formulas below:

As you see, single and double bonds alternate around the closed carbon chain. Moreover, two arrangements of these single and double bonds are possible. Kekulé suggested that the valence bonds in benzene shift back and forth between the two positions. In modern terminology the actual electron structure of a benzene molecule is known as a **resonance hybrid,** a blend of the two structures (page 111). For simplicity, chemists usually use either, but not both, graphic formulas to represent the fundamental aromatic hydrocarbon. For convenience, they frequently represent the ring structure of benzene and other aromatic compounds by the symbol shown below:

Aromatic Compounds—Condensed Ring Types

A number of aromatic substances obtained from coal tar, called coal-tar derivatives, have molecules with two, and sometimes three, rings. These compounds are frequently **condensed ring structures** in which two or three carbon atoms are common to the two ring structures. The simplest condensed ring hydrocarbon is naphthalene.

naphthalene

It consists essentially of two benzene rings condensed, or fused, together. You are probably familiar with naphthalene ($C_{10}H_8$) as a white crystalline solid with the odor of moth balls. It sublimes at room temperature to form a gas that destroys moth larvae.

Anthracene ($C_{14}H_{10}$) is an aromatic compound in which three benzene rings are fused.

anthracene

It is a white crystalline solid that is used to produce dyes and other organic compounds.

Sources and Uses of Aromatic Compounds

The chief source of benzene and other aromatic compounds is coal tar, a by-product of the manufacture of coke. Benzene is also produced during the catalytic cracking of hydrocarbon molecules from petroleum. It can be made in the laboratory by passing ethyne or various alkenes through a heated tube. At high temperature these smaller alkene molecules **polymerize,** that is, add onto one another, forming more complex molecules. The process of **polymerization,** by which molecules add onto one another, is of utmost importance in producing numerous organic compounds studied in subsequent chapters.

Today, aromatic coal-tar derivatives like benzene are of the greatest industrial importance. Almost all modern dyes, for example, are synthetic dyes made from coal-tar derivatives (Fig. 34-12). Yet before 1856 no synthetic dyes existed. In that year an eighteen-year-old English chemist, William Perkin, founded the aniline dye industry by accident. Perkin was trying to synthesize quinine from a coal-tar derivative. Instead, he produced mauve, the first synthetic dye. Aro-

34-12 In these large vats synthetic dyes are made from coal-tar derivatives. Virtually all dyes used today are colorfast synthetic dyes.

matic compounds are also used today in the manufacture of explosives, perfumes, photographic developers, and synthetic vitamins.

Cycloalkanes

Unsaturated aromatic hydrocarbons are not the only organic compounds having a ring structure. This structure is also found in **cycloalkanes,** saturated ring compounds related to the alkanes. The simplest of the cycloalkanes is the gas cyclopropane (C_3H_6) which is used as an anesthetic. The graphic formula for cyclopropane is:

cyclopropane

The general molecular formula for the cycloalkanes is the same as that for the alkenes, C_nH_{2n}. Is not cyclopropane an isomer of propene? The cycloalkanes have a ring structure, while the alkenes are open-chain compounds.

Until now, your attention has been focused on some of the simpler hydrocarbons. In the next chapter you will see how these hydrocarbons, particularly the unsaturated ones, serve as the starting point for numerous organic reactions which result in many of the products in widest

daily use. Before going on, however, it might be well to study Table 34-5, which summarizes the relationships among the aliphatic hydrocarbons.

QUESTIONS AND PROBLEMS

1. How do ring hydrocarbons differ structurally from open-chain hydrocarbons?

2. Draw one graphic formula for the fundamental aromatic compound. If another graphic formula is possible, explain why.

3. (a) Write the molecular formula for the cycloalkane containing six carbon atoms. (b) Draw the graphic formula for a condensed-ring hydrocarbon having the formula $C_{18}H_{12}$.

VALUE OF THE CONCEPT

THE CONCEPT

Organic chemistry is the chemistry of carbon compounds. Many organic compounds exist because a carbon atom with four valence electrons can form four covalent bonds with other elements and can also link covalently with other carbon atoms. In addition, isomers—molecules with the same formula but different spatial arrangements of its atoms—are possible. Organic compounds usually melt at relatively low temperatures, decompose easily, are nonelectrolytes, are combustible, and react slowly except during combustion.

Several methods of writing formulas for organic compounds are used: molecular formulas, graphic formulas using a dash (—) to represent each shared pair of electrons, and structural formulas in which each carbon atom with all non-carbon atoms attached is written as a group.

The hydrocarbons which contain only carbon and hydrogen atoms are divided into two types: the aliphatic or open-chain, and the aromatic or ring type. In aliphatic hydrocarbons the carbon atoms at the ends of the chain are not bonded to

Table 34-5 **COMPARISON OF ALIPHATIC HYDROCARBONS**

Saturated	Unsaturated	
Alkanes	*Alkenes*	*Alkynes*
(Single bonds)	*(1 Double bond)*	*(1 Triple bond)*
C_nH_{2n+2}	C_nH_{2n}	C_nH_{2n-2}
CH_4 Methane	—	—
C_2H_6 Ethane	C_2H_4 Ethene	C_2H_2 Ethyne
C_3H_8 Propane	C_3H_6 Propene	C_3H_4 Propyne

each other; all the carbon atoms are joined in aromatic hydrocarbons.

The alkanes are open-chain, saturated hydrocarbons. That is, all the bonds between carbon atoms are single bonds, and each remaining valence electron is shared with a hydrogen atom. The general formula for the homologous series of alkanes or paraffins is C_nH_{2n+2}. Most alkanes are obtained from petroleum and natural gas.

The alkenes are open-chain, unsaturated hydrocarbons containing double bonds. In the ethylene or ethene series only one double bond is found within each chain. The general formula for the ethene homologous series is C_nH_{2n}. The alkynes are open-chain, unsaturated hydrocarbons containing triple bonds. In the acetylene or ethyne series only one triple bond is found in each chain. The general formula for the ethyne series is C_nH_{2n-2}. The alkenes and alkynes are unsaturated organic compounds, since the double and triple bonds between carbon atoms in these compounds enables them to react with hydrogen.

The members of each homologous series of open-chain hydrocarbons differ from each other by a CH_2 group. Adding CH_2 to the formula for one member of a series gives the formula of the next highest member.

The most important aromatic compound is benzene, C_6H_6, in which the six carbon atoms are arranged to form a hexagon bonded alternately by single and double bonds. Along with benzene, condensed ring compounds obtained from coal tar are important in the preparation of dyes, artificially prepared vitamins, and explosives. Cycloalkanes, or ring alkanes, also exist.

Several systems are in use for naming organic compounds. Today the I.U.C. or Geneva system is gaining wide acceptance.

USING THE CONCEPT

Using the Basic Concept

1. For many years organic compounds were considered to be only those related to living processes? (a) Why? (b) How do we define organic chemistry today?

2. (a) What are the characteristic chemical and physical properties of organic compounds? (b) Why do so many organic compounds exist?
3. (a) What is a hydrocarbon? (b) Describe, in general terms, the two main types of hydrocarbons.
4. (a) Give three characteristics of alkanes. (b) List three examples and give both their molecular and structural formulas.
5. What evidence do you have that natural gas and petroleum are mixtures of hydrocarbons?
6. (a) Write the names and molecular formulas for the first twelve members of the alkane series. (b) What is the general formula for this homologous series?
7. Draw the graphic formula for butane, isobutane, and three isomers of pentane.
8. (a) Why is the term *straight chain* not truly descriptive of most aliphatic compounds? (b) Why is the term *open chain* more appropriate?
9. (a) How are the structure of cyclopropane and propane similar? (b) How do they differ?
10. Write the structural formula and draw the graphic formula for each of the first five members of the ethene series. [Draw the straight-chain (normal) isomer when several are possible.]
11. Give the I.U.C. name for each of the following: ethylene, acetylene, isobutane.
12. How could you prove that ethene molecules are unsaturated?
13. (a) Draw the graphic formula for each isomer of butene. (b) What is the general formula for the members of the ethene homologous series?
14. (a) Compare the graphic formula for butadiene with that for butene. (b) Are both compounds members of the same homologous series? Support your answer.
15. (a) Draw the graphic formula for acetylene. (b) Do isomers of acetylene exist?
16. (a) Draw the graphic formula and write

the structural formula for the first five members of the ethyne series. (Draw the straight-chain isomer in each case.) (b) What is the general formula for the ethyne homologous series?

17. (a) Draw both ring formulas for benzene. (b) Which of these structures best represents benzene molecules as they are known to exist? (c) How is the structure "abbreviated"?

18. Define each of the following terms: *resonance hybrid, polymerization, condensed ring structures, coal-tar derivative, fractional distillation.*

19. (a) List several uses of ring compounds. (b) Why are they always, if sometimes inaccurately, referred to as aromatics?

Relating Terms Within the Concept

Select the letter of the term in the right column that is most closely related to each term in the left column. Do not use a term more than once.

COLUMN A	COLUMN B
1. methyl	a. a triple bond between two carbon atoms
2. methane	
3. ethene series	
4. isomers	b. benzene
5. aliphatic	c. coal-tar derivatives
6. aromatic	
7. acetylene	d. C_nH_{2n}
8. ethyne series	e. C_nH_{2n-2}
9. graphic formula	f. dash represents pair of shared electrons
	g. ethylene
	h. open chain
	i. organic radical
	j. ring compounds with general formula of C_nH_{2n}
	k. similar empirical or molecular formulas
	l. simplest hydrocarbon

Solving Problems Within the Concept

1. Compare the number of grams of O_2 needed to burn 1 mole of each of the following: ethane, ethene, ethyne.

2. Draw the graphic formula for each of the following: normal hexane, 2-hexane, 2-methyl pentane, 2,2-dimethyl pentane.

3. What volume of methane (**STP**) is obtained by reacting of 10 grams of sodium acetate with an excess of soda lime?

4. Draw graphic formulas for each of the following: propene; 2-butene; 2-butyne; 1,3-butadiene; 2,3-dimethylbutane.

5. (a) Draw the graphic formula for each isomer of C_6H_{14}. (b) Give the I.U.C. and derived name for each isomer.

Applying the Concept

1. How are the ammonium ion and the methane molecule similar? different?

2. The substance commonly called "wax" is usually paraffin, a mixture of high molecular weight alkanes. Compare the physical and chemical properties of these alkanes with those of methane.

3. Draw the graphic formula and give the I.U.C. name of an alkene that is not a member of the ethene series.

4. (a) Write the molecular formula for an alkane containing seventy carbon atoms. (b) Do likewise for a member of the ethene series having seventy carbon atoms per molecule.

5. When a reaction occurs between the permanganate ion and an unsaturated hydrocarbon, the violet color of the permanganate fades. Why?

Reading Further

A Direct Entry into Organic Chemistry, by John Read, New York, Harper & Row, 1960. An excellent introduction to the subject.

"Organic Chemical Reactions," by John D. Roberts, *Scientific American,* November 1957. Describes how the chemist traces the course or the mechanisms of reactions of simple organic compounds.

35

Hydrocarbon Derivatives

At the turn of the century the horse and buggy was still the usual means of transportation. The family wash and the dinner dishes had to be done without the help of detergents. Today coal is giving way to petroleum and natural gas for heating homes. Satellites are hurled into space by powerful liquid or solid fuels, some of which are specifically developed for that purpose. In these and many other respects our lives are different today because of substances which have been derived from hydrocarbons.

SUBSTITUTION AND ADDITION PRODUCTS

Most of the thousands of organic compounds are derived from the relatively simple aliphatic and aromatic hydrocarbons by a series of reactions. The starting point for most of these *hydrocarbon derivatives* is either benzene, ethyne, or one of the simple alkanes.

As an example of the latter, consider what happens if you bring an open bottle of ammonium hydroxide close to the mouth of a bottle of methane (Fig. 35-1). No reaction is observed. Now if a few drops of bromine (Br_2) are added cautiously to the methane, the reddish color of the bromine disappears. Could colorless hydrogen bromide (HBr) have been produced? If you again bring the bottle of ammonium hydroxide to the mouth of the other bottle, the white smoke of ammonium bromide (NH_4Br) appears. As this smoke could only have been formed by a combination of hydrogen bromide and ammonia, the reaction between the methane and the bromine must have produced HBr. Further chemical tests show that another and more important reaction also has occurred. In the formation of the hydro-

gen bromide, the removal of the hydrogen atom from each methane molecule (CH_4) leaves a methyl radical (CH_3). This radical reacts with the bromine in the solution to produce a gas, methyl bromide (CH_3Br).

This reaction can be shown by an electron dot equation.

$$\overset{\displaystyle H}{\underset{\displaystyle H}{H:\overset{..}{C}:H}} + :\overset{..}{\underset{..}{Br}}:\overset{..}{\underset{..}{Br}}: \longrightarrow \overset{\displaystyle H}{\underset{\displaystyle H}{H:\overset{..}{C}:\overset{..}{\underset{..}{Br}}:}} + H:\overset{..}{\underset{..}{Br}}:$$

The following equations, using either molecular or graphic formulas, are more frequently used to represent an organic reaction, such as that between methane and bromine:

$$CH_4 \quad + \quad Br_2 \quad \longrightarrow \quad CH_3Br{\uparrow} \quad + \quad HBr{\uparrow}$$

$$\underset{\text{methane}}{H-\overset{\displaystyle H}{\underset{\displaystyle H}{C}}-H} + \underset{\text{bromine}}{Br-Br} \longrightarrow \underset{\text{methyl bromide}}{H-\overset{\displaystyle H}{\underset{\displaystyle H}{C}}-Br} + \underset{\text{hydrogen bromide}}{H-Br}$$

The graphic formula equation indicates that during the reaction a single bromine atom from each bromine molecule (Br_2) is *substituted* for a hydrogen atom in each methane molecule, forming methyl bromide (Fig. 35-2). The hydrogen atom that has been replaced by the bromine atom combines with the second bromine atom of Br_2 to form hydrogen bromide.

This reaction between methane and bromine

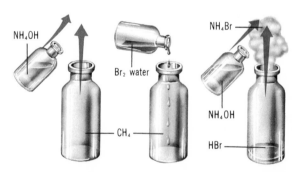

35-1 Ammonium hydroxide produces no reaction with methane (left) but serves as an indicator (right) that the color-fading reaction of bromine with methane (center) has produced hydrogen bromide.

592   CHEMISTRY OF CARBON COMPOUNDS

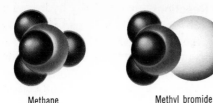

Methane   Methyl bromide

35-2 To produce a molecule of methyl bromide, one atom of bromine replaces one of the three atoms of hydrogen in a methane molecule.

is a **hydrocarbon substitution reaction.** *During substitution reactions* many types of *atoms,* including halogen atoms, *can be substituted for one or more hydrogen atoms* in an alkane or certain other *organic compounds.* The organic product of such a substitution reaction is called a **substitution product.** If the substitution reaction is between an alkane and a halogen, as in our example, the hydrocarbon derivative that results is called an **alkyl halide.** Thus, methyl bromide is an alkyl halide.

Halogen Substitution Reactions

Not one, but four different alkyl halides can be produced when chlorine and methane react in the presence of sunlight. As shown below, these are methyl chloride (CH_3Cl), a colorless gas used as a refrigerant; methylene chloride (CH_2Cl_2), a liquid solvent for paint; chloroform ($CHCl_3$), a liquid used as an anesthetic; and carbon tetrachloride (CCl_4), a dry-cleaning agent.

$$H-\overset{\displaystyle H}{\underset{\displaystyle H}{C}}-Cl$$

methyl chloride
(monochloro-
methane)

$$H-\overset{\displaystyle Cl}{\underset{\displaystyle H}{C}}-Cl$$

methylene chloride
(dichloromethane)

$$H-\overset{\displaystyle Cl}{\underset{\displaystyle Cl}{C}}-Cl$$

chloroform
(trichloro-
methane)

$$Cl-\overset{\displaystyle Cl}{\underset{\displaystyle Cl}{C}}-Cl$$

carbon tetrachloride
(tetrachloromethane)

The equations for the formation of these substitution products indicate that the replacement of the

hydrogen atoms by halogen atoms can continue until all the hydrogen atoms are replaced.

$$CH_4 + Cl_2 \longrightarrow CH_3Cl + HCl\uparrow$$
$$CH_3Cl + Cl_2 \longrightarrow CH_2Cl_2 + HCl\uparrow$$
$$CH_2Cl_2 + Cl_2 \longrightarrow CHCl_3 + HCl\uparrow$$
$$CHCl_3 + Cl_2 \longrightarrow CCl_4 + HCl\uparrow$$

In practice, the product of the reaction between methane and chlorine is a mixture of all four alkyl halides. The temperature of the reaction determines the percentage of each compound.

The reaction between chlorine and methane is explosive. So are the reactions in which certain other members of the alkane series react directly with halogens to form alkyl halides, notably the lighter alkanes and fluorine. Because the direct reactions are explosive, these alkyl halides are usually produced *by indirect means.* For example, carbon tetrachloride is produced indirectly by reacting carbon disulfide and chlorine in the presence of iron as a catalyst:

$$CS_2 + 3\,Cl_2 \xrightarrow{Fe} CCl_4 + S_2Cl_2$$

$$S{=}C{=}S + 3\,Cl_2 \xrightarrow{Fe} Cl-\overset{\displaystyle Cl}{\underset{\displaystyle Cl}{C}}-Cl + S_2Cl_2$$

carbon   carbon
disulfide   tetrachloride

Another example of a compound produced by indirect substitution is CCl_2F_2, one of the so-called **Freons.** The Freons are a group of alkyl halides which contain both fluorine and chlorine atoms and are used as refrigerants and propellants (Fig. 35-3). Dichlorodifluoromethane (CCl_2F_2), to use its I.U.C. name, may be produced indirectly by the reaction between carbon tetrachloride and antimony trifluoride:

$$3\,CCl_4 + SbF_3 \longrightarrow 3\,CCl_2F_2 + SbCl_3$$

$$(3)Cl-\overset{\displaystyle Cl}{\underset{\displaystyle Cl}{C}}-Cl + SbF_3 \longrightarrow (3)F-\overset{\displaystyle F}{\underset{\displaystyle Cl}{C}}-Cl + SbCl_3$$

carbon   antimony   dichloro-   antimony
tetrachloride   tri-   difluoro-   tri-
    fluoride   methane   chloride

35-3 This spray can of white paint, like many other products available in spray cans, uses a Freon as the propellant. How does it work?

Naming Halogen Derivatives

The chlorine substitution products of methane have been known for some time and are relatively simple substances. They are usually, and fairly adequately, described by their common names. However, with these and particularly with more complex hydrocarbon derivatives, the I.U.C. naming system is useful. In the common names for hydrocarbon derivatives, the name of the particular organic radical involved figures prominently. For example, CH_3Cl is commonly called *methyl* chloride. In the I.U.C. system, the names of radicals are not used. Instead the prefixes *mono-, di-, tri-*, and so forth are employed to show the number of atoms of another element attached to the hydrocarbon molecule.

In halogen derivatives the prefix is followed by the first syllable of the halogen name plus the letter *o*. Thus methyl chloride (CH_3Cl) becomes monochloromethane, while methylene chloride (CH_2Cl_2) becomes dichloromethane. Chloroform ($CHCl_3$) becomes trichloromethane, while carbon tetrachloride becomes tetrachloromethane. Under the I.U.C. system, the compound CH_2F_2 is difluoromethane; its graphic formula is:

$$H-\overset{\overset{\displaystyle H}{|}}{\underset{\underset{\displaystyle F}{|}}{C}}-F$$

Addition Reactions

If a few drops of bromine are added to a bottle of ethene, the reddish color of the bromine again disappears, indicating that a reaction has taken place (Fig. 35-4). But now if a bottle of ammonium hydroxide is brought close to the first bottle, the expected white smoke of ammonium bromide does not appear. Apparently this reaction has not produced HBr. In this instance the bromine does *not* substitute for hydrogen. To understand just what does happen, remember that ethene molecules, unlike those of methane, are unsaturated. Here, instead of substitution, two bromine atoms are *added to* each ethene molecule:

$$CH_2CH_2 \quad + \quad Br_2 \quad \longrightarrow \quad CH_2BrCH_2Br$$

$$\underset{\text{ethane}}{H-\overset{\overset{\displaystyle H}{|}}{C}=\overset{\overset{\displaystyle H}{|}}{C}-H} + \underset{\text{bromine}}{Br-Br} \longrightarrow \underset{\substack{\text{1,2-dibromoethane}\\\text{(ethylene dibromide)}}}{H-\overset{\overset{\displaystyle H}{|}}{\underset{\underset{\displaystyle Br}{|}}{C}}-\overset{\overset{\displaystyle H}{|}}{\underset{\underset{\displaystyle Br}{|}}{C}}-H}$$

As the equation indicates, the bromine causes the double bond of the ethene molecule to break. By comparing the graphic formulas for ethene and dibromoethane (ethylene dibromide) shown above, you see that while the ethene is unsaturated, the dibromoethane is saturated.

Because unsaturated hydrocarbons have double or triple bonds, their reactions with other types of atoms are usually not substitution reactions. Instead they are **addition reactions.** The

35-4 When bromine is added to ethane (left), a color-fading change indicates a chemical reaction. Ammonium hydroxide does not react with the product (right), indicating that hydrogen bromide was not produced.

organic product formed by an addition reaction is called an **addition product.** Though halogen derivatives are the most important products of addition reactions, they are not the only ones: many types of atoms can be combined with an unsaturated hydrocarbon in an addition reaction.

The graphic formula of dibromoethane shown above is only one of two isomers. Actually, it is 1,2-dibromoethane. In the second isomer both bromine atoms are attached to the same carbon atom. This 1,1-dibromoethane isomer is more difficult to prepare and less widely used.

Br H
| |
Br—C—C—H
| |
H H

1,1-dibromoethane

Substitution Products and Functional Groups

The more common hydrocarbon substitution derivatives are characterized by the presence of particular groups of atoms called **functional groups.** Functional groups, such as the —OH group, the —COOH group, and the —CHO group, are clusters of atoms, covalently bonded together. They are chiefly responsible for the chemical properties of each type of derivative. All alcohols, for example, contain the —OH or **hydroxyl** (*not* hydroxide) functional group. It is this group which makes the common alcohols soluble in water. Organic acids, on the other hand, contain the —COOH or **carboxyl** group. This group is responsible for the fact that organic acids ionize slightly in water to form hydronium ions. All aldehydes, such as formaldehyde, contain the —CHO or **formyl** functional group. There are also functional groups which contain no carbon atoms. Among these are the —NH₂ or amino group and the —NO₂ or nitro group.

Organic compounds (Fig. 35-5) are classified according to the type and number of the functional group, or groups, in their formulas. The names of some common organic compounds and the formulas, graphic formulas, and names of some organic functional groups are given in Table 35-1. In addition, the table contains an ex-

35-5 The technician is preparing an ester by adding an organic acid to an alcohol. Three other organic compounds—classified according to their functional groups as an ether, an aldehyde, and a ketone—also appear on the table.

ample of each class of organic compounds characterized by the different functional groups, and the formula for each compound.

The preparation of organic compounds usually involves more than simply attaching certain functional groups to certain organic radicals. However, the formulas for most organic compounds *can be thought of* as consisting of the formulas for one or more radicals, plus the formulas for one or more functional groups. In short, each organic compound is considered the functional group derivative of a particular hydrocarbon. Methyl alcohol, for example, has the formula CH₃OH. This formula combines the formula for the methyl radical (CH₃) with the formula for the hydroxyl group (—OH). Methyl alcohol is considered to be the hydroxyl derivative of methane.

QUESTIONS AND PROBLEMS

1. (a) Write graphic formula equations to indicate the addition of bromine to propene and the substitution of bromine in propane. (b) Why can't you indicate the addition of bromine to propane?

Table 35-1   ORGANIC COMPOUNDS AND FUNCTIONAL GROUPS

Class of compounds	Functional group	Formula	Graphic formula	Example of compound	Formula of compound
Alcohols	Hydroxyl	—OH	—OH	Methyl alcohol (methanol)	CH_3OH
Aldehydes	Formyl	—CHO	$-\overset{\overset{\displaystyle O}{\|\|}}{C}-H$	Formaldehyde (methanal)	HCHO
Ketones	Carbonyl	=CO	$-\overset{\overset{\displaystyle O}{\|\|}}{C}-$	Acetone (propanone)	CH_3COCH_3
Organic acids	Carboxyl	—COOH	$-\overset{\overset{\displaystyle O}{\|\|}}{C}-OH$	Acetic acid (ethanoic acid)	CH_3COOH
Ethers	Oxy	=O	—O—	Diethyl ether	$C_2H_5OC_2H_5$
Esters	- - -	—COO—	$-\overset{\overset{\displaystyle O}{\|\|}}{C}-O-$	Ethyl acetate Glyceryl stearate	$C_2H_5COOCH_3$ $(C_{17}H_{35}COO)_3C_3H_5$

2. Write the molecular and graphic formulas for dichloroethane and trifluoromethane.

3. (a) Write the molecular formula for ethyl alcohol. (b) Give the name and formula of its functional group.

ALCOHOLS

Most people incorrectly associate the name *alcohol* with a particular compound, the ethyl alcohol found in wines and liquors. But ethyl alcohol is only one of hundreds of substances that make up the class of compounds known as **alcohols.** The wood alcohol that frequently causes blindness or even death if taken internally, rubbing alcohol, and even glycerine produced in the intestine by the digestion of fat are all alcohols. All of them are hydroxyl derivatives of hydrocarbons. In every alcohol one or more hydroxyl (—OH) groups are substituted for one or more of the hydrogen atoms of a hydrocarbon (Fig. 35-6).

Methanol

Methyl alcohol, or wood alcohol (CH_3OH), is the simplest of all alcohols. For many years this alcohol was obtained from the distillation of wood during the preparation of charcoal, hence its name "wood alcohol." Today methyl alcohol is usually synthesized by the reaction between carbon monoxide and hydrogen in the presence of a zinc oxide catalyst:

$$CO + 2\,H_2 \xrightarrow[350°\,C]{ZnO} CH_3OH$$
$$\text{methyl alcohol}$$

It finds wide use as a solvent for shellac and certain other lacquers, and is the starting material in the production of many organic compounds.

According to the I.U.C. naming system, all

Methyl alcohol

35-6   In a molecule of methyl alcohol, one hydroxyl (—OH) group is substituted for one atom of hydrogen in a methane molecule. The oxygen molecule of the —OH group is bonded directly to a carbon atom.

alcohols take the name of the hydrocarbon to which they are related, plus the ending **-ol.** Thus methyl alcohol becomes **methanol.** Note carefully in the following graphic formula for methanol that although the oxygen and hydrogen atoms of the hydroxyl group are covalently bonded, there is no dash between these two atoms.

$$
\begin{array}{c}
\text{H} \\
| \\
\text{H}-\text{C}-\text{OH} \\
| \\
\text{H}
\end{array}
$$

methanol

This procedure is used to indicate that these atoms together make up a functional group, and it is usually followed in writing graphic formulas in which functional groups appear.

Ethanol

A second important alcohol is ethyl alcohol (C_2H_5OH or CH_3CH_2OH). This is considered to be the hydroxyl derivative of ethane and is given the I.U.C. name **ethanol.**

$$
\begin{array}{cc}
\text{H} & \text{H} \\
| & | \\
\text{H}-\text{C}-\text{C}-\text{OH} \\
| & | \\
\text{H} & \text{H}
\end{array}
$$

ethanol

For centuries ethanol was obtained by the fermentation of natural sugars and starches. Grapes, for example, have yeast cells growing on their skins. When the ripened grapes are picked and mashed, the enzyme *zymase* produced by these yeast cells causes the grape sugars to ferment, forming wine. Wine contains 12 to 20 percent by volume of ethanol. Another major source of ethanol is the fermentation of sugars found in molasses, a by-product of sugar refining.

A common name for ethanol is "grain alcohol." Along with carbon dioxide, it can be obtained by the fermentation of sugars from wheat and other grains. To do so, however, the starches and complex sugars in the grains must first be converted into simple sugars, such as glucose ($C_6H_{12}O_6$) by enzyme action.

$$C_6H_{12}O_6 \longrightarrow 2\,C_2H_5OH + 2\,CO_2$$

glucose · · · · · · · · · · ethanol

The ethanol is separated from the grain mash by distillation.

Ethanol is also prepared industrially by an addition reaction in which sulfuric acid is used instead of a halogen. The reaction between ethene and the sulfuric acid produces ethyl hydrogen sulfate. This addition product is then reacted with water to produce ethanol:

$$
\begin{array}{cc}
\text{H} & \text{H} \\
\text{C}=\text{C} \\
| & | \\
\text{H} & \text{H}
\end{array}
+ H_2SO_4 \longrightarrow
\begin{array}{cc}
\text{H} & \text{H} \\
| & | \\
\text{H}-\text{C}-\text{C}-\text{SO}_4\text{H} \\
| & | \\
\text{H} & \text{H}
\end{array}
$$

ethene · · · · · · · · · · · · · · · · ethyl hydrogen sulfate

$$
\begin{array}{cc}
\text{H} & \text{H} \\
| & | \\
\text{H}-\text{C}-\text{C}-\text{SO}_4\text{H} \\
| & | \\
\text{H} & \text{H}
\end{array}
+ H_2O \longrightarrow
$$

ethyl hydrogen sulfate

$$
\begin{array}{cc}
\text{H} & \text{H} \\
| & | \\
\text{H}-\text{C}-\text{C}-\text{OH} \\
| & | \\
\text{H} & \text{H}
\end{array}
+ H_2SO_4
$$

ethanol

Ethanol, or ethyl alcohol, is found in all alcoholic beverages. To render ordinary ethyl alcohol unfit to drink, substances like methanol, benzene, or pyridine are often added. The resulting substance is referred to as **"denatured alcohol"** (Fig. 35-7). As an industrial solvent, ethanol is second in importance only to water. It is also important in medicinal solutions such as tincture of iodine.

Isomers of Alcohols

Propanol, or propyl alcohol, the alcohol derived from the alkane propane, has two isomers. The molecular formula for both isomers is C_3H_7OH; but their structures, as seen by the location of the hydroxyl group in their graphic formulas, are quite different.

H H H
| | |
H—C—C—C—OH
| | |
H H H

normal propanol
1-propanol

H OH H
| | |
H—C—C—C—H
| | |
H H H

isopropanol
2-propanol

H H
| |
H—C—C—H
| |
OH OH

ethylene glycol

In normal propanol (1-propanol) the hydroxyl group is attached to a carbon atom at the end of the carbon chain. In the other isomer, isopropanol (2-propanol), the hydroxyl group is attached to the central carbon atom. A 70 percent solution of isopropanol (by volume) in water is sold as rubbing alcohol. All alcohols, such as propyl alcohol, whose formulas contain three or more carbon atoms in the chain, have two or more isomers.

Polyhydroxy Alcohols

Different types of alcohols are distinguished from one another by the number of —OH groups they contain. Those (such as methanol and ethanol) that contain only one hydroxyl group are called *mono*hydroxy alcohols. Those with two or three hydroxyl groups are called *poly*hydroxy alcohols—the Greek prefix *poly* signifying "many."

Alcohols that have two hydroxyl groups are called *di*hydroxy alcohols. Ethylene glycol [$C_2H_4(OH)_2$] is an example of a dihydroxy alcohol.

35-7 Ethanol or ethyl alcohol, in the barrel at the right, is found in drugs and alcoholic beverages. When denatured, as in the barrel at the left, the alcohol is no longer fit for human consumption.

Though it is prepared commercially by several different reactions, all result in the ultimate addition of two hydroxyl radicals to ethene.

H H
| |
H—C=C—H + 2 (—OH) ⟶

H H
| |
H—C—C—H
| |
OH OH

Look at the label on a can of permanent antifreeze used in automobile radiators. The antifreeze probably contains ethylene glycol. The boiling point of ethylene glycol is 197° C. This is much higher than that of water, and ethylene glycol does not evaporate as quickly as methanol, an alcohol used as a temporary antifreeze.

Glycerol or glycerine [$C_3H_5(OH)_3$] is an example of a *tri*hydroxy alcohol; each molecule contains three hydroxyl groups.

H
|
H—C—OH
|
H—C—OH
|
H—C—OH
|
H

glycerol

Glycerol is formed when soaps are prepared from fats and alkalies. One of the many uses of glycerol is in the manufacture of glyceryl trinitrate [$C_3H_5(ONO_2)_3$], the explosive known as nitroglycerine. It is a sweet, syrupy liquid that is the essential constituent of dynamite. It is mixed with nitrocellulose for use as a rocket propellant.

QUESTIONS AND PROBLEMS

1. How does normal butanol differ from the other isomers of butanol?

2. (a) Write the molecular and graphic formula for each alcohol: methanol, 1-butanol, and 3-pentanol. (b) How is ethanol prepared?

3. Differentiate between each of the following pairs of terms: (a) *monohydroxy alcohol* and *polyhydroxy alcohol* (b) *wood alcohol* and *grain alcohol* (c) *ethylene glycol* and *glycerol*.

ALCOHOL DERIVATIVES

Alcohols are produced commercially in very large quantities both because alcohols are extremely important in themselves and because their derivatives find wide use. The derivatives of the alcohols, which themselves are hydrocarbon derivatives, can be separated into four classes: **aldehydes, ketones, organic acids,** and **ethers.** The first three of these may be produced from alcohols by oxidation reactions, the last by dehydration.

Aldehydes

To prepare an *aldehyde, try the following:*

Place a small amount of methanol in a test tube and notice the identifying odor of the alcohol. Now heat a coil of copper wire in a Bunsen burner and thrust the wire into the

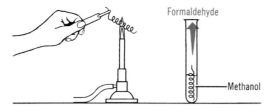

methanol. Repeat this several times, and notice the odor again. Has the original odor changed to the irritating odor of formaldehyde?

No doubt you are familiar with the odor from experiences in biology; aqueous solutions of formaldehyde, a gas at room temperature, are used to preserve biological specimens. The heated copper wire held in the alcohol, in the presence of air, brings about the mild oxidation of methanol

Formaldehyde

35-8 A molecule of formaldehyde contains a formyl or —CHO functional group and an atom of hydrogen. Both the oxygen atom and the hydrogen atom in the functional group of this and other aldehydes are attached directly to the same carbon atom (the only carbon atom in this aldehyde).

to formaldehyde. Formaldehyde (HCHO) is the simplest of a class of organic compounds called *aldehydes.* Formaldehyde (Fig. 35-8) can also be prepared by passing hot methanol and air over hot copper, or by treating methanol with a mild oxidizing agent.

$$CH_3OH + [O] \longrightarrow HCHO + H_2O$$

methanol   from oxidizing agent   formaldehyde (methanal)

$$\underset{\substack{H \\ | \\ H—C—OH \\ | \\ H}}{} + [O] \longrightarrow \underset{\substack{O \\ \| \\ H—C—H}}{} + H_2O$$

formaldehyde

The —CHO functional group in the graphic formula for formaldehyde is characteristic of all aldehydes. This **formyl** group always appears at the end of the carbon chain. If R is used to represent any organic radical, the general formula for aldehydes can be written **R—CHO.** (It is *never* written R—COH.) As shown below, the oxygen atom in the formyl group is always attached directly to the carbon atom by means of a double bond.

$$\underset{\substack{O \\ \| \\ —C—H}}{}$$

formyl group

Aldehydes, as a group, are prepared by the mild oxidation of *primary alcohols,* alcohols like methanol and ethanol in which no more than one organic radical is attached to the same carbon atom as the hydroxyl group.

primary alcohol + O_2 $\longrightarrow$ aldehyde + water

$$2\,R\overset{\displaystyle H}{\underset{\displaystyle H}{-\overset{|}{\underset{|}{C}}-}}OH\ +\ O_2\ \longrightarrow\ 2\,R\overset{\displaystyle O}{-\overset{\|}{C}-}H + 2\,H_2O$$

When aldehydes are prepared by the oxidation of alcohols, the oxygen essentially removes hydrogen from the alcohol to form water. This process is called **dehydrogenation.** The name *aldehyde,* in fact, is a contraction of the two words "*al*cohol *dehyd*rogenation."

In the I.U.C. system, an aldehyde takes its name from the name of the related hydrocarbon, followed by the ending *-al.* Thus HCHO, formaldehyde, is *methanal,* and CH_3CHO is *ethanal.*

Formaldehyde and other aldehydes are important in the preparation of resins and plastics. For example, the first Bakelite plastic was made by reacting formaldehyde and an aromatic compound called phenol. Ethanal, or acetaldehyde, is another important aldehyde used in the preparation of organic compounds and as an organic solvent. It is prepared from ethanol in a reaction similar to that for formaldehyde.

Ketones

If you attempt to oxidize a *secondary alcohol* like isopropanol, an alcohol in which two organic radicals are attached to the same carbon atom as the —OH group, an aldehyde does not form. Instead a **ketone** forms. The group of organic compounds called ketones is closely related to the aldehydes. Just as every aldehyde contains a formyl group, so all ketones contain a **carbonyl** group whose formula is:

$$-\overset{\displaystyle O}{\overset{\|}{C}}-$$

carbonyl group

This carbonyl group appears *between* the end carbon atoms in a carbon chain, not at the end. If again we let R represent any organic radical, the formula **RCOR'** can be used as the general formula for ketones. Observe below in the general

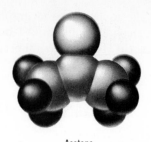

Acetone

35-9 A molecule of acetone consists of two methyl radicals joined together by the carbon atom of a carbonyl or =CO functional group.

formula for ketones that the two radicals are attached to the carbon atom of the carbonyl group.

$$R\overset{\displaystyle O}{-\overset{\|}{C}-}R'$$

ketones

The R and R' may represent either the same or different organic radicals.

Acetone (CH_3COCH_3) is the simplest and most important ketone (Fig. 35-9). It is used in great quantities as an organic solvent for resins and fatty substances. Acetone is produced by the oxidation of isopropanol, a secondary alcohol.

$$CH_3\overset{\displaystyle OH}{\underset{\displaystyle H}{-\overset{|}{\underset{|}{C}}-}}CH_3 + [O] \longrightarrow CH_3\overset{\displaystyle O}{-\overset{\|}{C}-}CH_3 + H_2O$$

isopropanol   from   acetone
(a secondary   oxidizing   (propanone)
alcohol)   agent

In acetone, as seen in the graphic formula above, two methyl radicals are attached to the carbon atom of the carbonyl group. In the I.U.C. system, a ketone takes its name from the total number of carbon atoms in the chain and ends in *-one.* Thus acetone, which contains three carbon atoms, has the I.U.C. name of *propanone.*

Organic Acids

You remember that ethanal, an aldehyde, is produced by the partial oxidation of ethanol, a primary alcohol:

Acetic acid

35-10 In a molecule of acetic acid, the carboxyl (—COOH) group is attached by its carbon atoms to the carbon atom of the methyl radical.

$$CH_3CH_2OH + [O] \longrightarrow CH_3CHO + H_2O$$
ethanol   ethanal

Further oxidation changes the aldehyde to acetic acid (CH_3COOH):

$$CH_3CHO + [O] \longrightarrow CH_3COOH$$
ethanal   acetic acid

Acetic acid (Fig. 35-10), the acid of vinegar, is an important member of a group of compounds called **organic acids.** All organic acids contain the —**COOH** or **carboxyl** functional group:

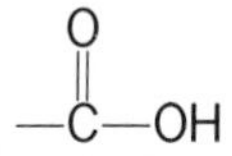

$$
\begin{array}{c}
O \\
\parallel \\
-C-OH
\end{array}
$$
carboxyl group

In the carboxyl group observe that one oxygen atom is attached by a *double* bond to the carbon atom. The other oxygen atom, that to which a hydrogen atom is bonded, is attached to the same carbon atom by a *single* bond.

Perhaps you have observed that cider without a preservative turns to vinegar within several days. The weak acetic acid solution sold as vinegar has been prepared for many years by the oxidation of the ethanol present in wines and fermented apple cider. The oxidation of ethanol to acetic acid is facilitated by the bacteria present in the sediment formed during the fermentation of the wine or cider. This sediment is called "mother of vinegar." Acetic acid, used in concentrated form as a solvent in the manufacture of acetate plastics, dyes, and some synthetic fibers like rayon, is prepared commercially by the hydration and oxidation of acetylene.

$$HC{\equiv}CH + H_2O + [O] \longrightarrow CH_3COOH$$

Although acetic acid is the most familiar organic acid, the simplest of all the organic acids is **formic acid.** This is the substance that causes itching or stinging if you are bitten by red ants or stung by bees.

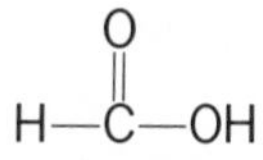

$$
\begin{array}{c}
O \\
\parallel \\
H-C-OH
\end{array}
$$
formic acid

In the I.U.C. system, the name of an organic acid begins with the name of the hydrocarbon to which it is related and ends in *-oic.* Thus acetic acid (CH_3COOH) is called *ethanoic acid,* and formic acid (HCOOH) is *methanoic* acid.

Other Organic Acids

Many organic acids, some simple and some quite complex, are in widespread use. Characteristically they result from *the oxidation of an*

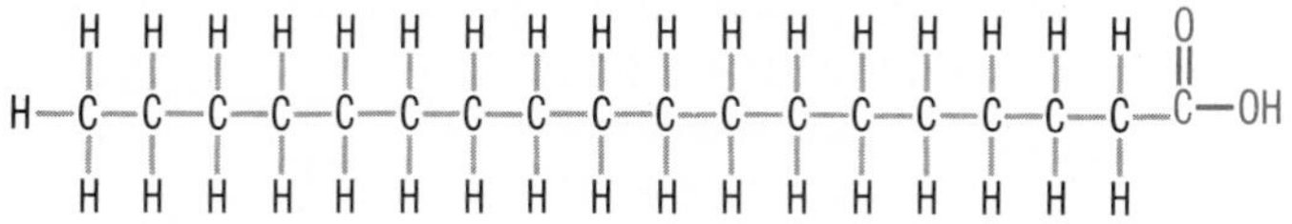

Stearic acid

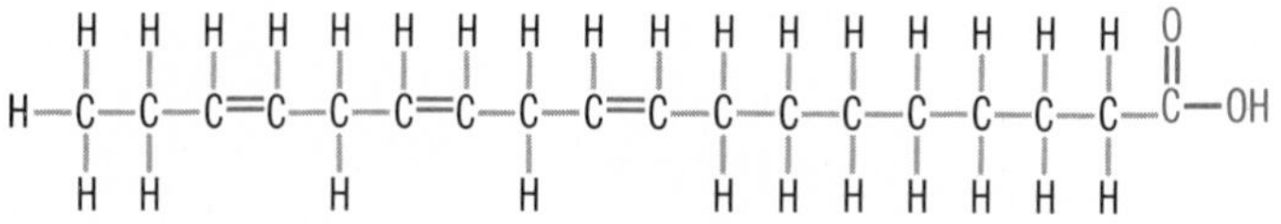

Linolenic acid

35-11 Stearic acid consists of a 17-carbon saturated chain to which a carboxyl group is attached. In contrast, linolenic acid consists of a 17-carbon chain with a carboxyl group attached, but with three double bonds in the chain. Linolenic acid is therefore an unsaturated fatty acid.

aldehyde. All are similar in that they contain one or more carboxyl groups and, if soluble, ionize in water to form hydronium ions. Here we will mention just a few of the more common acids.

Lactic acid, present in sour milk, is formed by the action of bacteria on lactose sugar. Notice from its graphic formula that lactic acid contains one hydroxyl and one carboxyl group:

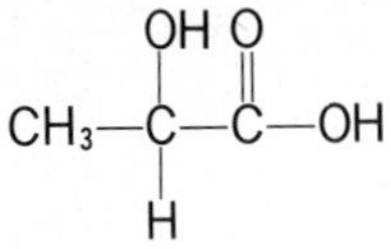

$$CH_3-\overset{\displaystyle OH}{\underset{\displaystyle H}{C}}-\overset{\displaystyle O}{C}-OH$$

lactic acid

Tartaric acid, used as a constituent of some baking powders, is obtained from the cream of tartar present in grapes. As its graphic formula indicates, tartaric acid contains two hydroxyl and two carboxyl groups:

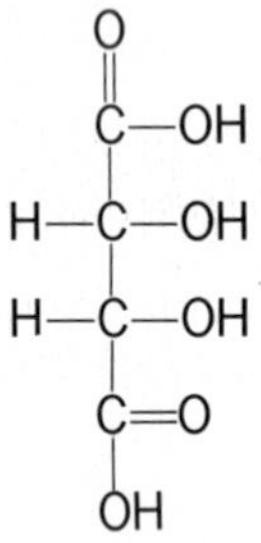

$$\begin{array}{c} \overset{\displaystyle O}{C}-OH \\ H-\overset{}{C}-OH \\ H-\overset{}{C}-OH \\ \overset{}{C}=O \\ OH \end{array}$$

tartaric acid

Citric acid is the acid found in oranges, grapefruit, and other citrus fruits. It is used for flavoring and also for making magnesium citrate, a laxative. The structural formula for citric acid shows that it contains three carboxyl groups:

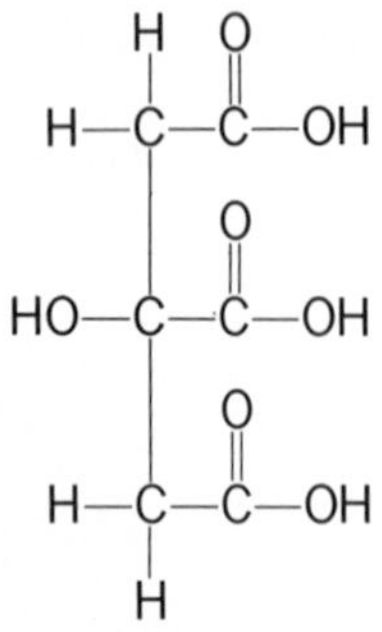

$$\begin{array}{c} H \quad O \\ H-\overset{}{C}-\overset{}{C}-OH \\ O \\ HO-\overset{}{C}-\overset{}{C}-OH \\ O \\ H-\overset{}{C}-\overset{}{C}-OH \\ H \end{array}$$

citric acid

Fatty acids are a series of acids which consist of a long carbon chain with attached hydrogen atoms and a —COOH group. They are called fatty acids because they are obtained by the hydrolysis of fat. Two important fatty acids are stearic acid ($C_{17}H_{35}COOH$), obtained from the hydrolysis of beef fat, and linolenic acid ($C_{17}H_{29}COOH$), obtained from linseed oil. The graphic formula for each of these acids is shown in Fig. 35-11.

Aromatic Acids

The acids considered thus far are derivatives of aliphatic or open-chain hydrocarbons. Numerous other acids, known as **aromatic acids,** are derivatives of the aromatic compound benzene. One of these is **benzoic acid,** in which a single carboxyl group replaces one hydrogen atom of a benzene molecule. Its formula, therefore, is C_6H_5COOH. Benzoic acid can be thought of as consisting of a carboxyl group attached to a **phenyl radical.** The phenyl radical (C_6H_5) is an aromatic radical derived from benzene, as indicated by its graphic formula.

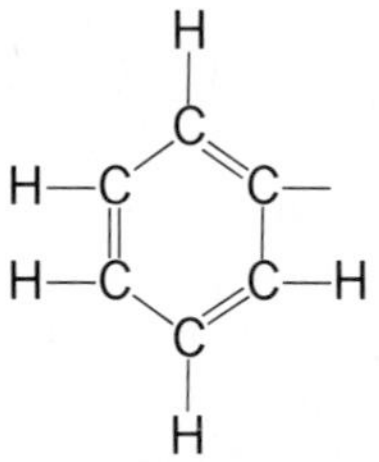

phenyl radical

Benzoic acid and sodium benzoate, a salt of the acid, are added to foods and beverages as a preservative (Fig. 35-12).

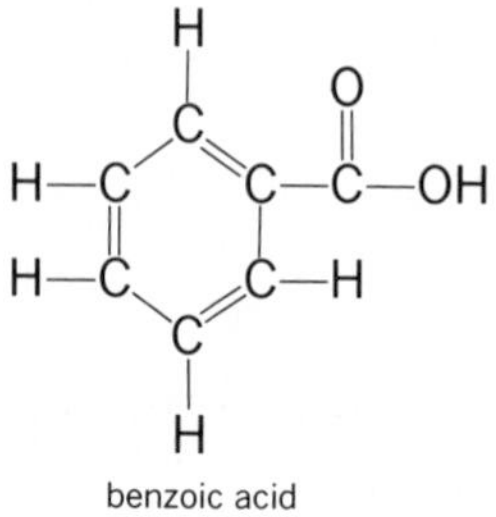

benzoic acid 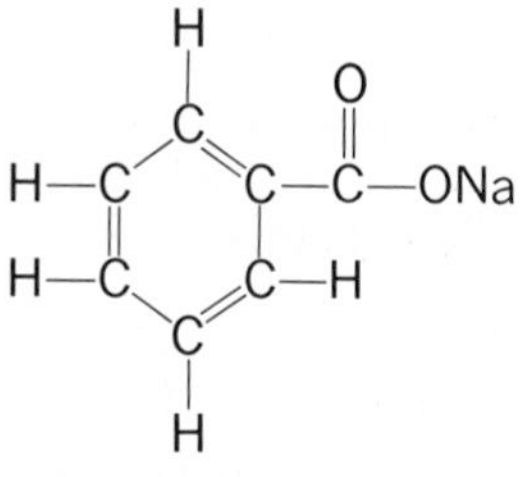   sodium benzoate

Salicylic acid, another aromatic acid derived from benzene, has the formula $C_6H_4OHCOOH$. Its structural formula (shown below) reveals that in this acid one hydrogen atom of benzene is replaced by a hydroxyl group, while a second hydrogen atom is replaced by a carboxyl group. Salicylic acid, like benzoic acid, is used as a preservative. A derivative of salicylic acid is *acetylsalicylic acid,* familiar to all of us as the aspirin used for relieving pain.

salicylic acid

acetylsalicylic acid

Ethers

The **ethers** are another group of organic compounds which can be prepared from alcohols. But ethers, unlike acids, aldehydes, and ketones, are *not* prepared by the oxidation of alcohols; they are prepared by the *dehydration* of alcohols. For instance, if a small amount of concentrated sulfuric acid is poured into a test tube of absolute ethanol (95 to 100 percent ethyl alcohol), and the tube is heated cautiously in a warm water bath, you can detect a distinct odor of ether. This is the odor of **diethyl ether,** the most important member of the ether group.

When sulfuric acid is added to ethanol, the acid serves as the dehydrating agent. As indicated by the dotted lines in the equation below, the concentrated H_2SO_4 removes a molecule of H_2O from the two molecules of ethanol. During this reaction two ethyl radicals become bonded together through a single oxygen atom to form diethyl ether:

$$C_2H_5\boxed{OH} + C_2H_5O\boxed{H} \xrightarrow{H_2SO_4} C_2H_5-O-C_2H_5 + H_2O$$

two molecules of ethanol

one molecule of diethyl ether

35-12 Each of these common foods or beverages contains a harmless organic preservative such as benzoic acid or sodium benzoate.

Diethyl ether (Fig. 35-13) is used as an anesthetic, but it is so highly flammable that great care must be taken in the operating room to prevent even a single spark from static electricity. It must *never be used near an open flame* since it combines readily with oxygen in all proportions to form an explosive mixture.

All common ethers may be thought of as organic compounds containing an **-oxy** functional group:

$$-O-$$

-oxy group

They have the general formula:

$$R-O-R'$$

ethers

Diethyl ether

35-13 In a molecule of diethyl ether, two ethyl radicals are bonded to a single oxygen molecule. Observe that the oxy- or —O— functional group is directly attached to a carbon atom of each ethyl group.

In the case of diethyl ether, both R's represent ethyl radicals.

$$H-\overset{\overset{\displaystyle H}{|}}{\underset{\underset{\displaystyle H}{|}}{C}}-\overset{\overset{\displaystyle H}{|}}{\underset{\underset{\displaystyle H}{|}}{C}}-O-\overset{\overset{\displaystyle H}{|}}{\underset{\underset{\displaystyle H}{|}}{C}}-\overset{\overset{\displaystyle H}{|}}{\underset{\underset{\displaystyle H}{|}}{C}}-H$$

diethyl ether

Ethers such as this in which both radicals are the same are called **simple ethers.** Ethers in which the two radicals are different are called **mixed ethers.** An example of the latter is methylethyl ether ($CH_3OC_2H_5$).

$$H-\overset{\overset{\displaystyle H}{|}}{\underset{\underset{\displaystyle H}{|}}{C}}-O-\overset{\overset{\displaystyle H}{|}}{\underset{\underset{\displaystyle H}{|}}{C}}-\overset{\overset{\displaystyle H}{|}}{\underset{\underset{\displaystyle H}{|}}{C}}-H$$

methylethyl ether

Examine the formulas below for normal butyl alcohol and for diethyl ether. Observe that the two substances are isomers, differing mainly in the position of the oxygen atoms, and yet their properties are quite different.

$$H-\overset{\overset{\displaystyle H}{|}}{\underset{\underset{\displaystyle H}{|}}{C}}-\overset{\overset{\displaystyle H}{|}}{\underset{\underset{\displaystyle H}{|}}{C}}-\overset{\overset{\displaystyle H}{|}}{\underset{\underset{\displaystyle H}{|}}{C}}-\overset{\overset{\displaystyle H}{|}}{\underset{\underset{\displaystyle OH}{|}}{C}}-H \qquad H-\overset{\overset{\displaystyle H}{|}}{\underset{\underset{\displaystyle H}{|}}{C}}-\overset{\overset{\displaystyle H}{|}}{\underset{\underset{\displaystyle H}{|}}{C}}-O-\overset{\overset{\displaystyle H}{|}}{\underset{\underset{\displaystyle H}{|}}{C}}-\overset{\overset{\displaystyle H}{|}}{\underset{\underset{\displaystyle H}{|}}{C}}-H$$

n-butyl alcohol   diethyl ether

Many ethers are isomers of alcohols. Name the alcohol of which dimethyl ether (CH_3OCH_3) is an isomer.

1. Give the name and graphic formula of the functional groups for each of the following: an alcohol, an aldehyde, a ketone, an ether, an acid.

2. (a) Which hydrocarbon derivatives are obtained by the oxidation of alcohols? (b) How are ethers related to alcohols? (c) How are acids related to alcohols? (d) How does the production of aldehydes differ from the production of ketones?

3. Write the graphic formulas for propanoic acid, methyl propyl ether.

4. (a) How do aromatic acids differ from fatty acids? (b) How does salicylic acid differ from benzoic acid?

ESTERS

None of the compounds considered in the last section is usually prepared by reactions between members of different classes of organic compounds. Aldehydes, for example, are prepared by the partial oxidation of alcohols, *not* by reactions between alcohols and acids, or alcohols and ethers. There is, however, a large group of organic compounds called **esters** which are usually prepared by reactions between alcohols and acids. The acids can be either organic or inorganic. Many simple esters, such as wintergreen, banana flavoring, and nail polish remover, are familiar to us because of their fragrant odors. Fats are examples of more complex esters.

The Formation of Esters

Girls are already familiar with the ester called ethyl acetate; it is one of the solvents used in nail polish. *You can prepare it yourself* in the laboratory (but your product must *not* be used as nail polish remover because H_2SO_4 is also present).

Mix 3 ml of ethyl alcohol and 5 ml of acetic acid in a test tube. *Cautiously* add 5 or 6 drops of concentrated H_2SO_4 and

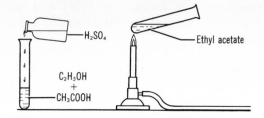

warm the test tube gently. The substance that forms, with its sweet but pungent smell, is ethyl acetate.

During the reaction, the acid and alcohol combine to form ethyl acetate and water.

$$CH_3CO\overline{[OH + H]}OC_2H_5 \xrightarrow{\text{H}^+} CH_3COOC_2H_5 + H_2O$$

acetic   ethyl   ethyl
acid   alcohol   acetate

Alcohol-acid reactions occur slowly and are usually reversible. Sulfuric acid (or another strong acid) is used to catalyze the reaction. A large excess of ethyl alcohol is used to shift the equilibrium to the right (Chap. 17), thus increasing the yield of the ester. The ethyl acetate is then separated from the unchanged materials by fractional distillation.

Water is formed by this reaction and so it appears at first that the reaction is comparable to the neutralization of an organic acid and a base. However, the two reactions are not actually analogous. Since alcohols do not ionize—they are not bases—no ions are involved when the alcohol and acid molecules react. The reaction between an alcohol and an acid to produce an ester is called **esterification.**

When an alcohol and an organic acid undergo esterification, you might expect that the —OH group from the alcohol would become part of the water that forms. But testing with radioactive oxygen-18 shows that this is not so. Instead, as indicated by the dotted line in the equation above, the alcohol is the source of the hydrogen and the acid is the source of the —OH group that combine to form water. Esterification, therefore, results from a mechanism very different from that of neutralization.

Reactions between many alcohols and organic acids produce esters which have the general formula RCOOR′. Their graphic formula is:

$$R-\overset{\displaystyle \overset{O}{\|}}{C}-O-R'$$

esters

Here R and R′ represent different radicals. Ethyl butyrate, an ester of ethanol and butyric acid, has the flavor and odor of pineapple. Methyl salicylate, formed from salicylic acid and methanol, is an ester with the odor and flavor of wintergreen (Fig. 35-14).

ethyl butyrate

methyl salicylate

If methanol and nitric acid, an inorganic acid, are mixed in the presence of sulfuric acid as a de-

35-14 Numerous esters are used as flavorings in candy, gum, and soda.

hydrating agent, they react to form the ester methyl nitrate:

$$CH_3OH + HNO_3 \xrightarrow{H_2SO_4} CH_3ONO_2 + H_2O$$

methanol   methyl nitrate

Methyl nitrate (CH_3ONO_2 or CH_3NO_3) is produced by an esterification reaction between an alcohol and an inorganic acid. A similar reaction between glycerol and nitric acid produces glyceryl trinitrate [$C_3H_5(ONO_2)_3$] or nitroglycerine.

Fats

Alcohols that contain more than one —OH group per molecule also react with organic acids to form esters. The most important of these esters are the **fats.** *Fats are naturally occurring esters of glycerol (a polyhydroxy alcohol) and fatty acids.* *Glyceryl stearate* is an ester found in animal fats, while *glyceryl oleate* and *palmitate* are esters found in vegetable fats. The formation of glyceryl stearate by the combination of one molecule of glycerol with three molecules of stearic acid is shown in the equation below and in Fig. 35-15.

$$3\ C_{17}H_{35}COOH + C_3H_5(OH)_3 \longrightarrow$$

stearic acid   glycerol

$$(C_{17}H_{35}COO)_3C_3H_5\ + 3\ H_2O$$

glyceryl stearate

Most fats are combinations of several esters. Those fats which are liquid at temperatures slightly below room temperature are called "oils." But these "oils" are chemically very different from the oil obtained from petroleum. Oil from petroleum is a mixture of liquid and gaseous hydrocarbons; the oils related to fats are liquid glyceryl esters.

Saturated and Unsaturated Fats

The carbon atoms in the fatty acid portion of glyceryl stearate are linked together by single bonds. Fats in which this occurs are called **saturated fats.** Like the molecules of alkane hydrocarbons, molecules of saturated fat do not react with hydrogen. Most animal fats are saturated and are solids at room temperatures. In contrast, the acid parts of many vegetable fats, such as glyceryl linolenate, are unsaturated. They have one or more double bonds (see Fig. 35-11).

Many unsaturated fats are liquid at room temperature. These liquid, unsaturated fats react with hydrogen under pressure, in the presence of a catalyst such as nickel, to form more saturated molecules. The reaction of hydrogen with unsaturated fats is an example of **hydrogenation**—the process of adding hydrogen to an unsaturated molecule (Fig. 35-16). The hydrogenation of a fat often converts the liquid fat into a solid, raising its melting point. Vegetable shortenings are examples of hydrogenated fats. Extensive research is now going on to find out whether there is any relationship between an excess of saturated fats in the diet and hardening of the arteries.

Soaps

When equal volumes of fat and concentrated NaOH solution are placed in a container, allowed

35-15 In the production of a molecule of glyceryl stearate, the three hydroxyl groups of a molecule of stearic acid react with three hydrogen atoms from a molecule of glycerol to form three molecules of water. The remaining portions of the acid and glycerol molecules react to form the fat, glyceryl stearate.

Stearic acid   Glycerol   Glyceryl stearate   Water

35-16 Corn oil is a typical unsaturated fat—that is, it is liquid at room temperature. When the double bonds in a molecule of corn oil are broken by the addition of hydrogen to form a saturated fat, a solid results. Some solid corn oil is used to make margarine.

to boil for about 10 minutes, and then cooled, a thick, colloidal suspension results. This suspension contains **soap.** *Soaps are metallic salts of fatty acids* having a large number of carbon atoms. For example, sodium stearate ($C_{17}H_{35}COONa$) is a soap.

Fats are important to the making of soaps because they serve as a source of fatty acids. If a fat such as stearin (glyceryl stearate) is combined with lye, a soap and glycerol are produced:

$$C_3H_5(C_{17}H_{35}COO)_3 + 3\,NaOH \longrightarrow$$
$$\underset{\text{stearin}}{} \qquad \underset{\text{lye}}{}$$

$$\underset{\text{soap}}{3\,C_{17}H_{35}COONa} + \underset{\text{glycerol}}{C_3H_5(OH)_3}$$

This process by which a fat and an alkali, like sodium hydroxide, react to form soap is called **saponification.** The soaps formed by the saponification of fats with NaOH are usually solids at room temperatures. On the other hand, saponification with KOH produces soaps that are liquid. Fats commonly used in the making of soaps include palmitin from palm oil, olein from olives, and cottonseed oil. The fat selected depends upon the purpose for which the soap is intended.

The older method of preparing soaps commercially is the **kettle method.** Here the fat and lye are boiled together in large kettles. After the reaction is complete, a concentrated solution of NaCl in which the soap is insoluble is added. In this "salting out" process (a practical example of the common ion effect), the soap separates, or floats away, from the glycerol and salt water. After the impurities are removed from the soap, it is run into **crutching pans.** Here rosin, perfumes (Fig. 35-17), and medicines are added to make the type of soap desired. To make a floating soap, air is beaten in. After further processing, the soap is made into bars, flakes, beads, or granules. The glycerol is recovered as a useful by-product by fractional distillation.

A more recent method of preparing soap, the **hydrolyzer method,** is based upon the hydrolysis of fats by steam. In this process the formation of soap can be thought of as occurring in two steps. Consider the production of sodium stearate as an example. In the first step, the glyceryl stearate ester hydrolyzes to form stearic acid and glycerol. The equation for this reaction, which is essentially the reverse of esterification, is:

$$\underset{\text{glyceryl stearate}}{(C_{17}H_{35}COO)_3C_3H_5} + 3\,H_2O \xrightarrow{\Delta}$$

$$\underset{\text{stearic acid}}{3\,C_{17}H_{35}COOH} + \underset{\text{glycerol}}{C_3H_5(OH)_3}$$

In the second step, sodium hydroxide reacts with the stearic acid to form sodium stearate soap and water:

$$\underset{\text{stearic acid}}{C_{17}H_{35}COOH} + NaOH \longrightarrow \underset{\text{sodium stearate}}{C_{17}H_{35}COONa} + H_2O$$

The advantage of the hydrolyzer method is that the process is continuous; the kettle method produces individual batches.

Cleansing Action of Soap

Half fill a 250-ml beaker with water and carefully pour a thin film of benzene onto the clear water. Stir the mixture vigorously. Do the benzene and water remain mixed or do they separate? Repeat the procedure, but this time pour the benzene over soapy water. What happens?

HYDROCARBON DERIVATIVES   607

35-17 In crutching pans such as this one, soap that will later be formed into bars of popular toilet soaps is blended with perfume.

The water and benzene separate quickly, but when soap is added, they emulsify to form a colloidal system, as described on page 317. The liquids which were once immiscible are now miscible.

Perhaps you live in an area that has "hard water." When soap is added to hard water a replacement reaction occurs between the soap and the alkaline earth ions (page 472). This reaction forms an insoluble soap or scum that prevents the original soap from acting as an effective cleansing agent.

$$2\,C_{17}H_{35}COONa + Ca^{+2} \longrightarrow$$

soluble   group IIA
soap   ion

$$(C_{17}H_{35}COO)_2Ca\!\downarrow + 2\,Na^+$$

insoluble   group IA
soap or scum   ion

Detergents

Any substance which lowers the surface tension of a liquid is called a "surface-active agent," or a **detergent.** Since all soaps have this effect,

strictly speaking all soaps are detergents. But today the term *detergents* is usually used to mean "soapless soaps" or synthetic agents resembling soap in their ability to emulsify oil and water and hold dirt in suspension. These synthetically made detergents are called **syndets.** One such syndet can be made by treating lauryl alcohol ($C_{12}H_{25}OH$), one of the long-chain alcohols, with sulfuric acid. Lauryl sulfate ($C_{12}H_{25}OSO_3H$) forms by an esterification reaction. The lauryl sulfate then reacts with sodium hydroxide to form the synthetic detergent sodium lauryl sulfate ($C_{12}H_{25}OSO_3Na$).

Although syndets behave much like soaps, their chemical structure is quite different. As a result of this structural difference syndets, unlike soaps, do not react with calcium and magnesium ions in hard water. This is why they do not leave a scum, or dirt ring, as soaps do. Also the suds formed by syndets are more lasting than soapsuds (Fig. 35-18). They are so long-lasting, in fact, that until recently they have constituted a serious sewage problem. Today, low-sudsing or "soft" detergents, in which the branched-chain alkyl group is replaced by a straight-chain group, are in widespread use. As these soft detergents are

35-18 From left to right, equal volumes of soap flakes, syndet (detergent), and low-sudsing detergent produced these suds. Which will fall?

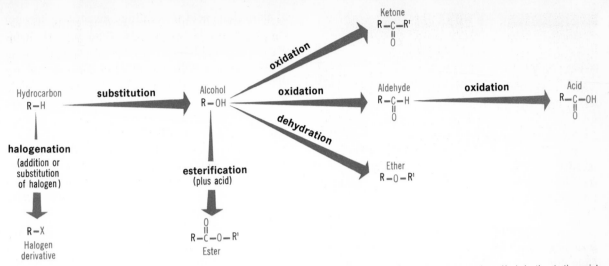

35-19 Halogen derivatives are produced from hydrocarbons by addition or substitution reactions. Alcohols, the starting point for many classes of organic compounds, are derived from hydrocarbons by substitution. Esters are derived from alcohol by the addition of acid, and ethers by dehydration; ketones and aldehydes are derived by oxidation. Further oxidation of aldehydes results in the formation of organic acids.

subject to faster bacterial decomposition, the foaming problem has been alleviated. Finally, the very effectiveness of syndets as a cleansing agent has its drawbacks. If used excessively on the human skin, they "rob" the skin of essential oils.

Relating Hydrocarbon Derivatives

To keep clearly in mind the relationships between the different classes of organic compounds (described in this chapter) that are derived from hydrocarbons, it is helpful to set forth these relationships in the form of a diagram. Such a diagram is shown in Fig. 35-19. In it the functional groups are printed in green; the alkyl radicals to which they are attached are all represented by the letter R.

In studying the diagram, you will see that the halogen derivatives are produced by either substitution or addition reactions, depending upon the original hydrocarbon involved. But the alcohols, aldehydes, ketones, acids, ethers, and esters can be considered as substitution products of the hydrocarbons. Primary alcohols undergo oxidation to become aldehydes, which in turn are oxidized to acids. Secondary alcohols are oxi-

dized to ketones. Various alcohols are dehydrated to form ethers and undergo esterification (react with acid) to form esters.

The number of complex organic compounds theoretically possible by reactions involving these relatively simple hydrocarbon derivatives is tremendous. The number of compounds actually available is limited only by the ingenuity of the organic chemist.

QUESTIONS AND PROBLEMS

1. (a) Write an equation for the production of the ester, ethyl nitrate. (b) Draw the graphic formula for the ester.

2. Write a graphic formula equation for: (a) the formation of the fat glyceryl palmitate from palmitic acid ($C_{15}H_{31}COOH$), (b) the preparation of the soap sodium palmitate from glyceryl palmitate.

3. (a) Describe briefly the cleansing action of soap. (b) Differentiate among detergent, syndet, and soap.

THE CONCEPT

Most organic compounds can be considered derivatives of the hydrocarbons. The starting point for many of these hydrocarbon derivatives is either benzene, acetylene, or one of the simple alkanes. Two types of reactions, substitution and addition, produce the simplest types of hydrocarbon derivatives. Substitution reactions involve the replacement of one or more hydrogen atoms per molecule by other atoms, such as those of the halogens. In addition reactions atoms are added to unsaturated molecules, causing the double or triple bonds to break. When halogen atoms react with hydrocarbons, whether by substitution or addition, the derivative is called an alkyl halide.

The more common hydrocarbon substitution derivatives are characterized by the presence of particular groups of atoms called functional groups. We have considered the following types of compounds containing functional groups:

1. Alcohols contain the —OH or hydroxyl group. Monohydroxy alcohols contain one —OH group per molecule; polyhydroxy alcohols contain two or more —OH groups per molecule. Methanol (CH_3OH), ethanol (C_2H_5OH), isopropanol ($CH_3CHOHCH_3$), and glycerol [$C_3H_5(OH)_3$] are among the common and important alcohols.

2. Aldehydes, which may be produced by the mild oxidation of primary alcohols, contain the —CHO or formyl group. Formaldehyde (HCHO) and acetaldehyde (CH_3CHO) are the most common aldehydes.

3. Ketones, which may be produced by the mild oxidation of secondary alcohols, contain the

$$\overset{\displaystyle O}{\underset{\displaystyle \|}{}}$$

carbonyl, or —C— group, anywhere between the ends of a chain of carbon atoms. Acetone or propanone (CH_3COCH_3) is a widely used ketone.

4. Organic acids contain the —COOH or carboxyl group; they may be produced by oxidizing aldehydes. Acetic acid (CH_3COOH), an example of an organic acid containing one carboxyl group per molecule, is among the most important of organic acids. Organic acids, such as lactic acid, contain one or more carboxyl groups, as well as one or more hydroxyl groups per molecule. Benzoic acid (C_6H_5COOH), a derivative of benzene, is an aromatic acid.

5. Ethers, produced by the dehydration of alcohols, contain organic radicals attached through an oxygen atom, R—O—R′. Diethyl ether, $(C_2H_5)_2O$, is the most important ether.

6. A large group of organic compounds called esters are prepared by reactions between members of different classes of organic compounds, usually between alcohols and acids. The preparation of some esters involves inorganic compounds as well. Ethyl acetate ($CH_3COOC_2H_5$) is an ester prepared from an alcohol and an organic acid, while methyl nitrate (CH_3ONO_2) is an ester resulting from the reaction between an alcohol and an inorganic acid. Fats, and some of the synthetic detergents, or syndets, are examples of very useful esters. Fats are esters of glycerol and organic acids, while soaps are formed from fatty acids and inorganic hydroxides.

USING THE CONCEPT

Using the Basic Concept

1. List three hydrocarbons that serve as basic materials from which many hydrocarbon derivatives may be made.

2. (a) Differentiate between an addition and a substitution reaction. (b) Write an equation for an addition reaction involving a hydrocarbon and a halogen. (c) Write an equation for a substitution reaction involving a hydrocarbon and a halogen.

3. (a) What is an alkyl halide? (b) Name the following alkyl halides by the I.U.C. system: CH_3I, CH_2Br_2, CCl_4, CBr_2F_2. (c) Draw the graphic formula for dichloromethane and 1,2-dichloropropane.

4. (a) Define *organic functional group*. (b) Name and write graphic formulas for five organic functional groups.

5. (a) Draw the graphic formula and write

the structural formula for each of the following alcohols: methanol, ethanol, propanol, isopropanol, 2-butanol. (b) Give the common name or names for three of the alcohols listed above.

6. (a) Identify each of the following: grain alcohol, denatured alcohol, rubbing alcohol. (b) Describe two methods for preparing ethanol.

7. (a) How does a monohydroxy alcohol differ from a polyhydroxy alcohol? (b) Give an example of each.

8. (a) Write an equation for the conversion of methanol into methanal (formaldehyde). (b) Why can this process be called either mild oxidation or dehydration?

9. (a) What is a primary alcohol? (b) Show that ethanol is a primary alcohol while isopropanol is not.

10. Draw the graphic formula and write the structural formula for the following aldehydes: ethanal, propanal, butanal.

11. (a) What is a secondary alcohol? (b) What type of compound is produced by the mild oxidation of secondary alcohols? (c) Write the functional group for this type of compound.

12. (a) Draw the graphic formula and write the structural formula for acetone and butanone. (b) What is the I.U.C. name for acetone?

13. (a) What is an organic acid, a fatty acid? (b) Write an equation for the general process by which acetic acid may be formed from ethanal.

14. (a) Draw graphic formulas for acetic, methanoic, and lactic acids. (b) How does the latter differ structurally from the first two?

15. (a) Write a general equation for the process by which ethers may be prepared from alcohols. (b) Draw the graphic formula for dimethyl ether and ethylpropyl ether.

16. (a) Write a general graphic formula for each of the following: ethers, aldehydes, ketones. (b) Specifically what do the letters R and R' represent in these formulas?

17. (a) Draw and compare the graphic formulas for n-butanol and diethyl ether. (b) Show that these two substances are isomers. (c) Name and draw the graphic formula for another isomer of diethyl ether.

18. (a) Differentiate between an organic ester and an inorganic ester. (b) Give an example of each. (c) Write an equation for the preparation of methyl acetate.

19. (a) Write the structural formula for each of the following: methyl nitrate, glyceryl trinitrate, n-butyl acetate, methyl formate. (b) How are these compounds related?

20. (a) Describe the process of esterification. (b) Write a general graphic formula for esters.

21. (a) How do fats differ from oils (assume both are esters)? (b) How does an oil that is an ester differ structurally from oil obtained from petroleum?

22. (a) Differentiate between a saturated and an unsaturated fat. (b) Give one example of each.

23. (a) Describe the hydrogenation of an oil. (b) How does this process affect the structure and physical properties of fats or oils?

24. (a) Describe the process of saponification. (b) Describe two methods employed in the industrial preparation of soap.

25. (a) Write an equation for the formation of sodium stearate from stearin and sodium hydroxide.

26. (a) Define the terms *detergent* and *syndet*. (b) Why don't syndets leave a scum when used with hard water?

Relating Terms Within the Concept
Each of the following statements contains two italicized terms. Select the *italicized* term that makes the statement correct.

1. The carboxyl functional group is ($-COOH$, $R-O-R'$).

2. An alkyl halide is a halogen derivative of an (*alkane, alkene*).
3. The formyl functional group is (—COO—, —CHO).
4. Alcohols that contain more than one —OH group per molecule must be (*primary alcohols, polyhydroxy alcohols*).
5. Long carbon chains with attached hydrogen atoms and a —COOH group are characteristics of (*fatty acids, ketones*).
6. The characteristic properties of various types of organic compounds are determined by their (*isomers, functional groups*).
7. Esterification is the production of an ester by the reaction between an alcohol and an (*acid, aldehyde*).
8. The formula of the phenyl radical is (C_2H_5, C_6H_5).
9. A fat is actually a (*mixed ether, glyceryl ester*).
10. The process by which a fat and an alkali react to form a soap is (*saponification, dehydration*).
11. Sodium lauryl sulfate is a (*Freon, syndet*).
12. The dehydrogenation of an alcohol is essentially the combining of oxygen with (*hydrogen, water*).

Solving Problems Within the Concept
1. Methanol is prepared commercially by the reaction between CO and H_2 at high temperatures and in the presence of a catalyst. How many moles of H_2 and of CO_2 must react to produce 1 mole of methanol?
2. How many grams of ethylene glycol must be added to each liter of water in an automobile radiator to lower the freezing point of the water to $-1.86°$ C?
3. Draw the graphic formulas for three isomers of the ester having the empirical formula $C_5H_{10}O_2$.
4. Suppose a chemist wishes to hydrogenate completely 2 moles of ethyne. (a) Write an equation for this hydrogenation reaction. (b) How many moles of hydrogen must react with the ethyne? (c) Name the product that would be formed.
5. Compare the percentage by weight of each element present in diethyl ether and normal butanol.
6. How many grams of NaOH are required to react completely with 1 ton of stearin in making sodium stearate?

Applying the Concept
1. Liquid alcohols, like water, have higher boiling points than might be expected. Give a possible explanation for this phenomenon.
2. Write, in order, the equations for the reactions that might be used to make ethanol from acetylene.
3. Draw a graphic formula for the product formed by the dehydration of isopropanol.
4. Write equations to show how you could prepare monobromoethane from (a) ethane, (b) ethene. What problem must be overcome when preparing any halogen derivative?
5. Write an equation to represent a reaction between an alcohol and a halogen acid to form an alkyl halide.
6. Sodium carbonate solution (washing soda) has been used instead of NaOH (lye) with fats in making soap. Explain why saponification occurs with Na_2CO_3.
7. Draw the graphic formula for phenyl ether. [Its empirical formula is $(C_6H_5)_2O$.]

Reading Further
The World of Carbon, by Isaac Asimov, New York, Abelard-Schuman, 1958. A clearly and simply written, yet excellent, introduction to the field of organic chemistry.
Organic Chemistry, 3d. ed., by R. Q. Brewster and W. E. McEwen, Englewood Cliffs, N.J., Prentice-Hall, 1961. If you would like to pursue organic chemistry in relation to electron theory and molecular orbital theory, you will find this book most useful.

36

Fuels—Sources of Energy

In Greek mythology, Prometheus was condemned to be chained to a rock and suffer everlasting torment because he stole fire from the gods and gave it to mankind. You may smile at this account, with oil burners, gas furnaces, fluorescent lamps, and electric stoves all around you, but the story emphasizes the reliance of early peoples on fire. With fire, man could warm his dwelling, provide light against the darkness, cook food, extract some metals from their ores, and shape the metals into tools or weapons. For most of recorded history, man has depended on fire to provide heat energy. In time, he learned to use many different *fuels,* substances that release heat energy upon combustion.

Waterfalls are sometimes an important source of energy, newly developed solar heaters and cookers are used occasionally, and nuclear energy is sometimes a source of heat; but for the present we still rely upon the combustion of carbon fuels as our main source of heat energy.

VARIATIONS AMONG FUELS

The consumption of fuel varies with time and place. People in many rural areas still use wood, although coal provides more heat, pound for pound. In a given locality within a large city, coal, gas, and oil are used by owners of similar buildings. What circumstances dictate the choice of fuel?

Even if all fuels contained the same amount of stored energy per pound, one difference among them would be that of availability. Rural dwellers have ready access to woodland, but the rapidly dwindling supply of this fuel plus the cost of transportation make it a poor choice for city dwellers. As a result, gas, oil, and coal are the principal fuels used in cities. Many communities far from the source of natural gas now use this fuel because pipelines have made it available (Fig. 36-1). Problems of storage, cleanliness, and convenience are also deciding factors in the choice of a fuel. Fuel oil tanks require less space than do coal bins, and by using fuel oil we avoid the nuisance of coal dust. Gas, piped into the home, requires no storage whatever in or near the home. Furthermore, gas and oil burn instantaneously to provide heat quickly; and their combustion can be controlled much more easily than that of coal, thus providing comfortable heating. In addition, the combustion of gas or oil does not form solid waste products.

Heating Value of Fuel

Since the purpose of any fuel, whether in the home or industry, is to provide energy, usually in the form of heat, we want the most heating value for our money. This requires knowledge of the heat energy produced when comparable amounts of various fuels are burned. Such measurement requires a unit of heat. The **calorie,** a unit of heat with which you are familiar, is defined as the quantity of heat required to raise the temperature of *one gram of water one degree Celsius.* The engineer employs the British thermal unit (Btu), a quantity of heat required to raise the temperature of *one pound of water one degree Fahrenheit.*

To compare the heating value of two solid fuels, simply measure the amount of heat produced when an equal weight of each is burned completely. Whether we measure the Btu's per pound or calories per gram of fuel burned, the technique of measurement is the same. A known weight of each fuel is placed in a calorimeter and ignited (page 155). From the data collected while the fuel undergoes combustion, the amount of heat produced by a given weight of each fuel is calculated. The heat produced by several fuels is given in Table 36-1.

The ultimate choice for home use of the many

Table 36-1 **HEAT PRODUCED BY MANUFACTURED AND NATURAL FUELS**

Fuel	Calories per gram	Chief combustible constituent
Wood	4000	Carbon (cellulose)
Anthracite coal	7700	Uncombined carbon
Bituminous coal	8000	Uncombined carbon Hydrocarbons
Coke	7800	Uncombined carbon
Fuel oil	9500	Hydrocarbons
Natural gas	10000	Hydrocarbons

fuels described must take into consideration each of the advantages and disadvantages mentioned previously—storage, cleanliness, ash removal, cost, and heat produced. Additional factors that are significant in industrial processes need not concern us at present.

Coal

Until almost the middle of this century, coal was our most widely used industrial fuel. What is the origin of coal? Many of the forests of distant ages have long since decayed, but the sun's energy that was originally stored in the vegetation has not been lost. Millions of years ago the earth's climate, which was much warmer and damper than it is today, stimulated a luxuriant growth of plant life. Ferns of those bygone eras were as large as some present-day trees (Fig. 36-2). Geological evidence indicates that the debris of these ancient forests was gradually buried under swamps and then covered with layers of soil. In the course of time, shifting of the land buried the vegetable debris deeper and deeper. At these depths, great heat and pressure compressed the debris and, probably assisted by bacterial decomposition, removed much of the hydrogen and oxygen present in the original plants. Left behind was compressed carbon, a substance capable of combining with oxygen to release energy. This is the fuel we call *coal*. Bacterial or some fungal action probably transformed some of the original debris into various types of *hydrocarbons* which were trapped in the coal.

36-1 This thirty-six-inch diameter pipeline carries natural gas from the Gulf Coast to cities hundreds of miles away.

36-2 Geologic evidence indicates that the debris of ancient forests of the Carboniferous Period was gradually buried under swamps and soil and was slowly converted to coal under great heat and pressure.

Coal shows evidence of these changes. **Peat,** the parent material of coal, is found today in peat bogs. When cut and dried to be used as fuel, it shows its vegetable origin. **Lignite,** a brownish coal serving as a fuel in some of our western states, shows less evidence of its vegetable origin than does peat. Decomposition of the original wood has proceeded further than in peat, and more oxygen and hydrogen have been removed. Both **bituminous** (soft) and **anthracite** (hard) coal represent advanced stages in the development of coal. The percentage of free carbon is much greater in these forms than in peat or lignite. Soft coal contains from 45 to 65 percent free carbon and a considerable amount of volatile hydrocarbons. Hard coal contains less of these compounds, but a correspondingly greater proportion of free carbon—70 to 85 percent.

Transforming Coal

Early methods of extracting metals from their ores utilized charcoal as a reducing agent. The shrinkage of forest lands and the growing use of wood for other purposes led to the use of coke in extracting metals. Coke is made by destructively distilling soft coal (bituminous) in a manner similar to the preparation of charcoal from wood.

The raw material is heated in the absence of air in order to drive off volatile substances, some of which condense to form coal tar. The resulting coke (or charcoal) then burns without smoke.

Originally, **destructive distillation,** or distillation in the absence of air, was carried out in order to transform wood or coal into a different solid fuel, and the gases and vapors were allowed to escape (Fig. 36-3). When these volatile by-products were found to be useful, new procedures were instituted for their recovery. Some of the gases have immediate use and others can serve as raw materials in the synthesis of organic compounds. A few of the many substances that can be separated from the volatile by-products obtained from wood and coal are listed with their uses in Table 36-2. Many more compounds can be obtained from coal tar, but those listed represent the major products.

The diversity of products listed in the table makes it clear why industry invests large sums in a process which changes one solid fuel into another. True, if the wood or coal were burned, these products of destructive distillation would

36-3 The destructive distillation of soft coal yields not only coke, but also coal gas, a fuel, and coal tar, a source of organic compounds.

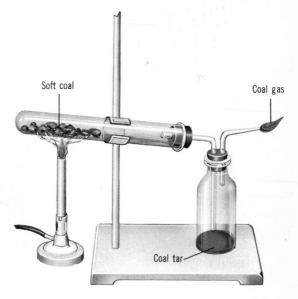

Wood			Coal		
By-product	*Derived product*	*Uses*	*By-product*	*Derived product*	*Uses*
Pyroligneous acid		Broken down to yield other products	Coal gas*		Fuel gas
	Methyl alcohol	Antifreeze, solvent for varnishes and lacquers, starting material in preparation of organic compounds		Methane	Fuel gas
				Carbon monoxide	Producer gas, water gas, reducing agent in metallurgy
	Acetic acid	Solvent for organic compounds, used in synthesizing cellulose acetate		Hydrogen	Fuel gases, torches, Haber process, hydrogenation
				Nitrogen	Haber process, fertilizers, explosives
	Acetone	Organic solvent, used in synthesizing organic compounds	Ammonia		Fertilizers, explosives
			Coal tar		Dyes, drugs, explosives, plastics, perfumes, paint, photographic chemicals
	Tar	Roads, roofs			
Combustible gas		Fuel gas		Benzene	Drugs, dyes, explosives
				Toluene	Explosives, drugs, dyes
	Methane	Fuel gas		Naphthalene	Moth preventive, dyes
	Hydrogen	Fuel gases, torches, Haber process, hydrogenation		Anthracene	Dyes
				Xylene	Synthesizing related organic compounds
	Carbon dioxide	Beverages, leavening agents, refrigeration, fire extinguishers		Phenol	Synthesizing plastics, antiseptics
	Carbon monoxide	Producer gas, water gas, reducing agent in metallurgy		Aniline	Dyes
				Pitch (tar)	Asphalt roads, roofs

* Usually not separated into component products.

also burn to provide heat; but they could not then be put to other uses. Acetone, methyl alcohol, and benzene are much more useful to the chemist as solvents and raw materials than as fuels. The simple ovens that previously sufficed to heat wood and coal have given way to complicated installations designed for the recovery of volatile by-products. After the destructive distillation of coal and wood, we still have solid charcoal and coke; but the chemist has wisely separated valuable materials which would otherwise have gone up in smoke. Table 36-3 summarizes the quantities of useful materials that can be obtained from a single ton of coal.

The Manufacture of Coke

In the destructive distillation of bituminous coal, a battery of oblong ovens is charged with coal from the top, and heated from below (Fig. 36-4). As the volatile products escape, they are conducted through pipes leading from the ovens to condensers in which the coal tar settles out. The ammonia gas is absorbed in water. The escaping insoluble gas, called **coal gas,** which has thus far been unaffected by this treatment, is washed further by passing it upward through water. It is then passed over iron oxide to remove gaseous sulfur compounds such as hydrogen sulfide. The purified gas, ready for use, is stored in

Table 36-3 YIELD FROM DESTRUCTIVE DISTILLATION OF 1 TON OF COAL

Product	Yield	
Coke	1,200–1,500	pounds
Coal tar	120	pounds
Coal gas	10,000–12,000	cubic feet
Ammonia	20	gallons
Light oil	2–3	gallons

giant gas holders. The resulting coke is pushed out of the oven into a freight car and moved to cooling towers where the red-hot coke is quenched by a spray of water. Since most of the coke made today is used in metallurgical processes, it is not surprising that "coking plants" are usually located near steel plants.

QUESTIONS AND PROBLEMS

1. (a) Into what forms, other than heat energy, can chemical energy be transformed? (b) Illustrate each of your answers.

2. (a) Differentiate between a calorie and a Btu. (b) When is each used?

3. The ultimate choice of a fuel in your home depends on many factors. Name as many factors as you can.

4. How is coal formed? Include in your answer the terms *lignite, peat, bituminous,* and *anthracite.*

5. Describe the destructive distillation of soft coal, indicating the products and by-products formed.

6. What value might destructive distillation have in our economy when applied to such materials as bones, oat hulls, and sugarcane stalks? (You might like to find out whether any of these has so been treated.)

GASEOUS FUELS

Since, in addition to the problems discussed previously, solid fuels do not ignite readily, they do not provide instantaneous heat. Gaseous fuels do not have these disadvantages. Because of their

36-4 Coke produced by the commercial destructive distillation of soft coal is used in steel mills. Coal tar is the starting point for many organic compounds, and coal gas is often used to heat additional coal in the retort.

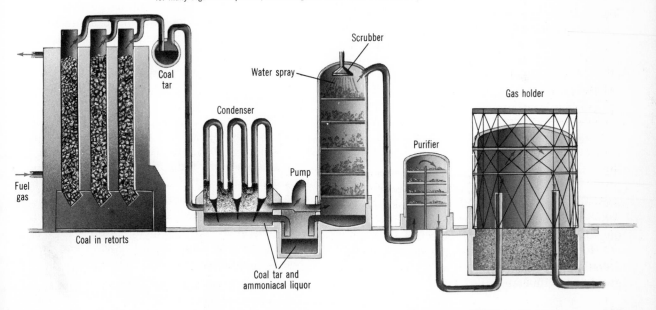

versatility, increasing emphasis has been placed on the development of gaseous products.

Coal Gas

For many years prior to the widespread utilization of natural gas as a fuel, a number of manufactured gaseous fuels were in use. The first of these, **coal gas,** is obtained by the destructive distillation of soft coal. It consists largely of hydrogen, methane, and other hydrocarbons, and some carbon monoxide. Before the electric light was developed, this gas was used to illuminate the streets of large cities. At present it is employed as a fuel gas, often by the same industries that produce it. The coal gas collected during destructive distillation of coal is often used to heat further batches of coal in the coke ovens.

Water Gas

The advantages of gaseous fuels over solid fuels led to attempts to transform coke into a combustible gaseous mixture. When steam is passed over *white-hot* coke, **water gas,** a mixture of carbon monoxide and hydrogen, is formed (Fig. 36-5).

$$C + H_2O \xrightarrow{\Delta} CO\uparrow + H_2\uparrow$$

This reaction is *endothermic,* and results in cooling of the coke. At lower temperatures (below white heat) carbon dioxide, without value as a fuel, is formed instead of carbon monoxide. In practice, when the temperature drops, the blast of steam is stopped and air is blown through the coke to raise it to a white heat once more. Steam is again introduced to continue the reaction. The process is thus intermittent in operation.

Water gas has two drawbacks. First, its fuel value is low; therefore it is enriched by introducing gases made by splitting (cracking) molecules of heavy oils at high temperatures. Second, the presence of carbon monoxide in the gaseous mixture creates a hazard. Not only is this gas poisonous, but, like hydrogen, it is colorless and odorless. It is therefore required by law that a gas with a distinct odor be added to fuel gas mixtures to give warning in case of leakage.

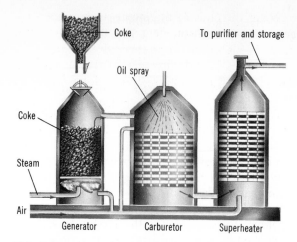

36-5 The manufacture of producer gas is an intermittent process; it must be stopped temporarily when the coke is no longer white-hot.

Producer Gas

Because low-grade coals leave an especially large amount of ash when burned, they are often converted to a gaseous fuel. When only a limited supply of air is blown through a bed of burning coals, combustion of the carbon is incomplete.

$$2 C + O_2 \xrightarrow{\Delta} 2 CO\uparrow$$

The carbon monoxide formed is diluted by the nitrogen of the air. The resulting gaseous mixture, **producer gas,** does not have a high fuel value; but it is relatively inexpensive and easy to produce. Producer gas is usually used by the industry that makes it or in furnaces requiring long, steady heating, such as in making glass.

Acetylene

Though the gaseous hydrocarbon acetylene (or ethyne, C_2H_2) finds little use as an ordinary fuel, it is an important industrial fuel. Its discovery provided a means of repairing broken metal parts in far better fashion than could be done by bolting, riveting, or soldering. The technique known as **welding** makes a single metal unit from two or more parts. The combustion of acetylene provides the high heat necessary.

$$2 C_2H_2 + 5 O_2 \longrightarrow 4 CO_2 + 2 H_2O + 624 \text{ kcal}$$

When the ends of the metals to be joined together have been softened, a "stick" of the same metal is placed between them to provide additional material and allowed to melt. On cooling, the two metal parts, plus the additional material, solidify as one piece.

The equation above reveals that 5 moles of oxygen, or twenty-five times that volume of air, are needed for the complete combustion of each 2 moles of acetylene. *To observe its incomplete combustion,* prepare acetylene by reacting water and calcium carbide as follows:

Arrange the apparatus as shown below to prepare acetylene and collect it by water displacement. Place several lumps of calcium carbide in a 250-ml flask and allow water from a separatory funnel to drip slowly onto the calcium carbide. In this way, acetylene is collected at a slow and steady rate. Allow the first gas evolved to escape. Why? Now

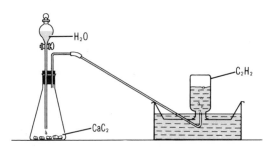

collect a bottle of acetylene, and place it upright on the table. *Cautiously* ignite the gas with a burning splint and observe the sooty flame produced. What does this flame indicate about the burning of the acetylene?

The water reacts with the calcium carbide to produce acetylene and calcium hydroxide.

$$CaC_2 + 2\,H_2O \longrightarrow C_2H_2\uparrow + Ca(OH)_2$$

In the air, acetylene undergoes incomplete combustion to yield soot (unburned carbon) as well as carbon dioxide and water. To insure complete combustion and maximum heat, acetylene is burned with pure oxygen in special burners (page

392). This intense heat of the oxyacetylene flame not only melts most metals but also can be used to cut metal (Fig. 36-6). It therefore finds good application in the scrap metal industry, where large metal pieces must be cut down to convenient size.

Natural Gas

Natural gas, the first-known gaseous fuel, is often found when drilling for petroleum and is a mixture of gaseous hydrocarbons. It was well known to the fire worshippers of ancient Persia as a flammable gas issuing from the earth, providing an apparently eternal flame. Natural gas consists of about 90 percent methane, CH_4, and some ethane, C_2H_6, combined with small amounts of similar compounds such as propane

36-6 The workman is adjusting the flame of an automatic cutting machine for the most efficient cut through a slab of steel. The oxyacetylene flame will cut quickly and evenly through the steel.

and butane. Helium is sometimes a constituent of natural gas. A clue to the formation of methane is provided by its occasional occurrence in swampy areas where vegetable matter is decaying —it is often known as **marsh gas.** Methane is also found in coal beds, where it may be a hazard to miners. Because of the convenience of gaseous fuels, and the large quantity of natural gas in the earth's crust in our country, natural gas is widely used. It is piped hundreds of miles to areas far from its place of origin (see page 614).

Bottled Gas

The gas range is a common feature in city homes, yet gas is also used in rural homes far from vast pipeline networks. The ethane, propane, and butane obtained from natural gas are readily separated by liquefaction, sealed under pressure in metal cylinders, and sold as **bottled gas** (page 582). Related hydrocarbon gases obtained in the processing of petroleum are used similarly under the name of **liquefied petroleum gases.** A European manufacturer is presently experimenting with the use of these liquefied gases as an automotive fuel.

Two important ideas are emphasized by this brief study of manufactured fuels. First, the conversion of solid fuels to gaseous fuels increases the supply of *useful* fuels. Second, the change of natural solid fuels (wood and charcoal) to other solid fuels (charcoal and coke) by destructive distillation yields not only gaseous fuels but also by-products of value as raw materials for the syntheses of other useful products.

QUESTIONS AND PROBLEMS

1. (a) How does water gas differ from producer gas? (b) How is each produced? (c) What are the chief disadvantages of each gas?

2. What relationship exists among natural gas, methane, and marsh gas?

3. Why is acetylene especially useful in the scrap metal industry?

4. (a) What is coal gas? (b) What is its main use?

5. What two types of gaseous fuels are sealed in cylinders, under pressure, and used for cooking in rural areas?

PETROLEUM AND ITS PRODUCTS

The availability of petroleum during the second half of the nineteenth century stimulated the development of the internal combustion engine. For petroleum, or more accurately the very volatile *gasoline* produced from petroleum, forms an explosive mixture with air inside the engine. The perfection of the internal combustion engine revolutionized our way of life. "Fill 'er up" is the end remark in our story of gasoline. What is the beginning?

The Nature of Petroleum

Petroleum or crude oil is a dark, viscous liquid widely distributed under the earth's surface. The liquid probably was formed by the decomposition, under layers of sediment or rock, of the remains of marine organisms that lived millions of years ago. Powerful neutron sources and studies of shock waves from dynamite blasts are used to study the rock strata and other features of oil-bearing regions. These studies indicate that petroleum-bearing regions have certain features in common. They consist of layers of rock and pools of petroleum like those shown in Fig. 36-7. If the shock wave patterns are similar to those found in subterranean oil fields, borings are made and studied for the presence of fossil remains that are usually found associated with petroleum. Today, drilling for oil is no longer the completely hit-or-miss affair it once was. The oil man can pick his spots and predict, in most instances, whether or not he will find oil.

For a long time petroleum was known only as a liquid which would burn with a smoky flame. It was even advertised and sold for medicinal purposes, although no medical basis existed for this practice. When petroleum was analyzed exhaustively, the oily liquid was found to be a storehouse of chemicals without equal in natural resources.

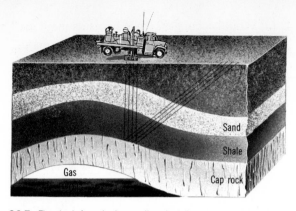

36-7 The shock for seismic soundings is delivered mechanically by this mobile unit from its jacker-up operating position. A pile-ram, powered by equipment on the truck bed, slams against the ground, and a seismograph downfield (not shown) records the pattern of deflections.

It is a mixture of thousands of hydrocarbons with very small amounts of nitrogen compounds and sulfur compounds. The hydrocarbons in petroleum are mainly saturated, straight-chain hydrocarbons; they range from those with very short carbon chains (gases and liquids) to long chains of thirty to forty carbon atoms (solid or semisolid compounds). Also present in petroleum are many other types of hydrocarbons, including straight-chain unsaturated hydrocarbons, cyclic saturated hydrocarbons (cycloalkanes), and cyclic unsaturated hydrocarbons related to benzene.

Distilling Petroleum

The composition of petroleum varies in different areas. Nevertheless, its constituents can be separated by *fractional distillation,* a process in which a mixture of volatile liquids that boil at different temperatures is separated according to successive boiling points of the ingredients. The boiling points of hydrocarbons depend mainly on their molecular weights—the smaller the molecule, the lower its boiling point. Observe this relationship for the first ten members of the methane series (straight-chain saturated hydrocarbons) shown in Table 34-1. The boiling points of the very short-chain hydrocarbons are so low that, except at high pressures or very low temperatures, they are gaseous. Even within the earth

these hydrocarbons separate from the other constituents of petroleum as natural gas.

Since the boiling points of many very short-chain hydrocarbons lie close together, they distill off together during fractional distillation. Often it is not necessary to separate further the individual members of such a group of compounds because they resemble each other in properties other than boiling point, and can therefore be put to the same uses. By fractional distillation, therefore, the components of petroleum are separated according to their *boiling ranges* rather than their boiling points.

In the laboratory, fractional distillation of a liquid mixture involves continuous heating, which allows the various components of the mixture to boil away and condense at successively higher temperatures. In industry, the fractional distillation of petroleum is achieved in a somewhat different manner. Instead of *boiling off* each component consecutively, the whole mixture is vaporized and each fraction is then *condensed* consecutively. In practice, crude oil is heated to boiling in a still and the vapors passed into a **fractionating tower** (Fig. 36-8). Here heavy residues, whose boiling points are so high that they do not vaporize, drop to the bottom, while the volatile compounds rise into the tower where they are cooled. On further cooling, substances with high boiling points (not easily vaporized) condense first and are collected in trays. Vapors of substances with lower boiling points rise higher in the tower before they are cooled below their boiling points. They condense, and collect in other trays. In this way, different successive *fractions* of petroleum continue to condense, that of lowest boiling point condensing last. Some substances have boiling points so low that they cannot be condensed by the cooling effect of the tower alone. They pass as vapors through the tower, and are condensed in water-cooled pipes, or they are piped to an aerial exhaust and burned.

Petroleum Fractions

The first step in refining petroleum is the division of the crude oil into three major fractions or

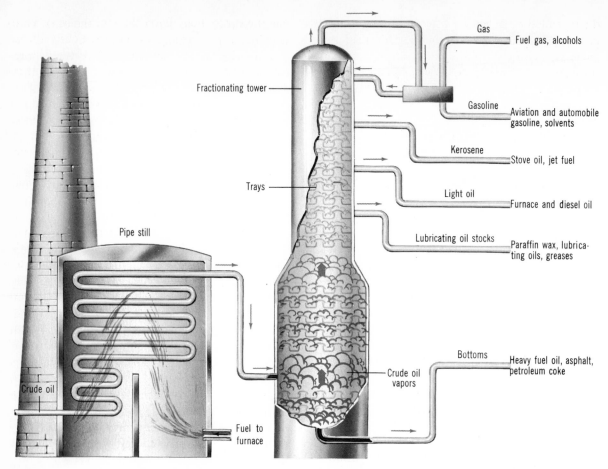

Fractionating tower

Trays

Pipe still

Crude oil

Fuel to furnace

Gas — Fuel gas, alcohols

Gasoline — Aviation and automobile gasoline, solvents

Kerosene — Stove oil, jet fuel

Light oil — Furnace and diesel oil

Lubricating oil stocks — Paraffin wax, lubricating oils, greases

Crude oil vapors

Bottoms — Heavy fuel oil, asphalt, petroleum coke

36-8 In this process of fractional distillation, petroleum is heated to boiling in the pipe still, and the vapors pass into the fractionating tower. The various fractions, or groups of compounds, condense as they cool, and each fraction is collected individually.

groups of compounds within a boiling range. The lightest fraction, containing gasoline and naphthas (compounds intermediate in properties between gasoline and kerosene), consists generally of hydrocarbon molecules containing five to twelve carbon atoms per molecule. The middle fraction, consisting of molecules of twelve to nineteen carbon atoms, includes kerosene, fuel oils, and lubricating oils. Left behind in the tower are the heavier hydrocarbons which are difficult to distill without decomposition. These include very viscous oils, and semisolid and solid materials such as the waxes and asphalts. Some decomposition of these hydrocarbons occurs in the still, to leave carbon in the form of petroleum

coke, which is used as a fuel or shaped and baked into electrodes.

Most of the fractions obtained by distillation of the crude oil still contain undesirable impurities; these must be removed before the products are ready for use. For example, the gasoline and fuel oil fractions must be freed of small amounts of sulfur compounds that would form sulfur trioxide when the fuel burned. The SO_3 would combine with water vapor to form sulfuric acid, which would corrode the car engine or house furnace. Lubricating oils must be freed from substances which would leave gummy deposits. Heavier oils are chilled to deposit wax and vaseline, which are then removed by filtration. Ingredients called *additives* are often added to refined petroleum products to improve their performance. Detergents added to motor oils help minimize the build-up of deposits on cylinder walls by keeping dirt and carbon particles in suspension.

Manufactured Gasoline

While the internal combustion engine makes possible both automobiles and airplanes, it also raises a question. Will the supply of fuel suffice to meet the demand? While more oil wells are drilled in this country and previously unexplored resources are developed in others, it has now become apparent that the demand for gasoline will in time outstrip the supply. In the past forty years gasoline consumption has increased tremendously. Figures show that the increased supply of gasoline cannot be accounted for by petroleum production alone. The work of the chemist and engineer has enabled the petroleum industry to produce more gasoline than is naturally present in the gasoline fraction of petroleum.

From the ordinary distillation of petroleum, the yield of kerosene, heavy oils, and waxes is more than sufficient to keep up with the demand

36-9 In the "cat cracker," long chain molecules of hydrocarbons are catalytically cracked or split into chains of moderate length. These chains are of the type found in the gasoline fraction of petroleum.

for these products. Even the recent use of kerosene in jet airplane engines has not greatly altered the demand for this petroleum fraction. The existence of these surpluses provided the petroleum chemist with a unique opportunity. Gasoline is a mixture of hydrocarbons containing from five to eleven carbon atoms per molecule. Actually, it contains chiefly isomers of six, seven, and eight carbon atom chains. Kerosene, heavy oil, and wax hydrocarbons contain from twelve to twenty-four carbon atoms per molecule. If the chemist could split one of these long-chain molecules, for example, one with sixteen carbon atoms, into equal parts, he would produce two chains of eight carbon atoms each. This splitting or **thermal cracking process** converts a *single long-chain molecule of a hydrocarbon into two or more molecules* of the type found in the gasoline fraction of petroleum. When fuel oil is heated under pressure at temperatures well above its boiling range, the hydrocarbons are "cracked" into shorter chains typical of those in gasoline.

Long-chain molecules do not always split into chains of the desired length in thermal cracking; shorter chains of one to four carbon atoms also result. By performing the cracking process in the presence of a catalyst, splitting of the chain into too-small units can be avoided. **Catalytic cracking** is carried out in tall (20-story) towers (Fig. 36-9) in which the finely powdered catalyst (alumina and silicon dioxide or aluminum silicate) is well mixed with the vapors of the hydrocarbons to be split. After either type of cracking, the gasoline molecules produced are separated by fractional distillation from the unchanged long-chain molecules and any small ones produced.

Small-chain hydrocarbons with only one to four carbon atoms per molecule, whether from petroleum and natural gas, or as by-products of the cracking process, can be joined together to form a typical eight-carbon gasoline molecule (Fig. 36-10). The process of combining two or more molecules of the same kind to form a larger unit is known as **polymerization.** The small molecule which serves as the unit for building the large molecule is known as a **monomer.** *Polymerization*

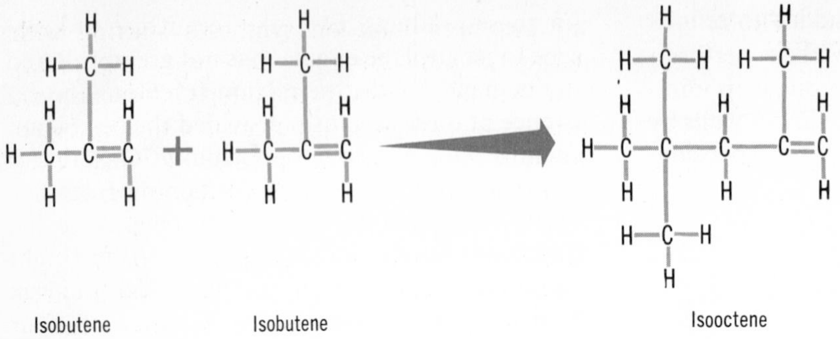

36-10 Two identical isobutene molecules serve as the monomers that are polymerized to form a molecule of isooctene, a typical eight-carbon gasoline molecule.

Isobutene   Isobutene   Isooctene

is actually the reverse of *cracking*. Whereas in cracking, large molecules are broken down to the size of gasoline molecules, polymerization builds small hydrocarbon units up to the size of gasoline molecules.

Improving Manufactured Gasoline

The efficiency of hydrocarbon molecules in a gasoline engine depends in part on the number of carbon atoms present. It also depends on whether each molecule in question is saturated or unsaturated, and whether the carbon atoms are combined to form a straight chain or a branched chain. The hydrocarbon molecules obtained in cracking or polymerization are often unsaturated and straight chain in nature. As neither of these types of molecules permits maximum efficiency of the gasoline engine, two further methods have been introduced for improving the performance of gasoline molecules. In the first, known as **hydrogenation,** the products of cracking are treated with hydrogen to form saturated compounds. Some of these are straight chain in nature; others are cyclic, saturated compounds, produced by the joining of the ends of a straight-chain molecule. Both types produced by hydrogenation show improved performance when burned.

The second method, known as **alkylation,** arose from the observation that, other things being equal, branched-chain hydrocarbons are more efficient fuels than straight-chain hydrocarbons. In alkylation, a process closely analogous to polymerization, small branched-chain hydrocarbons are combined with small straight-chain hydrocarbons to form larger, branched-chain molecules with superior properties as fuels (Fig. 36-11). These products may be hydrogenated to further improve their qualities. Because of cracking, polymerization, hydrogenation, and alkylation, it is now possible to obtain more than twice as much gasoline from a barrel of petroleum as was obtained fifty years ago. Table 36-4 indicates the gradual increase in yield since 1914.

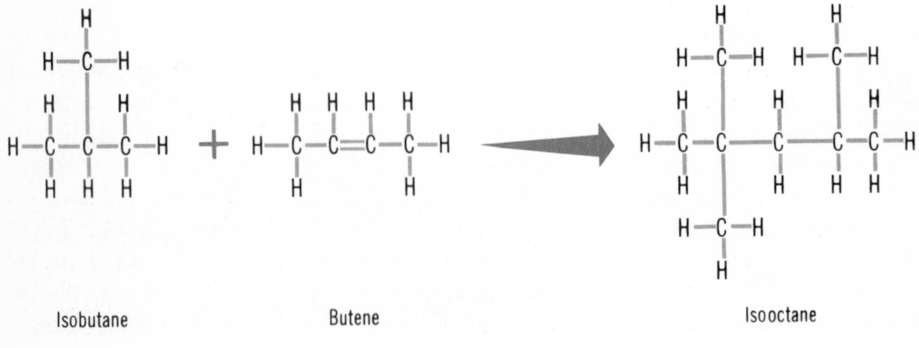

36-11 In alkylation small, branched molecules and straight-chain molecules, such as isobutane and butene, combine to form a longer branched-chain molecule, such as isooctane.

Isobutane   Butene   Isooctane

Table 36-4 YIELD OF PRODUCTS FROM 1000 GALLONS OF PETROLEUM

Product	Yield in Gallons		
	1914	1944	1963
Gasoline	182	394	441
Kerosene	241	47	51
Fuel oils	465	421	325
Lubricants (heavy oils)	66	25	20
Heavy bottom products (wax, asphalt, and others)	46	113	163

Synthesis from Solid and Gaseous Fuels

In time of war a nation may lack not only gasoline but petroleum as well. Gasoline cannot then be made either by cracking or by polymerization. Two other methods of making gasoline arose out of such crises. Each produces gasoline by going back to carbon and hydrogen, the fundamental constituents of any hydrocarbon. The first method, developed during World War I, is the **Bergius process** which makes gasoline from coal. Powdered coal is mixed with tar and heated with hydrogen under pressure (Fig. 36-12). Hydrocarbons ranging from gasoline to light oil molecules are produced. The second method, the **Fischer-Tropsch process,** makes gasoline from water gas. At high temperatures, and in the presence of a catalyst, the two components of water gas, carbon monoxide and hydrogen, react to form methane and water.

$$CO + 3 H_2 \longrightarrow CH_4\uparrow + H_2O$$

With the proper catalyst, this reaction will produce not just methane but a series of long-chain hydrocarbons typical of the gasoline fraction.

While these synthetic methods have augmented our gasoline supply considerably, research into new methods of producing gasoline still continues. Many substances which bear little or no relation to the hydrocarbons of gasoline are being investigated as new raw materials for the preparation of this fuel. Since World War II, for example, a whole new branch of organic chemistry has been built on syntheses starting with acetylene. Some syntheses have been directed toward the building of gasoline-type hydrocarbons. In addition, long-chain alcohols, easily produced by fermentation methods, can readily be converted to their corresponding hydrocarbons.

Combustion in Gasoline Engines

Gasoline can be used to provide power because its volatility enables formation of explosive mixtures with air. When the mixture explodes within the cylinders of the engine, hot compressed gases are formed and energy is released. The instantaneous expansion of these gases exerts pressure on the pistons, forcing them down. However, not only do we want energy to move the pistons; but also we want a smooth, steady push on the piston. If the explosion in the cylinder is too rapid, the push on the piston is sudden and results in jar-

36-12 In this reactor for the Bergius process, coal is converted to gasoline. Powdered coal is mixed with tar and subjected to a pressure of 10,000 pounds per square inch. Light oils are produced as by-products.

ring. This effect is known as *engine-knock*, which represents an ultimate loss of power. The explosion must be slowed down so that the available energy is applied smoothly for a maximum time.

If knocking results from too rapid an explosion, how can the reaction be slowed down? Only after some three thousand additives selected by trial and error had failed was it found that tetraethyl lead $[Pb(C_2H_5)_4]$ could "tame" the explosion of gasoline. The familiar signs on gasoline pumps reading "ethyl gasoline," or "contains lead," speak for the continued success of this method of preventing knocking. Unfortunately, the presence of a lead compound in gasoline raises the problem of preventing the deposition of metallic lead within the cylinder. Ethylene dibromide (dibromoethane) is used to control these deposits by forming volatile lead bromide (see page 383).

Octane Rating

A comparison of the rate of combustion of various hydrocarbon molecules in test engines shows that normal heptane, a straight-chain alkane of seven carbon atoms, burns rapidly and causes excessive knocking. Of the other gasoline hydrocarbons known, isooctane (or 2,2,4-trimethylpentane), a branched-chain alkane of eight carbon atoms, burns most smoothly and produces the least knocking.

normal heptane

isooctane

These two substances serve as the basis of the *octane rating scale*. On this scale *n*-heptane is as-

signed a value of 0 and isooctane a value of 100. Mixtures of *n*-heptane and isooctane are rated between 0 and 100 according to the percent of isooctane present. Other fuels containing neither *n*-heptane nor isooctane are also rated in octane numbers by comparing their performance with that of mixtures of the two former hydrocarbons. For example, any fuel which produces the same degree of knocking as a mixture of 30 percent normal heptane and 70 percent isooctane has an octane rating of 70.

Mixtures of branched-chain and ring hydrocarbon molecules are produced which cause even less knocking than isooctane; their octane rating is above 100. Gasolines composed of such molecules, produced by catalytic cracking of selected long-chain molecules or by polymerization of certain unsaturated branched-chain molecules, are now standard fuels in high-compression automobile and airplane engines.

The Combustion of Hydrocarbons

Observe the exhaust of a bus or automobile on a cold day. Trailing on the roadway just below the exhaust pipe is a dark streak that disappears shortly. What substance causes the streak? What other substance is produced when a hydrocarbon burns? To find out, *try the following*.

Play a Bunsen burner flame lightly over a cold metal surface. A similar dark streak appears briefly and then vanishes. Play the Bunsen burner on the metal surface again. What causes the streak? To verify your hypothesis quickly touch the darkened area with dry cobalt chloride paper. Does it change from blue to pink, indicating the presence of water? Now direct the flame at the surface of some limewater in a watch glass. What do you observe?

The dark streaks from both the Bunsen burner and the automobile are a result of the momentary condensation of the water vapor produced by the combustion of the hydrogen in the fuel molecules. The cloudy condition of the limewater indicates the formation of carbon dioxide resulting from the complete oxidation of the carbon in the fuel molecules. The evidence is in agreement with what should be expected from the complete combustion of a hydrocarbon; water and carbon dioxide are formed.

We can now write equations for the *complete* combustion of typical hydrocarbons.

For natural gas (methane):

$$CH_4 + 2 O_2 \xrightarrow{\Delta} CO_2\uparrow + 2 H_2O$$

For gasoline:

$$2 C_8H_{18} + 25 O_2 \xrightarrow{\Delta} 16 CO_2\uparrow + 18 H_2O$$

Observe in the last equation the considerable amount of oxygen needed for combustion. When the amount of oxygen is insufficient to oxidize both the carbon and hydrogen, as in the burning of gasoline in an internal combustion engine, only the hydrogen is oxidized to form water, while carbon is deposited. In the combustion of a hydrocarbon, the amount of air present may be less than that needed for complete combustion and more than the amount needed for the combustion of hydrogen alone. When this occurs, the carbon may be oxidized only partly to form poisonous carbon monoxide.

$$2 C_8H_{18} + 17 O_2 \longrightarrow 16 CO\uparrow + 18 H_2O$$

New Needs—New Fuels

The space age, initiated by the first Sputnik and continued by subsequent satellites, has placed a new emphasis on fuels. The energy of the older fuels did not give an object the necessary velocity either to go into orbit around the earth or to escape from its gravitational pull. And a new factor only added to the problem. Since rockets designed for space travel go far beyond the earth's atmosphere, the oxygen (or other oxidizing agent) necessary for combustion of the fuel must be provided within the rocket itself.

Two methods of fueling rockets have developed out of this circumstance. In rockets utilizing solid fuels, the oxidizer (often, but not always, oxygen) is either part of the fuel molecule, as in explosives, or it is provided in the form of a separate solid oxidizing agent mixed intimately with the fuel. Unlike explosives, these fuels are designed, by proper shaping of the solid, to burn at controlled rates rather than all at once. The second method utilizes a liquid fuel and a liquid oxidizing agent, each of which is stored in a separate tank within the rocket. Both are fed to the burners, where the stream of hot exhaust gases provides the thrust needed to propel the rocket. Rocket fuels include gasoline and kerosene, as well as newer fuels such as aniline, hydrazine, and ethyl alcohol. Oxidizing agents include fuming nitric acid, fluorine, hydrogen peroxide, and liquid oxygen, known as LOX. Together the fuel and oxidizing agent are known as *propellants*.

Liquid propellants provide higher energy than do solids, and their rate of burning can be controlled more easily. However, these fuels and oxidizing agents require a much more complex mechanism inside the rocket; and they may (as is true of liquid oxygen) be difficult or dangerous to handle. Both types of propellants may be utilized in the same rocket; the liquid may be used to power the initial stages of the rocket, while the solid form may be used to eject the capsule in the final stage. Figure 36-13 summarizes pictorially a typical application of rocket fuels to space flights.

QUESTIONS AND PROBLEMS

1. (a) What is fractional distillation? (b) In which part of a fractionating tower would you expect fuel oil hydrocarbons to condense? Why?

2. Differentiate between thermal and catalytic cracking.

3. Why must sulfur compounds be removed from gasoline?

4. When tetraethyl lead is burned in gasoline, lead deposits form in the engine cylinders. How are they removed?

5. Distinguish among *alkylation, polymerization,* and *hydrogenation.*

ROCKET FUELS

The Atlas Centaur rocket (left) is being fueled for flight from tanks of liquid nitrogen.

A solid-fuel antiaircraft missile (below) is being launched from an aircraft carrier.

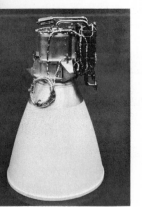

Compare this 4-foot $4\frac{1}{2}$-inch engine, which propelled the first manned lunar module off the moon, with the 278-foot rocket at the right, which propelled *Apollo 11* off the earth. This simple engine burned a mixture of hydrazines, which ignite spontaneously with the oxidizer, nitrogen tetroxide.

The liquid oxygen tank (above) contains the oxidizer for the kerosene fuel used in the nearby Saturn SA-2.

This gigantic, three-stage, Saturn 5 rocket that hurled *Apollo 11* into orbit contained kerosene and liquid oxygen in its first stage, and liquid hydrogen and liquid oxygen in its second and third stages.

THE CONCEPT

Fuels, materials which can be burned to provide heat energy, have two major uses. The first major use is in the operation of heat engines, illustrated by steam or gasoline engines. The second use is in raising the temperature of our environment. The choice of a fuel depends upon numerous details, most important of which are the purpose for which it is being used, availability, convenience, heating value, and cost.

The oldest known fuel is that which was most readily available—wood. In time it was discovered that peat could be dried to provide a fuel, and that wood could be transformed into charcoal, another solid fuel. The discovery of coal—a black stone that could burn—increased greatly the resources of solid fuels. The disadvantages involved in the use of solid fuels stimulated efforts to convert them into gaseous fuels. These efforts led to the destructive distillation of soft coal to yield coal gas, to the conversion of low-grade coals into producer gas, and to the conversion of coke into water gas. Although the use of coal gas, producer gas, and coal as fuels has diminished, the destructive distillation of coal has grown into a major chemical industry. The many by-products of the process serve as the raw materials for synthetic organic compounds.

The oldest known gaseous fuel is natural gas, once known as a mysterious, flammable gas issuing from the earth. Not until the present century, when the gas could be located in connection with petroleum deposits, tapped, and stored, did natural gas become a major fuel. The construction of long-distance pipelines has made this fuel available throughout the country. Another source of gaseous fuel is petroleum. Its lighter, gaseous molecules are separated and liquefied under pressure to provide tanks of bottled gas.

The most versatile source of fuels is petroleum, a complex mixture of thousands of hydrocarbons. The technique of fractional distillation has enabled the separation of petroleum into broad groups of fuels, each suitable for particular types of heat engines as well as for home heating. From petroleum we obtain fuels suitable for piston and jet engines, lubricants for machines, petroleum jelly for the pharmacist, and wax for candles.

By studying the combustion of gasoline hydrocarbons, the chemist has learned that some types of molecules are more efficient fuels than others. Branched-chain molecules are more efficient than straight-chain, cyclic molecules are superior to the straight-chain, and saturated molecules are preferable to the unsaturated. As a result, today's gasolines are "tailor-made." Some methods developed for extending our supply of gasoline involve splitting molecules that are too long to burn efficiently. This technique of cracking converts long kerosene or oil molecules into shorter, gasoline-type molecules. In thermal cracking heat alone is used, while catalytic cracking requires the presence of catalysts. Polymerization and alkylation builds gasoline-type molecules out of smaller, gaseous molecules, while hydrogenation changes the less efficient unsaturated molecules into more efficient saturated hydrocarbons.

USING THE CONCEPT

Using the Basic Concept

1. (a) What are the chief factors to be considered in selecting a fuel? (b) What is a calorie, a Btu?
2. (a) How does hard coal differ from soft coal? (b) Why isn't anthracite coal subjected to destructive distillation?
3. What use is made of the by-products of coke production?
4. (a) What is natural gas? (b) Why is it considered a good fuel?
5. (a) How is water gas produced? (b) What are its main drawbacks?
6. Differentiate among the following gases: producer gas, natural gas, marsh gas, bottled gas, liquefied petroleum gas.
7. (a) How is acetylene produced in the laboratory? (b) List two uses of acetylene.

8. What are the main types of hydrocarbons present in petroleum?
9. What compounds are present in the three major fractions produced by the process of fractional distillation of petroleum?
10. Under what circumstance is each of the following processes used: polymerization, hydrogenation, alkylation?
11. Describe briefly two processes by which gasoline is synthesized from solid or gaseous fuels.
12. Explain why kerosene does not make a suitable fuel in gasoline engines.
13. In contrast with kerosene, methyl, ethyl, and isopropyl alcohols burn cleanly. Why?
14. (a) Draw structural formulas for all of the isomers of hexane, C_6H_{14}. (b) Name each compound.
15. (a) Why are tetraethyl lead and ethylene dibromide added to gasoline? (b) What is meant by the octane rating of gasoline?
16. (a) Write an equation for the complete combustion of a gasoline molecule containing six carbon atoms. (b) Write an equation for its incomplete combustion.
17. List several factors that must be considered in choosing a rocket fuel.

Relating Terms Within the Concept

From the terms below select the term that best completes each of the following statements. Do not use a term more than once.

acetylene, alkylation, anthracite coal, bituminous coal, coal gas, cracking, destructive distillation, fractional distillation, methane, octane rating, petroleum, polymerization, water gas.

1. Charcoal is produced by _____.
2. Natural gas is about 90 percent _____.
3. A mixture of carbon monoxide and hydrogen is known as _____.
4. A gaseous hydrocarbon used in welding is _____.
5. Coke is made from _____.

6. The components of petroleum are separated according to their boiling ranges by _____.
7. Long-chain hydrocarbons are split into molecules of gasoline by _____.
8. Small straight-chain and branched-chain hydrocarbons are combined by _____.
9. Monomers are built into large molecules by _____.
10. The "knocking" quality of a gasoline decreases with an increase in _____.

Solving Problems Within the Concept

1. A mixture of 10 liters of methane and 10 liters of oxygen (**STP**) is exploded. (a) What is the volume of the residual gas (**STP**)? (b) What is its composition?
2. (a) How many liters of oxygen are needed for the complete combustion of 20 liters (**STP**) of heptane, C_7H_{16}? (b) How many liters of air are required?
3. How many grams of ethylene dibromide ($C_2H_4Br_2$) must be added to 1 ton of gasoline containing 0.1 percent by weight of tetraethyl lead?
4. One and one-half grams of a solid fuel were burned in a calorimeter. The water surrounding the sample weighed 250 grams and rose in temperature 40 degrees Celsius. What was the heating value of the fuel in calories per gram?
5. A weight of 7.11 grams of calcium carbide is reacted completely with water. After the reaction has ceased, the remaining liquid is neutralized with 1.0 M HCl. If 100 ml of the acid solution are required, what is the percentage purity of the calcium carbide?
6. A sample of water gas contains equal proportions of carbon monoxide and hydrogen. (a) What volume of *air* will be needed to burn completely 15 liters of the sample (**STP**)? (b) If the carbon dioxide which results is passed into an excess of limewater, what weight of calcium carbonate will be formed?

7. Fifty liters of air are needed for the complete combustion of 100 liters of producer gas (**STP**). What is the percent by volume of carbon monoxide in the producer gas?
8. A hydrocarbon contains 7.7 percent by weight of hydrogen. One liter of the gas (**STP**) weighs 1.16 grams. What is the formula of the compound?

Applying the Concept
1. Gasoline is more dangerous to handle than kerosene. Why?
2. If you were given an oily liquid, how could you prove whether it was a vegetable oil or a hydrocarbon oil?
3. How would you identify carbon monoxide in the exhaust gases from an automobile?
4. Why do some states have laws requiring that the exhaust systems of automobiles be equipped with afterburners?
5. Some gasoline pumps bear the warning, CAUTION—CONTAINS LEADED GASOLINE. Why?
6. An expedition to the South Pole during the 1920's found coal in some of the mountain ranges there. How can this be explained?
7. How could the chemist prove that the acetylene molecule contains a triple bond between the carbon atoms?

Reading Further
Several articles in *Scientific American* give excellent presentations of problems related to fuel. You will enjoy reading: "Coal," by Lawrence Lessing, July 1955; "The Fuel Problem," by Eugene Ayres, December 1949; and "The Arrival of Acetylene," by Herbert Yahraes, January 1949.

"Natural Gas—The Eternal Flame," by A. W. Atwood, *National Geographic,* October 1951, is a well-told story in words and photographs.

37

Rubber, Plastics, and Fibers

That new sports car you may have admired is actually a product of the chemist's test tube. As you sit on the nylon-covered seat inside its plastic body, you ride on styrene rubber tires on a road that may itself contain rubber particles. These products of modern technology have two things in common: they are synthetic, and they are polymers.

The discovery of the processes that produce polymers has been of profound significance to the chemist seeking to duplicate natural products. If he can prepare the monomer and then make it polymerize in imitation of a natural product, he may be able to prepare the natural polymer synthetically, or he may even be able to improve upon the properties of the naturally occurring substance. The development of superior types of synthetic rubber over the last forty years clearly illustrates how the study of polymerization enabled chemists to improve upon nature's product. It is in the chemistry of polymers that we find not only the story behind synthetic rubber (Fig. 37-1), but also that of fibers and plastics which are now so commonplace.

RUBBER

When incisions are made in the outer bark of the rubber tree, a plant found in various tropical areas, a milky liquid known as **latex** oozes out of the tree. Latex consists of a colloidal suspension of rubber particles in water. Originally, raw rubber was obtained from the liquid latex by careful evaporation of the water. Today it is obtained more easily by acidifying the colloidal latex with weak acids, such as acetic acid. The acid causes the rubber to coagulate into a white, doughy mass. The resulting raw rubber is sometimes milled, rolled into sheets, and smoked to produce smoked sheet rubber. If the latex is to be stored for a long time, or shipped long distances, coagulation of the rubber particles is prevented by the addition of ammonia water. You can observe some of the properties of raw rubber by *trying the following procedure.*

Stir a small quantity of acetic or formic acid into a beaker half full of latex. When the latex has coagulated into a number of large lumps of raw rubber, remove these and wash them repeatedly in water to remove the acid. Stretch, squeeze, and bounce one piece of this rubber. Dry some of these lumps of rubber. With one, try to erase the marks of a lead pencil. Immerse a second lump in hot water for 1 minute; now try to stretch it. Can you? Chill a third piece of this rubber in a refrigerator for 2 hours; then try stretching it. What happens?

Your observations illustrate the defects which limit the use of raw rubber. In hot weather, the rubber softens and becomes sticky; in very cold

37-1 Synthetic latex, like the natural product, is a colloidal suspension. When the synthetic latex is dispersed in water, its milky, rubbery appearance is clearly seen.

weather, it becomes hard and brittle. At both extremes of temperature, there is a reduction in elasticity.

Fabricating Rubber Articles

In 1839 Charles Goodyear accidentally discovered that the addition of sulfur to raw rubber improved its elasticity at varying temperatures and made it stronger and more resistant to wear. His discovery led to the modern practice of **vulcanization,** which involves heating raw rubber with sulfur or sulfur compounds. Vulcanized rubber is not only more elastic and flexible than raw rubber, but also it has other desirable characteristics. It is airtight and waterproof, absorbs vibrations, is a nonconductor of electricity, and can be made into an excellent adhesive.

The fabrication of rubber articles involves a series of steps which varies somewhat with the nature and purpose of the final article, and with the special ingredients which may be added for desired properties. Some of these ingredients are antioxidants, slowing the normal oxidation that causes rubber to become brittle. Zinc oxide and carbon black not only color the rubber but improve the toughness. Antimony sulfide and metallic oxides are also used to provide color.

Some articles, such as balloons, gloves, sponges, and bathing caps, are made directly from the latex. Sulfur and other ingredients are added to the liquid latex, and a mold of the desired article is dipped into the suspension. A thin film of rubber adheres to the mold, is coagulated by treatment with acid and drying, and is vulcanized by heating while still on the form. Thicker deposits of rubber can be made by repeating the procedure. A variation on this scheme is possible because the rubber particles in the latex suspension are electrically charged. If the mold is made an electrode, passage of an electric current through the latex causes the rubber particles to be deposited on the surface of the mold. Foam rubber products are made by whipping air into latex to which other ingredients have been added. The frothy foam produced is poured into molds and vulcanized by heating (Fig. 37-2).

37-2 The workman is stripping a latex foam cushion, produced from a frothy foam, from a vulcanizing "waffle iron."

Synthetic Rubber

The dream of synthesizing natural products is always recurrent because it frees man from the uncertainty of a dwindling natural supply. A further motivation behind the dream lies in the desire to improve the properties of the natural product. While the vulcanizing process improves the properties of natural rubber, certain shortcomings are still evident. If rubber bands made of vulcanized rubber have been stretched for many months, they lose their elasticity; they do not return to their original dimensions. Similarly, natural rubber absorbs certain organic liquids (kerosene and benzene), swells, and deteriorates. Yet even these weaknesses have been overcome.

The analysis of natural rubber, freed from associated vegetable fats, proteins, and mineral matter, leads to the formula C_5H_8. A study of the molecular weight of rubber indicates that it is a polymer of thousands of these monomer units. The true formula is actually best represented by $(C_5H_8)_n$—where n is measured in the thousands. Destructive distillation of rubber yields, among other substances, a hydrocarbon of the formula C_5H_8, known as *isoprene*.

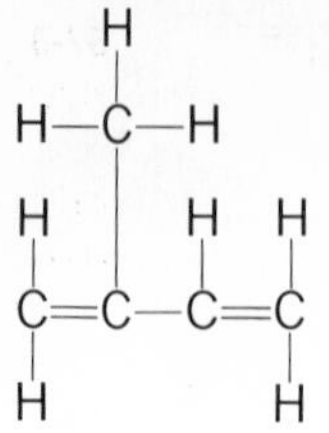

isoprene

Attempts to polymerize isoprene produced rubberlike materials, none of which equaled natural rubber in its properties. The polymerization of other unsaturated compounds not only resulted in the formation of rubberlike polymers, but also in materials having properties superior to those of natural rubber. Such research took advantage of the various ways in which polymerization proceeds.

Polymerization

The isoprene molecule has double bonds at the ends of the molecule. If these open out, the newly formed structural unit (monomer) has a reactive bond in each terminal carbon atom. The two inner carbon atoms of the isoprene molecule also form an additional covalent bond, resulting in a double bond.

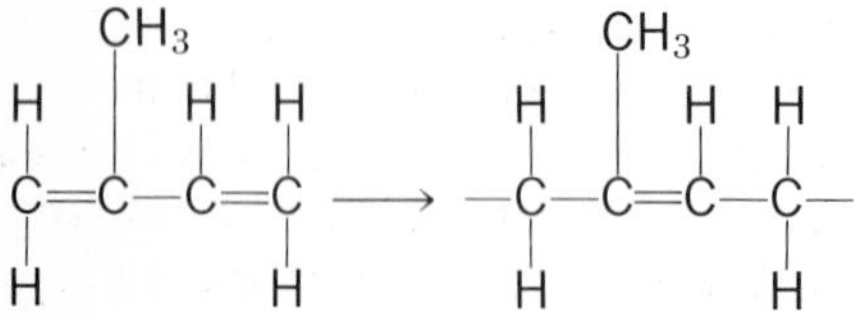

isoprene → isoprene monomer

A covalent bond can now form between the *end* carbon atoms of two isoprene molecules, *thus lengthening the chain of carbon atoms.*

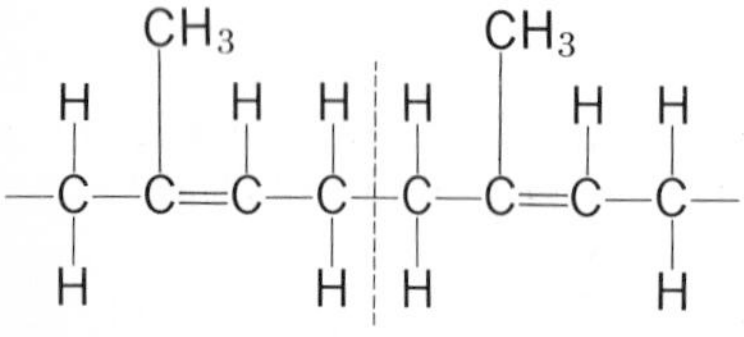

This *head-to-tail* process of addition of isoprene molecules (indicated by the dotted line in the formula above) can continue indefinitely. Polymers,

such as natural rubber, that form in this manner are known as **linear polymers.**

Consider two chains or *dimers,* each of which is formed by the linear polymerization of two isoprene molecules. If appropriate procedures involving heat and catalysts are used, new covalent bonds can be formed *between the two dimers.* The resulting structure represents a **cross-linked polymer,** capable of forming further polymers, either by cross-linkage or by head-to-tail addition. In vulcanization, sulfur atoms serve to provide the cross-link between the unsaturated carbon atoms of the polymer chains (Fig. 37-3). The cross-links vary with the vulcanizing procedures, the details of which are not completely understood. Nevertheless, it is this cross-linkage that accounts for the improved properties of vulcanized rubber. This type of polymerization, wherever it occurs, can be controlled by the catalyst employed and by the temperature used in the process.

In synthesizing new rubber molecules by polymerization, there is available to the chemist a possibility not found in nature. Natural rubber is a polymer of isoprene monomers. In the laboratory the chemist can combine *two different* monomers to form a new structural unit which is called a **copolymer. Copolymerization** provides the research chemist with a greater number of possibilities in his work. Not only can the properties of the product be varied by the choice of the monomers, but for any given pair of monomers, the properties of the product can be varied still further by varying the ratio of the monomers. Table 37-1, on page 637, summarizing a number of synthetic rubber products, shows how a variety of monomers is used to make today's synthetic rubber polymers. These raw materials are produced largely from unsaturated hydrocarbons obtained from coal tar or petroleum, or from their substitution products containing chlorine or nitrogen.

One of the first successful rubber substitutes was *neoprene,* made from acetylene and hydrogen chloride. These raw materials are reacted to form *chloroprene,* the monomer which is then polymerized (Fig. 37-4). Because chloroprene is unaf-

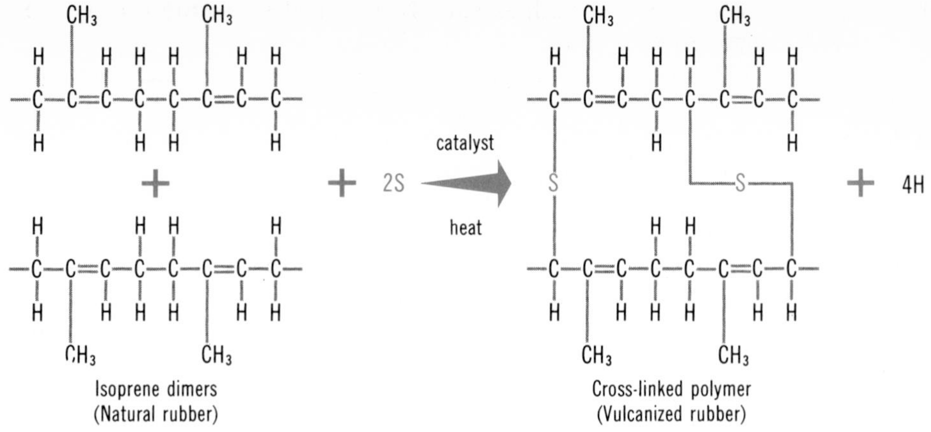

37-3 When two isoprene dimers undergo cross-linked polymerization in the presence of sulfur, heat, and an appropriate catalyst, sulfur atoms provide the cross-links in the product, vulcanized rubber.

Isoprene dimers
(Natural rubber)

Cross-linked polymer
(Vulcanized rubber)

fected by petroleum hydrocarbons, this synthetic has found wide use in hose designed to deliver gasoline and oil. Another rubber substitute was developed out of wartime needs. This is GR-S (Buna) rubber, made by copolymerizing butadiene (from petroleum) and styrene, an unsaturated hydrocarbon related to benzene (Fig. 37-5).

From Table 37-1, you can see that although the various polymers are superior to natural rubber in some properties, none of them shows very good heat resistance. Extremes of temperature cause a rapid decrease in the desirable properties of both natural and synthetic rubber. Elasticity is greatly reduced at low temperatures, and the polymers become brittle. In contrast, higher temperatures cause oxidation and destruction of the rubber. Recent developments in this field have overcome these handicaps by building polymers of an entirely different raw material. These units are not hydrocarbons but *silicones,* certain compounds of silicon.

Siloxanes

Atoms of silicon bond together much like atoms of carbon in the hydrocarbons. Although the bonds between silicon atoms are broken more readily than those between carbon atoms, the bonds between silicon and oxygen atoms are highly stable. The chemist has therefore been able to synthesize molecules in which silicon and oxygen atoms are bonded alternately to one another to form a stable chain. All organic silicon polymers composed of such silicon-oxygen chains with hydrocarbon groups attached to the silicon atoms are frequently classed as **silicones.**

Simple organic silicon compounds are usually prepared by heating the element silicon and alkyl chlorides in the presence of a copper catalyst.

$$RCl + Si \xrightarrow[\Delta]{Cu} RSiCl_3 + R_2SiCl_2 + R_3SiCl$$

The mixture of products is separated by fractional distillation. Reaction of any one of these

37-4 When chloroprene polymerizes to neoprene, the double bonds of the chloroprene molecule open out and form a reactive bond at each terminal carbon atom. A double bond also forms simultaneously between the two inner carbon atoms.

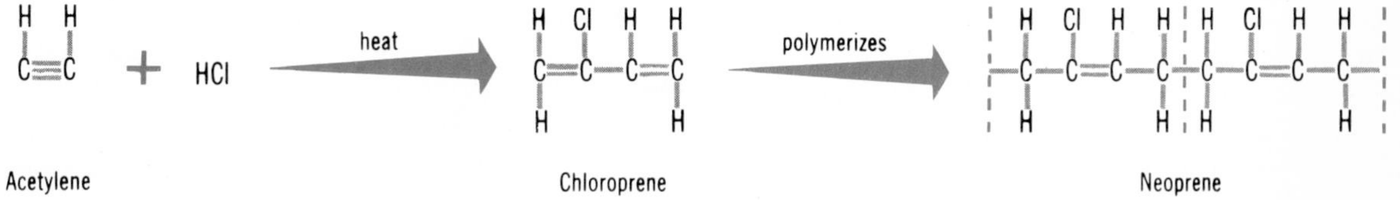

Acetylene

Chloroprene

Neoprene

RUBBER, PLASTICS, AND FIBERS   635

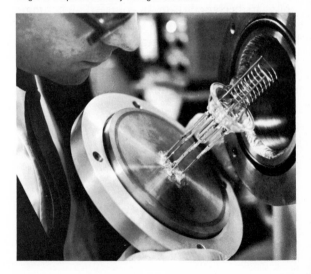

37-5 Butadiene and styrene are copolymerized to produce a long chain rubber polymer. The reactive bonds at each end of the latter molecule indicate that additional, similar units are bonded together in the production of GR-S (Buna) rubber.

compounds with water yields a chain of alternate silicon and oxygen atoms in which the alkyl groups are bonded to the silicone atoms.

$$-O-\underset{\underset{R}{|}}{\overset{\overset{R}{|}}{Si}}-O-\underset{\underset{R}{|}}{\overset{\overset{R}{|}}{Si}}-O-\underset{\underset{R}{|}}{\overset{\overset{R}{|}}{Si}}-O-$$

The resulting **siloxanes** vary considerably in their properties, depending on the nature of the alkyl groups and whether they are linear or cross-linked. Some are oils, some are jellies, and others are puttylike, rubbery solids. Some can even be deposited on the surface of textile fibers to yield water-repellent coatings. Certain silicone oils are constituents of cosmetic creams or protective coatings such as car waxes, where their water-repellent properties make them useful. Other silicone oils, which do not decompose at high temperatures or become very viscous at low temperatures, are especially valuable as lubricants in aircraft engines and other engines subjected to extremes of temperature.

Silicone Rubber

By varying the linkage and side groups in the siloxanes, various types of **silicone rubber** are produced. Silicone rubber remains flexible even at temperatures well below freezing, and is more stable to heat, oxidation, and chemical agents than natural rubber and other synthetics. It, like silicone oils, is valuable in aircraft operation where wide ranges of temperature are encountered. Various types of silicone rubber are particularly well suited for electrical insulation used under high-vacuum (Fig. 37-6), high-temperature, and high-voltage conditions.

The steady increase in the use of synthetic rubber indicates that these various polymers are superior to natural rubber for certain uses. The properties of these new products enable rubber to be used where it has never been used before. Today, synthetic rubber serves as the base for quick-drying paints suitable for cement and stone as well as wood and plaster.

QUESTIONS AND PROBLEMS

1. Differentiate between each of the following pairs of terms: (a) *monomer* and *polymer,* (b) *polymer* and *copolymer.*

37-6 In the high vacuum of outer space many sealants crack and fail. Here a silicone rubber is used as a seal around copper wires where they enter a steel, high-vacuum test chamber. The silicone rubber is unaffected by wide ranges of temperature and by flexing of the wires.

Table 37-1 **SYNTHETIC RUBBER**

Name	Monomer	Structural unit	Elasticity	Heat resistance	Resistance to organic solvents	Resistance to air oxidation	Impermeability to air	Uses
Natural rubber	Isoprene	(structural unit)	Good	Poor	Poor	Fair	Good	Soles and heels, overshoes and raincoats
Neoprene	Chloroprene	(structural unit)	Fair	Poor	Good	Good	Good	Hose for gasoline and petroleum chemicals, conveyer belts
Nitrile rubber	Butadiene + Acrylonitrile	(structural unit)	Good	Fair	Very good	Good	Fair	Hose for gasoline and oil, self-sealing gas tanks
Butyl rubber	Butadiene + Isobutene	(structural unit)	Good	Good	Good	Very good	Very good	Inner tubes, electrical insulation for high voltage
Thiokol rubber	Ethylene dichloride + Na_2S_4 Sodium tetrasulfide	(structural unit)	Fair	Fair	Good	Good	Fair	Tank linings and hose for petroleum products
GR-S (Buna) rubber	Styrene + Butadiene	(structural unit)	Fair	Good	Fair	Good	Fair	Tire treads

2. How does a linear polymer differ from a cross-linked polymer?

3. Define *isoprene, neoprene,* and *siloxane.*

4. Name several advantages of silicone and other synthetic types of rubber over natural rubber.

PLASTICS

The results of another branch of synthetic polymer research are the **plastics** in dinnerware, floor tiles, upholstery, safety glass, steering wheels, and patio roofs. Tough yet resilient, impervious to water and many chemicals, available in many shapes and forms, produced in a wide variety of colors, capable of being cut, drilled, and machined, these plastics are rapidly replacing many natural products. In less than 50 years, chemistry has provided new and better materials that have helped to conserve our natural resources.

Anything that is capable of being molded or shaped into a final definite form may be said to be plastic. On this basis, wax, rubber, glass, and clay are plastic materials. Today, however, the term *plastic* is used to represent a synthetic organic product that is made from coal, petroleum, or related raw materials and shaped into final form by heat and pressure.

Soften a lump of wax and mold it into any shape you wish. If the results are unsatisfactory, it is a simple matter to soften the wax and try again. The same procedure can be followed with clay, as long as the finished piece is not "fired." Once the piece has been fired and hardened into shape, it can no longer be softened and reworked.

Similarly, all plastic materials fall into two broad classes. Those which imitate wax in their behavior are known simply as **thermoplastics;** they can be softened by heating and molded into a new shape. Those materials that are shaped permanently by heat and pressure are known as **thermosetting plastics.** The difference between these types is found in the mechanism of polymerization. When the chains are formed by head-to-tail addition of the monomer units, the resulting product is usually a thermoplastic. If the new bonds are formed between *chains* as well as between units, the cross-linking produces an infusible (difficult to melt), thermosetting plastic.

Shaping the Plastic

Thermosetting materials lend themselves to the technique of **compression molding.** The raw material, in the form of powder or pellets, is placed in a heated mold, then considerable pressure is applied. The softened material is forced into the details of the mold to reproduce accurately the shape of the mold (Fig. 37-7). Thermoplastic materials permit another procedure known as **injection molding.** Here, the raw material is preheated and made soft or fluid; it is then fed into the mold where final pressure is applied. Rods, tubes, and sheets are formed in this manner by *extruding* the softened materials through openings of various shapes and sizes (Fig 37-8). The addition of accelerators (organic catalysts) hastens hardening of the plastic while eliminating the need for excessive pressure.

Bend a thin stick or rod between your hands; it snaps. Tie a number of sticks together, and

Phenol + Formaldehyde $\xrightarrow{\text{alkaline conditions}}$ Substituted phenol $\xrightarrow{\text{heat and acid catalyst}}$ H_2O (Water) + Intermediate product $\xrightarrow{\text{heat and pressure}}$

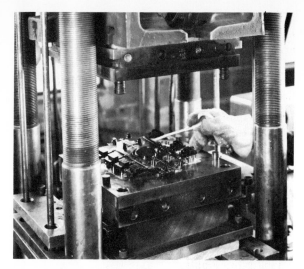

37-7 A thermosetting, phenol-formaldehyde plastic has been molded by compression into an electrical part that is being lifted from the mold.

37-8 Polyethylene, a thermoplastic, is being molded by extrusion. The plastic tubes are cooled in the water bath and cut into small pellets.

you find it difficult to bend, much less break them. The technique of building up layers of materials to form a strong union produces *laminated* products. Plywood, made of thin layers of wood bonded together, is an example of a laminated product produced before plastics were developed. If layers of glass cloth (or other fabric) are impregnated with plastic and the whole then subjected to heat and pressure, the result is a many-layered sandwich of strongly reinforced plastic. Such laminated plastics have been used in the construction of small boat hulls, as well as in patching plastic automobile bodies. When it is impossible to apply pressure, hardening of the plastic is achieved by the addition of accelerators and by "curing" under infrared lamps.

Thermosetting Plastics

When phenol (C_6H_5OH) and formaldehyde (HCHO) are kept together under weakly alkaline conditions, the formaldehyde molecules are added to the benzene ring of the phenol to form a series of substituted phenols. In the presence of acid catalysts at moderate temperatures, water is eliminated *between molecules* of these compounds to form products that are liquid or soft solids, somewhat soluble in alcohol, and fusible. This is the first stage in the building of larger polymer units (Fig. 37-9). At a higher temperature, water is eliminated *between these chains* to yield a longer-chain product that is less soluble in alcohol but still fusible. If the temperature is raised further and pressure is applied, a final re-

Phenol-formaldehyde polymer

37-9 Phenol and formaldehyde undergo a series of reactions to form a giant three-dimensional, high-molecular-weight, phenol-formaldehyde polymer. As its formation involves the elimination of water, phenol-formaldehyde is a condensation polymer.

RUBBER, PLASTICS, AND FIBERS   639

action occurs to form insoluble, infusible products which consist of a giant, three-dimensional network of units. High-molecular-weight materials formed in this way by the *elimination of water* are known as **condensation polymers.**

Condensation polymerization was the beginning of the story of *Bakelite,* the first modern thermosetting plastic, produced by the painstaking research of Dr. Leo Baekeland early in this century (Fig. 37-10). In practice, a molding material is produced by carrying the reaction to the second stage. The material is poured into trays to cool and harden, after which it is ground into a fine powder. Fillers are added to provide bulk and special properties to the final product. **Plasticizers,** substances which make the whole mass easier to shape, are also added. It is this combination of materials that is placed in a mold and transformed by heat and pressure into the third stage material—thermosetting Bakelite.

Bakelite, the foremost example of the **phenolformaldehyde** plastics, found a ready market in such articles as radio cabinets, electrical parts, and bottle caps. Solutions of the second-stage, less-soluble plastic could be used as varnishes and baking enamels. In recent years, Bakelite has been used to make agitators for washing machines and has been adapted to make coatings for the interior surfaces of tin cans. It is admirably suited for this use, being tasteless, odorless, resistant to food acids and chemicals, and able to withstand the heat of sterilization.

A whole new series of thermosetting plastics, or *resins,* has been developed by replacing the

37-10 Dr. Leo Baekeland's laboratory, photographed around 1909. Much of the laboratory glassware and apparatus used by this pioneer in the study of thermosetting plastics is typical of a laboratory of today.

phenol or formaldehyde (or both) in the original Bakelite formula with other chemicals. The resins produced have a great variety of useful properties. For example, if urea $[CO(NH_2)_2]$ and formaldehyde are mixed at a pH of 7.6 to 7.8, compounds that are water-soluble and colorless form. At higher temperatures and pressures, these com-

37-11 In the formation of urea-formaldehyde resin by condensation, molecules of formaldehyde bond with molecules of urea to form two increasingly complex intermediate products, prior to the formation of the final polymer.

Formaldehyde   Urea

Intermediate product

pounds polymerize further by condensation (elimination of water between molecules) to yield thermosetting long-chain polymers (Fig. 37-11). These and other thermosetting plastics are summarized in Table 37-2.

Thermoplastic Materials

The first successful thermoplastic material, and at the same time the first commercially successful plastic, was **Celluloid,** developed a hundred years ago by John Hyatt. The cellulose used in producing cellulose nitrate and then Celluloid is nitrated only partially because the fully nitrated compound is highly explosive. Though the cellulose nitrate alone cannot be molded, Hyatt discovered that camphor serves as an excellent plasticizer. In practice, cellulose nitrate is mixed with fillers, coloring matter, camphor, and alcohol to form a gel. This material is allowed to age while some of the alcohol evaporates; the remaining combination of materials is then molded into rods, tubes, and sheets. **Cellulose nitrate plastics** are tough, water-resistant, and easy to color and machine. Fountain-pen barrels and comb and brush sets were typical applications.

But this material is highly flammable and discolors in strong sunlight. Cellulose nitrate plastics have therefore been largely replaced by other cellulose esters without these shortcomings. Cellulose acetate, one of these esters, is made by reacting cellulose with acetic acid and acetic anhydride in the presence of sulfuric acid. **Cellulose acetate plastics** are less flammable and less affected by sunlight than nitrate plastics and are superior to them in mechanical strength, shock resistance, and electrical properties. The use of cellulose acetate plastics in airplane cockpit enclosures, automobile steering wheels, electrical appliances, and knife handles reflects these various properties.

A combination of cellulose acetate and *cellulose butyrate* duplicates these excellent properties with the added feature of lower water absorption. Articles made of this combination therefore maintain their dimensions better than those fashioned from either cellulose acetate or nitrate alone. Steering wheels, telephone sets, and knife handles are large-scale applications. Safety glass is made by bonding a sheet of this plastic between two sheets of plate glass by means of heat and pressure. Though safety glass will break, it will not shatter because the plastic holds the broken pieces of glass in place.

Noncellulose Thermoplastics

Cellulose ester plastics were followed by a series of completely different thermoplastic materials with a great variety of new and useful properties. Best known and first of these is *nylon,* perhaps more familiar as a fiber but nonetheless a perfect example of a plastic material. The raw materials for the original nylon were cyclohexane and butadiene, derivatives of petroleum and coal tar. These two compounds are converted to adipic acid $[C_4H_8(COOH)_2]$ and hexamethylene diamine $[C_6H_{12}(NH_2)_2]$, respectively. A combination of these compounds forms hexamethylene diamine adipate (nylon salt), the monomer for the

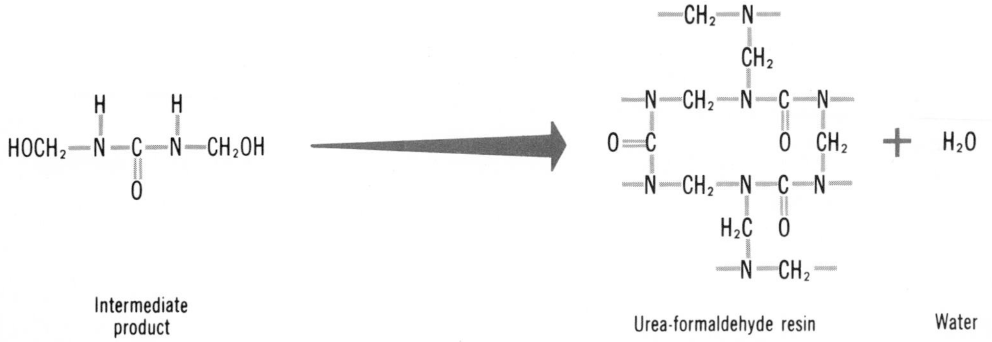

Intermediate product

Urea-formaldehyde resin   Water

Table 37-2 **THERMOSETTING PLASTICS**

Name	Raw materials	Properties	Uses
Bakelite	Phenol + HCHO Formaldehyde	Usually black or brown; good insulator, hard but brittle; can be sawed, drilled and machined	Cabinets, electrical insulators, bottle caps, varnishes and baking enamels; can be prepared in light colors to provide a casting material suitable for buttons and plastic jewelry
Resorcinol-formaldehyde	Resorcinol + HCHO Formaldehyde	Strong adhesive; unaffected by moisture, bacteria or fungi	Bonding wood or wood products, such as plywood
Urea-formaldehyde	$CO(NH_2)_2$ Urea + HCHO Formaldehyde	Easily colored; strong, adhesive, white in color	Adhesives, buttons, dishes, novelties, "wet-strength" paper products, baking enamels
Melamine-formaldehyde	Melamine + HCHO Formaldehyde	Easily colored; strong, adhesive, white in color	Dinnerware, adhesive for laminated products
Alkyd	Polyhydroxy alcohol (ethylene glycol, glycerine) esters of phthalic acid	Products are not moldable but can be suspended or dissolved in suitable liquids	Varnishes or baking enamels
Polyesters	Esters of unsaturated alcohols or unsaturated acids	Low density, transparent, brilliant colors, good strength	Translucent panels, reinforced (glass fiber) chemical tanks
Epoxy	Ethylene oxide H_2C-CH_2 + Phenols	Resistant to water and chemicals, abrasion-resistant, shockproof	Varnishes, adhesives for bonding wood and wood products

Table 37-3   THERMOPLASTIC MATERIALS

Name	Raw materials	Properties	Uses
Nylon (polyamides)	Hexamethylene diamine + adipic acid	Tough, flexible, low density, low water absorption	Gears, bearings, rope As a copolymer: small boat bodies
Cellulose nitrate (Celluloid)	Cellulose nitrate	Flexible, tough, water resistant, easily colored and machined, flammable, discolored in sunlight	Fountain-pen barrels, comb and brush sets
Acetate	Cellulose acetate	Smolders but does not burn, strong, shock resistant, good insulator	Automobile steering wheels, electrical appliances, knife handles, transparent sheeting, safety-type photographic film
Polyethylene	Ethene (ethylene) $H_2C{=}CH_2$	Resistant to water and chemicals, low density, good insulator, flexible	Piping, squeeze bottles, insulation, protective tape for underground metal pipe, for packaging film
Teflon	Tetrafluoroethene $F_2C{=}CF_2$ other halogenated ethenes	Resistant to almost all chemicals	Valves and gaskets for handling corrosive chemicals
Acrylates (Lucite, Plexiglas)	Esters of acrylic acid	Colorless, transparent, stable to light, moderate temperature and weathering	Canopies for airplane cockpits and gun turrets, display items, picture frames, comb and brush sets
Vinyl	Vinyl chloride $\overset{\displaystyle H}{\underset{}{}}\ \overset{\displaystyle H}{\underset{}{}}$ $HC{=}C{-}Cl$	Tough, resistant to water and chemicals, flexible	Unbreakable records, floor tile, garden hose, cable coatings, lining for tanks, waterproofing for fabrics As a copolymer: piping, upholstery, and sheet packaging material
Polystyrene	Styrene $-CH{=}CH_2$	Transparent and brilliant, easily colored, good insulator	Insulator for electronic components, refrigerator containers As a copolymer: piping, battery cases, lightweight building material and insulation
Silicone plastics	Silicones	Low water absorption, withstands extremes of temperature, provides water repellency, good insulator	Waterproofing concrete and shingles, for high-temperature applications

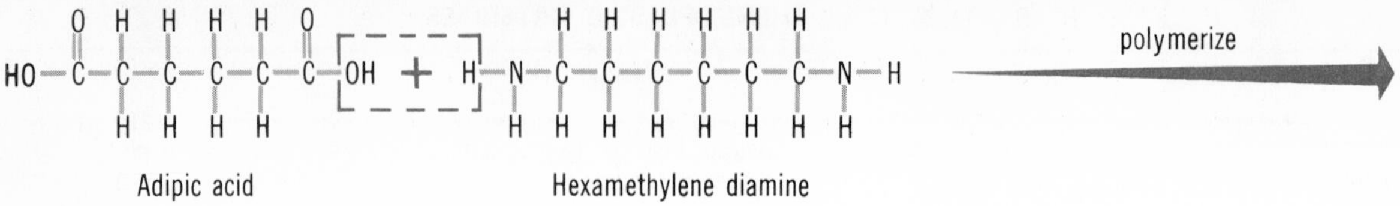

37-12 By condensation, molecules of adipic acid and hexamethylene diamine combine to form the monomer, hexamethylene diamine adipate. Nylon is a polymer or continuous chain of these monomers bonded together.

process. At elevated temperatures the nylon salt polymerizes by condensation to form long-chain polymers (Fig. 37-12).

Variation in the raw materials has enabled the chemist to prepare a whole series of nylons with a wide range of properties. Being tough and flexible, nylon is shaped into gears and bearings for machines, as well as into cables and wire coatings where rough use is encountered. Many of the bobbins used to wind fibers are made of nylon, less subject than metal or wood to attack by the chemicals used in other fibers. You will study some additional properties and uses of nylon shortly in your study of synthetic fibers. Nylon can be copolymerized with epoxy plastics (made from ethylene oxide and phenols) to yield products which maintain high strength over a considerable range of temperature. Such compositions are used to make small boat hulls, piping, and aircraft components.

37-13 This polyethylene suit—affectionately dubbed Homer's Hideous Hallucination—prevents radioactive dust from contaminating workers. The long, hollow tail, through which the worker crawls into the suit, stretches into an adjoining "safe room."

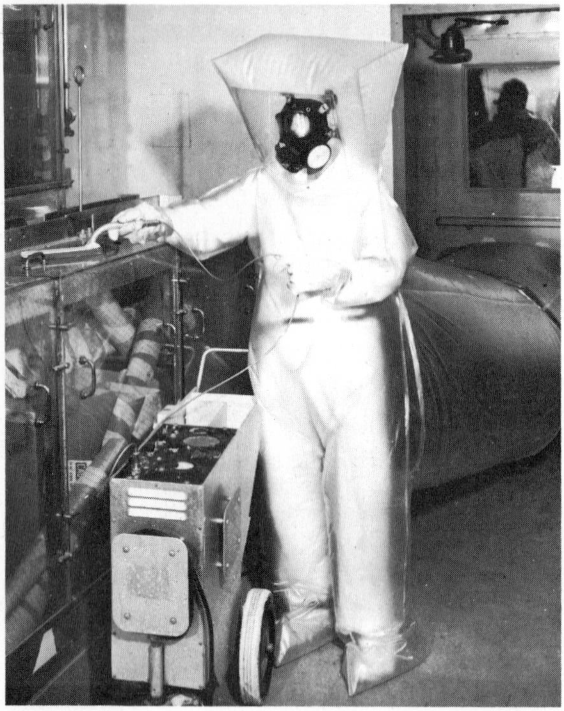

When ethene (ethylene) is subjected to varying pressures at moderate temperatures, this simple hydrocarbon polymerizes into large units known as **polyethylene.** Resistant to water and chemicals, flexible at temperatures well below freezing, and low in density, polyethylene is used extensively as piping for the chemical and petroleum industries, and in irrigation and waste disposal. Polyethylene's flexibility permits its use in squeeze bottles for powders and liquids—and in the unusual suit shown in Fig. 37-13. Since its insulating properties are superb, polyethylene is used as an insulator in high-voltage circuits. In the form of a tape, polyethylene is being wrapped around underground metal piping to prevent corrosion. Suspensions of this plastic are also being used to coat paper and cloth. A closely related plastic is now being made by polymerizing propene. Some of the many other thermoplastic materials which have been developed in recent years are summarized in Table 37-3.

Why are there so many plastic types, with more being developed? The discussion of properties and uses for the many materials described indicates that no one plastic suffices for all purposes. Some are hard and easily machined and maintain their dimensions; but they fracture on impact.

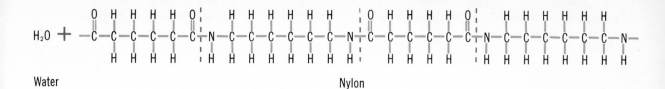

H_2O +

Water   Nylon

Others withstand shock but absorb water, thereby changing their dimensions. Some make ideal insulators at low voltage, but fail at high voltages. Resistance to chemicals may be the desired quality for some applications, resistance to sunlight for others. Some are crystal clear and colorless, while others can be made only in dark shades. And so each plastic fits particular needs, and new ones not only find a place but also may create new uses by virtue of new properties.

QUESTIONS AND PROBLEMS

1. Define each of the following terms: *plastic, condensation polymer, polyethylene, nylon.*

2. Differentiate between each of the following pairs of terms: (a) *thermoplastic* and *thermosetting plastic,* (b) *Bakelite* and *Celluloid.*

3. (a) By what two methods are plastics shaped? (b) Describe each process briefly.

4. Compare and contrast each of the following: (a) phenol-formaldehyde and urea-formaldehyde plastics, (b) cellulose nitrate and cellulose acetate plastics.

FIBERS

Fibers from which yarn can be spun and cloth woven have been known to man for centuries. Cotton and linen were readily obtainable from plant life, and wool from sheep and goats. Observation of the life habits of the mulberry moth led the Chinese to the discovery of silk, long a preciously guarded secret. Besides their difference in origin, these fibers vary in a number of properties. If you view them under the microscope, they are distinctively different (Fig. 37-14). Cotton fibers are flat and twisted, while linen occurs in jointed tubes resembling the structure of bamboo. Wool has a scaly structure, so that fibers stick readily to each other; silk has a smooth, tubular structure. Chemically, cotton and linen are polymers of glucose. Wool and silk are protein in nature; they are polymers of simple chains of various amino acids.

The properties and chemical behavior of these fibers are a direct consequence of the features just mentioned. Because wool fibers stick together readily, woolen cloth traps a considerable amount of air; it is this air which makes wool a good insulator. Since this feature is lacking in cotton,

37-14 These phase contrast microscope photographs of fibers of cotton, linen, wool, and silk, respectively, reveal the distinctive characteristic of each fiber. From their external structure you cannot predict their origin (1000 ×).

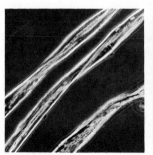   

linen, and silk, cloth woven from these fibers is cooler than wool.

When cotton and linen are burned, little or no ash is left, and the odor of burning paper, itself a cellulose product, is evident. Destructive distillation of cotton and linen fibers produces fumes acid to litmus. Wool and silk burn with difficulty, charring to form gummy residues. When these fibers are destructively distilled, the nitrogen in their proteins is transformed into ammonia, detectable by moist pink litmus paper. The sulfur in wool is changed to hydrogen sulfide, recognized by its effect on moist lead acetate paper. Both cotton and linen are unaffected by solutions of bases, although attacked by acids. Wool and silk are attacked and weakened by warm solutions of both acids and bases, particularly when concentrated.

Asbestos

No study of natural fibers would be complete without mention of two fibers which find wide use in forms other than garments. One of these is asbestos, an example of a mineral fiber. Asbestos is a linear hydrated magnesium silicate, easily separated into its fibers. It is fireproof, unaffected by almost all chemicals, and a good insulator; therefore it is used extensively in the chemistry laboratory in the form of sheets. The fibers can be woven into blankets and curtains designed to extinguish or prevent the spread of fires. Asbestos fibers are also fashioned into suits for those engaged in extinguishing particularly hazardous fires.

Paper

The most important use of a fiber other than in clothing is in paper. Paper is made from the cellulose of various trees; a relatively small source of the raw material is scrap cotton and linen cloth. In the tree the cellulose fibers are "cemented" together by a substance called *lignin*. In the preparation of paper pulp, the logs, already cut into small lengths and freed of their bark, are cut into small chips by rotating knives. These chips are now cooked under pressure in solutions of various chemicals, such as sodium hydroxide, calcium bisulfite, and sodium sulfide. The particular chemicals used and the temperature and time required vary with the source of the cellulose. This treatment frees the cellulose from its lignin bond; the fibers can now be washed free of the lignin and other vegetable matter in the original wood. These fibers are usually bleached before being made into paper.

In the manufacture of paper (Fig. 37-15), cellulose fibers are mixed with water and agitated in special machines (beaters). This treatment helps the fibers to form a closer and more dense mat, making the final paper more opaque. It is in this stage of the process that various other materials such as fillers, sizing, or coloring matter are added. Fillers are designed to fill the spaces among the cellulose fibers and make the paper easier to write on. Fillers are usually insoluble inorganic materials such as calcium carbonate, titanium dioxide, or talc and clay. The sizing of paper serves to produce a smooth, lustrous coating on the surface of the paper. Starches and gums may be used as sizing; another practice is to deposit an aluminum soap coating on the paper.

After the paper pulp is "beaten" and the chemicals added, the suspension is fed into a moving wire screen which vibrates from side to side as it moves along. The water in the suspension drains through the screen, leaving a closely matted layer of cellulose fibers. This mat is passed through a series of rollers that mechanically squeeze out most of the remaining moisture. Then additional rollers, steam-heated, compress and dry the mat to its finished form. Developments in the plastics field have led to the use of plastic materials for sizing; these not only produce a smoother surface on the paper but increase its wet strength considerably.

Synthetic Fibers

The great expense of silk, even after the secret of the silkworm had been learned from the Chinese, stimulated efforts to imitate or duplicate this fiber. One early method was devised by John

a Tremendous piles of wood chips (above) serve as the raw material for making paper.

b In the digester (far right) the wood chips are "cooked" with chemicals under steam pressure and reduced to a wet mass of pulp.

c In the washer (above right), the pulp revolves on large drums, where it is sprayed to remove leftover chemicals and non-fibrous substances.

d In large beaters (right), the fibers in the pulp are separated for bonding. Coloring, sizing, and fillers are also added here.

e After the fibers are rubbed, cut, and reduced to proper length, water is added and the pulp moved over the giant wire mesh where a wet sheet is formed (right). Finally the sheet is dried, given required smoothness, and placed on rollers.

Mercer, an Englishman. He discovered that when cotton is placed under tension and soaked in concentrated solutions of sodium hydroxide, the fiber becomes more lustrous and more easily dyed. In this treatment the dull, flat, twisted cotton fibers are straightened and rounded, thus imitating the structure of the silk fiber. But the resulting **mercerized cotton** is still quite unlike natural silk—so the search for synthetic fibers goes on. Today you are well acquainted with numerous silklike synthetic fibers, some of which not only equal but surpass the natural fiber. How did these fibers come into being? The answer to this question is provided by a study of the habits of the silkworm.

The mulberry leaf, which serves as the raw material, is eaten by the worm and digested into a liquid substance. The liquid is then forced through openings in the lower lip of the insect; it hardens on exposure to air. An analysis of this process indicates that there are three fundamental factors in silk fiber formation. First, the raw material, being of vegetable origin, bears a close relationship to the cellulose of cotton and trees; this material is readily available to the chemist. Second, the digestion process of both plants and animals is designed to transform food into a soluble form. Cellulose (or other raw material) must somehow be changed to the liquid state. And finally, the solution process must be reversed so that a solid material appears in the final stage. It is important to note at this point that our analysis, while good, has been oversimplified. Although the silkworm feeds on cellulose material, its digestive process changes the cellulose into a *protein* material, the silk. The chemist has been unable to duplicate this process. In his preparation of synthetic silk, he often uses totally different raw materials.

These steps, with variations, are the basis of *any* method now used in the preparation of artificial fibers. The raw material, once only cellulose, now includes chemicals derived from petroleum and soft coal. While some of these are dissolved, others are melted to provide a liquid. The liquefied material is forced through many fine openings called **spinnerets** (Fig. 37-16) to form threads. Any process of shaping a substance by forcing it through fine holes or very narrow slits is known as **extrusion.** In some cases (viscose silk) the chemicals used to dissolve the raw material are neutralized and the fibrous material precipitated. In others (cellulose acetate) the solvent is evaporated from the extruded liquid by a current of ascending warm air as the liquid passes down through a tower. The remaining solid forms the fiber or filament. Where the liquid is formed by melting the raw material, as in nylon, a similar operation forms the fiber as the extruded material cools. Each of the techniques described is also adapted to the formation of a sheet of material; the liquid is extruded through a narrow slit, usually onto a rotating drum.

The Viscose Process

Cellulose itself serves as the raw material for two methods of making a silk substitute commonly known as rayon. Because few solvents are known for cellulose, it must be converted into a

37-16 This close-up view shows filaments emerging from a spinneret that transforms liquid acetate into threadlike synthetic fibers.

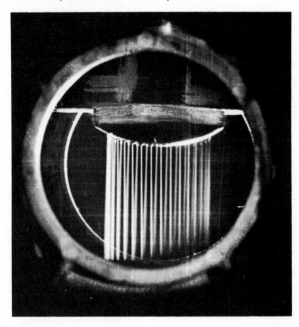

more easily soluble substance. The first of these methods, producing the major fraction of synthetic silk made from cellulose, is the **viscose process** which involves three steps summarized in Fig. 37-17.

First, purified cellulose is soaked in warm, moderately concentrated sodium hydroxide solution for a number of hours. After the basic solution has been squeezed out, the resulting *alkali cellulose* is shredded and kept for two or three hours at a moderate temperature. A further period of aging follows at a slightly higher temperature. These periods of aging result in chemical changes which cause the succeeding steps to occur more easily.

Next, carbon disulfide (CS_2) is added; it reacts with the alkali cellulose to form an orange-red solid that is soluble in sodium hydroxide solution. Desired pigments may be added to this solution, which is "ripened" for a period of four to five days at a moderate temperature. During these periods of aging and ripening, the liquid is filtered to remove any suspended matter. Gas bubbles, which would break the continuity of the filament in the final steps, are removed by placing the liquid under low pressure.

Finally, the solution is extruded through spinnerets into a bath containing dilute sulfuric acid. The action of the sulfuric acid decomposes the originally soluble (orange-red) compound to form a precipitated filament composed of cellulose. The filament, however, is no longer flat and twisted as in cotton, but it has the smooth, tubular structure of natural silk. The filament prepared in this manner is thoroughly washed to remove decomposition products resulting from the acid treatment, then bleached and washed again.

Viscose silk is an example of *regenerated* cellulose. Although the original solid raw material is converted into a soluble compound, the final step changes this liquid back to solid cellulose. The fiber, however, is now tubular and lustrous, in imitation of silk. Extrusion of this fiber in sheet form results in the formation of well-known *cellophane.*

The Cellulose Acetate Process

The second process, the **acetate process,** takes advantage of the fact that cellulose esters are much more soluble in organic solvents than cellulose itself. In fact, the first silklike fiber was made from the ester cellulose nitrate in 1884 by Count Hilaire B. de Chardonnet. Three years later the first gown made from "artificial silk" was displayed at the Paris Exposition—and a new industry was born.

The extreme flammability of cellulose nitrate material made its use in fabrics hazardous, and within a short time cellulose acetate was found to be a more suitable raw material. Cellulose acetate is made by treating purified cellulose with a mixture of acetic acid and acetic anhydride, sulfuric acid serving as the catalyst. When the reaction is complete, the product is washed free of these chemicals, dried, and dissolved in acetone. The filtered solution is extruded downward into a tower against a current of warm air; the air removes the acetone vapors and leaves the cellulose acetate in the form of a continuous filament. Extrusion of the solution through a narrow slit produces the acetate in the form of a sheet which is both pliable and moistureproof. You have already met it in the form of the "window" in a mailing envelope, and as the base in photographic safety film which smolders but does not burn. In the acetate process, economy is effected by reuse of the solvent. Acetate silk loses less strength than viscose silk when wet; but a hot iron destroys it and certain organic solvents dissolve it.

Fibers from Protein

While some chemists were transforming cellulose into silklike fibers, other chemists were busy utilizing natural proteins as raw materials for fibers. One such researcher prepared a woolly fiber from the nitrogenous casein of milk, but the product never came into general use. Recent work has produced a more successful fiber resembling wool by using *zein,* the protein in corn. Known commercially as *Vicara,* the fiber is woolly in appearance, and is widely used in blends with other fibers. It is not as strong as cotton or most

a   Cellulose, the raw material for production of viscose, may be taken from the wood pulp of pine trees (left).

b   Cellulose also is taken from cotton linters, short fibers left on seeds after being separated from the cotton boll (above).

d   After aging, the "crumb" is combined with carbon disulfide. The product, orange-red in color, is being removed from the drum (left).

c   After the raw material is changed to pulp, it is pressed into sheets that are changed chemically to "alkali cellulose." When the latter is dry, revolving blades in the machine above tear the sheets into fluffy particles or crumbs.

e   The cellulose crumb, mixed with a weak solution of caustic soda, is converted to a liquid "viscose solution."

f   The viscose solution is pumped through fine holes in the spinneret into an acid bath (above). On contact with the acid, the viscose solidifies into solid filaments of viscose silk—rayon.

650

synthetic fibers. Similar research is being conducted with proteins from peanuts and soy beans.

A True Synthetic Fiber

True synthetic silk fibers arose out of attempts to synthesize compounds bearing a structural relationship to the proteins. But such fibers begin life far from the animal and vegetable kingdoms, utilizing as raw materials benzene from coal tar, butadiene from petroleum, chlorine and hydrogen. This research led to the preparation of nylon, the first truly synthetic silklike fiber, in 1935. The preparation of the nylon monomer (Fig. 37-18) has already been discussed under plastics (page 644). The polymer prepared from the nylon monomer salt bears a resemblance to the protein in silk. By modifying this salt, a whole series of nylons of varying properties is produced.

While natural fibers consist of a bundle of *parallel* chains of polymers, the chains in nylon and other synthetic fibers are arranged in a random fashion which reduces the strength of the product. The spinning process therefore includes a step in which the fiber is stretched to a number of times its own length. This treatment arranges the chains in parallel fashion and greatly increases the strength of the fiber.

Nylon, which is stronger than natural silk, has the advantage of losing only a small fraction of its strength when wet. However, it must be ironed with care since it melts if overheated. Nylon is used in making stockings, wearing apparel, and parachutes, as well as the cord fabric in rubber tires. Its great strength and low water absorption have made it equally useful for fishing lines and for hawsers used in mooring ocean liners. The control of filament diameter during extrusion provides a range of fibers suitable for the sheerest of stockings to bristles for brushes.

Other Synthetic Fibers

Many synthetic fibers using other raw materials followed nylon. These differ from nylon just as nylon differs from cotton. *Dacron*, like nylon, represents the results of research into an entirely new polymer material, created by polymerizing

certain esters. The polymer is prepared for extrusion, and the filament is treated similarly to nylon (Fig. 37-19). Dacron's strength, resilience, and resistance to wrinkles makes it suitable for use in clothing and draperies. It has the disadvantage of melting and burning easily. Equally successful in the apparel field has been *Orlon*, a polymer of acrylonitrile used in rubber synthesis. The filament is prepared by extruding a solution of the polymer in the same manner as cellulose acetate; the fiber is then stretched. Orlon is outstanding with respect to strength and durability; it is used for shirts, suits, and pile fabrics.

Continuing research in the field of synthetic fibers is doubly valuable. It not only helps to create useful materials, but it also finds new uses for waste plant materials such as stalks, bark, and

37-18 The molecular arrangement of these two liquids (Figure 37-12) is such that they polymerize upon meeting to form a film of nylon strong enough to be pulled from the beaker and twisted into a rope.

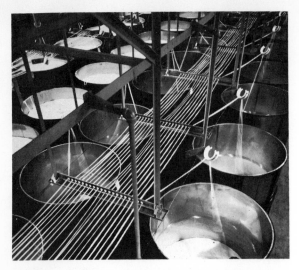

37-19 Moving down from the upper right, Dacron strands accumulate as another strand is added from each bin to the ropelike tow. A total of about twenty "endless" strands flow into a machine, where all are stretched to give them added strength.

stumps. The development of synthetic fibers has also stimulated the processors of natural fibers to seek ways of improving these fibers, such as in shrinkproofing and mothproofing wool.

Have we finished the list of synthetic fibers? Hardly—at best our list is complete only for the moment. While you read this sentence, some chemist is preparing a new raw material, or another chemist is anxiously awaiting the result of his first experiment with a new polymer.

QUESTIONS AND PROBLEMS

1. Describe the appearance of wool, silk, cotton, and linen fibers under the microscope.

2. Define each of the following: *Dacron, Orlon, Vicara, mercerized cotton, asbestos.*

3. Describe briefly the process of paper making.

4. How does the viscose process for making rayon differ from the cellulose acetate process?

5. (a) What are the raw materials used in making nylon? (b) List three distinct uses of nylon, and

indicate what property of nylon determines its use in each instance.

VALUE OF THE CONCEPT

THE CONCEPT

The keystone behind the preparation of synthetic rubber, plastics, and fibers may be summed up in one word—polymers. Natural rubber and fibers exist as polymers of simple molecules. Glucose is the unit in cellulose, amino acids in protein fibers, and isoprene in rubber. These monomers may be linked in head-to-tail fashion to form linear polymers; or bonding may occur between such chains to form cross-linked two- or three-dimensional polymers. The final polymer is an aggregate of hundreds or thousands of the monomer molecules. Condensation polymers may be formed by elimination of water between simple molecules; such polymers may represent either linear or cross-linked polymers.

The preparation of synthetic polymers which duplicate or improve on the natural product has followed two main courses. The first seeks to modify a natural polymer and give it new properties. Thus cellulose is modified by conversion to a soluble form which can be shaped into fibers or sheets. In the acetate process, the cellulose is changed into cellulose acetate in the finished product. In the viscose process, the finished product consists of cellulose that has been regenerated to acquire silklike characteristics.

The second course of polymer research starts with materials bearing some structural resemblance to the natural monomer. This procedure is best illustrated in the preparation of nylon. The synthetic monomer contains the same elements present in the silk protein, in a similar arrangement. This course of polymer research was notably successful in the preparation of synthetic rubber, using monomers related to, but different from, the natural isoprene polymer. The use of synthetic monomers provides the chemist with means of varying the properties of the final product. It further enables him to use the technique of copolymerizing two different monomers. Further modifications result in synthetic polymers without the disadvantages of natural products but superior in other respects.

Plastic polymers, regardless of the raw materials used, fall into two broad classes. Those which can be softened by heat after they have been formed and reshaped are called thermoplastics. Cellulose acetate, nylon, and polyethylene fall into this group. Urea-formaldehyde plastics and Bakelite, infusible after they have been formed, are called thermosetting plastics. Either type of plastic may be shaped by compression in a heated mold, or it may be extruded through dies to form rods, tubes, sheets, and other shapes.

USING THE CONCEPT

Using the Basic Concept

1. (a) Why is natural rubber vulcanized? (b) What substance is used in vulcanization?
2. (a) Write the formula for isoprene. (b) Why is this not considered the formula for latex?
3. How does a polymer differ from a copolymer?
4. How is condensation polymerization related to linear polymerization and cross-linked polymerization?
5. Show by diagram how *each* of the polymers below could polymerize by linear polymerization:

(a) $H_2C{=}\overset{\underset{\textstyle |}{F}}{C}{-}CH_3$ (b) $H_2C{=}\overset{\underset{\textstyle |}{Cl}}{C}{-}\overset{\underset{\textstyle |}{H}}{C}{=}CH_2$

(c) $C_6H_5{-}CH{=}CHBr$

6. How do neoprene and GR-S rubber differ from natural rubber?
7. (a) What is silicone rubber? (b) Give several uses of different types of silicone rubber and state the property on which each use is based.
8. Would the chemist use thermoplastics or thermosetting plastics in attempting to produce a new synthetic fiber? Why?

9. (a) How does compression molding of plastics differ from injection molding? (b) How does an extruded plastic differ from a laminated plastic?
10. (a) What type of plastics have replaced the early Bakelite (phenol-formaldehyde) plastic? (b) What are the advantages of the newer plastics?
11. (a) What type of plastics have replaced the first Celluloid (cellulose nitrate) plastics? (b) What are the advantages of the newer plastics?
12. (a) Name two widely used noncellulose thermoplastics. (b) Give three uses of each product named.
13. (a) List the three main problems that had to be solved before synthetic fibers could be produced. (b) Describe the general process by which synthetic fibers are produced.
14. (a) What is the difference between viscose rayon and cellophane? (b) between mercerized cotton and viscose silk? (c) between regenerated cellulose fibers and cellulose acetate fibers?
15. (a) How is nylon processed to increase its strength? (b) List several other synthetic fibers and indicate briefly their chemical origin.
16. Using articles found in the home, list those materials which are used both as fibers and as plastics.
17. From a study of the raw material used to make synthetic plastics and rubber, explain why it can be said that these synthetics are made from "coal, air, salt, and water."
18. How would the molecular weights of the cellulose esters compare with that of cellulose? Why?

Relating Terms Within the Concept

Select the letter of the term in Column B on the following page that is most closely related to each term in Column A. Do not use a term more than once.

COLUMN A	COLUMN B
1. nylon	a. boat hulls
2. cross-linked polymer	b. colloidal particles
	c. condensation polymer
3. rubber	d. extrusion
4. silicones	e. glucose
5. mercerized cotton	f. isoprene
6. wide temperature range	g. molding plastics
7. regenerated cellulose	h. neoprene
	i. phenol-formaldehyde plastic
8. acetate rayon	j. polyethylene
9. plasticizer	k. Si—O bonding
10. cellulose	l. sodium hydroxide
11. latex	m. thermoplastics
12. laminated plastics	n. thermosetting
	o. viscose

Solving Problems Within the Concept

1. What are the percentage compositions of $(C_6H_{10}O_5)_{5,000}$ and $(C_6H_{10}O_5)_{10,000}$? (Can you make a statement about the answers to be expected before doing any calculations?)
2. Determine the molecular weight of a structural unit of GR-S rubber.
3. A sample of cloth containing both woolen and cotton fibers weighs 2.50 grams. It is heated in 10 percent NaOH for 1 hour, filtered, washed, and dried. The residue weighs 0.375 gram. What is the percentage composition of the cloth?
4. A monomer has the composition: C 45.0 percent, H 3.8 percent, F 17.8 percent, and Cl 33.4 percent by weight. What is its formula?

Applying the Concept

1. Monomers will polymerize slowly if they are kept for a long time. How might the producers of monomers prevent such polymerization until the monomer is ready for use?
2. Why should fatty or waxy stains on nylon or cellulose acetate fabrics *not* be removed by means of acetone?
3. If you were given a supply of various plastics, how would you determine which are thermoplastic and which are thermosetting?
4. What advantage would plastic material have in the production of laminated materials, such as plywood, compared to the glues formerly used for this purpose?
5. A shirt made of Dacron-cotton fibers does not wrinkle easily, but a linen shirt does. Account for the difference.
6. Silicone rubber and plastics are less flammable than those made of hydrocarbon monomers. Why should this be so?
7. Why is ammonium carbonate sometimes added to batches of rubber designed to make foam rubber articles?

Reading Further

Textiles: Fiber to Fabric, 4th. ed., by M. D. Potter and B. P. Corbman, New York, McGraw-Hill, 1967. The story of the development, production, dyeing, and characteristics of natural and synthetic fibers. Includes details of the burning tests for identifying twenty different fibers.

A Concise Guide to Plastics, 2d. ed., by Herbert Simonds, New York, Reinhold Publishing, 1963. The sources, properties, production techniques, and applications of a large number of plastics.

Scientific American, September 1957. The entire issue is devoted to giant molecules. Of special interest are the three articles: "How Giant Molecules Are Made," by Giulio Natta; "Giant Molecules," by Herman Mark; and "How Giant Molecules Are Measured," by Peter Debye.

38

Chemistry of the Cell

What is the difference between the chemistry of a living thing, such as a tree, and the chemistry of an apparently lifeless rock? Chemical reactions occur in both, but the reactions that take place in the rock go in one direction only: they lead to the rock's eventual decomposition. In living things, on the other hand, chemical reactions are so organized that the organism maintains itself in a more or less steady state. A tree takes carbon dioxide from the air and inorganic ions and water molecules from the soil, and from these materials it fashions more "tree substance." A cat eats organic food and from this it fashions more "cat substance." In short, a living organism takes material—inorganic or organic—from its environment and converts it into its own kind of substance. The organism also gets rid of wastes that result from the breakdown, or decomposition, of compounds within its body. Within the organism, materials undergo the chemical reactions that make life possible—and **biochemistry** deals with the study of these chemical processes in living things.

As you may remember from biology, any organism is composed of one or more cells, the content of which is a living substance. This cell substance is a highly complex colloid of organic and inorganic molecules and ions. Water is its chief component; but it also contains carbohydrates, fats and oils (lipids), proteins, minerals, and vitamins. No formula can be written for the cell substance—it is ever changing. Yet its very constituents differentiate it from all inert or lifeless substances known. In some way not understood,

though probably related to the complex proteins, the cell contents are alive. The problem is complicated since this living colloidal substance acts both as a sol and as a gel. It differs in consistency in different cells, such as in an ameba and a muscle cell, and in different parts of the same cell, such as the cytoplasm and the cell nucleus. And the cell substance is unique in still another way—in the complexity of the numerous organic molecules of which it is composed. Human hemoglobin, for example, has the formula $C_{3032}H_{4816}O_{872}N_{780}S_8Fe_4$.

The constituents of the cell interact with each other to take in raw materials, to decompose the materials and synthesize new ones, and to elimate waste—in essence, to carry on the metabolism of the cell. Each cell (Fig. 38-1) is surrounded by a membrane through which pass ions and small organic and inorganic molecules. Within the cells are the **organelles,** which have a variety of functions. The **nucleus,** for example, is the organelle

38-1 In this electron micrograph, part of a cell's nucleus can be seen at the bottom. The two organelles at the top are mitochondria, important as enzymes sites in providing energy for the cell (44,000 ×).

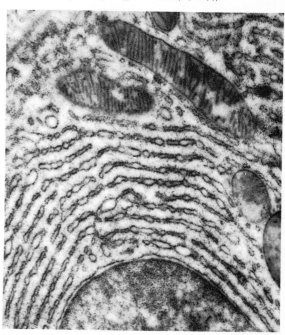

that contains the chromosomes, the determiners of heredity. The organelles called **mitochondria** are important to the energy relationships of the cell (page 660). Intimately associated with the mitochondria are the numerous organic catalysts called **enzymes.** Enzymes, like other catalysts, change the rate of chemical reactions, usually by speeding them up. Enzymes also control the reactions that are necessary for the life of the organism even at very low temperatures.

CARBOHYDRATES

The processes which take place in the cells of organisms require energy as a driving force. The ultimate source of man's energy is the food he eats—foods containing carbohydrates, fats, and proteins. Among man's most widely consumed foods have always been those containing **carbohydrates,** which include sugars and starches. As a nation's standard of living rises, the importance of carbohydrates in its diet decreases somewhat. Yet even in the United States, with one of the highest standards of living in the world, wheat and corn, two sources of starch, are still our most important foods. We also consume large quantities of glucose, sugar that occurs widely in edible plant parts. In fact, glucose is man's most important source of energy.

Glucose

All carbohydrates, such as glucose ($C_6H_{12}O_6$), are carbon compounds containing hydrogen atoms and oxygen atoms in the ratio of 2 to 1. Glucose contains six carbon atoms per molecule; a carbohydrate of this kind is called a **hexose.** The hexoses, in turn, form part of a group of sugars known as **monosaccharides.** The name monosaccharide is given to sugars which cannot be broken down into simpler sugar molecules.

In the graphic formula for glucose (at the right above), observe the chain of six carbon atoms. Observe, too, the formyl group at one end of the chain and the position of the five hydroxyl groups. To explain certain properties of glucose, chemists sometimes write its graphic formula as

shown at the right below. In this diagram observe that an oxygen atom serves as a "bridge" or bond between the first and fifth carbon atom in the molecule.

glucose

Though you cannot determine for yourself the structure of glucose, *you can determine* why it is sometimes referred to as a *reducing* sugar.

Place equal amounts of Benedict's solution in three Pyrex test tubes. Now add a few grains of glucose to the second test tube and a few drops of corn syrup to the third. Carefully heat all three test tubes until the solu-

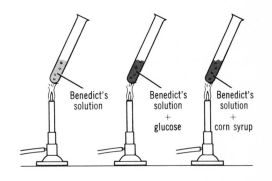

Benedict's solution

Benedict's solution + glucose

Benedict's solution + corn syrup

tions boil. As you continue heating the second and third tubes, you probably observe a green precipitate that gradually turns yellow and finally brick red. Does any color change occur in the boiled Benedict's solution in the first test tube?

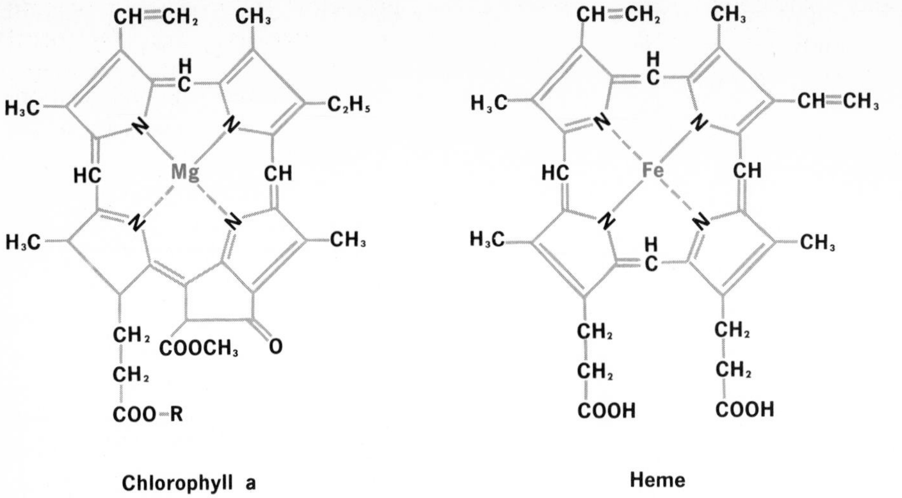

Chlorophyll a

Heme

38-2 A close relationship exists between the chlorophyll a molecule and the heme portion of a hemoglobin molecule. In the latter an atom of iron occupies the same position as an atom of magnesium in chlorophyll a. (Observe also below and upper right, where other differences appear.)

The formation of the precipitate and the color changes result from the action of an aldehydelike substance on the soluble copper(II) ions in the Benedict's solution. During the reaction, the blue copper(II) ions are *reduced* by the formyl (or aldehyde) group to the copper(I) ion of the brightly colored cuprous oxide. Glucose, which contains a formyl group, brings about the reduction of the copper ions in the second test tube. What monosaccharide is present in corn syrup?

Photosynthesis

You know from biology the overall reaction by which plants produce glucose. During photosynthesis carbon dioxide combines with water, in the presence of chlorophyll and light, to produce glucose and oxygen.

$$6\,CO_2 + 6\,H_2O \xrightarrow[\text{light}]{\text{chlorophyll}} C_6H_{12}O_6 + 6\,O_2\uparrow$$

But the above equation is really a great oversimplification of what takes place. In the monosaccharide which results from the linking together of carbon dioxide and hydrogen, the radiant energy of light is captured and stored as chemical energy. In the first stage of photosynthesis the light energy is absorbed by the chlorophyll. The energy excites some electrons in the chlorophyll, and these excited electrons are

then passed through a series of electron carriers in such a way that their energy is gradually released. In this *electron-carrier* system, numerous enzymes are involved as organic catalysts.

The water in the photosynthesis reaction is probably split into H^+ and OH^- ions. Oxidation of the OH^- ion to OH followed by the combining of the OH groups yields water and the oxygen given off as a by-product of the photosynthesis. The H^+ ions formed by the splitting of the water are picked up by a powerful "hydrogen acceptor" which carries them along to the carbon dioxide molecules. In a series of reactions the carbon dioxide and some of the hydrogen link together to form glucose.

Most of the glucose is transported out of the leaves to the roots and stem of the plant. Here it may be stored as glucose or converted by a series of chemical reactions to other carbohydrates and then stored.

Observe the graphic formula for chlorophyll a in Fig. 38-2. Even a quick glance reveals the complexity of compounds involved in biochemical reactions—actually this chlorophyll molecule is relatively simple as biochemical compounds go. Compare the formula for chlorophyll a with that of the heme portion of hemoglobin, the substance that carries oxygen in red blood cells. Structurally the latter compound is closely related to chlorophyll, but it contains iron instead of magnesium. The similarity of these compounds, one in green plants and one in higher animals, illustrates that despite the complexity of biochemical molecules there is a pattern in biochemistry.

Other Hexoses

Isomers of glucose are also formed and stored in plant cells. One of these isomers is *fructose.* Though its formula is $C_6H_{12}O_6$, it must differ structurally from glucose because it does not react with Benedict's solution. In the graphic formula below for fructose, observe that instead of the formyl group of glucose, fructose contains a carbonyl group at the position of the second carbon atom. A second isomer of glucose is *galactose.* A comparison of the graphic formulas for galactose and glucose (page 656) reveals that the hydroxyl group attached to the fourth carbon atom is on opposite sides in the two molecules.

fructose   galactose

Disaccharides

How do plants transform the hexoses (monosaccharides) they produce into larger, more complex carbohydrates such as sucrose, starch, and cellulose? The simplest of these carbohydrates is sucrose or common table sugar ($C_{12}H_{22}O_{11}$). Sucrose, which is found in sugar cane and sugar beets, is a double sugar or **disaccharide.** Both in the laboratory and in plants one molecule of glucose and one molecule of fructose are combined to form a molecule of sucrose. During the combination a molecule of water also forms.

$$C_6H_{12}O_6 + C_6H_{12}O_6 \longrightarrow C_{12}H_{22}O_{11} + H_2O$$

glucose   fructose   sucrose

This process is a **dehydration** (or condensation) **reaction** and is similar to the process by which a number of polymers are formed. The *process of dehydration* is one of the unifying principles of biochemistry, for fats and proteins are also produced from certain smaller molecules by dehydration synthesis.

Maltose, another disaccharide, is produced by dehydration between two molecules of glucose. Observe from the graphic equation in Fig. 38-3 that an —OH group splits off from one glucose molecule and combines with a —H from the other to form a molecule of H_2O. The remaining portions of the two glucose molecules link together to form one molecule of maltose.

By placing a disaccharide in an acid (HCl) solution, the process of forming a disaccharide can be reversed. A molecule of water, in effect, is put back to form the original monosaccharide.

$$C_{12}H_{22}O_{11} + H_2O \xrightarrow{acid} C_6H_{12}O_6 + C_6H_{12}O_6$$

sucrose   glucose   fructose

This reaction, which is the opposite of dehydration, is, of course, a **hydrolysis reaction.** This "breaking with water" reaction of sucrose could have been indicated by simply reversing the arrows in the dehydration equation for its production. *Hydrolysis of complex compounds* is a second unifying principle of biochemistry. In living things, for example, hydrolysis *catalyzed by enzymes* is the essential process in the digestion of carbohydrates, fats, and proteins.

Polysaccharides

When more than two monosaccharide molecules undergo dehydration simultaneously, they form **polysaccharides** and water. Three typical and very important polysaccharides are *starch* and *cellulose,* which occur in plant cells, and *glycogen,* which occurs in the cells of animals. Starch (Fig. 38-4), cellulose, and glycogen are actually closely related polymers.

Starch. Starch is a polysaccharide found abun-

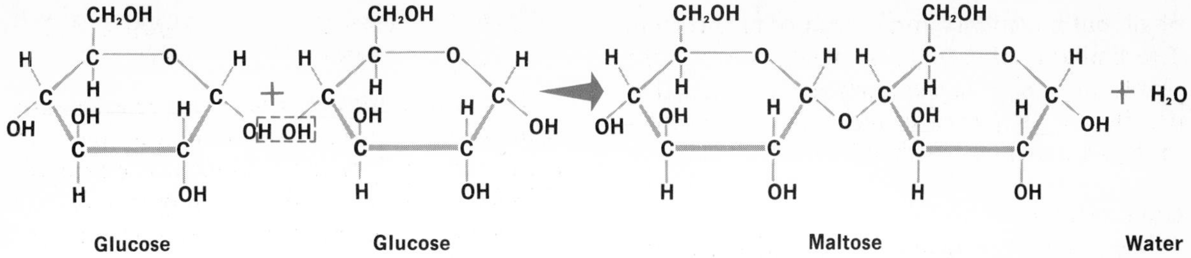

CH₂OH ... Glucose + Glucose → Maltose + H₂O

(Figure 38-3 chemical structures with labels:)

Glucose   **Glucose**   **Maltose**   **Water**

38-3 The —OH group from one glucose molecule combines with the —H from another to form a molecule of water. The remaining portions of the glucose molecules then join together to form a maltose molecule—dehydration has occurred.

dantly in the seeds of wheat, corn, and other grains, as well as in potatoes. Starch molecules consist of many glucose units joined together by dehydration. But starch molecules have no fixed size; they may contain from 100 to 10,000 glucose units. In the equation below for the formation of starch, x represents this varying number of units.

$$x\,C_6H_{12}O_6 \longrightarrow (C_6H_{10}O_5)x\downarrow + x\,H_2O$$

glucose   starch   water

Starch, either in an acid medium or by enzyme action, undergoes hydrolysis to form many glucose molecules. The reaction is essentially the reverse of dehydration.

Cellulose. The polysaccharide cellulose is the main constituent of the walls of plant cells. Cotton, linen, and wood all contain large amounts of cellulose. From these substances man gets the cellulose to make paper, cotton cloth, rayon, cellulose acetate, and a host of other products.

Cellulose has the same empirical formula as starch, but the arrangement of the glucose units in cellulose differs from that in starch. Human

beings cannot digest cellulose as they do starch. On the other hand, cows and some other animals have in their digestive tracts microorganisms which enable them to hydrolyze cellulose into glucose.

Glycogen. A third important polysaccharide, glycogen, is an isomer of starch and is found in the bodies of animals. Glycogen is stored in large quantities in muscle tissue and in the liver. Animal tissues contain a series of enzymes that can both hydrolyze (digest) glycogen into glucose and dehydrate glucose back into glycogen. These enzymes enable us to call on reserves of glycogen for energy whenever our body's immediate supply of glucose has become depleted.

Energy from Glucose

In the body the disaccharides and polysaccharides are, as you have seen, finally changed to glucose—the source of energy for the life processes. But how is this energy made available to the cells? When glucose is oxidized completely, whether in the laboratory or in the body, carbon

38-4 The diagram shows a portion of a starch molecule in synthesis. In starch molecules, varying numbers of glucose units are joined together in long chains by condensation reactions.

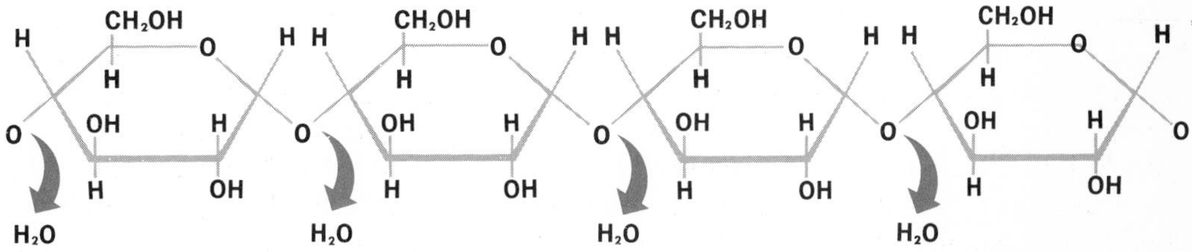

(Figure 38-4 chemical structures with labels CH₂OH and H₂O repeated)

H₂O   H₂O   H₂O   H₂O

dioxide and water are formed and energy is released.

$$C_6H_{12}O_6 + 6\,O_2 \longrightarrow 6\,H_2O + 6\,CO_2\uparrow + energy$$

In the laboratory, this process occurs quickly *and at high temperatures to release heat energy.* In the body such high temperatures are impossible; and though some heat energy is released, most of the energy released is chemical energy. In the body the oxidation of glucose occurs in many steps, each catalyzed by a specific enzyme. These enzymes, in effect, cause oxidation to occur at a lower temperature and to release mainly chemical energy.

Although the **cellular oxidation** of glucose involves a total of several dozen steps, four main ones may be singled out.

1. Cellular oxidation begins with glucose, a six-carbon compound. The atoms in the glucose molecule are rearranged; the molecule splits in half. In this way pyruvic acid, a three-carbon compound, is formed, four hydrogen atoms are removed, and a very small amount of energy is released.

$$C_6H_{12}O_6 \xrightarrow{\text{enzymes}} 2\,CH_3COCOOH + 4\,H + energy$$
glucose   pyruvic acid

It is important to note that this series of oxidation reactions consists of the removal of hydrogen atoms, *not* the addition of oxygen.

2. Next the pyruvic acid is broken down by another series of enzyme-catalyzed reactions into acetic acid, a two-carbon compound, carbon dioxide, and hydrogen. More energy is released here. (Because of the complex nature of these reactions, this and the following equations are shown unbalanced.)

$$CH_3COCOOH \xrightarrow{\text{enzymes}}$$
pyruvic acid $$CH_3COOH + CO_2\uparrow + H + energy$$
acetic acid

3. Then, through a complex cycle known as the Krebs cycle, the acetic acid is degraded (changed by a series of catalyzed reactions) to

carbon dioxide and hydrogen atoms. In this cycle, the amount of energy released is quite large.

$$CH_3COOH \xrightarrow{\text{Krebs cycle}} CO_2\uparrow + 4\,H + energy$$

4. Finally, in a "mopping-up" operation, the H atoms are combined with oxygen to form water.

$$4\,H + O_2 \xrightarrow{\text{enzymes}} 2\,H_2O$$

As you see, only the first three of the above four steps produce energy; and of these, the third step releases the most energy. Though glucose is degraded to carbon dioxide and water, the CO_2 and H_2O are only by-products; the release of chemical energy is the important part of the processes.

Many enzymes and certain vitamins play an essential role in cellular oxidation. The first step is believed to occur in the watery medium of the cytoplasm, but the all important oxidation of pyruvic acid to carbon dioxide and water takes place in the mitochondria. The whole oxidation process is summarized in Fig. 38-5.

Anaerobic Respiration

If little or no oxygen is present, some organisms, such as yeast, do not break down glucose into CO_2 and H_2O. Rather, they bring about the fermentation of glucose to carbon dioxide and alcohol. During fermentation or **anaerobic respiration,** respiration without oxygen, glucose is still changed to pyruvic acid. But the pyruvic acid is then reduced to ethyl alcohol and carbon dioxide.

pyruvic acid   ethyl alcohol

This incomplete breakdown of glucose involves no oxygen and releases very little energy.

In actively contracting muscle cells, an incomplete breakdown of glucose (hydrolyzed from

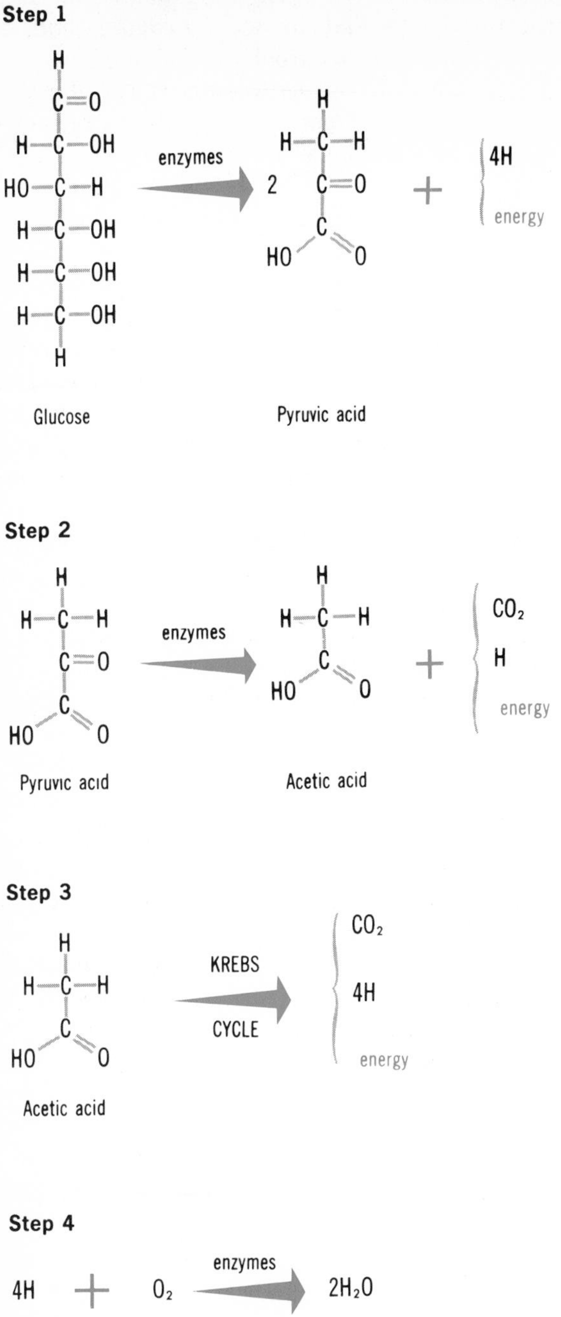

Step 1

Glucose → Pyruvic acid

$$\text{Glucose} \xrightarrow{\text{enzymes}} 2 \text{ (Pyruvic acid)} + 4H \text{ (energy)}$$

Step 2

$$\text{Pyruvic acid} \xrightarrow{\text{enzymes}} \text{Acetic acid} + \{CO_2, H\} \text{ (energy)}$$

Step 3

$$\text{Acetic acid} \xrightarrow{\text{KREBS CYCLE}} \{CO_2, 4H\} \text{ (energy)}$$

Step 4

$$4H + O_2 \xrightarrow{\text{enzymes}} 2H_2O$$

38-5 These four main steps in the cellular oxidation of glucose summarize a complex process that takes place in body cells. Each step begins with a product of the preceding step. The energy released, not the product formed, is what makes the process essential to most organisms.

glycogen) also takes place. During violent exercise the blood simply cannot transport oxygen quickly enough from the lungs, through the blood, to the muscle cells. In such muscle cells glucose is still changed to pyruvic acid, but this pyruvic acid is then reduced to lactic acid. The entire process releases little energy. When an excess of lactic acid forms, muscles become fatigued.

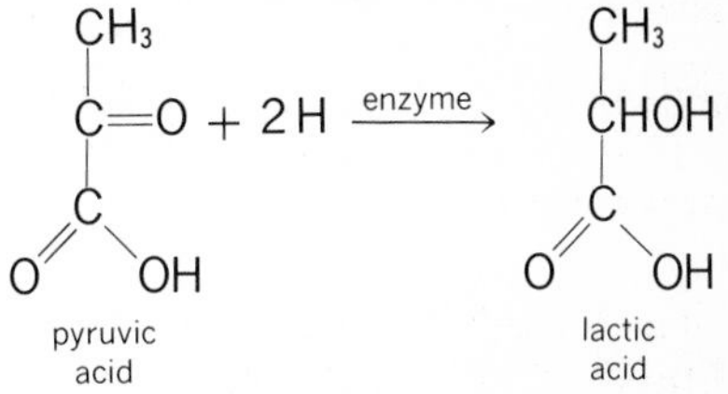

$$\underset{\text{pyruvic acid}}{\begin{array}{c} CH_3 \\ C=O \\ C \\ O \quad OH \end{array}} + 2H \xrightarrow{\text{enzyme}} \underset{\text{lactic acid}}{\begin{array}{c} CH_3 \\ CHOH \\ C \\ O \quad OH \end{array}}$$

When the muscle is again at rest, the major portion of the lactic acid is resynthesized into glycogen; but part of the lactic acid is oxidized to CO_2 and H_2O, liberating energy.

Energy and ATP

Regardless of the process used by plant and animal cells to release the energy stored in glucose, this energy is *not* used directly for life activities, such as contracting muscles and transmitting nerve impulses. Rather it is used to generate *adenosine triphosphate,* the substance that supplies energy directly to the cells. Adenosine triphosphate, abbreviated ATP, is composed of adenosine (containing a five-carbon sugar) and three phosphate groups (Fig. 38-6). It is the phosphate groups that make ATP so important in the exchange of energy. A great deal of energy is tied up in the chemical bonds that link two of the phosphate groups to the remainder of the molecules. These bonds, known as high-energy bonds, are represented by the wavy lines in Fig. 38-6.

When the cell processes require energy, the outermost of the high-energy bonds in the ATP molecules is split; the energy released in this splitting is used in the cell processes. At the same time the ATP, because it has given up one of its three phosphate groups, is changed into *adenosine diphosphate,* or ADP (Fig. 38-7).

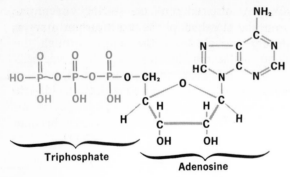

38-6 In ATP, two of the three phosphate groups are linked by high-energy bonds to adenosine, which contains a five-carbon sugar. The splitting off of one phosphate group yields energy and adenosine diphosphate.

Since the cell's supply of ATP has been reduced by the release of energy and the formation of ADP, the cell must make more ATP from the ADP. This process also requires energy, but where is the cell to obtain it? The energy to generate more ATP from ADP and a phosphate group is supplied to the cell by the oxidation of glucose. We see, then, that ATP is only the *immediate* source or carrier of the energy the cells require. It simply transmits energy which has been stored in the chemical bonds of glucose. In essence, when glucose is oxidized, the energy released is used to generate ATP.

Interconversion of Carbohydrates and Fats

Thus far we have stressed the importance of carbohydrates as the source of energy for body activities. But the body is able to utilize fats, and even proteins when necessary, as sources of

reserve energy. Research using deuterium as a tracer indicates that the body is capable both of converting fats into carbohydrates, and carbohydrates into fats. This conversion is a continuous process. The fat supply, converted into carbohydrates and used as a source of energy, is constantly being replaced by new fat molecules.

Each of these fat molecules, which is produced by a dehydration reaction between one glycerol and three fatty acid molecules (page 606), is hydrolyzed during digestion into its original components—another example of the unifying principle of hydrolysis and dehydration in biochemistry. Once fats are converted into these simpler organic compounds, the interconversion to carbohydrates can occur. From the above, it is easy to see why people who eat an excess of carbohydrates may end up overweight because of the storage of excess fat within the body.

QUESTIONS AND PROBLEMS

1. (a) Write a graphic formula equation for the production of sucrose from glucose and fructose. (b) What type of reaction is represented by the equation?

2. (a) Write a graphic formula equation for the production of glucose from maltose. (b) What type of reaction is represented by the equation?

3. Differentiate between each of the following pairs of terms:
   (a) *dehydration* and *hydrolysis*
   (b) *monosaccharide* and *polysaccharide*
   (c) *carbohydrate* and *fat*

4. Differentiate among each of the following groups of terms:
   (a) *glucose, fructose,* and *galactose*
   (b) *starch, cellulose,* and *glycogen*

5. (a) Describe briefly the major steps in the cellular oxidation of glucose. (b) How does anaerobic respiration differ from the cellular oxidation of glucose?

38-7 Energy for cell processes is released by splitting off one phosphate group from ATP, changing it to ADP. ATP is regenerated, using energy from the oxidation of glucose to add one phosphate group to ADP.

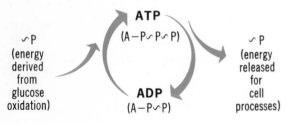

᷉P
(energy derived from glucose oxidation)

ATP
(A—P᷉P᷉P)

᷉P
(energy released for cell processes)

ADP
(A—P᷉P)

6. How are ADP and ATP related to the energy needs of the cell?

PROTEINS

Proteins constitute a very important part of our diet, for they supply the essential building blocks of living substances. Proteins are organic compounds containing carbon, hydrogen, oxygen, and nitrogen, as well as sulfur and phosphorus. Nitrogen is the particular element that distinguishes all proteins. When proteins react with acids or special enzymes, they hydrolyze to form more than 20 types of **amino acids.** It is the number, type, and arrangement of their amino acids that cause proteins to differ from one another. Just as monosaccharides are the building blocks for polysaccharides, so amino acids are the building blocks of proteins.

Amino Acids

Amino acids, like other organic acids, consist of chains of carbon atoms to which one or more carboxyl groups are attached. But in addition, all amino acids contain an $-NH_2$ or *amino* group. The similarity between acetic acid and glycine, the amino acid related to it, is indicated by their graphic formulas.

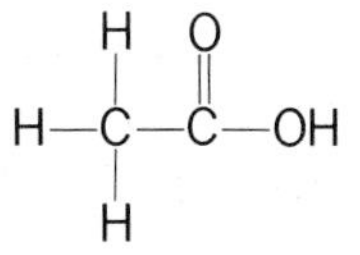

acetic acid 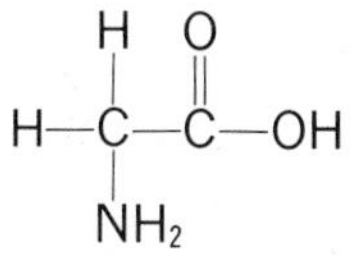   glycine

Observe that one of the $-H$ present in acetic acid is replaced in glycine by an $-NH_2$ group.

From the graphic formulas for several additional amino acids (alanine, valine, phenyl-

alanine), observe that the $-NH_2$, or amino group, is attached to the same carbon atom as the carboxyl group.

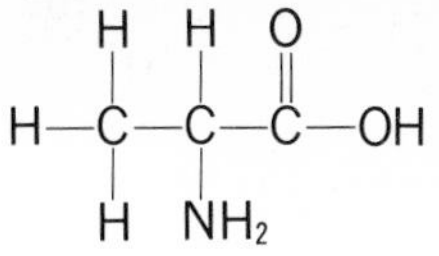

alanine 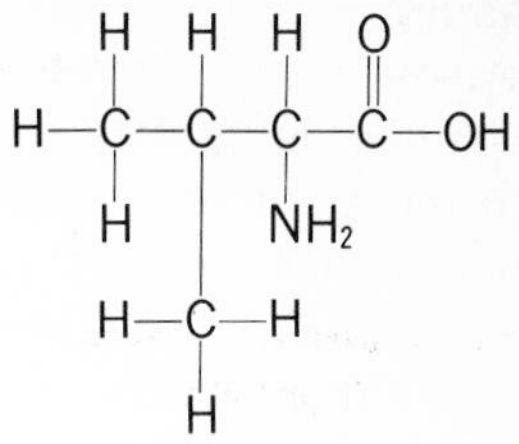   valine

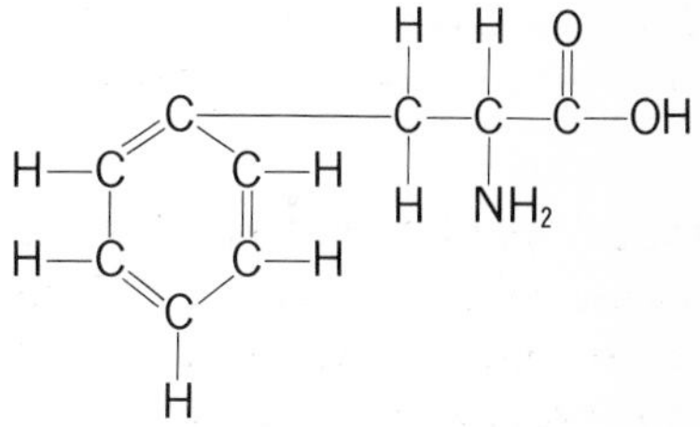

phenylalanine

This method of attachment is characteristic of all amino acids used by the body, even in those acids that are much more complex in structure.

Amino Acids and Peptide Chains

In linking together to form proteins, the amino acids first form larger molecules called **peptides.** The way this linkage takes place is indicated in Fig. 38-8. Here a molecule of the amino acid glycine is joined together with a molecule of alanine to form the peptide *glycylalanine* by the elimination of one molecule of water. This water molecule forms as the $-OH$ part of the carboxyl group of one acid molecule combines with an $-H$ from the amino group of the other acid molecules. Once again we have a process of *dehydration,* or

38-8 A molecule of the peptide glycylalanine is produced by the condensation of two unlike amino acid molecules—by the removal of the $-OH$ portion of the carboxyl group of glycine and an $-H$ from the amine group of alanine.

Glycine   Alanine   Glycylalanine   Water

condensation. The resulting carbon-nitrogen bond is referred to as a **peptide linkage.** Observe in Fig. 38-8 that each peptide linkage leaves one free amino group and a free carboxyl group at the opposite end of the molecule to continue the chain-building. Peptides do indeed join together through additional peptide linkages to form **polypeptide chains**—chains composed of numerous peptides strung together. Any given protein —and there are thousands of different proteins— is made up of one or more polypeptide chains.

To determine whether any substance contains certain common proteins, be it a bit of fingernail or egg white, *try the following.* You may already be familiar with this test if you have ever dropped even a small amount of nitric acid on your skin!

> Place a bit of powdered casein (the protein in milk) in one test tube and a small piece of cooked egg white in another. Now add a few drops of concentrated nitric acid to each. Does a deep yellow color appear? Pour off the excess acid and add a small amount of ammonium hydroxide. If protein is present, the yellow color changes to a deep orange.

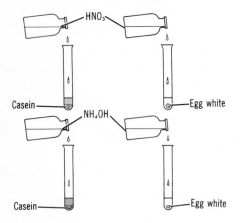

> Does the color change occur on the surface of the egg white as well as in the test tube with the dissolved casein?

If the color change occurs, you have demonstrated that egg white contains protein. Perhaps

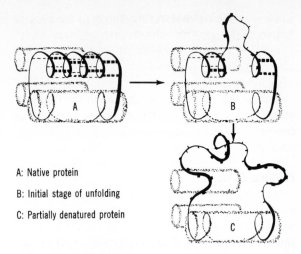

A: Native protein

B: Initial stage of unfolding

C: Partially denatured protein

38-9 In the diagrammatic representation of protein denaturation, a protein (in A) is shown as a long, continuous coil, cross-linked in several places. In B, breaking of the cross-links begins, while in C the coiled arrangement changes to an irregular diffuse arrangement.

you can test several other substances for the presence of protein by this **xanthroproteic test** for protein.

Protein Structure

A detailed knowledge of protein structure is fundamental to unraveling some of the basic secrets of living substances. An advance in our knowledge of protein structure came in 1954 when, for the first time, the intricate geometrical structure of a protein—the hormone insulin— was determined. Frederick Sanger of Cambridge, England, determined that the insulin molecule consists of fifty-one amino acid groups arranged in two chains, as well as six sulfur atoms and six —NH_2 groups.

Evidence from X-ray diffraction studies indicates that insulin and other protein molecules have a coiled arrangement in which hydrogen bonds exist between different peptide chains (Fig. 38-9). You know that when egg white (a typical protein) is cooked, it changes from a colloidal sol to a gel. Heating brings about a change in the protein's structure. The coiled arrangement changes to an irregular, diffuse arrangement. During this disorganization, which is know as **protein denaturation,** the hydrogen bonds between the peptide chains are broken. Often denaturation is irreversible, an indication of the importance of hydrogen bonding in the structure of proteins.

The process of establishing the structure of proteins continues. As recently as 1964, scientists finally succeeded in synthesizing a protein—insulin.

Enzyme Action

Without proteins all hydrolysis, dehydration, oxidation—in fact, all reactions in the body—would cease. Why? Enzymes are needed for all these reactions—and all enzymes are proteins. Let us look briefly at how enzymes work in one reaction as an indication of how they may operate in all reactions.

Consider the process by which a molecule of maltose is hydrolyzed into two molecules of glucose. The reaction is catalyzed by the enzyme malt*ase.* At the outset, the malt*ose* bonds with the malt*ase* by a most unusual reaction. Malt*ase,* like all enzymes, is a very large molecule. In contrast, malt*ose* is a small molecule. Malt*ose* is considered the **substrate,** the substance with which an enzyme reacts. When the substrate and enzyme react, apparently the malt*ose* fits into only a small portion of the malt*ase* molecule. This reaction is represented in Fig. 38-10.

In a series of extremely rapid reactions, the —O— bond between the two glucose units of the maltose molecules is broken at one site. Next, the —H from a water molecule bonds with the O atom at the broken site, forming one glucose molecule. The —OH from the water molecule bonds with the other unit to form a second glucose molecule. The reaction is complete: a maltose molecule is hydrolyzed to two glucose molecules and the enzyme remains unchanged to be used over and over again.

Enzyme Inhibition

An unusual application of enzyme specificity is in the field of **chemotherapy,** the use of chemicals to destroy germs without destroying the patient's useful tissue. As an example of a *chemotherapeutic* drug, consider sulfanilamide, developed by Gerhard Domagk in Germany in 1935. It was believed originally that sulfanilamide acted similarly to acids and other antiseptics by simply destroying bacteria. Continued research indicated, however, that the process by which sulfanilamide acts is not by mere destruction. Its action is related to the function of vitamins and enzymes.

You know that all organisms require vitamins to carry out normal life processes. One of the B complex vitamins, *para*-aminobenzoic acid, which is essential in the normal metabolism of bacteria, is closely related in structure to sulfanilamide.

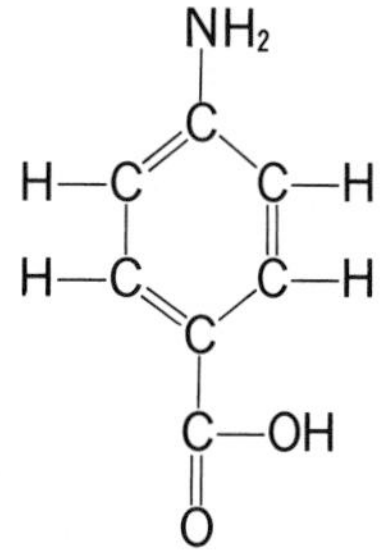

para-aminobenzoic acid 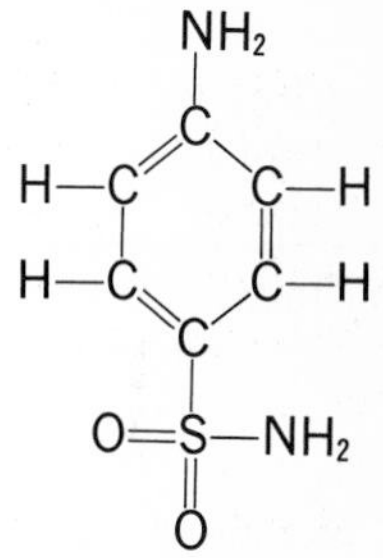   sulfanilamide

It seems that bacteria normally utilize *para*-aminobenzoic acid as the substrate for a particular enzyme-substrate reaction necessary for their

38-10   In the presence of the enzyme maltase (represented by the ochre area), a molecule of water is added to a molecule of maltose. At the site of enzyme action, the maltose molecule breaks and two molecules of glucose are synthesized by hydrolysis.

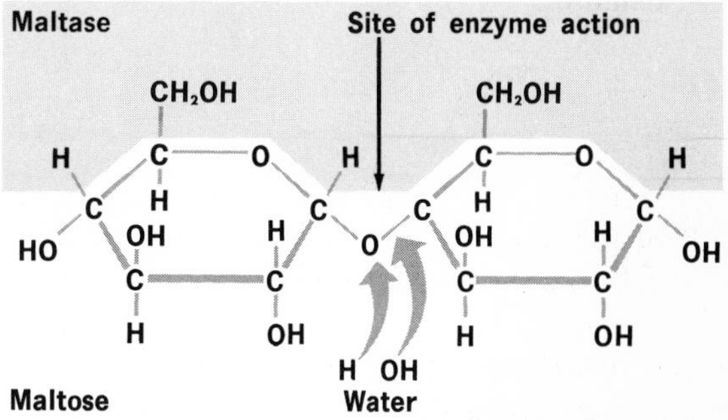

metabolism. Because of the close structural relationship of the two organic compounds, certain bacteria are "deceived" and use sulfanilamide as the substrate in place of *para*-aminobenzoic acid. If large doses of sulfanilamide are given, it bonds with the functional portion of the enzyme and effectively prevents the enzyme from reacting with the *para*-aminobenzoic acid. Since the bacteria are unable to utilize the *para*-aminobenzoic acid, their normal metabolism does not occur. Without proper nutrition the bacterial cells cannot reproduce. The development of sulfanilamide and other sulfa drugs led the way to the development of numerous other drugs, including the antibiotics, that are effective against many types of harmful bacteria.

Nucleoproteins and Nucleic Acids

One final class of protein molecules is uniquely important. These are the nucleoproteins, probably the most complex of all chemical substances. The hydrolysis of nucleoproteins shows that they

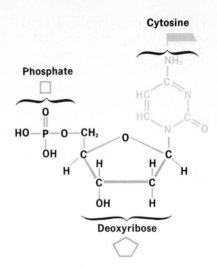

38-12 This nucleotide molecule is composed of phosphoric acid ("phosphate"), the pyrimidine cytosine, and deoxyribose, a sugar molecule containing one fewer oxygen atom than the usual five-carbon sugar.

consist of proteins combined with special types of organic acids called nucleic acids. Today both chemists and biologists believe that these nucleic acids hold the secret of life itself—for chromosomes are composed of nucleic acid attached to protein. Though the precise manner of attachment is still unknown, experimental evidence indicates that the portion of the chromosomes essential in heredity is the nucleic acid.

DNA

Deoxyribonucleic acid, better known as DNA, is the nucleic acid usually found in chromosomes. The **genes,** which transmit characteristics from parent to offspring, are now known to be portions of a DNA molecule. Since the turn of the century, scientists have discovered that the DNA molecule is made up of six different units. A molecule of DNA contains *phosphoric acid, deoxyribose* (a five-carbon sugar), and *four types of basic molecules containing nitrogen*. Just how many of the sugar molecules (the deoxyribose) there may be in a molecule of DNA we don't know; there may be thousands. To each one of these sugar units is attached one phosphoric acid molecule and one basic molecule containing nitrogen.

38-11 The ring structure of any pyrimidine contains four carbon and two nitrogen atoms; additional atoms vary. Purines are condensed ring compounds; the six-membered ring is similar to pyrimidine structure.

Cytosine

Thymine

a. PYRIMIDINES

Adenine

Guanine

b. PURINES

These molecules with nitrogen are of two kinds: **pyrimidines** and **purines.** The pyrimidines have a ring structure, each containing four carbon and two nitrogen atoms (Fig. 38-11a). The purines are condensed ring compounds having the type of carbon-nitrogen skeleton shown in Fig. 38-11b. The pyrimidines and purines, in turn, are each of two types. The two pyrimidines are **cytosine** and **thymine;** the two purines are **adenine** and **guanine.** When a pyrimidine or purine is bonded to a sugar molecule, and this in turn is bonded to a molecule of phosphoric acid, the resulting molecule is called a **nucleotide** (Fig. 38-12). These nucleotides bond together to form nucleic acids. A deoxyribonucleic acid molecule is made up of four—and only four—different nucleotides.

By detailed studies of X-ray diffraction pictures and by intelligent guesswork, F. H. C. Crick and J. D. Watson, working at the Cavendish Laboratory at Cambridge, England, were able to determine not only the arrangement of the units making up DNA but also the positions in space that these units occupy. Watson and Crick conceived of the overall structure of DNA as a ladder. The deoxyribose and the phosphoric acid portion of the nucleotide make up the uprights of the ladder; the purines and pyrimidines are the crosspieces

38-14 The technician is completing a portion of a solid model of a DNA molecule. The twisting of the uprights into a double helix is clearly seen. The complexity results from use of a ball for each atom.

38-13 In this fragment of a ladderlike molecule of DNA, the deoxyribose and phosphoric acid portions of the nucleotides form the uprights, and the specific purines and pyrimidines form the crosspieces.

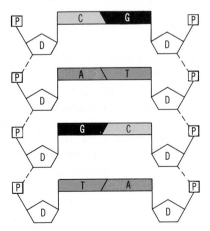

(Fig. 38-13). In these crosspieces of the DNA ladder, a purine is always bonded to a pyrimidine. Either adenine (a purine) is bonded to thymine (a pyrimidine) or the purine guanine is bonded to the pyrimidine cytosine. These, and only these, combinations of purines and pyrimidines are possible. Watson and Crick indicated, moreover, that the uprights are twisted about each other, forming a double helix (Fig. 38-14).

Along one upright of the ladder, the nucleotides are arranged in any possible sequence. Once this arrangement is set, the pattern of the other upright is determined. An adenine nucleotide always bonds with a thymine nucleotide, and a guanine nucleotide always bonds with a cytosine nucleotide. Although the DNA molecule is limited to only four nucleotides, these can be strung together in an almost infinite variety of sequences. And since a gene is a *sequence of nucleotides,* it is the sequence of nucleotides that determines the characteristics of any living organism.

DNA has the unique ability to reproduce, or **replicate,** itself; and it is this ability that makes possible the formation of new living cells. We can think of *replication* as the opening of the DNA ladder down the middle, as if by a zipper. As the ladder unzips (chemical bonds break), paired chemical units in each rung draw apart. By a series of complex reactions, identical units moving freely in the cell's nucleus rebuild half of each ladder (chemical bonds re-form). When the duplicating process is over, we have two DNA ladders that are exact replicas of the original. Instead of one chromosome we have two. The replication process can be repeated in healthy, living cells indefinitely—and it is this ability that makes possible the growth of all living things.

Biochemistry, indeed, is beginning to unravel the chemical secrets of life. Your understanding of processes such as hydrolysis, dehydration, and replication, together with an understanding of the nature of chemical bonds, may someday enable you to make a substantial and important contribution to man's fund of knowledge.

QUESTIONS AND PROBLEMS

1. (a) By a series of graphic formula equations indicate the relationships among amino acids, peptides, and polypeptides. (b) How are polypeptides and proteins related?

2. Describe briefly the mode of action by which the enzyme suc*rase* catalyzes the hydrolysis of suc*rose* into glucose and fructose.

3. How does denaturation of proteins differ from hydrolysis of proteins?

4. Define each of the following terms: *peptide linkage, amino group, nucleic acid, nucleotide, chemotherapy.*

5. Describe briefly the structure of a DNA molecule.

VALUE OF THE CONCEPT

THE CONCEPT

Biochemical processes usually occur within cells, which take in raw materials, decompose them, synthesize new substances, and eliminate wastes. Each cell is surrounded by a selectively permeable membrane and contains organelles which serve a variety of functions. The nucleus, for example, contains chromosomes, the determiners of heredity. Associated with mitochondria, which are important to the cells' energy relationships, are numerous organic catalysts, or enzymes.

The carbohydrates, fats, and proteins in food are the ultimate source of our energy. Carbohydrates such as glucose and fructose, both monosaccharides, contain carbon atoms in addition to hydrogen and oxygen atoms in a ratio of 2 to 1. Sucrose is a common disaccharide, while starch, cellulose, and glycogen are polysaccharides. Disaccharides and polysaccharides are formed from monosaccharides by dehydration; conversely, the latter are changed (digested) to the former by hydrolysis. Sugars such as glucose or galactose are called reducing sugars because they contain a formyl group that serves as a reducing agent. Carbohydrates are formed within the cells of green plants by the process of photosynthesis —the conversion of carbon dioxide and water into glucose and oxygen by a series of complex chemical processes.

During cellular oxidation (respiration) glucose is oxidized to carbon dioxide and water, and energy is released. This process occurs in many steps, each catalyzed by a specific enzyme. During one of these steps acetic acid is broken down or degraded to form carbon dioxide, hydrogen atoms, and energy. The degradation process is referred to as the Krebs cycle.

A second type of respiration, anaerobic respiration, or fermentation, occurs within the cells of certain organisms. During fermentation—respiration without oxygen—carbon dioxide and ethyl alcohol or other complex substances form.

In neither plant cells nor animal cells is the energy released from the oxidation of glucose used directly to carry on life activities. Instead, the energy is used to generate adenosine triphosphate, or ATP. When life processes require energy, ATP molecules release energy and are converted to adenosine diphosphate, or ADP.

Proteins are complex molecules consisting of long chains of amino acids. These acids are similar to other organic acids, except that some H atoms present in common organic acids are replaced by $-NH_2$ or amino groups. Amino acids join together through dehydration to form peptide chains. These link together into polypeptide chains, which combine into proteins.

Enzymes are complex protein molecules that act as catalysts. Enzymes seem to react with substrates enabling certain redistributions of chemical bonds to occur. Drugs such as the sulfa drugs are effective because they act as enzyme inhibitors within certain microorganisms causing disease.

Nucleoproteins are complex substances composed of proteins and nucleic acids. Chromosomes are composed of nucleoproteins containing deoxyribonucleic acid, or DNA. Each gene is now believed to be a sequence of a DNA molecule. Each molecule of DNA contains phosphoric acid, deoxyribose (a five-carbon sugar) and four types of basic molecules containing nitrogen, linked together into two long spiral chains. DNA has the unique ability of reproducing or replicating itself.

USING THE CONCEPT

Using the Basic Concept
1. (a) In what general way do the chemistry of living things and nonliving things differ? (b) What is the scope of biochemistry?
2. (a) Name the three energy-providing classes of foods. (b) Which of these classes makes up the bulk of man's diet?
3. (a) What is the chief structural characteristic of each of the following types of

sugar: hexose, pentose, monosaccharide, disaccharide, polysaccharide? (b) Give an example of each of the above classes of sugars.
4. (a) How does glucose differ in structure from fructose? (b) Why are these two sugars examples of isomers?
5. (a) In terms of its molecular structure, why is glucose called a reducing sugar? (b) Describe a test for a reducing sugar.
6. (a) What is the chemical purpose of chlorophyll in the process of photosynthesis? (b) Trace the probable path of the H_2O in the photosynthesis reaction.
7. (a) Give the name and empirical formula for the disaccharide that is most common in our diets. (b) Where is this disaccharide found in nature?
8. (a) What happens to sucrose when it is placed in an acid solution? (b) Write the equation for the chemical change that takes place. (c) Is the reaction an example of hydrolysis or of dehydration? Explain.
9. (a) Write a chemical equation indicating the combination of glucose units to form starch. (b) Is this an example of hydrolysis or dehydration? Explain.
10. (a) Name three important polysaccharide isomers. (b) Give a general source and use of each.
11. (a) Write an equation for the overall oxidation of glucose. (b) Describe the four main steps of cellular oxidation.
12. (a) Describe three differences between cellular oxidation (respiration) and anaerobic respiration. (b) Give examples of cells in which each of the above forms of oxidation occur.
13. (a) Describe the purpose of ATP in the process of respiration. (b) How is ADP formed from ATP? (c) How is ATP reformed from ADP? (d) What is the source of energy for this latter process?
14. What evidence can you present for the conversion of carbohydrates into fats, and vice versa, within the human body?

15. Indicate in terms of structure two ways in which the ten essential amino acids are similar.
16. Describe the general process by which amino acids combine with each other to form (a) peptides, (b) polypeptide chains.
17. Write a chemical equation to indicate the formation of glycylvaline from the two amino acids, glycine and valine.
18. Describe the xanthroproteic test used to indicate the presence of many common proteins.
19. What does the following statement mean? Each enzyme serves as a catalyst "at which" a specific chemical reaction occurs.
20. (a) What is chemotherapy? (b) What evidence exists that sulfanilamide and *para*-aminobenzoic acid are related in bacterial metabolism? (c) Is either *para*-aminobenzoic acid or sulfanilamide an enzyme? Explain your answer.
21. (a) Which portion of a chromosome determines the heredity of an individual? (b) Give the specific name of the essential substance.
22. (a) List the three components of each DNA molecule. (b) What are the components of nucleotides? (c) How are nucleotides and DNA related?
23. (a) Describe the basic difference between the chemical structure of purines and pyrimidines. (b) What two purines are found in DNA? What two pyrimidines?
24. (a) Describe the physical appearance of a DNA molecule. (b) How do biochemists explain chemically the ability of DNA molecules to replicate?

Relating Terms Within the Concept
From the terms below select the term that best completes each of the following statements. Do not use a term more than once.

ADP, ATP, DNA, amino acids, carbohydrates, dehydration, denaturation, fermentation, hydrolysis, Krebs cycle, lactic acid, *monosaccharide, nucleotide, peptide linkage, polysaccharide, proteins, pyruvic acid, replication.*

1. Hydrogen bonds are broken during protein _____ .
2. Starch is an example of a _____ .
3. $C_6H_{12}O_6$ is both a hexose and a _____ .
4. The first product of cellular oxidation is _____ .
5. Acetic acid is degraded to carbon dioxide and hydrogen in the _____ .
6. Yeast cells produced alcohol and carbon dioxide by the process of anaerobic respiration or _____ .
7. Energy from the oxidation of glucose is used to generate _____ .
8. Starch can be converted to glucose by the process of _____ .
9. Both cellulose and fructose are _____ .
10. The building blocks of proteins are _____ .
11. The condensation of two amino acids results in a _____ .
12. The nucleic acid in chromosomes is _____ .
13. All enzymes, or organic catalysts, are _____ .
14. The process by which DNA duplicates itself is _____ .

Solving Problems Within the Concept
1. Determine the molecular weight of a hemoglobin molecule.
2. Assume that 5 percent of the food eaten in a 3,000-calorie-per-day diet is converted and stored as fat in the body. How much weight per day would this amount of fat add to the body? (A pound of fat burned in a calorimeter yields approximately 3,600 calories.)
3. (a) How many molecules of glucose would be needed to produce one molecule of starch $(C_6H_{10}O_5)_x$ in which x is 1,000? (b) How many grams of water would be liberated as 1 mole of starch molecules forms by dehydration?
4. How many grams of glucose are produced

by the hydrolysis of 1 mole of maltose?

5. How many grams of chlorophyll (of the portion of the molecule on page 657) would have to be decomposed to obtain sufficient carbon to synthesize (if possible) 1 gram-molecular weight of the heme portion of a molecule of hemoglobin?

Applying the Concept

1. Explain in terms of bonding energy how heating denatures some liquid proteins.
2. In diabetes, an excess of glucose remains in the bloodstream because the body is unable to oxidize glucose properly. Some of the excess glucose is given off as body waste. Describe a test that can be used to determine whether or not a patient has diabetes.
3. (a) Are the essential amino acids soluble or insoluble? (b) How do you know?
4. In an investigation, iodine solution is used to show that a suspension contains starch. In a few hours the blue color of the solution gradually fades, indicating that starch is no longer present. What might have been the purpose of the investigation?
5. Glucose is rarely found in leaves and other parts of green plants; yet sucrose and starch are. Suggest a reason why this is true.
6. Mention six biochemical problems that are as yet unsolved.
7. Where do viruses obtain the nutrients necessary for replication?

Reading Further

The Double Helix, by James Watson, New York, Atheneum, 1968. A highly readable account of the struggle of Watson and F. Crick to unravel the structure of DNA.

Biochemistry: A Brief Course, by A. Mazur and B. Harrow, Philadephia, Saunders, 1968. A clear and logical presentation of the chemistry of living cells.

Biological Science: An Inquiry into Life, 2d ed., New York, Harcourt, Brace & World, 1968. Note especially Chapters, 5, 6, and 36 for a concise presentation of the biochemistry of cells and energy relationships.

METRIC AND ENGLISH SYSTEMS AND THEIR EQUIVALENTS

m = meter	mm^2 = square millimeter	ml = milliliter
cm = centimeter	cm^2 = square centimeter	g = gram
mm = millimeter	mm^3 = cubic millimeter	mg = milligram
km = kilometer	cm^3 = cubic centimeter	kg = kilogram
	cc = cubic centimeter	

METRIC SYSTEM	ENGLISH SYSTEM	EQUIVALENTS
Length		
10 mm = 1 cm	12 in = 1 ft	1 in = 2.54 cm
100 cm = 1 m	3 ft = 1 yd	1 ft = 30.48 cm
1,000 mm = 1 m	5,280 ft = 1 mi	1 m = 39.37 in
1,000 m = 1 km		1 km = 0.62 mi
Area		
$100\ mm^2 = 1\ cm^2$	$144\ in^2 = 1\ ft^2$	$1\ in^2 = 6.45\ cm^2$
		$1\ ft^2 = 929\ cm^2$
Volume		
$1{,}000\ mm^3 = 1\ cm^3$ (1 cc)	$1{,}728\ in^3 = 1\ ft^3$	1 liter = 1.06 qt
$1\ ml = 1\ cm^3$ (1 cc)	$231\ in^3 = 1\ gal$	1 gallon = 3.78 liters
1 liter = 1,000 ml		
Mass		
1,000 mg = 1 g	16 oz = 1 lb	1 kg = 2.2 lb
1,000 g = 1 kg	2,000 lb = 1 ton	1 lb = 454 g

SIGNIFICANT FIGURES

The measurement 32.4 ml is assumed to be accurate to the nearest tenth of a milliliter—its true value is between 32.35 ml and 32.45 ml. Two digits to the left of the decimal point and one to the right are fixed. Since the digits that express the measurement are called *significant figures,* the measurement contains *three* significant figures. If the measurement had been 324 ml or 3.24 ml, it would still contain three significant figures; the location of the decimal point is unrelated to the number of significant figures in this determination.

The more significant figures in a measurement, the more precise it is; but zeros pose a special problem. Zeros used to indicate a value are significant figures. If the measurement above had been 32.40 ml, the zero would have indicated that the measurement was accurate to the nearest hundredth; hence the measurement would have contained four significant figures. But zeros used solely to fix the decimal point are *not* significant figures. In the examples below the significant zeros are underlined:

1205 has four significant figures
12050 has five significant figures
0.1205 has four significant figures
.0125 has three significant figures
0.0125 has three significant figures
0.10125 has five significant figures
0.01205 has four significant figures

The procedure for rounding out measurements is relatively simple. When the first digit to be dropped is less than 5, do not change the last digit retained. If the first digit to be dropped is more than 5, increase by one the last digit retained. A frequently used procedure when the first digit to be dropped is 5 is *not* to change the last digit retained if it is an even number, but to increase it by one if the last digit is an odd number. For example:

125,639 rounded off to four significant figures becomes 125600
.012544 rounded off to four significant figures becomes .01254
125,668 rounded off to four significant figures becomes 125700
0.12556 rounded off to four significant figures becomes 0.1256
12565 rounded off to four significant figures becomes 12560
12575 rounded off to four significant figures becomes 12580

For ease in working with atomic weights, the values often are rounded off to whole numbers or to one decimal place (if approximately 0.5). The table of atomic weights on page 30 gives the atomic weights of each element to the known number of significant figures. The table on the inside back cover gives the figures usually used in calculations involving atomic weights of elements.

SCIENTIFIC NOTATION—POWERS OF TEN

In science the very large and the very small often complicate calculations. Avogadro's number is 602,350,000,000,000,000,000,000; it is much easier to handle when expressed in powers of ten as 6.02×10^{23}. Any number can be expressed as a power of ten multiplied by a second number between 1 and 10. This procedure is usually called *scientific notation*.

Numbers larger than one may be written as positive powers of ten. Thus, 250, which is 2.5×100, may be written as 2.5×10^2. And 602,000 may be written as 6.02×10^5. In writing any number in scientific notation, a move of the decimal point one digit to the left is "balanced" by an increase of one to the exponent of ten.

Numbers smaller than one may be written as negative powers of ten. Thus, 0.00072, which is the same as $\frac{72}{100,000}$ or $\frac{72}{10^5}$, may be written as 72×10^{-5}, or in scientific notation as 7.2×10^{-4}. And .006583 may be written as 6.583×10^{-3}. In writing any number in scientific notation, a move of the decimal point one digit to the right is "balanced" by a decrease of one (increase of *minus* one) to the exponent of ten.

To multiply numbers expressed in scientific notation, add the exponents of ten and multiply only the numbers preceding the powers of ten. For example:

$$(1.5 \times 10^3)(3.0 \times 10^5) = (1.5 \times 3.0)(10^{3+5}) = 4.5 \times 10^8$$

To divide numbers expressed in scientific notation, subtract the exponents of ten and divide only the numbers preceding the powers of ten. For example:

$$\frac{(7.2 \times 10^3)}{(6.0 \times 10^{-2})} = \frac{(7.2)}{(6.0)}(10^{3-[-2]}) = 1.2 \times 10^5$$

(S = soluble; Ss = slightly soluble; I = insoluble or nearly insoluble;
D = decomposes in water; — = does not exist or is unstable)

	Acetate	Bromide	Carbonate	Chlorate	Chloride	Hydroxide	Iodide	Nitrate	Oxide	Phosphate	Silicate	Sulfate	Sulfide	Sulfite
Aluminum	S	S	—	S	S	I	S	S	I	I	I	S	D	—
Ammonium	S	S	S	S	S	S	S	S	—	S	—	S	S	S
Antimony	—	D	—	—	S	—	D	—	Ss	—	—	D	I	—
Arsenic	—	D	—	—	D	—	S	—	Ss	—	—	—	I	—
Barium	S	S	I	S	S	Ss	S	S	Ss	I	S	I	D	I
Bismuth	—	D	I	—	D	I	I	D	I	I	—	D	I	—
Cadmium	D	D	I	S	S	I	S	S	I	I	I	S	I	Ss
Calcium	S	S	I	S	S	Ss	S	S	Ss	I	I	Ss	D	I
Chromium	S	S	—	—	S	I	—	S	I	Ss	—	S	I	—
Cobalt	S	S	I	S	S	I	S	S	I	I	I	S	I	I
Copper II	S	S	I	S	S	I	—	S	I	I	—	S	I	—
Iron II	S	S	I	—	S	I	S	S	I	I	I	S	I	Ss
Iron III	—	S	—	—	S	I	—	S	I	I	—	S	D	—
Hydrogen	S	S	—	S	S	—	S	S	—	S	S	S	S	—
Lead	S	Ss	I	S	Ss	I	Ss	S	I	I	I	I	I	I
Magnesium	S	S	I	S	S	I	S	S	I	Ss	I	S	D	Ss
Manganese	S	S	I	S	S	I	S	S	I	I	I	S	I	—
Mercury I	Ss	I	I	S	I	—	I	S	I	I	—	Ss	I	—
Mercury II	S	Ss	I	S	S	I	I	S	I	I	—	D	I	—
Nickel	S	S	I	S	S	I	S	S	I	I	—	S	I	I
Potassium	S	S	S	S	S	S	S	S	S	S	S	S	S	S
Silver	Ss	I	I	S	I	—	I	S	I	I	—	Ss	I	Ss
Sodium	S	S	S	S	S	S	S	S	S	S	S	S	S	S
Strontium	S	S	I	S	S	Ss	S	S	Ss	I	I	Ss	D	I
Tin II	D	S	—	S	S	I	S	D	I	I	—	S	I	—
Zinc	S	S	I	S	S	I	S	S	I	I	I	S	I	Ss

General Rules for Solubility in Water

1. All common ammonium, potassium, and sodium compounds are soluble.
2. All common acetates, chlorates, and nitrates are soluble.
   Acetates of mercury I and silver are only slightly soluble.
3. All common chlorides are soluble *except* chlorides of silver, mercury I, and lead. (Lead chloride is only slightly soluble in cold water, but highly soluble in hot water.)
4. All common sulfates are soluble *except* those of barium and lead. Sulfates of calcium, mercury I, silver, and strontium are only slightly soluble.
5. The common carbonates, oxides, phosphates, silicates, sulfides, and sulfites are generally insoluble *except* those of ammonium, potassium, and sodium.
6. All common hydroxides are insoluble *except* those of ammonium, potassium, and sodium. The hydroxides of barium, calcium, and strontium are only slightly soluble.

ATOMIC NUMBERS AND ATOMIC WEIGHTS

Name of element	Symbol	Atomic number	Atomic weight	Name of element	Symbol	Atomic number	Atomic weight
Actinium	Ac	89	[227]*	Mercury	Hg	80	200.59
Aluminum	Al	13	26.98	Molybdenum	Mo	42	95.94
Americium	Am	95	[243]	Neodymium	Nd	60	144.24
Antimony	Sb	51	121.75	Neon	Ne	10	20.18
Argon	Ar	18	39.95	Neptunium	Np	93	[237]
Arsenic	As	33	74.9	Nickel	Ni	28	58.71
Astatine	At	85	[210]	Niobium	Nb	41	92.91
Barium	Ba	56	137.34	Nobelium	No	102	[253]
Berkelium	Bk	97	[247]	Nitrogen	N	7	14.01
Beryllium	Be	4	9.01	Osmium	Os	76	190.2
Bismuth	Bi	83	208.98	Oxygen	O	8	15.99†
Boron	B	5	10.81	Palladium	Pd	46	106.4
Bromine	Br	35	79.91	Phosphorus	P	15	30.98
Cadmium	Cd	48	112.40	Platinum	Pt	78	195.09
Calcium	Ca	20	40.08	Plutonium	Pu	94	[242]
Californium	Cf	98	[249]	Polonium	Po	84	[210]
Carbon	C	6	12.01	Potassium	K	19	39.10
Cerium	Ce	58	140.12	Praseodymium	Pr	59	140.91
Cesium	Cs	55	132.91	Promethium	Pm	61	[147]
Chlorine	Cl	17	35.45	Protactinium	Pa	91	[231]
Chromium	Cr	24	51.99†	Radium	Ra	88	[226]
Cobalt	Co	27	58.93	Radon	Rn	86	[222]
Copper	Cu	29	63.54	Rhenium	Re	75	186.2
Curium	Cm	96	[247]	Rhodium	Rh	45	102.91
Dysprosium	Dy	66	162.50	Rubidium	Rb	37	85.47
Einsteinium	Es	99	[254]	Ruthenium	Ru	44	101.07
Erbium	Er	68	167.26	Samarium	Sm	62	150.35
Europium	Eu	63	151.96	Scandium	Sc	21	44.96
Fermium	Fm	100	[253]	Selenium	Se	34	78.96
Fluorine	F	9	18.99†	Silicon	Si	14	28.09
Francium	Fr	87	[223]	Silver	Ag	47	107.87
Gadolinium	Gd	64	157.25	Sodium	Na	11	22.99
Gallium	Ga	31	69.72	Strontium	Sr	38	87.62
Germanium	Ge	32	72.59	Sulfur	S	16	32.06
Gold	Au	79	196.97	Tantalum	Ta	73	180.95
Hafnium	Hf	72	178.49	Technetium	Tc	43	[99]
Helium	He	2	4.00	Tellurium	Te	52	127.60
Holmium	Ho	67	164.93	Terbium	Tb	65	158.93
Hydrogen	H	1	1.008	Thallium	Tl	81	204.37
Indium	In	49	114.82	Thorium	Th	90	232.04
Iodine	I	53	126.90	Thulium	Tm	69	168.93
Iridium	Ir	77	192.2	Tin	Sn	50	118.69
Iron	Fe	26	55.85	Titanium	Ti	22	47.90
Krypton	Kr	36	83.80	Tungsten	W	74	183.85
Lanthanum	La	57	138.91	Uranium	U	92	238.03
Lawrencium	Lw	103	[257]	Vanadium	V	23	50.94
Lead	Pb	82	207.19	Xenon	Xe	54	131.30
Lithium	Li	3	6.94	Ytterbium	Yb	70	173.04
Lutetium	Lu	71	174.97	Yttrium	Y	39	88.91
Magnesium	Mg	12	24.31	Zinc	Zn	30	65.37
Manganese	Mn	25	54.94	Zirconium	Zr	40	91.22
Mendelevium	Md	101	[256]	(Name undetermined)		104	[257]

* Brackets denote replacement of atomic weight by the mass number of the isotope with the longest half life.
† These values can be rounded out to the next whole number, because the third figure following the decimal point is greater than 5 and has been dropped.

PICTURE ACKNOWLEDGMENTS

Key: (t) top; (c) center; (b) bottom; (l) left; (r) right

UNIT I: p. 1, Niels Bohr Institutet; p. 4, (t) Ciba Corp., Ltd; (b) Illustration Research Service; p. 9, Illustration Research Service; pp. 12–13, reproduced by permission of The Royal Institution, London; p. 14, Radio Corp. of America; p. 31, by permission of the Editors of the "Philosophical Magazine"; p. 33, from F. W. Aston's *Mass Spectra and Isotopes,* Edward Arnold (Publishers) Ltd., London; p. 42, courtesy G. P. Thomson; p. 55, Argonne National Laboratory; p. 58, Boris Paretzkin and H. Steffen Peiser, "Science," vol. 146, Oct. 9, 1964, pp. 260–261. Copyright 1964 by the American Association for the Advancement of Science; p. 60, Morton Salt Co.

UNIT II: p. 179, Tekniska Museet, Stockholm; p. 181, Fundamental Photographs; p. 196, Harbrace; p. 224, Grant Heilman; p. 227, Harbrace; p, 228, Beckman Instruments; pp. 235, 242, and 248, Fundamental Photographs; p. 249, Dow Chemical Corp., p. 254, Harbrace; p. 256, Beckman Instruments; pp. 271, 276, 285, 289, 297, 298, and 313, Fundamental Photographs; p. 277, Harbrace; p. 293, from *General Chemistry* by Markham and Smith, copyright 1954, Houghton Mifflin Co., Boston, Mass.; p. 314, Bausch & Lomb, Inc.; p. 315, Courtesy of Professor Ralph W. G. Wyckoff, University of Arizona; p. 316, Borden Co.; p. 317, Chemicolloid Laboratories, Inc.

UNIT III: p. 325, Courtesy of The University of Chicago; p. 332, American Cancer Society; p. 333, from Glasstone's *Sourcebook on Atomic Energy,* copyright 1958, D. Van Nostrand Co., Inc., Princeton, N.J.; p. 338, (t) Pergamon Press, (c) Lawrence Radiation Laboratory, (b) CERN Scientific Information Service; p. 342, (t) A. J. Dempster, (b) University of California, Berkeley; p. 351, Brookhaven National Laboratory; p. 353, Lawrence Radiation Laboratory; p. 354, Westinghouse Research Laboratories; p. 355, Lawrence Radiation Laboratory; p. 356, (t) Brookhaven National Laboratory, (b) Union Carbide Corp.; p. 357, Lawrence Radiation Laboratory; p. 359, (t) Lawrence Radiation Laboratory, (b) Brookhaven National Laboratory; p. 360, both Lawrence Radiation Laboratory; p. 362, Courtesy of Professor P. I. Dee, University of Glasgow, Scotland; p. 363, (t) U.S. Atomic Energy Commission, (b) Courtesy, Los Alamos Scientific Laboratory.

UNIT IV: p. 367, Wide World; p. 372, Harbrace; p. 376, Dow Chemical Corp.; p. 378, Jones & Laughlin Steel Corp.; p. 379, Pennsalt; p. 380, E. I. duPont de Nemours & Co, Inc.; p. 381, Dow Chemical Corp.; p. 383, Eastman Kodak; p. 386, Harbrace; p. 393, Courtesy, Aluminum Co. of America; p. 397, Texas Gulf Sulphur Co., Inc.; p. 399, Harbrace; p. 405, E. I. duPont de Nemours & Co., Inc.; p. 409, Merck Sharp & Dohme; p. 412, Vactec, Inc.; p. 419, General Electric Co.; pp. 420 and 421, (t) Fundamental Photographs; p. 421, (b) Hugh Spencer; p. 426, Courtesy of The Royal Institution, London; p. 429, Monsanto Chemical; p. 432, Shell Oil Co.; p. 436, Harbrace; p. 437, Grinnell Co., Inc.; p. 450, Dow Chemical Co.; pp. 451 and 452, Fundamental Photographs; p. 453, International Salt Co.; p. 455, (tl) National Provisioner, (tr) Morton Salt Co., (cl) Wyandotte Chemicals Corp., (cr) Perkin-Elmer Corp., (b) Habrace; p. 460, Courtesy of Dr. Henry Gilman; p. 465, Harbrace; p. 466,

Dow Chemical Corp.; p. 467, Beryllium Corp.; p. 468, Harbrace; p. 469, (t) Charles Rotkin, P.F.I., (b) Owens-Corning Fiberglass Corp.; p. 470, Libby-Owens-Ford Glass Co.; p. 471, Sanford H. Roth from Rapho-Guillumette; p. 472, Fundamental Photographs; p. 473, Dow Chemical Corp.; p. 474, Johns-Manville Corp.; p. 484, Union Carbide Corp.; p. 486, Fundamental Photographs; p. 487, Anaconda Co.; p. 488, Copper Development Association, Inc.; p. 489, International Smelting & Refining Co.; p. 490, Copper Development Association, Inc.; p. 491, Susan McCartney; p. 494, Newmont Mining Corp.; p. 495, Reed & Barton; p. 497, Courtesy of Marvin Neivert; pp. 501, 502, 504, and 505, Jones & Laughlin Steel Corp.; pp. 507 and 509, U.S. Steel Corp.; p. 510, a., b., and c., U.S. Steel Corp., d., Republic Steel Corp.; p. 514, Jones & Laughlin Steel Corp.; p. 515, Dow Chemical Corp.; p. 516, Fundamental Photographs; p. 517, Harbrace; p. 518, Frederic P. Wiedersum Associates, Architects and Engineers, Valley Stream, N.Y., and Trenton, N.J.; p. 519, Harbrace; p. 524, Courtesy, Aluminum Co. of America; p. 527, Courtesy, Aluminum Co. of America; p. 528, Fundamental Photographs; p. 529, Perkin-Elmer Corp.; p. 530, Harbrace; p. 531, Bell Telephone Laboratories, Inc.; p. 532, Pfizer & Co.; p. 534, U.S. Borax; p. 535, Corning Glass Works; p. 536, Courstesy, Aluminum Co. of America; p. 549, Keystone Press; p. 553, (t) General Electric Research Laboratory, (b) N. W. Ayer & Sons, Inc.; p. 554, American Optical Company; p. 555, Ashland Oil & Refining Co.; p. 557, (t) Carborundum Co., (b) Speer Carbon Co., a division of Air Reduction Co., Inc.; p. 560, General Dynamics Corp.; p. 562, Wide World; p. 563, Walter Kidde & Co., Inc.; p. 565, Harbrace; p. 566, (bl) and (bc) Harbrace, (br) Johns-Manville Corp.; p. 567, Raytheon Co.; p. 569, General Dynamics Corp.

UNIT V: p. 573, UPI; p. 575, Charles Bonnay from Black Star; p. 582, Harbrace; p. 584, Standard Oil of N.J.; p. 586, Harbrace; p. 588, Ciba; pp. 594 and 595, Harbrace; p. 598, Union Carbide; pp. 603, 605, and 607, Harbrace; p. 608, (t) Proctor & Gamble, (b) Fundamental Photographs; p. 614, Tennessee Gas Transmission Co.; p. 615, Field Museum of Natural History; p. 623, Charles Rotkin, P.F.I.; p. 625, Bureau of Mines, U.S. Dept. of Interior; p. 628, (t) NASA, (cl) The New York Times, (cr) Convair, a division of General Dynamics Corp., (bl) Wide World, (br) NASA; p. 632, Dow Chemical Corp.; p. 633, U.S. Rubber Co.; p. 636, Dow Corning Corp.; p. 639, Dow Chemical Corp.; p. 640, Union Carbide; p. 644, General Electric Co.; p. 645, Walter Dawn; p. 647, a., d., e., and f., S. D. Warren Co., b., International Paper Co., c., American Forest Products Industries; p. 648, E. I. duPont de Nemours & Co., Inc.; p. 650, a., Michigan Dept. of Conservation, b., National Cotton Council, c., d., e., and f., American Viscose Corp.; p. 651, Ivan Massar from Black Star; p. 652, E. I. duPont de Nemours & Co., Inc.; p. 655, George E. Pallade, Rockefeller Institute; p. 664, from *The Mechanism of Enzyme Action,* edited by McElroy and Glass, copyright 1954, the Johns Hopkins Press, Baltimore, Md.; p. 667, Courtesy, Los Alamos Scientific Laboratory.

FOUR-COLOR PICTURE ACKNOWLEDGMENTS: Insert between pages 84 and 85 adapted from Spectrum Chart, copyright by The Welch Scientific Co., insert between pages 548 and 549, all Harbrace photos.

Illustrations by BMA Associates, Inc. and ANco Technical Services, Inc.

Index

(Page numbers in boldface refer to illustrations.)

Abelson, P. H., 360
abrasives, 531, 556
absolute temperature, *see* Kelvin scale
absolute zero, defined, 147
accelerators, particle, *see* particle accelerators
acetaldehyde (ethanal), 600, 601
acetanilide, 267, 394
acetate ion, 110, 209, 231, 277
acetate process, 649
acetic acid, 209, 210, 219, 220, 253, **254,** 255, 256, 442, 601, **601,** 616, 632; and conjugate pairs, 231; degraded through Krebs cycle, 660, **661;** formula for, 119, 596, 663; pH of, 226, 277; synthesized by Kolbe, 574; as weak acid, 220, 632; as weak electrolyte, 203, 209, 275
acetone, 596, 600, **600,** 616, 649
acetylene (ethyne), 574, 585, **585,** 586, 589, 592, 618–19, 635, **635;** preparation of, 619, **619**
acetylsalicylic acid, 253, 603
acid anhydrides, 218, 242–43, 279, 403, 405, 420, 435
acid-base indicators, table of, 227, **colorplate** facing 548
acid salts, 234–35, **235,** 252, 253
acids: from acid hydrides, 242–43, 242; amino, *see* amino acids; aromatic, 602–03; binary, 244; Brønsted-Lowery theory of, 217, 230, 231, 232; and conjugate bases, 231; defined, 118, 217, 229; diprotic, 234, 245; fatty, 602, 606, 607; formulas for common, 119; hydrogen from, 218, 220–21, **221;** hydrogen halide, 219, 244; indicators for, table of, 227; industrial uses of, 241; ionization of molecules in, **218,** 218–19; litmus test for, 218, **218;** and metallic oxides, reactions between, 250; monoprotic, 234, 245; naming, 244–45; nonvolatile, 243, **243,** 250 251; normal solutions of, 188–89; nucleic, 666; organic, 596, 600–02, **601;** preparation of, 241–45, 250–51, 409; properties of, **218;** from reactions between salts and nonvolatile acids, 243; in soil, 224; strong, **219,** 220, 231, 235, 236; ternary, **244,** 244–45;

triprotic, 234, 245; uses of, 241; volatile, 243; weak, **219,** 220, 231, 235, 236
acrylates, 643
actinide series, **77,** 82, 360, 481, **483, 484,** 485
actinium, **77,** 78, 82, 450, 481, 484, 485
activated complex, 163–65, **164,** 166, **166**
activation energy, 163, 164, **164, 165,** 166; defined, 163
active element, defined, 9, 55
active metals, 295, 296, 298, 373, 446; and active nonmetals, reactions between, 251, 372–73; and dilute acids, reactions between, 250; and water, reactions between, 247
activity series of metals (replacement series), 296–97, **296, 297**
addition product, defined, 595
addition reactions, of hydrocarbons, 594–95
adenine, **666,** 667
adenosine diphosphate (ADP), 661, 662, **662**
adenosine triphosphate (ATP), 661, 662, **662**
adipic acid, 641, 643, **644**
ADP (adenosine diphosphate), 661, 662, **662**
adsorption: by charcoal, 553, 554, **554;** defined, 321; by solid surfaces, 321–22, **321**
aerosols, 315
air: composition of, 18, 54, 58, 59; pressure of, at sea level, 146
-*al* suffix, 600
alanine, 663, **663**
alchemists, 3–4, **4,** 15, 217, 425
alcohol derivatives, **599,** 599–604, 600, **600, 601, 604**
alcohols, **596,** 596–99; denatured, 597, **598;** dihydroxy, 598; isomers of, 597–98; monohydroxy, 598; as nonelectrolytes, 202, 203; polyhydroxy, 598; trihydroxy, 598; *see also* ethyl alcohol; methyl alcohol; propyl alcohol
aldehydes, 595, 596, **599,** 599–600
aliphatic hydrocarbons, 576, 587, 589; *see also* alkanes; alkenes; alkynes
alkadienes, 585

alkali, defined, 224
alkali cellulose, 649
alkali metals (group IA), 79, 449–59, **451;** atomic structure of, 451; compounds of, 454–59; ions of, 451, 543, 544, 547; oxidation state of, 486; and periodic table, 449, 485; preparation of, 449–50; properties of, 449, 450–51; as reducing agents, 451–52; table of, 449; testing for, 544–45, 547; uses of, 452–53
alkaline earth metals (group IIA), 79, 224, 464–80; compounds of, 467–72, 476–77; ionization potentials of, **colorplate** facing 85, 464; ions of, 465, 543, 544, 547; and periodic table, 464, 465; preparation of, 465–66; properties of, 464; as reducing agents, 464; table of, 464; testing for, 544, 547; uses of, 466–67
alkanes, 576–82, 589, 592; boiling points of, 578, 579; catalytic cracking of, 584; graphic formulas for, 578; isomers of, 579–80, **579, 580;** molecular formulas for, 578, 579; naming, 580–81; series of, 577, **578;** sources and uses of, 581, **582, 624**
alkenes, **582,** 582–85, **583,** 589; boiling points of, 583; graphic formulas for, 583–84; molecular formulas for, 583; naming, 584; sources and uses of, 584–85
alkyd, 642
alkyl halide, defined, 593
alkyl radical, defined, 580
alkylation, 624
alkynes, **585,** 585–86, 589
allotrope, defined, 266, 393
alloys, 4, 181, 466; cobalt and nickel, 520; magnalium, 466, 530; steel, 506; tin and lead, 568
Alnico alloys, 520, 530–31, **531**
alpha particles, 24, 25, **25, 329,** 330, 334, 335, 336, 342, 347, 450; ionization effects of, on body cells, 339; nitrogen bombarded with, 334, **334,** 343, 357; symbols for, 341
alum, 532
alumina (aluminum oxide), 72, 116, 526, 528, 529, 531–32, 546

aluminum, 57, 86, 111, 379, 514, 524, **524,** 525; activity of, 296, 528; alloys of, 466, 529, 530–31; atomic number of, 72, 73, 74, 525; atomic radius of, 74, **colorplate** facing 85; atomic weight of, 525; beta particles absorbed by, 340, **341;** boiling point of, 525; bombarded with alpha particles, 335; cobalt nitrate test for, 546, **colorplate VI** facing 549; compounds of, 531–33; density of, 74, 525; electrical conductivity of, 529, electron configuration of, 46–49, **47,** 525; fused with sulfur to form aluminum sulfide, 251; hydrogen released by, in reaction with strong base, 528; ionization potential of, 39–41, **41,** 74, **colorplate** facing 85; 525; ions of, 527, 528; melting point of, 525; metallurgy of, 526–28, **527, 528;** oxidation potential of, 302; oxidation state of, 525; properties of, 73, 74, 525, 528–29; as reducing agent, 529, 530; salts of, 532; symbol for, 72, 73, 74; uses of, 529; valence number of, 116, 118

aluminum bronze, 530

aluminum chloride, 236, 532; as catalyst, 532; formula for, 96; from reaction between aluminum hydroxide and hydrochloric acid, 248; at temperatures below 400°C, 525, **527;** uses of, 376

aluminum family (group IIIA), 524–38; electron structure of, 525, **525;** oxidation states of, 524; and periodic table, 524, 525; properties of, 525; table of, 525

aluminum fluoride, 524

aluminum hydroxide, 236, 237, 248, 526, 532–33, **533,** 561

aluminum oxide, 72, 116, 526, 528, 529, 531–32, **531,** 546

aluminum sulfate, 531, 532

aluminum sulfide, 251

Alundum, 531

amalgamation process, 493

americium, 16, 360, **360,** 361, 485

amino acids, 645, 663; and peptides, 663–64, **664;** *see also* proteins

ammonia, 424, 428, 616, 617; and ammonium radical, 431; aqueous, *see,* aqueous ammonia; compounds of, 428, 430–33; as covalent compound, 100, 101, 223; fountain, 223; molecular weight of, 430; molecule of, 50, **51, 100,** 101, 107, **107,** 430, **431;** and nitride ion, 446; and Ostwald process, 422;

preparation of, 277, 278, 279, **279,** 422, **429,** 429–30, **430;** properties of, 430–31; and ratio by volume of nitrogen to hydrogen, 64; as reducing agent, 294; solid model of molecule of, 50, **51;** solubility of, in water, 430; and Solvay process, 457; as strong base, 231; uses of, 432, **432**

ammonium acetate, 236

ammonium bicarbonate, 457

ammonium bromide, 384, 592, **592,** 594

ammonium carbonate, 331, **331**

ammonium chloride, 417, 431, 457; formula for, 117; as normal salt, 234; preparation of, 235–37; solubility of, in water, 184; uses of, 432

ammonium hydroxide, 235, 236, 425, 429, 431, 443, 444, 456, 457, 543, 547, 592, 594; decomposed to form ammonia, 430; pH of, 226; as weak base, 223, 235; as weak electrolyte, 203

ammonium ion, 110, 117, 223, 230, **230,** 235, 424, 431, 544; test for, **431**

ammonium molybdate, 447

ammonium nitrate, 424, 426, 427, 432; in explosive, 249

ammonium nitrite, 417

ammonium phosphate, 432, 435

ammonium phosphomolybdate, 447

ammonium sulfate, 394, 432

amorphous solids, 139, 398

amphiprotic, defined, 230

amphoteric hydroxides, 248, 533, 550

amu, *see* atomic mass units

anaerobic respiration, 660–61

analysis, chemical, defined, 441

analytical groups: of metallic ions, 539–44; group I, 540–41, **540;** group II, 542, **542;** group III, 542–43; group IV, 543–44, **543;** group V, 544

-ane suffix, 583, 585

Angstrom, defined, 29

angular molecules, **103,** 107, **107**

anhydrous substance, defined, 195

aniline dyes, 588, 616

anions, *see* negative ions

annealing process, 469

anode, 23, **23,** 208, **208, 213, 248**

anthracene, 588, 616

anthracite coal, 614, 615

antibiotics, 666

antifreeze, 598

antiknock gasoline, 383, 452, 569, 626

antimony, 3, 371, 373, **420,** 433, 436; ions of, 446; properties of, 420, **420**

antimony chloride, 373, 402

antimony sulfide, 436, 547, **colorplate III** following 548, 633

antimony trichloride, 593

antimony trifluoride, 593

antineutrino, 360

aqua regia, 425, 436, 495

aquamarine, 465, **465**

aqueous ammonia, 420, 492; and conjugate acid–base pairs, 231; equation for, 223

aqueous solutions, 181–86, **182, 183;** electrical properties of, 201–04; and table of solutes, 184

Arabs, and concepts of matter, 3, 4

aragonite, 467

arc furnace, 556, **556**

arc lamp, 419, **419**

arc process, for preparation of nitric acid, 422

argon, 54, 75, 418, 419, 482; in air, 18; atom of, 56, **56;** atomic number of, 72, 73, 74, 417; atomic radius of, 74, **colorplate** facing 85; atomic weight of, 417; boiling point of, 417; density of, 74, 417; electron configuration of 46–47, **47,** 417; ionization potential of, 75, **75, colorplate** facing 85, 417; melting point of, 417; and periodic table, 76, 77, **77,** 78, 80, 81; properties of, 73, 74, 417; symbol for, 72, 73, 74; uses of, 419; and valence electrons, 73

Aristotle, 3, 433

aromatic acids, 602–03

aromatic hydrocarbons, 576, **587,** 587–89, **588**

Arrhenius, Svante, 179, 204, 205, 210

arsenic, 3, 298, 420, **420,** 433; in activity series, 296; compounds of, 433, ions of, 446; as metalloid, 86; preparation of, 435; properties of, 420, 435–36; uses of, 436

arsenic sulfide, 433, 547, **colorplate III** following 548

arsenious sulfide, colloidal, 318, 321, **321**

arsine, 435

asbestos, 476, 566, **566,** 646

ascorbic acid, 253

aspirin, 253, 603

association theory of hydrolysis, 235

astatine, 15, 333, 369, 385

Aston, F. W., 33

-ate suffix, 252

atomic bomb, 14, 34, 350, 351, 352, 356

atomic fission (*see* nuclear fission)

atomic hydrogen torch, 461

atomic mass units, atomic weight in, 25, 122

atomic notation, 34

atomic number: defined, 31; and periodic table, 30, 77–78, 79, inside back cover; and radioisotopes, 342

atomic pile, 325, 350, 351; control rods in, 351, **351**

atomic radii, 58, 74–75, 84, 88, 93; table of, **colorplate** facing 85

atomic theory, Dalton's, 11–14, 23

atomic weights, 25, 88; defined, 25; expressed in atomic mass units, 25; 122; expressed in grams, 123; and periodic table, 76–77, 78, 79, 88; table of, 26, inside back cover

atoms, 2, 3, 5, 23; and bond length, 107; branched, 579, 580; density of, 73–74; electron arrangements of, 55–56; electrons accepted by, 93; electrons donated by, 93; energy levels within, 30–31 (see also electron shells); in excited state, 31 in ground state 31, 46, 47; kernel of, 49; models of, 34–35, **34–35, 41,** 50–51, **51;** nucleus of, see nucleus, atomic; periodic properties of, 71; radii of, 58, 74–75, 84, **colorplate** facing 85, 88, 93; structure of, and ionization potential, 39; transmutation of, see transmutation of atoms; unbranched, 579, 580; see also electrons; ions; neutrons; protons

ATP (adenosine triphosphate), 661, 662, **662**

auto-oxidation reactions, 294, 395; defined, 294

Avogadro, Amadeo, 131, 132

Avogadro's Law, 132; defined, 132

Avogadro's number, 133; and mole, 133

Babbit metal, 568

background radiation, 338

Baekeland, Leo, 640

Bakelite, 600, 640, **640,** 642

baking powder, 560

baking soda, 432, 456, 457, 560, 561

balanced equations, 120–21, 308

Balard, Antoine, 381

ball-and-spring model of molecule, 51, **51**

ball-and-stick model of molecule, 51, **51**

barium, 348, 450, 467; compounds of, 477; electron configuration of, 485; flame test for, 545, 547, **colorplate IV** following 548; ions of, 543; and oxygen, affin-

ity for, 467; properties of, 464, 465; spectrum, **colorplate** facing 84; valence number of, 116

barium chloride, 275, 447; formula for, 96; in testing for ions containing sulfur, 445, 446

barium chromate, 544, 547

barium hydroxide, 189, 222

barium nitrate, 270

barium oxide, 222

barium peroxide, 394, 395

barium platinocyanide, 326, 327, **327**

barium sulfate, 270, 271, 275, 276, 394, 445, 446, 477

barometer, 125, **125**

Bartlett, Neil, 55

bases: from basic anhydrides, 246; caustic, 222, 223; as conductors of electricity, 222; and conjugate acids, 231; defined, 222, 229, 248; dihydroxy, 248; dissociation of compounds in, 222–23; indicators for, table of, 227; industrial uses of, 245; insoluble, from reactions between salts and strong bases, 247; litmus test for, 222, **222;** monohydroxy, 248; naming, 248; and nonmetallic oxides, reactions between, 250; normal solutions of, 189; preparation of, 245–48; properties of, **222;** from reactions between active metals and water, 247; strong, 223, 231, 235, 236, 247; trihydroxy, 248; uses of, 245; weak, 223, 231, 235, 236

basic anhydrides: bases prepared from, 246; defined, 223; prepared from salts, 246, **246**

basic salts, 235

battery: nickel-cadmium, 520; storage, 301, **410,** 410–11, 436, 569

battery plate, 568

bauxite, 526, 531, 532

Becker, H., 335

Becquerel, Henri, 326–28, 331–32, 338

Bémont, G., 329

"bends," prevention of, 419

Benedict's solution, 656, **656**

benzene, 382, 385, 409, 411, 451, 576, 585, 587, **587,** 592, 602, 603, 616

benzene hexachloride, 375

benzene ring, 587, **587**

benzoic acid, 602, **603**

Bergius process, 625, **625**

berkelium, 360, 361, 485

beryllium: 35; alloys of, 466; bombarded with alpha particles, 335; compounds

of, 477; electron configuration of, 47, 48, 81; ionization potential of, **41,** 49, 74, **colorplate** facing 85; produced by bombardment of lithium-7 with protons, 362; properties of, 73, 74, 464, 465, 466; and valence electrons, 73

beryllium bronze, 466, **467**

beryllium oxide, 71, 72

Berzelius, Jakob, 15, 16, 28, 170

Bessemer, Henry, 506

Bessemer converter, 506–07, **507**

beta particles, **329,** 330, 336, 342, 347, 360; absorption of, 340, **340,** 356; ionization effects of, on body cells, 339; symbols for, 341, 342

Bethe, H. A., 362

bi-prefix, 252; *hydrogen* substituted for, 253

bicarbonate radical, 110

binding energy of atomic nucleus, 350

biochemistry: defined, 655; unifying principles in, 658

bismuth, 420, **420,** 433, 436–37; compounds of, 436–37; ions of, 446; properties of, 420, 436; radioactive, 330, 333, 334, 339, 357; uses of, 437, **437**

bismuth nitrate, 234, 437

bismuth oxide, 436

bismuth sulfide, 542, **colorplate III** following 548

bisulfate ion, 234

bituminous coal, 614, 615, **615**

Black, Joseph, 5, 558

blast effect of nuclear fission bomb, 356

blast furnace, 501, **501, 503,** 503–04; airlocks in, 503, **503;** products of, 505; reactions in, 504–05

bleaching: with chlorine, 374–75, **375,** 376; with sulfur dioxide, 403–04, 405

bleaching powder, 472

blister copper, 489

blueprinting, and oxidation-reduction reactions, 518–19

body-centered cubic crystal, 140, **140**

body-centered cubic packing, 140

Bohr, Niels, 1, 30, 31, 35, 38, 39, 40, 41, 51

boiler scale, 473, **473**

boiling point, defined, 136; of solutions, **192**

bond angle, **103,** 107, **107**

bond length, 107, **107**

bonds: blending of covalent and ionic, 102–05, **103;** coordinate, 110; covalent, see covalent bonds; double covalent, 102, 575; hydrogen, 136–37, **137,** 183; ionic, see ionic bonds; metallic, 111,

111; nonpolar, 103, **103**; polar, **103**, 103–04; predicting types of, 106; single covalent, 101, 575; single electron, 535; special types of, **109**, 109–11, **110**, **111**; triple covalent, 102, 575

boneblack, 554, **554**

boranes, 535

borax, 524, 534, **534**, 535

borax bead test, **545**, 545–46, 547; **colorplate V** following 548

borazon, 535, 552

boric acid, 226, 442, 535, **535**

boric oxide, 535

boron, 524, 533; bombarded with alpha particles, 335; compounds of, 524, 533, 534, 535; as metalloid, 86; electron configuration 47, 48, 81; ionization potential of **41**, 49, 74, **colorplate** facing 85; preparation of, 533–34; properties of 74, 525, 534; valence number of, 116

boron carbide, 535, 556

boron fluoride, 525

boron nitride, 535

boron oxide, 72, 470

Bothe, W., 335

bottled gas, 620

Boyle, Robert, 4, 5, 9, 125, 127, 129, 131

Boyle's Law, 4, 127, **127**, 130, 131, 146–47; defined, 127

brass, 181, 490

Bredig arc, 317, **317**

breeder reactor, 354, **354**

bright-line spectrum, 28, **colorplate** facing 84

British thermal unit, 613

bromic acid, 245, **245**

bromide ion, 381, 444

bromine, 87, 106, 374, 592, 594; atomic number of, 369; atomic weight of, 369; boiling point of, 369; compounds of, 383–84; density of, 369, 382; electron configuration of, 369; and ethene, reaction between, 594, **594**; ionization potential of, **colorplate** facing 85; 369; melting point of, 369; and metals, reactions between, 382; and methane, reaction between, 592, **592**; oxidation state of, 369; and potassium hydroxide, reaction between, preparation of, **381**, 381–82, **382**; properties of, 369, 382–83; and replacement of other halogens, 383; solubility of, 369, 382; uses of compounds of, 383–84; valence number of, 116; and water, reaction between, 383

bromous acid, 245, **245**

bromthymol blue, 227, **colorplate** facing 548

Brønsted, J. N., 217

Brønsted-Lowry theory, 217, 230–32, 248

bronze, 481, 490–91, 530

Brown, Robert, 129

Brownian movement, 129, **129**, 314

bubble chamber, 337, **338**

Buna rubber, 635, **636**, 637

butadiene, **584**, 585, 635, **636**

butane, 578, 579, **579**, 580, 581

butene, 576, 583, 624

butyne, 585, 586,

cadmium, 16, 351, 484, 515; spectrum, **colorplate** facing 84

cadmium nitrate, 402

cadmium sulfate, 402, 547

cadmium sulfide, 542, **colorplate III** following 548

calcite, 467, **468**

calcium, 57, 59, 410, 464, 482; in activity series, 296; arsenates of, 436; atomic number of, 72, 73, 74, 464; atomic radius of, 74, **colorplate** facing 85; atomic weight of, 464; boiling point of, 464; compounds of, 467–72; density of, 464; discovery of, 450; electron configuration of, **47**, 464; flame test for, 545, **colorplate IV** following 548; ionization potential of, **41**, 74, **colorplate** facing 85, 464; ions of, 474, 475, 543, 544; melting point of, 464; necessary to life, 249; oxidation state of, 464; properties of, 464, 465; radioactive (calcium-45), 356; spectrum, **colorplate** facing 84; symbol for, 16, 72, 74; uses of, 466–67; valence number of, 97, 116, 118

calcium bicarbonate, 473, 474, 475, 559

calcium carbide, 556

calcium carbonate, 249, 473, 475, 558, 559; decomposition of, 246, 259, 468, **468**; in formation of caves, 474, **474**; properties and uses of, 467–68

calcium chloride, 443, 457, 471–72; from reaction between calcium carbonate and hydrochloric acid, 261; from reaction between calcium oxide and hydrochloric acid, 250; deliquescent, 196, **196**; formula for, 115; uses of, 376, 472

calcium dihydrogen phosphate, 560

calcium fluoride, 92, 95, **95**, 251, 380

calcium hydroxide, 189, 222, 224, 227, **248**, 249, 430, 447, 470–71, 475; as dihydroxy base, 248; from reaction between calcium oxide and water, 246, **246**, 468, 471; as strong base, 223

calcium nitrate, 117

calcium oxide, 222, 223, 246, 466, 468; formula for, 71, 72, 92, 95; as ionic compound, 94–95, **95**; preparation of, 468, 470, **470**; uses of, 470

calcium phosphate, 122, 170–71, 433, 435

calcium phosphide, 434

calcium sulfate, 117, 249, 250, 435, 469, 471, 473, 474, 475

californium, 360, 361, 485

calorie, defined, 613

calorimeter, 155, **156**, 613

carbides, 555; production of, 556

carbohydrates, 656–62; and fats, interconversion of, 662

carbon, 58, **550**, 550–57; allotropes of, 551, 555; amorphous, 553–55; atomic number of, 72, 73, 74, 550; atomic radius of, 74, **colorplate** facing 85; atomic weight of, 29, 550; compounds of, 555 *ff.*, 574, 575 *ff.*; density of, 74, 550; electron configuration of, **47**, 48, 83, 550, **551**; electron dot diagram for, **50**; half life of radioisotope of (carbon-14), 339, 549; hydrogen sulfide adsorbed by, 322; ionization potential of **41**, 74, **colorplate** facing 85, 550; isotope of (carbon-12): 30, 33, **33**, 355; (carbon-14): 34; melting point of, 550; oxidation of, 286–87, **287**, 291, 308; oxidation state of, 291, 550; and periodic table, 82; properties of, 72, 73, 74, 550; radioactive (carbon-14), 330, 339, 355, 356, 549, **549**; as reducing agent, 299; and smelting, 503; solid model of atom of, 51, **51**; symbol for, 16, 72, 73, 74; two-carbon chain formed by atoms of, 577; valence numbers of, 118; *see also* organic chemistry

carbon black, 554, 555, **555**

carbon cycle, 362, **362**, 558, **558**

carbon dioxide, 5, 60, 71, 181, 182, 259, 286, 288, 291, 395, 550, 574, 616; in air, 18; electron dot diagram for, 102, **102**; in fire extinguishers, 560–62, **561**, **562**, **563**; and food, 559–60; formula for, 72; heat of reaction of, 162; molecular weight of, 122–23; molecule of, **103**, 104; percentage composition of, 170; and potassium hydroxide, reaction between, 250; preparation of, 261, **558,** 558–59; properties of, 559; from reaction between calcium carbonate and hydrochloric acid, 261, 559; and rubber raft, 562; solid (dry ice), 138 142, 158, 560; and Solvay process, 457; uses of, 616

carbon disulfide, 19, 385, 397, 399–400, 434, 556–57, 593

carbon family (group IVA), 79, 549–72; and periodic table, 549–50; properties of, 549–50; table of, 550

carbon monoxide, 271, 272, 273, 275, 291, 308, 550, 563, 574, 616; molecular weight of, 564; preparation of, 563–64, **564;** properties of, 564; uses of, 564, 616

carbon tetrachloride, 182, 265, 266, 373, 375, 382, 385, 444, 593

carbon tetrafluoride, 108

carbonates: decomposition of, 246; ions of, 110, 447, 456, 559; from reactions between oxides and carbon dioxide, 451; testing for, 447; uses of, 456

carbonic acid, **218,** 219, 235, 468, 472; formula for, 119; from reactions between carbonates and acids, 261, 447; as weak acid, 220; as weak electrolyte, 203

carbonyl functional group, 596, 600

carborundum, 556, **557**

carboxyl functional group, 595, 596, 601

carnotite, 465

case hardening, defined, 511

cassiterite, 567

cast iron, 505

catalase, 267

catalysts: action of, 166; defined, 8, 165; and equilibrium, 278; negative, 165, 166, 267; positive, 165, 166, 267; and rate of reaction, 266–67

catalytic cracking process, 584, 623, **623,** *see also* thermal cracking process

cathode, 23, **23,** 24, **24,** 208, **208, 213, 248**

cathode ray, 23, 326, 327

cations, *see* positive ions

caustic potash, *see* potassium hydroxide

caustic soda, *see* sodium hydroxide

Cavendish, Henry, **8,** 9, 10, 11, **11,** 417

cellophane, 649

cells: electrochemical, 299–303, 513; Hooker, **370,** 371; living, chemistry of, **655,** 655–71, **657, 659, 661, 662, 663, 664, 665, 666, 667;** photoelectric, 412, **412,** 453; voltaic, 301; Vorce, 371

cellular oxidation, 660, **661**

Celluloid, 426, 641, 643

cellulose, 426, 648, 649, 658, 659

cellulose acetate, 641, 643, 649

cellulose butyrate, 641

cellulose nitrate, 426, 641, 643, 649

Celsius scale, 128 and *n.,* 147, 613

cement, 464, 467; preparation of, 468–69

cerium, 78, 484, 485

cesium: atomic number of, 449; atomic radius of, 48, **colorplate** facing 85; atomic weight of, 449; boiling point of, 449; crystals of, 451; density of, 449; in earth's crust, 450; electron configuration of, 449, 485; electronegativity of, 106; in high-vacuum tubes, 453; ionization potential of, 85, **colorplate** facing 85, 449, 451; metling point of, 449, 451, **451;** oxidation state of, 449; and periodic table, 79; and photoelectric cell, 453; properties of, 449; radioactive (cesium-137), 453; uses of, 453 properties of, 449; radioactive (cesium-137), 453; uses of, 453

Chadwick, James, 32, 335

chain reactions, 350–51, **350;** proton-proton, 362, **362**

chalcopyrites, 399

charcoal, 551, 553–54, 615, 616

Chardonnet, Hilaire B. de, 649

charge cloud diagram, 43

Charles, Jacques, 127, 129, 131, 132, 147

Charles' Law, 128, **128,** 130, 131, 148–49; defined, 128

chemical action, theory of, 153–69

chemical analysis, defined, 441

chemical change, **154, 155;** defined, 19; and mass, 154–56, **155, 156**

chemical equation, defined, 7

chemical equilibrium, 135, 269–70, **269;** and catalysts, 278; control of, 271–80; effect of concentration on, 272–73, **273;** effect of heat on, 277–78; importance of controlling, 279–80; pressure affecting, 278, **278;** stresses on systems at, controlling, 278–79

chemical property, defined, 9

chemistry: analysis in, 441; inorganic, 574; as laboratory science, 2; organic, 58, 574

chemotherapy, 665

Chile saltpeter, 384, 422

Chloramid, 374

chlorauric acid, 426

chlordane, 375

chloric acid, 245, 252

chloride ion, **60, 93,** 94, **94,** 228, 229, 230,

231, 236, 247, 266, 276, 290, 443, 444, 449, 476

chlorine, 93, 369–76, 381, 425, 426, 449, 494; activity of, 57, 372–73; atomic number of, 31, 72, 73, 74, 369; atomic radius of, 74, 75, **colorplate** facing 85; atomic weight of, 31, 32, 122, 369; as bleaching agent, 374–75, **375,** 376; boiling point of, 369; combustion supported by, 251, 284, 285, **372,** 372–73; compounds of, 375–76, 471–72; and copper, reaction between, 251, 379; density of, 74, 369; discovery of, 79; electron cloud diagram for, 50, **50;** electron configuration of, **47,** 369; electron dot diagram for, **50;** electronegativity of, 107; half life of radioisotope of (chlorine-36), 339; and hydrogen, reaction between, 244, 372; ionization potential of, **41,** 74, **colorplate** facing 85, 87, 369; and iron, reaction between, 284, 285, 286, 290, 307–08; isotopes of, 34, 339; melting point of, 369; and metals, reactions between, 372–73, 379; and methane, reaction between, 593; molecular weight of, 371; molecule of, 99, **99;** oxidation state of, 294, 369; and potassium bromide reaction between, 260; preparation of, 370, 370–71, **371;** properties of, 72, 73, 88–89, 369, 371–73; as purifying agent for water, 374, **374;** radioactive (chlorine-36), 330, 339; from reaction between hydrogen chloride and oxygen, 279; and replacement of other halogens, 373–74; and sodium, reaction between, 251, 372–73; solubility of, in water, 369, 371; symbol for, 16, 72, 74; in testing for halogen ions, 444; uses of, 374–75; valence numbers of, 97, 108, 116, 118; and water, reaction between, 373, **373,** 375

chlorine dioxide, 376

chloroform, 593, 594

chlorophyll, 657, **657**

chloroprene, 634–35, **635**

chlorous acid, 245, 252, **252**

chromatogram, 532, **532**

chromatography, 531–32, **532**

chrome steel, 506

chrome-vanadium steel, 506

chromite ion, 248

chromium, 42, 77, 84, 296, 514, 515, 530, 546; borax bead test for, **colorplate V** following 548

chromium hydroxide, 248

chromium oxide, 531
chromosomes, 666, 668
cinnabar, 396
citric acid, 220, 602
cladding process, 515
clay, 468
clinkers, in preparation of cement, 468–69
closed system, defined, 153–54
cloud chamber, 337, **337**
cloud track, 337, **338**, 358
coal, 551, 614–16, **615**, 617; *see also* anthra-cite coal and bituminous coal
coal gas, 616, 617, **617**, 618
coal tar, 588, 615, 616, 617
cobalt, 501, 511, 519; alloys of, 520, 521; borax bead test for, 546, **colorplate V** following 548; compounds of, 520; electron configuration of, 42; half life of radioisotope of (cobalt-60), 339; ions of, 520; and periodic table, 76, 77, 78; properties of, 502, 519, 520; radioactive (cobalt-60), 330, 339, 356, 520; symbol for, 16; as transition element, 501; uses of, 520; valence number of, 116
cobalt nitrate test, 545, 546, **546**, 547; **color-plate** facing 549
cobalt oxide, 470, 546
Cockcroft, J. D., 357, 358
coefficients, formulas preceded by, 119, 123
coke, 503, 504, 551, 615, 616–17, 618, **619**
colemanite, 524, 534
collision theory, 163, **163**, 166, 264
colloid mill, 317, **317**
colloidal dispersions, *see* colloids
colloidal particles: adsorption by, 321; charged, 319–22; defined, 312; and electrophoresis, 319–20; neutralizing of charged, 320–21; precipitation of, 319; produced by displacement, 318; size of, 313; and Tyndall effect, 313–14, 315, 316
colloidal systems, *see* colloids
colloids, 303, 311–24 *passim;* defined, 314; lyophilic, 316; lyophobic, 316; precipitation of, 319; preparing and maintaining, 316–19, **317**, **318**; protective, 319; types of, 315–16
colorplates: Acid-Base Indicators, facing 548; Atomic Radii, facing 85; Borax Bead Tests, following 548; Cobalt Nitrate Tests, facing 549; Differentiating Among Halogen Ions, following 548; Emission Spectra, facing 84; Flame Tests, following 548; Ionization Potential of the Elements facing 85;

Periodic Table following 84; Precipitated Sulfides, following 548.
combined gas law, 149–50
Combining Volumes of Gases, Gay-Lussac's Law of, 64, 131, 132, **132**; defined, 64
combustion, 263, 284, **284**, 285, 287; in gasoline engine, 625–26; of hydrocarbons, 626–27; *see also* oxidation
common ion effect, 276, **276**, 277, **277**
complex ions, 492; dissociation of, 493; table of, **493**
components of solution, defined, 180
composition reactions, 259
compounds: of alkali metals, 454–59; of alkaline earth metals, 467–72, 476–77; aluminum, 531–33; ammonia, 428, 430–33; aromatic, 576, **587**, 587–89; arsenic, 433; barium, 477; beryllium, 477; bismuth, 436–37; boron, 524, 533, 535; bromine, 383–84; calcium, 467–72; carbon, 555 *ff.*, 574, 575 *ff.*; chlorine, 375–76, 471–72; cobalt, 520; composition of, 59–60, 62–67; copper, 491–92; covalent, *see* covalent compounds; Dalton's symbols for, 13, **13**; decomposition of, 59, 60–62, **61**, 298–99; defined, 13, 17, 66; fluorine, 379–80, 418; hydrogen, 459; inorganic, *see* inorganic compounds; iodine, 386; ionic, *see* ionic compounds; iron, 516–19; lead, 569; lithium, 458; magnesium, 476–77; nature of, 59–60; nickel, 520; nitrogen, 67, 420, 421 *ff.*; organic, *see* organic compounds; of oxygen and nitrogen, 67, 417, 421, 426–27; percentage composition of, 170; reactions involving molecular, 308–09; silicon, 565–66, 635–36; stability of, 60; strontium, 477; sulfur, oxidation and reduction among, 410, 411; tin, 567–68; writing formulas for, 115–19
compression molding, of thermosetting materials, 638, **639**
concrete, 464; manufacture of, 469 reinforced, 469
condensation, 134–35; in biochemical reactions, 650, **659, 663**, 664; colloidal system prepared by, 317, 318–19; defined, 134
condensation polymers, 640
condensed ring structures, of aromatic compounds, 588
confirmatory tests, in analytical chemistry, 541, 542, 543, 544, 545, 547

Congo red, 227, 442; **colorplate I** facing 548
conjugate acid-base pairs, 230–32; table of, 233
Conservation of Energy, Law of, 156, 349; defined, 156
Conservation of Mass, Law of, 154, **154, 155, 155,** 349; defined, 154
Conservation of Mass-Energy, Law of, 349–50; defined, 349
constant: equilibrium, *see* equilibrium constant; ionization, 275
contact process, for preparation of sulfuric acid, 405, 406, 410, 411
continuous spectrum, 27, **colorplate** facing 84
control rods, in atomic pile, 325, 351, **351**
coordinate bonds, 110
copolymerization, 634
copper, 8, 57, 59, **59**, 117, 300, 424, 460, 481, 487–92, 514; in activity series, 295, 296, 297, 298; alloys of, 490–91; atomic number of, 486; atomic radius of, **color-plate** facing 85; atomic weight of, 486; boiling point of, 486; bombarded with deuterons, 358; borax bead test for, 546, **colorplate V** following 548; and chlorine, reaction between, 251, 379; compounds of, 491–92; density of, 486, 489; ductility of, 489, **490**; electron configuration of, 45, **490**; electrorefining of, 489, **489**; flame test for, 545, **colorplate IV** following 548; and fluorine, reaction between, 379; ionization potential of **colorplate** facing 85, 486; ions of, 292, 489, 491; and iron, rection between, 399; malleability of, 489; melting point of, 486, 489; metallurgy of, **487**, 487–89, **488, 489**; and nitric acid, reaction between, 309, 426, 427, **427**; ore, **487**; oxidation potential of, 302; oxidation states of, 486; and periodic table, 81, 485, 486; and printing, 491, **491**; properties of, 486, 489–90; and sulfuric acid, reaction between, 408; symbol for, 16; as transition element, 79–80, 486; uses of, 490; valence numbers of, 116, 118
copper carbonate, 490
copper chloride, 251
copper family (group IB), 486–87; density of, **486;** table of, 486
copper halides, 491
copper hydroxide, 492
copper nitrate, 309, 446
copper oxide, 394, 460

copper sulfate, 195, 236, 252, 491; anhydrous, 195; as electrolyte, 203, 491; hydrated, 195; and iron, reaction between, 260; preparation of, 491; uses of, 491

copper sulfide, 64, 65, 66, **66**, 67, 117, 399, **colorplate III** following 548

corrosion, 512, electrolysis in, 512–13, **513**; prevention of, **514**, 514–15, **515**; *see also* rust

corundum, 531

cosmic radiation, 338

cosmotron, 359

cotton, 645, 646; mercerized, 648

Cottrell precipitator, 320–21, **321**

covalence numbers, 108

covalent bond forces, 158

covalent bonds, 98, **98, 99, 100, 101**; blending with ionic, 102–05; **103**; defined, 98; single, double, triple, 101–02, **101, 102**

covalent compounds, **100**, 100–02, **101, 102, 103**, 373, 383; and oxidation numbers, 291; and valence numbers, 108

covalent molecules, 98, **98**, 99, **99**, 100–01, **100, 101, 103**

Crick, F. H. C., 667

criss-cross method, in writing formulas, 116, 117, 118

critical mass, defined, 350

critical temperature of gas, 135

Crookes, William, 331

Crookes tube, 23, 24, **24**, 26

cross-linked polymers, 634, **635**

crutching pans, in soap manufacture, 607

cryolite, 526, 527

crystal copper sulfate, formula weight of, 123

crystallization, 194–95; defined, 195

crystallization, water of, 195

crystals, 60, **60**, 184; types of, 139–40, **139 140, 141**, 397–98, **398**

cubic crystal, 139, 140, **140**

Curie, Marie, 16, 326, 328, 329,

Curie, Pierre, 16, 326, 328, 329

curium, 16, **360**, 361, 485

cyanamide process, for preparation of ammonia, 428

cyanide ion, 493

cyanide process, for extraction of gold and silver, 493, **494**

cycloalkanes, 589

cyclopropane, 589

cyclotron, 357, **357**, 358–59, **358**, 360

cytoplasm 660

cytosine, **666**, 667

Dacron, 651

Dalton, John, 11–15, 18, 23, 24, 25, 26, 48, 51, 64, 115, 170

Dalton's Law of Partial Pressure, **11–12**, 12

dating, radiocarbon, 549, **549**

Davisson, C. J., 42

Davy, Edmund, 585

Davy, Humphry, 153, 217, 369–70, 450

DDT, 315, 375

de Broglie, Louis, 42

decaborane, 535

decane, 578, 580

decay, radioactive, 332, 334

decomposition of compounds, 59–62

decomposition reactions, 259

dees, in cyclotron, 358, **358**

Definite Proportions, Law of, 65, 66; defined, 65

dehydration, 408, **408**, 658, **659**, 663, **663**

dehydrogenation, 600

deliquescence, 196, **196**

delta H, in equations, 160, 161, **161**

Democritus, 2, 3, 11

denatured alcohol, 597, **598**

density of atoms, 73–74

density and molecular weight of gases, 150

deoxyribonucleic acid (DNA), 666, 667, 668

deoxyribose, 666, **666**, 667, **667**

derived system of naming alkanes, 580–81

desalinated sea water, 180

destructive distillation, 553, 554, 615, **615**, 616, 617; of coal, 616, 617; of fibers, 646; of rubber, 633; of wood, 616

detergents, **608**, 608–09

deuterium, 33, **33**, 65, 363, 364, 461

deuterons, 357, 358, 360

di- prefix, 594

dialysis, 312–13, **312, 313**; defined, 312

diammonium hydrogen phosphate, 432

diamond, 551, 553, 565; crystal structure of, 140–41, 552, **552**; density of, 550; hardness of, 141, 552; industrial, 367, 552, **553**; molecule of, 17; properties of, 141, 550, 552

diatomic molecules, 16, **16**, 17, 98, 99–100, **99, 100**

dibromoethane (ethylene dibromide), 594, 595, 626

dichlorodifluoromethane, 593

dichloromethane, 593, 594

-diene suffix, 585

diethyl ether, 596, 603, 604, **604**

difluoromethane, 594

dihydroxy alcohols, 598

dihydroxy bases, 248

dimer, defined, 634

dipole, **103**, 103–04

diprotic acids, 233, 245

disaccharides, 658

disintegration, radioactive, 331–32, 334

disodium hydrogen phosphate, 234

dispersing medium, for colloidal particles, 314, 315

dispersion, colloidal system prepared by, 317

displacement, colloidal particles produced by, 318

disproportionations, 294

dissociation, defined, 205

distillate, defined, 194

distillation, 194, **194**; defined, 194; destructive, *see* destructive distillation; fractional, 392, 394, 581, 607, 621, 635

DNA (deoxyribonucleic acid), 666, 667, **667**, 668

dolomite, 466, 476

Domagk, Gerhard, 665

double covalent bonds, 102, 575

double repalcement reactions, 251, 259, 261–62, 409

doublets, of hydrogen, 42

Dowmetals, 530

Downs process: for preparation of chlorine, 371; for preparation of sodium, 450, **450**

dry atmospheres, sulfuric acid used in providing, 409, **409**

dry cell, 301, 411, 432

dry ice, 138, 142, 158, 560, **560**

Duralumin, 530

Duriron, 506

dyes, 420, 428, 436, 533, 588, **588**, 616

dynamic equilibrium, defined, 269–70, *see* chemical equilibrium

dynamite, 421

efflorescence, 196, **196**

eicosane, 580

Einstein, Albert, 1, 16, 348

einsteinium, 16, 354, 361, 485

electric current, as flow of electrons, 85, 111, 207, 300

electric furnace, 506, 508–09, **509**, 555–56, **556**, 557

electrochemical cells, 303, **300, 302**, 513

electrochemical series (electromotive

series), 302–03

electrolysis, **201**, 201–02; blister copper refined by, 489, **489**; in corrosion, 512–13, **513**; decomposition by, 60–61, **61**, 299; for determining ratio by volume of gaseous elements in compounds, **62**, 62–64, **63**; of hydrochloric acid, **207**, 207–08, **208**; of salt solutions, 247–48, **248**, 370; of water, 60–61, **61**, 154, **154**, 212–13, **213**

electrolytes: defined, 202; interionic attraction in strong, 210–11; and ions, 203–04; **204**; strong, 203; strong and weak, **210**; weak, 203, 275

electrolytic dissociation, theory of, 204, 210

electromagnetic radiation, 327; detection of, 335–38, **336**, **337**, **338**, **342**; effects of, 339–40; shielding from, 399–40, 351, **351**; types of, 329–30

electromotive series, *see* electrochemical series

electron affinity, 58–59, 106; table of, 59

electron clouds, 43

electron cloud diagrams, 43, **45**, **46**, 49, **49**, 98

electron configurations, 47–49, table of, 47; transition elements, table of, 83, 485, **485**

electron dot diagrams, 49–51, **50**, **83**, **93**, **94**, **95**, **100**, **526**

electron exchange, balancing, 307–8

electron orbital diagrams, 46–48, **46**, **47**, **55**, **57**, **83**, **98**, **99**, **100**, 101, **102**, **525**, **550**

electron shells, 39, 42–46, 482, 484; complete, 93; distribution of electrons among, table of, 56; incomplete, 93; and periodic table, 80–83; principal quantum number of, 43; *see also* atoms, energy levels within; subshell diagrams; subshells

electron spin, 45

electron transfer method, of balancing electron exchange, 307, 309

electronegativities of elements: defined, 105, 106; table of, **106**

electrons, 24, 25, 26, **26**, 32, 38, 342; affinity of, 58–59; charge assigned to, 341; discovery of, 24; flow of, as electric current, 85, 111, 207, 300; and oxidation, 285–86; rearrangement of outer-shell, between atoms, **93**, 93–94, **95**; structure of, 81–83, 86 (*see also* electron shells); valence, *see* valence electrons; wave nature of, 42–43, **43**

electrophoresis, 319–20, **320**

electroplating, 495, **495**, 515

electroscope, 336–37, **337**

electrostatic forces, 158

electrotype, 491

elements: activity of, 56–57, **56**; alchemists' symbols for, 15, **15**; ancient concept of, 3, **3**; atomic radii of, **colorplate** facing 85; Dalton's symbols for, 13, **13**, 15; defined, 2, 4–5; density of, 74; electron configurations, **47**, electronegativities of, 105, 106; families of, 76, 79, 80, 82–83, 85, 87; Greek symbols for, 15, **15**; ionization potentials of, **41**, 74, **75**, 75–76, 84–85, **colorplate** facing 85, 86, 87, 88, 369, 390, 417, 420, 449, 464, 486, 502, 525, 550; modern system of symbols for, 15–16; most abundant, table of, 58; number of, 14, 15, 21; and Periodic Law, 76, 77 (*see also* periodic table); properties of first twenty, 74; radioactive, 328–29 (*see also* radioactive isotopes); search for new, 9; spectral analysis of, 27–29, **27**, **29**; tracer, 355; transition, *see* transition elements; transuranic, *see* transuranic elements; valence electrons for, *see* valence electrons; valence numbers for common, table of, 116; with variable valence numbers, 118; X-ray spectra of, 31

emerald, 465, **465**

emery, 531

emission spectra, **colorplate** facing 84

Empedocles, 3

empirical formulas, 60, 171; defined, 60

emulsifying agents, 317–18, **318**

emulsion, defined, 316, **316**

end point, 254

endothermic reactions, **159**, 160, 161, **161**, 164, **164**, 165, **165**, 191, 192, 277, 618

-*ene* suffix, 583

energy: activation, 163, 164, **164**, 166; conservation of, 156, 349; conversion of, 157, **157**; hydration, 183, 192; kinetic, 157, 158, 163; lattice, 159, 192; from nuclear reactions, 347–66 *passim*; potential, 157–58; solar, 347

energy level crossovers, **48**, **81**

energy level diagram, 46, **46**, **453**; for transition elements, **483**

energy levels, 30, 46, 482,

entropy, 267; defined, 267

enzymes, 165, 656, 658, 660, **661**, 665; inhibition of, 665–66; needed for reactions in body, 665, **665**

epoxy plastics, 642, 644

Epsom salts (hydrated magnesium sulfate), 195, 477

equation weights, 123

equations: for artificial transmutations, 343; balanced, 120–21, 308; chemical, defined, 7; delta H in, 160, 161, **161**; ionic, 260, 261–62; net, 260, 262; nuclear, symbols for radiation in, 342–43; redox, 309–310; word, defined, 7; writing chemical, 120–21

equilibrium, chemical, *see* chemical equilibrium

equilibrium constant: application of, 275–76; and mass action, 273–75

esterification, 605

esters, 596, 604–09; formation of, **595**, 604–06, **605**; and fats, 606, **606**

etching, 426, **426**

ethanal, 600, 601

ethane, 172, 576, 577, **577**, 578, 579, 581, 583, **583**, 589, 594

ethanoic acid, *see* acetic acid

ethanol (ethyl alcohol), 582, 583, 597, 601, 603, 627

ethene (ethylene), 582–84, **583**, 643, 644; series of, 583

ethers, 427, 596, 603–04, **604**

ethyl, defined, 580

ethyl acetate, 596, 604, 605, **605**

ethyl alcohol (ethanol), 582, 583, 597, 601, 603, 627

ethyl butyrate, 605

ethylene (ethene), 582–84, **583**, 643, 644

ethylene bromide, 383, 452, 453, 594

ethylene dibromide (dibromoethane), 594, 595, 626

ethylene glycol, 191, 598

ethyne (acetylene), 574, 585, **585**, 586, **586**, 589, 592, 618–19, 635, **635**; series of, 585

eudiometer tube, 63, **63**

evaporation of liquids, 135

Everdur, 491

excited state of atom, 31

exclusion principle, 46

exothermic reactions, 159, **159**, 161, **161**, 162, 164, **164**, 165, **165**, 191, 192, 277

explosives, 249, 420, 421, 426, 428, 432, 589, 598

extrusion process, 638, **639**, 648

face-centered cubic close packing, 140

face-centered cubic crystal, 140, **140**

Fahrenheit scale, 613

fallout, 357

families, of periodic table, 76, 79–80; long, 81, 82; unfinished, 82; *see also* groups

Faraday, Michael, 201, 315, 587

fats: and carbohydrates, interconversion of, 662; as esters, 606, **606;** saturated, 606; unsaturated, 606

fatty acids, 602, 606, 607

feldspar, 565, **566**

Fermi, Enrico, 325, 347, 348, 351

fermium, 354, 361, 485

ferric ammonium alum, 532

ferric (iron III) chloride, 252, 284, 285, 286, 288, 290, 291, 373, 517, 518

ferric citrate, 518, 519

ferric hydroxide, 312, 320, 518

ferric ion, 118, 394, 517

ferric (iron III) oxide, 267, 285, 286, 299, 517

ferromagnetism, 511

ferromanganese, 507

ferrosilicon, 466

ferrous (iron II) chloride, 252, 286, 290, 291, 517, 518

ferrous ion, 118, 394, 517

ferrous (iron II) oxide, 267

ferrous sulfate (iron sulfate), 518

ferrous sulfide (iron sulfide), 19, 20, 400, 446

ferrous tannate, 518

fertilizers, 249, 410, 420, 426, 428, 432, 435, 458, 505

fibers, **645,** 645–52; from protein, 649, 651; synthetic, 646, 648, 651–52

filled orbital, defined, 47

"fine," as designation for silver, 495

fire extinguishers, 456, 532, 560–62, **561, 562, 563**

Fischer-Tropsch process, 625

fission, nuclear, *see* nuclear fission

fission fragment, 348, **348**

flame test, 544–45, 547; **colorplate IV** following 548

fluoborate ion, 525, **526**

fluoride ion, 95, 379, 444, 525, **526**

fluorine, 369, 418, 593, 627; activity of, 55, 58, 378–79; atomic number of, 72, 73, 74, 369; atomic radius of, 48, 58, 74, 75, **colorplate** facing 85; atomic weight of, 369; boiling point of, 369; compounds of, 379–80, 418; and copper, reaction between, 379; density of, 74, 369; electron configuration of, **47,** 369; electronegativity of, 106, 379; and hydrogen, reaction between, 244, 379,

380; ionization potential of, **41,** 74, 85, **colorplate** facing 85, 87, 369; melting point of, 369; and metals, reactions between, 379; molecular weight of, 378; as nonmetal, 58, 378; oxidation state of, 369; as oxidizing agent, 379; preparation of, 378; properties of, 72, 73, 74, 369, 378–79; symbol for, 72, 73, 74; uses of compounds of, 379–80; valence number of, 116; and water, reaction between, 369, 378, 379, **379**

fluorspar (calcium fluoride), 92, 95, **95,** 251, 380

foam fire extinguisher, 561–62, **562**

foam rubber, 633

fog, as colloid, 315

Food and Drug Administration, 254

"fool's gold" (iron pyrites), 54, 396, 502

formaldehyde, 264, 265, 595, 596, 599, 638, **638,** 639, 640; preparation of, **599**

formic acid, 563, 601, 632

formula weight: defined, 122; expressed in grams, 124, 133

formulas: coefficients placed before, 119, 123; defined, 17; empirical, 60, 171; graphic, for structures of organic molecules, 578, 583–84; in ionic form, 95–96, 97, 117; molecular, for structures of organic molecules, 171–72, 578, 583, 585; structural, 579; valence numbers of radicals determined from, 118–19; water of hydration indicated by, 195; writing, 115–19

formyl functional group, 595, 596, 599

fractional distillation, 392, 394, 581, 607, 621, 635

fractioning tower, 621, **622**

francium, 48, 77, 79, 106, 449, 450, 485

Frankland, Edward, 92

Frasch, Herman, 396, 397

Frasch process, **396,** 396–97, **397**

free energy change, 268

freezing point, defined, 138–39, **138;** depression, 193, **203**

Freons, 379, 593, **594**

frequency, 29, **29,** defined, 29

Frisch, Otto, 348

froth flotation, 488, **488,** 568

fructose, 575, 658

fuel oil, 614, 625

fuels, 347, 613; gaseous, 617–20, 625; heat produced by, 614; for rockets, 627, **628**

functional groups, 595, 609; table of, 596

furnace: blast, *see* blast furnace; electric, 506, 508–09, **509,** 555–56, **556,** 557;

open-hearth, 506, 507–08, **508**

fusion, nuclear, *see* nuclear fusion

galactose, 658

galena, 396, 568

Galileo, 125

gallium, 524, 535, **536;** properties of, 525

Galvani, Luigi, 299

galvanized iron, **514,** 515

gamma radiation, **329,** 330, 336, **342,** 342–43, 354, 355, 357, 362; absorption of, 340; ionization effects of, on body cells, 339; symbol for, 342

Gamow, George, 357

gangue, 488

gas chromatography, 531–32

gas laws, *see* Boyle's Law; Charles' Law; combined gas law; Gay-Lussac's Laws

gaseous diffusion plant, 352, 353

gases: combining volumes of, **62,** 62–64, **63;** critical temperatures of, 135; inert (rare), 54–55, 80, 93, 417, 418, 419; kinetic molecular theory of, 129–33; molar volumes of, 133, **133;** molecular weights of, 150–51; physical nature of, 130; and pressure changes, 125–27, **126;** and relationship between pressure and temperature changes, 128–29, **128, 130;** and temperature changes, 127–28, **127**

gasoline, 620, 623, 625, 627; antiknock, 383, 452, 569, 626; improved by hydrogenation and alkylation, 624; manufactured by cracking, 623, **623,** 624; manufactured by polymerization, 623–24; synthesized from solid and gaseous fuels, 625

gasoline engine, combustion in, 625–26

gastric juice, human, pH of, 241

Gay-Lussac's Law of Combining Volumes of Gases, 64, 131, 132, **132;** defined, 64

Gay-Lussac's Law relating pressure and temperature of gases, 129, 149; defined, 129

Geiger counter, 336, **336,** 337, 338, 340, 419

gel, defined, 315, **315**

genes, 666, 667

Geneva (I.C.U.) system of nomenclature, 581, 583, 584, 586, 593, 594, 596–97, 600

germanium, **77,** 82, 83, 567, **567;** properties of, 550, 567

Gibbs, J. Willard, 267

glacial acetic acid, 203, 209, 210

glass manufacture, **469,** 469–70, **470,** 535

glucose, 193, 597, 656, 657, 658, 659, **659;** cellulan oxidation of, 660, **661, 662;** formula for, 575, 656, 657, 659; isomers of, 575, 658; molecular weight of, 194; as nonelectrolyte, 202, 203; as source of energy for life processes, 659–60, **661, 662;** stored in plants, 657

glycerine, 426, 598, 662

glycerol, 598, 606, 607

glyceryl oleate, 606

glyceryl stearate, 596, 606, **606,** 607

glycine, 663, **663**

glycogen, 658, 659

glycylalanine, 663, **663**

goiter, simple, caused by iodine deficiency, 386

gold, 57, 58, 59, 373, 481, 492–93; in activity series, 295, 296; and alchemists, 4; alloys of, 495; atomic number of, 486; atomic radius of, 58, **colorplate** facing 85; atomic weight of, 486; boiling point of, 486; as by-product, 494; as catalyst, 386; chemical extraction of, 493, 494, **494;** colloidal, 318–19; density of, 486; dissolved in aqua regia, 425; and fluorine, reaction between, 379; ionization potential of, 486; melting point of, 486; oxidation states of, 486; and periodic table, 80, 81, 485, 486; properties of, 486, 494, 495; radioactive, produced by transmutation, 357; symbol for, 16; as transition element, 486; uses of, 495, 496

gold chloride, 426

gold leaf, 495–96

Goodyear, Charles, 633

Graham, Thomas, 312, 313

gram atomic weights, 123

gram equivalent weights, 188

gram formula weights, 124, 133

gram molecular weights, 123, 133

granite, 565

graphic formulas, for structures of organic molecules, 578, 583–84

graphite, 551, 552–53; crystal structure of, 552, **552;** production of, 557, **557;** properties of, 550, 552, 553; uses of, 553

Greeks, early, and concepts of matter, 2, 3, **3**

ground state of atom, 31, 46

group IA, *see* alkali metals

group IB, *see* copper family

group IIA, *see* alkaline earth metals

group IIIA, *see* aluminum family

group IVA, *see* carbon family

group VA, *see* nitrogen family

group VIA, *see* oxygen family

group VIIA, *see* halogen family

group VIII, *see* transition elements

group O, *see* inert gases

groups, of periodic table, 79–80

GR-S (Buna) rubber, 635, **636,** 637

guanine, **666,** 667

Guldberg, Cato, 273

gypsum, *see* calcium sulfate

Haber, Fritz, 429

Haber process, 277, 278, 279, **279,** 422, 429, **429**

hafnium, 78, 81

Hahn, Otto, 347

half-cell reactions, 300–03, **301, 302,** 307, 308, 401

half life, of radioactive isotope, 338–39, **339**

halide salts, of sodium and potassium, 454

halides, hydrogen, 219, 244

Hall, Charles Martin, 524, 526

Hall-Héroult process, 527–28, **527**

halogen derivatives, 595; naming, 594

halogen family (group VIIA), 79, 80, 368–89, 391; and periodic table, 368; preparation of, 369; properties of, 369; and replacement by bromine, 383; and replacement by chlorine, 373–74, **373;** table of, 369; uses of, 369

halogen ions, **colorplate II** following 548; differentiating among, 444–45; qualitative analysis of, **443,** 443–45

halogen substitution reactions, 593

Halozone, 374

hard water, **472,** 472–76, 608; cause of, 474; formation of, 473; and ion exchange, **475,** 475–76; permanent, 475, 476; softening, 474–75, **475,** 475–76; temporary, 475, 476

heat: decomposition by, 61, **61:** effect of, on chemical equilibrium, 277–78

heat of formation, 162, **162**

heat of fusion, defined, 139

heat of reaction, 161–62

heat of solution, 191–92; defined, 191

heat of vaporization, defined, 138

heavy water, 32, 66

Heisenberg, Werner, 42–43

helium, 16, 17, 34, 40, 47, 54, 75, 99, 263, 363, 368, 418–19, 482, 581; in air, 418; atomic number of, 2, 31, 73, 74, 417; atomic radius of, 74, **colorplate** facing 85; atomic weight of, 48, 417; boiling point of, 417; as coolant in nuclear reactor, 351–52, 418; density of, 74, 417, 418; diagram of atom of, **55;** and disintegration of lithium-7 atoms, 358; electron configuration of, 47, **47,** 417; ionization potential of, **41,** 74, 75, **75, colorplate** facing 85, 417; melting point of, 417; nucleus of, mass of, 330, 349, 350; and periodic table, 80; in prevention of "bends," 419; properties of, 72, 73, 74, 417; spectral analysis of, 40, **colorplate** facing 84; symbol for, 17, 72, 73, 74; uses of, 418–19; and valence electrons, 73

hematite, 502

heme, **657**

hemoglobin, 60, 563, 655, 657

heptane, 578, 626

heptene, 583

heptyne, 585

Héroult, Paul, 524

hexagonal close packing, 140, **141**

hexagonal crystal, 140, **140, 141**

hexamethylene diamine, 641, 643, **644**

hexane, 578

hexene, 583

hexose, 656, 658

hexyne, 585

higher oxidation state, defined, 290

high-speed tool steel, 506

Hittorf, Johann, 204

Hoffman apparatus, 62, **62**

homogenization, 317

homologous series, 578

Hooker cell, **370,** 371

Hoopes process, 527–28, **528**

hot dipping process, 515

Hyatt, John, 641

hydrated copper sulfate, 195

hydrated ions, 183, 206–07, 222, 232, 236

hydrated magnesium sulfate, 195, 477

hydrated sodium carbonate, efflorescence of, 196

hydrated sodium sulfate, 196, **196**

hydrates, defined, 195

hydration energy, 183, 192

hydration, water of, 195

hydrazine, 627

hydriodic acid, 219, 385, 386

Hydrion paper, **227,** 227–28, 227

hydro-prefix, 244

hydrobromic acid, 219, 244, 381, 384, 468

hydrocarbon derivatives, 592–612; diagram on relationships between, **609;** naming, 594

hydrocarbon substitution reactions, 593

hydrocarbons, 554, 574–91, 614; aliphatic, 576, **576,** 587, 589 (*see also* alkanes; alkenes; alkynes); aromatic, 576, **576, 587,** 587–89, **588;** branched, 579; classification of, 575–76; combustion of, 626–27; in petroleum, 621, 622; open-chain, 579; ring, **587,** 587–89, **588;** saturated, 576–81, **579, 580, 582,** 589 (*see also* alkanes); straight chain, 579; unbranched, 579; unsaturated, **582,** 582–86, **583, 585,** 589 (*see also* alkenes and alkynes)

hydrochloric acid, 9, 10, **10,** 188, 189, 207, 208, 217, 219, 220, 227, 228, 235, 236, 237, 276, 371, 447, 528, 529; in aqua regia, 425; as binary acid, 244, **244;** and calcium carbonate, reaction between, 261; and conjugate pairs, 231; electrolysis of, **207,** 207–08, **208;** as electrolyte, 203, 205–06; and ferrous (iron II) sulfide, reaction between, 400, **400;** formula for, 119, 244; from hydrochlorous acid, decomposition of, 373; interionic attraction in 1 *m* solution of, 210, 211; and iron, reaction between, 286, **286,** 288, 290, 517; laboratory preparation of, 376–77, **377;** as monoprotic acid, 245; pH of, 226; and ratio by volume of hydrogen to chlorine, 63; from reaction between hydrogen chloride and water, 206, 244; related to sodium chloride, 251, **252;** and sodium carbonate, reaction between, 447, **447;** and sodium hydroxide, reaction between, 228, 261; and sodium sulfate, reaction between, 272, **272;** as strong acid, 220, 231, 235, 236; sulfides precipitated in, 542; in testing for ions containing sulfur, 445, **445,** 446, 542, 543; titrated against sodium hydroxide, **254,** 254–55; uses of, 377–78; as volatile acid, 243; and zinc, reaction between, 10, 250, 260, 270, 295, 460; *see also* hydrogen chloride

hydrocyanic acid, 217

hydrofluoric acid, 219, 380, 566

hydrogen, 15, 16, 20, 28, 29, 263, 459–61, 616; from acids, 218, 220–21, **221;** in air, 18, 58; atomic number of, 31, 72, 73, 74, 449; atomic radius of, 47, 48, 74, **colorplate** facing 85; atomic weight of, 32, 48, 122, 449; boiling point of, 449; and chlorine, reaction between, 244, 372; in compounds, 459; density of, 74, 449; diagram for atom of, 33, **55;** discovery of, 9–10; in earth's waters, 58, 59; from electrolysis of sodium chloride solution, 247; electron cloud diagram for, 50; electron configuration of 46, **47,** 449; electronegativity of, 106; and fluorine, reaction between, 244, 379, 380; and iodine, reaction between, 385, 386; ionization of, 39; ionization potential of, **41,** 74, **colorplate** facing 85, 449, 459; ions of, 211, 224–35 *passim,* **224, 225,** 246, 247, 249, 407, 408, 449, 459, 460, 513, 657 (*see also* hydronium ion); isotopes of, 32–33, **33,** 34, 49, **49,** 342–43, 363, 461; melting point of, 449; metals less active than, 297–98; molecular weight of, 122; molecule of, **98,** 98–99, **99,** 460; nitrogen combined with, 256, 277; orbitals of, 44–45, **45;** oxidation states of, 292, 293, 296, 449, 452; and periodic table, 80, 459; preparation of, 10, **10,** 218, 220–21, **221,** 250, **459,** 459–60; properties of, 72, 73, 74, 449, 459, 460, **460;** and ratio to oxygen by volume in heavy water, 66; and ratio to oxygen by volume in water, **62,** 62–63; and ratio to oxygen by weight in water, 64; from reaction between aluminum and strong base, 528; from reaction between magnesium and dilute nitric acid, 424; from reaction between magnesium and sulfuric acid, 260; from reaction between sodium and water, 247, 260; from reaction between zinc and hydrochloric acid, 250, 260; and reduction, 460; spectrum, **colorplate** facing 84; symbol for, 16, 72, 73, 74; as unique element, 459, 461; test for, 11; uses of, 461; valence number of, 108, 116, 118–19; weight of, in relation to air, 11

hydrogen bomb, 363, 461

hydrogen bonding, 136–37, 141, 183, 430, 665

hydrogen bonds, 137, **137, 141,** 665

hydrogen bromide, 381, 384, 592

hydrogen chloride, 205, 206, 217, 243, 272, 276, 372; as covalent compound, 100, **100,** 101; as dipole, **103,** 103–04; electron structure of molecule of, **100,** 101; as oxidizing agent, 296; and oxygen, reaction between, 279; properties of, 377; and ratio by volume of hydrogen to chlorine, 63, 64; and water, reaction between, 206, 244; *see also* hydrochloric acid

hydrogen cyanide, 102,

hydrogen fluoride, 137, **137,** 378, 379, **379,** 380, 444

hydrogen halides, 219, 244

hydrogen iodide, 166, **166,** 268, 385, 386

hydrogen peroxide, 266, 267, 292, 394, **395,** 627; formula for, 66; preparation of, 394; properties of, 394; and ratio by weight of hydrogen to oxygen, 66; and sulfurous acid, reaction between, 404; uses of, 395

hydrogen sulfide, 237, 251, 400, 402, 543; adsorption of, 322; molecular weight of, 401; preparation of, **400,** 400–01; properties of, 401–02, **401;** as reducing agent, 294; and sulfur dioxide, reaction between, 294; testing for, 445; testing in analytical groups II and III, 542–43, **542**

hydrogen sulfite, *see* sulfurous acid

hydrogenation, 461, 606, **607,** 624

hydrolyzer method, of preparing soaps, 607

hydrolysis, 235, **235,** 237, 261, 270, 318, 658; in biochemical reactions, 658, 665, **665**

hydronium ion, 206, **207,** 209, 211, **211,** 218, 219, 220, 221, **221,** 229, 230, 231, 236, 244, 262, 377, 407, 409, 424, 468

hydrosulfuric acid, 244, **244,** 401

hydroxide ion, 109, **109,** 110, 117, 211, 222–35 *passim,* **225,** 246, 247, 248, 249, 264, 267, 370, 450, 476, 513, 657; qualitative analysis of, 441–43, **442**

hydroxides, 454, 456; amphoteric, 248, 533, 550

hydroxyl functional group, 595, 596

hygroscopic substance, defined, 196

hyperon, 360

hypo-prefix, 245, 252

hypobromous acid, 245, **245,** 252, 383

hypochlorous acid, 245, 252, 373, 375, 518

hypophosphite salts, 435

hypophosphorus acid, 435

-*ic* suffix, 118, 244, 245, 252

ice, structure of, 141, **141**

-*ide* suffix, 94, 251

immiscible liquids, 181, **181**

incandescent bulb, argon in, 419

incomplete reactions, 270

indicators, **colorplate I** following 548; acid–base, 227; in qualitative analysis of hydroxide ion, 441–43, **442;** universal, 227–28

indium, 43, 59, 524, 535; properties of, 525

-*ine* suffix, 94

inert (rare) gases (group 0), 40, 54, 55, 80, 93, 417, 418, 419; table of, 417

ingot of steel, 509

injection molding, of thermosetting materials, 638, **639**

inner transition elements, 82

inorganic chemistry, defined, 574

inorganic compounds, 574; compared with organic, 575

insecticides, 375, 436

insoluble substance, defined, 184

inspection method, of balancing equations, 121

insulation, pipe and furnace, 476, **477**

insulin, 664, 665

interionic attraction, in strong electrolytes, 210–11

interionic forces, 158

International Union of Chemistry system of nomenclature, 581, 583, 584, 586, 593, 594, 596–97, 600

Invar, 506, 520

iodide ion, 383, 386, 444

iodine, 369, 373, 374, 383, 391, 491; antiseptic action of, 386, **386;** atomic number of, 369; atomic radius of, 58, **colorplate** facing 85; atomic weight of, 369; boiling point of, 369; compounds of, 386; crystals of, 385; density of, 87, 369; discovery of, 384; electron configuration of, 369; electronegativity of, 106; goiter caused by deficiency of, 386; half life of radioisotope of (iodine-131), 338, 339; and hydrogen, reaction between, 385, 386; ionization potential of, 85, **colorplate** facing 85, 87, 369; melting point of, 369; necessary to thyroid gland, 249, 386; oxidation state of, 369; and periodic table, 76, 77, 78, 87, 88; preparation of, 384–85, **385;** properties of, 369, 385–86; radioactive (iodine-131), 330, 338, 339, 340, 356, 386; as test for starch, 386; tincture of, 385, 386; uses of compounds of, 386; valence number of, 116

iodized salt, 386

ion exchange method, of softening hard water, **475,** 475–76

ion exchange resins, 476

ion product constant of water, 224–25

ionic bonds, **93,** 94, **94,** 95, **95,** 102; blending with covalent, 102–05, **103;** defined, 94

ionic compounds, **93, 94,** 94–95, **95,** 373; formula weights of, 122; formulas for,

95–96, 97, 117; gram formula weights of, 124; and oxidation numbers, 290–91; and valence numbers, 96–97

ionic equations, 260, 261–62

ionic radii, 95; table of, **96**

ionization, 206, **206,** 209–10; energy of, 39; factors affecting, 210; of acids, 209, **209;** of hydrogen atom, 39 of molecules in acids, **218,** 218–19; theory of, 204, 210

ionization constant, 275, **275**

ionization energy, 38–39

ionization potentials of elements, 39, 40, 74, **75,** 75–76, 85, 86, 87, 88, 369, 390, 417, 420, 449, 464, 486, 502, 525, 550; defined, 40; table of, 41 and **colorplate** facing 85

ions, 60, **60,** 93, 102; acetate, 110, 209, 231, 277; of alkali metals, 451, 543, 544, 547; of alkaline earth metals, 465, 543, 544, 547; aluminum, 527, 528; ammonium, 110, 117, 223, 230, **230,** 235, 424, 431, 544; antimony, 446; arsenic, 3, 298, 420, 433; barium, 543; bicarbonate, 110; bismuth, 446; bisulfate, 233; bromide, 381, 444; calcium, 474, 475, 543, 544; carbonate, 110, 447, 456, 559; chlorate, 110; chloride, 94, **94,** 228, 229, 230, 231, 236, 247, 266, 276, 290, 443, 444, 449, 476; chromite, 248; cobalt, 520; complex, *see* complex ions; cupric, 292, 489, 491; cuprous, 292, 491; cyanide, 493; defined, 60, 93; dichromate, 292; and dissociation, 205; electricity conducted by, 207–08; and electrolytes, 203–04, **204;** ferric, 118, 394, 517; ferrous, 118, 394, 517; fluoborate, 525, **526;** fluoride, 379, 444, 525, **526;** halogen, *see* halogen ions; hydrated, 183, 222, 232, 236; hydrogen, 211, 224–35 *passim,* **225,** 246, 247, 249, 407, 408, 449, 459, 460, 513, 657 (*see also* hydronium ion); hydronium, 206, **207,** 209, 211, 218, 219, 220, 221, 229, 230, 231, 236, 244, 262, 377, 407, 409, 424, 468; hydroxide, *see* hydroxide ion; iodide, 383, 386, 444; magnesium, 474, 513, 516; manganous, 404; mercuric, 118; mercurous, 118; metallic, *see* metallic ions; negative, *see* negative ions; nickel, 520; nitrate, 109, 110, **110,** 117, 292, 446; nitride, 446; number of, in solutions, 188; oxidation numbers of, 292; perdisulfate, 394; permanganate, 395, 404, 411; peroxide, 394, 395, 404; phosphate, 110,

235, 447; plumbite, 569; positive, *see* positive ions; sodium, 94, **94,** 109, 228, 235, 247, 276, 449, 475, 544; strontium, 543, 544; sulfate, 109, 110, **110,** 117, 233, 404, 409, 445, 476; sulfide, 411, 445, 542, 543; sulfite, 110, 119, 445;

iron, 9, 18, 19, 57, 59, 84, 111, 424, 511–16; abundance of, 502; in acitvity series, 296; allotropes of, 511; atomic number of, 502; atomic radius of, **colorplate** facing 85; atomic weight of, 502; boiling point of, 502; borax bead test for, 546, **colorplate V** following 548; cast, 505; and chlorine, reaction between, 284, 285, 286, 290, 307–08; compounds of, 516–19; and copper, reaction between, 399; and copper sulfate, reaction between, 260; density of, 502; ductility of, 511; electron configuration of, 502; extracted from iron ore, 61–62, 467, 501, 502, **502, 503,** 503–05, **504;** and ferromagnetism, 511; galvanized, 515; half life of radioisotope of (iron-59), 339; and hydrochloric acid, reaction between, 286, **286,** 288, 290, 517; ionization potential of, 502, **colorplate** facing 85; ions of, 118, 394, 517; malleability of, 511; melting point of, 502; necessary to red blood cells, 249; oxidation potential of, 302; oxidation-reduction of, in iron compounds, 516–17, **516;** oxidation states of, 290, 502; oxides of, 278, 517; and oxygen reduction portion of reaction between, 287–88; and periodic table, 76, 83; pig, 504, 505, 508; properties of, 502, 511; radioactive (iron-59), 330, 356; reduction of, reaction between ferric (iron III) oxide and carbon, 299; rusting of, 264, 285, **285,** 512, **512,** 513, **513,** 514; and sulfur, reaction between, 19, 398–99; symbol for, 16; as transition element, 80, 501; valence number of, 116

iron (II) chloride (ferrous chloride), 252, 286, 290, 291, 517, 518

iron (III) chloride (ferric chloride), 252, 284, 285, 286, 288, 290, 291, 373, 517, 518

iron ore, 61–62, 467, 501, 502

iron (II) oxide (ferrous oxide) 267

iron (III) oxide (ferric oxide), 267, 285, 286, 299, 517

iron pyrites ("fool's gold"), 54, 396, 502

iron sulfate (ferrous sulfate), 518

iron sulfide (ferrous sulfide), 19, 120, 400, 446

iron triad (of group VIII), 501–24; and ferromagnetism, 511; properties of, 502; table of, 502

irreversible reactions, 270, **270**, 271, **271**

iso-prefix, 580

isobutane, 579, 580, **580**, 624

isomers, 575, 579–80, 584, 586

isooctane, 624, **624**, 626

isooctene, **624**

isopentane, 580

isoprene, 633–34, 635, **635**

isopropanol, 598, 600

isotopes, 32–33; and Law of Definite Proportions, 65–66; mass numbers of, 33; of hydrogen, diagrams of, 34; radioactive, *see* radioactive isotopes; symbols for, 34

-ite suffix, 252

Joliot, Frederic, 335

Joliot-Curie, Irene, 335

K shell, 45, 49, 50, **50**, 55, 80, 81, 482

karat, defined, 495

Kekulé von Stradonitz, Friedrich, 587

Kelly, William, 506

Kelvin scale, 147 and *n.*, 148

kernite, 534

kerosene, 451, 623, 625, 627

ketones, 596, 600

kettle method, of preparing soaps, 607

kiln, rotary, 468, **469**, 470

kinetic energy, 157, **157**, 158, 163

kinetic molecular theory, 129–33, 134, 135, 137, 153, 157

Kossel, W., 35

Kolbe, Adolf, 574

Krebs cycle, 660, **661**

krypton, 54, 81, 348, 417, 418, 419

L shell, 45, 49, 50, **50**, 56, 81, 94, 482

lacquers, 426

lactic acid, 442, 602, 661

laminated plastics, 639

lamp: arc, 419, **419**; mercury vapor, 419; sodium vapor, 452, **452**

lampblack, 554–55

lanthanide series, 82, 481, **483**, 484, 485

lanthanum, 78, 481, 484, 485

latex, 632, **632**, 633

lattice energy, 159, 192

lattice point, 140

Lavoisier, Antoine, 5, 6, 10, 217, 284, 285

Lawrence, Ernest O., 358, 359

lawrencium, 78, 82, 361, 485

lead, 298, 332, 333, 379, 567; in activity series, 296; antimony alloyed with, 436; arsenates of, 436; atomic number of, 550; atomic radius of, **colorplate** facing 85; atomic weight of, 550; boiling point of, 550; compounds of, 569; density of, 550; electron configuration of, 83, 550; gamma radiation absorbed by, 340, **341;** ionization potential of, **colorplate** facing 85, 550; melting point of, 550; metallurgy of, 494; oxidation states of, 550; properties of, 549, 550, 569; tin alloyed with, 568; in uranium disintegration series, 333

lead acetate, 402, 445

lead bromide, 383

lead chamber process, for preparation of sulfuric acid, 406, **406**

lead chloride, 540

lead dioxide, 395, 411

lead iodide, 154, 184

lead nitrate, 154, 234, 261

lead oxide, 470, 568, 569

lead sulfate, 411, 568

lead sulfide, 445

leavening agent, 559

LeChatelier, Henri, 278, 429

LeChatelier's Principle, 278, 279, 429, 457, 519; defined, 278

Leucippus, 2, 11

Lewis, G. N., 92

lignin, 646

lignite, 615

lime, *see* calcium oxide

limestone, 59, 261, 457, 464, 467, 468, 503, 504, 508

limestone caves, formation of, 473–74, **474**

limewater, 447, 473

limonite, 502

linear accelerations, defined, 359

linear arrangement, of atoms in molecule, **103**, 104

linear polymers, 634

linen, 645, 646

linolenic acid, 601, 602

liquefied petroleum gases, 620

liquid chromatography, 532

liquid fuels, for rockets, 627, **628**

liquids: boiling point of, 136; and condensation, 134–35; evaporation of, 135;

freezing [?] oration of, ?–39; heat of evaporation of [?] cible, 181 [?]scible, 181; mislithium, 35, **35, 47,** [?] in activity series, ? 363, 460, **460;** 357, 358; atomic n[?]m of, 56, **56,** 449; atomic radius o? 72, 73, 74, facing 85; atomic wei**colorplate** ing point of, 449; bo?49; boilprotons, 362; compounds?d with tals of, 451; density of, 7?; crystelectron configuration of, 4?451; flame test for, 545, **colorplate** 449; lowing 548; ionization potenti?l-40, **41,** 74, **75,** 76, **colorplate** facing 449; melting point of, 449; oxidati? state of, 449; and periodic table, 79, 81; preparation of, 450; properties of, 72, 73, 74, 449; spectrum, **colorplate** facing 84; symbol for, 72, 73, 74; and valence electrons, 73

lithium aluminum hydride, 458

lithium chloride, 458

lithium hydroxide, 456

lithium oxide, 71; bombarded with accelerated protons, 357–58; formula for, 71, 72

litmus, 227, 370, **colorplate** facing 548

litmus paper: for testing acids, 218, **218;** for testing bases, 222, **222**

lodestone, 517, **517**

long periods, of periodic table, 81, 82

Lowry, T. M., 217, 229

LOX, 263, 392, 627

lubricants, 625

Lucite, 643

lutecium, 78, 485

lye, *see* sodium hydroxide

lyophilic colloids, 316

lyophobic colloids, 316

M shell, 45, 49, 56, 81, 84, 93, 94, 482

McMillan, E. M., 360

magnalium alloys, 466, 530

magnesia, milk of, 226, 477

magnesium, 56, 57, 220, 221, 260, 265, 296, 513; as active metal, 296, 373; alloys of, 466; atomic number of, 72, 73, 74, 464; atomic radius of, 74, **colorplate** facing 85; atomic weight of, 464; boiling point of, 464; cobalt nitrate test for, 546, **colorplate VI** facing 549; compounds of, 476–77; density of, 74, 464; electron configuration of, **47,** 464, ionization

...**plate** fac-
potential of, 39, 4... 516; melting 85, 464; ions ... acid, reac-
ing point of, 464 ... itrogen reaction between, ... 421; oxidation
tion between ...tion of, 466, **466;**
state of, 464..., 74, 464, 465; for
properties ...n against corrosion,
protectio... er as source of, 465–66,
515–16; ...uric acid, reaction be-
466; ... symbol for, 72, 73, 74; va-
tween...ber of, 116
len... bicarbonate, 475
mag...m bromide, 60
ma...ium carbonate, 476
...esium chloride, 61, 116, 443
...gnesium hydroxide, 222, 246, 247, 476
magnesium nitride, 421
magnesium oxide, 222, 223, 476–77, 546;
    formula for, 71, 72, 96; formula for, in
    ionic form, 96; and ratio by weight of
    magnesium to oxygen, 65; uses of, 477;
    and water, reaction between, 246, 477
magnesium sulfate, 465, 475, 477
magnesium sulfide, 115, 116
magnetite, 517, **517**
maltase, 665, **665**
maltose, 658, **659,** 665, **665**
manganese, 42, 466, 507, 530, 546; borax
    bead test for, **colorplate V** following
    548
manganese dioxide, 8, 96, 165, 267, 371,
    381, 382, 385
manganese steel, 506
marble, 59, 464, 467, 468
marsh gas, 620
Mass Action, Law of, 273, **273,** 274, 276;
    defined, 273
mass defect, 350
mass-energy relationship, 348, 349–50; and
    Einstein's equation, 349, 350
mass number: defined, 33; and radioiso-
    topes, 342, 343
mass spectrometer, **33**
matte, 488
mechanism of reaction, 166–67, **166**
medicine: and nitrous oxide, 427, radio-
    isotopes used in, 355–56, **356**
Meitner, Lise, 348
melamine-formaldehyde, 642
melting point, defined, 139
Mendeleev, Dmitri, 76, 78, 79, 84, 417, 485,
    497
mendelevium, 361, 485
Mercer, John, 646, 648

mercerized cotton, 648
mercuric chloride, 528, 529
mercuric ion, 118
mercuric oxide, 5, **5,** 6, **6,** 7, 17, 60; decom-
    posed by heating, 2, **2,** 5, **5,** 6, **6;** equa-
    tion for, when heated, 7, 120–21, 123;
    formula for, 2, 7
mercuric sulfide, 542, **colorplate III** follow-
    ing 548
mercurous chloride, 540, 541
mercurous ion, 118
mercury, **5,** 6, **6,** 59; in activity series, 296;
    in amalgamation process, 493; bom-
    barded with deuterons, 357; spectrum,
    colorplate facing 84; valence number
    of, 116
mercury vapor lamp, 419
mesons, 360
metaboric acid, 535
metal carbonates, 246
metallic bonds, 111, **111**
metallic chlorides, 376
metallic ions, 539; analytical groups of,
    539, 540, 542, 543–44; confirmatory
    tests for, 541, 542, 543, 544, 545, 547;
    in filtrates, 541; precipitation of, 540,
    541, 542, 543, 544, 546–47; qualitative
    analysis of, 539–48, **540, 542, 543, 544,
    545, 546;** in residues, 541; separation
    of, 539–40, 541; specific tests for, **545,**
    545–46
metallic nitrates, 426
metallic oxides, 246, 250, 298
metallic sulfides, 402
metalloids, 87
metallurgy, 481, 488, 503; *see* specific ele-
    ments
metals, 57, **57,** 58, 86, 87; active, *see* active
    metals; activity series of, 296–97; alkali,
    see alkali metals; and bromine, reac-
    tions between, 382; and chlorine, reac-
    tions between, 372–73, 379; as con-
    ductors of heat and electricity, 57, 85,
    111; corrosion of, prevention of, **514,**
    514–15, **515;** ductility of, 57; effect of
    atomic size in, 58; and fluorine, reac-
    tions between, 379; inactive, 295, 296;
    ionization potentials of, 86, **colorplate**
    facing 85; less active than hydrogen,
    297–98; malleability of, 57; in negative
    ions, 446–47; and nitric acid, reactions
    between, 423–24, 426; and periodic
    table, 85, 86; pickling of, 410, 515, 518;
    "sea of valence electrons" in, 111; and
    sulfur, reactions between, 398–99, **399**

methanal (formaldehyde), 264, 265, 595,
    599, 638, 639, **639,** 640
methane, 551, 555, 576, 581, 589, **593,** 616,
    619, 620; boiling point of, 578, 579; and
    bromine, reaction between, 592, **592;**
    and chlorine, reaction between, 593;
    as covalent compound, 100, 101;
    graphic formula for, 578; molecular
    formula for, 578, 579; molecular
    weight of, from density, 151; molecule
    of, 100, 107, 577; preparation of, 576–
    77; as reducing agent, 294; and steam,
    reaction between, 460
methanoic (formic) acid, 563, 601, 632
methanol (methyl alcohol), 191, 595, **596,**
    596–97, 616
methyl, defined, 580
methyl alcohol, 191, 595, **596,** 596–97, 616
methyl bromide, 593, **593**
methyl chloride, 593, 594
methyl nitrate, 606
methyl orange, 227, 233, **colorplate** facing
    548
methyl red, 227, **colorplate** facing 548
methyl salicylate, 605
methyl violet, 227, **colorplate** facing 548
metric system, *see* Appendix
Meyer, J. Lothar, 76
mica, 565, **566**
microcurie, defined, 388 *n.*
microscopy system, **14**
milk: homogenized, 316, 317, 318; stron-
    tium-90 removed from, 477
milk of magnesia, 226, 477
Millikan, Robert, 24
mineral wool, 505
miscible liquid, **181;** defined, 181
mitochondria, 656, 660
mixed ethers, 604
mixture: defined, 18; iron and sulfur, 18–19,
    18–19
moderator, in core of nuclear reactor, 351,
    351
modified electron shell diagrams, 49, **49**
Moissan, Henri, 367, 378
molal solution, 187, 189–90, **190;** defined,
    189
molar solution, **187,** 187–88, **189;** defined,
    187, **190**
molar volume of gas, 133, **133**
mole, 133; defined, 133
mole method, of solving weight and vol-
    ume problems, 172–174
mole principle, 172
molecular formulas, 171–72, 578, 583, 585

molecular weights: of covalent compounds, determination of, 193–94; defined, 122; expressed in grams, 123, 133; of gases, 150–51

molecules: in acids, ionization of, 218–19; angular, **103**, 107, **107;** and Brownian movement, 129, **129;** covalent, 98, **98,** 99, **99,** 99, 100–01, **101;** defined, 16; diatomic, 16, **16,** 17, 98, 99–100, **100;** DNA, 66, 667; and kinetic molecular theory, 129–33, 134, 135, 137, 153, 157; mole of, 133; monatomic, **16,** 17; nonpolar, 103; polar, **103;** 103–04; pyramidal, 107, **107;** rotational motion of, 158, **158,** 159; shapes of, **107,** 107–08; space-filling models of, 50–51, **51,** 99, **99;** straight chain, 579; tetrahedral **107,** 108; translational motion of, 158, **158,** 159; triatomic, 104–05; vibrational motion of, 158, **158,** 159

molybdenum steel, 506

monatomic molecules, **16,** 17

Mond process, 519

Monel metal, 520

monitoring instruments, for detecting radiation, 335–38, **336, 337**

mono- prefix, 594

monocalcium phosphate, 410, 435

monochloromethane, 593, 594

monoclinic crystal, 139–40, **140,** 397, 398, **398**

monohydroxy alcohols, 598

monohydroxy bases, 248

monomer, defined, 623

monoprotic acids, 232, 245

monosaccharides, 656

monosodium phosphate, 234

mordant, fibers treated with, 436, 533

Moseley, H. G. J., 31, 77

motion of molecules: rotational, 158, **158,** 159; translational, 158, **158,** 159; vibrational, 158, **158,** 159

Multiple Proportions, Law of, 14 *n.,* 67; defined, 67

muriatic acid, *see* hydrochloric acid

n- prefix, 579, 580

N shell, 56, 81, 482, 484

naphthalene, 141, 142, 411, 588, 616

natural gas, 581, 613, 614, **614,** 619–20

natural radioactive series, 333–34

natural radioactivity, discovery of, 326, 328; *see also* electromagnetic radiation

natural radioisotopes, 329, 330

natural rubber, 633, 634, 636; properties and uses of, 637

negative, in photography, 496, 497, **497**

negative ions, 58, 95, 106, 208; testing for, 441–48, **442, 443, 445, 446, 447**

neo- prefix, 580

neon, 17, 28, 33, 54, 75, 80, 418, 419, 482; in air, 18; atomic number of, 72, 73, 74, 417; atomic radius of, 74, **colorplate** facing 85; atomic weight of, 32, 417; boiling point of, 417; density of, 74, 417; diagram of atom of, **56;** electron configuration of, **47** 417; ions of, 33; ionization potential of, **41,** 75, **75, colorplate** facing 85; 417; isotopes of, 32; melting point of, 417; and periodic table 81; properties of, 72, 73, 74, 417; symbol for, 72, 73, 74; uses of, 419; and valence electrons, 73

neopentane, 580

neoprene, 634, **635,** 637

neptunium, 353, **354,** 355, 360, 361, 485

net equations, 260, 262

neutralization reactions, **228,** 228–29, 233, 248, 249–50, 254, 262, 270, 271

neutrons, 32, 36, **50,** 335, 342; and atomic number, 33–34; properties of, 27; symbol for, 341; thermal, 351; uranium bombarded with, 347, 348, **348,** 350, **350, 353,** 354, 360

Newlands, John, 76

Newton, Sir Issac, 27

nichrome, 520

nickel, 501, 511, 514, 515; in activity series, 296; alloys of, 520, 521; borax bead test for, 546, **colorplate V** following 548; compounds of, 520; electron configuration of, 42; ions of, 520; Mond process for purifying, 519; oxidation potential of, 302; and periodic table, 76, 77, 78; properties of, 502, 519, 520; as transition element, 80, 501; uses of, 520

nickel-cadmium battery, **519,** 520

nickel carbonyl, 519

nickelous oxide, 520

nitrate ion, 109, 110, **110,** 117, 292, 446

nitrates: testing for, 446, **446;** uses of, 426, 432, 457–58

nitric acid, 217, 232, 241, 243, 406, 421–22, 468, 627; in aqua regia, 425; and benzene, reaction between, 409; concentrated, 423, 425; and copper, reaction between, 309, 426, 427, **427;** dilute, 423, 424, 426, 427; formula for, 119, 244, 245; and magnesium, reaction between, 424; and metals, reactions between, 423–24, **424,** 426; and nonmetals, reactions between, 425, **425,** as oxidizing agent, 423, 424, 425, 627; preparation of, 250, **422,** 422–23, **423,** 431; properties of, 423; and proteins, 425; related to sodium nitrate, 252, **252;** as strong acid, 220; as ternary acid, 244, **244;** in testing for chloride ion, 443, **443,** 444; in testing for phosphate ion, 447; titrated against potassium hydroxide, 255; uses of, 426; as volatile acid, 243

nitric oxide, 67, 162, 422, 424, 426–27, 446

nitrides, testing for, 446

nitriding, defined, 511

nitrites, and nitrous acid, 428

nitrobenzene, 409

nitrocellulose, 426

nitrogen, 58, 392, 446, 616; in air, 18, 58, 59, 263, 419; atomic number of, 72, 73, 74, 420; atomic radius of, 74, **colorplate** facing 85; atomic weight of, 420; boiling point of, 420; bombarded with alpha particles, 334, **334,** 343, 357; compounds of, 67, 420, 421 *ff.;* density of, 74, 417, 420; diagram for atom of, 49, **49;** electron configuration of, **47,** 420; fixation of, 421, **421;** hydrogen combined with, 256, 277; ionization potential of, **41,** 49, 74, **colorplate** facing 85; 420; isotopes of, 33, **33,** 334, 343, 355; and magnesium, reaction between, 418, 421, **421;** melting point of, 420; molecule of, 102, **102;** oxidation states of, 292, 420, 428; oxides of, 67, 417, 421, 426–27; preparation of, 417, **418;** properties of, 72, 73, 74, 420; and proteins, 663, 666; radioactive (nitrogen-15), 355–56; symbol for, 72, 73, 74; valence number of, 116

nitrogen dioxide, 64, 67, 406, 422, 423, 424, 426–27

nitrogen family (group VA), 419–40; and periodic table, 417; properties of, 420; table of, 420

nitrogen pentoxide, 67, 71, 72

nitrogen triode, 60

nitrogen trioxide, 67

nitroglycerine, 421, 422, 426, 598, 606

nitrosyl chloride, 426

nitrous acid, 119, 244, 245, 428

nitrous oxide, 67, 427, **427**

nobelium, 361, 485

nonane, 578

nonelectrolyte, defined, 202
nonmetals, 57, **57**, 58, 86, 87; effect of atomic size in, 58; ionization potentials of, 85; and nitric acid, reactions between, 425; and periodic table, 85, 86
nonpolar bonds, 103, **103**
nonpolar molecules, 103
nonvolatile acids, 243, 250–51
normal solutions, 187, 188–89, **189;** defined, 188
nuclear atom, 25
nuclear equations, symbols for radiation in, 342–43
nuclear fission (atomic fission), 347–48, **348;** bombs produced by, 366; energy from, 348–60 *passim*
nuclear fusion, 361–64, **363;** and accelerators, 362; controlled, 363–64; self-sustaining, 362–63
nuclear reactions, energy from, 347–66 *passim;* symbols in, 341–42
nuclear reactors, 351–52, **354,** 452; core in, 351, **351;** energy from, 352–57; moderator in core of, 351, **351;** transuranic elements as fuels for, 353–54; types of, 354–55
nucleic acids, 666
nucleoproteins, 666
nucleotides, **666,** 667, 668
nucleus, atomic, 25, 38, **38,** 39, **39;** and atomic number, 31; binding energy of, 350; mass defect of, 349–50
nylon, 574, 641, 643, 644, **645,** 648, 651, **651, 652**

O shell, 81, 82
octane, 578, 627; *see also* isooctane
octane rating scale, 626
-*oic* suffix, 601
-*ol* suffix, 597
oleum, 406
open-hearth furnace, 506, 507–08, **508**
orbitals, 44, 45, **45,** 46, **46,** 47, 48, **48,** 49, 482, 484, 501; table of, 47
orbital overlap diagrams, 98, **98,** 99, **99,** 100, **100,** 102
orbits, 30, energy levels or shells, 361; movement between, 25
organelles, 655–56
organic acids, 596, 600–02, **601**
organic chemistry, defined, 58, 574
organic compounds, 574, 575; compared with inorganic, 575; and functional groups, 595, **595,** 596

Orlon, 651
orthodichlor-benzene, 375
orthorhombic crystal, 139, **140**
Ostwald process, 422–23, 431
-*ous* suffix, 118, 244, 245, 252
oxalic acid, 574
oxidation, 285, 287, 288, 369, 390; of carbon, 286–87, **287,** 291, 308; cellular, of glucose, 660, **661, 662;** defined, 286, 293; and electrons, 285–86; of metals, 298; **298;** slow, 285; *see also* combustion
oxidation numbers, 289–95, 382; in covalent compounds, 291; determination of, 291–92, **291, 292, 294;** by groups, **293;** in ionic compounds, 290–91
oxidation potential, 301–02, 303; table of, 302
oxidation-reduction (redox) reactions, 259, 287–89, **288, 289,** 293–94, 295–96, 300, 301, 318–19, 370, 371, 373, 374, 383, 395, 399, 401, 404, 424, 460, 489; applied to blueprints, 518–19; balancing, 307–10; in iron compounds, 516–19; of sulfur, 410
oxides: defined, 71; distinguished from peroxides, 395; formulas for, with elements of atomic numbers *1* through *20,* 72; of iron, 278, 517; of nitrogen, 67, 417, 421, 426–27; nonmetallic, and bases, reactions between, 250; periodic arrangement of, 72; of phosphorus, 434, 435; *see also* metallic oxides
oxidizing agent: defined, 288, 369; determination of, 294, 295
-*oxy* functional group, 596, 603
oxyacetylene torch, 392, **392,** 619, **619**
oxygen, 20, 28, 93, 368, 390, **399,** 417; in air, 18, 54, 58, 59; atomic number of, 72, 73, 74, 390; atomic radius of, 48, 74, **colorplate** facing 85; atomic weight of, 28–29, 48, 88, 122, 123, 390; boiling point of, 390; combustion supported by, 8, 9, 284, 285, 391 (*see also* oxidation); commerical preparation of, 391–92, **392;** density of, 74, 390; discovery, 5, **5,** 6, **6, 8, 9;** in earth's crust, 58; in earth's waters, 58, 59; electron configuration of, **47, 49,** 390; gram atomic weight of, 123; gram molecular weight of, 151; and hydrogen chloride, reaction between, 279; ionization potential of, **41, colorplate** facing 85, 390; and iron, reduction portion of reaction between, 287–88;

isotopes of, 33, **33,** 34; laboratory preparation of, **391;** liquid, 263, 392, 627; magnetic property of, 100; melting point of, 390; molecular weight of, 151; molecule of, 99–100, **100, 394;** necessary to life, 390; and nitrogen, compounds of, 67, 417, 421, 426–27; as nonmetallic element, 57; oxidation states of, 292, 390; potassium chlorate, released from, 7–8, 165; preparation of, 6, 7, **7;** properties of, 8–9, 72, 73, 74, 390; and ratio to hydrogen by volume in water, **62,** 62–63; and ratio to hydrogen by weight in heavy water, 66; and ratio to hydrogen by weight in hydrogen peroxide, 66; and ratio to hydrogen by weight in water, 64, 66; symbol for, 16, 72, 73, 74; test for, 6; uses of, 392–93; valence number of, 97, 116
oxygen family (group VIA), 79, 368, 390–416; and periodic table, 368, 390; properties of, 390; table of, 390
oxygen tent, 393
oxyhydrogen torch, 392, **393,** 461, **461**
ozone, 17, 393–94, **394;** preparation of, **393**

P shell, 81, 82, 484
palmitate, 606
paper manufacture, 646, **647**
para-aminobenzoic acid, 665, 666
paradichlorobenzene, 141, 142
paraffins, *see* alkanes
Parkes process, 494
Partial Pressure, Dalton's Law of, 12
particle accelerators, **357,** 357–60, **358, 359;** and nuclear fusion, 362; and transuranic elements, 360; use of, 359–60
Pauli, Wolfgang, exclusion principle of, 46
pentachlor-phenol, 375, **376**
pentadiene, 585
pentane, 578, 580
pentene, 583
pentyne, 585, 586
pepsin, 165, 267
peptides, and amino acids, 663–64, **664**
peptization, 317
per- perfix, 245, 252
perbromic acid, 245, **245,** 252
percentage composition, of compound, 170
perchloric acid, 245, 252
perdisulfate ion, 394
perdisulfuric acid, 394

Periodic Law, 76, 77

periodic table, 76–88, *passim,* **colorplate** following 84, 248, 348, 360, 482, 485–86, 497; A and B subgroups, 83, 485–86; alkali metals in, 449, 485; alkaline earth metals in, 464, 465; aluminum family in, 524, 525; amphoteric hydroxides in, 248; and atomic numbers, 77–78, 79; and atomic weights 76–77, 78, 79, 88; B groups and short form, 83; carbon family in, 549–50; groups of, 79–80; halogen family in, 368; long or extended form, 78, **colorplate** following 84; Mendeleev's short form, **77**; metals in, 85, 86; nitrogen family in, 417; nonmetals in, 85, 86; oxygen family in, 368, 390; periods of, 80–82; transition elements in, 482, 485–86, 497; and triads of group VIII, 501; used for predicting properties of elements, 87–88; and valence numbers, 118

periods, of periodic table, 80–83; 482–84

periods 4, 5, 6, and 7, 482–84

Perkins, William Henry, 588

Permalloy, 520

permanganate ion, 395, 404, 411

peroxides, distinguished from oxides, 395; ions of, 394, 395, 404

petroleum, 620, 621, **621,** additives to improve performance of, 623; fractional distillation of, 621; fractions of, 621–23; nature of, 620–21; as sources of alkanes, 581; "washed" with concentrated sulfuric acid, 410; yield from, 625

pewter, 568

pH scale, **225,** 225–26

pH values: of blood, human, 241; of common substances, 226; determination of, 226–28; of gastric juice, human, 241; meter for, 228, **228;** of salt solutions, prediction of, 235–36; of soil, 241

phenol, 616, 638, 639, **639,** 640

phenol red, 227, **colorplate** facing 548

phenolphthalein, 226, 227, 233, 254, 255, 264, 442, 513, **colorplate** facing 548

phenyl radical, 602

phenylanaline, 663

phlogiston, 284

phosphate, **666;** high energy bonds of, 661, **662**

phosphate ion, 235, 447

phosphine, 434

phosphor bronze, 434, 490, 491

phosphoric acid, 218, **218,** 234, 235, 435, 666, 667, **667;** formula for, 119, 435; as tripotic acid, 233, 245, 435; uses of, 435

phosphorous acid, 384, 435

phosphorus, 8, 242, 410, 420, 433, 446; acids of, 434, 435; allotropes of, 266, 434; atomic number of, 72, 73, 74, 420; atomic radius of, 74, **colorplate** facing 85; atomic weight of, 420; boiling point of, 420; density of, 74, 420; electron configuration of, **47,** 50, **50,** 420; electron dot diagram for, **50;** half life of radioisotope of (phosphorus-32), 339; ionization potential of, **41,** 74, **colorplate** facing 85, 420; necessary to life, 433; as nonmetal, 57, 86; oxidation states of, 420; oxides of, 434, 435; preparation of, 433, **434;** properties of, 72, 73, 74, 420, 434; radioactive, 330, 335, 339, 340, 355, 356; red, 266, 434; sources of, 433; symbol for, 72, 73, 74; uses of, 434, **434;** valence numbers of, 116, 118; white, 266, 434

phosphorus pentoxide, 71–72, 217, 242, **242,** 434, 435

phosphorus sesquisulfide, 434

phosphorus tribromide, 384

phosphorus trioxide, 434

photoelectric cells, 412, **412,** 453

photographic film and paper, coated with light-sensitive emulsions, 383, **383,** 386

photographic lamp, xenon used in, 419

photographic process, and silver, **496,** 496–97, **497**

photons, 29

photosynthesis, 355, **355,** 558, **558,** 657

physical change, defined, 19; and mass, 155–56

physical property, defined, 9

pickling, of metals, 410, 515, 518

pig iron, 504, 505, 508

pinch effect, in nuclear fusion, 363

pitchblende, 328, 329, 465

Planck, Max, 1, **1,** 29, 367

plasma, in nuclear fusion, 363

plaster of Paris, 471, **471**

plasticizers, 640

plastics, 379, 380, 420, 426, 574, 600, 638–45; laminated, 639; phenol-formaldehyde, 639–40; shaping, 638–39, **639;** thermosetting, *see* thermosetting plastics; *see also* thermoplastics

platinum, 55, 165, 373, 386, 394, 405, 422, 429; in activity series, 296

Plexiglas, 643

plutonium, 351, 353, **353,** 354, **354,** 355, 361, 485

plywood, 639

polar bonds, **103,** 103–04; defined, 104

polonium, 24, 59, 333, 390, 391, 412; atomic number of, 390; atomic weight of, 88, 390; discovery of, 328; electron configuration of, 390; half lives of radioisotopes of, 339; and periodic table, 368; radioactive, 330, 333, 335, 339

polyesters, 642

polyethylene, 585, 643, 644, **644**

polyhydroxy alcohols, 598

polymerization, 588, 623–24, 632, 634–35; cross-linked, 634, **635;** linear, 634

polymers, 634; condensation, **639,** 640

polypeptide chains, 664

polysaccharides, 658–59

polystyrene, 643

positive, in photography, 497, **497**

positive ions, 58, 95, 106, 208; testing for, 539–48, **540, 542, 543, 544, 545, 546;** *see also* metallic ions

potassium, 48, 368, 482, 526; activity of, 58, 295, 296; atomic number of, 72, 73, 74, 449; atomic radius of, 48, 58, 74, 75, **colorplate** facing 85; atomic weight of, 122, 449; boiling point of, 449; crystals of, 451; density of, 74, 449; diagram for atom of, 49, **49;** discovery of, 450; electron configuration of, **47,** 449; flame test for, 545, **colorplate IV** following 548; and fluorine, reaction between, 379; halide salts of, 454; ionization potential of, **41, 75,** 76, 449; melting point of, 449; oxidation state of, 449; and periodic table, 76, 77, 78, 79, 81; preparation of, 450; properties of, 72, 73, 74, 449; radioactive (potassium-40), 338; spectrum, **colorplate** facing 84; symbol for, 72, 73, 74; valence number of, 116

potassium alum, 532

potassium bicarbonate, 457

potassium bromate, 294

potassium bromide, 260, 294, 384

potassium carbonate, 457, 470

potassium chlorate, 7, **7,** 8, 17, 165, 256; balanced equation for heating of, to yield potassium chloride and oxygen, 121; as electrolyte, 202, **202;** as oxidizing agent, 294; oxygen released from, 7–8, 165; related to chloric acid, 252 potassium chloride, 7, 8, 443, 454, 513; formula for, 96, 115; formula for, in ionic form, 96

patassium chlorite, 252, **252**

potassium chromate, 547

potassium chrome alum, 532

potassium ferricyanide, 513, 518, 519

potassium ferrocyanide, 517

potassium fluoborate, 534

potassium hydroxide, 232, 236, 417, 456; and bromine, reaction between, 294; and carbon dioxide, reaction between, 250; nitric acid titrated against, 255; as strong base, 236; and sulfuric acid, reaction between, 228

potassium hypobromite, 252

potassium iodide, 154, 186, 261, 383, 385, 386, 491

potassium nitrate, 457; as ionic substance, 232; as oxidizing agent, 294; from reaction between sodium nitrate and potassium chloride, 458; solubility of, in water, 185; and sulfuric acid, reaction between, 250; uses of, 458

potassium oxide, 71, 72

potassium perbromate, 252

potassium permanganate, 395, 404, 407, 445

potassium sulfate: formula for, 117; formula for, in ionic form, 117; from reaction between potassium hydroxide and sulfuric acid, 236; from reaction between potassium nitrate and sulfuric acid, 250

potassium sulfide, 251

potassium uranyl sulfate, 328

potential energy, of particles of matter, 157–58, **157**

power reactor, nuclear, 354, **354**

precipitation: of colloids, 319; defined, 319; of metallic ions, 540, 541, 542, 543, 544, 546–47; of negative ions, 443, 444, 445, **445**, 447, **447**

precipitator, Cottrell, 320–21, **321**

Priestley, Joseph, 5, 6, 8, 9, 10, 16, 259, 284, 427, 559

principal quantum number, defined, 45

producer gas, 181, 618

product of reaction, defined, 120

production reactor, nuclear, 354, 355

propane, 554, 577, 578, 579, **579**, 581, 589

propanol, 597–98

propanone (acetone), 596, 600, **600**, 616, 649

propellants, for rockets, 627

propene, 583, 589

properties: defined, 8; physical and chemical, 9

propyl, defined, 580

propyl alcohol, 597–98

propyne, 585, 586, 589

protactinium-234, 333, 334, 342

proteins, 60, **663**, 663–68; denaturation of, **664**, 665; fibers from, 649, 651; and nitrogen, 663, 666; structure of, 664–65; xanthroproteic test for, 664, **664**; *see also* amino acids; enzymes

proton donor-proton acceptor theory, **229**, 229–30, **230**

proton-proton chain reaction, 362, **362**

proton-synchroton, 359

protons, 32, 206, 207, 342, 343; accelerated, lithium bombarded with, 357–58, 362; properties of, 27; symbol for, 341

Proust, Louis, 65

ptyalin, 165

purines, **666**, 667, **667**

pyramidal molecules, 107, **107**

pyramidines, **666**, 667, **667**

pyroboric acid, 535

pyroligneous acid, 616

pyruvic acid, 660, 661, **661**

Q shell, 82

qualitative analysis: defined, 441; of metallic ions, 539–48, **540, 542, 543, 544, 545, 546;** of negative ions, 441–48, **442, 443, 445, 446, 447**

quanta, defined, 29

quantitative analysis, defined, 441, 448

quantum mechanics, 43

quantum numbers, 45

quantum theory, of light, 29

quartz, 565, 566

quicklime, *see* calcium oxide

radiation, 329–30, **329** (*see also* alpha, beta, and gamma)

radiation, electromagnetic, *see* electromagnetic radiation

radicals, **109**, 109–10, **110**, 580, 602; defined, 109; table of, 110, 116; valence numbers of, 116, 118–19; writing formulas for compounds containing, 117; *see also* ions

radioactive disintegration, 331–32, **331, 332**, 333, 334

radioactive isotopes (radioisotopes), 329, 330, 331–35; and atomic number, 342; half life of, 338–39; and mass number, 342, 343; natural, 329, 330; uses of, 355–56, **355, 356**

radioactive series: natural, 333–34; produced by man, 335

radioactive tracers, 355

radioactivity, natural, discovery of, 326–28, **328**

radiocarbon dating, 549, **549**

radioisotopes, *see* radioactive isotopes

radium, 332, 333, 336, 339, 464; discovery of, 326, 329; electron configuration of, 485; properties of, 464, 465; uses of, 467

radium chloride, 329

radon, 54, 55, 332, 333, 368, 417, 418

radon fluoride, 55

Ramsay, William, 34, 54, 417, 418

rare earths (lanthanide series), 481, **483**, 484, **484**

rare (inert) gases, 54, 55, 80, 93, 417, 418, 419; compared with ions, **94;** orbital diagrams of, **482**

rate of reaction: and catalysts, 266–67, **267;** defined, 264; effect of concentration on, 264–65, **264, 265;** and increase of surface area, 266; and reactants, 265–66, **265;** and temperature, 265, **266**

Rayleigh, Lord, 54, 417, 418

rayon, 456, 648

reactants: defined, 120; and reaction rate, 265–66

reactions: addition, 594–95; autooxidation, 294, 395; chain, *see* chain reactions; combustion, 263, 284, 285, 287; to completion, *see* irreversible reaction; composition, 259; decomposition, 259; dehydration, 408, 658, 663; double replacement, 251, 259, 261–62, 409; endothermic, **159**, 160, 161, **161**, 164, **164**, 165, **165**, 191, 192, 277, 618; exothermic, 159, **159**, 161, **161**, 162, 164, **164**, 165, **165**, 191, 192, 277; half-cell, 301, 302, 307, 308, 401; hydrocarbon substitution, 593; hydrogenation, 461, 606, 624; hydrolysis, **234**, 234–35, **235**, 236, 261, 270, 318, 658; involving molecular compounds, 308–09; irreversible, 270, 271; mechanism of, 166–67; neutralization, **228**, 228–29, 233, 248, 249–50, 254, 262, 270, 271; nuclear, *see* nuclear reactions; rate of, *see* rate of reaction; redox, *see* oxidation-reduction reactions; predicting, 303–04; reversible, 269; single replacement, 259–60; thermonuclear, 362–63

reactors, nuclear, *see* nuclear reactors

realgar, 435

recrystallization, salt purified by, 454

red lead, 569

redox (oxidation-reduction) reactions, *see* oxidation-reduction (redox) reactions

reducing agents, 303; defined, 288; determination of, 294, 295

reduction, defined, 287, 293; *see* oxidation-reduction

refractory material, defined, 556

refrigerants, 379, 593

regenerated cellulose, 649

replacement series, *see* activity series

replication, of DNA, 668

research reactor, nuclear, 354

resins, 600, 640, **641**

resistance furnace, 555–56, **556**

resonance hybrids, 110–11, **110, 111,** 587

resorcinol-formaldehyde, 642

respiration, anaerobic, 660–61

reversible reactions, 269, 270, **270**

rhodium, 515

rhombic crystal, 397, 398, **398**

ring hydrocarbons, **587,** 587–89

rockets, fuels for, 627, **628**

Roentgen, Wilhelm von, 326, 327

rolling mill, steel ingot shaped by, 509, **510**

rotary kiln, 468, **469,** 470

rotational motion of molecules, 158, **158,** 159

rubber: butyl, 637; foam, 633; formula for, 633; natural, *see* natural rubber; nitrile, 637; silicone, 636, **636;** synthetic, *see* synthetic rubber; thiokol, 637; vulcanized, 396, 633, **633,** 635, **635**

rubidium, 79, 449, 450, 451, 453

rust, 264, 285, **285,** 512, 513, 514; *see also* corrosion

Rutherford, Ernest, 24, 25, 51, 329, 331, 332, 334, 335, 336, 338, 343, 347, 357

salicylic acid, 603

salt, table, *see* sodium chloride

saltpeter, Chile, 384, 422

salts: acid, 233–35, 252, 253; basic, 234; basic anhydrides prepared from, 246; binary, 251, **252;** defined, 232; double (alums), 532; halide, 454; hydrolysis of, 234, **235,** 237; industrial uses of, 249; naming, 251–53 (table of, 253); normal, 233–34; preparation of, 249–51, **251;** in

solution, electrolysis of, 247–48, **248,** 370; of strong acids and strong bases, 237–38; of strong acids and weak bases, 236–37; of strong bases and weak acids, 236, related, 252; ternary, 252, **252;** of weak acids and weak bases, 237

Sanger, Frederick, 573, 664

saponification, 607

saturated fats, 606

saturated hydrocarbons, *see* hydrocarbons

saturated solution, defined, 184

scandium, 42, 482, 484

Sceptical Chymist, The, 4, **4**

Scheele, Carl Wilhelm, 5, 6, 8, 9, 369, 371, 574

Schroedinger, Irwin, 43

scientific notation, powers of ten, *see* Appendix

scintillation counter, 337

sea water: desalinated, 180; as homogeneous substance, 180

selenic acid, 412

selenium, 88, 368, 390, 412

selenous acid, 412

series: actinide, 82, 360, 481, **483,** 484; activity, of metals, 296–97; electrochemical, 303; ethene (ethylene), 582–84, **583;** ethyne (acetylene), 585, **585,** 586; homologous, 578; lanthanide, 81–82, 481, **483,** 484; uranium disintegration, 333–34, 342, 412

shells, electron *see* electron shells

shielding, from effects of radiation, 339–40, 351, **351**

short form, of periodic table, 84

siderite, 502

significant figures, in calculating atomic weights, 122; *see also* Appendix

silanes, 566–67

silica gel, 566

silicide, 567

silicon, 17, 82, 335, 549, 565; compounds of, 565–66, **565,** 635–36; electron configuration of, 42, 83, 550; as metalloid, 86; properties of, 72, 73, 74, 549, 550; and valence electrons, 73

silicon carbide, 535, 556, 565

silicon dioxide, 395, 565, 566

silicon steel, 506

silicon tetrachloride, 376, 565

silicone rubber, *see* rubber

silicones, 567, 635–36, 643

silk, 645, 646, 648, 649; *see also* synthetic fibers

siloxanes, 636

silver, 57, 59, 111, 394, 424, 493; in activity series, 296, 297; alloys of, 495; atomic number of, 486; atomic radius of, **colorplate** facing 85; atomic weight of, 486; boiling point of, 486; as by-product, 494; chemical extraction of, 493, 494, **494;** density of, 486; electron configuration of, 486; "fine" as designation for, 495; and fluorine, reaction between, 379; ionization potential of, **colorplate** facing 85, 486; melting point of, 486; oxidation potential of, 302; oxidation states of, 486; and periodic table, 485, 486; and photographic process, **496,** 496–97, **497,** properties of, 486, 494, 495; as transition element, 80, 486; uses of, 495, 496–97; valence number of, 116

silver bromide, 383, 444, 496

silver carbonate, 443

silver chloride, 184, 186, 251, 261, 443, 444, 496, 540–41, 547

silver fluoride, 444

silver halides, 496

silver iodide, 386, 444, 496

silver nitrate, 251, 261, 265, 266, 297, 384; and photographic process, 426, 496; in testing for chloride ion, 443, 444

silver oxalate, 443

silver sulfate, 443, 494

silver sulfide, 399, **399**

simple cubic crystal, 140, **140**

simple ethers, 604

single covalent bonds, 101, 575

single electron bonds, 535

single replacement reactions, 259–60

"sky-writing," 376

slag, 505, **505,** 508

slaked lime, *see* calcium hydroxide

smelting, defined, 503

smog, as colloid, 315

soap, 606–08; as emulsifying and wetting agent, 318, **318,** 607–08; manufacture of, 456, 607, **608**

soapstone, 476

soda-acid fire extinguisher, 560–61, **561**

soda ash, 457

soda lime process, for preparation of sodium hydroxide, 456

Soddy, Frederick, 33, 331, 332, 338

sodium, 28, 93, 368, 384; activity of, 56, 57, 296, 373; atomic number of, 72, 73, 74, 449; atomic radius of, 74, 75, **colorplate** facing 85; atomic weight of, 449; boiling point of, 449; and chlorine, reaction between, 251, 372–73; crystals of, 451;

density of, 74, 449; diagram for atom of, 49, **49, 56;** electron cloud diagram for, 50, **50;** electron configuration of, **47,** 449; electronegativity of, 106; flame test for, 545, **colorplate IV** following 548; and fluorine, reaction between, 379; half life of radioisotope of (sodium-24), 339; halide salts of, 454; ionization potential of, 39, **41, 75, colorplate** facing 85, 449; ions of, 94, **94,** 109, 228, 235, 247, 276, 449, 475, 544; melting point of, 449; as metal, 57, 86; orbital diagram, **525;** oxidation state of, 449; and periodic table, 79, 81; preparation of, 450, **450;** properties of, 72, 73, 74, 449; radioactive (sodium-24), 330, 339, 356; as reducing agent, 452; spectral analysis of, 39, **colorplate** facing 84; symbol for, 72, 73, 74; uses of, 452–53; valence number of, 97, 116, 118; and water, reaction between, 247, 260, 451, **451**

sodium acetate, 233, 234, 270, 277, 442

sodium aluminate, 248, 460, 528

sodium aluminum sulfate, 560

sodium benzoate, 602, **603**

sodium bicarbonate, 432, 456, 457, 560, 561

sodium bisulfate (sodium hydrogen sulfate), 233, 252, 377, 384

sodium bisulfite (sodium hydrogen sulfite), 252, 264, 265

sodium bromide, 373, 374, 382, 384

sodium butyrate, 577

sodium carbonate, 432, 433, 447, 456, 574; hydrated, efflorescence of, 196; and hydrochloric acid, reaction between, 447, **447;** industrial (soda ash), 457; in lime glass manufacture, 456; pH of, 226; preparation of, 457; from reaction between sodium hydroxide and carbonic acid, 235; uses of, 456

sodium chloride (table salt), 17, 54, 57, 60, 107, 182, 188, 190, 192, 193, 232, 234, 243, 276, 454; as binary salt, 252, **252;** crystals of **60,** 94, **94,** 139, **139,** 194; electrolysis of, 247, **370,** 449, 450; as electrolyte, **201,** 201–02, 203, 575; electron structure of, **93,** 93–94, **94;** formula for, 60, 251; gram formula weight of, 124; as hygroscopic substance, 196; industrial uses of, 376, 454, **455;** interionic attraction in 1 *m* solution of, 210, 211; ionic equation for formation of, by neutralization, 228; ionic formula for, 95; as ionic solid, 140, 232; melting point of, 575;

mining operations for, **453,** 454; necessary to life, 249, 454; pH of solution of, 234, 236; from reaction between sodium hydroxide and hydrochloric acid, 228, 236, 237, 249; from reaction between sodium oxide and hydrochloric acid, 250; from reaction between sodium sulfate and hydrochloric acid, 272, **272;** related to hydrochloric acid, 251, **252;** and silver nitrate, reaction between solutions of, 251, 261, 443; from sodium burned in chlorine, 251, 372–73; solubility of, in water, 184, 185, 234; in Solvay process, 457; and sulfuric acid, reaction between, 261, 272, 377; uses of, 376, 454, **455;** X-ray diffraction of, 139

sodium chlorite, 376

sodium cyanide, 453, 493

sodium fluoride, 379

sodium hydride, 459; electron shell diagram of, **459**

sodium hydrogen sulfate (sodium bisulfate), 233, 252, 377, 384

sodium hydrogen sulfite (sodium bisulfite), 252, 264, 265

sodium hydroxide, 186, 189, 212, 228, 234, 235, 236, 237, **248,** 249, 375, **375,** 417, 442; and carbonic acid, sodium carbonate prepared from, 235; and deliquescence, 196; from electrolysis of sodium chloride solution, 247, 370; as electrolyte, 203, 210; formula for, 117; and heat of solution, 191, **191;** and hydrochloric acid, reaction between, 228, 261; hydrochloric acid titrated against, **254,** 254–55; ionic formula for, 117; molten, in preparation of sodium, 450; as monohydroxy base, 248; pH of, 226; preparation of, 247, 370, 391, **391,** 451, **451;** from reaction between sodium and water, 247, 451, **451;** from reaction between sodium carbonate and calcium hydroxide, 454, 456; from reaction between sodium peroxide and water, 391, **391;** and sodium butyrate, reaction between, 577; as solid, 224, 247; as strong base, 223, 236; uses of, 456; vinegar titrated against, 255–56

sodium hypochlorite, 252, 375, **375,** 376

sodium iodate, 384

sodium iodide, 373, 374

sodium nitrate, 183, 184, 252, 271, 423, 428, 446; as electrolyte, 202, 203; in fertilizer, 458; formula for, 252; and heat of so-

lution, 191, **191;** as normal salt, 233; from reaction between silver nitrate and sodium chloride, 251; from reaction between sodium carbonate and nitric acid, 458; related to nitric acid, 252, **252;** as ternary salt, 252, **252**

sodium nitrite, 417, 428

sodium oxalate, 443

sodium oxide, 71, 72, 246, 250

sodium perchlorate, 252

sodium peroxide, 391, **391,** 395, 453

sodium phosphate, 234, 267, 447

sodium stearate, 607

sodium sulfate, 188, 212, 270, 443; gram formula weight of, 124; hydrated, 196, **196;** and hydrochloric acid, reaction between, 272, **272;** ionic equation for formation of, by neutralization, 233; as normal salt, 233, **233;** related to sodium bisulfate, 252; testing for, 445, **445**

sodium sulfide, 96, 445, **445**

sodium sulfite, 233, 252, 445, **445**

sodium thiosulfate, 313, 318, 319, 375, **375,** 496

sodium vapor lamp, 452, **452**

sol, defined, 315

solder, 181, 568, 569, **569**

solid models, 50–51, **51**

solid fuels, for rockets, 627, **628**

solids: amorphous, 139; ionic, 140; melting point of, 139; metallic, 140; molecular, 141; network, 141; particles in, 140–41; structure of, 139; sublimation of, 141–42, 385

solubility, defined, 182

solubility curves, **184,** 184–85

solubility product, 276, **276**

solubility table, *see* Appendix

solute particles, in molar solution, 187–88

solutes: defined, 182; separated from solvents, **194,** 194–95; table of, dissolved per 100 grams of water, 184

solutions: acid, *see* acids; aqueous, *see* aqueous solutions; basic, *see* bases; boiling points of, 192–93; concentrated, 186, **186,** 187, 188, 189, 190; defined, 180, 311; dilute, 186, **186;** electrical properties of, 201–04; freezing points of, 193; gaseous, 191; ions in, number of, 188; liquid, 181 *ff*; molality of, 187, 189–90, **190;** molarity of, **187,** 187–88, **189, 190;** normality of, 187, 188–89; **189;** saturated, 184; solid, **180,** 181; standard, 187; supersaturated, 185; unsaturated, 184

Solvay, Ernest, 456
Solvay process, 456–57, **457, 458,** 470, 472
solvent: defined, 182; separated from solute, **194,** 194–95
soot, 551, **551**
Sörenson, S. P. L., 225
space-filling models, of atoms, 91, **91**
space lattice, 139, **139**
spark chamber, 337
spectrometer, mass, 33, **33**
spectroscope, 28, **28,** 418, 545
spectrum: bright-line, 28; continuous, 27, **27,** visible, 27, **colorplate** facing 84
spinnerets, 648, **648**
spin number, 45–46
stainless steel, 506, 516, **516**
standard pressure, defined, 146
standard solution, defined, 187
standard temperature: defined, 148; and pressure, 150, 151
stannic sulfide, 542, **colorplate III** following 548
stannous fluoride, 379
stannous sulfide, 542, **colorplate III** following 548
starch: iodine test for, 386; as polysaccharide, 658–59, **659**
stearic acid, 601, 602, 606, 607
steel, 181, 501, 502, 505–11; carbon content of, 509; heat treatment of, 509, 511; pickling of, **378;** production of, 506–11, **507, 508, 509, 510**
steel alloys, 506, 516, **516**
sterling silver, 181, 495
stibine, 436
stibnite, 399, 436
Stock, Alfred, 118
Stock system, 118
storage battery, 301, **410,** 410–11, 436, 569
STP, *see* standard temperature and pressure
Strassmann, Fritz, 347
streptomycin, 554
strontium: compounds of, 477; flame test for, 545, **colorplate IV** following, 548; ions of, 543, 544; and oxygen, affinity for, 467; properties of, 464, 465; radioactive (strontium-90), 330, 339, 356, 447; spectrum, **colorplate** facing 84
structural formulas, 579
styrene, 632, 635, **636,** 634
subatomic particles, 32, 341; *see also* electrons; neutrons; protons
sublimation, 141–42, 385; defined, 142
subshells, 44, **44,** 45; defined, 44; and orbitals, 44, **44,** 45, **45,** 46, **46, 50**

substitution product of hydrocarbons, 595–604; defined, 593
substrate, defined, 665
sucrose (sugar), 17, 61, 190, 192, 193, 658; decomposition of, 61; formula for, 575; melting point of, 575; as nonelectrolyte, 202, 203, 205, 575
sugar, *see* sucrose
sulfanilamide, 665, 666
sulfates: ions of, 109, 110, **110,** 117, 233, 404, 409, 445, 476; testing for, 445, 446
sulfides: ions of, 411, 445, 542, 543; testing for, 445, 446, 542, 543
sulfites, 428; ions of, 110, 119, 445; testing for 445, 446
sulfur, 9, 18, 19, 54, 57, 58, 368, 391, 396, **399,** 401; allotropes of, 397–98; amorphous, 398, **398;** atomic number of, 72, 73, 74, 390; atomic radius of, 74, **colorplate** facing 85; atomic weight of, 88, 122, 390; atoms of, in solid state, 398, **398;** boiling point of, 390; colloidal, 314, 318; combustion supported by, 399; compounds of, oxidation and reduction among, 410, 411; crystals of, 397–98, **398;** density of, 74, 87, 390; electron configuration of, **47,** 390; flowers of, 396, 397, **397,** 398; fused with aluminum to form aluminum sulfide, 251; ionization potential of, **41,** 74, **colorplate** facing 85, 390; ions of, 109, 110, **110,** 117, 119, 233, 404, 409, 411, 445–46, 476, 542, 543; and iron, reaction between 19, 398–99; isotopes of, 34, 355, 356; melting point of, 390; and metals, reactions between, 398–99, **399;** mined by Frasch process, 397, **397;** molecule of, 17; oxidation states of, 294, 390; as oxidizing agent, 398, 410, 411; and periodic table, 87, 88; prismatic, 397, 398, **398;** properties of, 72, 73, 74, 390, 397; radioactive (sulfur-35), 356; reactions of, prediction of, 398–99; as reducing agent, 410, 411; rhombic, 397, 398, **398;** roll, 396, 399; in solid state, atoms of, 398, **398;** symbol for, 72, 73, 74, 396, 398; valence number of, 116
sulfur dioxide, 218, 242, 243, 279, 398, 402, 411; as bleaching agent, 403–04, 405; and bromine, reaction between, 381; and hydrogen sulfide, reaction between, 294; molecule of, 110–11, **110, 111;** preparation of, 402–03, **403;** properties of, 403; testing for, 445; uses of, 404–05
sulfur monoxide, 101, **101,** 102

sulfur trioxide, 163, 165, 220, 279, 405, 411
sulfuric acid, 189, 212, 219, 220, 242, 250, 381, 382, 385, 394, 400, 402–03, **403,** 423, 603; and calcium fluoride, reaction between, 380; concentrated, 185, 186, 406–07, **407,** 408, 409; and copper, reaction between, 408; in cotton-bleaching process, 375, **375;** as dehydrating agent, 408, 409–10; dilute, 186, 192, 203, 408–09; as diprotic acid, 233, 245; dry atmospheres provided by, 409, **409;** as electrolyte, 203; formula for, 119, 244, 245; fuming, 406; and magnesium, reaction between, 265; and metals, reactions between, 407–08; as nonvolatile acid, 243; as oxidizing agent, 408; pH of, 226; and potassium hydroxide, reaction between, 228; and potassium nitrate reaction between, 250; preparation of, 163, 220, **404, 405,** 405–06, **406;** properties of, 406–09; from reaction between sulfur trioxide and water, 220, 405–06; and sodium bromide, reaction between, 384; and sodium chloride, reaction between, 261, 272, 377; as strong acid, 220, 236; as ternary acid, 244, **244;** in testing for nitrate ion, 446; uses of, 409–11
sulfurous acid, 218, **218,** 219, 220, 242, 411, **411;** formula for, 119, 244, 245, 428; and hydrogen peroxide, reaction between, 404; from reaction between sulfur dioxide and water, 220; as reducing agent, 404; related to sodium sulfite, 252; as ternary acid, 244; as weak acid, 220
superphosphate of lime, 410, 433
supersaturation, 185, **185**
suspension, defined, 311
symbol: Berzelius', 15; Dalton's **13;** of elements, 16; Greek and alchemists', **15**
synchroton, 359, **359**
syndets, **608,** 608–09
synthetic fibers, 646, 648, 651–52
synthetic rubber, 452, 585, 632, 633–34, 635, 636; properties and uses of, 637
system, closed, defined, 153–54

taconite, 503
talc, 476
tannic acid, 442
tar, 616
tartar emetic, 436
tartaric acid, 602

tear gas, 384

Teflon, 379–80, **380,** 643

telluric acid, 412

tellurium, 390, 391, 412; compounds of, 412; and periodic table, 76, 78, 87–88, 368; properties of, 87–88, 390; uses of, 412

tellurous acid, 412

tempering, defined, 511

ternary acids, **244,** 244–45

ternary salts, 252, **252**

tetrachloromethane (carbon tetrachloride), 182, 265, 266, 373, 375, 382, 385, 444, 593

tetraethyl lead, 165, 383, 452, 453, 569, 626

tetragonal crystal, 139, **140**

tetrahedral molecules, **107,** 108

thallium, 59, 333, 524, 525, 535–36; properties of, 525

thermal cracking process, 623

Thermit process, 530, **530**

thermonuclear reactions, 362–63

thermoplastics, 638, 641; cellulose acetate, 641, 643; cellulose nitrate, 641, 643; noncellulose, 641, 644–45; properties and uses of, 643; silicone, 643

thermosetting plastics, 638, 639–41; properties and uses of, 642

Thompson, William, 147

Thomson, G. P., 42

Thomson, J. J., 24, **24**

Thomson, Thomas, 15

thorium, 78, 331, 332, 355; electron configuration of, 485; in uranium disintegration series, 333, 334, 342

thorium X, 331, 332

thymine, **666,** 667

thymolphthalein, 227, 442, **442, colorplate** facing 548

thyroid gland cancer, treated with radioactive iodine, 356, 386

tin, 9, 77, 296, 481, 567; in activity series, 296; compounds of, 567–68; electron configuration of, 83, 550; and lead, alloys of, 568; oxidation potential of, 302; properties of, 549, 550, 567; valence number of, 116

tin plate, 515

titanium, 42, 376, 452

titanium oxide, 531

titanium tetrachloride, 376

titration, 253–56, **254, 256;** for determination of percentage by weight of solutes in solutions, 255–56; end point of, 254, 255

toluene, 616

Torr, 126, 146

Torricelli, Evangelista, 125

tracer elements, 355

transition elements, 79–80, 83, 85, 481–86, 501; electron configuration of, 484–85; energy level diagram for, **483;** and energy value of white light, for removal of electrons, 484–85; and periodic table, **481,** 482, 485–86, 497; of period, 4, 482; of periods 5, 6, and 7, 484

translational motion of molecules, 158, **158,** 159

transmutation of atoms, 332, 347; artificial, 334–35, **334,** 343, 357–58, 359

transuranic elements, 332, 347, 348, 354, 355, 484; and particle accelerators, 360; as reactor fuels, 353–54; table of, 361

tri- prefix, 594

triads of group VIII, and periodic table, 501

triatomic molecules, 104–05

tricalcium phosphate, 410

trichloromethane, 593, 594

triclinic crystal, 140, **140**

trihydroxy alcohols, 598

trihydroxy bases, 248

triple covalent bonds, 102, 575

triprotic acids, 233, 245

trisodium phosphate, 192, 475; as cleansing agent, 234, 435; dissociated in water, 235; as normal salt, 233, 234

tritium, 33, **33, 362,** 363, 364, 461

tungsten, field ion microscope photograph of, 48

tungsten carbide, 535

Tyndall, John, 314

Tyndall effect, 313–14, **313,** 315, 316

type metal, 436, **436,** 491, 568

ultramicroscope, 314, **314**

ultraviolet light, 394

uncertainty principle, 43–44, **44**

unfilled orbital, defined, 48

unfinished period, of periodic table, 82

unit cell, of space lattice, 139, **139**

universal indicators, 227–28

unsaturated fats, 606

unsaturated hydrocarbons, *see* hydrocarbons

unsaturated solution, defined, 184

uranium, 15, 328, 331, 332; atomic number of, 31; atomic radius of, **colorplate** facing 85; bombarded with neutrons, 347, 348, **348,** 350, **350, 353,** 354, 360; crystals of, 328, **328;** electron configuration of, 485; and fluorine, reaction between, 380; half lives of radioisotopes of, 339; ionization potential of, **colorplate** facing 85; isotopes of, 34, 330, 333, 334, 339, 342, 351, 352, 353, 355, 360

uranium disintegration series, 333–34, 342, 412

uranium hexafluoride, **352,** 353, 380

uranium nitrate, 331, **331**

uranium X, 331, 332

urea, 574, 640

urea-formaldehyde, 640, 641, 642

valence: defined, 92, 97; variable, 117–18

valence electrons, 73, 80, 83, 84, 85, 86, 93; defined, 73; unpaired, 100

valence numbers, 115, 292; and clasification of reactions, 259; of elements and radicals, table of, 116; and covalent compounds, 108; and ionic compounds, 96–97; and periodic table, 118

valence, variable, 117–18

valine, 663

Van de Graaff, R. J., 358

Van de Graaff generator, 358

van der Waals, Johannes Diderils, 131

van der Waals forces, 131, **131,** 134, 135, 158, 159

vanadium pentoxide, 405

vapor pressure, 135–36, **135, 136**

vibrational motion of molecules, 158, **158,** 159

Vicara, 649

vinegar, 253, 255

vinyl, 643

viscose process, 648–49, **650**

viscose silk, 649

visible spectrum, **colorplate** facing 84

vitamins, 253, 665

volatile acids, 243

voltaic cell, 300

voltmeter, 300, **300**

volume, ratio of gaseous elements expressed in terms of, 62 *ff.*

volume-volume problems, 175–76

Vorce cell, 371

vulcanization, 396, 633, **633,** 635, **635**

Waage, Peter, 273

Walton, E. T. S., 357, 358

washing soda, *see* sodium carbonate

water: and active metals, reactions between, 247; angular molecule of, 103, 107, **107;** arrangement of atoms in molecule of, 17, **17;** boiling point of, 136–37, 192; and bromine, reaction between, 383; and chlorine, reaction between, 373, **373,** 375; as covalent compound, 100, 101; of crystallization, 195; distilled, 194, 201; dual nature, as Brønsted-Lowry acid or base, 230; electrolysis of, 60–61, **61,** 212–13, **213;** electron structure of molecule of, **100,** 101; and fluorine, reaction between, 369, 378, 379, **379;** formula for, 13, 18, 71, 72; freezing point of, 148; gram molecular weight of, 123; hard, *see* hard water; heat of reaction of, 161, 162; heavy, 32, 66; of hydration, 195, **195;** hydrogen bonds of, *see* hydrogen bonds; ion product constant of, 224–25; ionization of, **211,** 211–12; molecular weight of, 122, molecule of, **100,** 104–05, **141;** pH of, 226; purified with chlorine, 374; and ratio by volume of hydrogen to oxygen, **62,** 62–63; and ratio by weight of hydrogen to oxygen, 64, 66; sea, 180; and sodium, reaction between, 247, 260, 451, **451;** and sodium peroxide, reaction between, 391, **391;** soft, 473, 475; as weak electrolyte, 211, **211;** *see also* aqueous solutions
water displacement, defined, 8

water gas, 618, **618**
Watson, J. D., 667
wavelength, 28–29
wave mechanical model, of atom, 43–51, **49, 50**
wave mechanics, 43
weight, ratio of each element in compound expressed in terms of, 62, 64 *ff.*
weight-volume problems, 176–77
weight-weight problems, 174–75
welding, 419, 618, 619, **619**
wetting agent, 318
white light, energy value of, for removal of electrons from transition elements, 484–85
Wilson, C. T. R., 337
Wilson cloud chamber, 337, **337**
Wöhler, Friedrich, 574
wood: as fuel, 614; volatile byproducts of destructive distillation of, 616
Woodward, Robert, 573
wool, 645, 646, 652
word equation, defined, 7

xanthroproteic test, for protein, 664
xenon, 17, 54, 55, 59, 81, 417, 418, 419
xenon tetrafluoride, 55, **55**
X-ray diffraction, 58, **58,** 107, **137,** 587, 664, 667
X rays, 31, **31,** 77, 139, 466; discovery of, 326–27; wavelengths of, 327

xylenes, 616

yeast, 559
-yne suffix, 585
yttrium, 484

zein, 649
zeolites, 475, 476
zinc, 9, 10, **10,** 218, 298, 300, 482, 494; in activity series, 296; cobalt nitrate test for, 546, **colorplate VI** facing 549; in cyanide process, 493; electron configuration of, 42, 43, **43;** and galvanized iron, 515; and hydrochloric acid, reaction between, 10, 250, 260, 270, 295, 460; ions of, 300, 515; and nitric acid, reaction between, 424; oxidation potential of, 302; oxidation state of, 296; and periodic table, 80; as reducing agent, 296; and sulfur, reaction between, 399; and sulfuric acid, reaction between, 407; as transition element, 80; valence number of, 116
zinc blende, 396
zinc chloride, 234, 250, 270, 296
zinc oxide, 243, 546, 633
zinc sulfate, 402, 407
zinc sulfide, 243, 336, 399, 467, 543, **colorplate III** following 548
zirconium, 376, 452
zymase, 597

ATOMIC NUMBERS AND ATOMIC WEIGHTS

Name of element	Symbol	Atomic number	Atomic weight	Name of element	Symbol	Atomic number	Atomic weight
Actinium	Ac	89	[227]*	Mercury	Hg	80	200.59
Aluminum	Al	13	26.98	Molybdenum	Mo	42	95.94
Americium	Am	95	[243]	Neodymium	Nd	60	144.24
Antimony	Sb	51	121.75	Neon	Ne	10	20.18
Argon	Ar	18	39.95	Neptunium	Np	93	[237]
Arsenic	As	33	74.9	Nickel	Ni	28	58.71
Astatine	At	85	[210]	Niobium	Nb	41	92.91
Barium	Ba	56	137.34	Nobelium	No	102	[253]
Berkelium	Bk	97	[247]	Nitrogen	N	7	14.01
Beryllium	Be	4	9.01	Osmium	Os	76	190.2
Bismuth	Bi	83	208.98	Oxygen	O	8	15.99†
Boron	B	5	10.81	Palladium	Pd	46	106.4
Bromine	Br	35	79.91	Phosphorus	P	15	30.98
Cadmium	Cd	48	112.40	Platinum	Pt	78	195.09
Calcium	Ca	20	40.08	Plutonium	Pu	94	[242]
Californium	Cf	98	[249]	Polonium	Po	84	[210]
Carbon	C	6	12.01	Potassium	K	19	39.10
Cerium	Ce	58	140.12	Praseodymium	Pr	59	140.91
Cesium	Cs	55	132.91	Promethium	Pm	61	[147]
Chlorine	Cl	17	35.45	Protactinium	Pa	91	[231]
Chromium	Cr	24	51.99†	Radium	Ra	88	[226]
Cobalt	Co	27	58.93	Radon	Rn	86	[222]
Copper	Cu	29	63.54	Rhenium	Re	75	186.2
Curium	Cm	96	[247]	Rhodium	Rh	45	102.91
Dysprosium	Dy	66	162.50	Rubidium	Rb	37	85.47
Einsteinium	Es	99	[254]	Ruthenium	Ru	44	101.07
Erbium	Er	68	167.26	Samarium	Sm	62	150.35
Europium	Eu	63	151.96	Scandium	Sc	21	44.96
Fermium	Fm	100	[253]	Selenium	Se	34	78.96
Fluorine	F	9	18.99†	Silicon	Si	14	28.09
Francium	Fr	87	[223]	Silver	Ag	47	107.87
Gadolinium	Gd	64	157.25	Sodium	Na	11	22.99
Gallium	Ga	31	69.72	Strontium	Sr	38	87.62
Germanium	Ge	32	72.59	Sulfur	S	16	32.06
Gold	Au	79	196.97	Tantalum	Ta	73	180.95
Hafnium	Hf	72	178.49	Technetium	Tc	43	[99]
Helium	He	2	4.00	Tellurium	Te	52	127.60
Holmium	Ho	67	164.93	Terbium	Tb	65	158.93
Hydrogen	H	1	1.008	Thallium	Tl	81	204.37
Indium	In	49	114.82	Thorium	Th	90	232.04
Iodine	I	53	126.90	Thulium	Tm	69	168.93
Iridium	Ir	77	192.2	Tin	Sn	50	118.69
Iron	Fe	26	55.85	Titanium	Ti	22	47.90
Krypton	Kr	36	83.80	Tungsten	W	74	183.85
Lanthanum	La	57	138.91	Uranium	U	92	238.03
Lawrencium	Lw	103	[257]	Vanadium	V	23	50.94
Lead	Pb	82	207.19	Xenon	Xe	54	131.30
Lithium	Li	3	6.94	Ytterbium	Yb	70	173.04
Lutetium	Lu	71	174.97	Yttrium	Y	39	88.91
Magnesium	Mg	12	24.31	Zinc	Zn	30	65.37
Manganese	Mn	25	54.94	Zirconium	Zr	40	91.22
Mendelevium	Md	101	[256]	(Name undetermined)		104	[257]

* Brackets denote replacement of atomic weight by the mass number of the isotope with the longest half life.
† These values can be rounded out to the next whole number, because the third figure following the decimal point is greater than 5 and has been dropped.